GILBERT STUART, "Mrs. Perez Morton" (sketch)

ESTIMATES IN ART

SERIES II

SIXTEEN ESSAYS ON AMERICAN PAINT-
ERS OF THE NINETEENTH CENTURY

BY

FRANK JEWETT MATHER, Jr.

NEW YORK
HENRY HOLT AND COMPANY

COPYRIGHT, 1931,
BY
HENRY HOLT AND COMPANY, INC.

First Printing

To

MY DAUGHTER

SHARER OF MY TASTES

FOREWORD

From a series of essays written over a period of twenty years no intelligent reader will demand complete consistency of opinion. So, while I have retouched and amplified these studies where it seemed necessary, I have made no attempt to edit them into an artificial coherence. They must stand as the best I could do at the time of writing. Most have been published in magazines, but the Inness and Fuller are here first printed. While there has been no endeavor to make a group of essays serve as a systematic history, I believe no highly significant American painter of the nineteenth century has been omitted, saving always John La Farge, whom the reader will find not inappropriately treated among the old masters, in the former volume of "Estimates." For courteous permission to reprint copyright matter thanks are expressed to the publishers of *Scribner's, The Nation, The Review, Art in America, The International Studio,* and *The Saturday Review of Literature*. A special acknowledgment is due to *The Phillips Publications* and to Mr. Frederic Fairchild Sherman for the

exceptional magnanimity with which they have
authorized the reprinting of considerable passages from their books, respectively on Arthur
B. Davies and Homer D. Martin.

F. J. M., Jr.

Princeton, N. J.

CONTENTS

FACE-PAINTER AND FEMINIST

THE ART OF S. F. B. MORSE

GEORGE INNESS

ELIHU VEDDER

AFTERTHOUGHTS ON WHISTLER

GEORGE FULLER

HOMER D. MARTIN

ALBERT PINKHAM RYDER

CONTENTS

ARTHUR B. DAVIES

ILLUSTRATIONS

I

GILBERT STUART
FACE-PAINTER AND FEMINIST

FACE-PAINTER AND FEMINIST

An excellent painter, Gilbert Stuart was far from an exemplary character. He was capable of neglecting attached parents, of ridiculing a benefactor, of accepting advances for portraits which he never painted and possibly never intended to paint. His return to America, far from being a patriotic pilgrimage to the feet of Washington, as Dunlap glowingly represents it, was an incursion into an unspoiled field of patronage, London, and Dublin having become too hot for the artist adventurer. All this may seem unimportant, but I think not. A face-painter with fewer foibles of his own would not have caught with Stuart's uncanny insight the foibles of others, while an almost illiterate colonial youth of low degree would hardly have made himself a favorite in the best society of Dr. Johnson's London had he offered as qualification simply a steady and dependable character. Instead Gilbert Stuart offered an extraordinary tact and wit and a competent mastery of his craft. It was enough wherever he turned.

3

For some weeks I have been turning over the plates in Lawrence Park's monumental catalogue, reviving old memories of the originals, with the result that one old impression has been confirmed, and an entirely new impression has been gained. I remain of the old opinion that while Gilbert Stuart was not quite a great portrait painter, he was one of the greatest of face-painters, whereas I realize for the first time that Stuart was one of the ablest interpreters of womanhood that the art of painting has seen. Intending nothing derogatory by the term, I feel that the word face-painter precisely defines Stuart's notable excellences and his equally patent limitations. Within his lifetime worked Reynolds, Gainsborough, Raeburn, Goya, David, and Ingres. None of them painted a face better than Stuart, and several of them painted it less well, but all of them have a stronger claim to be regarded as great portraitists. Stuart's interest was usually exhausted with capturing the forms and character of a face. He was a specialist, and contentedly so. There was an early moment when under the influence of Gainsborough he aimed at style. Later he cared only for likeness and character. His compositions are the entirely adequate improvisations of a very clever person. His accessories and costumes are brilliantly touched in, but often remain extraneous to the pictorial effect. And this neglect was from choice and not from lack of ability. The costumes and accessories in the portraits of Don Josef de Jaudenes y Nebot and his wife in the Metropolitan Museum are of exquisite fitness and character. Stuart could paint hands beautifully, but usually avoided the task, and often painted them badly. Except for the very picturesque "A Gentleman Skating—William Grant, of Congalton," a canvas emulative of Gainsborough, Stuart's rare full-lengths are tritely composed. Again, unlike all his portrait-painting contemporaries, Stuart was never tempted away from his specialty. But is not the great portrait painter normally a great painter who incidently makes portraits?

Indeed it is doubtful if the man who paints only portraits will ever paint great portraits. Stuart painted hundreds of amazingly true and vivid masks—the Vaughan Washington, the Mrs. Perez Morton are types, but did he ever paint a portrait that would hang quite comfortably beside a Titian, a Vandyke, a Goya, a David, or an Ingres? Which only means that Stuart could or would not provide that surplus beyond fine face-painting, that sustained pictorial richness and character, which the finest portrait painting demands. In Titian's "Ariosto" the quilted satin sleeve is as eloquent as the sensitive olive face and the silky raven beard. Rembrandt's "Lady with a Fan" would without the exquisitely painted fan lose half her existence. It is doubtful if these extensions of meaning, this animism in the inanimate, can be learned solely in portrait painting. At least Stuart never did learn this magic, and his place, a very honorable one, is rather with the Moros, Mierevelts, and Knellers than with the Holbeins, Velasquezes, and Hogarths.

Again a scrutiny of Park's fine reproductions produces the disconcerting surprise that the male portraits which Stuart made in his eighteen British years are as a class far superior to those which he painted in America, and withal that one could form from his entire work a group of women's portraits which for character and vitality have been surpassed by no painter except Rembrandt. In order that the reader may check these bald assertions, let me propose a game with him. I will make a group of a dozen British male portraits by Stuart, challenging the reader to make a group of male Americans by Stuart that shall be equal in character and pictorial beauty. Throughout, the British group will show with an equally vivid character a finer and more studied pictorialism. Here is the British group; it may readily be considered in Park's illustrations, which are alphabetically arranged: Sir Cropley Ashley-Cooper, James Boydell, William Kerin Constable, Dr. John Fothergill, James Heath, Ozias Humphrey, Dr. William Smith, Gilbert Stuart, Thomas Baron Sydney, James Ward, Benjamin West, Edmond Sexton, Viscount Pery. If the reader loses in this game, as I am confident he will, I must further remark that, with a few exceptions, the finest male portraits that Stuart painted after his return to America are those of foreigners—notably Don Josef de Jaudenes y Nebot, Count Volney, the Marquis d'Yrujo. These are all finer pictorially than most of the American male portraits, and expressed with a more complete sympathy.

Let us play the second hand of the game. I will choose a list of a dozen American female portraits which for sheer vitality and vivid personal presence will bear comparison with any dozen female portraits by any painter whatsoever—Rembrandt only barred. The list is: Mrs. William Bingham, Miss Maria Bartlett,

Miss Clementina Beach, Mrs. John Bullus, Mrs. Samuel Cary, Mrs. Henry Clymer, Mrs. Charles Dearborn, Mrs. James Greenleaf, Miss Elizabeth Inches, Mrs. Perez Morton (the sketch), Mrs. Edward Tuckerman, the Marchioness d'Yrujo (née Maria McKean). The addition of an English portrait or two, such as that of the Marchioness of Dufferin, would enrich the list. Now I am perfectly aware that from many painters could be chosen a dozen female portraits of finer pictorial accomplishment, but I doubt if any other dozen save Rembrandt's would yield so many keen and irresistible impressions of so many actual women. Merely turning over the relatively unspeaking reproductions, there comes over me the old pathos of François Villon's deathless ballade—the deep pity that so much charm, character, and warm life are now but scattered bones, white as the snows of yesteryear, and a handful of brown dust.

I feel the reader will find not only that my list will bear the proposed hard test, but that two or three alternative lists could be chosen that would meet the test nearly as well. If this be so, my initial assertion that Stuart is the greatest painter of woman's character stands, and we gain the further point of view that when Stuart painted women the usually clear line between fine portraiture and consummate face-painting tends to disappear.

We may attempt to interpret these facts in terms of Gilbert Stuart's life and character. Returning at forty to the native land which he had willingly left at her moment of greatest need, Stuart really returned as a distinguished foreigner, with a foreigner's attitude. For that robust and varied man's world of which he had been a large part, in the London of Dr. Johnson, Reynolds, and Pitt, Stuart found no equivalent in New York, Philadelphia, or Boston. His nostalgia he was too tactful to reveal, though it appears plainly enough in his anecdotage, and he assuaged it by wit and work. To the American man he gave what the American man wanted, a most resolute and resemblant face-painting. The value of this work as record has been acclaimed from the first and needs no further eulogy. But he rarely found in any American man that challenging charm which graces nearly all the portraits of his London patrons and familiars. In part this may have rested on lack of sympathy or on simple inattention to whatever lay behind the appearance. There could, for example, hardly have been a more interesting male anywhere at the moment than Aaron Burr, yet Stuart painted a dull and perfunctory portrait of him. This is merely the extreme case of Stuart's always fine face-painting falling short of fine portraiture.

Towards the American woman Gilbert Stuart's attitude was that of all perceptive foreigners. She was a marvel, a puzzle, and a delight. She was irresistibly herself, an independent and unconditioned existence, in a sense that the American man busied with nation making could not be. So Stuart read her, confessed her, and most gallantly celebrated her, with the result that the mothers and daughters of the early Republic are today about twice as alive as the fathers and sons. And Stuart's admirable face-painting of women is ever tending to be much more than face-painting, going over the line towards fine portraiture. How Gilbert Stuart learned his magic as a feminist is between himself, Mrs. Stuart, and his God. It is enough to ascertain the fact without seeking an explanation.

I should be glad if these reinterpretations of an artist who through official and patriotic eminence has nearly vanished as a man should be considered my homage to the late Lawrence Park's long labor of love upon which this and all subsequent interpretations of Gilbert Stuart must chiefly depend.

[1925.]

II

THE ART OF S. F. B. MORSE

S. F. B. MORSE, "Mr. David de Forest"

THE ART OF S. F. B. MORSE

Samuel Finley Breese Morse, despite his
fame as inventor of the telegraph, was born
out of due time. He has that eighteenth century many-sidedness which was exemplified in
Franklin and Jefferson and, in a measure, by
his master, the poet-painter Allston. His
fame as inventor of the telegraph has almost
wholly obscured his considerable accomplishment as an artist. One of the most valuable
features of the excellent official memoir by his
son is the clearing up of this early and tragically abridged chapter. Morse was a good correspondent and diarist. Thus it is possible to
trace his life almost entirely in his own words.

Finley Morse, as his friends called him, was
born in Charlestown, Massachusetts, on the
27th of April, 1791. His father, Jedediah
Morse, was an orthodox Congregational clergy-
man, an energetic person of various talents.
He compiled the first American geography and
gazetteer, thus eking out a slender salary; he
was an esteemed correspondent of Washington,
and of such early British Liberals as Zachary

15

Macaulay, Wilberforce, and Owen. The mother, Elizabeth Finley, was a daughter of the President of Princeton College, a shrewd, humorous, masterful woman as her letters show her, resilient though she had borne eleven children and lost eight. Of this patriarchal family Finley Morse was the eldest. At nine he was a preparatory student at Andover. At ten his father admonished him—"steady and undissipated attention to one object is a sure sign of superior genius, as hurry, bustle, and agitation are the never-failing symptoms of a weak and frivolous mind."

At the age of fourteen, 1805, the boy was enrolled at Yale, the family college. There is amusing correspondence about his expenses. It was necessary to keep brandy, wine and "segars" in his room. But in the intervals of snipe shooting and miniature painting on ivory, at five dollars a likeness, he seems to have been a fairly diligent student. Literary tastes began to crop out, guided, however, by an austere Yankee morality. At Mr. Beers's shop he bought a Montaigne in French, eight volumes handsomely bound, for two dollars. On horrified inspection he writes: "The reason they are so cheap is because they are wicked and bad books for me or anybody else to read. I got them because they were cheap, and have exchanged them for a handsome English edition of Gil Blas, price $4.50." Evidently moral fastidiousness had its compensations in the case of this sixteen-year-old lad. It is possibly the only time that "Gil Blas" has served as first aid to the morally injured. But the paradox after all illustrates that permanent trait in Calvinistic morals by which sin is located not in practice but in theory. There was no theory of any sort in "Gil Blas," hence no harm.

Morse did not leave Yale without seeing electrical experiments under Professor Dwight, in the "Philosophical Chamber," and hearing Mr. Day lecture on this new science. These phenomena, so important for his subsequent career as an inventor, interested him only in second order. In his senior vacation he writes to his father in the somewhat Olympian vein already well marked. "As to my choice of a profession, I still think that I was made for a painter, and I would be obliged to you to make such an arrangement with Mr. Allston for my studying with him as you shall think expedient. I should desire to study with him during the winter, and, as he expects to return to England in the spring, I should admire to be able to go with him." There was an interval of conformity to parental reluctance—as a clerk in a book shop. Then the dream accomplished itself. Finley became Allston's disciple, planned a composition in the grand style, "Marius on the Ruins of Carthage," and by the middle of July 1811 was sailing with the Allstons for England, on the good ship *Lydia*.

So for four years Morse was one of that remarkable colony of Americans who for a generation postponed the inevitable decline of the British School of painting. Copley was already senile, but Benjamin West ruled and did much for the young man, until the magnanimous Allston humorously insisted that Morse was after all his pupil. Soon Morse joined forces with the genial and able Philadelphian, C. R. Leslie. In London De Quincey's adept of murder as a fine art was still at large, and the young men habitually slept with pistols at their bolsters. Morse duly visited the Elgin marbles at Burlington House. He observed that they show "the inferiority of all subsequent sculpture. Even those celebrated works, the Apollo Belvedere, Venus di Medicis, and the rest of those noble statues must yield to them." Every morning Morse and Leslie woke at five and walked for a mile and a half to sketch the Phidian marbles. At the moment when the Par-

thenon pediments were accounted rubbish by
the multitude this was no banal enthusiasm.

For a drawing from the Laocoön Morse was
admitted to the life class of the Royal Academy. Within a year he was working at his
first painting of heroic scale and subject, "The
Dying Hercules," first modelling it in clay.
The model won the prize for sculpture at the
Society of Arts, the picture made something
of a sensation in the Royal Academy. There
is little enough pleasure to be got today from
this bituminous canvas, which adorns the Yale
Art School. It illustrates the more glaring
faults of a master whom Morse unhappily admired, Ribera. Yet for a half-trained youth of
twenty-two, it is a powerful and by no means
unpromising performance.

Soon after Morse's arrival at London the relations between England and America, already
embittered by the orders in council and the em-
bargo, drifted into war. He was unmolested
personally, but harassed by poverty, opposi-
tion, declining patronage, and even more by
the faineancy of his family at home. They
were complacent peace-at-any-pricers, irritat-
ingly indulgent to the active patriotism of the
eldest son. Yet there were compensations
amid war's vexations and alarms. He saw fre-

quently and with admiration the conquerors of Napoleon, the noble figure of Czar Alexander I., Blücher, Yorck, the Cossack hetman, Platoff. He saw Wilberforce weep for joy when the guns verified the news of "a great victory in Flanders." The great philanthropist "expatiated largely on the prospects of a universal peace in consequence of the probable overthrow of Napoleon." Here surely one comes near a permanent fount of equally vain hopes and tears in things mortal.

England was becoming impossible for a high-spirited young American. His valedictory to London was a mythological piece, "Jupiter in the Case of Apollo, Marpessa and Idas." It failed of an Academy prize through a technicality. A letter to his parents reveals the pathetic high hopes with which he turned homeward:

"If I could get a commission or two for some large pictures for a church or public hall, to the amount of two or three hundred dollars I should feel much gratified. I do not despair of such an event, for, through your influence with the clergy and their influence with the people, I think some commission for a scripture subject for a church might be obtained, a crucifixion, for instance. Had I no higher thoughts than being a first-rate portrait painter, I would have chosen a far different profession. My ambition is to be among those who shall revive the splendor of the fifteenth century, to rival the genius of a Raphael, a Michael Angelo, or a Titian; my ambition is to be enlisted in the constellation of genius now rising in this country; I wish to shine, not by a light borrowed from them, but to shine the brightest."

It would be a mistake to dismiss this plan simply as evidence of a young man's inordinate ambition. The generation nourished æsthetically on Sir Joshua Reynolds's "Discourses," had a programme which it regarded both as meritorious and practicable. In particular the Americans had the grace or the naïveté to take Sir Joshua literally. Where he merely preached, they most strenuously practiced. Copley in his military canvases, West in his copious mythological production, Allston in his great imaginative designs—these were regarded as the harbingers of the resurgent Historical School. They and their works have gone the way of Southey's epics. Ambition and even nobility of spirit alone are poor gages for immortality. To us they are merely thwarted dreamers of the impossible. Happily they were not that to themselves. Only the unfortunate Haydon was to live through the whole tragedy of this mistaken high endeavor. Morse was to settle down to being nearly a first-rate portrait painter. But fortunately the realization that it was merely for that that he was foregoing the evening chats with Coleridge and the practice of the historic style came to him gradually.

Boston characteristically cold-shouldered her returned prodigy, so, after the practice of face-painters of the day, he went on the road. As he painted heads up and down rural New Hampshire and Massachusetts at fifteen dollars apiece, his intention was to collect funds for an Italian trip. Love at this point intervened in the person of Lucretia Pickering Walker, of Concord, New Hampshire. Her short-lived and rather pensive grace still lives in the charming picture which he did of her with their two children. Under his persuasion she experienced religious conversion, thus unwittingly preparing herself for her early death. The young lovers had pitifully little of each other's society. During most of the engagement he was south, in Charleston, where for the first time he found a really generous patronage. There he took his young bride in the winter of

1818-1819. There he received his first public commission, to paint the full-length portrait of President Monroe which still hangs in the City Hall.

It was knocked off in two weeks of December 1819, with enthusiasm, though amid all manner of interruptions. The city of Charleston commissioned it at what was then the handsome fee of seven hundred and fifty dollars, and it got what is one of the best examples of official portraiture ever executed in America. The presentment has picturesqueness without sacrifice of dignity; there is something unexpected and alert about the characterization. The sense of race is strong in the work. Very notable is the focus of the strong and sensitive face retained unimpaired amid the oddness of the accessories. President Monroe was not wrong in preferring it to the more famous full-length portrait by Stuart.

At the moment Charleston was probably the best trained city in art in America. In the mansions which lined the Battery were Raeburns, Romneys, Sir Joshuas. The Huguenot colony possessed excellent pictures of the recent French school. The planter aristocracy was proud, generous, hospitable. Charleston was probably the only city in America where a number of painters had lived by their art like gentlemen. Morse thought of settling there, but in three years he had exhausted what was after all a limited field. His hazards of new fortunes in Albany and New York it is unnecessary to follow. Struggling along, deprived mostly of the companionship of his wife and children, he felt himself settling down to the average gait of the journeymen face-painters of the day. In something like desperation he obtained an appointment as attaché on a special legation to Mexico. The precedent of Rubens encouraged him to the step, but the legation was recalled long before reaching the border. Meanwhile, in 1823, he did the group of the House of Representatives which is now in the Corcoran Gallery. It brought him a certain repute but no money. From every point of view this picture is the most remarkable American painting of its moment. In it Morse with a flexibility all his own concentrated all that he had learnt twenty years earlier from the great Napoleonic canvases of David. The scale and dignity of the fine interior are fully realized as is the delicate effect of early candle-light. The tiny portraits are at once characterful and unobtrusive. They have a seriousness worthy of their spacious setting. Among

American painters then living only Henry Sargent, painter of the charming "Tea Party" and
"Dinner Party," in the Boston Art Museum,
could have coped with the technical difficulties
of the theme with any success, and indeed of
all contemporary painters only the aged Goya
could have carried off the thing with an equal
beauty and impressiveness. David still lingering on in Brussels was no longer capable of anything so sincere and accomplished. To find
such a work unappreciated must have been a
breaking point for Morse.

In these wandering years he had painted
many fine portraits. Two of the most famous
and accessible are those of Mr. and Mrs.
David C. de Forest, which were painted in
1823, and are now in the Yale School of the
Fine Arts. What immediately strikes one in
the man's portrait is its probity, force, and
geniality. It has the candor and simplicity of
make of a fine Hogarth or a Raeburn. The
quite modern attack of Morse is perhaps even
better shown in the gaunt sketch of the head of
Lafayette now in the New York Public Library.
It is not an agreeable work, but full of character
and the memory insists on retaining the impression. Morse in his portraiture of men had in
a higher degree the merits common to the face-

painters of that day. He seems to me as much superior to the Hardings, Jarvises, Rembrandt Peales and Jouetts of the time as he is generally inferior to Copley and Gilbert Stuart.

As a technician he seems more contemporary and a bit further from the old masters. Startlingly modern is the Mrs. de Forest at Yale, probably the most brilliant portrait painted in America between the death of Stuart and maturity of Sargent. Without loss of character, it has extraordinary material richness. The touch is swift, the impast heavy, the sharp balance between the full blue of the turban and the deep cream and red of an India shawl as happy as hazardous. There is a gorgeousness and fulness of life in the work which is most exceptional in American portraiture of that time. It is as far from the safe discretion of Stuart as it is from the superficial prettiness of Sully. On entering the gallery you are both dominated and perplexed by it. Oddly it carries no English or American suggestion. One would say a magnificent Isabey. That work of this merit should have had little vogue is probably due to the fact that portraiture was as yet regarded not as an art but as a purely commemorative function. I should add that this richness and gusto are somewhat exceptional even in the work of Morse. His portrait of his daughter Susan in a yellow gown, for example, is lovely as a characterization, but thinly and timidly painted.

In 1825, his thirty-fourth year, he once more tried his fortunes in New York, this time successfully. It was the moment of Lafayette's triumphal return to America. Morse was chosen to paint the hero's portrait for the city over such competitors as Vanderlyn, Sully and Peale. The sittings at Washington resulted in a lifelong friendship. The work was tragically interrupted by news of the sudden death of Morse's young wife. "With her was connected all that I expected of happiness on earth," he writes to a friend. The full-length portrait of Lafayette in the New York City Hall betrays something of the lassitude and despondency under which it was completed, yet it also has a bizarre and romantic impressiveness—something compellingly Byronic. The sketch which has already been mentioned is probably the truer memorial. What was to have been the means of reuniting the little family at New York was to be the prelude to a lonely struggle that also must end in bitterness.

I suppose bereavement has made many a public career. It was so in Morse's case. His high seriousness made its impression on the easy-going New York of the 'twenties. The artists of the city were restless under the mismanagement of the American Academy of Arts by that testy veteran of the Revolution, Colonel John Trumbull. On the 8th of October, 1825, this discontent organized itself in the rooms of the Historical Society, in the innocent guise of a New York Drawing Association. Morse was elected president. January 1826 the Association became the National Academy of the Arts of Design with thirty professional members, of whom oblivion has spared for one reason or another only half a dozen—Durand, Dunlap, Rembrandt Peale, Thomas Cole and Alexander Anderson. For ten years Morse held the presidency. He lectured regularly in behalf of the movement. "The cause of the artists," he writes, "seems, under Providence, to be in some degree, confided to me, and I cannot shrink from the cares and troubles at present put upon me." He probably did more than any other man to bring about what if not the best period of American art was at least the most normal and generous condition of art patronage in America. The time he thus diverted from his painting he made up by intense industry, "sitting in my chair from seven in the morning until twelve or one the next morning, with only about an hour's intermission."

His position as a portrait painter was now established, but we hear little of the old ambitions. Still, the warmth with which he welcomed a commission for an historical subject for the cabin of a new steamboat proves that the old desire was not dead. It was probably with some notion of returning to the grand style, that Morse, in 1829, sailed for a long trip in Europe. It was perhaps too late for the fullest enjoyment and profit from such an experience. He was already thirty-eight, celebrated, and fixed in his artistic habits and admirations. It is an interesting question what his development might have been had he studied in the Louvre, as was his plan, in the ardent years of preparation. At London in his pupilage there was far too little accessible in the way of old art to offset the teaching of Allston and the precepts of West.

His impressions of travel give a mixed flavor of openmindedness and commonplaceness. It was not at the time a usual sentiment to write of Canterbury: "The effect of the long aisles and towering clustered pillars and richly carved screens of a Gothic church upon the imagination can scarcely be described—the emotion is that of awe." Such notes are rare in the scanty journals of this belated *Wanderjahr*. At Paris he was cordially received by Lafayette. At Rome he met his old friends the Fenimore Coopers, made pleasant acquaintance with Horace Vernet, then chief of the Villa Médécis, and Cardinal Wiseman. He painted the portrait of the venerable sculptor Thorwaldsen, and years later the painter had the pleasure of presenting it to the Danish government. At Naples he was inclined to think the "Dead Christ with the three Marys and Joseph," by Ribera, the finest picture he had yet seen. After this it is reassuring that he took the pains to copy Tintoretto's "Miracle of the Slave" at Venice. It was lightly considered there and as he worked actually threatened with damage from a thunder storm through a leaky roof. Generally speaking the journals of 1829 to 1832 are perfunctory. He notes small annoyances, is outraged by the theatre, beggary and Sabbath breaking. The Puritan seems to dominate the artist. Or Morse may merely be exercising the middle-aged man's privilege of indulging whim and taking much for granted.

At Paris he shared rooms with the sculptor Greenough. Lafayette, generously occupied with the doomed cause of Polish freedom, was most hospitable to his two artist friends. There were hopeful talks of impending government patronage of art at home, doubtless the decoration of the rotunda of the Capitol. For his homecoming Morse planned an innocent sensation, an interior of the Louvre gallery with a great array of miniature copies of the masterpieces. It fell flat, was sold at a loss. Worse disillusionment was in store. In 1834 Congress had voted four great historical pictures to adorn the rotunda of the Capitol. Morse, from his general prominence and as president of the National Academy, seemed sure of one. But President John Quincy Adams, distrustful of native talent, submitted a resolution opening the competition to foreign artists. This was the occasion of indignant protest in the already censorious *Evening Post,* and the article was generally but erroneously believed to be Morse's. It was, as a matter of fact, James Fenimore Cooper who thus unwittingly dealt a death blow to the lifelong hopes of his friend. Morse never recovered from the disappointment. Yielding to persuasion, he retained the presidency of the Academy until 1845, and resumed it for the year of emergency, 1861. But it had become an impersonal loyalty; his heart was elsewhere.

On the return voyage in 1832 the idea of the telegraph had dawned clearly. A new struggle was at hand. To tell of it is like describing another man, and it does not now concern us. From his art Morse declined longer to ask a livelihood, although it would have maintained him and the bantling invention most handsomely. In 1835 he accepted a pittance from the University of New York as Professor of the Literature of the Arts of Design. It was, I suppose, the first post of the sort in America. He occupied living and laboratory quarters in the old Gothic building on Washington Square, the scene of much romance in its day, and there he worked out heroically through all adversity the telegraph for the world, and for himself wealth and immortality.

In 1849, when victory in the new adventure was assured, he wrote a pathetic letter to Fenimore Cooper:

"Alas, My dear sir, the very name of pictures produces a sadness of heart I cannot describe. Painting has been a smiling mistress to many, but she has been a cruel jilt to me. I did not abandon her, she abandoned me. I have scarcely taken any interest in painting for many years. Will you believe it? When last in Paris, in 1845, I did not go into the Louvre, nor did I visit a single picture gallery.

"I sometimes indulge a vague dream that I may paint again. It is rather the memory of past pleasures, when hope was enticing me onward only to deceive me at last. Except some family portraits, valuable to me from their likenesses only, I could wish that every picture I ever painted was destroyed. I have no wish to be remembered as a painter, for I never was a painter. My ideal of that profession was, perhaps, too exalted—I may say is too exalted. I leave it to others more worthy to fill the niches of art."

To salve the disappointment of the Capitol decorations his friends raised a handsome subscription for a historical canvas of like scale. He began on "The Signing of the First Compact on the Mayflower," but all zest for such work was gone. He dropped the project and honorably repaid the subscribers with interest. In 1864, being seventy-three, he had "many yearnings towards painting," and made the endeavor to draw once more, but found his eyesight hopelessly defective. In his later years the only evidence of his former accomplishment is the handsome little skull with which he habitually "dead-headed" his telegrams.

His own judgment, that he failed from holding too exalted an ideal of his profession seems not far amiss, but he possibly did not realize the full tragedy of his own case. Like Haydon and many another he was a victim to Sir Joshua's dictum of the transcendency of the historical style. Unhappily the devout readers of the "Discourses" while taking the teaching at face value, omitted to supplement it by studying Sir Joshua's actual practice and the ground of his great repute. His vivacity and distinction, his graceful artifices of composition, his rich and learned color, in short his eminently decorative quality, were so many sealed books to them. Instead they entertained a delusion which he was personally far too shrewd to cherish, that by an effort of the will one could re-create the mood of the great masters of the Renaissance. Besides there was unfortunate ambiguity as to who the great masters were. For Morse, Ribera was one of the most admirable. So a whole generation of ambitious souls, the Wests, Corneliuses, Girodets, and Hayezes came up with the delusion that one could wish himself into the grand style. Watts, with a clearer vision of the old Italians,

in a manner did it. But most of the more ambitious spirits were wholly oblivious of the
truth that decorative skill must underlie all
monumental painting. The man who can
decorate a space may go on as far as his
powers permit. History and the grand style
are open to him. To attempt history without
first mastering decoration is to court sure disaster. While Morse was still plastic he might
have learned the true way from Delacroix, had
he had the eyes to see him, as La Farge did
later. But Morse saw Delacroix too late and
probably with disapproval.

As it was, Morse voluntarily forewent a
sure and honorable career. He was a portraitist of no common order. In imaginative
painting he reached a passable academic competence. For the asking he might have had the
repute and prosperity of his older and younger
contemporaries, Washington Allston and Daniel Huntington. He was clearly their equal in
seriousness and imagination, and in skill distinctly their superior. In my opinion he attained about the artistic development that his
powers and the conditions permitted. When
he deserted art for the telegraph, some just
instinct told him that nothing but repetition was
ahead. Of his own painting, after his great dis-

illusionment, he thought far too poorly. He was a sterling and skilful portraitist, one of the soundest and withal most brilliant practitioners of his time. His modest place in the history of American painting is a perfectly sure one. He will not be forgotten, and his eventual repute is likely rather to rise than to fall.

[1923.]

III

GEORGE INNESS

GEORGE INNESS, "Evening, Medfield"

GEORGE INNESS

American painting started with portraiture, and in the work of West, Stuart, Malbone, Jarvis, Harding, and Morse early attained real distinction. The portrait easily multiplied itself into the group, and the group as readily became a subject picture. Thus the contemporary triumphs of Benjamin West, Washington Allston, John Trumbull, and Henry Inman rested on historical painting in the traditional grand style. The theoretical basis was the "Discourses of Sir Joshua Reynolds," the technical basis, the practice of the English or French academies. The whole movement was a brilliant importation which failed to root itself and soon faded.

American landscape, on the contrary, was of humbler origin and native. It grew out of topography, as it had earlier in England. Seaports, ships, civic improvements, country places, were sketched and commemorated in engraving. The work was rude but honest. Soon draughtsmen of fairly professional competence like the partners Alvan Fisher and William G.

Wall published colored sheets and entire albums of our scenery. Meanwhile the writings of Washington Irving and of Fenimore Cooper had cast the glamour of legend about both our wild and cultivated sites, and the cult of Bryant's and of Wordsworth's poetry had added to legend and naïve love of nature the sanction of religious mysticism. By 1830 the artistic current was setting from the grand style to landscape. It had the interest of being exclusively and intensely a native movement.

If such an amiable topographer as Thomas Doughty stems from the English tonalists, such more characteristic figures as Thomas Cole and Asher B. Durand are entirely self-taught. They are formed before Düsseldorf and Barbizon have gained sway, they grow in strange obliviousness of the contemporary glories of Constable and Turner. Thus the Hudson River School may be rather a poor thing, but it is emphatically our own, and it presents to the student at least the charm of modesty, seriousness, and primitive sincerity—and that in an age elsewhere given over to sophistication. It also offers the phenomenon, rare enough in the last century, of a common point of view in artist and public. It was the faith of young America in the pioneers of the Hud-

son River School that made possible the
achievement of a Homer Martin, an Alexander
Wyant, and a George Inness.

George Inness was born at Kingston, New
York, May 1, 1825. His father was of Scotch
extraction and a grocer by trade. The boy
grew to young manhood at Newark, New Jersey, then not a whirl of machinery and trams,
but a sleepy little city with abundant local tradition and pride. About it stretched one of the
loveliest prospects in the world, now defaced
by reeking chimneys and blatant advertising
boards—the Passaic and Hackensack meadows
with their noble rim of encircling heights.
These great marshes with their swinging
estuaries, their abundance of seasonal flowers,
have an infinite variety of charm within their
apparent monotony, and the glory of dawn and
sunset nowhere yields richer or more delicate
incandescences than it does among the reeds
and cattails that carpet this old bed of the
Hudson. Treeless or nearly so, these meadows
are bordered by gently rolling country adorned
by the finest elms, white oaks, scarlet oaks,
maples and beeches. Even New England
presents in autumn no such clamor of scarlet,
crimson, yellow, and glowing russet as does
the Orange Mountain where it rolls up from

the meadows. It was then a farming country broken into glades and hillocks, offering juxta-position of left-over forest trees with orchard or pasture—an agreeable, intimate, half-tamed landscape, with plentiful reminders of its primi-tive solemnity. The love of this sort of land-scape beauty is the single permanent character-istic of our most versatile and volatile painter.

George Inness shifted his sketching grounds widely. The Roman Campagna, the coast of France, and England, the Alleghenies, the White Mountains and the Sierras, the Moors of Scotland, at one time or another engrossed him. But he is always at his best in such pictures as recall the rim of the meadows of the Hackensack. For him, as for so many artists, the first keen revelation of beauty was to de-termine the career. When in old age he came back to Eagleswood and later to Montclair, it was with a sure instinct that his supreme and most personal effort as an artist could only be made amid the recollections of childhood.

For George Inness's education we have the slightest information. He was delicate and high-strung—an epileptic. Neither his health, his inclination, nor the circumstances of his family permitted much schooling. There was an attempt to make a shop clerk of him, but his

vivacities repelled customers. His education
was to come slowly and adequately, from books
and from life. He is said to have studied in a
drawing school and to have worked with an
engraver at Newark when but a lad. Later he
worked for a bare month in 1845 with Régis
Gignoux at New York. Gignoux was about
nine years Inness's senior. A product of
French academic training, a favorite pupil of
Delaroche, he had at least shown initiative in
following a pretty American girl to New York,
persuading her to marry him, and making a
good living for her. As the first specialist in
snow scenes he retains a modest place in the history of American landscape painting. In his
practice he tried to realize a happy mean between the dryness of the academic style and
the apparently dangerous richness of the new
Romantic technic.

It is customary to deny any influence of Gignoux on Inness. I feel, on the contrary, that
Gignoux in that brief month came within an
ace of spoiling our best landscape painter.
Gignoux, as compared with such naïve American landscape painters as Thomas Cole and
Asher B. Durand, was a professional, and con-
versant with all the tricks. He didn't look very
hard at anything, but he knew the tree touch,

as exemplified by Hobbema, the cloud and snow
touches as worked out by Aart van der Neer.
Inness not unnaturally grasped eagerly at this
facile lore. His early landscapes are so insincere and superficial, and withal so discourag-
ingly accomplished, that it is hard to see the
makings of a good painter in him. Such a landscape as "Early Recollections," dated 1849,
Inness's twenty-fifth year, is an appalling picture for any young artist to live down. There
is no trace of honest observation in it. It is
built up of approved touches, recipes, contrasts,
has the merit of careful composition, and in
a shallow rural vein is entirely charming. No
young landscape painter has a right to be as
smartly competent as Inness here shows himself. He himself was soon to see the error and
most resolutely to turn his back upon such
cheap successes.

Compare with "Early Recollections" the
river scene "On the Juniata" painted only seven
years later, in 1856. It is hard to see the same
mind in the two works. From being facile,
nondescript, and vaguely picturesque, everything has become tense, specific, and local. In
the marvellously studied trees and weeds and
sedges, in the exact and exquisite notation of
shadow and reflection, the picture offers all the

gifts of the eager and patient eye. And if it is rather microscopically seen, it is nobly composed. The grandeur and serenity of the idea transcends all smallness of execution.

Plainly something has happened to an artist who is chipper and ostentatious at twenty-five and reverent and humble as regards nature at thirty-two. And a good deal had happened to George Inness in the interval. He had married and gone twice abroad, sojourned in Paris and lingered in Rome. His wife had borne him a son to inherit his name and talent. Above all he had experienced a definite religious conversion under the influence of his elder colleague, William Page. Page was one of those impressive personalities which fail of complete expression in their works. A few faded portraits of a great accent tell us that Page had sat at the feet of Titian. In the correspondence of the Brownings there is a recurrent phrase for Page —"that noble Page" is repeated through the letters. One does not easily or falsely make such an impression upon such intimates as the Brownings. And the earnestness, dignity and sweetness of William Page were precisely the corrective needed by the clever and volatile Inness. Their association at Rome and at Eagleswood was most beneficial for the younger man. Page had struggled with the severe Calvinism of Andover Seminary and had finally found peace in the singularly mathematical optimism of Emmanuel Swedenborg.

George Inness now fed his religious spirit from this source. He also found peace both in the expansive sublimity of his new creed and in its quaint logical trimness and formality. He no longer saw nature as an attractive something to be cleverly mimicked, but as the very vesture of Deity, the hem of which an artist might touch only with awe. Landscape painting became no longer a mere accomplishment, but a search for truth and an act of worship. This mystical side of Inness's art we must consider later, and at some length; meanwhile this lovely view on the Juniata shows the endeavor for strength and accuracy which is to mark Inness's pictures for the next twenty years. It is remarkable that a young American of genius should bring back from Europe only the counsel of fidelity to our American nature. Yet it must be remembered that Inness was no frequenter of galleries, while in the early 'fifties the Constables and Rousseaus and Corots from which he was soon to learn much were neither in public galleries nor at all available for a casual tourist. I have no doubt that he studied the Claudes at Rome, and thereby fortified his own natural gift for composition, but I am satisfied that he studied the landscape of Asher B. Durand more faithfully than he ever did that of any European master.

Durand is the true ancestor of whatever is strenuous and experimental in American painting, as his friend and contemporary Thomas Cole is of our temperamental and poetic art. Both, unluckily, had painted good pictures before they had seen good pictures. Durand had passed from the drudgery of copper-plate engraving to portraiture and thence to landscape. He worked with the microscopic eye, trying for the specific, in texture of bark and moss, in substance of rock and earth. He loved combinations of meadowland and wild scenery such as the Hudson River and the intervales of the White Mountains afforded. He loved the equable light of clouded afternoons. He brought to landscape the simple natural enthusiasm of the average cultivated American of the time, and he painted the face of nature with pious notation of every dimple or wrinkle. He achieved a solid descriptive kind of prose, but of a singularly colorless kind. In an infinity of little crisp touches, each locally right enough, one color annuls another and the whole picture sinks into a featureless and negative grayness. He never sees how the whole is coming out, but reverently and hopefully labors the parts.

Thomas Cole on the contrary had a prophetic notion of the intended picture, and a positive accent. But he had too little knowledge of details and only a passable sense of color. A roamer in the wilds of Ohio and Pennsylvania, he felt the melancholy poetry of our great forested mountains. There are places so still that a bird's note is startling. Cole spread these vast forest silences upon his canvases with fine feeling and adequate skill. He is panoramic where Durand often chose the limited view. Cole's landscapes have the severe, cool note of Bryant's poetry, and it is Bryant who has written the finest and truest words on Cole's art:

"Pictures which carried the eye to a scene of wild grandeur peculiar to our country, over our aerial mountain tops, with their mighty growth of forests never touched by the axe, along the banks of streams never deformed by culture, and into the depths of skies bright with the hues of our own climate . . . and into the transparent abysses of which it seemed as if you might send an arrow out of sight."

Cole was a poet and musician as well as a

painter, a sensitive and companionable man. He went to Europe for new subjects rather than for new methods. He worked out a sparse Puritan method of his own in which neutral browns, grays and greens afforded a sufficient harmony to accompany his grave and simple lyrics. The gift of richness and color was never his, and in the moral allegories into which he let himself be drawn his defects are patent and lamentable. Still he is the poet among our pioneer landscapists, and this vein found the richest fulfilment in Homer Martin.

Inness himself in his latest phase was to take up and give splendor to the ideals of Cole, but at the outset Inness was wise enough to see the dangers of this panoramic picture making. Instead he chose the entirely sound and available naturalism of Durand. And Inness had what Durand lacked—a fine instinctive sense of color. Between 1856 and 1868 we can trace in Inness the disappearance of detail in behalf of color effect, the growth of power in rendering swing and texture—the easy accomplishment of all that Durand had tried so hard for and never wholly attained.

Through the 'fifties Inness worked mostly in New York, living in Brooklyn. His painting steadily grows in breadth, the larger truth of

effect superseding the smaller truth of detail.
His color comes clearer and in larger masses,
his paint is often loaded and worked about—
the whole look more modern and European.
The quick progress along these lines is well
shown by contrasting with the "Juniata River"
of 1856, the "Hackensack Meadows" of 1859,
which is in the New York Public Library. It is
a less agreeable picture than the earlier one, the
contrasts are exaggerated, the simplification of
masses of foliage and herbage a little bare, the
handling of the paint, though resolute, somewhat heavy and monotonous. Something of
the virginal loveliness of the earlier work has
gone. But there is great gain in skill, and a real
growth towards unity. Already we have wonderful edges that characterize almost unaided
the masses therein contained, and we have instead of copies of weeds and twigs fine manipulations of paint that suggest such features
without impairing the general effect. Inness is
travelling the way of Théodore Rousseau and
Jules Dupré and by this time is conscious of
their value as examples.

By his fortieth year, 1865, Inness had attained a complete mastery of spacious themes.
In that year he signed the great picture "Peace
and Plenty" and the even greater little canvas

"The Delaware Valley," both in the Metropolitan Museum. In the "Peace and Plenty" he has taken, possibly in deliberate competition, a subject similar to Cole's "The Ox Bow." He has introduced an infinity of rustic detail without cumbering the arrangement, has saturated the whole with harvest color and invested it with shimmering air. The panorama misses grandeur, but has instead a direct and hearty sense of the charm of fat fields in harvest time. One has only to compare with it the artificial rusticity of the "Recollections of Childhood" of sixteen years earlier to note Inness's artistic growth.

But "The Delaware Valley" is a far more important picture, as showing Inness's positive command of effects of cloud and wind and air. It is painted with utmost freedom, with beautiful expressions for texture, nearness and farness, for the rolling up of clouds, and the loss of mountain slopes in their grazing edges. It is worked in freely broken color in a way not less masterful than Constable's. Above all it has a definite unity of mood and vision—nothing could be added or taken away. And this unity depends largely on the light which invades all forms. It is a picture of absorptions and reflections—as if between the clouds and the

earth the light were an active spirit, transforming at will whatever it touches. Thus the
painter grasps not merely the poetical motive
of unity, but also the scientific spirit of flux.
The clouds will settle and break, the rain will
fall, a new light will create a new scene.

In view of such work as this, Inness's elec-
tion in 1868 to the National Academy seems
tardy. Doubtless the immense repute of Albert
Bierstadt and F. E. Church—painters of gran-
diose mountain scenes—stood between Inness
and the public. Their pictures were shown
amid red plush curtains before footlights, and
sold for fabulous sums. On the other hand the
prim and trim art of John F. Kensett offered a
more available attraction. His lake and mountain scenes, smoothly painted, picturesquely arranged, affecting the pearliness of dawn or the
glow of evening, enjoyed an enormous popu-
larity. Kensett was a genial sociable person as
well, whereas Inness was already a somewhat
solitary and eccentric man. Plainly he bewil-
dered both the critics and the amateurs of the
black walnut era. The generally expansive
Henry T. Tuckerman writes of him, in 1867,
in "The Book of the Artists":

"Inness, in his best moods, is effective
through his freedom and boldness, whereby he

often grasps the truth with refreshing power;
sometimes this manner overleaps the modesty
of nature, and license takes the place of freedom; somewhat too much of the French style is
often complained of as vitiating the legitimate
individuality of this artist; and there is in him,
as in so many of his peers, a provoking want of
sustained excellence, a spasmodic rather than a
consistent merit."

With the wisdom of hindsight it is easy to
smile at Tuckerman's condescension towards
the only capable landscape school of his time.
It is harder to pardon him his failure to perceive the immense superiority of George Inness
over the Durands, Kensetts, and Sanford Gif-
fords, whom he had so unqualifiedly praised.
Yet in a blundering way Tuckerman had touched
the weakness of a great painter—Inness's im-
moderation, his tendency rather to improvise
than to reflect. As a matter of fact it was the
variety of Inness that bothered his contemporaries to the very end. It is an art that never
wholly standardizes itself, and the art dealer
and art patron alike crave characteristic pictures. Of course Inness himself was very little
interested in the dealer and patron and completely engrossed with his own mystical cos-
mologies and his painting. In ten years of in-

tense study he had thoroughly mastered the forms of American landscape—had indeed memorized them, and had simultaneously worked out a technic as free and modern as that of his great French exemplars. Indeed it might seem as if no progress were likely beyond such pictures as the Delaware Valley group or so gracious and imposing a canvas as the "Autumn," in the Rhode Island School of Design. To Inness, however, these apparent perfections were merely so many dissatisfactions—reasons not for stopping but for pressing onward.

The extraordinary personality of the man has so much engrossed his critics and biographers that they have neglected the plain business of telling where he lived and sketched and travelled. So far as I can gather from scattered and vague evidence, he was at Medfield, near Boston, from about 1859 to 1864. There he made wonderful sketches which were elaborated into pictures for many years to come. From about 1865 to 1870 he was mostly at Eagleswood, New Jersey, near Perth Amboy, in reach of his native tidal meadows. From 1870 to 1874 or so he was in Europe, chiefly in Italy. Thenceforth he lived mostly at New York, and in his last ten years on the heights above Montclair, New Jersey. He made occasional trips to England, to Florida, and to the Sierras. As to sketching grounds, he made few real sketches out of doors after the Italian trip of the early 'seventies. There the sheer novelty and loveliness of the scenery lured him into old pursuits now no longer necessary, his memory being stored with beautiful forms. After his first beginnings I think Inness rarely painted pictures in the open air. In this he differed from his fellows of the Hudson River School who put themselves to the most needless pains in the interest of a quite imaginary fidelity to nature. And as Inness grew older and his habitual invalidism increased, nature became rather a personal solace than a direct model, and his pictures represented so many ardent improvisations upon themes long ago memorized.

The Italian trip which closed with his fiftieth year constituted a pause for reflection. It saw the consummation of his early practice and the preparation for his last manner. In particular he restudied composition with new zeal, and within the old fine arrangements he achieved a new simplicity of workmanship. It is as if he had considered admiringly the untroubled surfaces of Claude and Poussin and under their spell was momentarily constrained to curb the impetuosities of his own restless mind and hand. There is a great power and modesty about the representation of the forms in such a picture as the "Barberini Pines." Nothing is scamped, nothing overasserted. It is a massive, solid apparition with nothing of the evanescence of the Delaware Valley pictures. The balance and placing of the dull greens of the pines and the olives are impeccable. Masterly is the handling of that very difficult problem—a down-hill perspective. One or two such supreme examples of gravity and sobriety Inness was to give us, before cutting loose from representation and indulging the most fantastic visions. We find the perfect application of the Italian manner in the great canvas, "Evening at Medfield," painted like the "Barberini Pines" in 1875. We have the simplest and finest indications of the essential forms, the superb pollard saturated with the afterglow, the darkling ground with the curving path that leads the eye graciously to the grand mass of the grove. Other indications of cattle and buildings are of the finest and the whole thing swims in the deepest and most resonant evening glory—the illumined "dark air" of Dante. Such a picture in its grave and simple composition represents the application of the Italian method to memories of ten years earlier. It does consummately what Aalbert Cuyp, Old Crome, and young Turner had earlier essayed. These Italian and Italianate Innesses are not favorites—for the adequate reason that we properly associate Inness with the scenery of his native land, and for the poorer reason that, representing a transient perfection, they are not characteristic. They are after all America's most notable contribution to the old masterly tradition of landscape. They would hang better in the Louvre or the Uffizi than the more famous late Innesses. This by way of description and not to raise prematurely the issue of rank between the late Innesses and their predecessors.

From 1875 to 1880 or later a curious change comes over George Inness's painting. It seems mixed and confused. The color has no longer the depth of the mature works, while it has not attained the ineffable volatility of the last phase. The pictures seem to lack the earlier substance and to be aiming at an ethereality not yet fully realized. There is a not quite pleasant sense of ferment about them—a yeastiness in the very pigment. On the technical side this means that Inness has ceased to lay in the picture in brown, and no longer proceeds by successive over paintings. Spiritually the change corresponds so definitely to the intensification of his peculiar personality that we must perforce turn from the works to the man himself in order to arrive at any adequate explanation.

George Inness's master ideal was religious mysticism, of which his painting was merely an incidental expression. For many years he read little but theology—not I fear the wise and moderate fathers of Latin Christianity, but the enthusiasts of the recent sects. Fortunately G. W. Sheldon, an excellent critic of the early 'eighties, has left abundant -ana in his book on "American Painters" and in an article in the *Century Magazine* for 1898. Inness, we learn, talked incessantly and excitedly on religious and philosophical subjects, and left thousands of pages of quite unreadable manuscripts on these mysteries. Quite in the Neo-Platonic tradition, he had a mystical interpretation of the numbers. One meant infinity; two, conjunction; three, potency. Four signified substance and five germination. Of his painting he once said, "I would not give a fig for art ideas except as they represent what I perceive behind them; and I love to think most of what I, in common with all men, need most—the good of our practice in the art of life. Rivers, streams, the rippling brook, the hillside, the sky, clouds—all things

that we see—will convey the sentiment of the
highest art if we are in the love of God and
the desire of truth." It was this love of truth
that wrung from him apropos of Turner's hor-
ribly theatrical "Slave Ship" the harshest words
any artist has ever used of another. He
condemned that much discussed picture as "the
most infernal piece of claptrap ever painted."

Often Inness's religion worked very practically. He besieged the magazines in vain with
a 5000 word essay on Zola's "L'Assommoir"
as a consummate plea for temperance. Generally he regarded man and nature as a partial
revelation or representation of the great unity
that is God—a thought beautifully expressed
in a remark on one of his own pictures of falling leaves in autumn—each leaf being "a little
truth from off the tree of life."

Such hints must suffice for the mysticism of
George Inness. We have to do with an eccentric, with a crank if you will. His thinking
lacks background of culture, is often ragged
and confused. And the lucidity of his views on
art is in refreshing contrast to the cloudiness of
his views on religion.

He saw clearly that art does not address itself directly to the moral sense. It merely conveys an emotion (Tolstoy's view). This emo-

tion must be single, that the work of art may have unity. "The true beauty of the work consists in the beauty of the sentiment or emotion which it inspires. Its real greatness consists in the quality and force of this emotion." Again he has said, "A work of art is beautiful if the sentiment is beautiful, it is great if the sentiment is vital."

With such views, George Inness naturally despised insincere or weak painting. His favorite word of scorn for ill-constructed or inexpressive work was "dishwater," and he often applied it to his own pictures in their first stages. Mr. Daingerfield tells an instructive anecdote of a diaphanous Inness, all pearly grays and faint greens, with a pale sun. The painter regarded this faint loveliness with impatience, murmured his imprecation "dishwater," rubbed his thumb in the chrome yellow of his palette, and smeared the sharp color across the painted sun crying, "Stay there till you look white." This gesture meant repainting the entire picture, carrying all its values up to a point where the keen yellow should count no longer as color but merely as light.

The impulsive act recalls the readiness with which he destroyed or transformed his own works. He once came in excited from a thunderstorm, and in a few hours painted "The Coming Storm," now in the St. Louis Museum, over his own big canvas of "Mount Washington." Again, the frame maker one day sent in a frame which proved to be a misfit for a new canvas. Inness sent out for a canvas to fit the frame and finished it in a couple of hours. A purchaser sent back a delicate spring landscape to have the foreground indications of cows sharpened. After half a day of furious work Mr. Daingerfield saw on the easel "a stormy sunset, over a much-torn, surf-broken ocean," and Inness exulting over "the finest thing I've ever done," and chuckling, "I guess I touched up his cows for him."

This creative fury is characteristic of Inness. He never sat down to paint. When his right hand was for a time disabled, he readily learned to work with his left. He sometimes toiled for fifteen-hour stretches, often working on as many as twenty canvases during the long day. He effaced ruthlessly many exquisite pictures. He was ever talking of principles and ever changing them. His memory so teemed with images that the merest hint or analogy in nature released a picture—as when he looked down his little lane at Montclair and the vision of one of his finest river prospects rose clear before him.

If George Inness, then, seems the very type of the purely impulsive genius, impulse was corrected in him by very systematic theories and habits of work. The broader relations of light and dark in a picture must be determined by the value of the sky at the horizon, which should be a middle tone between the lightest and darkest parts. Nearly all of his mature works obey this law. These relations are true to natural appearance only when there are strong reflected lights from earth or water. Generally, the procedure involves an unnatural darkening of the sky. All the same it makes for unity in the effect by diminishing the contrast between sky and earth. For that matter it was the consistent practice of the great Dutch landscape painters Ruysdael and Hobbema and Van Goyen.

Inness's theory also required the division of the picture from the bottom to the horizon into three well-defined planes of which the second should contain the motives of chief interest. All minor objects should be kept within the sky line. Pedantic as the rule may seem, it makes for unity and the rather empty and open first plane lures the eye far into the picture and creates a positive sense of spaciousness.

More original than these precepts for composition, was Inness's endeavor to achieve the fullest harmony of tone through the fullest assertion of color. In this he approaches Cézanne's theory that where the color is strongest the form should be most perceptible. Here Inness was in the line of the most modern painting and at odds with his great model, Rousseau, and his own contemporaries Wyant and Homer D. Martin, who for the sake of unity reduced all colors to middle tones. Such a method, though legitimate enough and for certain emotional expressions perhaps inevitable, seemed an uncourageous evasion to Inness—a concession to that "dishwater" and "pea soup" which his robust soul ever loathed.

About 1880, after five years of apparent fumbling, but really of strenuous research, he worked out the method which distinguishes the "typical" Innesses of the dealers and museums. Meanwhile he produced certain lovely transitional works such as the little sketch "Pompton River," at Chicago, in which the intricate tender greens are balanced with the skill of a Daubigny. The latest method is so well described by Mr. Daingerfield that I have only to transcribe him, condensing slightly:

"In working upon a new canvas the subject was drawn in with a few bold strokes, the structure and principle underlying the theme being fully grasped, this was then stained in with due regard for breadth and light and shade, but the tones were not extremely varied nor was the full power of contrast sought. The pigment was always transparent and thinned with a vehicle. . . . As this stain set or grew tacky, it was rubbed or scrubbed into the canvas, lights were scratched out with a thumbnail or brush handle, or wiped out with a rag—always modelling, drawing, developing, in the most surprising manner: never at a loss for a form . . . they seemed to shape themselves at his touch, and the brush was spread with extreme force, as it scrubbed until in its scratching there developed wonderful growths of grass, or weeds, or trees. As this color tightened in the drying the forms were sharpened . . . The picture now being fairly set, and the whole theme fairly pulsating with the vibrant unctuous flow of it all, for as yet there were no touches of opaque color, he would sharpen a few lights by scratching—perhaps with a knife, more often with the finger nail—add a note here and there of stronger color and stop for the time."

Plainly such pictures were, as Whistler insisted all pictures should be, "finished from the first." The sparing addition of local color was a secondary process which might or might not be necessary, and on such a foundation a very little frank color would give the most resonant effects. The initial creative energy was what counted. The method of cautiously enriching a complete transparent preparation was that of Rubens. It admits of no sullying the purity of the color, rejects bold contrasts, and produces a coruscation from within the picture itself.

Thus were painted the pictures that represent George Inness's splendid afterglow—the Innesses in which solid earth melts into air, and light penetrates grass and treetops, and the world seems to throb and shiver under the kiss of the sun. One need only compare a picture of the 'sixties with one of the early 'nineties to see what has happened.

Everything has been simplified and volatilized. Any corner of nature, any motive—just the shimmer of a beech trunk in the swelter of summer, a few of the tall columns of a southern pine grove, the fountain of blossoms that is an apple tree in spring, the glooming of a dark pool before a grove—the simplest and most usual features of our landscape are now motive enough for a great picture. Through these few and carefully placed forms the light comes and goes in waves of purest color—crimsons, emeralds, topazes, sapphires. There is a sort of struggle and clash of light and color with form —a tendency of the colored light to dissolve the form, and a contrary tendency of the form to assert itself. The result is a singular harmony—tense, exciting, a bit unstable, very unlike the serene and sustained harmonies that we expect to find in most great landscape painters. Instead we have the somewhat vague ardor of George Inness's religious mysticism —a pictorial unity not quite inevitable but a little hectic and forced. The artist no longer intimates the unity of nature, he rather insists on it, but he does so with a grand and sonorous eloquence.

In the summer of 1894 George Inness died at the Brig of Allan in Scotland. His last years were his most creative, and fame was rapidly overtaking his endeavor. He had had abundant honors, had exhibited at Paris as early as 1850 and been medalled there at the World Exposition of 1889. Three years after his death his pictures were vigorously disputed in the auction room and now they fetch the prices of fine Rousseaus and Corots. He is the only American landscape painter who is generally known today in Europe and he has received generous praise from such historians of modern art as Richard Muther.

It is superfluous to call the roll of the last great pictures. The "Mill Pond," "Rainbow after Rain," at Chicago; "Spring Blossoms," at the Metropolitan Museum; "Sundown" at the National Gallery, Washington; "Afterglow" and the "Wood Gatherers," in private collections, are universally known and loved. It seems also too early to fix his precise place in American landscape painting. Certainly none of our landscapists was more various and skilful. I may perhaps most clearly suggest his limitations by asking the question—What are the great Innesses? It would be a very difficult question to answer. All the Innesses are fine and in their degree great, but nothing stands out as consummately so. This is not the case with such contemporaries as Wyant and Homer Martin. We say confidently that the fullest expression of Wyant's thin, elegiac poetry is the "Adirondack Clearing" in the Metropolitan Museum. We are in no doubt as to Homer Martin's few masterpieces—the grand melan-

choly of "Westchester Hills," the crushing
pathos of the "Haunted Manor," the supreme
gracefulness of the "Harp of the Winds."

With Inness it is different—the impression is
more uniformly exhilarating and all-overish.
He himself would have insisted that his work
must be judged strictly by the value of the sentiment. And the sentiment in the later works
is a sort of abstract sun-worship—a somewhat
dehumanized ideal. Towards the later glories
of Turner, Inness was curiously unsympathetic,
perhaps for the good reason that he saw in
Turner's gorgeous improvisations many of his
own defects. Like Turner he lacked patience.
He lacked as well the deeply reflective quality
of such born landscape painters as Jacob Ruysdael and Théodore Rousseau, while he never
achieved the instinctively balanced spontaneity
of Corot. George Inness ever struggled with
the sore difficulty of combining subjectivity of
mood with a reasonable objectivity of presentation. In his later years subjectivity ran riot.
It may be then that the future will effect some
readjustment of valuation in his case. I can
imagine a time when for their slightness and ex-
travagance the late or characteristic Innesses
will lose a little, and the marvellously balanced

and robustly conceived pictures of the late 'sixties and early 'seventies will gain.

But these are ungenerous and perhaps unprofitable speculations. America will always remember with admiration the most flame-like spirit her art has offered.

[1927.]

IV

ELIHU VEDDER

ELIHU VEDDER, "Rome, Patroness of the Arts"

ELIHU VEDDER

Elihu Vedder was the last of those early American artists who were Italianate by residence and by inspiration—and far the greatest of a line on the whole more interesting personally than notable artistically. He himself was remarkable on both counts, being not only one of the great imaginative designers of his time, but also, and somewhat paradoxically, a most witty and whimsically delightful man.

All this was hardly to be expected from his ancestry. He came of a solid and much-intermarried line of Dutch stock, pioneers at Schenectady, New York. He was born in Varick Street, in the city of New York, in 1836, sent to the usual schools, and in early boyhood displayed of his future talents only a desire to make almost anything and a restless inventiveness.

His father, a merchant in the Cuban sugar trade, was mostly absent. Visits to him in Cuba, charmingly described in "The Digressions of V," must have gone far to make the future artist. There was a freer life, glory of

73

ponies and boots and spurs, dark-eyed little girls who gave look for look and sometimes kiss for kiss, slaves, pestilence, cheapness of human life, and waving of giant palms between blue sky and bluer sea.

Things happened, too, to make the eager little boy face grave issues. He one day found a beloved lodger crumpled and quiet against the wainscot. The memory of the thing twenty years later created one of his best little canvases, "The Dying Alchemist." When an old cemetery was moved at Schenectady, he saw come out of the ground the white bones of an uncle whom he had never seen in the flesh. An Aunt Sarah habitually saw visions and told them and, having committed the unpardonable sin, quietly awaited damnation. An Uncle Custer went mad, but not before predicting that carriages would move by their own power and that machines would fly. Young Elihu himself was shot and nearly killed in hunting. At sixteen he saw his mother fade and die. In Cuba he viewed the strand where the unbaptized dead were cast out to the sun and the buzzards. That memory of festering rags and worse later got into his picture, "The Plague in Florence." Then there were always girls—encounters casual or ardent. All this meant an exercise in seeing and feeling such as an American lad rarely gets. It greatly enhanced what he later called "the rich, romantic sadness of youth."

From his 'teens he began to draw, and after a vain attempt to break him in in an architect's office, his father faced the inevitable and put him with a drawing master, nicknamed "Pilgrim Matheson," from his favorite theme, at Sherbourne, New York.

At twenty, 1856, Vedder set out for Paris, where he drifted into Picot's class for the antique. Some fatality kept him from, perhaps protected him from, the current successful masters, Couture and Boisbaudran, and he missed also the new wonder of Courbet, Manet, Millet. To the established glories of Ingres and Delacroix he was equally oblivious. Fate willed it that his art should be, in his own words "home-made," but it was not precisely that, for it was soon to possess itself of the richest of backgrounds—that of the Italian Golden Age.

What luck led him tramping along the Cornice Road to Italy he does not tell. At Florence the pedantic Bonaiuti furthered him little more than Picot had at Paris, but at least gave the student the example of a strenuous and elevated spirit—a lesson not lost on such a youngster as Vedder. But his artistic education came from Italy itself—the old masters, the villa-clad hills, the crumbling streets of old cities, the climbing cypresses on the winding roads. These things he sketched with gusto and growing skill and with a freer brush than he later commanded.

In 1861 it became impossible for his father to continue the six hundred dollars a year that had spelt Italy and liberty. After a perilous voyage from Cadiz, young Vedder, now twenty-five, anchored off New York on the day when Sumter was fired on.

Vedder's old gunshot wound, which caused the left arm to be permanently weakened, made the eagerly desired military service impossible. He settled to a bitter struggle, slept on a pallet, at times lacked food. Working for the wood-block cutters, the wages were fifty cents for a pictorial idea, a dollar and a half for a suggestive sketch, three dollars for a finished drawing on the wood. But in the lean war-time years he imagined and created "The Questioner of the Sphinx," "The Fisherman and the Genii," "The Roc's Egg," "The Lair of the Sea Serpent," "The Lost Mind." Akin to these is that handful of admirable illustrations which he made in 1865 for an edition of Tennyson's "Enoch Arden." Few young paint-

ers have ever made a more solid and brilliant
début in imaginative design. The critics hailed
him. In 1865 he was elected to the National
Academy, being probably the youngest painter
who has ever received that honor. These early
canvases are among the biggest little pictures
that have ever been painted. "The Lair of the
Sea Serpent," with its sense of vastness and
loneliness and its hint of terror and its exceptionally lovely color, has for years been one of
the best seen pictures in the Boston Museum.
"The Lost Mind," in the Metropolitan Museum, is one of the dozen most impressive pictures on its richly garnished walls. Vedder had
achieved what no American painter before him
had seriously attempted—Albert Ryder and
John La Farge had not asserted themselves—
an art fraught with gravity, simplicity, and
noble imaginative content—as Mr. W. C.
Brownell wrote many years ago, a work "pene-
trated with thought, with reflection, with significance."

If I could persuade the reader to turn to
Mr. Brownell's essay in *Scribner's* for 1895, I
could both abridge and greatly better, vicari-
ously, my task of appreciation. As it is I shall
here and there quote from it.

That Vedder should run away from such

a success and settle in Italy seems at once odd and characteristic. Various considerations prompted the decision. First, in five laborious years he had barely made a poor living—and at that had been driven into all manner of hack work. Next, as the Italian associations faded, he found nothing to replace them. He made various excursions in New England and found nothing he wanted to paint. But the true reason is well recounted in the "Digressions," in an interview with Emerson. The sage of Concord had repeatedly insisted that, nature being one, all heavens should be alike for the artist, who had better remain under that which saw his birth. To this Vedder objected:

"Mr. Emerson, I think there is a great difference between the literary man and the artist in regard to Europe. Nature is the same everywhere, but literature and art are nature seen through other eyes, and a literary man in Patagonia without books to consult would be at a great disadvantage. Here he has all that is essential in the way of books; but to the artist, whose books are pictures, this land is Patagonia. Take from your shelves your Bible, Plato, Shakespeare, Bacon, Montaigne, etc., and make it so that you could not consult them

without going to Europe, and I think it would
soon be—Ho, for Europe!"

So Ho for Europe it was. There was an
interval in Paris and Brittany with the William
Hunts and the lifelong friend, Charles Caryl
Coleman. In 1867 Vedder became engaged to
Caroline Rosekrans, and the period of episodic
girls ended. In 1869 he married the stately
and accomplished woman who was to be his
helpmate for forty years, and settled rather by
habit than by intention in Italy. In the remarkable records of works of art sold between 1869
and 1883, the year of the Omar illustrations—
see the "Digressions" for the list—these seem
on the whole fallow years. The four children
came rapidly. The little picture available for
the passing tourist had to be cultivated: there
was the joy of exploration and sketching in the
hill towns, the pleasure of working in wood and
metal, and amusingness of reviving the little
painting—the *cassone* manner of the Italian
Renaissance. In these years, divided between
Perugia and Rome, Vedder seems to have lived
on the small change of his art. Perhaps the
best things are still hidden in his portfolios—
for he hated to let a fine sketch go. Anyhow
there are crayon sketches of magical cleverness
and dexterity—an unexpected note in the illus-

trator of Omar—dating from these years, un-
awarded prizes still open to the intelligent
museum director or open-minded amateur.
And there are sketches which have the sense of
tears in them.   For these days saw the death of
many comrades and of two beloved sons.   To
the "rich romantic sadness of youth" was added
abundantly those real sorrows of maturity—
those tears which best water the plant of
genius.

For better or for worse Vedder is likely to
be known as the illustrator of Omar.   He
learned of the quatrains at Perugia through
Henry Ellis, adept in Chaucer and in Blake.
Blake and the "Rubáiyát" gave to Vedder's
mature imagination just the shock needed to
detach new visions from the Renaissance background.   Vedder never seems to derive from
one master in the sense that his friend La Farge
may be said to draw from Delacroix and from
Titian.   Vedder assimilated rather the leading
principle of the Italian Renaissance than the
particular practice of any master.   And that
principle was that the human body is not only
beautiful apart from any ulterior meaning, but
is also universally available and adequate for
the noblest symbolism.   So in the century of
illustrations for Omar, "accompaniments" Ved-

der appropriately called them, we have grand and elemental figures, nude or lightly draped, which not only convey the meaning of the quatrains, but often seem to raise these meanings to a higher significance. We are dealing in text and picture with the simplest poetry of the race —the short sweetness of life and love, the keen but uncertain solaces of that wine which is both drink and philosophy, the pathos of death and parting, the mystery in life and the darker obscurity beyond—in short, with those great but generally unperceived commonplaces which are of the very essence both of meditative poetry and of monumental design.

To embody all this, Vedder's crayon wrought out massive and gracious forms of men and women, fit receptacles for all that love and life can pour forth, as for all that death and fate can drain away. There is passion in these forms, with resignation and melancholy. No painter of the century, with the single exception of George Frederic Watts, has found such vivid and convincing symbols for those great reflective emotions which, if we will, are ours simply by our right as human beings. The drawings were put through in a gush of inspiration in twelve months of 1883 and 1884, amid the dank, funereal laurels and cypresses of the Villa

Strohl-Fern at Rome. Unhappily they were but indifferently reproduced in the original large edition. They come better in the successive small editions, but the real publication remains to be made. Since the drawings are still kept together a real reproduction is still possible. It would not only be a signal monument to Vedder's genius, but also one of the most significant memorials of our imaginative design.

Following the Omar, came some of the best paintings: the noble and sensitive head of Lazarus, "The Enemy Sowing Tares," "The Cumæan Sibyl." Any seeing eye could read in the designs for Omar the assertion of a great gift for mural painting. Charles McKim first made this discovery and endeavored to enlist Vedder for the World's Exhibition at Chicago in 1893. The conditions of time being impossible for him, Vedder escaped from Daniel C. Burnham's joyous crew of painters and accepted a commission for a ceiling in the New York residence of Collis P. Huntington. It has been transferred since to the Yale Art Museum. He chose, as a Renaissance decorator would have done, the obvious impersonations that lent themselves to abstract handling of the figure—the "Sun with the Four Sea-

sons," in a great medallion; the "Moon and
Fortune," in narrow spandrels with a winding
pattern of arabesques and small nude caryatids.
The whole was disposed, after Raphael's precedent, as a gracious and significant filling of
chosen geometrical spaces, without such tricks
and illusions of perspective as are usual in ceiling designs. The decoration was conducted
with emphatic linear rhythm and without much
positive color. There is a plastic quality about
the modelling, and the design—as in all of
Vedder's mural paintings—could be acceptably
rendered in low relief and in monochrome.
To this plastic quality many critics have objected and Vedder himself, in the "Digressions," seems to deplore the rather negative
quality of his later color. Indeed, he used to
say ruefully, and I think self-deceived, that a
fine colorist had gone astray in himself.

Personally I think the objection and the regret were both ill-founded. What Vedder had
to say was complete in line, mass, and composition. His idea of decoration needed only an
enriched monochrome; more color, or a more
realistic treatment, would have compromised
the terse and logical abstractness of the
method. The intimate and particular graces of
painting are not valid in the field of general

ideas. Raphael knew that and so did Ingres. Thus Vedder's economy of color and incident should be regarded really as a mark of richness —of complete clarification and control of the intellectual conception.

While the Huntington decorations were going on, McKim got Vedder to do a lunette, "The Idea of Art," for the Walker Art Gallery at Bowdoin College. The year was 1894. The theme was Nature flanked by personifications of Sculpture, Architecture, and Poetry on one side, and by Harmony, Love, and Painting on the other. We have the gracious unfunctional postures of the Renaissance style, a fine contrast of types and figures, and a simple and compelling rhythm.

In 1896 and 1897 Vedder designed for the Library of Congress five lunettes representing good and bad government and their results— subjects dear to such mediæval painters as Giotto and Ambrogio Lorenzetti—and the mosaic of Minerva. He affected to think lightly of these designs, but I fancy it was a whimsical pose. The lunette of Anarchy seems to me one of the best things in the mural painting of the century. It has not only the customary largeness and rightness of design, but legitimate intellectual subtleties all its own.

The joy of ruthless destruction, of a power that has passed beyond human good and evil, could not be better expressed.

Here Vedder's work as an artist virtually closes. It had consisted of three great spurts —the early imaginative pictures of 1863 to 1865, the Omar illustrations of 1883 to 1884, the mural paintings of 1893 to 1897. For lack of training and opportunity Vedder had come tardily to his own. The great impulse toward mural painting and the waning of our æsthetic parochialism found him an old man, if a singularly sturdy one, and ready to rest on his oars. The proceeds of his mural painting went into his Xanadu, the delightful Villa dei Quattro Venti, which he built astride the saddle between the two great mountains of the Island of Capri. There and in Roman winters he lived mostly in memories, cultivated old and new friendships, wrote his delightful autobiography, "The Digressions of V," 1910, and two books of quaint verses, "Moods," 1914, and "Doubts and Other Things," 1921. The last book—beautiful in its make and illustrations—came into his hands the evening before he died peacefully in his sleep. For that I am glad, since "V" adored his own verses. He had outlived his strength by six years, but not his wit and his musings.

What Vedder might have accomplished could he have chosen a later birthday, had he been professionally trained instead of having to train himself, had he enjoyed that small but certain and adequate income which he wistfully envisaged as the root of all artistic righteous-ness—is an interesting matter of speculation. It is the under-note of elegy in the fun and fancy of the "Digressions." As it is, it may seem enough that he was the greatest intellectualist painter of America in his day, and with few rivals among his contemporaries anywhere. With all his limitations—and painfully he knew them—he had, in Mr. Brownell's words, em-phatically expressed his own "native inclination for whatever is large and noble in form," and as well "a penetrating feeling for beauty in its full rather than in its fleeting aspects."

[1922.]

V

AFTERTHOUGHTS ON WHISTLER

JAMES MCNEILL WHISTLER, "Rosa Corder"

AFTERTHOUGHTS ON WHISTLER

A gentleman once came into a painter's studio, and in the course of chat admitted an income of fourteen thousand crowns. Before leaving, he inquired the price of a landscape and was told two hundred crowns; smilingly, he said he would call again, in hope of a lower price. On a second visit, the price was three hundred. Scenting a joke, the patron redoubled his praises of the picture and made a third inquiry. "Four hundred crowns," said the painter, "and a hundred crowns more every time you ask, and to rid myself of your importunity, and show up your stinginess, and finally, to prove that with all your fourteen thousand crowns you cannot buy one picture of mine, here goes." Whereupon the painter kicked the canvas into rags. This story is told, not of Whistler, but of one Salvator Rosa, who, more than two centuries earlier, had unpardonably anticipated many of the devices of the author of the "Gentle Art of Making Enemies."

Salvator's pictures are still in the galleries, but how little the pose he elaborately maintained now matters! The time will come when Whistler's symphonies and arrangements will have no advantage in mere notoriety over the reliques of stupid men. Horsley, of whose campaign against the nude was contemptuously written *Horsley soit qui mal y pense*, may look nearly as impressive as Whistler in a museum catalogue of the twenty-second century.

Already the mere wonder of Whistler is lessening. The legend which he assiduously built up is crumbling, despite the official hagiographers. Such comprehensive exhibitions as those of Boston and London tended at once to make more normal and slightly to diminish the impression of his art. The smaller anthology later presented by the Metropolitan Museum left one positively rubbing one's eyes and wondering what these battles already long ago were all about. Only a few weeks since this ill-proportioned square hall had been hung with Rembrandt, Steen, Ruysdael, Vermeer. The contrast was a bit overwhelming.

The three great portraits (what need to name the "Mother," the "Carlyle," and the "Miss Alexander?") were necessarily absent. Everything else was well represented, though one missed such a masterpiece of the early realistic days as "Westminster Bridge." For it

"The Blue Wave," a kind of sublimation of Courbet, was a fair substitute. The portraits were, with the exception of the etherial and baffling "Florence Leyland," which the Brooklyn Museum lent, conquerors in many previous shows. Here was that strange expression of wistful agility, the violinist Pablo Sarasate, and the fragile aristocracy of the poet Robert de Montesquiou. Here was the melancholy mask of that sorely tried and trying patron, Francis Leyland, the æsthetic ship master. In one corner, aloof, yet conscious of you, the "Andalousienne" glanced over her shoulder; across the hall was poised in complete unconsciousness "Rosa Corder," true Diana of Park Lane. Her presence almost compensated for the absence of the "Mother" and the adorable "Miss Alexander." The absolute discretion of Whistler's art is in this portrait of a young gentlewoman. Observing the pallor of the face proudly unconscious in its setting of vibrant browns and grays, Mr. Huneker happily read into the whole the legend of inaccessibility— *Noli me tangere.*

Beside the smaller portraits, the Japanese manner was exemplified in "The Golden Screen," and "Lange Leizen," the blues of which are a feast, and "The Ocean." Of the nocturnes and similar open-air arrangements, there were five, including the delicious "Blue and Silver——Battersea Reach" and the notorious "Falling Rocket," which cost Ruskin a farthing and several painful quarter-hours. In what, for want of a better name, we may call the English manner are the "Music Room" and the "Little White Girl." Singularly apart stood the big "White Girl," and to crown the exhibition there was a fine group of those nudes and semi-nudes in pastel which are rather obviously called the "Tanagra" series. The Museums, the Freer, Whittemore, Pope, and Johnson, and Canfield collections, among others, had given of their best. So great was the diversity of style that one was reminded of the analysis of the German critic Meier-Graefe, for whom Whistler was a case of multiple personality.

But under the evident variety of its components, the show had unity enough. A principle of ultrarefinement, of sensitiveness, and appealing charm ran through the whole. There is a Whistler manner as distinct as the Greuze mannerism. Realist, impressionist, mere prestidigitator—in all rôles, he is prince charming. The conviction grows insensibly, as one notes how many of these pictures lack the more substantial qualities of fine painting, that his art

is one of avoidance; negative, not positive.
There are certain exquisitely disciplined personalities to whom we yield ourselves uncondition-
ally, only to perceive later, and with a little
shock, that they prevail through elimination of
the common and wholesome asperities. This
thought we may pursue later. What is important is to note that, save for this evasive charm,
all Whistler's work has taken on a more usual
look. Possibly the miracle of the symphonies
and arrangements depended largely upon the
background of the Royal Academy, which as-
suredly was a world to satisfy a Huxley—a
world in which miracles did not happen.

Whistler's dæmon never served him better
than in suggesting London as a residence. His
native America was plainly out of the question.
Paris, the city of Whistler's love, afforded no
appropriate stage. Had he grown to maturity
alongside Boudin, Manet, Cazin, Fantin,
Degas, he would probably have been a better
painter. This was his own opinion. But,
clearly, he would have been much less of a portent. Even his wit would there have seemed not
outrageous, but merely exceptional. In the
Parisian drama he could hardly have been a
protagonist; London from the first gladly
awarded him the part of Apollyon, and trem-

bled while it hated. The result is that we have taken his works as the cartels of a champion. Against the murkiness of the Royal Academy they have glowed like an oriflamme. Seen simply as paintings, they must take on a different aspect. That, surely, is the reason why just the shade of a misgiving now accompanies the attempt to renew the old, fond adventure of a soul among symphonies and arrangements.

It will clarify our vision if we go to the galleries of old masters in the Metropolitan Museum for a moment and there take a glance at a few superlative examples of fine painting. Let us choose Vermeer of Delft, Hals in his portrait of a woman, Renoir's Mme. Charpentier among her children, Manet's "Boy with a Sword." Then to the Vanderbilt Gallery, observing on the way a supreme example of charm, Rossetti's Lady Lilith. In the long corridor, for charm and masterly execution combined, let us halt before the best of the Alfred Stevenses. As we pursue the long way back, it will be well to lug in Velasquez. Thus we shall have set for the Whistlers the very severest comparisons, and I think that only a fanatic will deny that his art, with all its winsomeness, is distinctly of a smaller accent, at times of a rather thin preciosity.

Let us ask a blunt question? Was there a superlatively fine picture in the memorial exhibition? The present writer is sure only of one—"The Little White Girl." Surely, no time will stale the lovely pensiveness of the mood, the dulcet quality of a workmanship everywhere perfectly assured, the dainty accord of the various whites. In comparison, the big "White Girl" is far-fetched and rapidly becoming merely odd. To paint white on white has ceased to be a marvel; in fact, it never was except in a color-blind age. Aside from this, the big "White Girl" is uncertainly balanced and uncomfortable to look at for long.

The Japanese pictures are refined to a degree, subtly harmonized, and present individual passages of the finest color. They are so evidently mere confections—self-confessed stages towards the "Little White Girl"—that their analysis may be waived.

The "Music Room," perhaps the most accomplished of the early pictures, keeps one long in doubt. It is the most strenuously complicated of Whistler's interiors. What seems to place it just a little lower than first-class is an eccentric edginess, and some lack of complete unity.

The "Rosa Corder" is so lovely an apparition that I will not argue the technical reasons that make it not quite a great portrait. To a discerning eye the whole of Whistler is in this canvas. Enhance it a trifle and you would get the "Mother" or "Miss Alexander," transfer the manner to landscape, and the symphonies and nocturnes logically ensue. The essence of it is an infallible pictorial sense. The focus of that pallid face in its setting of brown and gray is perfect. Where the picture comes a little short of the best is in a too-ready sacrifice of the beauty of definition to that of unity, in a *parti-pris* of tone which makes the artist impose the harmony arbitrarily instead of extorting it from the data.

This tendency, barely discernible in the "Rosa Corder," becomes pronounced in the nocturnes. There is a thrill in most of them that makes one forget their high degree of artificiality. Cazin's moonlights, in a manner far abler, lack the glamour. Millet has done the thing with equal charm and greater majesty. Whistler invented a most useful decorative formula, which he abused a little himself. His followers have shown how much of a trick it was. His art is so personal and distinguished that European painting hardly suffices to demonstrate its insubstantiality. One may fairly judge a picture like "Symphony in Gray and Green: the Ocean," only by comparing it with what it simulates—the color-prints of Japan. Better yet, take landscape painting of the Chinese school. The Eastern product is finer at every point, more spacious, more mysterious, and, above all, more knowing. It gets by direct and exquisite selection from nature what Whistler got by evasion. To a Japanese connoisseur most of his work would seem superficial, and just a bit slovenly. And this means that, while he valiantly shook off the cheap naturalism of Europe, he never underwent the discipline necessary to attain to the mystical naturalism of the Far East. Artistically, he remains a man without a country.

Here he was more or less of a victim. In his etching, his most important achievement, he managed to keep his feet on the ground. Doubtless, he would have done so in his painting also, but for the presence of the "enemies." Of them he was morbidly conscious. He dwarfed himself by resolutely being as unlike the Royal Academy as possible. He moved in an atmosphere of hostility tempered by adulation equally excessive. He fatally lacked the company and the criticism of his peers. The work he did in such unwholesome isolation tes-

tifies to the extraordinary natural gift of the
man.   His quality, however, was not to be
great, but to be charming.

Possibly, the "Tanagra" pastels show him
quintessentially.   The refinement with which
these little figures are set within the tinted
sheet, the deftness of the spotting, the value
of the sparsely applied color, a sensuousness
that for being discreetly attenuated is all the
more effective—such are the salient qualities
of this work.   It recalls, as the word Tanagra
does, the subtly coquettish flavor of Hellenistic
art.   There is a hint of Correggio, though not
his vigor, and a stronger reminiscence of the
pensive charm of Watteau.   Not merely in
enduing the figure with a peculiarly aristocratic
glamour, but, more technically, in adopting the
blue tints as harmonizers, the poet-painter of
Paris anticipated the poet-painter of Chelsea.

By an occasional *tour de force*—a few of
the Thames etchings, the three great portraits
—Whistler imposes himself upon us.   But
we fail to note how exceptional work of this
quality is.   The real Whistler is not in the
sabre stroke, but in the caress or the equally
feline scratch.   It was this that made him so
readily lean toward Rossetti.   In fact, his relation to the early English illustrators and paint-

ers has strangely been overlooked. Like them, he inherited much from the mannerly school of the eighteenth century. What is the title etching to the "French Set," one of his most engaging groups of figures, really like? Is it not like a superlative Stothard sketch, and even more like a Dicky Doyle? Walter Crane, as a decorator, shows qualities and defects singularly akin to those of Whistler as a painter. These analogies are raised merely to show that, normally, Whistler's place is not with the men of power, but with the men of charm. In painting he must have learned much from Gainsborough and more from Turner, who, in fact, has anticipated more robustly many of the triumphs of the arrangements and symphonies.

Withal, Whistler remains absolutely personal and apart. His art, being one of avoidance, evading certain fundamental requirements of structure, is on the whole a small one, but exquisite, idiomatic, and refreshing. An excess of languor, too great a dependence upon the hypnotic effect of the merely vague, is its defect. It heralded a needed reaction against the color-blindness of the official art of France and England, but, unhappily, it set a generation of secessionists to weaving abstract and rather trivial iridescences. In the doctrine of preciousness of surface, Whistler did both harm and good. To show how really hideous was much that passed for fine painting was a public service. To suggest that manipulated pigments can or should vie with the specific beauties of ceramic enamels or with Eastern weavings was to launch a forlorn hope.

On this theme of "quality" much nonsense has been put about. Simply as an agreeable colored texture no painting compares with a fine Persian rug or tile. In other words, the painter must atone in other perfections—in a masterly sense of form, in beautiful and complicated arrangements, in spaciousness, in personal interpretation of bare appearances—for the relative meanness of his materials.

Whistler met these requirements only about halfway, hence falls out of the class of great and well-rounded painters. His tact was sufficient to keep him clear of the more demoralizing implications of his own theories. Naturally, his imitators lacked the subtlety to see that the master frequently took himself in a Pickwickian sense. They lacked even more lamentably the discipline of sound early studies. Without having done their Thames etchings, they undertook their nocturnes. Where Whistler was limpid, they made a virtue of deliquescence. In him were the seeds of the best and the worst tendencies in modern painting. Fighting magnificently for the decorative ideal of picture-making—a truly regenerative principle—he also reduced the painter's art to mere epidermal bloom, a dangerous counsel of empty æstheticism. Hence no one can be quite indifferent to him.

Is not this according to his strictest definition of success? Nor would one gauge too crabbedly his evident limitations. He is so charming that one will generally take him at his own valuation. As time goes on, however, it will become clear that his abode in the Elysian fields is nearer the pleasant garden-houses of Watteau and Fragonard than the more imposing mansions of Turner and Velasquez.
[1910.]

VI

GEORGE FULLER

GEORGE FULLER, "Winifred Dysart"

GEORGE FULLER

Even chronologically, George Fuller's art was a twilight development. After early and relatively insignificant experiences as a portrait painter, the needs of his family drove him back for fifteen years to the paternal farm near the confluence of the Deerfield and Connecticut rivers. And it was the failure of the farming episode that restored him to painting, a man of fifty-four. The handful of pictures by which he is remembered were painted as he passed into old age. He died at sixty-two. There is something morally heroic in this art born of adversity, and accomplished almost in the face of death, but the paintings themselves tell nothing of the outwardly guiding circumstances. They are so many visions of the mystery of nature, of the fragility of maidenhood, of the hesitancies and frustrations of personalities too finely wrought for such a struggle as Fuller himself had faced.

And all this is intimated rather than expressed, and caught in a singularly uniform, almost monotonous, medium. "Brown sauce"

I hear a young and impatient reader interrupt. Yes, brown sauce, but with a saving difference, for it is not a studio recipe but a true inference from those late October twilights in Massachusetts, when the air shimmers with a luminous dust that has been crushed up from dried leaves. The simple magic of George Fuller was to grasp the quality of this hour and season, as evocative of pensive dreams.

From this quintessential moment of the dying year he distils a universal pathos. A man who sees æsthetically only the whip-poor-will's hour, and then within a narrow circle, may be a notable elegiac poet, and that Fuller was, but hardly a great artist, if we are to count fecundity and athleticism for anything. And since within his limitations Fuller is a fascinating critical problem, in attacking which I shall surely now and then fall into overstatement, let me once for all make my general estimate of him clear. I do not think any master of understatement, however distinguished, any artist whose forte is chiefly reticence, can be regarded as a great artist. It is this failure to speak out which makes Hawthorne, in every way an exquisite writer, hardly a great writer. W. D. Howells, who wrote an admirable memoir of Fuller, again is a writer who has more taste

than vitality, being withal an impeccable crafts-
man. Fuller, after all, in this devotion to un-
derstatement and half-tones is in an authentic
New England tradition which reaches from
Hawthorne's "Twicetold Tales" to President
Coolidge's enigmatic "I do not choose to run."

George Fuller was born near the lovely village of Deerfield, Mass., a spot redolent of
history and legend, in 1822. His father was a
farmer, and from him the son inherited not
much more than a mediocre farm, a quiet patience and a love of the soil. On the side of
his mother, Fanny Negus, there was talent.
Her stock was Welsh, and an amateur of
ethnic origins would be inclined to see a Celtic
strain in the elfin and elusive art of the son.
By his fourteenth year, George Fuller's schooling was over, and he was a clerk, transiently,
in a grocery and in a shoe store. His liberation came in a small position on a railroad survey in Illinois. Of the party was the talented
sculptor, H. K. Brown. Under his advice
Fuller trained himself as a face-painter, working eventually at Boston, Albany, in northern
New York and in the South. In his nineteenth
year he writes elatedly to his family that he
is able to raise his price from twenty to thirty
dollars. That year there was a pleasant inter-

lude at Albany with Brown and with the benign idealist sculptor, Erastus Palmer. Brown wrote Fuller as he left Albany: "Look upon your drawing and painting as your language, the medium through which you express to others your feelings." Admirable humanistic counsel which Fuller was later to ponder deeply.

From his twentieth to his thirtieth year Fuller was an itinerant face-painter, but made considerable stations in Boston and New York. His personal distinction got him good acquaintance everywhere. The habit of the world and of great books brought him an education and a culture peculiarly his own. In his art he had studied diligently Stuart and Allston. But his achievement was at best respectable, and when in 1853, his thirty-first year, he was elected an Associate of the National Academy the compliment was quite as much to his personality as to his portraiture. So he carried on, esteemed but inconspicuous, to his thirty-eighth year.

Meanwhile things went badly at the Deerfield farm. The gains were rare and hazardous; there were slowly increasing debts; some loved one was always battling hopelessly and tragically with New England's white plague. It came to a pass where the farm and the family plainly needed him, and, never a Christian believer himself, he made the art of Christian abnegation unhesitatingly. It turned out to be his own making as an artist, but this he could not foresee.

So it was in the spirit of a farewell to his art that before assuming the yoke, he gave himself a few months in Europe. His companion was that brilliant picaresque critic, W. J. Stillman. The trip, a rapid one for those leisurely times, reached from Sicily to Holland. It would be pleasant to quote from his correspondence at this time observations which show a fine and lucid taste, and a surprising degree of real education, but the scale of this essay forbids such alluring by-ways. He met Ruskin at Geneva, but was never drawn toward Ruskin's primitivism. Of Rembrandt's "Night Watch" Fuller notes: "The mystery of color and the poetic suggestiveness in a degree which has only been expressed by his masterly hand." Here was matter on which to ponder in the rare surcease of mental worry and physical exhaustion on the Deerfield farm.

By his thirty-ninth year George Fuller had taken up his work as a farmer. The next year he married Agnes Higginson. With the blessing of many children, came the accompanying cares. He did not entirely give up painting.

A simple studio building rose alongside the old farmhouse. But there was little time for pictures. He cleared thirty acres of swamp land, largely with his own hand. One must think of him growing prematurely old, already venerable with his great white beard, gazing at once wearily and intently on autumn evenings when the cliffs of Sugar Loaf rose warm and lustrous out of the brown air that filled the intervening river bottom—meditating pictures which he had no time to paint. One must also think of a simple and noble acceptance of the lot of patriarch and tiller of an ungrateful soil.

After fifteen years of it, the farm was bankrupt; there were half a dozen little mouths to feed. It was now a question whether painting would save the farm. Within his fifty-third year he painted twelve pictures; adding two earlier ones, he exhibited the fourteen, in 1876, at Boston, sold most of them, received a generous criticism, and secured a patronage which he held and increased during his remaining eight years. And when the young painters surcharged with high ideals from Paris set up in rivalry with the old Academy the Society of American Artists, Fuller was one of the very few seniors whom they honored with an invitation to their select membership. The whole story is a little like an attenuated New England version of the Book of Job. Something of it reappears in George Fuller's upright, wistful and quietistic art.

The Job of the Bible seems to have readily forgotten his pains and chagrins in restored and enhanced good fortunes. Fuller experienced a rejuvenation, but his new art drew its character of refined obscurity from the hard intervening years. In his pictures it is always eventide. His figures do not act and have never acted. They simply exist and seek sympathy. Their appeal is discreet and muted, merely implicit. Their mood is as veiled as their forms, which shimmer uncertainly in the enveloping dusk. They live not in any world of ours, but, as Fuller once said he wanted them to live, "in a world of their own." Inevitable analogies with Rembrandt, with Whistler, with Carrière, are unprofitable, for there is no community of mood. Fuller was far less able than any of these technically kindred spirits, and, while he lacked their varying spiritual clarity, he had something quite precious and his own. It may be sensed in any one of those maiden forms that are at once mere wraiths in a luminous dusk, and nevertheless vivid apparitions to any sensitive imagination. "Winifred Dysart,"

"Priscilla," "Nydia"—these are the memorable
Fullers, and to these ideal figures may be added
a few portraits of similar distinction, always
portraits of young people.

Before approaching the real theme, a word
on the landscapes. I do not share the general
admiration for them. Having a certain relation to specific appearances, they are not
specific enough, and being fantastic, they are
not fantastic enough. Indeed the otherworldliness of Fuller's art evidently disabled him
from being a sound landscape painter in our
native realistic tradition, while his temperament was too romantic to permit him to seek
merely decorative conventions, and his spirituality was of a diffused type that did not readily transform specific appearances into equally
concrete symbols. It seems to me that Blakelock, who was distinctly a more limited nature,
saw better what Fuller wanted to see in landscape and painted it better. There are charming landscapes by Fuller. The little sketch,
"Shearing the Donkey," is entrancing. I guess
it to be a happy accident. The "Turkey Pasture" has dignity and more than usual richness
of color, and a singularly noble sky line of live
oaks. But in general the landscapes of Fuller,
while very tenderly felt, seem to me inade-

quately seen. The poetry is not reinforced by
any lucid rhetoric of form. The expression
anticipates something of the slipperiness of recent image-making in free verse. Nothing is
dense and measurable and permanent. So I
think the vogue of the landscapes is really a
kind of overflow from the well-grounded admiration for the figure pieces. Had Fuller not
painted Winifred Dysart and her crepuscular
fellow sprites, I am sure that the landscapes
would have passed almost unnoticed.

To put into words what one feels about the
half-dozen fine figure pieces is difficult. No
description covers the case. Of what avail is
it to note that these lovely figures of young
women are suffused and buried in a russet and
pearly mist, that they stand gracefully and hesitatingly with a breadth of vibrating gloom at
either side, that they are rapt in their own
musings, yet singularly appeal to sympathy,
that they exist in no time and place but in a
quiet effulgence of all the autumns? When one
has said this, we have gained only pale generalizations for a very specific charm. Yet there
is no other way, for these fair girls of George
Fuller's imagination are themselves generalizations and symbols, quintessences of all that was
exquisitely candid and pure in young woman-

hood as he saw it; of all, too, that was elusive and intangible. It makes no difference whether the apparition is named from our Colonial days or from Roman history. It is simply a Fuller —a reverent vision with its element of wistful longing. Such more specific creations as "Fedalma" in oriental travesty, or "The Quadroon," in wearied, perplexed and perhaps half-rebellious meditation, fall out of the class. Indeed "The Quadroon" makes Fuller look a minor painter less from lack of gift than from force of circumstances. The picture has a reality, a formidable existence in our own world, which the others lack. Their existence in their own world and George Fuller's is, however, complete and undeniable.

To be sure, the mere construction is hesitating and unhandy—much scraping out and over painting, many changes, much ploughing the wet paint with the brush-handle—all the marks of a capricious and unsystematic handling. But all this is really of the least importance. There is no messing of the surface simply for quality; everything ministers to expression. The admirable white-line wood-engraver George Closson, who engraved the cuts for the memorial volume, testifies that the imprecision of the work is only apparent. Everything lent itself to the very precise formulas of his own art, while taxing all the resources of his most skilful burin. How such effects are obtained is really no business of the layman. His curiosity in such points is usually at the expense of any real appreciation. It is better in George Fuller's case simply to share that highly sublimated nostalgia with which in advanced years he faces the lovely mystery of the adolescence of the Yankee girl.

For the validity of his symbolism lies in the fact that one is dealing after all with daughters of New England. They are not portraits, but they have an odd and inexplicable reference to girls we have known. They are at once so fragile and so confident, their gracefulness is so unconscious and often so near to a captivating awkwardness. They have an air of existing in their own right, of being unrelated to other people or to affairs. Indeed the old cult of American girlhood in its delicate institutionalism perhaps finds its best celebrant in George Fuller. And since the cult itself has waned, and the idol has successively changed and stepped down from the dream-made pedestal, George Fuller's pictures add to their intrinsic charm a distinct pathos of distance, and a value of spiritual documentation.

The word feminist has not the pleasantest

connotations, but in every good sense Fuller was just that, and beyond that he had very little to offer. So were two of his younger contemporaries, feminists—Abbott Thayer and Alden Weir. Thayer heroized his young women morally and mentally. Weir felt chiefly the complicated delicacies of their minds. Fuller is at once farther from and nearer to the fair girls he saw and transformed in imagination, than is either of the other two. He approached the mystery with less curiosity than either, with less desire to understand, but he gives a more complete and unquestioning homage. He has neither the somewhat stoical chivalry of Thayer, nor yet the cerebral admiration of Weir. Fuller has no desire to be noble nor yet to be discerning; he lets himself go in wistful, bitter-sweet imaginings. Autumn muses upon spring until her diaphanous form is evoked. It moves hesitantly among the dead leaves and stirs from them a veil of saffron dust which is at once a barrier and a medium of revelation.

It would be easy to take this as a classic case in the psychology of senescence, easy to be ingenious on the theme, and still easier to be disgusting. I shall hope to be neither. One does not need to cite the young maiden who warmed King David's feet; one may without reading

Mr. Galsworthy's "The Dark Flower," imagine the ordinary outgoing of every aging male towards young womanhood. But one finds the experience also in the form of a wistful and troubled homage which has in it no element of desire. There is no need of analyzing what is a matter of common observation, and, according to its quality, fit subject for the comic strip and the night club or for a high and delicate poetry. In this matter George Fuller was on the side of the angels, and they visited him familiarly, and the record of their epiphanies is in his pictures.

[1929.]

VII

HOMER D. MARTIN

HOMER D. MARTIN, "The Old Manor House"

HOMER D. MARTIN

By 1830 two main tendencies had asserted
themselves in our landscape painting. With
inadequate technical resources Thomas Cole
had developed scenic breadth, had made visible
the sober or savage poetry of our forested
mountains. His art was one of deliberate
selection in the interest of mood. With infinite patience and the austerity of an analytical
eye Asher B. Durand set down the minute facts
of our landscape. The work is descriptive and
inventorial, mood being secondary to truth as
Durand understood it. Our later landscape
painters have followed one precept or the
other, or have mediated between the two. The
eventual triumph was to be with Cole, who had
independently divined what was to be the point
of view of the great landscapists of England
and France.

It is the historical distinction of Homer D.
Martin that he followed unwaveringly the tradition of Cole, enriching it with new resources
and a finer sense of color and adapting it finally
to more intimate subjects. It was Martin's per-

sonal distinction to convey more powerfully
than any American contemporary the elegiac
poetry of our primeval scenery, while also
catching the richer pathos of sea-beaten and immemorially inhabited Normandy. This he did
with reverence for average appearances and
without the glamorous inventiveness of, say,
Inness. Thus within a somewhat limited range,
and judged by his best pictures, Martin, I think,
should be regarded as our best landscape
painter of the generation following Cole, and
I am not sure that anyone since has really surpassed his discreet and noble deployment of his
favorite themes.

His beginnings were unlikely even for the
'fifties. He was born in 1836, a carpenter's
son, at Albany, New York, with a congenital
astigmatism. The family were strict Method-
ists. They attempted to turn him from a taste
for drawing by making him first a shop clerk
and next an architect's draughtsman, and when
they yielded to his evident vocation, no better
master was available than the feeble James M.
Hart. Homer Martin soon left him, and, except for a brief association with James Smillie,
never again sought a master. From the venerable sculptor E. D. Palmer, from Launt
Thompson, from such young friends as Edward

Gay and George D. Boughton, proud possessor of a Corot, Martin received fellowship and encouragement, but his real training was in the face of nature.

There exist scores of his early drawings. After the timid fashion of the time these are pencil outlines on buff paper cautiously shaded and touched with white. The Catskills, Adirondacks and White Mountains furnished the themes. The attitude is panoramic; great spaces are represented and, except for a certain nervous energy in tree forms, without much skill. To a modern art student indeed the series would seem contemptible. Yet these austere sheets have a quality which the modern art student rarely attains—namely studied and beautiful composition. The point of view is carefully chosen; the necessary omissions and emphases are instinctively grasped; each sheet, so far as arrangement is concerned, is a lucidly conceived picture. In short these rather feeble drawings constitute after all a notable training in composition and in memorizing the greater forms of nature. Without these early exercises it is doubtful whether Homer Martin broken and nearly blind could have created his noblest forests, mountains and moorlands from memory aided only by his own early pictures. Throughout his career this innate concern with composition is evinced by his habit of making a new picture out of an old one by revision and simplification. He forgot nothing. His fastidiousness in arrangement may account for an occasional lack of robustness in details. It is the limitation of Claude whom, I fancy, Martin early came to know in big copper plates adorning the walls of travelled Albany families.

The few of Martin's paintings which have come down from the late 'fifties are so poor that their only interest is to show that a great talent may entirely fail to show itself in an ill-understood medium. Slickly and thinly painted, with the quality of a bad oilcloth, grays out of key enlivened with poisonous passages of vermillion, they represent the worst amateur practice of the moment. However, from 1857, they were occasionally accepted by the Academy, which deserves some credit for discerning the fine arrangements disfigured by an incompetent practice.

In the early 'sixties his practice improves, as a result probably of his training with James Smillie in New York, 1862-1863. The veteran engraver and landscape painter was no giant in landscape himself, but he knew everybody worth knowing in artistic New York. Homer

Martin's love of unity, expressing itself as tonality in his painting, kept him aloof from the somewhat raw polychromy of Bierstadt, F. E. Church, and early Inness, as it had earlier from that of the Harts. He must, I think, have studied the great Coles with their sombre breadth, and he probably took counsel of the popular J. F. Kensett with his crisp notations of form and his ingenious if superficial color harmonies.

At twenty-five, in 1861, Homer Martin married Elizabeth Gilbert Davis, a brilliant woman whose novels and book reviews, for the *Nation,* helped much during the thirty-five years of struggle upon which the young pair had embarked. She was his social superior, but they had almost everything else in common. Both were completely unworldly, both artists, both loved good talk, good books and good music, both were agnostics before Herbert Spencer had coined the word. On the religious side their bond was later to be strained by Mrs. Martin's conversion, under the auspices of La Farge and Father Hecker to Roman Catholicism, but she played her subsequently difficult part with entire loyalty and reasonable discretion, and the bond held.

Their future evidently lay beyond Albany.

In 1864 Martin brought wife and baby to New York, and set up his studio in the Tenth Street building already inhabited by La Farge and Winslow Homer, who were to be his only artist friends.   At New York his art and associations rapidly broadened.   He passed beyond the idyllism of his best early picture, "The Old Mill," 1860, and restudied his early forest and mountain themes, treating them with the old compositional felicity while adding thereto a more incisive drawing, a finer handling and a color richer and more harmonious.   His art already seems complete in "Lake Sanford," one of the treasures of the Century Club.   It was painted in 1870 from sketches made considerably earlier.   The scene is tragically harsh. One looks across a ledgy hummock, spiky with blasted spruces, immemorially ravaged by fire and wind, to a pewtery lake beyond which dull clouds hide the distant ledges and the sky.   The dark color is of the emotional essence.   It seems, as Martin's friend, William Dennett, castigator of contemporary political corruption in the *Evening Post,* used to say, as if nobody but God and the artist had looked upon the scene.   The picture is typical for its moment. If, as Amiel was to write, landscape is a state of mind, this was the most distinguished land-

scape America had produced, as noble as Cole's
best with more conscience and precision, nobler
and more selective, if less colorful and urbane,
than the contemporary Innesses. And the
Martins of his early New York days have
often a blither note. In a canvas of 1873
painted for his friend, the late William C.
Brownell, one glimpses the iridescent sheen of
Lake Champlain across sunny slopes, while
above the haze that veils the farther shore one
finds the near-by green repeated in that blue-
green, thinly covered sky which was to be fairly
the trademark of the fine early Martins.

When, in 1874, the National Academy
elected him to full membership, they probably
were exercising rather magnanimity than artistic discernment, for Martin had become something of an outlaw among his fellow artists.
Their intellectual superior, he cared little for
their company. They in turn feared his extraordinary wit which, if usually genial, could
at times be cutting. So his ambrosial nights at
the Century Club were passed preferably with
such higher journalists as the veteran Dennett
and young Brownell, with the future critic
of architecture, Montgomery Schuyler; with
prominent physicians like Dr. Mosher, health
officer of the port, or the vigorous and accom-

plished Dr. Daniel M. Stimson. In the Century the legend of Martin's talk is still vivid, but there seems to have been something untranscribable about it. The few *verbatim* examples which I managed to secure for my biography of him suggest only a ready and somewhat brittle wit. The overtones are no longer there. The charm of his talk had the perhaps valuable foil of a visage marred by a chronic eruption. His mere acquaintances say that he was physically repellent; his close friends, that the disfigurement was slight and negligible. Concerning Homer Martin men have never held tepid opinions.

In New York of the black-walnut era the Martins soon won the companionship and the admiration of the best without becoming prosperous. They both were temperamental, and indifferent managers. Her mind was on her writing and on new and poignant religious experiences, his on his painting and on convivialities more delightful than contingently profitable. Mathematically they earned the modest living they required, but the money was spent before it accrued, and, I suppose, they were never wholly out of debt. His painting, enthusiastically hailed by those who were or were soon to be our best critics, never struck the

popular and wealthy taste. Its frequent som-
breness was against it in an age very cheerful
over its own vulgarity. New riches did not
care to linger in desolate places which only God
and Homer Martin had found good. He was
suspected of painting in French and unpatriotic
ways, and, though he had painted many exquisite pictures, he lacked Inness's knack of now
and then bowling over a doubting public with
a palpable and very big masterpiece. Indeed
he kept going only through the generous and
intelligent patronage of friends. In 1873 he
wrote to his friend Mosher, "It is better to be
in hell than in art."

As he carried on amid difficulties, his style
mellowed. His compositions, now cleared of
traditional details, gain breadth; his discreet
tonalities become more subtle; the brush works
no longer with alternations of exasperated
energy and heaviness, but caressingly with little
pigment; the themes are more limited and intimate—brooks, the bends of slow moving rivers.
This foreordained progress was doubtless accelerated by the European trip which he made
in 1876. He saw the masterpieces at London,
Paris, Amsterdam and The Hague. Unhappily
no record of these formative impressions survives except his shock over the artificialities

and sensationalisms of Turner and his joy over the tranquil perfections of Claude. At London he had the high companionship of Albert Moore and Whistler. It was the moment of the nocturnes, and I think their exquisite economy of material passingly influenced the Martins of the late 'eighties. When he returned from England, the young progressives of the Society of American Artists invited his membership, a compliment which on the material side only emphasized his unorthodoxy. He undertook hack work for *Scribner's,* illustrations of the literary shrines about Concord. This commission, however reluctantly undertaken, was highly important, for a similar charge in England was to bring him to his few years of relative ease and before his most congenial themes in Normandy.

The verdict of the auction rooms is clear that the good Martins are the Normandy Martins and those that he later made in the new style acquired in France. I do not dispute it, but I feel that the best of the American Martins are thereby gravely underestimated, and that if he gained immensely in France, he possibly sacrificed an alternative development of an even more precious sort. It is the memory of the lovely picture of 1880, "Andante, Fifth

Symphony," which evokes these might-have-beens. It is a visible tribute to the noble music, and much of it was painted while a friend played the piano partition in the studio. Here is the picture, as much as inadequate words may express it: A forest brook broadens into a shallow pool to which vague reflections of rocks and trees and broken sky lend depth and mystery. In the upper vista, boulders glint in the half-light before a screen of misty foliage. The rock-rimmed bounds of the pool and some foreground weeds are accented with great vigor, while everything in the forest above is soft and evanescent. Tree trunks loom spectrally before a general forest gloom which is enlivened by the scarlet flash of a precociously autumnal maple. The general color is extraordinarily modulated grays qualified by broad touches of russet and green. The surface is of a silken thinness and of a similarly subdued luminosity. In its contrasts of preciseness and mystery the picture obeys the Japanese law that every composition must be clearly divided into a masculine and a feminine part. Perfect tone is achieved without sacrifice of local color.

The picture exemplifies admirably a high point of momentary perfection, the culmination of that delicate naturalism in which Martin had begun. The analogy of the stream broadening amid forest loveliness to the great Andante is by no means far-fetched. In some ways the picture is more attractive than his more highly prized later work with its broader manipulation of paint and its more systematically asserted tone. I sometimes wonder what would have happened had the public seen fit to support work of this excellence and made it possible for Homer Martin to reach his full development in his own land. All his future course was more or less accidentally shaped by the fact that the great art editor of the new *Century*, A. W. Drake, liked the Concord sketches better than Martin himself did and ordered a trip to England to sketch in George Eliot's Warwickshire. I say advisedly ordered, for Martin was in no position to decline a commission however uncongenial. So in the early autumn of 1881 he sailed for England, not as one of the half dozen foremost landscape painters of his day, but as an obscure and needy magazine illustrator.

He reknit the old friendship with Whistler and saw much of the poet Henley. His old Albany mate, George H. Boughton, now become complacently prosperous, has left an ungracious record of Martin's disquieting shabbiness. The hospitable Edmund Gosses confirm this impression and add that he seemed "muffled and quite discouraged." Little was done on the Warwickshire sketches. No paintings of these nine months are known. At forty-five Homer Martin seemed finished. It was the coming of Mrs. Martin, in the summer of 1882, that lifted him from this slough of despond. The sketches for the *Century* were soon completed. She was promptly taken to see Whistler, but the flutterings of the Butterfly and her own high seriousness were antipathetic, and the visit was not repeated.

With a little ready money from the illustrations, the Martins were able to accept the invitation of his old boon companion William J. Hennessy to come to upper Normandy. After twenty years as a justly popular book and magazine illustrator, Hennessy had saved enough to live abroad and paint his now forgotten pictures. He was a genial person, a notable figure at Pennedepie, and he knew the ropes. From his suggestion to settle near by at Villerville the Homer Martins gained the nearest view they were ever to have of the Delectable Mountains. It was a time of drawing together. Both loved the place, in which men and their habitations seemed to have become a veritable part of nature. He observed and sketched it while she wrote about it delightfully in paragraphs that are so many verbal obbligatos for his now famous pictures. To be sure they were as poor as ever, but it was easier to be poor where nobody was important or lived behind a brownstone front. They were sustained by a sense of his progress, for although he was little productive—only half a dozen large canvases can be traced to the four years spent between Villerville and Honfleur—his art was rapidly broadening, and he was regaining confidence.

Much has been written about Homer Martin's last manner, and its difference from his early style has been somewhat exaggerated. The change came chiefly to painting with a denser material, with the palette knife rather than with the brush and with a more subtle division of tones. He observed the new impressionist technique at Paris, but did not adopt it. I guess that he learned more from that master of tonality, Boudin, who was then painting in the neighborhood. What was new was the subject matter and not the attitude. As Samuel Isham has well written, "The real essentials (the feeling for the relations of mass,

for the exact difference of tone between the sky
and the solid earth, the sense of subtle color)
are the same, and under every change of surface remains the same deep, grave melancholy,
sobering but not saddening, which is the key-
note of Martin's work." It should be remarked also that the best picture he brought
back from France was "Sand Dunes, Lake Ontario," a theme which he had first essayed
twelve years earlier and carried through several
versions. It may also be noted that the finest
pictures which after his return from America
he made in the new technique are again on his
old native themes and with few exceptions re-
visions of compositions painted many years
earlier. Such reflections point the entirely
native and essentially intellectual character of
Homer Martin's art.

In 1886, being fifty years old, he decided to
renew the struggle in New York. He brought
few pictures back but many rich memories, and
numerous small sketches. Season by season
for seven years great picture followed great
picture, the canvases that now are the pride of
our museums and the goal of our wealthy
amateurs. Few of these masterpieces sold, and
those at a base price. Even two years after
Martin's death, and when it was already good

business to forge Martins, that fairly enlightened collector, William T. Evans, was with difficulty persuaded to buy "Westchester Hills" for
a thousand dollars. Six years later he sold it
for about five times the money, thereby depriv-
ing his bequest to the National Gallery of what
would have been its chief ornament. Universally praised by the critics, Martin's fame
brought him few dollars. By 1892 the sight
of one eye had entirely failed, and that of the
other was seriously impaired. Worn down at
last by the endless struggle, his wife's nerves
broke, and she fled for rest and support to their
son Ralph in St. Paul. Six months later, driven
by poverty and ill health, he followed her there.

In poverty, in a social isolation which he had
never before experienced, going blind, with a
cancer gnawing at his throat, Homer Martin
painted four of his greatest pictures—"Criquebœuf Church," "The Harp of the Winds,"
"The Normandy Farm," "Adirondack Scenery." The foe, as he wrote to a friend, was
"eating the gizzard" out of him, but at last in
his own opinion he had learned to paint, and
that kept him up. When his wife, surmising it
might be his last picture, congratulated him on
finishing his noble picture, "Adirondack Scenery," he answered, "I have learned to paint at

last. If I were quite blind now, and knew just where the colors were on my palette, I could express myself." He was mercifully prevented from justifying these proud words. By February of 1897 the dull discomfort in the throat changed into a brief space of corroding agony, and on the twelfth of that month the much-worn man entered into rest unnoticed. Within five years of his death half a dozen of his pictures were sold for a total sum that would have kept him comfortably for life.

There is perhaps no moral to be drawn and no reproach to be implied. Martin's great accomplishment fell at a time when the patronage of American art was in abeyance. Our collectors were buying from France. The shifting of standards in the 'eighties and 'nineties, made all contemporary paintings seem dubious investments, and American painting peculiarly so. No dealer could confidently engage to take an American picture back at the price paid. With dead men's pictures he could and did safely do this. And the dealers morally owned the so-called amateurs. New York had sprawled all over Manhattan Island, had ceased to be a social unit. The old easy relationship between artist and well-to-do folk, which had constituted the black-walnut era a golden age, so far as the patronage of art was concerned, had wholly broken down. The old patrons were poorer, the new patrons speculatively inclined and too busy to track a poor, however talented, painter to his unseemly lair. An artist had to be very energetic and managing, to live in those days, and Homer Martin was quite indolent and too proud to scheme for success. Like most witty men he was at once entirely lucid and something of an ironist. He never blamed the times, and I feel that he would have agreed he was merely unlucky in having been born with a great painter's talent, of poor parents and in the wrong decade.

Homer Martin once maintained among friends who were discussing the subject of story-telling pictures, that there was in every picture something of this. And being asked to prove it from his own "Westchester Hills," he answered, "Oh, the old home has been deserted, and all the family has gone West along that road." The retort was only half a jest. The pathos of the scene does largely depend upon the impression that these fields and slopes and groves are derelict, abandoned by man and not quite given back to nature. No picture of Homer Martin is merely retinal and objective after approved modern formulas. He was too

deeply conscious of the vicissitudes of the earth
for that. There is in the Adirondack and Lake
Ontario subjects a sense of the moulding or
fracturing agency of storm, of the passing of
fire or rain, of the furrowing of gullies and
crumbling of ledges. A kind of pity for the old
earth blended with awe at the immemorial processes of growth and decay is ever present. In
the Normandy pictures we have the effort of
man arresting and guiding these vicissitudes,
and there is usually a hint of the refractoriness
of the earth to such pains. His favorite hour
and light are those of early evening, when, undisturbed by the shifting pageantry of the sun,
one may meditate upon the uncertain tenure
that man shares with mute creation. There are
pictures of the early time and a few late ones,
like "Sun Worshippers," in which he yields
himself gladly to the intoxication of frank color
and to the joy of sunlight. But this festal and
candid mood is at all times exceptional. He
brings usually to the observation and pictorial
interpretation of nature, a definite and poetical
mood full of that noble and measured melancholy, which in poetry we call elegiac. It was
the mood proper to a lover of Keats and
Beethoven.

Every picture of Martin, then, represents a

complex of recurrent moods, observations and memories. His tradition is the contemplative one, and absolutely alien to the instantaneous reactions of impressionism. And his habit of constantly returning to old themes is significant. Between 1874 and 1887 there must be four or five versions of "Sand Dunes, Lake Ontario," each one coming a little nearer the light poise of the remote dunes between sky and water, and each working out finer symbols of swart aridity in the forms of the foreground trees. Indeed every picture of his is quite slowly and thoughtfully elaborated as a conscious arrangement. The matter stands very plain in his own words to Thomas B. Clarke in a letter dated February 25, 1896. "As to the pictures in sight . . . in sight, that is to me, the 28 x 40" (probably Mr. Babbott's "Newport") "is all thought out except one or two cloud forms which trouble me greatly. The larger picture in which I intend to sum up about what I think of the woods" (apparently it was never finished) "needs considerable scene shifting before the curtain can be raised. . . . It might be ready for the autumn openings if I settle on the arrangements of the parts soon." Such testimony as to the wholly conscious intellectuality of Homer Martin's invention dis-

penses me from further analysis. I wish in lieu
of a formal criticism to trace the quality of the
inspiration and pictorial idiom in three consummate examples,—"An Old Manor House,"
"The Harp of the Winds," and "Adirondack
Scenery."

Beneath a troubled gray sky, in which a
single flash of red gives the last signal of dying
day, the old manor house stands amid a copse
of leafless, untrimmed poplars. Vacant doors
and windows are so many dark gashes in the
warm-brown, crumbling wall. The sordid
trees are swarthy and their branches give forth
a peculiar murkiness that invests the deserted
mansion. It seems as if some memory of Poe's
"House of Usher" must have been in the
artist's mind as he painted, so exactly does he
make visual the familiar words:

"About the whole mansion and domain there hung
an atmosphere peculiar to themselves and their immediate vicinity—an atmosphere which had no affinity with the air of Heaven, but which had reeked up
from the decayed trees and the gray wall and the
silent tarn,—a pestilent and mystic vapor, dull, slug-
gish, faintly discernible, and leaden-hued."

Between the spectator and the lonely manor
lies a lustrous, stagnant pool, marbled strangely
with confused reflections from shore and sky,

and containing more clearly the chill image of the desolate house. Such a house and such a pool exist at Criquebœuf, but again the conviction imposes itself that this is "the bleak and lurid tarn that lay in unruffled lustre" by the "House of Usher," wherein one might look shudderingly upon "the remodelled and inverted images of the gray sedges, and the ghastly tree stems, and the vacant and eye-like windows." Yet the mood of this intensely tragic picture is not one of horror. There is a kind of overwhelming pity in it, as if the departing gleam were the sign of countless days that had gone down in sadness; the old manor among its sordid imprisoning trees, a veritable symbol of all glories that have departed.

Unless it be "Criquebœuf Church," the "Harp of the Winds" is Homer Martin's most famous picture, as it is his most admired and accessible. That appropriate title, which he and his wife always used between themselves, he declined to use publicly, fearing lest it seem too sentimental. "But that," writes his wife, "was what it meant to him, for he was thinking of music all the while he was painting it." She tells us, too, that the trees were originally much higher, and, with their reflections in the slow current, assumed more explicitly the form of a

harp. The change she regretted, in which I
think few will follow her, for nothing could be
more satisfyingly gracious than this file of slender trees bending suavely with the curve of a
broadening river. Upstream, the light touches
the white-washed houses of a village. A slight
dip in the low sky line suggests the upper winding course of the quiet river. The clouded sky,
shot with pale bars of gold and silver over a
tenuous blue, has that peculiar diagonal rise
which gives height and movement. Silvery
gray is the prevailing tone, into which are
worked discreet enrichments of yellow, dull
green, and blue. The rough and lustreless surface is remarkably luminous. A sober preciousness, both earthy and ethereal, comparable to
the mysterious bloom of fine Japanese pottery,
is characteristic of the whole effect. One may
note the ingenuity by which all the curves which
are arbitrary elements in a beautiful pattern in
plane are also essential factors in depth. Such
harmonizing of arabesque with spatial suggestion is of the very essence of fine composition.
Better than such pedantries, it may be simply
to say that no landscape in the Metropolitan
Museum will more immediately arrest the attention, and few will better endure prolonged
contemplation.

"Adirondack Scenery" is perhaps the best epitome of Homer Martin's entire achievement, being based on memories that had been turned over and refined for more than thirty years. Its direct prototype was a small canvas called the "Source of the Hudson." It is the richest in color of all the later works and possibly the broadest and most skilful in handling. The eye looks beyond gray, flat ledges over a stretch of brown second-growth, amid which flash rare scarlet maples, beyond a shallow valley and a shaggy distant ridge, to a steely lake where all the mountain slopes converge. The further ascent catches a golden permeating bloom from a dense vapor bank that recoils from the higher barrier and casts down a shadow. These vapors surge forward in a lurid and swirling yellow mass, thinning at the sides and top into the serene blue of a rain-washed sky. A peculiar and soothing gravity, proper to the vast spaces represented, is the ruling impression. One would be dull of heart indeed who could stand before this picture without a renewed and consoling awe at the secular balance of earth, air, and water which brings beauty out of ravage and calm out of strife. Nor is there anything mystic or far-fetched about the picture. Its highly generalized forms are firm, its textures of forest, rock, and cloud, unexaggeratedly veracious. I think it would appeal almost as strongly to a woodsman as to a poet.

Unless I have grossly misread these pictures, we have to do with a most distinguished kind of imagination, with a mind keenly lyrical and meditative. The inspiration is not so much various as authentic and deep. From beginning to end of Homer Martin's painting we have much the same kind of transaction between a sensitive, clairvoyant spirit and natural appearances. What he seeks in nature is solace, suspension of the will, expansion of the contemplative self. This mood I have in passing called Virgilian. It might be well to add—of a Virgil exiled in an untamed land. The feeling is essentially pagan, and not to be confused with the Wordsworthian and mystical temper which it superficially recalls, nor with the sentimental primitivism of the Rousseauists. It is somewhat stoical, valuing nature, chiefly as a means for regaining in tranquillity the form of one's own spirit. The sentiment might be paralleled in Milton and is not uncommon in the eighteenth century poets, such as Gray, though then it sometimes implies a quite unstoical revolt against society. I find nothing of this

Rousseauism in Martin. It seems to me that his temper is quite classically poised and his real concern with the governance of his own soul. We find a similar stoicism paradoxically inter-blent with the Christianity of Bryant. One of his best poems, "A Winter Piece," a poem that curiously anticipates much recent pictorial concern with winter scenery, breathes in a somewhat simpler tone much of the mood of Homer Martin's pictures.

The time has been that these wild solitudes,
Yet beautiful as wild, were trod by me
Oftener than now, and when the ills of life
Had chafed my spirit—when the unsteady pulse
Beat with strange flutterings—I would wander forth
And seek the woods. The sunshine on my path
Was to me a friend. The swelling hills,
The quiet dells retiring far between,
With gentle invitation to explore
Their windings, were a calm society
That talked with me and soothed me.

Such a mood may sometimes be merely the evasion of a weak spirit, but Homer Martin, if wayward, was not weak. He expresses a solace that strong spirits have often felt in nature, a sentiment that has been the staple of poetry from the days of the sages of India and China, through Œdipus at Colonus and the stoics, to our own century. His vein is narrow but in the finest tradition and of the most evident personal authenticity.

Yet, saving only La Farge and Vedder, I have never heard a painter speak in unreserved praise of Martin's work, and I have heard painters whose opinions are usually worth while declare that it is negligible. No formal rebuttal of such opinions seems to me necessary, but a word as to standards may be in order. The value of any work of art, I believe, is solely that it should communicate a choice and desirable emotion. This is true even of so-called impersonal art. In Manet, for example, quite the most objective of painters, one shares a tense and distinguished curiosity. Now the person who gets no such choice and desirable emotion from the art of Homer Martin, may, if he be assured that his sensibilities have reached their limit of education, quite properly neglect work from which he derives no pleasure. Which comes to saying that the reasonable criticism of a work of art is always of its emotional content, and so in a manner of the artist himself. It is always competent to declare that this emotional content, however strongly and consistently expressed, does violence to our own nature and is for us undesirable. Indeed any other unfavorable criticism of a work of art seems in the nature of things superfluous and absurd.

If this very simple principle were understood, it would save much confusion. There is abroad an ultraromantic assumption that we are always bound to accept the point of view of the artist, but perfectly at liberty to object to his technique. Precisely the reverse is the case. His point of view, having all sorts of general and vital implications, we are entirely free to accept or reject, being bound merely to understand it, while the particular rhetoric of his expression, being idiosyncratic and necessary, we must accept, and the less we bother about it the better. To do otherwise is to miss the whole point. You may, for instance, attack Claude as a poor imagination, but not as a flimsy executant. Yet, many, with Ruskin, admit his poetry and deplore his tree-forms or the thinness of his pigment or what not—which is one of the more asininely specious forms of æsthetic pedantry.

With men for whom a George Fuller is primarily a feeble draughtsman I cannot argue. Let them come out honestly and say they think the sentiment is forced or cheap, and we can self-respectingly agree to disagree. And my grudge against my painter friends who decry

Homer Martin is that they do not discuss his sentiment, but assert some weakness in his diction. He splits his pictorial infinitives or ends his phrases feebly with a preposition, or otherwise breaks the rules. Whose rules? I marvel at those who know so exactly how a vision should be conveyed which they have never glimpsed save through what they call a defective form of expression. Yet there is a professional realm in which these technical matters are subjects of legitimate interest. Only we should keep in mind that such considerations are subæsthetic and quite secondary.

Taking the work of Homer Martin on this lower plane, it is obvious that he is not, strictly speaking, a great painter. The zest, variety, swiftness, and deftness of the consummate practitioner he has fitfully, and on the whole, rarely. An impeccable sense of mass and close-knit atmospheric balance was not his. Tryon, who, in some respects, may be regarded as his closest American affinity, was more skilful and curious in these matters. I have sometimes felt that Henry Wolf's admirable woodcut copy of the "Harp of the Winds" was just a shade more substantial and fine than the original. Yet it is precisely the twilight and occasionally unsure vision of Homer Martin that we value.

And the unsureness in no wise affects what he
has to say to us. Beautiful pattern, vibrating
color, distinguished mood—all these things are
precisely and fully conveyed. What matters it
while the "Harp of the Winds" balances rhyth-
mically in pellucid air and shimmering water
that perhaps you couldn't walk on the nearer
strand? The fact that you conceive the feat
shows that you have missed the picture entirely.

To those who are sensitive to the gracious
and highbred melancholy of Homer Martin's
work, this explanation will be superfluous. To
others it may be said that his alleged technical
weaknesses are of the emotional essence and
stand or fall with the emotion itself. He was
a lover of clear thinking, and this must be my
excuse for a digression that may clear up a confused attitude towards his work. He seems to
me a singularly appealing type of the minor
artist, the kind one often loves better than those
of accredited greatness. For variety, copious-
ness and vitality, Inness and Winslow Homer
are clearly his superiors; both of these come
nearer to meeting the usual notion of a great
painter, and yet I would sacrifice all their work
if I might keep the "Manor House," or
"Adirondack Scenery." Not because I under-

rate these large and genial personalities just mentioned, but because I believe that the future is more likely to duplicate approximately their type of vision and degree of skill.

I imagine Homer Martin's fame as compared with theirs will suffer vicissitudes. He is more aloof and complicated; they, more simply explicable and more nearly related to average wholesome predilections. They are more democratic and of our land and time, he more aristocratic and more free of the whole world of contemplation. I can imagine Homer Martin at times forgotten. I am equally certain that he will be perennially rediscovered, and always with that thrill which the finding of some bygone poet of minor but delicately certain flight brings to the man of open heart and sympathetic imagination.

[1912, 1926.]

VIII

ALBERT PINKHAM RYDER

ALBERT P. RYDER, "Moonlight by the Sea"

ALBERT PINKHAM RYDER

The usually dependable stork sometimes quaintly loses his bearings and drops his precious burden in unlikely places. This happened when James McNeill Whistler was born in Lowell, Mass., in 1834, and when Albert Pinkham Ryder arrived in Mill Street, New Bedford, Mass., on March 19, 1847. Whistler did not fail to protest against the stork, on grounds both of geography and chronology. To a would-be fellow townsman and contemporary he declared that he would be born when and where he chose. Albert Ryder never quarrelled with the date or place of his birth, and though it is hard to reconcile his lunar poetry with his upbringing, he shows certain traces of his origin. His people for several generations back were Cape Codders from Yarmouth—mechanics, shopkeepers, seagoing men. Ryder was himself what is called on the Cape an "independent" person, hard to move, immune from outside pressures. Well-meaning friends at different times tried to lure him into comfortable quarters and to induce him to produce regularly and be prosperous. Ryder's answer was to lock himself more tightly in his Eleventh Street attic. No Cape Codder will be driven or even much urged. To the chagrin of long-suffering patrons, Ryder often kept a promised picture in hand for a score of years. Concerning a client who had been gradually trained to patience, he once remarked, "Lately he has been very nice about it, only comes around once a year or so." The precise humorous inflection will be more readily grasped on the Cape than anywhere else in the world.

Cape Cod too is a haunted region. Spiritualism swept over it in the 'thirties and 'forties. And the abundant new ghosts found already installed the spirits of the victims that Captain Kidd slaughtered over his buried treasure. The pines around Tarpaulin Cove have seen the pirates, the British and the Yankee privateers dropping anchor opposite their sweet spring. And the soft, humid air of the Cape entraps more moonlight than any air I know, and then the tiny sand dunes loom gigantic between the moon path in the sea and the veiled sky. And the little fish-houses offer spectral walls and blue-black mysteries of gaping doorways. Such were the visual memories of

Ryder's stock. It proved a sufficient artistic inheritance, and in his later years he willingly
went back to confirm and enhance it.

Albert Pinkham Ryder came up in the de-
cency of old New Bedford, graduated in due
course from the Middle Street Grammar
School, and began to paint. Most of his
juvenilia have perished. Indeed we are as
badly off for his first steps as we are for those
of the average old master. One or two pieces
that I have seen suggest in their sirupy brown-
ness the influence of Albert Bierstadt. A repellent, metallic painter in his Rocky Mountain
vein, Bierstadt was a mildly attractive land-
scapist when off his guard. He dealt in luminous browns and yellows after the fashion of
Hobbema as understood at contemporary Düsseldorf. Every well-regulated New Bedford
home is still likely to have a Bierstadt of this
livable type. He was one of the wealthiest and
most prominent citizens of the town and perhaps the most highly considered American
artist of the 'sixties. Ryder's developed style
may be considered as merely an intensification
of Bierstadt's minor vein, the yellow-brown
being carried down towards black, the timid
veiled blue assuming a green resonance. Possibly certain tawny pictures of large size lying

in disrepute among the dealers are really the
early Ryders. They are at any rate what the
early Ryders should be if his point of departure were Bierstadt. It is a ticklish critical
question which I cannot presume to settle.
Moreover, its artistic importance is rather
slight.

Young Ryder came to art and indeed to life
sorely handicapped. His great frame had been
poisoned through vaccination. In particular
his eyes had been so weakened that any strain
tended to produce ulcers. Naturally he drifted
into an owlish sort of life, wandering off into
the moonlight at all hours and avoiding the
glare of the high sun. The physical and moral
solace of these moonlight strolls is a chief emotional content of his pictures. Indeed the forms
of most of his compositions can be directly
traced to such memories. His trees in their dis-
tortions and bold pattern are merely the wind-
blown dwarf oaks of the Cape seen against an
evening sky; his misshapen hulks are those obsolete carcasses that darkle on that little grave-
yard of ships, Crow Island; his misty stretches
of calm water in moonlight washing the feet of
shadowy dunes can be seen at South Dart-
mouth. Even the rare bits of stately architecture in his pictures suggest the late Geor-

gian porticoes and belfries and gables along County Street. All his life long he assiduously reinforced his particular type of vision, but I think he added rather little to the visual memories of adolescence. Likewise the element of glamour and peril in his sea pieces grows out of New Bedford. Her hardy sons pursued the whale to the ends of ocean. Ships came back bleached and battered, mere wraiths. The little schooners plied to George's Banks through leagues of treacherous shoals and baffling currents. Ryder never attempted a literal record of this, nor of anything, but the spirit of adventure and hazard in his work found its nourishment along the New Bedford wharves. His scudding ships are wholly fantastic, yet very like some hard-clammer's skiff staggering up towards Fort Phœnix before a souther, its bellying, tiny spritsail at once deformed by the urging blast and full of moonlight.

In a precious autobiographical fragment Albert Ryder tells us how the vision of his art suddenly came to him. He began by studying the great masters, naturally in engravings, and copying them.

Like many old Yankee families the Ryders produced just one money-maker, and he loyally helped out the rest. William Davis Ryder came to New York soon after the Civil War and set up the eating-house of Ryder and Jones at 432 Broadway. It prospered. By 1879 William was proprietor of the Hotel Albert in West Eleventh Street. The rest of the family followed his fortunes to New York. In 1871 we first find Albert Ryder with his father Alexander registered at 348 West Thirty-fifth Street. They were only waiting for brother William to move into larger quarters at 280 West Fourth Street. That was the family home for many years, until 1879, when William moved to 16 East Twelfth Street near his hotel, and Albert Ryder set up his studio.

Doggedly the old father tried to do his bit, and not too successfully. We find him in 1871 running a restaurant at 36 Pine Street. Evidently it was a bad venture, for within a year he is registered as a milk man. That lasts a year or two. In 1877 he is superintendent, sexton, of St. Stephen's at 35 Howard Street. That job again lasted little more than a year and was the old man's last activity. By that time perhaps William had managed to convince the patriarch that it was in the financial interest of all that he should forego the luxury of self-support.

For two years from 1871 Albert Ryder is described in the directories as an "artist." Doubtless this is the period of his association with William E. Marshall, the portrait painter and engraver. Marshall had made solid studies with Couture, and was a serious craftsman. Ryder was possibly rather an assistant than a pupil. This we may surmise from the scrupulousness with which in 1873 he registers himself as a "student" when he enters the school of the National Academy of Design. Since neither the training of Marshall nor that of the Academy is reflected in Ryder's work I pass both briefly. His position as a student of the Academy gave him the chance to exhibit a landscape called "Clearing Away" in the exhibition of 1873. In 1876 he showed a "Cattle Piece" and thereafter contributed with fair regularity. He tardily became an Associate in 1902 and was soon promoted to be an N.A., in 1906. The sojourn with Marshall invites exploration. It raises the probability that Ryder painted portraits which have been lost. One such was seen and described by Sadakichi Hartmann about 1900. He writes of it in his "History of American Art."

"The first glance told me it was a man in American uniform, after that I saw only the face, the tightened lips, the eyes; it was as if a soul were bursting from them. . . . This portrait immediately gave me a keener insight into his artistic character than any other picture. Everything was sacrificed to express the radiance of the innermost, the most subtle and intense expression of a human soul."

About 1876 the Scotch connoisseur and dealer Daniel Cottier discovered Ryder. He and his partner James Inglis thenceforward counted for much in whatever small prosperity Ryder ever enjoyed. Cottier's influence was great with the few æsthetically aspiring New Yorkers of the moment. He promptly showed Ryder's pictures alongside those of Abbott Thayer and Francis Lathrop. When in 1877, the Paris-trained insurgents founded the Society of American Artists, Ryder was among the first to be invited. It showed liberality for these apostles of dexterity to choose a man whose methods were as fumbling as his imagination was exquisite. Ryder very faithfully exhibited with the Society and became an academician with the rest at the time of the merger in 1902. His few artist friends, Alden Weir, Charles Melville Dewey, Albert Groll, and Alexander Schilling were in the new movement. The few critics who deigned to notice his early efforts

admitted his force of invention but gently de-
plored his lack of fidelity to nature. Indeed a
chiding paragraph on Ryder and Blakelock was
almost ritual in sound criticism of the day.

In 1881 a miracle of liberation befell Ryder.
Up to his thirty-fourth year he had lived as a
semi-dependent, with his family. The solitude
and disorder which were the very necessity of
any creative existence for him had been impossible. Now he set up his own studio in the old
Benedick on Washington Square East. It was
then new, an effrontery of unwonted height
with its six stories, a sinister symbol of an impending emancipation of American bachelor-
hood from the semi-domesticity of the boarding
house. There Ryder worked for ten years and
there I am confident three-quarters of his pictures were conceived. Thereafter he had three
attic studies, all portents of dire disorder, in
Greenwich Village. He lived as a shy recluse,
building up in his later years a small group of
fervid and patient admirers who assured him
such modest prosperity as he wished and as his
dilatory habits permitted. His final year was
one of invalidism and during it he was tenderly
cared for by his friends, the Fitzpatricks, at
Elmhurst, L. I. In their house he died in 1917,
being seventy years old. His creative period

was brief, maybe from 1880 to 1895 or so, from his forty-third to his fifty-eighth year. The habit of retouching and the necessity of repairing his pictures, which were painted in a most perishable technique, kept him in occupation when he was no longer a creator. It is no exaggeration to say that the last twenty years of his life were largely devoted to patching up his early work. Thus it is generally idle to ask when a Ryder was painted. When "Henry Eckford" (Charles de Kay) wrote the first generous and adequate criticism of Ryder, in the *Century* for 1890, he had seen all the great Ryders except the "Jonah" and the "Race Track" picture and the "Siegfried." These were in hand before Sadakichi Hartmann's visit about 1900. By then the creative impulse was pretty well exhausted. Probably there never had been enough physical energy to inform the great frame, or enough will to carry through a career, and as Mr. Sherman, Ryder's best biographer, suggests, Ryder declined to repeat himself even when repetition would have been lucrative. He remained a shy and secluded bachelor, content with a few intimacies and his dreams. He made three brief trips to Europe in 1877, 1887, and 1893, but was uncomfortable in travel and nearly impervious to the old masters.

He is said to have proposed to a woman he had never seen, but whose violin playing from a neighboring studio had enraptured him. He read deeply a few great books, his Bible, Chaucer and Shakespeare. At the opera he occasionally drank freely of the Teutonic myths through Wagner's music. He willingly composed for his pictures rhymes and sentiments which have a Blake-like simplicity and appeal. He remained all his life a great child with no views except about his own art. The Institute, Barbizon, Manet, and Monet successively revolutionized American painting in his time. Like Dante, he kept out of movements, making "a party by himself." Unconventional, he had no quarrels with the conventions. Many still remember him as an old man, very gentle, shy, and charming. His head was too small both for his great body and patriarchal red beard. How he looked may be seen in Alden Weir's admirable portrait of 1894. It conveys something of the Yankee amenity of the man, and is more truthful than Kenneth Hayes Miller's better known and more obviously impressive effigy. Altogether Ryder belonged to the sporadic genus of dreamers. They turn up everywhere to our æsthetic delight and sometimes to our practical distress. They decline to be

classified except in terms of their own preferences, and on their own conditions.

Of the great Chinese painter Kao K'o-ming
is written: "He was a lover of darkness and
silence; he loved to roam about in wild country and gaze abstractedly for a whole day on
the beauties of mountain and forest. Then,
when he returned home, he would remain in
some quiet room, shut off from all thoughts and
cares, and allow his soul to pass beyond the
bounds of this world."

This eloquent passage from Dr. Giles's
"Chinese Pictorial Art" very well expresses the
relation of observation to creation in Albert
Ryder. He was a lover of the mystery of twilight and moonlight, but he has left no sketches
from nature. He roamed about and in his own
words "soaked in" the scene. Of his one hundred and fifty paintings more than half are
landscapes or marines. Of the landscapes
three only depict an actual locality. If we include sheep and cattle pieces among the landscapes, the list rises to fifty. Of little figure
subjects, generally a single woman's figure with
a literary suggestion, there are thirty-three.
Mythology and symbolism claim eleven pictures, and here are his masterpieces. There
are two or three oriental scenes, two little com-

positions of nudes, and one extraordinary still life of a dead canary. Two-thirds of the pictures are tiny, less than a foot in largest dimension, the biggest are still small, perhaps three feet in greatest measurement. Perhaps no artist has won such fame for so little manual labor, and again few pictures show such unremitting work of the mind.

The little marines and landscapes can only be treated as a class, and as the preparation for the higher flights they should be first considered. Let me describe the one I know best, "Moonlight by the Sea," for the good reason that it is under my eye as I write. It is number 153 in Mr. Sherman's catalogue. The little oblong is exactly divided by the warm brown of a sand dune and the blue-green light of an evening sea and sky. The dune sweeps down from the left in an S curve, which is extended to the right in a bit of level land. The land and the sky-sea part of the pictures are equal reciprocals, each having about the form of a row-boat rudder. Any unpleasant evenness in the division is immediately effaced by giving the vaporous sea a value much darker than the sky. The sea is worked with dry little touches of pale blue over a red ochre preparation. The warm ground comes through at the horizon, carrying in warmer tone the brown of the earth into both sea and sky. Towards the land there is a faint yellowish moon path. A level mist over the horizon cuts a moon at the middle. One gets in faint lemon yellow an aerial illusion of a very long building with a low dome.

Above, the sky shades off into greenish blue, lightly glazed and streaked throughout with warm brown. All this seems to have gone ahead fast. It is a lovely bit of tonality, cold and positive in the glimpse of sea, warm and mysterious in the veiled sky. The scene gets its validity largely from the quality of the shaded edge of the dune. Nothing could look more fumbling on near view or be really more skilful. It hardens where needed, escapes the sky, showing bits of the reddish preparation, occasionally interlocks with the level brush strokes in the sky. All this means irradiation and the sufficient rounding over of the mass, and it lends great scale to what in actuality was a small motive.

So far we are still, I think, in the first intention of the artist. Remained the task of enriching the somewhat monotonous brown mass of the earth. Where the dune curves a little too sweetly into the water is set the sharp prow and bowsprit of a stranded sloop. The backward raking mast supports a rag of silvery triangular sail, at this stage the brightest spot in the picture. We have the needed angular contrast to the simple curves of the design, and the interest is moving forward from sky to earth. Next a little of the very pale blue of the water is flicked across the foot of the dune in indeterminate short strokes. It gets some warmth from the brown and seems a faint, narrow band of moonlight stealing over the dune. At the end of this strip is a little fish-house facing the sea. It is lighter and warmer than the ground and a little of the blue moonlight comes up on its foundation. Such touches of light are carried sparsely out towards the foreground.

The intention is now to locate the interest under the dune, for two red cows at the right and a heavy stake at the left of the foreground, though boldly put in with the palette knife, are also subordinated. They constitute an enrichment of the level stretch, but are visible only when you search for them. Such low visibility would be quite impossible in nature.

At this point the interest of the picture wavered between the silvery sail and the fish-house. The last touch, which made the picture, will have been to diminish the size of the sail and to paint in a new gabled house facing the spectator. The front glistens with moonlight under what seems warm reddish-brown thatch and around a mysterious dark doorway. Nothing explains the redness of the roof. It is chosen simply as the focus of all the warm values of the pictures. And the moonlit front, which becomes brightest light and focus of all the lights in the picture, is painted in no expected color, but in a sharp if also pale lemon yellow. The new fish-house is slapped in without much relation to the old one, which almost disappears behind it, and of course there could be no such gleam or deep red roof lines in a building that faces directly away from the moon. In short, while the great relations all rest on observation, or rather on very fine memory, and the whole thing has the "air of drawing" which Ryder modestly claimed for his work, the determining details are treated with complete freedom, disregarding probability and even possibility for some higher law of the picture itself.

I need only add that the paint is mixed with a heavy varnish, the picture being a series of glazes. Over all, more varnish has been floated, which has developed a large but handsome crackle. The whole thing has the ma-

terial preciousness of an enamel or lacquer.
And with these purely decorative preoccupa-
tions so marked, it has a paradoxical richness
of mood. Everything that soothes and awes
one when a veiled moon rises at sea and the
mystery reaches landward is expressed on the
little eight-by-ten-inch canvas.

Similar qualities are in all the landscapes and
marines. Always the great simple design, always the fundamental contrast between a blue-
green sky and a darker sea or earth, ever the
subtle enrichment of the darks and the working
of the surface into a lustrous enamel. In the
marines the pattern of the sky often furnishes
the chief interest, a fantastic sail serving merely
as a contrasting accent to the dense leaden
clouds with sharp yellow borders where the
moonlight breaks around them. Generally the
faint light comes out of the picture. Nearly
without exception, the work has been repainted
and revised, features moved about and added
until the final effect is reached. Very exceptional is such a masterpiece of simple untroubled composition as "The Wreck," which seems
to have gone through by first intention.

Many of these pictures are marred by deep
fissures. Some have faded almost into irrec-
ognizability. Ryder used varnish upon var-

nish, as Whistler often did, with the same disastrous results. Retouches were often made in light upon a dark ground. Poorly grounded canvases or panels without a ground were too often used. I have seen a noble design painted on what looks like a small bread-board. The soft wood has drunk up the pigment till only a wraith is left. In short Ryder disregarded all technical considerations in the endeavor to get his pictorial effect and his lustrous enamel. During his lifetime he had to restore perhaps half of his paintings, and very few will survive our generation undiminished. On the whole the marines seem likely to stand best, having less underpainting of brown, and by a rare good luck the half dozen masterpieces, with the exception of "The Flying Dutchman," are painted in a fashion that promises reasonable duration.

While Ryder touched in the figures in his great compositions with great energy and expressiveness, his little single figures seem to me the most negligible side of his work. They have their poetry often, as in the charming creation "Passing Song," which was emphasized by the artist's own rhymes, but they are as a class ignorantly done. Ryder had never studied the body as he had moonlit landscape, and the slovenliness of the work goes far to detract from the value of the sentiment. They lack that distinguished "air of drawing" which his landscapes and marines have so markedly. Exceptions are the noble descending Pegasus in the Worcester Museum and the two very intense if almost over-sweet versions of Jesus revealed to the Magdalene.

Perhaps the greatest Ryders are "The Flying Dutchman," "The Jonah," "The Race Track," and the "Custance." Many would add the "Siegfried." It has steely coruscations worthy of a Greco, and in mere pattern is consummate; it conveys most energetically its sense of doom, and is just a little melodramatic. The "Jonah" is the best exhibition piece, marvellous in the way in which is carefully built up a boiling of great waves, superb in the relations of the laboring boat and the heavily darting great fish, most skilful in the way in which the mere arms and head of the sinking prophet dominate the picture. One sees it all as if from a neighboring boat, shares as a participator in the sublimity and terror of the moment. Tintoretto himself could not have bettered it. Even more beautiful in its rich blues and lilac grays, and even more distinctive as a composition is "The Flying Dutchman." The mere work is simpler and stronger, the towering of the phantom ship above the doomed skiff magnificently asserted, the mixing up of spectral sails and driving tempest clouds most effective. It is tense and lyrical where "The Jonah" is dramatic. The sheer glory of the vision captures the old castaways in peril of death. Again much of the effect comes from our being drawn bodily into the picture. We see the vision precisely as the men in the foundering boat see it, sharing their dread and exhilaration.

"Death on the race track" has a place apart, for we can trace its origins both in life and art. The occasion of this great symbol was the suicide of a waiter who used to serve Ryder in his brother's hotel. The waiter had a sure tip from the famous Dwyer stables and put all his savings on Hanover. Ryder, who was in his confidence, tried to dissuade him. Returning to the café of the Hotel Albert after the race and missing the waiter, Ryder learned that Hanover had lost and that his unlucky backer had shot himself. Thus the great picture of a skeleton horse and rider galloping about a dusky and forsaken track grew simply out of Ryder's shock at this tragedy of gambling. As he cast about for a symbol, there flashed in his memory the conqueror death in Old Bruegel's

picture of the plague, which he had lately seen
at the Prado. He sets the withered, speeding
figures of horse and rider at the turn of a
gloomy track, and the thing becomes a universal
symbol. Death rages in a dead world, his victims have been reaped, and still he rides and
ever must. It is the most concentrated creation of Ryder's genius, and the chief motive is
directly borrowed from one of the most diffuse
pictures in the world. Ryder's genius lies
largely in daring the obvious association of
Death with the solitary track. It is the most
child-like and right putting of two and two together. It makes the activities of death, which
in Old Bruegel's masterpiece were as complicated and interesting as that of a field-marshal,
seem as monotonous and mechanical as they are
sinister. It is a new note in *macabre* design.
Incidentally it is instructive to recall that Velasquez and Titian in their glories at the Prado
never affected Ryder's art, whereas the homely
and drastic art of Old Bruegel stuck in memory
and lent itself perfectly to one of Ryder's most
personal inventions.

Perhaps the loveliest of all the Ryders is the
"Custance." Under hesitating clouds—generally in Ryder clouds have determined pattern
and set—a great boat rocks gently and discloses

the pale face of a young girl who lies with a
baby on her breast. The water laps and curls
gently about the clumsy barque and is full of
tranquil moonlight. The little forms in the
boat, since its gunwales and shadowy depths
form a sort of dark nimbus, dominate the scene
extraordinarily. Ryder is incomparable in the
art of directing the attention where and as he
wants it. A benign sea and sky are pictorial
value for that Divine protection which Chaucer
emphasized in "The Man of Law's Tale."
One feels that the boat

> "dryvynge alway,
> Som-tymë, West and som-tyme North and South
> And som-tyme Est, ful many a wery day,"

is bound for a happy port.

If the greatest Ryders are those that enlist
legend and human interest, their difference from
the little landscapes and marines is after all
merely one of degree. The essential poetry is
ever the same, the difference being only that
of emphasis or accent. Any scrap of an angry
sea with the big winds equally driving metallic
clouds and a laboring sail through the moonlight conveys hardly diminished the glamour
and peril of "The Jonah" or "The Flying
Dutchman," while any one of a score of tiny

nocturnes distils the enveloping peace and high serenity of the "Custance."

The imaginative content of Ryder's painting is so direct and elemental that any verbal transcript becomes at once a hopeless competition and a sort of impertinence. Most of his critics have wisely taken refuge in analogies. Mr. Duncan Phillips has cited illuminatively the eerie quality of Coleridge in "The Ancient Mariner." Less happy is the almost stock parallel with Monticelli and Blakelock, both men of tone not of contrast, and of slighter inspiration. A little better is the customary allegation of Thys Maris and George Fuller. But they too are more tonal, more subtly psychological, less profound and general. Charles de Kay has more perceptively indicated a real kinship with Millet.

"Not by the way he paints or the subjects he chooses but along more intricate channels of resemblance, by his humble boldness, if one may be forgiven the seeming paradox, by his imagination, seriousness, and childlike temperament." Sadakichi Hartmann very aptly recalls the marvellous Virgil woodcuts of William Blake. For me, this is the nearest shot of all, and I may add that a still closer affinity is Blake's best pupil, the painter and etcher,

Samuel Palmer. His was a similar intense and simple poetry, a kindred love of the great relations between earth and sky, a common desire to enrich the darks to the limit of lucidity, an identical patience and thoughtfulness, the same twilight preferences. Add to this the small scale of the work, and a generalized sweetness and serenity, and the parallel approaches completeness.

Albert Ryder may or may not have known the Palmers. It is probable that the Cottiers often showed them, and it would be hard to persuade me that Ryder did not know and study the lovely etchings and drawings for Virgil's "Eclogues," which were published in 1883 after Palmer's death. Palmer's letters on his own practice would form an excellent commentary on Ryder's methods. Palmer writes to his son: "Somehow or other, let a design be never so studiously simple in the masses, it will fill itself as it goes on, like the weasel in the fable who got into the meal-tub, and when the pleasure begins, in attempting tone, and mystery and intricacy, away go the hours at a gallop." Again he writes to Hamerton of his drawings, "They take a long time for the very reason that I am longing to see them done, and know that the shortest and only way is to aim at no mechanical finish and to put only touches of love."

Compare Ryder's sayings, "The artist should fear to become the slave of detail. He should try to express his thought and not the surface of it. What avails a storm cloud accurate in form and color if the storm is not therein. A daub of white will serve as a robe for Miranda if one feels the shrinking timidity of the young maiden as the heavens pour down upon her their vials of wrath. . . . The canvas I began ten years ago I shall perhaps complete today or tomorrow. It has been ripening under the sunlight of the years that come and go. It is not that a canvas should not be worked at. It is a wise artist who knows when to cry 'halt' in his composition, but it should be pondered over in his heart and worked out with prayer and fasting."

I have no desire to press unduly parallels that may be only coincidences. Yet nothing could be more Palmer-like than Ryder's greatest landscape, that owned by Miss Bloodgood. The elevation of the feeling, with a certain elation in it, the harmonious organization of the clouds with the lights and darks of the rolling hills, even the accent of the tiny forms of men and animals could best be matched in Palmer's designs for Virgil and Milton. I need hardly add that if Palmer seems to me the more accomplished, Ryder seems to me the greater artist. In pure composition, in the right adjustment of economy and richness, in the capacity to make completely and unerringly his precise pictorial point, no artist of his time excelled him, and very few of any time.

[1917.]

IX

WINSLOW HOMER

WINSLOW HOMER, "Sunlight on the Coast"

WINSLOW HOMER

Since for many years I had admired the pictures of Winslow Homer, just this side idolatry, I hate to acknowledge that the first glimpse of the memorial exhibition at the Metropolitan Museum made me wince. It seemed impossible that so many fine works by one hand should be so discordant. Here were so many openings in the wall, but the vistas revealed no principle of harmony. Except for a uniform energy in the work, these pictures might be the product of several men of different ages and training. Here was a man who apparently faced nature with no preferences and preconceptions, and set himself to study almost impersonally her dynamic phases. Plainly, it was the struggle of men with the sea, of the waves with the land, the slow, powerful heave of tropic seas, the poise and buoyancy of boats among threatening billows, the battling of trees with the tempest—in general, a world of ceaseless strife and motion that engaged Winslow Homer's imagination.

What is baffling in his art is the absence of

formulas. He seems to have had no liking for this or that form of color emphasis, no habits of the hand, no desire to unify or attenuate the rawness of the thing seen. He faces nature with a kind of ruthless impersonality. He repels while he attracts, is distinguished in virtue of a magnificent commonness and a wilfully prosaic probity. He gives a keen and paradoxical sensation that I have encountered nowhere else in art except in the superb and more civilized brusqueness of Édouard Manet. And again in Winslow Homer one frequently sees the great single contour, the direct assertion of color and plane, the general primitive aspect that the post-impressionists affect without attaining. Had he only consented to be eccentric in color, he might have anticipated the notoriety of Gauguin. As it was, Winslow Homer kept to his studio at Prout's Neck, in view of his beloved sea, and painted with advice of no one, in oblivion of praise or blame.

A kind of primitivism is of the essence of this art. Here is a self-schooled man, free from transatlantic influences, who paints as if Düsseldorf, Barbizon, and Giverny had never been heard of. Christian Brinton, in an interesting essay in *Scribner's Magazine,* has celebrated this Americanism of Winslow Homer. And, indeed, in impetuous scorn of conventions and adoration of energy he may be regarded as the most American of men. Yet I feel that the isolated position of Winslow Homer makes him something more or less than American. Obviously, no other nation can claim him; but did we really possess him, or does he by an exceptional and wholly individualistic superiority dominate us? For me he does not fit easily into our American scheme, as Frederick Remington did, but quite disconcertingly evades classification, after the fashion of Walt Whitman. And of the two, Whitman was more of our sort, if only for his diffuseness and enormous easygoingness. Nothing of this in Winslow Homer. His mode is concise and tense. Some taciturn trapper or skipper reckoning with natural appearances might paint like this.

These pictures have no look of things that are composed or meditated in a studio, but of things that vehemently occur amid the clash of waves and rapids. In this memorial exhibition of some fifty pictures, two or three quite exceptionally have great charm, but without this demonstration I should have supposed it impossible that so many fine works should have of charm just nothing. It may seem a pity to begin our analysis with negations, but this conscious asperity is the central quality of the man, and from it grow both his greatness and his limitations.

Take his last work, the unfinished picture, "Shooting the Rapids, Saguenay River." A sweep of inky gray gives the heave of a treacherous chute down which races a birch-bark canoe. Guides at bow and stern strain to keep clear of the rock which reveals itself in a heavy spurt of yellow foam. In the centre a sportsman braces himself with that exhilaration which is just a little qualified by fear. The whole thing is gaunt, powerful, emphatic; the mere indication of the tense distorted faces of the paddlers is caricature of a striking type. It is, let us say it frankly, very ugly, and quite unforgettable. What the artist wanted was clearly the assertion of the heave and rush of the rapids, of the strain of the figures, and for the rest he contented himself with an approximate notation of the local color. And this means that the picture was not conceived in what we call beauty, but in energy that implied nothing more harmonious than nature herself. Had the finished picture attained charm of color or rhythm of line or mass, these qualities would have been secondary and imputed, and it is difficult to imagine that anything charming could or would have been superimposed upon these repellent sooty preparations.

Now recall Whistler's truest paradox that the fine picture is finished as soon as begun, reveals, that is, at every stage some principle of harmony and arrangement, and a very serious shortcoming in Winslow Homer's vision and method will be apparent. He is often harsh beyond the needs of his particular form of expression. Observe those masses of white paint—most perishable of pigments—that indicate the uprush of waves shattered on the rocks. That procedure suggests very well the massiveness of the ocean's attack, the formidable hydraulic fact, but how little it suggests the color of such translucent columns or the subtle weaving of festooning curves between sky and sea! In short, while the artist's business, generally speaking, is to make things more orderly than they seem, Winslow Homer, for the sake of anarchic force, has made them less orderly. And here again one recalls Whitman, who, not satisfied with spurning the trammels of verse, created a rhetoric looser than that of prose.

The analogy does less than justice to the magnificent lucidity of Winslow Homer. And I have felt freer to emphasize his sacrifice of the rhythms of form and color to expression of force, because the sacrifice was evidently a conscious one. The harmonies did not escape him; he evaded them. How lovely is the darkling blue and green in the wave depicted in "Sunlight on the Coast"! How filmy and fairly calligraphic the drift of spray to the left, how pictorially satisfying the slow roll of the steamer athwart distant billows! The whole thing has a sober, saturated radiance that we shall rarely meet except in the water-colors. Beautiful in tone, again, is the "Banks Fishermen," with a dory splendidly poised above a net shimmering with herring. Their metallic lustre dominates the accessory blues and grays of the picture, and a red buoy balanced in green water is a fine note of contrast. Again the coppery flesh colors and leaden hue of the sea in the strange canvas, "Sunset and Moonrise: Kissing the Moon," are keenly original and effective. The whole composition——the grim heads that rise abruptly from a dory lost in the trough of the sea, the crest of a wave that licks up to the cold disk of the moon in a sky of slaty violet——all this is most personally invented; much less the cross section of reality than it seems.

But it is evident in this and many other pictures that color had no preciousness to him intrinsically. It was a powerful language that told of the motion of things, and rendered facts of farness and nearness, nothing more. Colors to him were instruments, not friends and foes. Of that sense of arbitrary fitness and harmony which is the mark of the great painter he had nothing; and if harmony appears in his pictures, we may fairly suppose that it was not invented, but caught fresh from nature. The thought occurs that one who recked so little of the beauties of color should perhaps have worked in monochrome. And the gaunt silhouettes of Capes Trinity and Eternity are here to suggest what he might have done in this manner. The titanic scale of the subject he has captured, and with a little more richness and variety in the grays and a pleasanter surface quality, what is a superb study would be a masterpiece.

Yet if Winslow Homer had eschewed color, we should be the poorer. His parsimonious palette, based solely upon realistic intention, is, after all, highly symbolical of the coldly destructive seas of the north and of the sturdy folk who cope with the ocean for their livelihood. Moreover, it is instructive to see what truth and vigor of color construction can exist apart from tone. That is almost a new chapter in the technique of painting, and it paradoxically links the primitive artist Winslow Homer

with such musical anarchists as Richard Strauss
and Dubussy, who have discovered that musical
construction need not imply overt melody or
harmony.

The last twenty years of Winslow Homer's
life were spent in relative seclusion at Prout's
Neck, Maine.   With occasional flights to the
deep woods or the West Indies and Florida, he
settled down to two subjects: the sea gnawing
at the land, and sea-folk struggling with the
sea.   The actual clash and fury that shapes the
edges of the continent he painted with a force
and energy attained by no other artist.   It is
unnecessary to specify pictures of this type.
There are not many of them, for he was a slow
worker, but they constitute possibly the most
generic achievement that American art has to
show for itself.

Yet the masterpieces are possibly elsewhere.
The best of Winslow Homer's fishermen are
seen with a simplicity and largeness that is instinct with style.   The most famous picture of
this sort is, of course, the gaunt moonlit face
of the lookout who rings eight bells.   Of equal
quality is the picture of the same title, with two
figures, which Mr. Stotesbury lends to the
memorial exhibition.   Here we have the great
contours and generalized modelling of Millet,

and a true sense of the physical littleness and spiritual might of those hardy men who go down to the sea in ships. Such pictures are more concentrated and less subject to defects of color than the more famous marines. There is in them a hint of manly admiration, the impersonal creator is caught off his guard, and a severe beauty gets into the work.

No estimate of Winslow Homer can be a fair one which fails to take into account the fact that he began as and in essentials remained an illustrator. The Civil War liberated him from hack work in a lithographer's shop. Besides war sketches for the wood block, which brought him fame, Winslow Homer found time to paint *genre* pictures of army and negro life. He displayed the knack of the journalist draughtsman and something more. A single study, showing negro soldiers lolling on the sunny side of their tent, is in the present exhibition. It has character, and the sky is beautifully painted. The National Academy of Design showed an uncommonly keen sense of merit when it elected him an associate in 1864 and the year after promoted him to full membership. In 1867, being thirty years old, he made the prescribed visit to Paris, whence, unlike thousands of his colleagues, he returned unscathed.

For a matter of ten years he roved widely in
the forests of Maine and Canada, in the still
wild Adirondacks, in Florida and Bermuda,
producing more sketches than pictures, and still
continuing the *genre* vein that was proper to
him as an illustrator. Some of his best work
of this sort, fish leaping at the fly, tenting
scenes, etc., transcends the stock illustration for
the sporting press only by its energy. A picture like "Snapping the Whip," with its line of
romping schoolboys, shows how undistinguished
his vision was as late as 1876. Close inspection of it will show a fine and masculine workmanship. The hand is ready, but the mind still
hesitates and does its seeing casually or at
second hand. A study of the illustrations which
he made abundantly for *Harper's Weekly* between 1867 and 1877 would reveal at once the
solidity of his self-discipline and an unexpected
versatility. He could have been great as a
genre painter had he chosen. It was not till
his fifties that we begin to get pictures of the
quality of "Banks Fishermen," 1885, "Under-
tow," and "Eight Bells," 1886, and it was still
a decade before the conviction began to spread
that we had a great painter among us. It was a
sojourn in Gloucester in 1878 that initiated him
into the life of seagoing fishermen, and his

finest pictures are more or less reminiscent of this period.

An interesting and not quite explicable episode in his development is his work done at Newcastle, England, between 1881 and 1883. It has an amenity nowhere else appearing in his art. It seems as if England mollified the wanderer. There are even odd suggestions that the sentimentalism of current British painting may have reacted ever so little upon his stern manner. The English sketches have a peculiar flavor. How account for that admirable monochrome of a lugger, lent by Mr. Drake, in which sit peasant girls with the classic poise of goddesses? Ingres would not have set them down with a subtler line, and Frederick Walker would not have conceived the subject very differently.

Within a few years Winslow Homer was in his retreat in Maine, and his work had already assumed that harshness which was to be his characteristic to the end. What caused this swift and radical reaction from the sweet new style acquired in England is a critical problem of some difficulty. We have no right to pry into the causes of that carefully guarded seclusion at Prout's Neck. Indeed, there is a sufficient obvious cause in the man's hatred of

crowds and love of the sea. As for the change
of style, it may rest upon the strange objectivity
of the man. Where there was atmosphere and
picturesqueness he painted it, where it was lacking he scorned to prettify the crude reality.
The case may be as simple as that. And yet
I fancy the intimates of Winslow Homer could,
if they would, give us a more psychological explanation. In any case, I would not press the
point of objectivity, for Winslow Homer was
much more the conscious personal artist than
he seems, his devices being merely unusual and
well concealed.

On several occasions, notably at the Pan-
American Exhibition at Buffalo, Winslow
Homer chose to be represented by his water-
colors. Doubtless he felt in them possibilities
of harmony lacking in his larger works. In
these water-colors, many of which were made
in sub-tropical seas, rules absolute simplicity of
statement. They are exhilarating from their
calculated audacity. A few sweeps of the
brush, an added accent or two, and a blue expanse of quiet sea spreads out before you, or
the lush tangle of Everglades, or the lustrous
shambling forms of half-nude negroes luxuriat-
ing in sea and sunshine. Of the series devoted
to American fishing and camping scenes Mr.

Huneker has somewhere said with a certain in-
nuendo that they will be liked by those who like
the subjects. The observation merely under-
lines the artist's proud habit of abstracting
himself from his work. Yet the water-colors
show a powerful and very likable accomplishment. They never attain the finer and more
mysterious harmonies, but they are sonorous in
a fashion foreign to the oil paintings. Most
of the water-colors betray a very definite illus-
trative intention. A capital instance is the
study for "Hunter and Hound." The hunter in
a canoe has caught a buck by the horn; the
swimming animal drags the boat downstream
while a hound paddles desperately in pursuit.
The determination of the hunter, the slip of the
boat over the water, are admirably expressed.
Strident whorls of white indicate the great rip-
ples that enfold the struggling beast. It is a
remarkable vision of energy unqualified by any
desire for arrangement. And here it is instructive to note the considerable changes made in
the oil painting. The crudity of the delineation has yielded to a certain mystery. To the
left the river turns in and affords a vista. In
short, though the compositional changes are
slight and in a manner obvious, they show the
artist seeking a greater unity through complex-

ity, working, that is, in the spirit in which good pictures have always been made.

It would be interesting to review the water-colors in the memorial exhibition, but it is better to take collectively those brilliant studies which catch the radiance and slow potency of tropic seas, the swing of moored boats in the shallows, and the battling of sailing craft with the gale. There is an extraordinary sketch of palms searched and shaken by the hurricane. For technical mastery nothing equals the sketch "Homosassa, Florida," in which two simple washes do duty for the sunlit front of jungles in foreground and middle distance, while a single murky wash of purple slightly accented suggests the whole complication and mystery of the inner forest. I suppose a painter would unhesitatingly stake the greatness of Winslow Homer on a few of these consummate sketches, and they are indeed among the unprecedented things. They recall vaguely certain triumphs of the Japanese in similar themes, but the American work is swifter, more potent, less schematic. I cannot imagine that work so in-dividual and invigorating will ever be for-gotten.

To anticipate the verdict of the future on Winslow Homer would be a presumption, yet this much may safely be said: that he bulks large today partly because of the debilitated estate of American painting during his lifetime. Whenever painting has resumed a normal force and expressiveness, his peculiar merit of energy will inevitably seem less rare, while in better times than ours his defects in arrangement and tone may well be judged more harshly. Meanwhile his memory deserves the most generous admiration from his contemporaries. If he narrowed himself and sacrificed merits that seemed cheap to him, it was for the sake of truth and intensity. He seems to have had little music in his soul, but he had a blunt and forceful way of saying what he meant. Unquestionably, he has deepened the common vision of our sea and forest and their folk. In short, he did about all that a potent individuality, isolated, unsustained by a sound tradition, can do in our day. A more fortunate age that has arrived at vital formulas may perhaps find his work a shade anarchical, brusque, and incomplete, but such criticism, I believe, will be tempered by profound admiration for a great spirit. The stark apparition of Winslow Homer may remind some future critic that in the off days of art in America we lacked not so much great personalities as a social tradition to give them support and an æsthetically enlightened remnant to afford them companionship.

[1911.]

X

THOMAS EAKINS

Courtesy of Jefferson Medical College, Philadelphia

THOMAS EAKINS, "The Gross Clinic"

THOMAS EAKINS

Born in 1844, Thomas Eakins had about ten years' seniority over that group of Paris-trained painters which includes Beckwith, Brush, Cox, Blashfield, Sargent and Weir. And Eakins was also a good ten years younger than such pioneers as William Hunt and John La Farge. These chronological facts and the contented obscurity with which he lived out his life in his native Philadelphia have prevented Eakins from being considered with the group to which æsthetically he belongs, and of which he was unquestionably the greatest member. Thus, though a pioneer of the Paris style in America, he never received pioneer honors. That heartening conspiracy of praise which it was the good luck of the founders of the Society of American Artists to enlist, had no Philadelphia branch by which Eakins might benefit. Indeed it did not even occur to the Society to invite to its membership that painter whose career had been singularly prophetic of its own ideals. Quite tardily, in 1902, the National Academy did elect Eakins. He re-

ceived his modicum of medals and awards, but
he had no press, and desired none.   Philadelphia had no equivalent for the promptly reported revels of the Tile Club.   The grubby
mansard of Eakins's house, his only studio,
never entertained the danseuse of the moment.
To be sure he painted many celebrities, but they
were Philadelphia celebrities.

No anecdotage enlivens Eakins's memory.
That report of fellow students at Paris which
makes young Sargent and young Weir still vivid
is in Eakins's case entirely lacking.   We know
that for some years before 1870, after preliminary studies with Leutze and Schuessle, at the
Pennsylvania Academy, he studied with Gérôme
at the École, and with Bonnat, that he was wandering in Spain during the Franco-Prussian war,
that shortly after his return to Philadelphia he
taught drawing and painting at the Academy,
and when a venial and even humorous indiscre-
tion ended this connection, he continued to
teach in the Independent Art Students' League
till within a few years of his death in 1916.
We know that he studied anatomy profoundly.
Everything about his work tells of the tenacious
student and intrepid thinker.   And the work
also tells of certain masculine propensities.   He
loved the prize ring at its spectacular moments,

the swish of the sweeps of a racing shell, the light swiftness of oversparred racing craft on quiet waters. So far as I know, he never painted a horse, but he was a horseman and modelled fine horses for great monuments at Trenton and Brooklyn. For the *décor* of the artist life he cared just nothing. His own great portraits, many of which he painted for friendship or for practice, gradually overran his comfortable, nondescript house, converting it into one of the most curious and personal of museums.

Great moments in painting, everything that we associate with Manet, Monet, and Cézanne, fell within his activity and observation, and we can only guess what he thought of them. His practice ignored these movements, changed little from his young manhood, and he never took the trouble to record his opinions, or possibly even to form them. One thinks, in contrast, of Thayer and Weir each painfully remaking a style, promptly repudiating the manner that served Eakins for a long lifetime. All this suggests a certain massiveness and immobility in Eakins, a certain narrowness, if you will, but it also shows wisdom and lucidity. In the way of style Eakins had from the first what he needed. As a portraitist and *genre* painter in that old tradition which delicately balances the claims of character with those of specific appearance, he knew his strength to lie. The new problems were not his problems, and although a few colorful landscapes prove that he could have gone forward had he wished, the old conventions perfectly served his genius, and he held faithfully to them. This gave him a gaunt, left-behind look and secured him only that grudging and qualified recognition which eager youth accords to an old-timer. Such neglect seems not to have mattered to him. With a few stanch admirers, mostly old friends, he carried on in his sixties much as he had in his thirties. In our day we have rarely seen so intelligent an artist so early and fully integrated. Indeed I recall no parallel except Renoir for so untroubled and consecutive a career, at perhaps the most agitated moment the art of painting has ever known.

The style which for a lifetime sufficed for Eakins's talent, seems, barring a partial survival in portraiture, as dead as the dodo. Yet it is a style that took two or three centuries to produce, and it is still worth analysis. It may be assumed that the youth who passed from Schuessle's classes to Paris, about 1866, was already an able linear draughtsman and brought with him what Paris still regarded as the beginning of pictorial righteousness. This is only an inference from Eakins's pictures, for, curiously enough, he almost never made drawings, unlike his contemporaries, was not tempted by etching, began his work ordinarily on the canvas itself, and painted such preliminary studies as were necessary with the brush. In short, while his taste was old-fashioned, his procedures were quite modern. He thought only in terms of paint. In contrast, one may recall the portfolio of fine pencil studies that would underlie any considerable painting of his master, Gérôme. At Paris the style of the Institute had already subdivided into a more linear and a more painter-like tradition. In the direct succession of the Empire style was Gérôme. He thought of everything in line, with color as a secondary grace. His ideals, naturally with personal modifications, passed to America in Kenyon Cox, George de Forest Brush, H. O. Walker, and Robert Vonnoh. Alongside the straight orthodoxy of Gérôme, there flourished a tolerated liberalism, with Bonnat as its prophet. From Couture down, the more liberal official painters, without breaking doctrinally with the Empire style, had been seeking a more flexible and painterlike practice. They consulted the museums. In Spanish painting particularly they found precedents for richer surfaces, greater luminosity, and a synthesis that made for unity. Bonnat and Ribot were working along these lines, while Whistler was ready to conduct similar experiments more audaciously in England, and Eastman Johnson, with inspiration chiefly Dutch, had already introduced something similar in America.

Essentially a painter spirit, Eakins naturally turned to Bonnat and the liberals. A few academies from the Paris days still preserved in the Eakins house are like more supple Bonnats. Indeed these studies have so much of the richness and discreet luminosity of Courbet's flesh painting that one must suppose Eakins perused the great heretic on the sly. This type of painting is so unduly discredited today that it needs a word of championship. It accepted a set of historical conventions which seem to me still sound. Everything, being done in the studio, showed the generally reduced light and sharpened contrasts of indoors. Illumination was effected not by precise registration of closely allied tones but by selected and strong contrasts of light and dark. This chiaroscuro was the means of creating form.

The necessity of strong contrast tended to eliminate distracting hues and to base the palette on black and white. Great care was taken with the blacks and whites, which thus got a kind of color value. Frank color was generally admitted only as a spot, a flash of red or gleam of blue justified by a costume or accessory. Something like this convention had served Rembrandt and the little Dutch masters, Velasquez and the Spanish realists; before them, Caravaggio; and after them, Chardin. It was the dark manner always competing with the equally conventional florid and colorful tradition of Rubens. Today such pictures from auctioneers to æsthetes are shrugged off as "dark pictures," which only means that it takes a certain amount of time and patience to read them, as it took time and patience to paint them.

Of course there is no merit in painting dark or in painting bright. Either way, the best and the worst pictures have been made. But the painter who wishes to linger over his theme, facing it in many moods, enriching it from repeated observation and reflection, correcting and reshaping as he goes—such a painter will quite logically be a dark painter. To say what he has to say he must liberate himself from the inexorable tyranny of the fugitive appearance and from the perplexities of an ever shifting light. He must content himself with wide approximations to appearances, just enough to give credibility to the mental images in which he deals. Such a painter today is hardly regarded either as an artist or even as a respectable craftsman, but that is due to the cheap contemporaneity of most modern taste and to the great delusion of a constant progress in the craft of painting.

All that is just in the prejudice against dark painting is the intuition that a stupid painter may impose himself more readily that way. This may be true but it is also true that it is harder to paint a great picture by the dark conventions than by the bright, nature and the luck of appearances and decorative novelty co-operating less in the effect. It is the conviction that Eakins's dark pictures are paradoxically great which has retained him the respect of a youth which dates the birth of painting from Cézanne. And the more imaginative even see, that being what he was, a profound student of his fellow men, he could no other than adopt and retain the methods proper to the painstakingly intellectualized work of art.

Possibly Eakins was really at his greatest in *genre* painting, but since portraiture was his life work, we should begin with it. An Eakins portrait is very largely conceived, but without parade of handling; and very minutely detailed, but without any smallness. The main balance, the cardinal articulations, the characteristic mass, are surely and strongly felt from the first. He saw what distinguishes anyone from a distance, before the features come into play. Here lay his specific genius. Whoever knew one of Eakins's sitters would easily recognize him at a hundred-foot remove from the canvas, simply by the way of sitting, standing, or walking. No amassing of details, and Eakins added them relentlessly, ever effaced or attenuated this first vivid apprehension. Now to catch a sufficient approximation to these larger facts of appearance is of course the common gift of the caricaturist, but I believe no one can transcribe such facts accurately and expressively on the scale of life unless he knows their cause. And here Eakins through profound anatomical study had attained the knowledge of those greater dynamic peculiarities which give to each of us his unique look and bearing.

And as Eakins multiplied details, he did so in a hierarchy of organization. Nothing was felt separately as unrelated to the larger structure. Hence the more details are added, the closer knit is the whole. And the details are expressed in an entirely painter-like way, as flecks or patches of tone which give the plastic suggestion. The feeling of the brush is every-where, it never hardens into a pencil. For this harmonious union of breadth with minute detail there are few precedents or analogies. In every way the closest is the early portraiture of Velasquez. The critics speak of it in the same terms of carefully guarded praise that you will find in the scanty critical writing about Eakins. And indeed I am willing to concede that whatever verdict is fit for Velasquez in his early maturity is approximately right for Eakins throughout. In both cases we have to do with extraordinary expressions of character without positive charm or felicity of mere handling.

Generally Eakins's sense of character is somewhat tragic. There are notable excep-tions—the two concert singers (at the Penn-sylvania Academy and at his house) in their full-throated vitality, the splendid lolling nudes in the "Bathing Pool," the lean athletes in the prize ring pictures, the brawny rowers, the noble nude woman in the "Nymph of the Schuylkill." But in the main Eakins liked to paint and did paint men and women strong though ravaged by the years, somewhat warped and furrowed by much action and thinking. In a few portraits, as that of his friend, Archbishop Wood, he dwelt upon the mellowness and benignity of old age, but he preferred to read character in terms of effort and fortitude. This Spartan mood was repugnant if not mysterious to an age that eschewed the tragic, or tolerated it only if attenuated by an alien urbanity. It was the moment when "The Lady of Lyons" passed for high tragedy while "La Traviata" was a favorite opera. In such days the lucid bleakness of Eakins could not be liked, and when approved, was approved hesitatingly or coldly. He was a fine draughtsman, but a mediocre painter.

This point of view was most elaborately expressed by that excellent critic, Samuel Isham, from whose "History of American Painting" I quote, premising that Isham bracketed Alfred Q. Collins and Eakins, as portraitists with a formidable grasp of character but without ease of charm of execution.

"In the same way Eakins, with a like grasp of the personality of his subjects, and an even greater enjoyment of the picturesqueness of their attitudes and apparel, yet fails of the popular appreciation that he merits because of his neglect of the beauties and graces

of painting,—not the beauties and graces of his subjects. No one would wish his sitters more modishly
clad or more self-conscious. Their interest lies in
their personality, and that is excellently given. The
drawing is the most searching and delicate, the figures
are well constructed and stand with notable firmness
on their feet, and every line of face and raiment has
character. The artist seems to say, 'Here is the man,
what more do you want,' but the paint is apt to be laid
on inelegantly. There are vast expanses of background that are thin or dry or muddy or cold. The
eye longs for beauty of surface, richness of impasto,
or transparent depths of shadow, and the lack is the
more felt because the artist has shown that when he
will he is quite competent to give them, but they do
not come naturally."

How this whole passage evokes a pathos of
distance! Only twenty-five years ago you could
write of the beauty of painting, and everybody
would know just what you meant. It all lay
in *cuisine,* and the proof of the pudding was the
eating. You sampled it, like little Jack Horner,
by putting in your thumb and pulling out a
plum. If the plum were not well textured, lustrous, discreetly iridescent, you condemned the
pudding. To consider the total concoction of
the pudding—culinary preconceptions that
might call for an unalluring sort of plum,
would have been to intrude alien literary issues
into a judgment purely æsthetic. It was wonderful to live in such certitudes. I who speak

have done it, and perhaps Mr. Isham may really be congratulated in failing of that full measure of years which would have brought him to a moment when beauty of painting, namely the artist's *cuisine,* save to one or two die-hards, means just nothing at all.

A joyous historian once remarked to me of the Three Fates of the Parthenon that they were "not very cuddlesome." He did not regard it as a serious criticism of Phidias. To Mr. Isham it did seem serious criticism to regret that an austere genius should not paint voluptuously. Today it would be impossible to persuade any amateur that an Eakins would be better if it were painted with the richness of a Chase. I need only add that the alleged defects in Eakins's practice would only be apparent if you looked for them in corners. The whole picture always has its inevitable rightness, metallic, if you will, but complete and profoundly impressive. The artist rarely wishes to charm you, was seldom charmed himself; he wishes to understand fully, to see clearly and to show clearly, and this he invariably does. One must simply accept a certain grim nobility and ruthless directness as proper to the man and inherent in his message. Perhaps the greatest of the very mixed benefits that Modernism has brought in its train is the habit of judging pictures as wholes and not from arbitrarily chosen extracts.

Any fine portraitist is perforce a historian, and Eakins's portraits give the fullest record that exists of the intellectual travail of our old American stock in the 1870's and 1880's. It was a period when there seemed to be an abyss between thought and action. The men who were seaming the land with railroads, bordering the rivers with mills, wresting coal, oil, and metals from the earth, harnessing electricity, applying chemistry to great industry—these men seem wholly detached from our tradition, constituting a new and baffling race of their own. None of them so far as I know was painted by Eakins. They would not have sought him. A kind of æsthetic simplicity about them drove them to popular and flattering portraitists when they had time to be painted at all. For the rest, few of them looked their admittedly important part. There were exceptions, captains of industry who lived broadly and generously and achieved a fine and personal culture. I would go far to see an Eakins portrait of J. J. Hill or of Sir William van Horne. But this was not to be. His sitters were artists and intellectuals, and there he wrote his indelible chapter.

It was in a singular sense a moment of hesitation. Darwin, Huxley, Herbert Spencer and Matthew Arnold were novelties, presenting urgent problems with which thinking people had to cope. Everything in belief and much in practice had to be radically reconstructed, with a dire off chance that only destruction was possible. There had been no time to think it through, nor yet to adopt the defeatist policy of letting it alone. Eakins's personal attitude in this matter I do not know, nor is it important. It is enough that he saw and caught the stigmata of such thinking in his most characteristic portraits. The few complacent sitters of Eakins were priests, and these as a class are his least interesting pictures. His gift was to understand a generation, seeking dimly to find itself, and saddened by an uncertain quest.

If the historical value of his single portraits is great, this value is at its maximum in the two big pictures of surgical clinics—"Dr. Gross's Clinic," at Jefferson Medical College; "Dr. Agnew's Clinic," at the Medical School of the University of Pennsylvania. Here Eakins is venturing in a field magnificently occupied by the early Dutch painters and vulgarized throughout the last century by the official painters of France. There is no question on which side Eakins belongs. You must parallel him not with Roll and Gervex, but with Hals and Rembrandt, and he does not too much suffer under the comparison. Between Eakins's two topically similar masterpieces there is a spiritual abyss. It is the difference between the old and the new surgery—surgery as legerdemain and surgery as science. In the "Gross Clinic" Eakins caught imperishably the very last of the old, for Lister had already published his discoveries.

With the enthusiasm of a beneficent magus, Dr. Gross presides over the oddest sort of witches' kitchen. Eager young men clutch about the gashed thigh. A woman in the operating circle hides her face. There is a general black fustiness, everywhere frock coats and white linen, sometimes blood-stained. A great surgeon retains the garb and capacity of a gentleman even when he operates. So doubtless did Amboise Paré. Behind and above is a mystery of faces, clear only that of the clerk who rigidly keeps pace with act and word. There is a separate study in the Worcester Museum for the head of Dr. Gross, and it is amazing how the mere posture implies the whole picture. He is wise, sad and determined. He has staked his skilful hands against death or decrepitude, but the event is uncertain, remains a God with whom possibly neither he nor the patient is on terms, and a fate which he cannot control. Skilful he has been, and forgetting the blood that crimsons his fingers to the knuckles, he poises his hand and tells as he may where his skill lies. It is a portrait of Dr. Gross, everything else, despite resolute secondary portraiture throughout, being incidental. He is a prophet among his disciples, and his act seems not one of routine, but a gesture implying a miraculous deliverance. It is a very great picture. Rembrandt's "Anatomy Lesson" seems to me inferior to it in taste and concentration. It was painted in 1875, when Eakins was forty-one, and it did not meet its predestined gold medal till twenty years later, at the St. Louis Exhibition.

With "Dr. Agnew's Clinic," painted some fifteen years later, we step into another world. There is no sense of urgency or inspiration. Instead, the beauty of an orderly ritual. The white-clothed surgeon stands apart with the nonchalant confidence of a military commander in his trained force. Three surgeons work deftly and quietly about the half-exposed body;

a trim nurse stands by. The formidable array of special cutlery that we note in the foreground of the "Gross Clinic" is absent. One just sees the edge of a modest instrument tray. The surgeon is no longer an inspired magus working his miracle in a dire emergency, but merely the principal actor in a well-knit drama. He no longer bets just his skilful hands against death, but a whole body of knowledge and a corps of capable assistants. There is no weeping relative in the circle. Science has learned that the weeping relative is as septic as the gentlemanly frock coat, and has banished both. There is nothing grim about the scene. The mood is rather serene and cheerful. Nobody but Eakins has so keenly felt the tense beauty of a modern surgical operation—a spectacle as lovely in its fashion as a solemn dance, and for the same reason, that it rests on an exquisite order.

Merely on the technical side this is an advance on the "Gross Clinic." The atmospheric envelopment is finer and more reasonable, the audience of medical students, including many admirable portraits, is at once more fully realized and better subordinated. But I think the "Gross Clinic" with its sinister intensity is after all the greater picture, evidently not so lucidly seen, but more impetuously imagined. Either picture would suffice to make an enduring fame. Modern painting affords no worthy parallels. Besnard, in the "École de Pharmacie," with all his ability, is far less penetrating. For our analogies we must go back to the Dutch corporation pictures and to the anatomy lessons of Keyser and Rembrandt; and Eakins, if his dexterity is less, is on the same high plane of insight and interpretation.

The single portraits of Eakins are as various as the sitters. Style they have abundantly, but it is scrupulously subordinated to character, and has to be looked for. I suppose he has lacked his due fame largely from the fact that his handling is never an earmark. There is nothing about a fine Eakins' portrait that gives the tyro the joy of saying offhand, "There's a good Eakins," as he would say, "There's a Chase, a Sargent, a Whistler." You would say instead, "There's a very serious portrait." In short in a generation that sorely overvalued brilliant handling, Eakins simply offered nothing that could be talked about or written about, and was naturally neglected. Today, I trust, we are more interested in what is expressed than in the rhetoric of expression, and Eakins is coming into his own, for no portrait painter of his age, whether in America or Europe, has left a more various and speaking gallery of thinking and feeling fellow mortals.

The very variety of these portraits makes any such generalization as I have attempted in an earlier page misleading and inadequate. What common denominator will fit the sombre gravity of "The Thinker," in the Metropolitan Museum, all grave blacks; the resolute frailness and delicacy of Miss van Buren, in the Phillips Memorial Gallery, with its bleakly lovely flash of silvery blue; the sprightly somewhat cynical assurance of Dr. Agnew in his white surgeon's jacket, at the Barnes Foundation; the slouching geniality of Walt Whitman; the crisp and almost inhuman detachment of the great physicist, Professor Rowland; the fine dandyism of J. Carroll Beckwith at his easel; the superb vitality of the Concert Singer, the stolid confidence of the little girl, Ruth, already assuming her defensive mask against a none too friendly world, the exquisite subhumorous quality of the young woman, Clara, with the grand oval of a face worthy of a Juno? Plainly these achievements can only be hinted, but the hint may be sufficiently verified and extended by consulting the illustrated catalogue which was published by the Metropolitan

Museum for the memorial exhibition of 1917.

It may still be argued that Eakins might have cared more for richness of painting and for composition. The answer would be that these pictorial graces are usually indulged at the expense of true portraiture. Only Velasquez in his maturity seems to have achieved fastidious arrangement and handling without waiver of the pristine veracity of his conception. Indeed the notion that a picture is a world made by the painter after his heart's desire has in portraiture a limited application. A portraitist of Eakins's kidney felt rather that the world of each portrait is primarily that of the sitter, that in each case it should be investigated and ascertained, and by no means predetermined on stylistic grounds. In portraits conceived with this severe probity, the personal style of the painter will all the same transpire, but rather as an intangible, a precious moral aroma, than in lusciousness of handling or measurable compositional ratios. It is entirely unprofitable to compare Eakins with those poetizing or caricaturing portraitists who are primarily painters and decorators—little brothers of Titian, Vandyke or Frans Hals. He is of another sort. It is safe to predict that his place is assured in a line of portraitists which after all includes Antonello da Messina, Il Moro, Raphael, Hogarth, Copley, David and Ingres.

In *genre* painting Eakins is so uniformly urbane and so positively charming that his lack of recognition in this field is amazing. Released from the formidable responsibility of painting portraits, dealing often with sports he loved or with intimate scenes at home, or, exceptionally, with whimsical evocations of the past, these little pictures offer no obstacle to appreciation. Yet he sold few of these little masterpieces. Most of them are still in his widow's possession or have passed through her generosity to the Pennsylvania Museum. The only one that was publicly visible during his lifetime, the admirable "Chess Players," in the Metropolitan Museum, was his gift. These pictures were his recreations, and he let it go at that. Why they did not sell when the Eastman Johnsons, the E. L. Henrys and the early Winslow Homers readily found purchasers is mysterious to me. Possibly Eakins rarely took the pains to exhibit them. Sure of a modest living from his teaching, selling pictures was about the last of Eakins's concern. It was enough to paint them.

Eakins was about twenty-eight when on his return from France he painted the rowing pic-

tures. He sent back to his master Gérôme
"John Biglen in a Single Scull," retaining for
himself a replica which is still in the Eakins
house. Both master and pupil had reason to be
proud of the picture, for it is very plainly told,
having, withal, an unaffected greatness. In a
shell cut sharply at the ends by the frame the
brawny form of the champion is arched forward ready for the catch, the wrists still
dropped in feathering position. The nose of
another shell just enters the picture from behind. Far beyond is the hazy farther bank of
the Delaware, a shade lower than the rower's
head. The dull blue expanse of river is troubled only by the long eddies from the last
stroke, gently breaking the reflection of the
figure and the shell, and by a couple of distant
white sails. Everything is homely and specific,
yet singularly grand. And this largeness of
effect is chiefly due to the way in which the burly
form, its heavy curves contrasting with the dominant horizontals, between two of which it is
held, imposes itself against the vast level of the
river. And the picture has in a high degree a
grace then novel and only beginning to be talked
about, an envelopment that catches the very
feel of that sultry mist which hangs over the
surface of our slow-running tidal rivers. Not

greater but more charming is "The Pair-oared Shell" driven powerfully through the shadow of a massive lustrous bridge pier towards broken rapids and a near-by wooded shore. Here the distribution of great masses of light and dark in a simple and noble geometrical arrangement is both lovely and impressive. A few fresh and jolly pictures of small sailing craft, of this same time, afford a relief for the tension of the rowing themes.

Of 1874, Eakins's thirty-first year, is the portrait of Professor Benjamin H. Rand, now in Jefferson Medical College. It is as much a magnified *genre* picture as a portrait, with the interest impartially distributed between the fine bearded head, the sharply lighted microscopes and papers, and the pet cat arching a luxurious back against her owner's solid left hand while a light paw reaches for the right hand heavily resting on the paper. Already we find that indefinable air of a witches' kitchen which was to be fully realized in "Dr. Gross's Clinic" of the next year; and already we discern the formula upon which the later subject pictures were to be built, a carefully chosen form strongly illuminated in foreground amid a barely penetrable obscurity. Upon a similar principle of contrast are constructed such masterpieces as "The

Zither Player," "The Chess Player," "The Home Ranch," the two versions of "The Nymph of the Schuylkill," the two prize ring pictures. It was the formula that had earlier served Caravaggio, young Velasquez, Rembrandt and Terborch. For that *genre* painting which seeks rather intensity of character than kaleidoscopic variety of appearances the convention seems permanently valid. One is not far from it in the superb "Card Players" of Cézanne, where the same principle of concentration rules. Here it is instructive to compare the admirable contemporary narratives of Winslow Homer in which a concern with specific ambience sacrifices mental to physical reality. Indeed the right use of established formulas may seem to be the fine wisdom of all great artists, as it is that of all men who with delicate intelligence lead the good life. Such a course relegates mere experimentalism to its due and minor place whether in art or life, resting, as such a progress must, on the conviction that discovery is best reached through a preliminary review and recovery.

Of the pictures painted in this convention "Salutat" is the more thrilling and "The Nymph of the Schuylkill" the more charming and satisfying. In the prize ring picture, the firm body of the champion tingles from the toe barely touching the floor to the upraised right hand; the homely and entirely natural poses of the towel-man and sponge-holder behind are of singular nobility; the background of applauding sportsmen, including portraits of Eakins and his friends, though seen in half-light, is admirably realized, but there is a baffling lack of unity. Perhaps it is as simple as that the two secondary figures are more interesting than the main figure, or that there is too much light behind the boxer. In short, one is inclined to believe that the picture would have been better had there been a greater sacrifice of naturalism to the convention.

No such reserves apply to the grander version of "The Nymph of the Schuylkill," which seems to me entirely perfect and worthy to be named with the great Terborchs or with Rembrandt's "Little Susanna." The motive of an artist working from a nude model has of course served for scores of the most tedious or vulgar Salon pictures. In no case could Eakins have stooped to such banalities, but he was fortunate in getting a hackneyed theme in a delightfully fresh and unexplored form. In the legendary of Philadelphia one learns that when William Rush, carver of figure-heads, wished to cut in wood the local nymph, finding no worthy model at a moment when the professional model hardly existed, "a celebrated belle of the time consented to pose." One wishes that legend had handed down her name, for she was a free spirit before freedom had become fashionable with her sex. The sittings took place in an old house still shown on the river bank within sound of the quiet running of the Schuylkill, and Mrs. Rush kept the "celebrated belle" in countenance with the sanction of her presence. I fully grasp the impatience of a sophisticated reader with these anecdotal, or, if you insist, sentimental preliminaries. But they are really of the pictorial essence. It is Eakins's sensitiveness to these considerations, which is implicit in all the arrangement and execution, that makes the little canvas at once so great and so delicious.

The noble form of the model blooms out of the dusk. The back, partly turned towards the spectator, is invested with a heavy and little modulated shadow while a superb blotch of light establishes the front profile of the entire figure. The figure itself, massive and graciously equipoised, the left side being free of the burden, has no seductiveness, but rather a beauty into which sex hardly enters, recalling the rare female nudes of early Greek sculpture. The seated form of Mrs. Rush, knitting, balanced by a fine confusion of the model's clothes on a chair, constitutes a picturesque half-circle in which the model stands or from which she seems slowly to rise like a Venus Anadyomene from her great shell. In the far corner, left, one sees the sculptor dimly, but realizes how carefully he studies his stroke before striking the big chisel set on the ankle of the statue. In the other corner is one of those bizarre features which Eakins, for all his sobriety, loved, the chalked outline of a figure-head on the wall with scribbled notes in chalk. Here is just a touch of that witches' kitchen quality which dominates earlier pictures. The slight bit of color conceded in a generally monochrome scheme, a bit of grayed blue in the fillet and a touch amid the mass of clothes, is very effective, while the whites and blacks are so modulated as to give a richness of tone, which I think no one would exchange for more positive color. Of course the greatness of the picture rests on an all pervading thoughtfulness. There is some sense of a solemn rite about it. The celebrated belle so carefully balancing the folio which simulates an urn could shift from the dusky room on the Schuylkill to the procession of urn-bearing maidens on the Parthenon frieze, and not find herself an alien. In such a picture, the entirely familiar meets the unexpected to create an effect of grandeur which has its overtones of glamour and even of a latent humor.

No review of the other *genre* pictures is possible. "The Negro Boy Dancing," the singing "Cowboy"—carried off with the gusto of a Hals, "Spinning," many another—all show the same grasp of the pictorial moment, the same sure and simple emphasis. Let us pass rather to the masterpiece of them all, "The Swimming Pool." The subject is nothing but six naked men and boys on or about a rude stone pier which juts out before a grove, with a glimpse upstream to a rising meadow, closed by woods, which cut off all but a patch of sky. The pyramidal group is as formally composed as any Renaissance picture, with contrast of forms tensely erect or lolling and relaxed, with lovely connecting gestures, everything studied and complete. But, by a singular grace, nothing is far-fetched or forced. Every pose, every gesture, is what might be seen. By a happy chance any confused group of bathing men might fall into this monumental order without anyone dropping a hand or turning a head. The in-

gredients are casual and natural, the whole
stately and monumental.

Of the principle of discovering beauty by selective observation of mere appearances there
could be no finer example, and of course this
was ever Eakins's road to beauty. The picture
is not built on the usual formula. The light
comes well forward on the pier, and more than
half the surface is rather bright. The shad-
owed pool is not rendered with the richness and
variety of color that was already in vogue about
this time, about 1898, but Eakins gives after all
the look of the scene to an eye focused on the
figures and taking the riverscape for granted.
This was an old-fashioned procedure. It was
the momentary fashion to let outdoor light dis-
integrate the nude. Hardly any good painter
except Renoir dared to stand out of the mode.
In the nature of the case, it is hard to see why
a figure should lose all interest as a figure
simply because it is out of doors, or, withal,
why specific illumination should seem the only
admirable attribute of nature. Cézanne was
soon to teach us better. And indeed has any
picture come nearer to Cézanne's own program
of "doing a Poussin after nature" than does
"The Swimming Pool"?

Thomas Eakins's genius was that of the

observer and discoverer. His aim was accuracy and truthfulness, his habit a self-effacement which was proud or humble, as you choose to look at it, but in any case rested on a devout acceptance of the thing seen. His art then consisted in study and a delicate probity. The personal transformation, which every good artist makes, was in his case confined to well-pondered omissions and discreet emphasis of the residual vision, in a very creative act of taste. This same inherent taste and culture saved him from the lure of unfit novelties, kept him from restless experimentation, led him surely to such established conventions as were akin to his thinking and feeling. Thus there is a massive and appealing wisdom in all his work, a value of interpretation which time will not efface. Amid the whirlwind that stirred the art of painting to its depths during his activity, he held his tiller true. No painter of his time better deserves Leonardo's praise for that artist whose judgment surpasses his mere dexterity. The time abounded in painters whose dexterity surpassed their judgment. Most of them are already forgotten, while Eakins's fame, which has never yet received its due celebration, mounts steadily.

[1929.]

XI

THE ENIGMA OF SARGENT

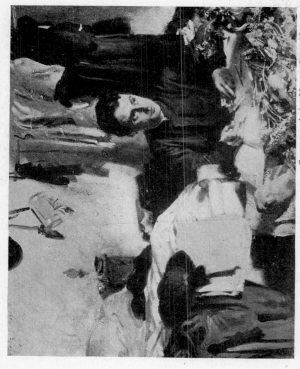

JOHN S. SARGENT, "Padre Sebastiano"

THE ENIGMA OF SARGENT

In reading very carefully Mr. Downes's life of John Sargent, I have been followed by a curious sense of frustration. It is evident that the accomplished art critic emeritus of the *Transcript* has assembled about all the material at hand, clear that he has written with the conviction of admiring acquaintance, but the man behind the painting completely eludes me. There is a baffling amount of widely differing opinion about Sargent: he was a sardonic prosecuting attorney, he was an honest and disinterested student of appearances; he was a heartless virtuoso, he was a loyal and considerate gentleman; he was one of the best painters of all times, he was a showy and shallow executant. And for all these contradictory views there is a perplexing variety of evidence. Nor do my own casual meetings with him and seeing his pictures for a matter of thirty-five years help me to simplify matters.

One recalls agreeably the nice, burly, Anglified American gentleman, entirely simple and affable when you took him as such, stiffening a little defensively when you took him as an artist. One recalls pictures as masterly as work as they are as human interpretation, others merely assertive and clever, still others showy and flimsy, again others objective and breathlessly faithful to the look of things; mural paintings overingeniously archæological, others highly decorative in an archaistic way, others highly undecorative in a melodramatic way, a few highly decorative and as deeply felt, some mildly decorative and hardly felt at all. Then one thinks of the water colors so marvelously seen and executed, but so little felt, and alongside of them of a landscape like "Lake O'Hara," profoundly seen and as deeply felt. The whirl of these paradoxes, while confusing, is also consistent. One has the spectacle of a first rate gift producing rarely at its height, but dealing often in the second rate or worse.

Mr. Downes's well-sustained eulogy naturally helps little to explain a paradox of which the eulogist seems unaware, but his ample collection of facts is serviceable as are the many cuts which quicken old memory of their originals. Evidently the life and work of any artist if closely questioned should betray any apparent mystery of his genius. Let us approach the enigma of John Sargent along these lines.

He was born in Florence in 1856, his father being of the New England Brahmin class and his mother a Philadelphia patrician. It was she who passed on to him a passionate love of music and painting, the father contributing that physical tenacity which plays a large part in any artistic success. John Sargent thus came up in an atmosphere of expatriate gentility, shifting his casual schooling and more continuous efforts as a draughtsman, as considerations of health, economy, or convenience moved his parents from Florence to Rome and Nice. Reading good books and learning languages by contact, he had a far better education than falls to most painters. However, I think he never wholly outlived the irreality of his upbringing. To think of life in terms of comfort and voluntary contacts may befit old age, but it is a poisonous programme for youth, as weakening the heroic sense of duty and reducing the exercise of the sympathies, which are really best fined and trained in compulsory contacts, to a kind of selective dilettantism. A great artist may well end, Goethe-like, as a citizen of the world, but no great artist has ever begun as that, and John Sargent was not to prove an exception. High seriousness is a homemade product. In short his morale was limited to that of the nomadic

American of culture, and that necessarily qualified his whole view of life, and naturally his
attitude towards his art.

In seeking Carolus-Duran at eighteen, young
Sargent merely found confirmation of defects
and qualities already established. The ideal
of the studio was a vivid but superficial curiosity towards appearances; the technical programme, the production of cleverly manipulated passages of paint to suggest any sort of
attractive epidermis in nature. Everything
was studied as so much still-life. Whatever
of a moral or physical sort might be within the
epidermis was not the painter's concern, did
not really interest him. That larger drawing,
which is really a psychical taking possession of
any subject-matter was not so much neglected as
completely unknown. Indeed only Puvis, Carrière, Fantin, and Degas——Cézanne had not
emerged——possessed it at the moment in
France, with Watts and Alfred Stevens in England, and Thomas Eakins and Winslow Homer
in America. It is interesting to guess what
Sargent might have become had he sought, instead of Carolus, one of these large seeing
masters, but I am inclined to agree with Mr.
Cortissoz that in Carolus's atelier Sargent
found precisely the training that befitted him.

The method there pursued had indeed its undeniable merits. It was grounded in a discreet revival of the sumptuous low tonalities of the Venetian and Spanish schools, in emulation of the bold yet learned manipulation of their great masters. It employed the safe and tested earth colors, avoiding those ephemeral stridencies which the synthetic chemist was putting at the disposal of the contemporary Impressionists. So reasonable and handsome a way of working was welcomed by the cosmopolitan youth who was by his capacity as an expatriate American of culture free from all the perilous curiosities and aspirations of the new radical schools. Within four years Sargent had fully mastered the method, exhibiting at twenty-two in the Salon of 1878 the excellent little canvas "Oyster Gatherers of Cancale," now in the Corcoran Gallery. It has much charm and alertness with a quiet and just sense of life and movement, and a sober pearliness in the illumination.

For more than twenty-five years Sargent occasionally produced little figure pieces of this sort, and the group constitutes the most satisfactory and untroubled expression of his personality. "The Sulphur Match," "Venice in

Gray Weather," "In the Luxembourg Gardens," the two "Venetian Interiors," "The Spanish Courtyard"—every well-informed art lover knows and likes these pictures, for their elegance, for their sober perfection of tone and handling, for a clear and simple evocation which is free from insistence. Their entire accessibility is their charm and perhaps their limitation. Anybody can see them. But just anybody cannot see Degas in similar vein. It requires superior vision. Sargent's complete and elegant accomplishment in this vein seems to me to result in a certain emptiness when the scale is enlarged as in "The Boit Children" and most of the other portrait groups. However, simply these little figure pieces would entitle him to be regarded as one of the best minor painters of his time, keeping him in grateful memory with such painters as Alfred Stevens, Frank Potter, and Tarbell.

As a portraitist, Sargent during his lifetime evoked the widest difference of opinion, and a critic will do well to cling so long as he may to what little unanimity there is. I suppose that everybody will agree that the "Carolus," the "Lady with a Rose," the "George Henschel," the two Marquand portraits, the Homer Saint Gaudens, and most of the Wertheimer portraits, with the "Coventry Patmore" and the "Lord Ribbesdale" and the "Ian Hamilton," together with the Mrs. Augustus Hemingway, the "Major Henry Lee Higginson," the "Joseph Pulitzer," and the group of the Four Doctors are not merely among the best portraits of our times, but also compare very favorably with the finest portraits of the past. I should not expect anybody but some Modernist who disbelieves in portraiture to differ from this view. Naturally the list might be considerably extended, but I feel the additions would soon be sharply contested. Personally, for instance, I find the much-admired "Beatrice Goelet" and the "Honorable Laura Lister" neither better nor worse than the similar pictures of little girls by Millais; I think the groups of aristocratic young women in the eighteenth century tradition far-fetched and tediously assertive; I loathe the "Ellen Terry" admiringly and am only mildly amused by the fabulously clever "Carmencita"; I think "The Boit Children," despite the adorable separate portraits, unpleasant in scale and feebly realized as a space. Naturally no authority is claimed for such prejudices. They are mentioned at all merely to show the wisdom of approaching Sargent through the group of about twenty admitted masterpieces of portraiture. Let us seek whatever principle of unity there may be among works quite various in handling, running from very sober treatment in the tradition of Carolus to the most audacious pyrotechnics.

In the first place these are all "sympathetic" Sargents. One feels that he cared more for the sitter in every case than for his own adroitness in divination or his own skill in rendering. Except in the case of the "Asher B. Wertheimer," the most ill-wishing critic could not say that Sargent had played the "prosecuting attorney," and here the critic would be wrong, for the Wertheimer is a high act of appreciation of the shrewdness and vitality of its subject. One has in every case an extraordinary virtuosity modestly subordinated to a congenial task of interpretation.

Next these are all early Sargents. Most of them were painted before 1898, and none of them later than 1903. These in short are the sort of portraits that engaged the enthusiasm of Sargent's most friendly and perceptive critics, Henry James and Alice Meynell. Beyond 1903 there are very few memorable Sargent portraits, and many bad and flimsy ones.

It seems to me that a certain obvious importance of these chronological facts has been ignored. We have the very peculiar fact that the man who was regarded as the greatest portraitist of his day did all his best work by his forty-eighth year and at fifty-five was sick of the task. Sargent had exhausted prematurely a vein which a Velasquez, a Titian, a Rembrandt, a Raeburn, a Stuart, cultivated and enriched so long as their hands could hold a brush.

What an artist quits is his own affair, and while quitting portraiture, Sargent remained immensely busy at mural decoration and water-color sketching in his last fifteen years. But for an artist of great and established achievement to go off badly is not entirely his own affair. The case wants explaining. I shall not forget the somewhat appalling revelations of the memorial exhibition held in the Metropolitan Museum. With half a dozen portraits that seemed fit company for the Halses, Rembrandts, and Velasquezes, and Vandykes in neighboring galleries, there were many of which to speak little is charity—figures that stood ambiguously or toppled out of their frames, speciously painted stuffs with no body inside, beautifully painted heads with nothing below the neck, much nondescript and some poor color, many pictures that seemed oddly out of fashion—a look that a first-rate picture never gets. Generally speaking the showy portraits were the bad portraits, the "Mrs. Swinton" being the type, with its brittle and hollow workmanship, its entire absence of any reasonable grammar of painting. It was there to show that Sargent was occasionally painting very badly near his best time, 1897.

To seek the reason for this paradox through those twenty triumphal years in London from 1884 is a task as difficult as ungrateful. Yet one may guess at the effect upon a very sensitive and self-conscious nature of such excesses of praise and blame as cheered or howled before the Chelsea door of a cultured and expatriate young American in his early thirties. He was one of the greatest portraitists of all times, he was merely a clever exhibitionist; he was a profound interpreter, he was a shallow and heartless virtuoso enriching and amusing himself at the expense of his infatuated sitters. Doubtless he pretended to himself that all this did not matter, but here and there it stung him so far that he broke a habitual reticence, to counterattack what seemed to him to attaint his character as a gentleman. More serious handicap, he had to live up or down to an early fame as the cleverest painter of a very clever age. It is the heavy penalty of cleverness that the clever person must conduct a continuous performance. To live up to such *tours de force* as "El Jaleo," 1882, and "Carmencita," 1899, was to live in overstrain. Both pictures are masterpieces bred of peculiar experience, of nerves tingling at the sinuous fury of the dance or at the splendid insolence of a Spanish she-devil in repose. The brush moves with the swiftness and certainty of a conductor's baton, evoking a visible music at once strident and superbly rhythmical. But Sargent was expected to be as excited over the aigrette of a British matron or over the towering late-Victorian shoulder sleeves of a reigning belle. He played fair with them. When they gave him something to think of while painting, he gave them his virtuosity and with it his insight and his sympathy, and when they gave him nothing, he honestly gave them what most of them wanted and were paying for—his mere virtuosity.

So I imagine the apparently ideal life in London, with its successful defence against unfit contacts and its rich companionship with fellow artists, musicians, men of letters, and understanding women was less satisfactory to Sargent than it seemed. Without developing either the constant insight and deep human respect of the great portrait painters or the sound perfunctory habits of the merely good portrait painters, he was harassed between two almost equally sinister reputations, that of superhuman virtuosity, and that of a malign "prosecuting attorney." So he remained chiefly a virtuoso who, like Hals and Rubens before him, painted many brilliant portraits, and, as admiration or affection moved him, a few portraits that are great.

By a circular route we have come back to our starting point that the great Sargents are the "sympathetic" Sargents. By this I do not mean that the sitters are likable, though often they are, but that they vividly enlisted Sargent's interest, that he thought much about them while painting them. Surely the "Marquand," the "Wertheimer," and the "Coventry Patmore" are not precisely likable effigies, nor is the amiability of the marvelous "Four Doctors" their most salient characteristic, but in every case we have personalities potent enough to arrest even an expatriate American of culture. Nor is

"Mme. X." really likable, but she is so alive in her steely perfection that one cannot see her with impunity. Perhaps Sargent's extraordinary sensitiveness is best shown by simply comparing "The Lady with the Rose" and "Mme. X.," recalling that less than three years separate the two portraits. One woman is painted with some magical distillation from flowers seen at dawn through the dew, the other welcomes and challenges the merciless light from raucous avenues; one is fully intimated with manifold respectful modulations, the other is fully and emphatically uttered in a single *élan* of male admiration. And both pictures are quite perfect.

Before leaving the "sympathetic" Sargents we do well to note that some of them enlist his greatest virtuosity. It is concealed in many, particularly in his valedictory to great painting, "The Four Doctors." The structure of the fine heads is so unobtrusive that it seems as if anybody must have painted them that way, and the really noble, spacious, and highly studied arrangement seems almost casual. The "Major Higginson," too, owes nothing of its massive and benign existence to any overt handling. One never thinks of the workmanship;

one thinks of the man. But the "Marquand," the "Patmore," and the "Wertheimer" are as brilliant as the "Carmencita," be it said with brilliancy of precise, emphatic, and understanding elucidation and without a shred of personal display in it. For the "Carmencita" so much cannot be maintained.

The relation of sympathy and interest which underlies all of Sargent's finest portraits evidently did not depend upon the intrinsic worth or interest of the sitter. It depended rather upon some mysterious and possibly capricious *rapport*. Sargent could do an inadequate Roosevelt, Woodrow Wilson, and President Eliot; an indifferent Booth and Irving. All of which goes to show either that he lacked the portrait painter's temperament, or more likely, that, having it, he soon lost it. How, we may hardly surmise. Possibly a too long and difficult inner struggle against adulation, abuse, and boredom may account for much. Few painters have been thrust so early into so ambiguous a notoriety. In any case, the great portraitist in him died young, emerging now and again posthumously in a few of the water colors and charcoal drawings of the later years.

So, measured by the standard of consistent performance, the general view that Sargent was the greatest portraitist of his times seems exaggerated. Watts, I feel, painted many more fine portraits, so did Fantin and Thomas Eakins. And the best portraits of Sargent seem to me less enduringly good than the best of Degas and Carrière and Augustus John, while Orpen's equally brilliant practice is far more evenly sustained. I do not press such comparisons; they are possibly unprofitable. As a portraitist, Sargent seems to me to have suffered from his natal cosmopolitanism, and from the absence of any pondered and settled attitude towards his art and presumably towards life. He was the fine flower of the Parisian dilettantism of Théophile Gautier and Carolus-Duran, and great only when he transcended his æsthetic origins. In many fields he was immensely able and intelligent, displaying a versatility which suggests some lack of inner centrality. Possibly he was too much in the fashion of his day and without that degree of detachment, that capacity for seeing in the aspect of eternity, which the greatest artists never lack. Hence a considerable abatement of his present fame is to be expected. But his best portraits, both for beautiful vision and workmanship, are his sure gage against that oblivion that quietly waits for the merely clever artist in any field.

In the early summer of 1890, in his forty-fifth year, Sargent was charged with the decoration of the upper hall of the Boston Public Library. The subject was to be the history of religion. This work was his most absorbing interest for his remaining twenty-five years, and it never was quite finished. It is one of the ironies that those architects, McKim, Mead and White, who were chief promoters of our mural painting, generally designed their monumental halls first, and often called the decorator to irrevocably bad conditions. They never designed an interior less fitted for monumental painting than that which was assigned to John Sargent. The long corridor was cut in two symmetrically by a big skylight above, and asymmetrically on the floor by the well of a staircase and its parapet. There remained available for the mural painter the two shallow barrel-vaulted alcoves at the ends, three big lunettes on either side and, below them, sadly isolated spaces on the side walls proper.

Within these limitations, Sargent was to do about everything that was possible. It worked out as three quite separate series: the two alcoves and the six lunettes. That a painter of Sargent's fine critical intelligence should have accepted so unpromising a task and worked at it so loyally requires explanation. There is evidently implied a great zeal to do mural painting. Next the very difficulties may have challenged one to whom difficulties were supposed to be merely opportunities. Again Sargent himself was the fine flower of a moment that, insisting on fine parts, had largely lost the sense of fine wholes. Good writing consisted wholly in fit words and fine phrases, good painting meant only fine passages. It is possible that Sargent at first welcomed conditions that limited his task to the creation of so many fine episodes, and only too late faced the problem of unification. Talking with him just after the lunettes and long vault were finished, I felt that his prodigious endeavor had not unnaturally produced an amiable self-deception. He had worked so hard to produce unity that he saw more unity than there was.

For four years Sargent worked at the first part of the decorations in the vast studio which he and Abbey shared at Fairford. There were trips to the Levant to saturate himself with the feeling of the old paganism. The contrast between the works proceeding at opposite ends of the Fairford studio is suggestive. Abbey was working out an idyllic and reflective sort of poetry in the Grail series, with retrospective and Tennysonian references; Sargent, largely guided by Flaubert and the actual monuments, was seeking to revive as spectacle the beauty and horror of the old beliefs. So in 1895 he set up the lunette which represents the Jews trampled by the strange gods of Egypt and Assyria, the adjoining vault heavily occupied by Moloch and Astarte,—cruelty and lust, with the broad frieze of aspiring and agonizing prophets below. In the lunette and vault Sargent intended to represent the Confusion of Religions, and here the intellectualism that somewhat vitiates all these decorations appears clearly. Evidently confusion may become a pictorial or decorative motive only on condition that it be brought into order, in which case it ceases to be confusion. Sargent was aware of the paradox, for he compromised. The lunette and the vault may be considered as half in order, equal concessions being made to the intellectual theme of confused religions and to the requirements of decorative arrangement. Naturally the effect was ambiguous. The tendency was to praise it ambiguously as a distinguished sort of novelty, and to reserve genuine praise for the entirely understandable frieze of prophets. The prophets were and are resolute academic studies. Without decorative unity, they had dignity and an interesting portrait character. Today they seem chiefly old-fashioned and the least effective part of the decoration. The promise lay in the chaos above the prophets, with its real inventiveness, despite its archæology, and its very personal color scheme, gold dominating sullen reds, as of glowing iron, and tenuous blue greens. To make a very splendid and wholly novel decoration nothing was needed but a finer and more formal ordonnance, and this was supplied some eight years later in the "Dogma of the Redemption" which adorns the opposite wall. Its vault and side panels were set up some fourteen years later, in 1916, and here is the perfect fulfilment of Sargent's talent as a mural painter.

Before designing the "Dogma of the Redemption," Sargent made a special trip to Spain, where he felt much of the spirit of mediæval Christianity had survived. There he made profound studies of a class of paintings, the great Catalonian altar backs, which at that time were little known even to professional historians of art. These strange paintings of the fifteenth century combine extraordinary realism in figure painting with the most sumptuous decorative abstractions. In a panel of Jaime Vergos you will see a face modelled with the knowledge of a Masaccio looking out from a nimbus of embossed and engraved stucco covered with gold. This art has a peculiar æsthetic effect. It is at once completely actual and completely otherworldly. Could an art based on the best realistic teaching of the Paris Schools attain otherworldliness by careful assimilation of the decorative conventions of early Catalonia?

Such was John Sargent's problem, and he solved it triumphantly. About the sculptured Christ rules a beautiful geometry of design. The three identical figures of the Trinity above glow somberly from behind their twisting banderoles in gilded relief with that red of cooling iron which we have observed in the earlier lunette. The motive of the Trinity fills the arch. Below the geometry is less insistent in the row of angels bearing the implements of the passion. The two patterns are connected by the figure of the Crucified Christ with Adam and Eve lashed to His pierced sides. Nothing is archæological except the arrangement, which after all rests on principles which have no date, and the decorative conventions. In figure painting and sculpture Sargent uses all his resources. Here there is nothing of Nazarene or pre-Raphaelite anæmia, everywhere splendid vitality, specific form, even something of the nineteenth century sense of the model. This is true of the angels, and they are perhaps Sargent's most beautiful creations. Again what would otherwise have a beaux-arts quality, gains aloofness and a sort of spirituality through the abstract splendor of the gold, and here are repeated those same thin, greenish ceruleans which we first saw in the diaphanous veil of Astarte.

The mood is one of intellectual understanding and reverent sympathy. Sargent could not be expected to believe that Euclidean theology which he so clearly visualized, but the man of historic imagination knew how nobly seventy generations of mankind had lived and died under the dogma of redemption. Sargent found no place in his scheme for the religion of the Renaissance, feeling it justly an anti-religious age. To complete the vault and short side walls of the alcove he passed directly from the Middle Ages to the seventeenth century and the Counter-reformation. In the notable omissions involved, his tact was complete. Protestantism, while it offered a sufficiently pictorial history, provided few symbols and less mythology, was unavailable for any comprehensive decorative scheme of which mythology and symbolism were the essence.

Above the two Madonnas on the side walls, he disposed the vault formally about great rectangles presenting the Annunciation and the Crucifixion, the smaller ovals and quatrefoils containing scenes from the life of the Virgin and of Christ. Within these narrow and formal bounds moves a passionate life. Sargent has caught perfectly that appeal to emotion with which the Church met the Protestant appeal to reason. He has assimilated the great painters who have expressed the new fervour— Sodoma, Baroccio, El Greco. But the inventions are his own, and the greatest of Sargent is in such little spaces as those which contain "Christ on the Mount of Olives," "The Visitation," the Boy Christ rushing into His Mother's Arms. The method is new. Everything is veiled and shimmering with broken light; it is as modern as a Besnard. But the formal gold mouldings and minor ornament including the heraldic symbols of the evangelists bind the Baroque vault into a perfect unity with the end wall. Unlike the end wall, which is sympathetically understood, the vault is deeply felt. Here is a paradox, for intellectually Sargent must have been as far from the religion of St.

Ignatius Loyola as he was from the theology of St. Bernard. But Sargent was temperamentally as much a musician as a painter, and his emotional self responded to a form of religious expression which without irreverence may be called nobly operatic.

Fortunately this alcove may be viewed as a unit. It is, I think, Sargent's greatest achievement, that in which he most fully gave all of himself. Technically it has a place by itself as the only modern mural painting that equals in material splendor that of the early Middle Ages and Renaissance. On the spiritual side it is replete with Sargent's perceptive intelligence and warm sympathy and intuitional scholarship. In a moment the chief spiritual product of which was the historic imagination, this is a highly representative work. It is a reconstruction not through archæological data—Abbey was proving the sterility of that in the Grail series in the hall below—but through the invention of symbols fit, though of our time, to express the soul of a time long past.

Were it a question of giving up the alcove of the "Dogma of the Redemption" or all the portraits, I should give up the portraits. Fair equivalents for them could be found; their absence would not essentially change the prospect of the painting of the turn of the century. But there is no equivalent for Sargent's finest decoration, and its absence would deprive us of a capital document for our times.

The desired contrast between the pagan and Christian ends of the long hall remained literary and was decoratively unachieved. In the six great lunettes representing the Apocalypse and Millennium, Sargent adopted a new method, or rather returned to the approved method of the schools. Blond nude bodies, rather flat modelling, much unifying blue and blue gray, some gold to echo the formula of the alcoves—everything is technically right and able. Gold braidwork about the vaults and around the dreadful skylights, much of it done by Sargent's own hands, does its best to make a decorative unit. The invention of the lunettes is alert, gracious and always ingenious, the mood pleasantly theatrical and quite unreal. There was nothing of the prophet in Sargent, and he paid off these prophetic themes, as he paid off many of his sitters, simply with his manual skill.

Not much more can be said for the great decorative series in the Boston Museum of Fine Arts. As an expression of Sargent's athleticism and general fine judgment this great suite

with its relief sculpture and ornament is remarkable. One is astounded that any man in
the late sixties could in a short time turn off
so creditably so great a task. Everything goes
along safe and established lines without very
heavily taxing invention or attention. Sargent
once remarked to me that all any decorator
could do was to make a place look better than
it did before, and this modest ambition was
agreeably fulfilled in the Museum. The compositions greet the visitor pleasantly without
arresting his entrance and exit unduly. To
the historian of art they will be chiefly interesting as proving that the early twentieth century could occasionally produce a mural painter
with the executive capacity of a Pietro da Cor-
tona or a Luca Giordano.

Concerning the two big World War panels
in the Widener Library, Harvard University,
silence is kindest. Sargent had lived the war,
had sketched at the British front. It was all
too near him to be symbolized. He should not
have undertaken a task which could only event-
uate in forcing his vein and in patriotic melo-
drama.

Reviewing Sargent's career as a mural
painter, we apparently get quite a different impression from that which Sargent the portrait-

ist yields. We find a reflective, scholarly spirit brooding retrospectively, and greatest in its more mediated efforts. It is a spirit also capable of amazing improvisations, and technical display, but æsthetically insignificant in this phase. It seems as if the cosmopolitan and expatriate with no tangible home in the present found a home for his imagination in the long endeavor of the race towards a righteousness and knowledge not of this world.

Such was his inward avenue of escape. The exit outward was sketching in the face of nature, the dearest pursuit of his last twenty years. In 1903 was published, with an introduction by Alice Meynell, a splendid folio of more than fifty plates after Sargent's portraits. With a very few exceptions it contains all his best portraits, and may fairly be regarded as his lasting monument in this field. Such was his own view, for thenceforth so far as possible he avoided portrait painting, made mural decoration his serious concern and sketching in water color his chief recreation. Though well short of fifty, he had earned his right to go his own way. Not to mention his four or five knighthoods and his membership in half a dozen academies, and a collection of gold medals formidable from mere weight, Sargent had behind him what for most artists would be a life work. He felt he was losing his touch in portraiture, Mr. Downes tells us. However that be, he had surely lost his interest, and doubtless felt justly that in portraiture nothing but repetition of past triumphs was possible. Despite the "Four Doctors" and the "John D. Rockefeller," this was broadly true.

In water color sketching he developed an extraordinary technical skill. If there were trials and failures, as is to be supposed, he destroyed them. And about the water colors there was not the bitter debate that had raged around the portraits. The aquarelles had a uniformly good press and were bought by scores for our American museums. According to one's standards, these water colors are the most wonderful performances or the most negligible. Possibly they are both. In technical quality, in clean and dextrous application of the pure wash, they are amazing and exemplary. In discovering simple formulas to suggest the most various textures and illuminations they are stupendously intelligent. If the task of the water-colorist be merely to catch the obvious and superficial look of things, there are no better water colors. If, however, his task is to evoke larger truths of nature's structure and essential organization, these sketches are of small importance. Like the poorer portraits, they are hollow—all outside. From the first I have felt their brittleness, their lack of anything like distinguished mood or interpretation. Their positive quality has always seemed to me to be restricted to their sure and expeditious execution and to the gusto that accompanies it.

All these immediate convictions were emphasized when for the first time I saw, in the Metropolitan Museum, the Sargents hung within sight of other fine American water colors. Not merely in confrontation with the Winslow Homers—dire juxtaposition for any aquarellist—but also in comparison with good average sheets of Gifford Beal, Paul Dougherty, Childe Hassam, John Marin, the Sargents as a group sunk into the gallery walls, lost color, lost validity. There was nothing behind the surface of the paper. It was a somewhat melancholy reflection that through a confusion of fashion with artistic merit, hundreds of such sheets were in transit from museum walls to museum portfolios and ultimate oblivion.

Naturally among a thousand brilliant misses there are a few hits, and these generally are not brilliant. For the water colors as for the oils the rule holds that the good Sargents are the sympathetic Sargents. The little outdoor portraits as a class are admirable, finely felt and unaffectedly executed. The men in a hay mow, the girls fishing, the numerous studies of his friends as they sketched with him, the burly apparition of himself on a hilltop—these are the fine Sargent water colors. And in these expressions of friendship he usually keeps in abeyance a color sense as audacious as uncertain, falling back upon the safe and simple harmonies of his early figure studies in oils.

It is unfortunate that the water colors have been so egregiously overrated. Only rarely enlisting the serious side of their painter, as the chosen escape of a great talent, they have their own interest. They also furthered certain remarkable achievements in outdoor painting in oils.

Throughout Sargent was a great talent in which genius was sporadic. It took genius, if chiefly of a technical sort, to paint that extraordinary study in sheer illusionism, "The Hermit," in the Metropolitan Museum. Amid the cross-lighted confusion of a forest one gradually makes discoveries—a gaunt hermit, two gazelles. The eye is not led, as in most pictures. It wanders in some bewilderment among shafts of sunlight, never quite coming to rest. Kenyon Cox in "Artist and Public" writes discerningly of this picture. The scene "is rendered as one might perceive it in the first flash of vision if one came upon it unexpectedly. This picture is better than Sorolla— it is better than almost any one. It is perhaps the most astonishing realization of the modern ideal, the most accomplished transcript of the actual appearance of nature, that has yet been produced."

"The Hermit" was painted about 1910 when the "modern ideal" was setting elsewhere, and Kenyon Cox's words were written in 1914, when the flood tide of a new Modernism had become torrential. "The Hermit" is likely to survive successive Modernisms if only for the good archæological reason that it is the consummate expression of the leading ideal of its moment.

During the World War Sargent trudged along the miry British trenches and made a few little sketches of such simplicity and power that one feels a great illustrator may have remained unrealized in him. It is a view which the mural paintings at Boston support, and it awakens a regret that Sargent called so rarely on what was a remarkable capacity for invention. The

Spartan episode of the trenches may well have weakened a heart that before long was going to refuse to serve his stalwart frame.

In 1916, having finished the Library decorations, John Sargent summered in the Rocky Mountains. Amid the grandeur of that scenery and in the unwonted relaxation of camp life he conceived and largely executed a handful of superb landscape sketches in oil and the large picture of Lake O'Hara. It is another of those surprises which his generally standardized production presents bafflingly from time to time. Great in scale and feeling, of American landscapes of this century only Abbott Thayer's "Monadnock," Albert Ryder's fantastic landscapes being obviously out of the comparison, seems to me to equal it in grandeur. It is very American in mood and even in general look, with odd affinities with Bierstadt's heroic landscapes. It has of course a sombre loveliness of color and a sense of moving mists and waters that Bierstadt never commanded or even perceived. It has dignity without either constraint or exaggeration and a rare felicity of workmanship without display of cleverness. I am glad to leave this the final impression of John Sargent's art.

This isolated masterpiece may recall our

initial guess that Sargent's work as a whole may be inferior to his native gift, and that there was a distinct frustration in his career. The causes for this I have already suggested in his youthful experiences, Paris training, and in the exaggerations of praise and dispraise that early troubled a sensitive temperament. It has been no pleasure to me to counter the *élan* of indiscriminate admiration that has followed his death. Yet a chief business of criticism is to distinguish between what is merely fashionable and successful and what is great in art. This I have tried to do in Sargent's case, simply bringing together views which are already on record and which were expressed when Sargent's vogue was at its height.

Whatever was possible for an expatriate American of culture, trained by Carolus and rising to fame in the London of the 'nineties John Sargent abundantly achieved. It was an achievement bewildering in its variety and ability, but in the main uncentral and impermanent. I summon one of Sargent's closest friends to explain why.

Henry James once wrote of the cosmopolitan C. S. Reinhart words that express much of his own case and more of that of his lifelong friend John Sargent. The quotation may save me a summing up.

"Does the cosmopolitan necessarily pay for his freedom by a want of function—the impersonality of not being representative? Must one be a little narrow to have a sentiment, and very local to have a quality, or at least a style; and would the missing type . . . yet haunt our artist—who is somehow, in his rare instrumental facility, outside of quality and style—a good deal more if he were not, amid the mixture of associations and the confusion of races, liable to fall into vagueness as to what the types are?" [1927.]

XII

EDWIN AUSTIN ABBEY

EDWIN A. ABBEY, "Spirit of Religious Liberty"

Pennsylvania Statehouse, Harrisburg

EDWIN AUSTIN ABBEY

The career of Edwin Abbey is at once very simple and quite baffling. He was born in 1852 in Philadelphia of New England stock. His vocation as an illustrator developed early, and, after a modicum of schooling in letters and art, he became a general utility man for the Harpers in New York. Those were the old wood-block days. To go into that mill of faking, redrawing, and being redrawn—all in a hurry—might have ruined a much better artist than nineteen-year-old Abbey. Instead, he underwent the drudgery unscathed and with profit. Soon he got better work, like the illustration of Dickens's "Christmas Stories" and of Frank R. Stockton's "Rudder Grange." By twenty-three he had passed out of apprenticeship and poverty and had developed his peculiar gift for the illustration of such old English writers as Herrick and Shakespeare. In this quick progress the great Victorian book illustrators, Houghton, Pinwell, and Millais, were his guiding lights. But he grew into a style quite different from theirs, less austere and more colorful. The multiplied small lines are beautiful as such, but they readily merge themselves into tone. Probably like Blum and Pennell he had in mind the brilliant pen-drawing of Fortuny. It was fortunate that the new photo-engraving processes were coming in, for such drawings simply defied the best efforts even of the meticulously patient woodcutters of the 'seventies. Doubtless the love of definition and of antiquarian detail sufficiently accounts for Abbey's technique as a pen draughtsman. He wanted not indications, but complete little silvery pictures, and he made them deliciously. Very likely the example of such French pen draughtsmen as Meissonier and Vièrge and of such etchers as Gaillard and Bracquemond counted for something, as may the early work of George du Maurier. In any case Abbey eschewed the precedents of such powerful, summary pen draughtsmen as Charles Keene and Tenniel, though he greatly admired them, and chose a manner in which delicacy and reflection and graciousness were to count for more than strength.

Already Abbey had developed that conscience of an antiquarian which was to govern all his work. He buys eighteenth century costumes and furniture regardless of cost, and when

originals are unattainable has copies made.
Yet never an archæologically minded designer
showed greater ease. The more pains he took
the more graceful was the result. This initial
paradox runs through his entire production.

Upon the Bohemian days in New York at the
old University Building, and upon the high
jinks of the newly founded Tile Club Mr. E. V.
Lucas, the official biographer, expands with
gusto. This companionable note accompanies
Abbey to the end. When he moved to England the best doors went ajar for him forth-
with. And no one better deserved friendship.
He took pains with it. For years at Morgan
Hall he held a cricket week, playing an intrepid
duffer's game himself well into middle life and
entertaining his entire eleven with unstinted
cordiality.

In 1878, being not yet twenty-six, Abbey,
having survived perilous farewell feasts from
Harpers and the Tile Club, sailed for England
with the contracts for half a dozen of his most
famous books in his baggage. In England he
was to spend most of his remaining thirty-three
years as most industrious of artists and most
accessible of country gentlemen. In 1882 appeared his first book, "The Songs of Herrick."

It was quickly followed by such charming masterpieces of illustration as "The School for Scandal," "The Quiet Life," "She Stoops to Conquer," "Old Songs," and the perhaps less uniformly successful Shakespeare illustrations. Within twelve years he won his first place among illustrators, had begun timidly to paint in oil, and had married, doing all these things cautiously and well.

In all but the matrimonial venture nothing but repetition was now to be expected. On the contrary, he soon was to cease illustrating and to win an equal prominence as an historical and mural painter. When in 1890 Charles F. McKim commissioned Abbey to do the Story of the Holy Grail for the Boston Public Library he exercised an extraordinary faith and insight. Abbey seemed essentially a little master, a maker of delicious illustrations, an adept at a rather small and idyllic type of water color. Abbey girded himself to the task, assembled a twelfth century armory and wardrobe, and in twelve years the series was complete. Meanwhile, he had astonished one Royal Academy after another with the most vigorous historical narratives, "King Lear and His Daughters," the "Courtship of Richard Crookback," and had painted great decorative idyls like the

"Song of Fiammetta." In 1896 he was elected
an Associate of the Royal Academy and in 1898
a full Academician. In 1902 he was chosen to
paint the Coronation picture, and this seems
almost a prerogative as a Philadelphian, for
had not Charles R. Leslie painted Queen Vic-
toria's coronation?

The Boston decorations are not the greatest
work of Abbey, but they most completely represent his artistic ideals. He set himself learn-
edly to re-create the century of Robert de
Borron as he had to revive the age of Gold-
smith, Herrick, and Shakespeare. He was new
at decoration and later admitted that the Grail
pictures were too elaborate. They are indeed
rather charming and romantic as episodes than
lucid and compelling as a series. In their ideal-
ism is just a taint of irreality. His very procedure of painting from made properties and
endeavoring to reproduce the look of so remote
a time seems, however upright, artistically er-
roneous. There is an æsthetic statute of limitations for archæology. The materials reasonably exist for re-creating the look of the
seventeenth century, but not for the twelfth.
Herrick, I think, would feel fairly at home with
the Abbey illustrations and Shakespeare not
too much a stranger, but Frederick Barbarossa

would feel utterly *dépaysé* in the delivery room of the Boston Public Library, nay indignant, for he might suspect caricature of the world he was defending against the Paynims. On the contrary, he or St. Francis would accept St. Geneviève's world as Puvis spread it on the walls of the Pantheon without benefit of archæology.

In short, the only artistically available past is the past that can be visualized in imagination. Such visualization cannot be effected by collecting data and translating these into properties and arranging and painting the properties. The imaginative visualization—Raphael's Greece, Rubens's Rome, Poussin's Arcadia—will have a kind of mental and sufficient reality, whereas the archæological reconstruction will have at best a Wardour Street illusion of reality. No completely intelligent artist has ever made Abbey's mistake, for instinct warns him that the land of legend can only be glimpsed with the mind's eye. Howard Pyle, who was much the better mediævalist, once wrote asking Abbey whether he really saw his settings or only "saw them in his nut." Abbey wrote reprovingly, and considerately left the letter unposted, for posterity, that he really saw everything, never realizing that it would have been better to look in his "nut" for them.

This he did tardily in his last great task, the decorations for the State Capitol at Harrisburg. Here everything is simpler and more coherent. Abbey realized that in certain spaces history was impossible and allegory and symbolism imperative. He once cited Raphael's "Jurisprudence" in the Vatican as the ideal of what a noble decoration should be, and the work at Harrisburg echoes that conviction. It is noble and effective, rightly audacious in mixture of reality with symbolism, as in the lunette, the "Treasures of the Earth," with the geniuses of science hovering over actual toiling miners. It is conceived heroically throughout; no American mural painter save La Farge and Vedder and Sargent has done anything as fine. Where it lacks is in scale, freedom and gravity; everything is magnificently thought out, but it is not quite seen.

This great task wore Abbey out. He died in 1911, aged fifty-nine, and the world was the poorer by a very great gentleman and a very distinguished painter. Edwin Abbey seems a case of an exquisite little genius promoted far towards but not quite to greatness by an indefatigable industry, probity, and intelligence. Abbey could do nothing badly. Had the ambition seized him, he would have painted an entirely creditable Last Judgment. He would not precisely have failed had he illustrated Dante, but nature plainly intended him for an illustrator of Sheridan and Herrick. He is most delightfully himself in the lovely drawings for "Old Songs" and "The Quiet Life." Posterity will remember him vividly by these things when it has to consult its guidebooks to make sure who created the decorations at Boston and Harrisburg. He was one of the great nostalgic talents, true *confrère* of his friend Austin Dobson. The nostalgic artist must somehow make a home for himself, and, when made, he leaves it with some peril. Abbey found his real home in the England of our great-great-grandfathers and so wholly possessed it that no eighteenth century English illustrator gives an equal conviction of the more gracious realities of that age. He is more real than the documents he so intelligently consulted. That in venturing far from his true domain he not only did not meet disaster but even achieved measurable success is an impressive tribute to his industrious and flexible talent.

Indeed, the exemplary value of this rich life so fully and genially celebrated by Mr. Lucas is

precisely that it shows how far an artist may go
with a limited allowance of genius, if only his
store of grit, patience, taste, intelligence, and
perseverance be large enough.

[1922.]

XIII

KENYON COX

KENYON COX, "Tradition"

KENYON COX

To estimate the personality of a man with whom one has had relatively short acquaintance may seem impertinent. Yet any criticism is perforce an estimate of personality, and that of Kenyon Cox was too masterful not to have a public character. When hardly out of the École des Beaux-arts, a struggling young artist in his late twenties, Kenyon Cox began to be a legend and a portent. People admired him and feared him; in his regard, no one thought of being lukewarm. He was one of that group of modernly trained young men from Antwerp, Munich, or Paris who perturbed and eventually dominated the old National Academy through the transient rivalry of the Society of American Artists. The treatment these honest reformers received is one of the mysteries of the history of American taste. Without difficulty they got social and critical approval, everything but purchasers. For a generation, under the tactful coaching of the dealers, the collectors of New York had bought dearly the "conscientious nudes" of Lefèbvre and Cabanel, not to mention Bouguereau. Why they should have ignored the equally able academies of Cox is not easy to fathom. Why the critics should have cavilled at these very skilful exercises of Cox, while applauding the precisely similar achievements of his Parisian exemplars, is again mysterious. Perhaps it seemed right for Frenchmen to indulge a taste for the academic nude, but wrong for an American. Or with a subtler epicurism the connoisseurs of our by no means naughty 'nineties may have felt that a conscientious nude, like a cask of sherry, needs a sea-voyage to make it desirable. However that be, Cox, like most of his artistic contemporaries, was driven back on teaching, writing, lecturing, illustrating, meanwhile, in neglect, laying the solid foundations for future success as a mural painter.

In neglect but not in obscurity. As a teacher in the Art Students' League and committeeman or official of the Society, his influence carried far. He was an embodied conservative conscience, a stalwart and dreaded champion of the great traditions of painting, a dangerous critic of successive new schools and fads, a formidable foe of every sort of sloppiness. The times were fairly sloppy, so he was not popular. It was a lot which he accepted, because he was thoroughly honest and fearless, and because it was the condition of his loyalty to what he believed the great tradition. His death must have caused relief if not rejoicing among the wild-eyed inspirationalists of Greenwich Village. For them he was an uncomfortable person to have around.

Cox came of extraordinary ancestry. His mother was the daughter of Doctor Finney, the great evangelist, and first president of Oberlin College. His father, Jacob Dolson Cox, had an amazingly various career. He was a Civil War major-general in the field, and later one of the best historians of the war; governor of the State of Ohio; and later senator and congressman; secretary of the interior for Grant, forced out of his place for resisting land-grabbing; president of the Wabash Railroad and of the University of Cincinnati. As if that were not enough, he was a lawyer, an admirable book reviewer for the *Nation,* a renowned microscopist, and had an uncommon knowledge of cathedral architecture. With all this versatility, he was a man of most stable competence and of highest integrity. To be born of such a father is a patent of intellectual nobility.

Kenyon Cox was born in Warren, Ohio, in 1856. The rich and pleasant scenery upon which his eyes opened was the subject of one of his rare landscapes, a beautiful picture called "Passing Shadows." His formal education was much hampered by illness, though in such a family as his the training of home was the best of educations. His chieftain father came back from the war to find the tall lad in bed. From his ninth to his thirteenth year he was bed-ridden, at times in peril of his life, and periodically under the surgeon's knife. To this deprivation of the usual activities of boyhood one may ascribe a sort of bodily ungainliness, oddly contradictory of the robust pattern of his mind. On acquaintance this paradox worked as a charm.

From early childhood his calling as a painter was manifest, and from his fourteenth year he was allowed to take drawing lessons. At twenty he sojourned for a rather unprofitable year in Philadelphia, at the Academy School, and at twenty-one, 1877, he sought the land of painter's promise, and Paris. Beginning with the master most in vogue, Carolus-Duran, he left him in a year for the severer tutelage of Gérôme. From 1879 to 1882 he was an exhibitor at the Salon. He returned to New York in that year, being twenty-six years old, was immediately elected to the Society of American Artists, and soon became prominent in its schools and councils. He had pursued with passionate conviction the academic study of the nude at Paris, and continued it in New York against the difficulties we have already noted.

With the plain man's disinclination to hang the academic nude in his home, I have considerable sympathy. He is naturally offish toward what he suspects is an exercise or a show-piece, and at best a hussy without clothes. The New Yorkers of the 'eighties and 'nineties, perhaps, deserve less blame for their uncovetous admiration of Cox's very able exercises than for the snobbishness with which they bought entirely similar and by no means better academies only because these were made by European artists. Cox was really preparing himself with dogged grit and intelligence for his ultimate work as a mural painter. One sees in these designs the struggle for freedom through discipline. And half a dozen of these nudes he hardly surpassed.

A discerning person might have inferred this from his delightful and too little known illustrations for Rossetti's "Blessed Damozel," 1886. Meanwhile he achieved a few figure compositions, such as "Moonrise," which will be more valued as time goes on, and did occa-

sional portraits of character and distinction.
In some fifteen years of purposeful effort, without attaining vogue, he attained what is more
difficult—personal authority. Then his chance
came as a decorator, at Bowdoin College, in
the Appellate Court, New York, at the Colum-
bian Exposition, Chicago, and in the Congres-
sional Library.

In these new and unproved activities, as he
has himself written, his development was characteristically slow and thorough. The color he
had learned in the Paris schools and the habit
of representing the model rather literally had to
be foregone in favor of colors and forms suitable for intricate compositions and great wall
spaces. His whole practice had to be renewed
in the light of the great masters of monumental
design. Too robust to seek the solution of
bleached tones, with the followers of Puvis, he
turned to the Venetians, Titian and Veronese.
Since Rubens and Vandyke probably no artist
has studied them more penetratingly. He believed that their richer forms and colors and
intricate rhythms in depth were more suitable
for our modern ornate buildings than the paler
hues and simpler forms based on the primitive
masters of fresco. In his practice, as later in
his writings, he scouted the idea that mere flat-

ness and paleness were in themselves decorative
necessities or decorative merits. I have often
heard him laugh at the current notion that
Veronese or Delacroix or Paul Baudry lacked
monumental quality in comparison with Giotto
or Ingres or Puvis. In such a view Cox stood
almost alone. Though the unobservant took
him as a formalist, he really was the foe of too
narrow formulas whether old or new.

From the year 1900 or thereabouts Cox's
decorative style assumed more urbanity and
sureness in design while his color grew richer
and more unified. I have not had the good
fortune to see Cox's best decorations in place,
but I did see the growth and promise in such
works as the lunette "The Light of Learning"
at Winona, Minnesota, when it was being finished in New York. Its beautifully calculated
rhythms are both easy and noble, its color
resplendent. Even more ingratiating are the
little lunettes for the Iowa State Capitol.
There are fine decorations in the court-house
of Wilkesbarre, Pennsylvania, and mosaics and
wall paintings in the State Capitol at St. Paul.
For these learned and gracious designs I doubt
if Cox ever got approximately due credit outside of the pages of *Scribner's Magazine*.

It is fair to say that the few competent newspaper critics are naturally embarrassed before the absurdity of judging a mural decoration in the studio. The appraisal naturally belongs to the art critics where the decoration abides. Unhappily, regions that can very well afford mural painting cannot afford critics, so many of our most noteworthy mural decorations never receive adequate criticism at all. Kenyon Cox had even worse luck in the grudging character of the mention he did get. He had been too long an Aristides, and the critics usually slurred him without intelligence. I present with only the comment of my own italics a passage which illustrates the journalistic formula for judging a Cox. It was written, it doesn't matter by whom, on Cox's "Marriage of the Atlantic and Pacific" at St. Paul. "One might have wished, *despite the beauty of design inherent in his work,* that Mr. Cox had chosen a less formal method of treatment."

Kenyon Cox was an art critic himself for a matter of twenty-five years, and it is safe to say that in all that period of work, and often of hack work, no sentence like that ever dribbled from his pen.

He early won his spurs as a writer by becoming a staff reviewer for the *Nation*. To *Scribner's* as well he was a frequent and welcome contributor. From 1905 begin his remarkable books collecting his periodical essays or embodying his lectures: "Old Masters and New," "Painters and Sculptors," "The Classic Point of View," "Artist and Public," "Concerning Painting." It was an unusual type of criticism—forthright, clear, emphatic. It drove straight to main issues, avoiding subtleties and by-paths. It was so clear and accessible that it was easy to underestimate its literary merit. I have heard the work dismissed as obvious. Such a judgment misses entirely the athletic compactness of Cox's English as it does the fine energy of his thought. There never was a greater error than to dismiss him as a cold person; he loved and scorned tremendously. Right-mindedness was a passion with him.

On the positive side Cox has left us unsurpassed appreciations of Veronese, Corot, Millet, Holbein, Saint Gaudens. These essays seem to me already classics in a field in which classics are few. The various studies of Rembrandt and that on Michelangelo add something to these well-worn themes. Whatever theme he touched he enriched. Leonardo da Vinci, Raphael, Vermeer of Delft, Puvis—much bewritten as these masters are, Cox supplied fresh points of view. It is not safe to neglect even the shorter essays and notes, most of which were taken over from the *Nation*. On Whistler and Burne-Jones, for instance, no one has written with more justice and discrimination.

Again, on the constructive side, Cox treated the whole matter of the education of the artist and of the right relation of artist to public. Here, against the headlong individualism of the day, Cox took his stand on the side of a traditional and social art. The idea that the artist could find all necessary warrants in himself he rejected as sure to lead to eccentricity. To such barbarous self-assertion he opposed the Classic Spirit. "It is the disinterested search for perfection; it is the love of clearness and reasonableness and self-control; it is, above all, the love of permanence and of continuity. It asks of a work of art, not that it shall be novel or effective, but that it shall be fine and noble. It seeks not merely to express individuality or emotion but to express disciplined emotion and individuality restrained by law." Such doctrine was naturally poison to young people who with neither knowledge of the past nor vision of continuity nor respect for law were trying to slap their souls rapidly on canvas. What could they make of the great half-truth, "The only study that has ever greatly helped the designer is the study of design as it has been practiced before him"?

On the all-pervasive Impressionism, the success of which within its proper limits Cox generously acknowledged, he wrote: "Impressionism, which makes light its only subject, and ruthlessly sacrifices clarity and structure in the interest of illusion, is acceptable in inverse proportion to the essential beauty and interest of the objects represented." For the rest he felt that the handling of the Impressionists was often brutal and ugly and hindered the attaining of a modern technic.

To note the limitations of Cox's manly and pondered criticism is, perhaps, to repeat the error of the scribe who at once admitted that one of Cox's decorations was beautifully designed and in the same breath wished it quite otherwise. Cox necessarily missed certain finesses of appreciation which one finds in such all-viewing masters as William C. Brownell and John La Farge. Being almost impeccably right, as it seems to me, he was sometimes right on terms of an artificial simplicity. His intense perception of general principles sometimes colored unhappily his particular judgments. He so loathed muddle-headedness that he insufficiently admitted that irony of life by which a quite wrong-thinking person may act rather well, while an artist with false ideas or none in evidence may do very beautiful work. He was so resolute in condemning what seemed to him subversive theory that he sometimes swept under the indictment rather notable works. Thus he did scant justice to Rodin's real greatness, it seems to me, largely because Rodin had unwittingly demoralized the young generation of sculptors.

But despite all these reservations the bulk of Cox's critical writing seems to me sound and hearty and permanent. To read contemporary criticism after fifty years is usually to thank God that we are not as other critics were. I don't think Cox will give much basis for this kind of complacency, say, in the year 1968. I believe his occasional reader then will rather marvel how so much fighting energy and conviction could be combined with so catholic a taste and so delicate an insight, and will marvel the more that these books with their fairly eighteenth century ease and lucidity could have come out of the welter of the early twentieth century.

From the competent, Cox never lacked honor. He was chosen an associate of the

National Academy in 1900 and a full member
in 1903. He was medalled by the Salon, the
National Academy, the Architectural League,
and at the recent world expositions. He had
honorary doctorates from Oberlin and Dart-
mouth and was an early member of the American Academy of Arts and Letters. He believed in organization and authority and
worked indefatigably in conservative propa-
ganda on the lecture platform or in the drudgery of art juries and committees. He had
force and discretion, was a natural leader. No
doubt, had occasion served, he would have led
a brigade in the field as competently as his
father did. His failure to gain from young
students the confidence his lay contemporaries
gave him was due to the fact that his teaching
countered sharply the restless spirit of the
times. Indeed, few of the art students of the
'nineties had historical background enough even
to know what Cox was driving at. For such
isolation there was balm in the fact that he was
able to nurture a delightful painter's gift akin
to his own in a wife and a son.

Dying at sixty-two, Kenyon Cox's career as
a painter snapped in the years when an artist
of his reflective type is just coming to his own.
Every mural design was finer than the last, his

practice was gradually measuring up to his high and arduous theories. Hence there is especial tragedy in his cutting off. What he had done up to his fiftieth year seems merely preparatory to great mural design, and it is only within ten years that he had been doing work that relatively satisfied his ideals. Hence, considerable as the work is, it is fragmentary as compared with what it might have been had strength and long years been granted to him. His was a painstaking and gradual development like that of certain of the old masters— Dürer, for example—whom he loved. Such artists rarely give the full measure of themselves in their painting. So I feel it is with Cox. Whether in his pictures or in his writings, the future will have difficulty in realizing the massive and brilliant integrity of the man who is gone.

[1918.]

XIV

ALDEN WEIR

ALDEN WEIR

The late Alden Weir carried into American painting a quality of æsthetic conscience akin to that of Mr. Howells, and Henry James in his early phase. To make a precise and delicate record of observation was his aim. Whether his theme were a New England factory village, a bunch of roses, or a finely bred American girl, he sought to tell the true truth of the matter. While insisting on its main characteristics, he neglected none of its shades and overtones. Thus his painting, while technically austere, was mentally very rich. He saw more than most painters, and he saw better. While he had the best training of the Paris schools, there never was a more American spirit, but American in a peculiar and limited sense. From the new America of immigration and quantity production he stood quite apart.

His task was to fix the survivals of an older America. His little towns that nestle quietly in their river valleys, amid maples, are such as Thoreau loved to sketch in prose or Whittier in verse. They have a frail, intense charm. Similar is the character of that notable gallery of young girls. They are fine and earnest, trained in scruple and nicety of thought and conduct. They are the descendants of Miss Catherine Sedgwick's heroines, and of Mrs. Harriet Beecher Stowe's—as rare in their somewhat brittle perfection as a Colonial meeting-house rising amid blast furnaces of yesterday. An observer of any imagination will ask: Will their daughters be like them? or are they the last wintry flowers of an autumn forever past?

Alden Weir was too much the artist, too good an eye and too fastidious a mind, to obtrude such legitimately sentimental considerations. These things are implied rather than underlined in his painting, but they are always there. And they give to his art a quality of race, which makes it unique. No one not an old American can understand the element of delicate truthfulness in his portraiture whether of persons or places.

To express this vision he made the fullest and most discreet use of all the resources of the new impressionism. Born May 30, 1852, at West Point, he had his first training from his father, an excellent historical painter, and instructor in drawing at the Military Academy. Alden Weir early followed the new current to Paris. From 1872 his talent and his extraordinary masculine beauty, as of an athlete by Polyclitus, soon made him a marked personage. He worked under the best of the academic teachers, Gérôme, and soon attained a style of great ease. In the age of the *morceau bien fait,* few could handle the brush with more elegance. Occasional flower and game pieces survive to show that Alden Weir could have rivalled Chase in the creation of lovely surfaces and textures. But there was something to express that could not be compassed in that fashionable mode.

Returning to America in 1876, Alden Weir undertook the long task of reshaping an established style in the light of the new luminism. His mature pictures are built in an infinity of strokes and tones. The surface constitutes a restrained iridescence between the observer and the object. Unlike the Parisian luminists, he never forsook the determined contour and the well-calculated pattern. His method was often unfavorably criticized. People complained of the kneaded and dissociated quality of his textures. The same objection was made to the very similar technic of George Frederick

Watts, who in the decorative, as Weir in the luministic field, built up his pictures by insensible increments reflecting his own thoughtfulness. Current criticism never is quite just to pictures that to attain their end must be much thought over and worked over. All the world loves a juggler, in whatever art.

To Alden Weir came a slow and solid recognition. The National Academy made him an associate in 1885, and a member in 1886. He was a leading figure in the Society of American Artists, and later in the Ten American Painters. He was for several years President of the National Academy. While his practice was early crystallized, his taste remained liberal. He was unafraid of the new experiments and eccentricities, having a quiet confidence that in the long run the more excellent methods would prevail. Probably no artist of our day in America was more generally respected or more genuinely admired by both conservatives and radicals. Among his peers he was an imposing and a winning personality—strong, sensitive, resolutely honest, courteous without affectation or compromise. His pictures are in the Luxembourg and our best American galleries. He had full and deserved meed of honor and regarded it modestly as merely an incentive to new endeavor. Even in his latter invalidism, he retained much of that classic beauty which is perpetuated by Olin Warner in one of the greatest of American portrait busts.

It is too early to appraise Alden Weir's accomplishment justly. No one but his friend Twachtman has expressed so well certain evanescent appearances in our American landscape. His series of women's portraits breathe training and discipline in pictorial intimations which are paradoxically precise and subtle. Whatever his final position as a painter, he has been immensely significant to us of older America. It is not likely that he will be wholly neglected by the new America which apparently is about to fulfill or supersede us.

[1919.]

XV

WILLIAM M. CHASE

WILLIAM M. CHASE, "Ready for the Ride"

WILLIAM M. CHASE

William Merritt Chase, who died, in 1916, in his sixty-seventh year, with energies unabated, was the ablest painter of face values that America has yet produced. It probably never occurred to him to paint what was not before his eye. He saw the world as a display of beautiful surfaces which challenged his skill. It was enough to set him painting to note the nacreous sheen of a fish, or the satiny bloom of fruit, or the wind-smoothed dunes about Shinnecock, or the fine, specific olive of a woman's face. The patination and texture of things aroused not merely his admiration, but his will to possess. He drew unceasingly into his home and his several studios thousands of bits of old brass and copper, less resplendent but more precious pewter, floor weavings of the Orient, wall weavings of France and Flanders, mellow old pictures, barbaric jewelry. Ruskin used to carry a few uncut gems in his pocket; Chase made a background for himself of such material. His eye was feline, caressing, and requiring to be caressed.

It is difficult to refer all this to Franklin, Indiana, where he was born, November 1, 1849, or to Munich, where he got his first serious training in art. He adopted rather the notion prevalent in Paris of the 'sixties that art is a fine manufacture. How he got this from his rather dull master, Wagner, and his only slightly clever master, the younger Kaulbach, is a bit mysterious. Very likely, Chase took the idea to Munich with him, confirming it at Paris en route. As a young portrait painter at St. Louis he had had his chief success with his still lives. Throughout his career he would either limber up or rest up by producing masterpieces of this order. He seemed most himself when the problem was simplified to one of eye and hand. His art was complete before he was thirty, and never greatly varied thereafter. He was medalled at the Centennial Exposition in 1876, being twenty-seven years old, and constantly won new honors. Despite a truly American shrewdness and unfailingly American sympathies, he became somewhat an exotic in walk and conversation. Through the 'eighties and 'nineties his flowing cloak and his flat-brimmed "cylinder" astounded the New York philistine as fifty years earlier Théophile Gautier's red waistcoat had scandalized the *bourgeois* of

Paris. But the somewhat bristling and Meph-
istophelian front of Chase covered a very
real wit and geniality. He was an ornament in
all company, a true citizen of the world.

The year 1876, his twenty-seventh, was
crucial. He could have had his appointment
at the Munich Academy as a Herr Professor,
but he came back to New York instead to be
the first instructor of the newly formed Art
Students' League. It is significant of the
modern divorce of art from economics that,
whereas it is very difficult for an artist to make
his living by practicing his trade, it is quite easy
for him to make a living by teaching others to
practice it. Chase may have become a teacher
chiefly for prudential reasons. But his theory
that painting is a fine manufacture implied that
it could and should be taught. Into his teaching he threw himself with rare wholehearted-
ness. If art should be discreetly manufactured,
by the same token it should be skilfully exhibited and profitably sold. With entire consistency, then, Chase associated himself with
that Society of American Artists which in 1877
began to claim for new talent a place on the
line. With much ability he served the Society
as its president from 1885 to 1895. Meanwhile he had painted some of his best portraits,

the "Woman in Black" at the Metropolitan Museum, the "White Shawl" at Philadelphia.

When this militant phase as an organizer was over, he set up his own art school, in 1897. It had and still has extraordinary success. It expanded in many directions. Shinnecock Hills, not yet holy ground for golfers, blossomed every summer with feminine talent. Chase varied the routine of teaching by recreations which involved personally conducting eager hordes for summers amid the art and nature of Holland, Italy, and Spain. It was a distinction of the Chase School that the master honestly tried to teach painting. Most art schools have taught drawing. Apparently the personal dictum of Ingres that anybody who can draw can paint well enough had frozen into a universal dogma. Chase rejected it. He strove to make his students see as painters. The color was to be the structure. Chase carried his pupils as far as he had gone himself. He was formed before the inventions of Manet and Monet had gained credence, and before the still more revolutionary procedures of Cézanne had declared themselves. To most of the problems of open-air illumination he was quite oblivious. He liked an attractive object that would "stay put" in the equable light of a studio. His art at its best lies very close to the more sober phase of Fortuny. The aim is merely fine and just observation, with swift and delicate execution.

Once asked how he got his sombre richness of color and fullness of form, the great Courbet answered simply: "I take pains with my tones—*Je cherche mes tons.*" By Chase's time the modest tones had become the "Values," with a very big V. He was their American Apostle. As a practical counsel this meant that appearances must be re-created in paint according to that optical law by which we grasp an object through interpretation of its salient, colored planes, the task being to read from these planes, the farness or nearness and the structure of the object. In a rough and ready way the average eye does this unconsciously, but the artist has to do this very consciously and delicately, since, where the layman need only identify, the artist must represent. Hals and Velasquez had carried this research far, and Manet had renewed it most brilliantly. Chase made of it an æsthetic and almost a religion, prudently seeking the values in the stable luminosity of the studio, while Theodore Robinson, John H. Twachtman and young Childe Hassam were more audaciously pursuing the quest out of doors. It was the main endeavor of the last years of the nineteenth century.

Given their belief that the business of painting is representation, it is impossible to quarrel with those who held that appearances should be dealt with according to their own laws. And it would be ungracious to minimize triumphs in representation which meant its exhaustion as a leading principle. When Chase was painting the alert and gracious Lady in a Riding Habit, in the Union League Club, Cézanne was painting those uncouth and generalized portraits which powerfully asserted that art was now to be transformation, that the hard-won values were obsolete, that the appearance was now to be dealt with according to human laws which were not necessarily its own.

It must have been about 1908, at Florence, when I used to chat with Chase, escaped from his disciples, over a glass of beer at Reininghaus's. Leo Stein had already appalled me with his portable gallery of Matisses, Cézannes, and Gauguins, but I never broke the word to Chase. He talked delightfully about everything, with now and then a return to the old masters. We were both dodos *sans le savoir*. But there is no shame in being a dodo, and as such Chase played his part magnificently, and after all legend usually holds the dodo longer in memory than it does the bird who supersedes him. I think it still a good bet that Matisse may fade out of the future histories of painting sooner than Chase. It was probably the teacher in Chase that prevented his even considering the new movements. The values could in a manner be taught; there was a training that reached to it. The bewildering transformations cried about by Expressionist, Cubist and Futurist, evidently could not be taught, and were no affair of his. Indeed as a champion of a closed system in the face of many varieties of revolution, Chase acted very well,—kept his temper, let the world wag, continued to pursue the values more delicately than his many rivals.

Being, as he was, distinctly of the school of the *morceau bien peint,* he was free from its besetting sin of showing off. The amiable ostentation which was in his personality he kept out of his art. There is a sobriety even about the most prodigiously clever Chases, even in those amazing codfish of his later years. His hand never goes off into sheer flourish. It is restrained by the loveliness of the thing, by the conscience that will not enlarge on its personal discovery, but will give true record.

Since Chase's concern was with beautiful surfaces, his art is necessarily one of epidermis. He avoided the syncopations, the sheer emphasis of structure, to which Manet had shown the way. He took objects quite at their face value, and rarely invested them with the tenderness, mystery, and understanding that comes from meditation and remembered feelings. He accepted to the full the Impressionist convention that every time is a first time, though otherwise he took nothing from Impressionism. We get in him a fine, bare vision, and must not expect therewith much contributory enrichment from mind and mood. He admired especially those painters whose eye is keenest, with mood in abeyance, Frans Hals and Velasquez.

So there are no great Chases, but there is a singularly fine and even accomplishment. His was an extraordinarily well-utilized talent. His pictures always suggest high analogies. To repeat the distinction of his finer portraits one must go to the best of Carolus-Duran, the early charming Carolus; in our time only Alfred Stevens has surpassed the cosey richness of Chase's little interiors; while the still-lives perhaps have no rival in our day for competent literalness. So far as we know, Chase never painted a decoration, nor desired to do so; never told a story in paint, rarely chose any subject that anybody else might not have seen. His superiority was merely to see it more clearly. In the lucidity with which he accepted these limitations he was eminently of his generation. The defect of his art is its professionalism, its savor of the studio. Few artists of our time have done more successfully what they set themselves to do. Chase believed art to be a fine manufacture, and in his hands it became such—a manufacture intelligently and delicately fine. To lovers of things his art will long keep its appeal. Few men have painted surfaces better. The time will come when men will marvel at such a degree of specialization in the artist, and in Chase's case the marvel, doubtless the regret, will be accompanied by an unwilling admiration.

[1916, 1930]

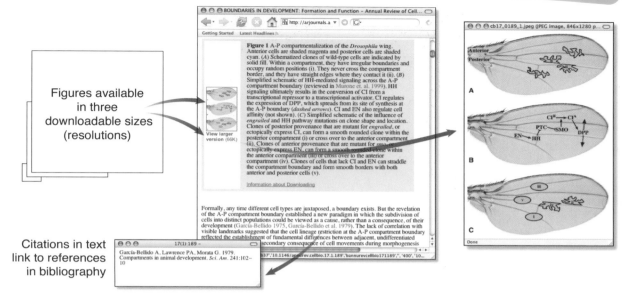

Figures available in three downloadable sizes (resolutions)

Citations in text link to references in bibliography

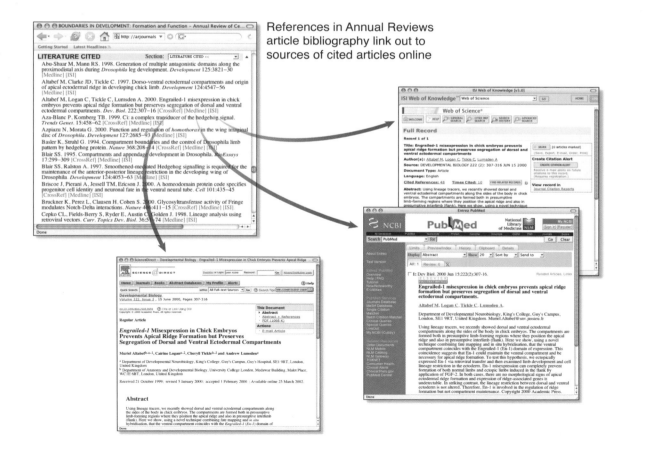

References in Annual Reviews article bibliography link out to sources of cited articles online

Annual Review of Cell and
Developmental Biology

Annual Review of Cell and Developmental Biology

Volume 24, 2008

Randy Schekman, *Editor*
University of California, Berkeley

Larry Goldstein, *Associate Editor*
University of California, San Diego, School of Medicine

Janet Rossant, *Associate Editor*
Hospital for Sick Children, University of Toronto

www.annualreviews.org • science@annualreviews.org • 650-493-4400

Annual Reviews
4139 El Camino Way • P.O. Box 10139 • Palo Alto, California 94303-0139

Annual Reviews
Palo Alto, California, USA

International Standard Serial Number: 1081-0706
International Standard Book Number: 978-0-8243-3124-5

TYPESET BY APTARA
PRINTED AND BOUND BY FRIESENS CORPORATION, ALTONA, MANITOBA, CANADA

Preface

The health of our biomedical enterprise depends on the steady growth of resources to support original and early career scholars. Although funding from federal and state sources has been in short supply in recent years, an equally pressing concern relates to the recognition of the special needs of beginning investigators and those among us who strike off in new directions. A recent study commissioned by the American Academy of Arts and Sciences (ARISE: **http://www.amacad.org/arisefolder/default.aspx**) provides evidence of dwindling support for early career and particularly innovative biomedical scientists.

We all have seen the evidence of age creep in the award of first RO1 grants and in the difficulty new investigators and original ideas have in the funding process. Although more generous support from federal sources will help, certain fundamental problems with the review process hinder the recognition of unproven talent and unusual ideas.

The ARISE report highlights several interesting and nonobvious remedies to the problem of funding high-risk, high-reward research. One proposal is to enhance the interaction between staff in the funding agencies and frontline investigators in emerging disciplines. In past years, program officers from the federal agencies participated actively in small research meetings, such as Gordon Conferences, where the newest unpublished and promising results are shared. Funding restrictions and a lack of reinforcement in the program officer career path curtailed such contact. Such disinvestment is unwise. A small allocation of travel funds and encouragement in career advancement would return those responsible for funding decisions back into contact with the best beginning and innovative investigators.

Private funding agencies can help. Selective private sources tend to favor the most highly acclaimed young scholars, some of whom may have more support than they really need. Support tends to focus on individuals in a select few elite institutions. The ARISE report encourages agencies to favor other scholars who may not yet have secured extramural funding.

Universities also have a role to play. Research buildings are erected as in a "field of dreams" with the expectation that investigators will take responsibility for core facilities. The ARISE report recommends that institutions fundraise for building endowments to support the creation and staffing of core facilities, rather than relying exclusively on expensive recharges to individual investigators. And even more importantly, universities and research institutes should assume greater responsibility for faculty salaries, particularly where faculty serve teaching and administrative functions that support the institution as well as the research enterprise. Such cost-sharing measures by federal grant recipients would stretch the research dollar to permit more support for beginning investigators.

For this year's Perspective chapter, our fourth in the series, we are privileged to honor the work of a founding father of high-resolution light microscopy, Dr. Shinya Inoué. His chapter recounts the many years of discovery in Japan and in the United States brought about by technical advances in microscope design, many of his own construction. His images of the spindle seen by polarizing light microscopy proved the existence and function of the spindle in living cells.

Randy Schekman
Editor
University of California, Berkeley

Figure 1

Annual Review of Cell and Developmental Biology Editorial Committee.

Figure 2

Anirvan Ghosh and Larry Goldstein.

Annual Review
of Cell and
Developmental
Biology

Volume 24, 2008

Contents

Indexes

Errata

An online log of corrections to *Annual Review of Cell and Developmental Biology* articles
may be found at http://cellbio.annualreviews.org/errata.shtml

Related Articles

From the *Annual Review of Genetics*, Volume 41 (2007)

Epigenetic Control of Centromere Behavior
Karl Ekwall

Cell Turnover and Adult Tissue Homeostasis: From Humans to Planarians
Jason Pellettieri and Alejandro Sánchez Alvarado

Specificity in Two-Component Signal Transduction Pathways
Michael T. Laub and Mark Goulian

The Origin and Establishment of the Plastid in Algae and Plants
Adrian Reyes-Prieto, Andreas P.M. Weber, and Debashish Bhattacharya

Transport of Sequence-Specific RNA Interference Information Between Cells
Antony M. Jose and Craig P. Hunter

Regulation of Sterol Synthesis in Eukaryotes
Peter J. Espenshade and Adam L. Hughes

Systems Biology of Caulobacter
Michael T. Laub, Lucy Shapiro, and Harley H. McAdams

From the *Annual Review of Genomics and Human Genetics*, Volume 8 (2007)

Genetic Basis of Thoracic Aortic Aneurysms and Dissections: Focus on Smooth
Muscle Cell Contractile Dysfunction
*Dianna M. Milewicz, Dong-Chuan Guo, Van Tran-Fadulu, Andrea L. Lafont,
Christina L. Papke, Sakiko Inamoto, and Hariyadarshi Pannu*

Disorders of Lysosome-Related Organelle Biogenesis: Clinical
and Molecular Genetics
*Marjan Huizing, Amanda Helip-Wooley, Wendy Westbroek, Meral Gunay-Aygun,
and William A. Gahl*

From the *Annual Review of Immunology*, Volume 25 (2007)

The Actin Cytoskeleton in T Cell Activation
Janis K. Burkhardt, Esteban Carrizosa, and Meredith H. Shaffer

Thymus Organogenesis
Hans-Reimer Rodewald

From the *Annual Review of Medicine*, Volume 58 (2007)

The Effect of Toll-Like Receptors and Toll-Like Receptor Genetics
in Human Disease
*Stavros Garantziotis, John W. Hollingsworth, Aimee K. Zaas,
and David A. Schwartz*

From the *Annual Review of Plant Bology*, Volume 59 (2008)

Shinya Inoué

Microtubule Dynamics in Cell Division: Exploring Living Cells with Polarized Light Microscopy

Shinya Inoué

Marine Biological Laboratory, Woods Hole, Massachusetts 02543;
email: jmacneil@mbl.edu

Annu. Rev. Cell Dev. Biol. 2008. 24:1–28

First published online as a Review in Advance on July 16, 2008

The *Annual Review of Cell and Developmental Biology* is online at cellbio.annualreviews.org

This article's doi:
10.1146/annurev.cellbio.24.110707.175323

Key Words

mitosis, spindle fibers, microtubules, dynamic equilibrium, colchicine, chromosome movement, polarized light microscopy, birefringence

Abstract

This Perspective is an account of my early experience while I studied the dynamic organization and behavior of the mitotic spindle and its submicroscopic filaments using polarized light microscopy. The birefringence of spindle filaments in normally dividing plant and animal cells, and those treated by various agents, revealed (*a*) the reality of spindle fibers and fibrils in healthy living cells; (*b*) the labile, dynamic nature of the molecular filaments making up the spindle fibers; (*c*) the mode of fibrogenesis and action of orienting centers; and (*d*) force-generating properties based on the disassembly and assembly of the fibrils. These studies, which were carried out directly on living cells using improved polarizing microscopes, in fact predicted the reversible assembly properties of microtubules.

Contents

INTRODUCTION

Classically the light microscope was used to examine preserved, thin-sectioned tissues and cells. More recently it has become an important tool for exploring the molecular basis of physiological functions directly in active living cells. The major transition to its modern use was prompted by optical advances in the mid-twentieth century, followed by another spurt in the 1980s brought about by electronic imaging and striking advances in molecular biology.

Although I was able to participate in both recent transitions in microscopy, this Perspective covers my experience during the earlier part of those events. By following the birefringence in live dividing cells with an improved polarizing microscope, we learned about the reality of spindle fibers, the dynamic organization of their filaments, and their labile assembly/disassembly and force-generating properties. The dynamic behavior of molecules making up the birefringent spindle filaments could now be followed directly in actively dividing cells.

Our studies on live cells were followed by the isolation of a colchicine-binding protein, identified as the microtubule protein, and by the discovery that microtubules could be disassembled or assembled in vitro. Those studies verified our analysis of the birefringence observed in living cells and opened up vast new avenues for exploring the molecules and mechanisms involved in mitosis and a wide range of related cellular events.

As may be apparent from my publications, including this essay, I have been interested in improving the capabilities of the light microscope and exploring its uses as much as in uncovering the submicroscopic structures and dynamic events taking place in the living cell. Recently many have contributed immensely to and made unbelievable advances in both of these fields (see, e.g., Howard & Hyman 2007, Maiato et al. 2004, Pawley 2006, Sluder & Wolf 2003, Wittmann et al. 2001). The current essay, thus, focuses on events relating to some early developments to which I had the good fortune to contribute.[1]

---

[1] This Perspective emphasizes our early studies on the mitotic spindle and microtubules but does not cover other topics that my colleagues and I have explored using polarized light and other advanced modes of microscopy. Articles reporting on a number of such biological studies and our contributions to advances in microscopy are assembled in *Collected Works of Shinya Inoué: Living Cells, Light Microscopy, and Molecular Dynamics,* just published by World Scientific Publishing (Inoué 2008a). This book also includes a DVD disk featuring many ciné- and video-micrographs of active living cells and narrated explanations on polarized light microscopy.

ENCOUNTER WITH KATIE AND JEAN DAN: INTRODUCTION TO LIVING CELLS

Born 1921 in London, England, as the eldest child of a Japanese diplomat, I was brought up together with my sisters in several countries. I enjoyed my early school years in Portland, Oregon, and Sydney, Australia, but from 1932 I remained in Japan to enter a municipal high school in Tokyo.

From my early days, I was interested in figuring out how to build electric motors and tiny portable radios that actually worked, but was not so interested in biology. My mother gave me a small microscope, but it was so disappointing; nothing in the prepared slides was doing anything. Still, at our home, I did raise silkworms and later even collected and mounted butterflies on occasion. But in high school, the only thing that really impressed me in biology was the behavior of a bird's feather that our teacher let us examine under a loupe. The tiny, barbed hooks allowed the feather to be ruffled yet be zippered neatly back together. The image seen through a magnifier finally explained how something actually worked!

My deeper interest in biology was aroused in 1941 while I was a student at Musashi Kōtō Gakko, a junior college in Tokyo. There I met Professor Katsuma Dan (frivolously nicknamed Katie by himself) in the first class that he taught in his home country (**Figure 1**). Katie had returned to Japan in 1937 with his American wife, Jean Clark Dan, a fellow graduate student who had also worked with L.V. Heilbrunn at the University of Pennsylvania and with whom he had spent summers at the Marine Biological Laboratory (MBL) in Woods Hole, Massachusetts.

As a student who had been unhappy with the high school classes in militaristic Japan, I was shocked but delighted by Katie's different attitude and approach. Instead of promoting rote learning, he told us about how he and his friends were figuring out how cells divided by tracing the movement of kaolin particles placed on the surface of developing sea urchin eggs. And he

Figure 1

Katsuma Dan (1905–1996) at the Centennial Celebration of Misaki Marine Biological Station in 1987. From Inoué (1994).

told us about how Karl von Frisch took advantage of the sugar rationing in Germany during World War I to explore how honeybees found their way back home by using polarization of the sky light to navigate, then dance and signal to their hive mates how to reach the nectar source.

In the lab, Katie let his students try experiments that might or might not work, rather than have us follow pretested procedures. I still cannot forget the excitement of having been able to show how Lillie's iron wire model of nerve conduction worked by successive electrical depolarization (of a passivated layer on a steel wire immersed in concentrated nitric acid) rather than by propagation of a chemical change, as argued by my classmates. And I found that even the conduction speed could be enhanced by making the current jump past a locally insulated segment of the model [just as Ichiji Tasaki demonstrated the same year for saltatory conduction in myelinated nerve fibers (Tasaki & Takeuchi 1941)]!

But that was the year the Japanese Navy attacked Pearl Harbor, and Japan and the United States became embroiled in World War II. Still, unlike many of my former high school classmates, especially the A students who had become navy officers and soon perished at sea, I was deferred from military service as a science major (until four months before the end of the war, when everybody was conscripted). Thus, I was able to enter Tokyo Imperial University in 1942 and finish the curtailed 2.5-year curriculum with a major in zoology.

One evening in 1943, Katie invited me to his home in Kudan, Tokyo, to try visualizing the spindle during cell division. Imaging the mitotic spindle in living cells was of particular interest to Katie; he posited that egg cells divided by an elongating spindle pushing apart the two astrospheres attached to its poles (Dan 1943). The problem was that the spindle itself was generally not visible under the microscope in living cells.

A notable exception, as Katie noted, was W.J. Schmidt's 1937 observation of developing sea urchin eggs, made with a polarizing microscope (**Figure 2**). As reinterpreted by Schmidt himself in 1939, those pictures showed the football-shaped spindles whose contrast depended on the birefringence produced by aligned protein molecules (Schmidt 1939; see **Figure 5** and associated caption, below, for an explanation of birefringence).

That evening in Tokyo, Katie fertilized clear eggs of sea urchins that he had brought home from the marine lab in Misaki. Under air-raid

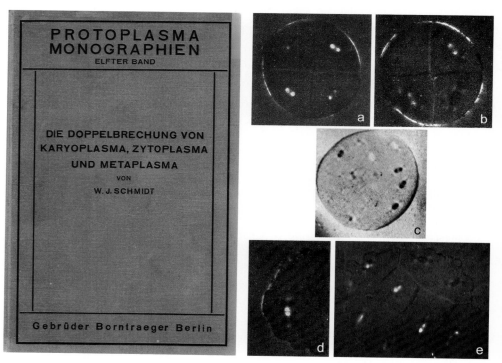

Figure 2

(*Left*) W.J. Schmidt's 1937 monograph. (*Right*) In this monograph, on p. 89, figure 31, Schmidt shows live, fertilized (flattened) sea urchin eggs observed between crossed Nicols with a polarizing microscope. (*a*) Four-cell stage in metaphase. (*b*) Four-cell stage in anaphase. (*c*) Anaphase sperm nuclei in polyspermic egg. (*d*) Spindle and chromosomes in a blastomere at the two-cell stage. (*e*) Spindles and chromosomes in a blastomere at the eight-cell stage. At the time of publication of his monograph, Schmidt interpreted the football-shaped white and dark birefringent structures as being chromosomes and only the asters (seen in panels *d* and *e*) as the nuclear spindle. Reproduced from Schmidt (1937) with kind permission of Gebrüder Bornträger (**http://www.borntraeger-cramer.de**).

blackout curtains, we spent several hours trying to see the spindle birefringence, using a polarizing microscope that Katie had borrowed from his colleague in Geology. But alas, the evening ended with inconclusive results.

THE "SHINYA-SCOPE"

Five years later we resumed these studies, this time at the Misaki Marine Biological Station, which Katie had recovered in 1945 from the allied occupation forces, using his message entitled "The last one to go" (reproduced in Article 56 in Inoué 2008a). At Misaki, rather than use a commercial polarizing microscope, I started from scratch by assembling parts on a cast-off machine gun base. (The Station had been taken over by the Japanese Navy for the last year of the war as a miniature submarine base, so some destroyed weapon parts were scattered.) On the cast-iron base, I tied by string a Zeiss microscope that Katie let me modify, a calcite polarizing prism loaned by Professor Koana of the Physics Department of Tokyo University, and an AH-4 mercury arc lamp that I found at a surplus store and that I placed in a tea can.

Using this home-made instrument (**Figure 3**), we could finally repeat Schmidt's observations. For several minutes before the egg underwent cleavage, we saw the birefringent spindle and asters emerge and grow, then the spindle splitting into two parts as the asters grew larger. But the initial success was dashed when I tried to improve the image by rotating the objective lens to minimize the stray light introduced by strain birefringence in the lenses. The field between crossed polarizers did, in fact, become darker, but where were the birefringent spindles? They had simply vanished!

Katie's admonition to me was, "I told you to leave well enough alone." But I was really curious and wanted to make the system work better. It did take a whole month, but I finally realized that the birefringence of the strained lens was, in fact, helping by acting as a compensator and raising the image contrast of the weakly birefringent spindle. So I split a piece of mica into

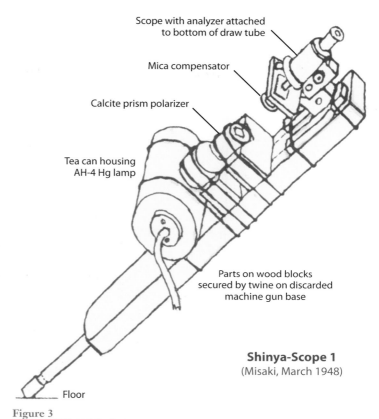

Scope with analyzer attached to bottom of draw tube

Mica compensator

Calcite prism polarizer

Tea can housing AH-4 Hg lamp

Parts on wood blocks secured by twine on discarded machine gun base

Shinya-Scope 1
(Misaki, March 1948)

Floor

Figure 3

The author's handmade polarizing microscope, built from salvaged components at the Misaki Marine Biological Station in 1948. Reproduced from Inoué (2008a) with kind permission of World Scientific Publishing.

a thin sheet and placed it on the microscope's rotatable substage filter holder so that its orientation could be adjusted, namely, so that it would act as a Brace-Koehler compensator.

Now, even though the microscope field was not completely dark, we could see the brighter or darker football-shaped spindle against a gray background (**Figure 4**). In fact, we could see quite a bit more than was reported in Schmidt's publication and even guess at the orientation of the component molecules.

By way of explanation, a compensator introduces uniform birefringence over the whole field of view so that, between crossed polarizers, the specimen appears brighter or darker, depending on whether its birefringence is adding or subtracting from the birefringence of the compensator. As shown in **Figures 4** and **5**,

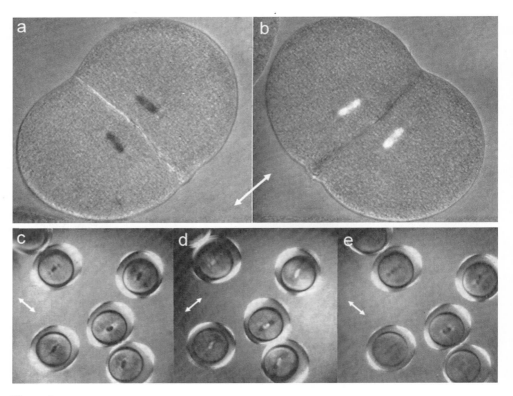

Figure 4

(*a,b*) Two-cell-stage jellyfish (*Spirocodon* sp.) egg with metaphase spindles observed with the microscope shown in **Figure 3**. In these live, optically clear cells, the positively birefringent spindle appears bright or dark, depending on its orientation relative to the compensator (see **Figure 5** for an explanation). The cell surface, which is negatively birefringent, appears in opposite contrast where it lies parallel to the spindle. Unlike in many other genera, eggs of jellyfish do not produce a fertilization envelope. (*c,d,e*) Fertilized, developing eggs of a sand dollar, *Clypeaster japonica*. The *Clypeaster* eggs (which are exceptionally transparent) are surrounded by a fertilization envelope, which shows a strong, tangentially positive birefringence. The spindle and asters also show a positive birefringence along their long axes. Double-headed arrows indicate the slow-axis direction of the compensator. From Inoué & Dan (1951).

where the slow axis of the specimen (e.g., the length of the spindle filaments) lies parallel to the slow axis of the compensator, the specimen appears brighter. Where the axes are crossed (lie in opposite quadrants), they appear darker, i.e., are compensated. [Every birefringent (i.e., doubly refractive) material has two refractive indexes that reflect the arrangement of their molecular lattice or fine structure. The direction for which (the electrical vector of) the light wave suffers the greatest refraction is called the slow axis, and the one with the lowest refraction is called the fast axis. For further explanations,

see, e.g., Bennett 1950, Appendix III in Inoué 1986, and Inoué 2002.]

In the paper reporting these observations (Inoué & Dan 1951), I also calculated the optimum amount of compensation required to maximize the image contrast of weakly birefringent objects in the presence of stray background light (as also published nearly concurrently by Swann & Mitchison in 1950).

Kayo Okazaki and Katie extensively used the microscope I built in Misaki (and sketched from memory in approximately 1989; see **Figure 3**) to follow the development of biocrystalline skeletal spicules in sea urchin embryos (Okazaki & Inoué 1976). After my departure to Princeton in 1948, Kayo and Katie called it the "Shinya-Scope."

In 1948, Jean Dan returned to Misaki from her first post–World War II trip back home to the United States. She was full of news about their friends in the States, especially those at the MBL in Woods Hole. And she brought home, as a present for her husband Katie, a Bausch & Lomb phase contrast microscope (the first one available in the United States and acquired courtesy of the American Philosophical Society). Jean, who soon discovered the acrosomal reaction, used this microscope extensively to study sperm-egg interactions at fertilization. For me, she arranged a financial loan from her sister Peggy Chittick of Milford, Connecticut, so that I could travel and study in the States.

TO PRINCETON (1948–51)

In the fall of 1948, with a postwar Japanese passport (which I recall was number 50), I arrived at Princeton's Biology Department. There, while building what I hoped was a better polarizing microscope, I was introduced to classical cytology by my mentor, Kenneth W. Cooper. Ken had studied with Franz Schrader, who in turn had followed E.B. Wilson's steps; all three were at Columbia University in New York. It was, therefore, natural for me to wonder how chromosomes moved in mitosis and about the enigmatic properties of the mitotic spindle.

At Princeton I was exposed to Wilson's classical volume on the hereditary role of chromosomes and the structure and function of the mitotic spindle in cell division (Wilson 1928). Summarizing four-decades-long studies on fixed and stained cells made by many cytologists, he describes the fibrillar structure of the achromatic spindle and astral rays. Still, he is puzzled about the ephemeral nature and invisibility of the spindle fibrils in living cells and questions the validity of the contractile fibrillar hypothesis for chromosome movement favored by many. At the same time, he is reluctant to accept "that the fibrillae seen in sections

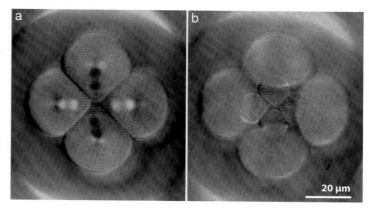

Figure 5

Micromere formation during the fourth division in a developing egg of a sand dollar, *Echinarachnius parma* (the images were taken with a rectified polarizing microscope in the 1970s). (*a*) The spindles in these four cells have converged to the egg's vegetal pole (the four animal pole cells are out of focus). Where the spindle long axis (orientation of microtubules) lies parallel to the compensator slow axis (SS′), the positively birefringent spindle appears bright. Where the axes are crossed, the spindle appears dark. (*b*) Cleavage planes bisect the spindle remnants and give rise to four micromeres (predecessor of spicules and gonads) and four macromeres. In the diagram below the photographs, PP′ and AA′ show the transmission axes of the polarizer and the analyzer (which are crossed), respectively, and SS′ and FF′ are the orientations of the slow and fast axes of the compensator, respectively. Reproduced from Inoué (1981) with kind permission of The Rockefeller University Press.

may not really pre-exist approximately as such in the living cell" and cautions us not to "prematurely condemn a theory which may yet be reconcilable with the so-called dynamical theories" (Chapter II, Section IV, *The Mechanism of Mitosis*, in Wilson 1928).

The more physicochemically oriented proponents of the dynamical theory experimented with living cells and tended to be skeptical of the existence of the fibrous elements of the spindle and asters. These investigators considered such elements to be artifacts of fixation.

In a 1929 article, Karl Bělař compared the behavior of live grasshopper spermatocytes with that of carefully fixed and stained cells (**Figure 6**). Although unable to see any spindle

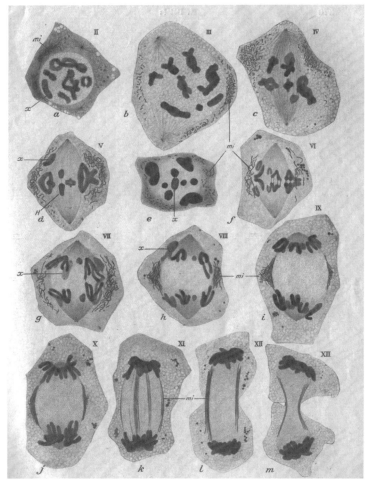

Figure 6

Spermatocytes of a grasshopper, *Chorthippus lineatus*, at different stages of meiosis I. The drawings were by Bělař (1929) of 6-μm sections of cells fixed in Flemming-Meves solution, stained with iron-hematoxilin. mi, mitochondria; x, sex chromosome; H, heteromorph tetrad.

up not of coherent filaments but of short thin rods, as in a liquid crystal (Wada 1950). Similarly, observing the migration of chromosomes that appeared to cut right through kinetochore fibers, Gunnar Östergren (1949) also favored the liquid crystalline nature of spindle fibers.

These and other views in the early 1950s on the physical nature of the mitotic spindle, as well as various proposals on how chromosomes move in mitosis, are summarized in Franz Schrader's monograph *Mitosis: The Movement of Chromosomes in Cell Division* (Schrader 1953). In this volume, he points out two cases in which spindle fibers were actually observed in intact dividing cells. These observations were made by L. R. Cleveland (1938) in *Barbulanympha*, a symbiotic protozoan in the wood-eating cockroach *Cryptocercus*, and by Kenneth Cooper (1941) in the eggs of a grass mite, *Pediculopsis graminum*. Still, Schrader points out that these were exceptional cases and could not be taken to represent cells undergoing mitosis generally. Thus, the reality of spindle fibers and their nature remained major unresolved issues.

While I was at Princeton, we also saw fascinating movies of dividing grasshopper spermatocytes, filmed by Kurt Michelle of Karl Zeiss, using its phase contrast microscope. Subsequently, Kyojiro Shimakura captured higher-resolution images of similar live cells (**Figure 7**), and Andrew and Wishia Bajer (1951, 1956) made many films of dividing endosperm cells of the African blood lily *Haemanthus katherinae* (**Figure 8**; see **Supplemental Movie 1**; for all supplemental material, follow the Supplemental Material link from the Annual Reviews home page at **http://www.annualreviews.org**). In these dividing cells, the phase contrast microscope displayed the movement and shape change of chromosomes most strikingly.

The phase contrast microscope accentuates the image contrast of those bodies whose refractive indexes are somewhat greater or less than the refractive indexes of their surroundings. In contrast to the chromosomes themselves, the spindle fibers that were supposed to move the chromosomes, and the fibrils laying down

structure, he observed in healthy, live cells Brownian motion preferentially along the direction of fibrils that would appear after fixation. Also, from the distortion of live cells treated with hyperosmotic media, he concluded that spindle fibrils or some longitudinal lamellar material must exist in the living cell despite their invisibility.

By observing chromosome movement in dividing stamen hair cells of *Tradescantia*, Bungo Wada proposed that spindle fibers were made

the cell plate in plant cells, were not visible in phase contrast.

In these early post–World War II years, the electron microscope also started to reveal many important cellular fine structures (see Sabatini 2005). But little could be seen of the fine structure in the spindle until glutaraldehyde fixation was introduced nearly two decades later (Sabatini et al. 1963).

Thus, the challenge for me in the late 1940s was to develop a polarizing microscope that had enough sensitivity and image resolution to show what, in fact, was going on inside dividing, living cells.

THE PRINCETON MICROSCOPE

At Princeton, I decided to start from scratch again so that I could improve on the microscope that I had built at Misaki. By then I was more aware of the standard use of polarizing (or petrographic) microscopes to study crystals and to identify minerals and ores (e.g., Hartshorne & Stuart 1960, Rinne & Bereck 1953, Wahlstrom 1960, Wright 1911). Biologists also used these microscopes to study mineralized tissue, skeletal muscle, plant cellulose walls, etc., which were all highly birefringent (see, e.g., Ambronn & Frey 1926, Bennett 1950, Frey-Wyssling 1953, Schmidt 1924). Schmidt (1937) also explored an extensive array of cellular components and cell products, many with much weaker birefringence, as summarized in this second monograph. The commercially available polarizing microscopes were, however, not optimally designed for observing or measuring the intricately organized, and very weakly birefringent, minute organelles in living cells.

It turned out that there was an inherent incompatibility between achieving high sensitivity for detecting weak birefringence and for gaining image resolution high enough to study structural details inside a living cell. At low condenser and objective lens numerical apertures (NAs), one could achieve high extinction and gain great sensitivity, but then the resolution was limited. Selecting objective and condenser lenses with exceptionally low strain birefrin-

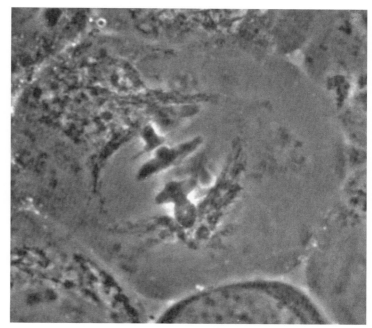

Figure 7

Phase contrast image of a live spermatocyte in a grasshopper, *Chloealtis genicularibus*, at full metaphase. Photograph courtesy of Dr. Kyojiro Shimakura of Hokkaido University. Reproduced from Inoué (1964) with kind permission of Elsevier.

gence, and polarizers and analyzers providing very high extinction, was not enough. The critical factor turned out to be the very fact that microscope lenses had to refract light to form an image. And the greater the angle of refraction (and high-NA lenses are characterized by high angles of refraction), the greater is the loss of extinction and, therefore, loss of sensitivity to detect weak birefringence.

I examined this paradox in detail at Princeton (Inoué 1952b) but had no basic solution, so I went ahead and built my second polarizing microscope, using the best arrangement and components available to me at that time (including strain-free objectives selected from several hundred by Bausch & Lomb, a much brighter AH-6 water-cooled high-pressure mercury arc lamp, a Leitz photo stand, etc.). The resulting microscope is illustrated in **Figure 9**.

With this microscope, I found that I could indeed gain moderately high resolution (if not

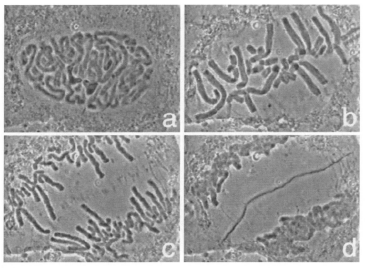

Figure 8

Phase contrast images of an endosperm cell of *Haemanthus katherinae* from (*a*) nuclear envelope breakdown, (*b*) metaphase, and (*c*) late anaphase, through (*d*) cell plate formation. See **Supplemental Movie 1**, reproduced from Inoué (2008a) with kind permission of World Scientific Publishing. Reproduced from Inoué & Oldenbourg (1998) with kind permission of American Society for Cell Biology (**http://www.molbiolcell.org/cgi/content/full/9/7/1603**).

yet at the oil-immersion level) of weakly birefringent structures inside living cells. Being aware that birefringence reflects the arrangement of fine structure and molecules far smaller than the resolution limit of the light microscope, and that the observations could be made without staining or otherwise interfering with the activity of the living cells, I was excited to see what I could explore with this new instrument.

FINALLY TO WOODS HOLE: REALITY AND BEHAVIOR OF SPINDLE FIBERS AND FIBRILS

In early summer of 1949, I finally arrived at the MBL in Woods Hole, together with my classmates Woody Hastings and Dave Stadler and with my new microscope in the trunk of Dave's family car.

In Woods Hole, I met many of the Dans' and Cooper's old friends about whom I had heard so much. I became acquainted with them at the mess hall (where we all shared tables), in the lecture room in the shingle-covered Old Main, in the labs, at Captain Kidd, and at Stony Beach.

These new acquaintances—Don Costello, Albert Tyler, Dan Mazia, and the Osterhouts—introduced me to several local marine invertebrates and showed me how to collect their freshly spawned gametes. The eggs from a few species were clear enough to see the birefringent spindle and asters directly, but many of the eggs were filled with yolk and other birefringent granules and were too opaque to see their internal structures. I solved this problem by using an air-turbine centrifuge, developed earlier by E. Newton Harvey and Bill Loomis at Princeton. Eggs layered on a cushion of isopycnotic sucrose-seawater solution could be stratified so that the spindle and asters would display their birefringence within a clear, yolk-free zone. Despite the stratification and even egg fragmentation, the spindle-containing egg fragments would continue to divide when fertilized.

By using centrifuged oocytes from the annelid parchment worm *Chaetopterus pergamentaceous*, I was able to see clearly the structure of their metaphase-arrested, first-meiosis spindle. This material was ideal for viewing details of spindle structure and for experimenting on the spindle. The cell stayed in metaphase without proceeding to anaphase for more than an hour unless the cell was activated, for example, by fertilization or osmotic shock.

To my delight, the image resolution of the new microscope was high enough so that I could now see that the *Chaetopterus* oocyte spindle was not just a birefringent football-shaped structure (as seen by Schmidt 1937, Swann & Mitchison 1950, and Katie and myself in Misaki). Instead, it was made up of birefringent fibers whose birefringence was stronger (*a*) where they converged and attached to the kinetochore on each of the nine chromosomes on the metaphase plate and (*b*) at the two spindle poles. Furthermore, each of the chromosomal, or kinetochore fibers, as well as the material of the astral rays, appeared to be made up of very thin, submicroscopic fibrils (**Figure 10**; Inoué 1953).

In the activated oocytes, the birefringence of the chromosomal fibers briefly rose as the cell entered anaphase, as it would also in a metaphase cell whose spindle was stretched (**Figure 11**). As the chromosomes were led by the chromosomal fibers to the spindle poles, the fiber birefringence dropped, except where it remained high adjacent to the kinetochore on chromosomes.

Also, as chromosomes moved poleward during anaphase, the diameter of each fiber did not increase as the fiber shortened. So I argued that, despite Schmidt's claim, the loss of birefringence of the spindle material during anaphase could not be explained by a folding of its polypeptide chains (Inoué 2008c).

From these observations I concluded that, although invisible in living cells with conventional microscopy, spindle fibers did really exist in living cells and were not artifacts of fixation, in contrast to what had been argued for half a century (Schrader 1953). Furthermore, the fibers were made up of a bundle of submicroscopic fibrils as depicted in the better-preserved fixed specimen recorded by early cytologists. But the skeptics who had not seen the dynamic images through my microscope had yet to be convinced.

CONVINCING THE SKEPTICS: SPINDLE FIBERS IN TIME-LAPSE MOVIES OF DIVIDING CELLS

During the school year at Princeton, I continued to improve my microscope so that I could measure birefringence in minute objects (Inoué 1951) and also make time-lapse movies of the weakly birefringent spindle in dividing plant cells.

Among the time-lapse movies showing the changing birefringence of the spindle coupled with the movement of chromosomes, the most informative came from cells in the anthers of an Easter lily, *Lilium longiflorum*. When I visited Dr. Ralph Ericson at the University of Pennsylvania, he told me that pollen mother cells in 22.4-mm-long flower buds undergo meiosis and gave me a few plants that were at just the

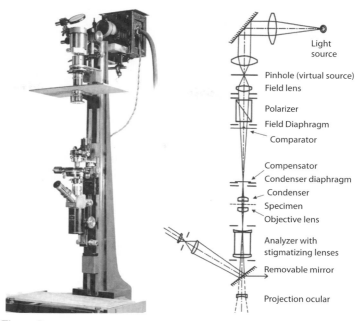

Figure 9

Shinya's Princeton microscope (*left*) with a schematic of the optical path (*right*). From Inoué (2008b), reproduced from Inoué (2008a) with kind permission of World Scientific Publishing.

right stage (for how the flower bud is measured, see Inoué & Oldenbourg 1998).

Before collecting cells from the lily anthers, I found that I had to centrifuge the flower bud in a clinical centrifuge to displace the highly birefringent cell inclusions, which otherwise prevented observing the live spindle. Also, culture media for lily pollen mother cells were not known, so I diluted frog Ringer to 7/8 (a concentration at which the cells would not plasmolize). Fortunately, the pollen mother cells, starting with nuclear envelope breakdown, would complete their two successive divisions despite the intense monochromatic green illumination required for many hours to record the full sequence on 16-mm film.

At MBL, I first publicly showed the movie of the dividing *Lilium* pollen mother cells in Lillie Auditorium (I believe it was in 1951). I still remember how Homer Smith, MBL's General Manager, light-proofed the room by personally climbing up and covering the auditorium's green house roof with a black sheet of cloth so

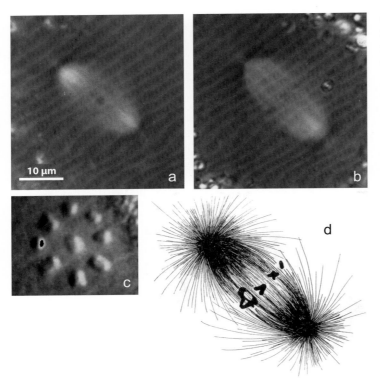

dles of the birefringent fibrils brought the chromosomes to the metaphase plate, and shortening fibers led them to the spindle poles. After the interzonal fibers diminished, new birefringent fibrils appeared between the daughter nuclei to generate the phragmoplast. In the midplane of the phragmoplast, the cell plate was assembled.

The question asked by Dr. Ethyl Brown Harvey, "Were those cells alive?", reflected the pervasive, long-held view by many that spindle fibers and their fibrils were not present in living cells but were artifacts of fixation. But these cells were happy enough to go through their two sequential divisions! The reality of spindle fibers in living cells could no longer be doubted.

Figure 10

(*a,b*) Birefringence of a metaphase-arrested meiosis I spindle in a live, centrifugally clarified *Chaetopterus* oocyte; scale bar for *a* and *b*, 10 μm. (*c*) Polar view of the metaphase plate seen in DIC (differential interference contrast). (*d*) Distribution of fibrils deduced from birefringence. Panels *a*, *b*, and *d* are reproduced from Inoué (1953) with kind permission of Springer Science+Business Media. Panel *c* is reproduced from Inoué & Inoué (1986) with kind permission of Wiley-Blackwell Publishing.

that I (a mere graduate student) could show the film!

The movie showed the chromosomes being brought to the metaphase plate and then led poleward by the birefringent spindle fibers. Finally, birefringent fibrils reemerged between the daughter nuclei to form the phragmoplast, and vesicles assembled in its mid-zone to form the cell plate (**Figure 12**; see **Supplemental Movie 2**, Inoué 1964, Inoué & Oldenbourg 1998).

The response to this showing was most gratifying. There was no doubt that spindle fibers and the fibrils making up the fibers (made visible with sensitive polarizing microscopy) were clearly present in the living, dividing cell. Bun-

THE LABILE NATURE OF SPINDLE FIBERS: REVERSIBLE DEPOLYMERIZATION AND ASSOCIATED CHROMOSOME MOVEMENTS

But what was most exciting for me was that the birefringence of the spindle fibers was not static. It not only fluctuated and changed during mitosis but disappeared reversibly when a cell was exposed to low temperature (**Figure 13**; see **Supplemental Movie 3**, Inoué 1952a, 1964) or to the antimitotic drug colchicine (**Figure 14**; Inoué 1952c). In other words, the fibrils making up the spindle fibers would depolymerize in cold or when exposed to colchicine, only to repolymerize when the condition was reversed.

The results with colchicine were especially intriguing. When metaphase-arrested *Chaetopterus* oocytes were exposed to colchicine, the spindle birefringence would gradually disappear as the fibrils depolymerized (the kinetochore fibers were the longest to persist), but in addition, the depolymerizing filaments actually led the chromosomes and inner spindle pole to the cell surface, where the outer meiotic spindle pole was attached (**Figure 14**). Thus, the colchicine experiments suggested that depolymerizing filaments could generate forces adequate to pull the

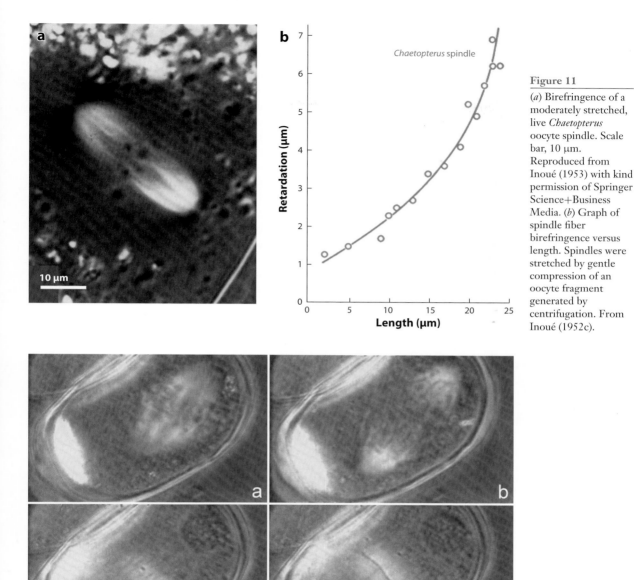

Figure 11

(*a*) Birefringence of a moderately stretched, live *Chaetopterus* oocyte spindle. Scale bar, 10 μm. Reproduced from Inoué (1953) with kind permission of Springer Science+Business Media. (*b*) Graph of spindle fiber birefringence versus length. Spindles were stretched by gentle compression of an oocyte fragment generated by centrifugation. From Inoué (1952c).

Figure 12

Birefringence of spindle fibers in a pollen mother cell of an Easter lily, *Lilium longiflorum*. A movie of dividing *Lilium* pollen mother cells finally convinced skeptics that spindle fibers (and their dynamic submicroscopic fibrils) were actually present in living cells and were not an artifact of fixation, in contrast to what had been argued for half a century. (*a*) Anaphase onset. (*b*) Mid-anaphase. (*c*) Phragmoplast formation. (*d*) Cell plate formation. Panels reproduced from Inoué (1964) with kind permission of Elsevier. See **Supplemental Movie 2**, reproduced from Inoué (2008a) with kind permission of World Scientific Publishing.

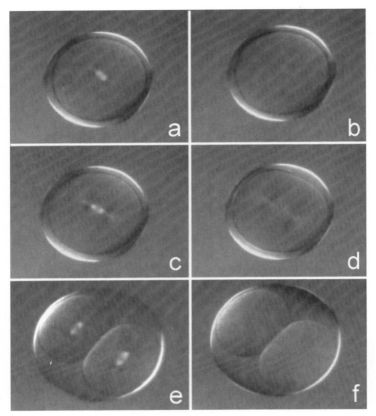

Figure 13

Reversible loss of spindle birefringence by cold treatment of a developing sea urchin egg. In these still frames taken from **Supplemental Movie 3**, the first cleavage spindle (*a*) is developing, (*b*) has disappeared by cold treatment, (*c*) has recovered and reached full metaphase, and (*d*) is at cleavage onset. After chilling and returning to room temperature, the second cleavage spindle is (*e*) in metaphase and (*f*) chilled again in anaphase. The same egg was chilled seven times; development was delayed by the duration of chilling but not arrested. Reproduced from Inoué (2008a) with kind permission of World Scientific Publishing. See **Supplemental Movie 3**, also reproduced from Inoué (2008a) with kind permission of World Scientific Publishing.

chromosomes and the spindle poles toward each other (Inoué 1952c).

Jumping forward to the 1970s, Ted Salmon and I showed that chromosome movement, associated with gradual loss of spindle fiber birefringence, could also be induced in metaphase-arrested *Chaetopterus* oocytes when we dropped the temperature to an intermediate value (**Figure 15**; Inoué & Ritter 1975). Furthermore, using a novel pressure chamber, Salmon showed that not only could birefringence loss

and chromosome movement be induced by elevating hydrostatic pressure, but both became faster (up to 400 atm) as more pressure was applied (**Figures 15** and **16**; Salmon 1975b, 1976; Salmon & Ellis 1975). Thus, it became increasingly likely that microtubules in vivo could generate pulling and pushing forces by their disassembly and assembly. Salmon further showed that purified microtubules assembled in vitro would also depolymerize under high hydrostatic pressure (Salmon 1975a).

In plant cells as well, the fibrils of the spindle and phragmoplast were just as labile as in animal cells. These fibrils would depolymerize when exposed to cold or treated with colchicine or even low concentrations of calcium ions, as was soon to be discovered.

ORIENTING CENTERS AND ULTRAVIOLET MICROBEAM EXPERIMENTS

By the late 1950s, we had developed the polarization rectifier and, thus, were able to achieve full resolution with a polarizing microscope, even using high-NA oil-immersion lenses, without losing the sensitivity needed to detect weak birefringence (Inoué & Hyde 1957).

Using this new capability, Andrew and Wishia Bajer and I followed the behavior of birefringent fibers and fibrils during mitosis in live endosperm cells of the African blood lily *H. katherinae*. The endosperm cell lacks a rigid cell wall and so could be flattened on an osmotically equilibrated agar sheet by gently drawing off the excess endosperm fluid. Using serial photographs and a time-lapse movie taken with rectified optics, we found positively birefringent fibrils that were aligned in the clear zone and polar cap outside of the intact nuclear envelope before the envelope started to break down (**Figure 17**, *left column*; Inoué & Bajer 1961).

As soon as chromosomes condensed further and the nuclear envelope started to break down, birefringent fibrils grew into the nucleus (**Figure 17**, *right column*) and attached

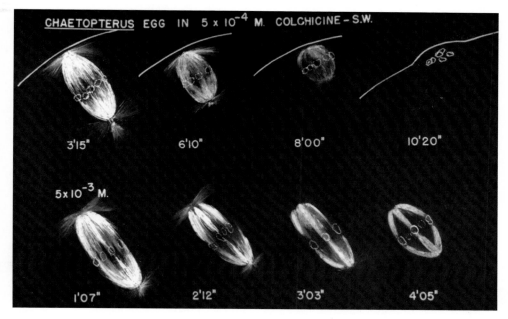

Figure 14

Shortening and loss of birefringence by a metaphase-arrested *Chaetopterus* spindle exposed to colchicine in seawater. Below each frame is the time in minutes and seconds after the application of 5×10^{-4} M colchicine (*upper row*) and 5×10^{-3} M colchicine (*lower row*). From Inoué (1952c).

to kinetochores to form birefringent chromosomal fibers. Some fibrils bundled into sheaths around chromosomes.

From metaphase through anaphase, fiber birefringence converged and remained strong at the kinetochore, as we had already seen in lily pollen mother cells and in animal cells (**Figure 18**; Inoué & Bajer 1961). In telophase, more birefringent fibrils appeared parallel to the spindle's remaining interpolar fibers and formed the phragmoplast, as had also occurred in Easter lily pollen mother cells. Small vesicles accumulated in the mid-zone of the phragmoplast, then fused to form the cell plate. When the cell plate started to appear, the birefringence of the phragmoplast fibrils was strongest by the cell plate, suggesting that it (along with the kinetochores) had taken over the role of keeping the fibrils oriented. Thus, the young cell plate and kinetochores both appeared to be acting as orienting centers (Inoué & Sato 1967).

Microbeam experiments further revealed the activity of orienting centers. Using carefully dose-controlled ultraviolet (UV) microbeam irradiation, we could reduce or abolish the birefringence of spindle fibers or phragmoplast filaments locally in the irradiated region. When a metaphase endosperm cell of *Haemanthus* (with its typical plant-type spindle) was irradiated, the spindle fiber lost its birefringence not only in the irradiated area but also toward the spindle pole. Nevertheless, the birefringence persisted between the irradiated area and the kinetochore (**Figure 19**). In telophase, the birefringent phragmoplast fibrils disappeared from the irradiated area and poleward but, again, persisted between the cell plate and the irradiated area.

But whether in metaphase or with a phragmoplast, the birefringent fibrils immediately started to grow back through the irradiated area and poleward as soon as UV irradiation was stopped. Thus, spindle fiber molecules clearly grow away from the kinetochore and from the cell plate.

Microbeam experiments with animal cells were further revealing. Using crane fly spermatocytes, Forer (1965) found that birefringence was lost from the area irradiated with a UV microbeam. But in these cells, birefringent fibers persisted not only between the irradiated area and the kinetochores but also between the irradiated area and the spindle pole! In other words the irradiated area appeared as an area of reduced birefringence (**Figure 20**).

Furthermore, after irradiation, the area of reduced birefringence traveled poleward at a steady pace and disappeared at the spindle pole. Thus, the birefringent material not only grew poleward away from the kinetochore into the irradiated area but also shortened toward the spindle pole.

These observations implied a treadmilling of the spindle fiber molecules from the kine-

tochore to the pole. (Interestingly, the spindle fibers in grasshopper spermatocytes exposed to UV microbeam show a different, more complex behavior, as reported by Gerry Gordon in 1979; see Article 32 in Inoué 2008a for additional note.)

Thus, on the basis of the dynamic distribution of spindle birefringence observed in several animal and plant cells and UV microbeam experiments, we postulated that three mechanisms align the molecular filaments that make up spindle fibers, phragmoplast fibrils, and astral rays. They are (*a*) the activity of orienting centers, (*b*) spontaneous alignment by concentrated formation of filaments, and (*c*) parallel alignment to previously formed filaments. Furthermore, the orienting centers [which are now called microtubule-organizing centers (MTOCs)] become active, one after another, with the progression of mitosis (Inoué & Sato 1967).

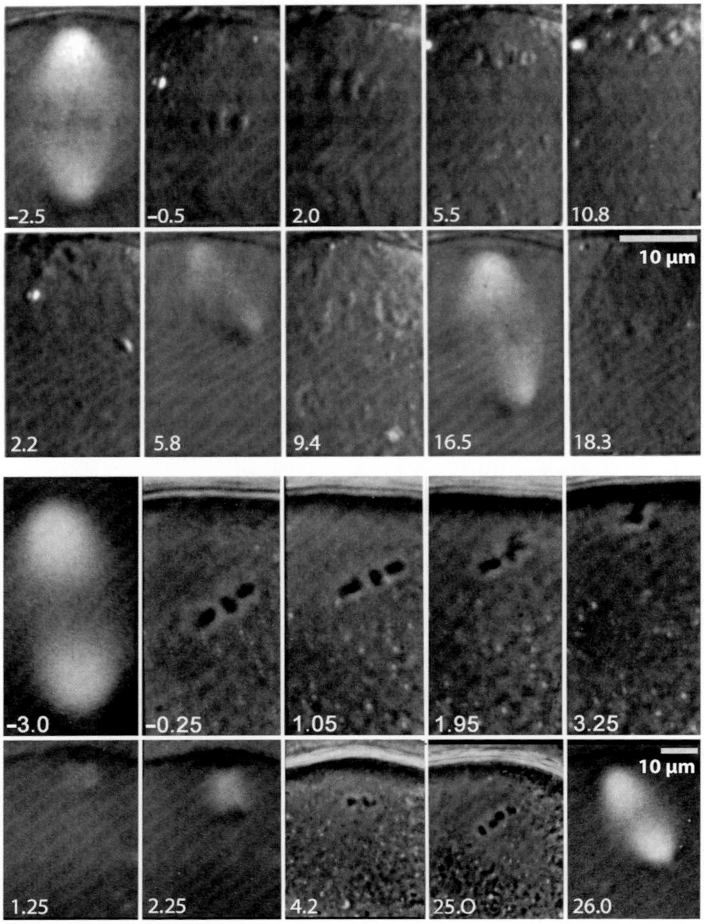

Figure 15

Chromosome movement induced by cooling or by elevated hydrostatic pressure in a metaphase-arrested *Chaetopterus* oocyte. In Row 1, the temperature is dropped from 23.5°C to 5.2°C at time 0.0 min. (The −2.5-min frame is in polarized light, and the other frames are in DIC.) Chromosomes move to the cell surface as spindle filaments depolymerize and shorten. In Row 2, the temperature is raised to 24°C at 0.0 min. (The 5.8- and 16.5-min frames are in polarized light, and the others are in DIC.) Chromosomes move away from the cell surface as spindle birefringence and length increase. Scale bar, 10 μm. Rows 1 and 2 are from Inoué & Ritter (1975). Row 3 shows 200 atm of hydrostatic pressure applied at time 0.0 min. (The −3.0 min frame in polarized light, and the other frames are in phase contrast; print magnification differs from that of Row 4.) Chromosomes move to the cell surface as spindle filaments depolymerize and shorten. In Row 4, pressure is reduced to 1 atm at time 0.0 min. (The 1.25-, 2.25-, and 26.0-min frames are in polarized light; the other frames are in phase contrast.) Chromosomes move away from the cell surface as spindle birefringence and length increase. Scale bar, 10 μm. Rows 3 and 4 are reproduced from Salmon (1975b) with kind permission of Wiley-Blackwell Publishing.

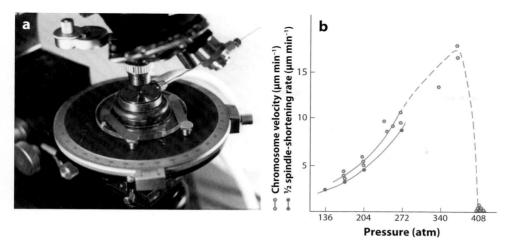

Figure 16

(*a*) Water-jacketed hydrostatic pressure chamber on Leitz polarizing microscope. Reproduced from Salmon & Ellis (1975) with kind permission of The Rockefeller University Press. (*b*) Speeds of chromosome movement and birefringence decay versus applied pressure. Both speeds increase as hydrostatic pressure is raised. But above 400 atm, chromosomes no longer move because spindle microtubules disassemble too rapidly. Reproduced from Salmon (1976) with kind permission of Cold Spring Harbor Laboratory Press.

SPINDLE BIREFRINGENCE, MICROTUBE DYNAMICS, AND FORCE GENERATION FOR CHROMOSOME MOVEMENT

In a symposium volume published in 1964, I provided photographs of birefringent spindle fibers and fibrils in a large variety of animal and plant cells undergoing normal mitosis as well as treated with cold or exposed to UV microbeam irradiation. The fibers and their oriented fibrils, which I proposed were capable of producing pulling and pushing forces by the removal or addition of material, appeared to be in a labile dynamic equilibrium with their subunit molecules (Inoué 1964).

In our summary paper in 1967, Hidemi Sato and I showed that 50% heavy water doubles the birefringence and size of spindles and asters, signaling the reversible incorporation of a subunit protein from a pool. The reversible assembly took place in less than 2 min and did not require the synthesis of new proteins. Thus, coupled with our earlier observations on the reversible disassembly and force-generating effects by cold and by colchicine, we postulated

the presence of a dynamic equilibrium between spindle fibers (filaments) and a cytoplasmic pool of their protein subunits and that shifts in the equilibrium were responsible for spindle assembly and also for chromosome movement (**Figure 21**; Inoué & Sato 1967; see also Inoué & Salmon 1995, Maiato et al. 2004).

In the meanwhile, Bruce Nicklas and coworkers carried out extensive micromanipulation studies on live grasshopper spermatocytes. By displacing a single chromosome with a microneedle, they demonstrated how the kinetochores are quite stably, but not irreversibly, linked by fibers to the spindle poles. Also, they showed how tension exerted on kinetochores by spindle fibers governed the position and arrangement of chromosome arms and even the coordinated onset of anaphase (Nicklas & Koch 1969, Nicklas & Staehly 1967, Nicklas et al. 2001). In an extensive review article discussing the role of microtubules in mitotic chromosome movements, Nicklas (1971) illustrates the detailed distribution of birefringence in spindle fibers of a living grasshopper spermatocyte undergoing anaphase as seen with a rectified polarizing microscope (**Figure 22**).

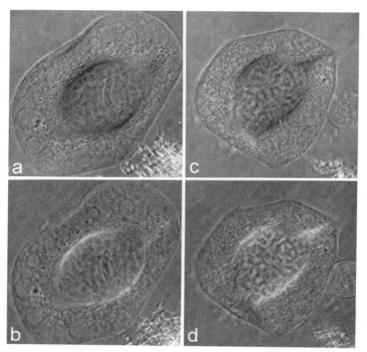

Figure 17

Endosperm cell of the African blood lily *Haemanthus katherinae* preparing to enter mitosis. (*Left column*) A few hours before nuclear envelope breakdown, birefringent fibrils appear in the clear zone outside of the envelope. (*Right column*) As the nuclear envelope starts to break down, additional fibrils from the polar cap grow into the nucleus. Shortly thereafter, the fibrils connect to chromosomes and form the spindle. The compensator slow axis is NW-SE in panels *a* and *c* and NE-SW in panels *b* and *d*. Reproduced from Inoué & Bajer (1961) with kind permission of Springer Science+Business Media.

In 1974, using a rectified polarizing microscope, Sato & Izutsu captured spectacular images of dynamic, birefringent spindle fibers in dividing spermatocytes of another species of grasshopper, *Chrysocraon japonicas* [see **Supplemental Movie 4**, reproduced from Inoué (2008a) with kind permission of World Scientific Publishing]. Although the incredible activity (Northern lights flickering of spindle fiber birefringence that reflects the highly dynamic spindle microtubules) seen in the film could not be fully explained in 1974 (because so little was yet known of interactions between motor proteins and microtubules), the activity was interpreted as reflecting the treadmilling and growth and shortening of microtubules that were stochastically assembling and disassem-

bling in dynamic equilibrium with their subunit molecules.

Our earlier physiological studies on dividing cells and the interpretation of the underlying submicroscopic events had received considerable attention. However, at the writing of our 1967 review, the nature of the protein molecules that made up the microtubules was still in dispute. Furthermore, no one had known that microtubules could be isolated or disassembled into subunits by cold treatment and that the chilled supernatant would reassemble into microtubules upon warming. As described below, Ed Taylor and his associates made those essential discoveries of the in vitro properties of microtubules shortly after Taylor (1965) managed to label the spindle protein, using H^3-colchicine.

EARLY BIOCHEMISTRY

In 1952 Dan Mazia and Katsuma Dan, using synchronously dividing sea urchin eggs, managed to isolate the mitotic apparatus in large quantities (Mazia & Dan 1952). The apparatus, which included the spindle, asters, and chromosomes, was isolated by stabilizing (in cold, ethanol-treated eggs) the presumed protein gel structure by converting its –SH groups to –SS with H_2O_2. The remaining cytoplasm and cell membrane were then solubilized with the detergent Duponol. Although the exact identity of the proteins that make up the fibrous elements of the spindle was yet to be discovered, the early work of Mazia and Dan showed that the mitotic apparatus could, in fact, be isolated as an integral physical body. This property was also used to display the configuration of the asymmetric asters, e.g., in unequally dividing egg cells.

In 1965, Taylor prepared H^3-colchicine with high specific activity, which bound reversibly to a subset of cellular sites. He also showed that in cells exposed to concentrations of colchicine as low as 2×10^{-7} M, mitosis was blocked and metaphase chromosomes accumulated without affecting DNA, RNA, or protein synthesis. From the data, he reasoned that if a critical fraction (3–5%) of the cellular sites that can bind

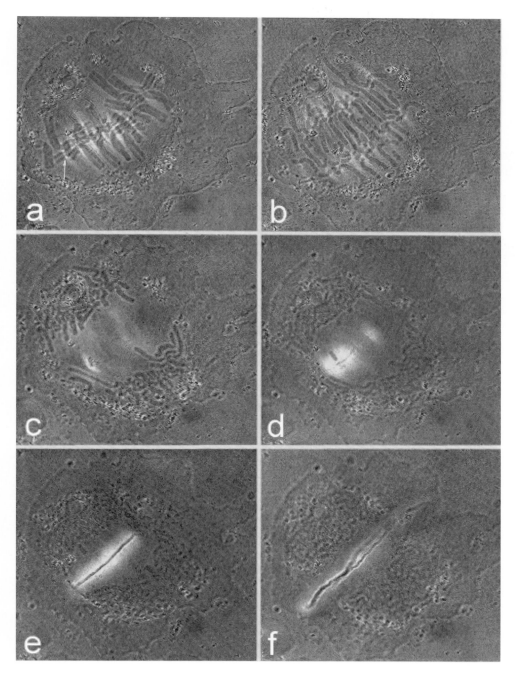

Figure 18

Mitosis and cell division in an endosperm cell of the African blood lily. Birefringence of chromosomal fibers in (*a*) metaphase and (*b*) anaphase shows clearly in this flattened cell. Likewise, birefringent fibrils are clear in (*c*) telophase, (*d,e*) the phragmoplast stage, and (*e, f*) cell plate formation. Reproduced from Inoué & Bajer (1961) with kind permission of Springer Science+Business Media.

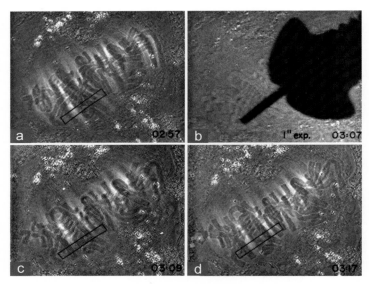

Figure 19

Microbeam irradiation and recovery of metaphase spindle fibers in an endosperm cell of *Haemanthus katherinae*. (*a*) Ten seconds before a 1-s UV irradiation. (*b*) Image of a UV micromirror and supporting screw. (*c*) Two seconds after irradiation, fiber birefringence has disappeared from the irradiated area and distally. (*d*) Ten seconds after irradiation, the spindle fibers have grown back through the irradiated area. Reproduced from Inoué (1964) with kind permission of Elsevier.

colchicine is complexed, the cell is unable to form a functional spindle (Taylor 1965).

In 1967, Taylor and his student Gary Borisy found that H^3-colchicine bound a 6S protein found in extracts from a variety of tissues and organelles. The amount of binding correlated with the presence of microtubules but not with the number of cells that were dividing. Thus, they suggested that the colchicine-binding 6S protein is a subunit of microtubules (Borisy & Taylor 1967).

In 1972, Richard Weisenberg reported the successful repolymerization of isolated microtubule protein and showed that a very low concentration of Ca^{2+} (much lower than that released from vesicles in living cells) was sufficient to depolymerize microtubules and block their polymerization. He showed that the 2°C supernatant obtained from an extract of rat brain would generate microtubules when warmed to 35°C in the presence of Mg^{2+}-ATP (or -GTP), a Ca^{2+} chelator (EGTA), and an

organic buffer (MES at pH 6.5). Very few microtubules formed when the supernatant was incubated with 0.1 mM colchicine (Weisenberg 1972).

The ability to reversibly depolymerize microtubules in vitro led both to the purification of tubulin, the dimeric subunit protein of microtubules, and to extensive studies of the biochemistry and assembly properties of microtubules. These included the discovery of microtubule dynamic instability, which depends on GTP hydrolysis within tubulin subunits after they polymerize into an end of a microtubule (Mitchison & Kirschner 1984).

EARLY ELECTRON MICROSCOPY

The existence of a vast array of microtubules in all tissues was revealed after Sabatini's discovery that glutaraldehyde fixation can preserve cytoplasmic microtubules (Sabatini et al. 1963). In a symposium article published in 1966, Keith Porter summarizes evidence for the presence of a ~250-Å-diameter, straight, ubiquitous filamentous cell component, which is particularly labile and sensitive to fixation by osmium tetroxide alone but not to fixation by glutaraldehyde followed by osmium tetroxide. In negative-stained samples, the components exhibited a ~80-Å pitch tilted ~10° to the long axis and apparently possessing a low-density axial component. They were thought to be tubular and were named microtubules (Porter 1966).

Porter goes on to say that the microtubules appear to govern primarily cell shape and form the structural framework of the mitotic spindle, etc., namely, to act as a "cytoskeleton." He also notes that their presence is apparently required for the transport of cell inclusions and organelles and for cytoplasmic streaming because the distribution and orientation of microtubules in the cell correlate with these functions. "But the force-generating role, if any, and the mechanism of force generation by microtubules are unclear."

Others, in the meantime, had observed "tubular spindle filaments" with the

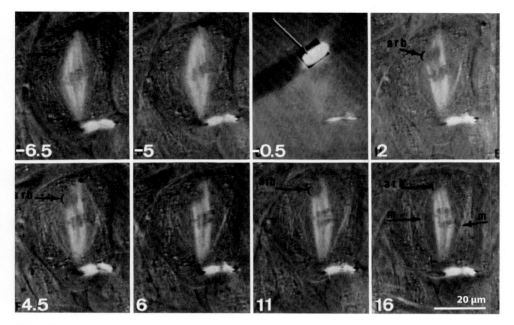

Figure 20

Poleward migration of the area of reduced birefringence induced by UV microbeam irradiation. Late-metaphase spindle fibers in the spermatocyte of a crane fly, *Nephrotoma suturalis*, were irradiated at time 0.0 min (in the *bright area* seen in the frame of –0.5 min). Where irradiated, a discrete area of reduced birefringence (arb) appeared, then migrated to the upper spindle pole and disappeared. Anaphase started 6 min after irradiation. m denotes mitochondria. Scale bar, 20 μm. Reproduced from Forer (1965) with kind permission of The Rockefeller University Press.

electron microscope (Brinkley & Stubblefield 1966, Harris 1962, Robbins & Gonatas 1964, Roth 1967). In the axopodia of a heliozoan, Tilney et al. (1966, 1967) demonstrated, by both electron microscopy and polarization optics, the reversible loss of microtubules exposed to cold or hydrostatic pressure and later to colchicine, just as we had seen earlier in the birefringent mitotic spindle filaments in dividing cells.

In 1975, using metaphase spindles isolated from a starfish oocyte (with a fixative that precisely preserved their birefringence), we were able to establish that the birefringence of the spindle fibers in living cells exactly measured the distribution and concentration of their microtubules. Thus, we finally gained proof that, so long as the spindle is fixed in such a way that its birefringence is precisely preserved, the (form) birefringence of the spindle fiber measures the number of microtubules per square micrometer in electron microscopy cross section (**Figure 23**; Sato et al. 1975).

CONCLUDING REMARKS AND UPDATE

In this Perspective, I reminisced on our early studies with polarized light microscopy to explore the detailed structure and dynamic properties of the mitotic (and meiotic) spindles directly in living cells. These studies proved that spindle fibers and fibrils were, indeed, present in healthy living cells, even though previously they could generally not be seen except after fixation and staining.

Our polarization optical studies on active, living cells also confirmed the highly labile nature of the spindle fibers and their fibrils and the fact that they were dynamically

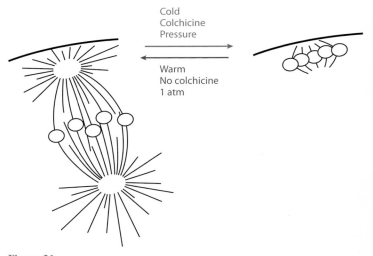

Cold
Colchicine
Pressure

Warm
No colchicine
1 atm

Figure 21

Schematic showing the reversible movement of chromosomes and inner spindle pole to the cell surface by agents that depolymerize birefringent spindle fibers. Reproduced from Inoué & Salmon (1995) with kind permission of American Society for Cell Biology.

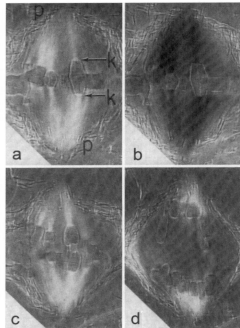

Figure 22

A spermatocyte of a grasshopper, *Pardalophra apiculata*, observed with rectified optics shows prominent birefringent chromosomal spindle fibers. (*a,b*) Metaphase of meiosis I, (*c*) early anaphase, and (*d*) late anaphase. (Panels *a, c, d* are in additive compensation; panel *b* is in subtractive compensation.) Kinetochores are indicated by k, and spindle poles by p. From Nicklas (1971).

organized by orienting centers such as kinetochores, spindle poles, and the cell plate. These findings, which had been surmised by classical cytologists, could now be followed within individual living cells with high time resolution and unambiguously within individual living cells. Thus, the behavior of spindle fibrils followed with polarized light microscopy foretold the reversible assembling, dynamic properties of isolated microtubules that had not yet been discovered. In addition, by observing the action of colchicine on the spindle structure in living cells, I suggested that chromosome movement could be induced by the depolymerization of spindle fibrils (Inoué 1952c).

Although met with some skepticism, and despite the discovery of microtubule sliding activities powered by the motor proteins dynein by Summer & Gibbons (1971) and, later, kinesin by Vale et al. (1985), what appeared to be a somewhat counterintuitive explanation of force generation by depolymerizing microtubules was finally demonstrated in vitro by Koshland et al. (1988) and verified through further experiments by Coue et al. (1991). The latter authors observed the traction of a chromosome by a single depolymerizing microtubule

in a cell-free system in the absence of energy-yielding nucleotides. Today force generation by motor proteins and force generation by assembly/disassembly of microtubules are both considered necessary for chromosome movement (Inoué & Salmon 1995, Mitchison & Salmon 2001, Mogilner et al. 2006).

By 1967, our accumulated data suggested that long, slender fibrils, oriented by organizing centers such as the kinetochore on the chromosomes and the spindle poles, were in a labile, dynamic equilibrium with their globular subunit protein molecules, which primarily polymerized at the kinetochores and depolymerized at the spindle poles (Inoué & Sato 1967).

Although these early suggestions are consistent with modern views on the assembly and

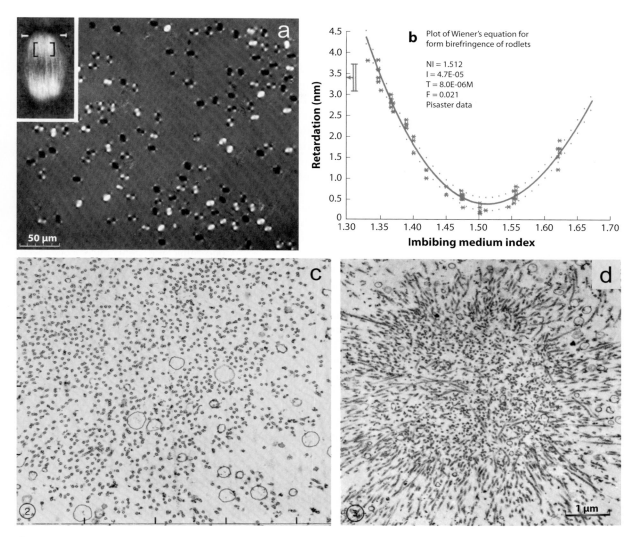

b Plot of Wiener's equation for form birefringence of rodlets

NI = 1.512
I = 4.7E-05
T = 8.0E-06M
F = 0.021
Pisaster data

Figure 23

Form birefringence of a meiotic spindle isolated from oocytes of a starfish, *Pisaster ochraceus*. (*a*) Mass isolation of metaphase-arrested spindles with 12% hexylene glycol. The black brackets in the inset show the spindle region where birefringence was measured. (*b*) At an immersion media refractive index of 1.35, birefringence of the isolated spindles (fixed with 3% glutaraldehyde–12% hexylene glycol at pH 6.3) remains as in life (*double vertical bar* to *left*). Perfused with carefully selected refractive index media, the measured birefringence (*asterisks*) exactly follows Wiener's form birefringence curve (generated with Bragg & Pippard's 1953 formula) for parallel rodlets whose refractive index is 1.52 and that occupy 2% volume. This volume fraction is identical to the fractional area occupied by the cross section of microtubules seen in the electron micrograph in panel *c* (1-μm grid at *bottom*). (*c*) The electron microscopy section was cut halfway across the brackets in the inset to panel *a*. (*d*) Electron micrograph through the polar region of the spindle (*white bar* in panel *a*, *inset*). Reproduced from Sato et al. (1975) with kind permission of The Rockefeller University Press.

force-generating properties of mitotic microtubules (Koshland et al. 1988, McIntosh et al. 1969), in the early days I was unaware that a microtubule assembles and disassembles almost exclusively at its ends, as demonstrated by Margolis & Wilson (1978), or that microtubules had an intrinsic polarity, with their two ends having different assembly properties (Heidemann & McIntosh 1981, Telzer & Haimo 1981).

Thus, on the one hand, in my 1953 report I interpreted the submicroscopic structure of the spindle fibers (on the basis of its birefringence in live *Chaetopterus* oocytes) as being made up of a population of long, uninterrupted thin fibrils connecting the chromosomes and spindle pole (**Figure 10***d*). Yet, on the other hand, in figures 3 and 56 of my 1964 article, I represent the spindle fibers as being made up of short rods to stress the highly labile nature and the equilibrium of fibers with their pool of subunits (Inoué 1964, reproduced as Article 22 in Inoué 2008a). This second representation almost suggests that I viewed the fibers to be tactoids, a possibility that I argued against in the concluding chapter of my doctorate thesis (Inoué 2008c).

The contradiction is now mainly resolved by Mitchison & Kirschner's discovery that mitotic microtubules are undergoing dynamic instability (Mitchison & Kirschner 1984). In other words, spindle fibers are made up of microtubules that individually grow long by assembly and then very rapidly shorten by disassembly. So long as that process happens stochastically, each spindle fiber is made up of microtubules of varying lengths, and collectively, they are turning over rapidly in exchange with their pool of subunit tubulin molecules (Mitchison & Salmon 2001, Waterman-Storer & Salmon 1998).

Although providing a general conceptual framework concerning force generation by assembly-disassembly of microtubules based on the dynamic equilibrium between polymer filaments and their subunits, my earlier reports did not envision the dynamic instability of mitotic microtubules (Mitchison & Kirschner 1984), microtubule assembly affected by specific enzymes (Howard & Hyman 2007), or the exceptionally complex and dynamic molecular events that are taking place between microtubules and motor proteins, especially at the kinetochore (e.g., Inoué & Salmon 1995, Maiato et al. 2004, Wittmann et al. 2001).

Nevertheless, our own studies on mitotic mechanisms and microscopy development have had the good fortune to play discernible historic roles. In retrospect, we were in a fortunate position to bridge the extensive knowledge accumulated by the classical cytologists, on the basis primarily of diligent and broad-ranging studies of fixed and stained tissues and cells (Schrader 1953, Wilson 1928), and modern cell biology, which emphasizes studies based on physiology and molecular biology in living cells. I hope that we do not forget the rich diversity of mitotic patterns unearthed by earlier cytologists. Some of these patterns will certainly shed unexpected insights into cellular organization and molecular mechanisms essential for mitosis (see **Supplemental Comment 1**).

Concerning the light microscope, well-corrected lenses were made and Zernicke's theory of microscope image formation had been fully formulated by the mid-twentieth century. Thus, the time was ripe for further innovations in microscopy that contributed to our ability to study active living cells over time, rather than only after fixation.

More recently, fluorescence microscopy, including multiphoton excitation, confocal, and other modes of imaging or processing, with its well-recognized advantages, has flourished. Yet, I believe polarization microscopy has further important roles to play. Not only can we image and measure birefringence that reflects ordered fine structure nondestructively, but also polarized light microscopy reveals inherent anisotropic interactions that take place between bond electrons and polarized electromagnetic light waves (see, e.g., Appendix III in Inoué 1986). Thus, using advanced polarization optics, we have the opportunity to precisely locate, orient, and follow changes in selected molecules or interactions taking place between molecules. Such studies should provide further insight into the intricate organizational mechanisms and the interacting signals that are exchanged in and between cells, which are essential for the continuation of cellular life and for the orderly development of organisms (see **Supplemental Comment 2**).

DISCLOSURE STATEMENT

The author is not aware of any biases that might be perceived as affecting the objectivity of this article.

ACKNOWLEDGMENTS

I wish to thank Editor Randy Schekman for urging me to write this Perspective, Ted Salmon of the University of North Carolina for his many valuable inputs, Jane MacNeil and Grant Harris of MBL for extensive help in preparing this manuscript and movies, and authors and publishers for allowing us to reproduce previously published figures. I also thank my many friends and supporters, in and out of MBL, who made my life-long pursuits possible. These exciting adventures would not have been possible without continued and understanding support from my family, especially my wife, Sylvia.

LITERATURE CITED

Ambronn H, Frey A. 1926. *Das Polarisationsmikroskop: Seine Anwendung in der Kolloidforschung und in der Färberei*. Leipzig: Akad. Verlag

Bajer A. 1951. Ciné-micrographic studies on mitosis in endosperm. III. The origin of the mitotic spindle. *Exp. Cell Res.* 13:493–502

Bajer A, Molé-Bajer J. 1956. Ciné-micrographic studies on mitosis in endosperm. II. Chromosome, cytoplasmic and Brownian movements. *Chromosoma* 7:558–607

Bělař K. 1929. Beitäge zur Kausalanalyse der Mitose. II. Untersuchungen an den Spermatocyten von *Chorthippus (Stenobothrus) lineatus* Panz. *Roux Archiv f. Entwmk.* 118:359–484 and Plates I–VIII

Bennett HS. 1950. The microscopical investigation of biological tissues with polarized light. In *Handbook of Biological Technique*, ed. CE McLung, pp. 591–677. New York: Harper & Row

Borisy GG, Taylor EW. 1967. The mechanism of action of colchicine: binding of colchicine-^{3}H to cellular protein. *J. Cell Biol.* 34:525–33

Bragg WL, Pippard AB. 1953. The form birefringence of macromolecules. *Acta Crystallogr. B* 6:865–67

Cleveland LR. 1938. Origin and development of the achromatic figure. *Biol. Bull.* 74:41–55

Cooper KW. 1941. Visibility of the primary spindle fibers and the course of mitosis in the living blastomeres of the mite, *Pediculopsis granimum* Reut. *Proc. Natl. Acad. Sci. USA* 27:480–83

Coue M, Lombillo VA, McIntosh JR. 1991. Microtubule depolymerization promotes particle and chromosome movement in vitro. *J. Cell Biol.* 112:1165–75

Dan K. 1943. Behavior of the cell surface during cleavage. VI. On the mechanism of cell division. *J. Fac. Sci. Tokyo Imp. Univ.* (Ser. IV) 6:323–68

Forer A. 1965. Local reduction in spindle birefringence in living *Nephrotoma suturalis* (Loew) spermatocytes induced by UV microbeam irradiation. *J. Cell Biol.* 25:95–117

Frey-Wyssling A. 1953. *Submicroscopic Morphology of Protoplasm*. Amsterdam: Elsevier

Gordon G. 1979. Unexpected increase in poleward velocities of mitotic chromosomes after UV irradiation of their kinetochore fibers. *J. Cell Biol.* 83:376a

Harris P. 1962. Some structural and functional aspects of the mitotic apparatus in sea urchin embryos. *J. Cell Biol.* 14:475–85

Hartshorne NH, Stuart A. 1960. *Crystals and the Polarising Microscope: A Handbook for Chemists and Others*. London: Arnold. 3rd ed.

Heidemann SR, McIntosh JR. 1981. Visualization of the structural polarity of microtubules. *Nature* 286:517–19

Howard J, Hyman AA. 2007. Microtubule polymerases and depolymerases. *Curr. Opin. Cell Biol.* 19:31–35

Inoué S. 1951. A method for measuring small retardations of structures in living cells. *Exp. Cell Res.* 2:513–17

Inoué S. 1952a. Effect of temperature on the birefringence of the mitotic spindle. *Biol. Bull.* 103:316

Inoué S. 1952b. Studies on depolarization of light at microscope lens surfaces. I. The origin of stray light by rotation at the lens surfaces. *Exp. Cell Res.* 3:199–208

Inoué S. 1952c. The effect of colchicine on the microscopic and submicroscopic structure of the mitotic spindle. *Exp. Cell Res. Suppl.* 2:305–18

Inoué S. 1953. Polarization optical studies of the mitotic spindle. I. The demonstration of spindle fibers in living cells. *Chromosoma* 5:487–500

Inoué S. 1964. Organization and function of the mitotic spindle. In *Primitive Motile Systems in Cell Biology*, ed. RD Allen, N Kamiya, pp. 549–98. New York: Academic

Inoué S. 1981. Cell division and the mitotic spindle. *J. Cell Biol.* 91:131s–47s

Inoué S. 1986. *Video Microscopy*. New York: Plenum

Inoué S. 1994. A tribute to Katsuma Dan. *Biol. Bull.* 187:125–31

Inoué S. 2002. Polarization microscopy. *Curr. Protoc. Cell Biol. Suppl.* 13:4.9.1–27

Inoué S. 2008a. *Collected Works of Shinya Inoué: Microscopes, Living Cells, and Dynamic Molecules*. Singapore: World Sci. Publ.

Inoué S. 2008b (1951). Doctoral thesis, *Studies of the structure of the mitotic spindle in living cells with an improved polarization microscope*, Part I: Introduction. Published as Article 7 in Inoué 2008a

Inoué S. 2008c (1951). Doctoral thesis, *Studies of the structure of the mitotic spindle in living cells with an improved polarization microscope*, Part VI: The submicroscopic structure of the spindle in living cells. Published as Article 12 in Inoué 2008a

Inoué S, Bajer A. 1961. Birefringence in endosperm mitosis. *Chromosoma* 12:48–63

Inoué S, Dan K. 1951. Birefringence of the dividing cell. *J. Morphol.* 89:423–56

Inoué S, Hyde WL. 1957. Studies on depolarization of light at microscope lens surfaces. II. The simultaneous realization of high resolution and high sensitivity with the polarizing microscope. *J. Biophys. Biochem. Cytol.* 3:831–38

Inoué S, Inoué TD. 1986. Computer-aided stereoscopic video reconstruction and serial display from high-resolution light-microscope optical sections. *Ann. N.Y. Acad. Sci.* 483:392–404

Inoué S, Oldenbourg R. 1998. Microtubule dynamics in mitotic spindle displayed by polarized light microscopy. *Mol. Biol. Cell* 9:1603–7 (**http://www.molbiolcell.org/cgi/content/full/9/7/1603**)

Inoué S, Ritter H Jr. 1975. Dynamics of mitotic spindle organization and function. In *Molecules and Cell Movement*, ed. S. Inoué, RE Stephens, pp. 3–30. New York: Raven Press

Inoué S, Salmon ED. 1995. Force generation by assembly/disassembly in mitosis and related movements. *Mol. Biol. Cell* 6:1619–40

Inoué S, Sato H. 1967. Cell motility by labile association of molecules. *J. Gen. Physiol.* 50:259–92

Koshland DE, Mitchison TJ, Kirschner M. 1988. Polewards chromosome movement driven by microtubule depolymerization in vitro. *Nature* 331:499–504

Maiato H, DeLuca J, Salmon ED, Earnshaw WC. 2004. The dynamic kinetochore-microtubule interface. *J. Cell Sci.* 117:5461–77

Margolis RL, Wilson L. 1978. Opposite end assembly and disassembly of microtubules at steady state in vitro. *Cell* 13:1–8

Mazia D, Dan K. 1952. The isolation and biochemical characterization of the mitotic apparatus of the dividing cell. *Proc. Natl. Acad. Sci. USA* 38:826–38

McIntosh JR, Hepler PK, van Wie DG. 1969. Model for mitosis. *Nature* 224:659–63

Mitchison JM, Kirschner M. 1984. Dynamic instability of microtubule growth. *Nature* 312:237–42

Mitchison TJ, Salmon ED. 2001. Mitosis: a history of cell division. *Nat. Cell Biol.* 3:E17–21

Mogilner A, Wollman R, Civelekoglu-Scholey G, Scholey J. 2006. Modeling mitosis. *Trends Cell Biol.* 16:88–96

Nicklas RB. 1971. Mitosis. In *Advances in Cell Biology*, ed. DM Prescott, L Goldstein, E McConkey, 2:225–97. New York: Appleton-Century-Croft

Nicklas RB, Koch CA. 1969. Chromosome micromanipulation III. Spindle fiber tension and the reorientation of mal-oriented chromosomes. *J. Cell Biol.* 43:40–50

Nicklas RB, Staehly CA. 1967. Chromosome micromanipulation I. The mechanics of chromosome attachment to the spindle. *Chromosoma* 21:1–16

Nicklas RB, Waters JC, Salmon ED, Ward SC. 2001. Checkpoint signals in grasshopper meiosis are sensitive to microtubule attachment, but tension is still essential. *J. Cell Sci.* 114:4173–83

Okazaki K, Inoué S. 1976. Crystal property of the larval sea urchin spicule. *Dev. Growth Differ.* 18:413–34

Östergren G. 1949. Luzula and the mechanism of chromosome movements. *Hereditas* 35:445–68

Pawley JB, ed. 2006. *Handbook of Biological Confocal Microscopy*. New York: Plenum. 3rd ed.

Porter KR. 1966. Cytoplasmic microtubules and their function. In *Ciba Foundation Symposium on Principles of Biomolecular Organization*, ed. GEW Wolstenholme, M O'Connor, pp. 308–45. London: Churchill

Rinne FWB, Bereck M. 1953. *Anleitung zu optischen Unterzuchungen mit dem Polarizationsmikroskop*. Stuttgart: Schweizerbart

Robbins E, Gonatas NK. 1964. The ultrastructure of a mammalian cell during the mitotic cycle. *J. Cell Biol.* 21:429–63

Roth LE. 1967. Electron microscopy of mitosis in Amebae. III. Cold and urea treatments: a basis for tests of direct effects of mitotic inhibitors on microtubule formation. *J. Cell Biol.* 34:47–59

Sabatini DD. 2005. In awe of subcellular complexity: 50 years of trespassing boundaries within the cell. *Annu. Rev. Cell Dev. Biol.* 21:1–33

Sabatini DD, Bensch K, Barrnett RJ. 1963. Cytochemistry and electron microscopy. The preservation of cellular ultrastructure and enzymatic activity by aldehyde fixation. *J. Cell Biol.* 17:19–58

Salmon ED. 1975a. Pressure-induced depolymerization of brain microtubules in vitro. *Science* 189:884–86

Salmon ED. 1975b. Spindle microtubules: thermodynamics of in vivo assembly and role in chromosome movement. *Ann. N.Y. Acad. Sci.* 253:383–406

Salmon ED. 1976. Pressure-induced depolymerization of spindle microtubules: IV. Production and regulation of chromosome movement. In *Cold Spring Harbor Conferences on Cell Proliferation—Cell Motility*, ed. R Goldman, T Pollard, J Rosenbaum, 3:1329–42. New York: Cold Spring Harb. Lab. Press

Salmon ED, Ellis GW. 1975. A new miniature hydrostatic pressure chamber for microscopy: Strain-free optical glass windows facilitate phase contrast and polarized light microscopy of living cells. Optional fixture permits simultaneous control of pressure and temperature. *J. Cell Biol.* 65:587–602

Sato H, Ellis GW, Inoué S. 1975. Microtubular origin of mitotic spindle form birefringence. *J. Cell Biol.* 67:501–17

Schmidt WJ. 1924. *Die Bausteine des Tierkörpers in polarisiertem Lichte*. Bonn: Cohen

Schmidt WJ. 1937. *Die Doppelbrechung von Karyoplasma, Zytoplasma und Metaplasma*. Protoplasma Monographien, Vol. 11. Berlin: Gebrüder Bornträger

Schmidt WJ. 1939. Doppelbrechung der Kernspindel und Zugfasertheorie der Chromosomenbewegung. *Chromosoma* 1:253–64

Schrader F. 1953. *Mitosis: The Movement of Chromosomes in Cell Division*. New York: Columbia Univ. Press

Sluder G, Wolf DE, eds. 2003. *Digital Microscopy: A Second Edition of Video Microscopy. Methods in Cell Biology*, Vol. 72. San Diego: Academic

Summer KE, Gibbons IR. 1971. Adenosine triphosphate-induced sliding of tubules in trypsin-treated flagella of sea-urchin sperm. *Proc. Natl. Acad. Sci. USA* 68:3092–96

Swann MM, Mitchison JM. 1950. Refinements in polarized light microscopy. *J. Exp. Biol.* 27:226–37

Tasaki I, Takeuchi T. 1941. Der am Ranvierschen Knoten entstenhende Aktionsstrom und seine Bedeutung für die Erregengsleitung. *Pflügers Arch. Physiol.* 244:696–711

Taylor EW. 1965. The mechanism of colchicine inhibition of mitosis. I. Kinetics of inhibition and the binding of H^3-colchicine. *J. Cell Biol.* 25:145–60

Telzer BR, Haimo LT. 1981. Decoration of spindle microtubules with dynein: evidence for uniform polarity. *J. Cell Biol.* 89:373–78

Tilney LG, Hiramoto Y, Marsland D. 1966. Studies of microtubules in Heliozoa. III. A pressure analysis on the role of these structures on the formation and maintenance of the axopodia of *Actinosphaerium nucleofilum* (Barrett). *J. Cell Biol.* 29:77–95

Tilney LG, Porter KR. 1967. Studies of microtubules in Heliozoa. II. The effect of low temperature on these structures on the formation and maintenance of the axopodia. *J. Cell Biol.* 34:327–43

Vale RD, Reese TS, Sheetz MP. 1985. Identification of a novel force-generating protein, kinesin, involved in microtubule-based motility. *Cell* 42:39–50

Wada B. 1950. The mechanism of mitosis based on studies of the submicroscopic structure and of the living state of the *Tradescantia* cell. *Cytologia* 16:1–26

Wahlstrom FE. 1960. *Optical Crystallography*. New York: Wiley. 3rd ed.

Waterman-Storer CM, Salmon ED. 1998. How microtubules get fluorescent speckles. *Biophys. J.* 75:2059–69

Weisenberg RC. 1972. Microtubule formation in vitro in solutions containing low calcium ion concentrations. *Science* 177:1104–5

Wilson EB. 1928. *The Cell in Development and Heredity*. New York: MacMillan. 3rd ed.

Wittmann T, Hyman T, Desai A. 2001. The spindle: a dynamic assembly of microtubules and motors. *Nat. Cell Biol.* 3:E28–34

Wright FE. 1911. *The Methods of Petrographic-Microscopic Research: Their Relative Accuracy and Range of Application*. Washington: Carnegie Inst.

REFERENCE ADDED IN PROOF

Brinkley BR, Stubblefield E. 1966. The fine structure of the kinetochore of a mammalian cell in vitro. *Chromosoma* 19:28–43

Replicative Aging in Yeast: The Means to the End

K.A. Steinkraus,[1] M. Kaeberlein,[1,*] and B.K. Kennedy[2,*]

[1]Department of Pathology and [2]Department of Biochemistry, University of Washington, Seattle, Washington 98195; email: kaeber@u.washington.edu, bkenn@u.washington.edu

Annu. Rev. Cell Dev. Biol. 2008. 24:29–54

First published online as a Review in Advance on July 14, 2008

The *Annual Review of Cell and Developmental Biology* is online at cellbio.annualreviews.org

This article's doi:
10.1146/annurev.cellbio.23.090506.123509

*Corresponding authors.

Key Words

longevity, dietary restriction, SIR2, TOR, life span

Abstract

Progress in aging research is now rapid, and surprisingly, studies in a single-celled eukaryote are a driving force. The genetic modulators of replicative life span in yeast are being identified, the molecular events that accompany aging are being discovered, and the extent to which longevity pathways are conserved between yeast and multicellular eukaryotes is being tested. In this review, we provide a brief retrospective view on the development of yeast as a model for aging and then turn to recent discoveries that have pushed aging research into novel directions and also linked aging in yeast to well-developed hypotheses in mammals. Although the question of what causes aging still cannot be answered definitively, that day may be rapidly approaching.

Contents

INTRODUCTION

Aging is paradoxical. On the one hand, it is universal in mammals, and therefore, unlike specific diseases, it seems to be a natural process. On the other hand, the deterioration in health and ultimate mortality associated with aging have caused humans for millennia to look for ways of impeding its seemingly inevitable progress.

Molecular and genetic studies of aging have gained pace over the last century to the extent that aging research is a thriving field of endeavor. Studies of aging in mammals are limited by the long life span of common model organisms. Mice and rats live 3–5 years and primates up to 40. Nevertheless, aging studies, particularly in rodents, have been highly informative, framing much of our understanding of the genetic factors and environmental conditions modulating longevity. One solution to speed up studies of aging has been to study primary human or mouse cells in culture. These cells (usually fibroblasts are chosen for study) have a limited proliferative capacity before they undergo terminal cell-

cycle arrest (Hayflick 1965). Senescence in culture has been immensely informative, providing insights into cell-cycle control, differentiation, and cancer. However, its relevance to organismal aging remains a highly debated topic (Campisi & d'Adda di Fagagna 2007).

A second approach that has dramatically accelerated aging research is the use of invertebrate organisms, which age more rapidly and are readily amenable to genetic and environmental manipulation. Although a variety of organisms have been studied, a majority of studies have utilized fruit flies (*Drosophila melanogaster*) (Helfand & Rogina 2003), worms (*Caenorhabditis elegans*) (Houthoofd & Vanfleteren 2007, Olsen et al. 2006), or yeast (*Saccharomyces cerevisiae*) (Kaeberlein et al. 2007, Piper 2006). Worms live approximately 2–3 weeks and flies 2–3 months. Among the genetic interventions that result in life span extension in both organisms are mutations in the insulin/IGF-1 signaling pathway (Gami & Wolkow 2006). Because some mutations reducing insulin/IGF-1 signaling in mice also result in enhanced longevity (Bartke 2005), at least some lessons learned in worms and flies are likely to translate to mammals and, perhaps, humans.

As a single-celled eukaryote, *S. cerevisiae* seems an unlikely candidate for aging studies. Yet at least two aging assays have been developed and more than 100 studies have been published for this organism. In this review, we discuss genetic studies aimed at defining the pathways modulating yeast aging, and biochemical studies attempting to identify the root causes of one of the models: replicative aging. Readers are directed to other papers for a discussion of chronological aging in yeast (Fabrizio & Longo 2003, Laun et al. 2006). Furthermore, we address the likelihood that the aging process is conserved between yeast and multicellular eukaryotes.

REPLICATIVE AGING IN YEAST

S. cerevisiae divide by budding and therefore undergo asymmetrical cell division, with the mother cell retaining more volume than the

Insulin/IGF-1
signaling pathway: a
hormonal signaling
pathway conserved in
higher eukaryotes

daughter (Hartwell & Unger 1977). Taking advantage of this asymmetry, Robert Mortimer & John Johnston (1959) were the first scientists to perform a yeast life span experiment. A pioneer in the field of yeast genetics and recently deceased, Mortimer was best known for developing techniques to monitor yeast meiosis and using them to generate invaluable genetic maps (http://mcb.berkeley.edu/news-and-events/research-news/robert-mortimer/). In this study, a small needle was used to microdissect daughter cells away from mothers, and the number of divisions a mother could undergo [later defined as replicative life span (RLS)] (**Figure 1**) was tabulated (Mortimer & Johnston 1959). However, this pioneering study made no attempt to link the limited proliferative potential of individual yeast cells to aging in multicellular organisms.

The result of each division of a mother cell can also be detected by the appearance of a circular bud scar composed of chitin on the cell surface (Bacon et al. 1966, Barton 1950, Seichertova et al. 1973). Because bud scars do not normally overlap, the Mortimer study addressed the hypothesis that available sites for the formation of new bud scars on the cell surface would become limiting as yeast mother cells continue to divide, a mechanism likely restricted to yeast. This model was discounted, however, by the observation that cell surface area expands dramatically as mother cells age, more than compensating for the loss of available surface area (Mortimer & Johnston 1959). Instead, Mortimer & Johnston speculated that reduced surface-to-volume ratios in old mother cells may limit metabolic processes. Although the bud scar and surface-to-volume hypotheses are now largely disfavored (Egilmez & Jazwinski 1989, Kennedy et al. 1994), this original study set the stage for exploration into yeast replicative aging.

After the initial foray by Mortimer & Johnston (1959), two decades passed before a second group restored interest in yeast aging. This latter group (Müller et al. 1980) addressed an important question that remained unresolved: Is the life span of a yeast cell limited

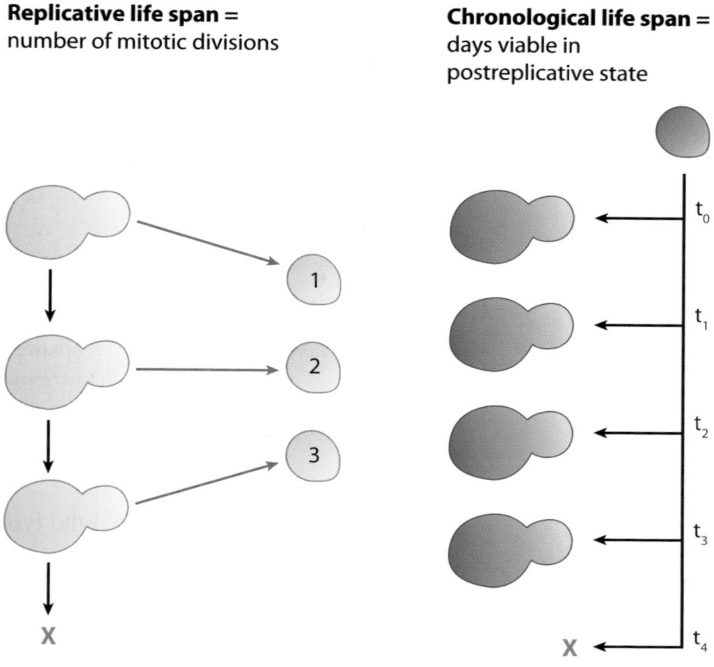

Replicative life span = number of mitotic divisions

Chronological life span = days viable in postreplicative state

Figure 1

Replicative and chronological life span assays in yeast. (*Left*) In a replicative life span (RLS) assay, one mother cell is allowed to divide, and the smaller daughters cells are removed by microdissection. The number of daughters produced is tallied as the RLS. (*Right*) In a chronological life span (CLS) assay, cells are maintained in an undividing state. At given time (*t*) intervals, a subset of the population is placed onto media to allow cell division to resume. The life span is determined as the time point at which those cells are unable to reenter the cell cycle.

by the number of mitotic cycles or calendar life span? A series of experiments led to the conclusion that the number of replicative cycles, and not the length of time since budding, was the primary determinant of life span (Müller et al. 1980). This is also supported by the observation by many groups that cells do not lyse immediately after reaching permanent cell-cycle arrest (Mortimer & Johnston 1959). Although lysis may be the final result, many cells can often remain metabolically active for days, similar to what is reported for senescent fibroblasts in cell culture. The chronological time a cell can remain viable in a postreplicative state [chronological life span (CLS)] has been established and extensively studied as a second model of aging in yeast (Fabrizio & Longo 2003, Longo et al. 1996). Which of these two assays

Replicative life span (RLS): the cumulative number of mitotic divisions a cell can undergo

Chronological life span (CLS): the amount of time a cell can remain viable while in a nondividing state

better models aging in other eukaryotes remains unanswered. In fact, there may be an interesting interplay between the replicative and the chronological aging of yeast; passage of a cell through a postreplicative stage reduces its RLS once it reenters the cell cycle (Ashrafi et al. 1999). Therefore, postmitotic aging of a cell can delimit its RLS.

ASYMMETRY AND YEAST AGING

To survive in the wild, *S. cerevisiae* has adapted to undergo rapid mitotic expansion in nutrient-rich conditions. It must accomplish this feat while simultaneously maintaining the vitality of the population, and it accomplishes this in part through asymmetric division (**Figure 2**). Whereas the larger mother cell ages and ultimately loses replicative capacity, daughters produced by the aging mother generally are renewed in their capacity; this ensures that the colony survives even though aging mothers within the colony might perish. Asymmetric division may cause mother cells to retain an aging factor, thus sacrificing individual replicative potential while retaining full potential in resulting daughter cells (Egilmez & Jazwinski 1989, Kennedy et al. 1994).

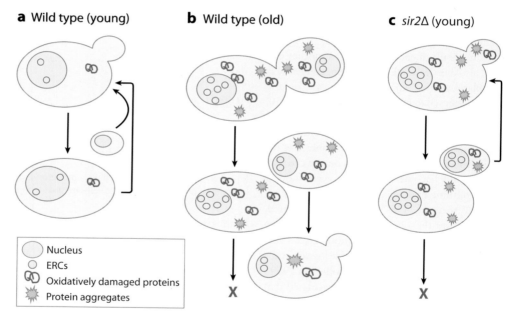

Figure 2

The asymmetry of division is lost in old mother cells and *sir2Δ* cells. The three aging factors diagrammed here are extrachromosomal ribosomal DNA circles (ERCs), oxidatively damaged proteins, and protein aggregates. (*a*) In young wild-type cells, levels of all three factors are low, and the factors are preferentially sequestered in the mother cell. Note the size differential between the mother cell and the budding daughter cell. Both mother and daughter will go on to further budding. (*b*) In old wild-type cells, the three factors accumulate to high levels. The budding daughter cell is similar in size to the mother cell and inherits all three of the aging factors. The old mother cell can no longer divide at the end of its replicative life span (RLS). The daughter cell, although the product of asymmetrical division, will proceed to normal asymmetric division. (*c*) *sir2Δ* cells accumulate abnormally high levels of ERCs and protein aggregates. Division is partially symmetric in that, although the daughter cell is much smaller than the mother, these aging factors are not preferentially sequestered away from the daughter. The precocious accumulation of aging factors limits the RLS of the mother, although the daughter can go on to divide.

A molecular confirmation of this hypothesis was provided by the identification of extrachromosomal ribosomal DNA circles (ERCs) as one cause of aging in yeast (Sinclair & Guarente 1997). The yeast ribosomal DNA (rDNA) consists of approximately 100 to 150 tandemly arrayed copies of a 9.1-kb repeat containing all the information necessary to code for the rRNA (Petes & Botstein 1977, Philippsen et al. 1978, Rustchenko & Sherman 1994). ERCs are formed by homologous recombination between rDNA repeats; are self-replicating, owing to the presence of an origin of replication within the rDNA repeat; and, because they lack a CEN element, display biased segregation to mother cells (Murray & Szostak 1983). This combination of asymmetric inheritance and self-replication leads to a mother cell–specific increase in ERC copy number with age. It is believed that, once a threshold level of ERCs accumulates in the mother cell, senescence occurs, perhaps owing to titration of essential cellular factors by the abundant rDNA sequence present as ERCs.

Interestingly, asymmetry breaks down in the oldest mothers, resulting in an increased frequency of symmetric divisions (Jazwinski et al. 1989, Johnston 1966, Kennedy et al. 1994). In these aberrant mitotic events, the mother cell and daughter cell are indistinguishable in size, and the daughter has a reduced life span that is comparable to the remaining life span of the mother cell. Progeny from symmetrical daughters recover full life span potential following asymmetric division (Kennedy et al. 1994), however, indicating that the damage that accumulates to limit mother cell life span is not permanent. For instance, if nuclear DNA damage to the mother cell accumulated during old age, it would be inherited in the daughter cells and would not be diluted out in the daughter lineage, and full life span would not be restored.

More recently, a screen has been performed to identify yeast mutants that fail to maintain age asymmetry with respect to divisions (Lai et al. 2002). These conditional mutants clonally senesce at the restrictive temperature. According to one proposal, normally functional mitochondria are specifically segregated to daughter cells, and this process is disrupted in symmetry mutants (Jazwinski 2005, Lai et al. 2002). More recently, Seo et al. (2007) reported that the abnormal segregation of mitochondria in one of these symmetry mutants (a point mutation in *ATP2*) could be suppressed by the overexpression of a peroxin protein (Pex6). They propose that Pex6, at least when overexpressed, can contribute to mitochondrial biogenesis in addition to its known peroxisomal roles. A second fruitful source of information regarding asymmetry may come from mathematical modeling, and studies have attempted to model yeast aging parameters in this fashion (Gillespie et al. 2004, Hirsch 1993, Jazwinski & Wawryn 2001).

At the molecular level, exciting data from Nyström and colleagues have shown that, after cytokinesis, levels of protein carbonyls and other forms of oxidatively damaged proteins are much higher in the mother cell than in the daughter (Aguilaniu et al. 2003, Erjavec & Nystrom 2007). Protein aggregates containing heavily carbonylated proteins are also retained in mother cells (Erjavec et al. 2007). Given that the accumulation of damage caused by reactive oxygen species (ROS) may be one cause of aging (discussed below), these findings suggest that minimizing the segregation of preexisting damage to the newly formed daughter cell is one method of ensuring a full life span (Nyström 2005).

The mechanism(s) by which asymmetry is achieved with respect to oxidized and aggregated proteins is beginning to be delineated. For instance, asymmetry must require a functional actin cytoskeleton because transient disruption of the cytoskeleton with Latrunculin-A disrupts the asymmetry of oxidized proteins and aggregates (Aguilaniu et al. 2003, Erjavec et al. 2007). The actin cytoskeleton has also been linked directly to life span in yeast; deletion of the actin bundling protein Scp1 results in increased actin dynamics, reduced ROS, and extended life span (Gourlay et al. 2004). However, protection of daughter cells during division seems to be accomplished not only by restricting access of damaged proteins

Extrachromosomal ribosomal DNA circles (ERCs): formed by recombination between rDNA repeats and preferentially sequestered in mother cells

Ribosomal DNA (rDNA): consists of 100 to 150 tandemly arrayed copies of the sequence coding for rRNA

Reactive oxygen species (ROS): highly reactive molecules due to the presence of unpaired valence shell electrons

to daughters but also by increasing the ability of daughter cells to combat damage. This latter process occurs in part through a daughter-specific enhancement of catalase activity (Erjavec & Nystrom 2007). During aberrant symmetric divisions initiated by old mothers, one or more of these processes presumably break down, allowing both leakage of ERCs and higher levels of oxidized or aggregated proteins to migrate to daughters. Finally, the Sir2 histone deacetylase, a conserved longevity-promoting factor in yeast, worms, and flies, is also required for mother-daughter asymmetry with respect to oxidized aggregated proteins (Aguilaniu et al. 2003, Erjavec & Nystrom 2007, Erjavec et al. 2007). We discuss the role of Sir2 in this process in more detail in the subsection on sirtuins (below).

Other proteins (e.g., cell wall components) are segregated asymmetrically between mothers and daughters. However, old components are not always left in mother cells because the old spindle pole body always segregates to the daughter (Pereira et al. 2001). Studying the molecular asymmetry associated with mitotic division in yeast and how it relates to aging will no doubt continue to provide further novel insights into the aging process.

GENETIC MODULATION OF YEAST REPLICATIVE LIFE SPAN

Fundamentally, studies of the basic mechanisms of aging can be approached from two directions, and both have been exploited in yeast. Either one can study the genetic (or environmental) interventions that alter the rate of aging, or one can determine the phenotypic and molecular changes that are associated with aging (e.g., yeast cell volume increases with age). In this and the next section, we address both approaches in yeast replicative aging, beginning here with genetic approaches.

As with other model organisms, genetic changes can dramatically influence the longevity of yeast. This was first demonstrated by the finding that expression of an oncogenic retroviral derivative of human RAS, v-Ha-RAS, in yeast cells resulted in extension of RLS (Chen et al. 1990). Because expression of this oncogene was known to contribute to immortalization of mammalian fibroblasts, it was a reasonable starting point in yeast. Senescence in fibroblasts has long been studied in an attempt to gain an understanding of the mammalian aging process and has yielded extensive information about the control of cell proliferation and its links to cancer. The relationship between fibroblast senescence and organismal aging is still debated (Campisi & d'Adda di Fagagna 2007). Because yeast is a single-celled organism, it was also argued whether the RLS assay would be a better model for organismal aging or cellular senescence. Although this debate is not completely resolved, the genetic factors controlling yeast aging seem to align better with those controlling organismal aging in multicellular eukaryotes than with those controlling senescence (see below). However, many of the known regulators of mammalian cell senescence are not conserved in yeast, making a direct comparison difficult.

Life span extension by expression of v-Ha-RAS in yeast served as the motivation for testing the possibility that the two yeast RAS orthologs might function to modulate replicative aging. Paradoxically, deletion of $RAS1$ resulted in life span extension, whereas deletion of $RAS2$ shortened life span (Sun et al. 1994). The reasons for these divergent effects are not yet understood. Since these early studies, numerous yeast aging genes have been identified and are discussed in relevant places throughout this review. In this section, we highlight efforts to perform unbiased screens to identify yeast aging genes and the extent to which they have led to a better understanding of yeast replicative aging.

Although there are many benefits to studying aging in yeast, there are also limitations, in particular, the difficulty associated with procuring large populations of truly old cells. In a rapidly growing culture of yeast, ages of individual cells will distribute geometrically, with half of the population virgins, 1/4 one-division-old mothers, 1/8 two-division-old mothers, etc.

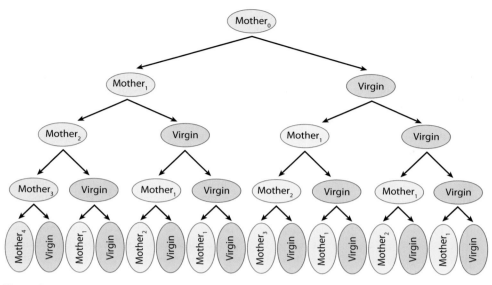

Figure 3

Old mother cells represent a fraction of an experimental population. The schematic shows the distribution of ages of cells in a dividing population. The number of divisions each mother cell has undergone is indicated in the subtext. Virgin daughters (*purple*) represent half of the population at each division. Among the remaining population are the younger mothers (*blue*) and the original mother (*green*).

(**Figure 3**). Therefore, the fraction of truly old cells (>20 generations) is negligible. This fact raises questions about whether the life span of individual yeast cells is relevant from the perspective of natural selection (discussed below), and also makes obtaining enough old cells for biochemical studies difficult. Several schemes have been employed to enrich for old cells, and populations of reasonably old cells can be obtained (Chen & Contreras 2007, Egilmez et al. 1989, Park et al. 2002, Smeal et al. 1996). Nevertheless, and in spite of attempts to automate life span analysis (Jarolim et al. 2004), the only truly accurate method for measuring RLS to date is micromanipulation of daughter cells away from mother cells while counting the number of daughters produced by each individual mother cell. The brute-force nature of this assay is not conducive to large-scale screens.

The first attempt around this problem by Jazwinski and colleagues involved purification of old (and young) cells, followed by RNA collection and differential hybridization to iden-

tify transcripts up- or downregulated with age (Egilmez et al. 1989). This led to the identification of a gene whose expression is dramatically downregulated with age and that later was named *LAG1* (D'Mello et al. 1994). *LAG1* encodes a ceramide synthase (Dickson et al. 2006, Guillas et al. 2001, Schorling et al. 2001, Spassieva et al. 2006). This is quite intriguing, given proposed roles for ceramides in stress response pathways, apoptosis, and cell senescence (Obeid & Hannun 2003). The relationship of *LAG1* to yeast life span is complex, as either deletion or mild overexpression results in life span extension (D'Mello et al. 1994). In contrast, deletion of another ceramide synthase gene (*LAC1*) does not alter RLS (Guillas et al. 2001, Jiang et al. 1998, Schorling et al. 2001).

In another attempt to study yeast aging, the Guarante lab's primary goal was to perform unbiased screens to identify aging genes. An initial screen was made possible by the finding that stress resistance and the maintenance of viability at 4°C correlated with longevity. Although this correlation later proved to be strain specific, it was grounds for screening stress-resistant mutants for enhanced longevity (Kennedy et al. 1995). The first mutant characterized was a complex mutation in the gene encoding Sir4, which, along with Sir2 and Sir3, forms a complex that mediates transcriptional repression at telomeres and silent mating-type loci *HML* and *HMR* (Ivy et al. 1986, Rine & Herskowitz 1987). *SIR2* encodes a histone/protein deacetylase, and this enzymatic activity is required for its silencing functions (Imai et al. 2000, Landry et al. 2000, Smith et al. 2000).

The long-lived *SIR4-42* allele was loss of function for telomere and *HM* silencing; however, it behaved as a dominant allele for longevity (Kennedy et al. 1995). This finding, although dampening interest in direct links between telomeres and yeast aging, proved highly valuable in the establishment of a model whereby the SIR4-42 mutation directed the SIR complex away from telomeres and *HM* loci to an undefined *AGE* locus (Kennedy et al. 1995), which was later proposed to be the rDNA (Kennedy et al. 1997). Consistently, mutations that reduce recruitment sites for the SIR complex at telomeres lead to life span extension (Austriaco & Guarente 1997). For a more detailed discussion of SIR2 and yeast aging, see the subsection on sirtuins, below.

Two other genes were linked to yeast aging in this initial screen. Recessive mutations in (or deletion of) *UTH1* were found to cause a modest increase in life span (Austriaco 1996, Kennedy et al. 1995). *UTH1* expression is induced by oxidative stress, and *uth1Δ* strains have altered sensitivities to different sources of oxidative stress (Bandara et al. 1998, Camougrand et al. 2004). Reported to be an outer mitochondrial membrane protein (Velours et al. 2002), *UTH1* is also required for induction of apoptosis in yeast by expression of mammalian Bax and for autophagy-mediated degradation of mitochondria (Camougrand et al. 2003, Kissova et al. 2004). Which, if any, of these activities are causally involved in the longevity-modulating role of Uth1 remains to be determined. The link to autophagy is partic-

ularly intriguing, however, given that reduced Tor signaling, a process known to induce autophagy (Martin & Hall 2005), leads to RLS extension (Kaeberlein et al. 2005c). In addition, autophagy has been implicated in life span–extending mutations in *C. elegans* (Melendez et al. 2003).

The final gene identified in this screen was *UTH4* (Kennedy et al. 1997), also referred to as *MPT5*. Identification of *MPT5* was fortuitous because the parental strain for this screen contained a C-terminal truncation allele, and the life span–extending *UTH4* mutation was a reversion that restored the wild-type open reading frame (ORF) and allowed production of the full-length protein. Overexpression of *MPT5* increases life span in two other strain backgrounds, and deletion of *MPT5* shortens life span (Kaeberlein & Guarente 2002, Kaeberlein et al. 2005b, Kennedy et al. 1997). It remains unclear how increased Mpt5 activity affects yeast aging. Mpt5 function leads to altered SIR-dependent silencing (Kennedy et al. 1997) but also regulates the integrity of the cell wall (Kaeberlein & Guarente 2002, Stewart et al. 2007) and a MAP kinase pathway linked to pseudohyphal growth (Prinz et al. 2007). Mpt5 also interacts genetically with Ssd1, a protein that promotes longevity via a Sir2-independent pathway (Kaeberlein & Guarente 2002, Kaeberlein et al. 2004). Structurally, Uth4 is one member of a family of yeast proteins that resemble *Drosophila* pumilio, an RNA binding protein that regulates the translation of specific messages (Wharton & Aggarwal 2006). Mpt5 controls the translation and/or degradation of a few mRNAs (Goldstrohm et al. 2006, 2007; Hook et al. 2007; Prinz et al. 2007; Stewart et al. 2007). Whether these transcripts (or as-yet-unidentified ones) are linked to longevity regulation by Mpt5 remains to be determined.

To date, only one unbiased screen for mutations that increase RLS has been reported; in this screen, longevity was used as the primary phenotype (Kaeberlein et al. 2005c). This work involved screening 564 single-gene deletion strains as part of an ongoing effort to quantify replicative aging properties across the haploid yeast ORF deletion collection (Kaeberlein et al. 2005c), a set of ~4800 isogenic single-gene deletion strains (Brachmann et al. 1998, Winzeler et al. 1999). Generally, to get a reliable estimate of the mean RLS of a given strain, it is desirable to measure the life span of at least 40–50 mother cells in repeated assays. Given that the average life span of the deletion set parental strain (BY4742) is ~26 generations, this would require microdissection of approximately 19.5 million daughter cells. Thus, it was necessary to take an alternative approach. Accordingly, Kaeberlein et al. (2005c) developed an iterative strategy that provides semiquantitative life span data for each deletion strain and allows for classification of each strain as potentially (or unlikely to be) long-lived. Potentially long-lived deletions are then subjected to rigorous validation in strains from both haploid mating types.

From the initial analysis of 564 gene deletions, 13 (2.3%) were verified to be long-lived (Kaeberlein et al. 2005c). Among the yeast aging genes identified was *TOR1*, providing the first link in yeast between Tor signaling and aging (see below subsection, Translational Regulation and Dietary Restriction). Also of note, approximately 20% of deletions were statistically short-lived. Although a very small number of cells were analyzed for most short-lived deletions, this high approximate frequency points to the challenge of mechanistically interpreting shortened life span. It is currently not possible to determine whether the normal aging process is accelerated in short-lived cells or whether cells are dying owing to defects unrelated to normal aging. We have now generated preliminary data on all nonessential yeast deletion strains, and the estimate of 2.3% for the percentage of long-lived deletions appears accurate, leading us to predict that, upon completion of verification, approximately 100–120 yeast aging genes will be identified. These numbers are in keeping with estimates from RNAi-based screens in *C. elegans* (Hamilton et al. 2005, Hansen et al. 2005, Lee et al. 2003).

MOLECULAR PHENOTYPES ASSOCIATED WITH REPLICATIVE AGING

Through micromanipulation, Mortimer & Johnston (1959) were the first to determine that aging mother cells take increasingly longer times to progress through the cell cycle and produce daughters. Accumulation of the proposed aging factor and/or cellular damage likely makes it progressively harder for aging mothers to continue mitotic division. Two such factors have been identified: ERCs (Sinclair & Guarente 1997) and oxidatively damaged proteins (Aguilaniu et al. 2003). Interestingly, both are regulated by the activity of the protein deacetylase Sir2 (discussed below) (Aguilaniu et al. 2003, Kaeberlein et al. 1999).

Several lines of evidence indicate that ERCs can cause the senescence of mother cells, at least under some conditions. The most elegant of these derives from a study by Sinclair & Guarente (1997), in which a plasmid containing an ERC- and *LoxP*-flanked ARS-CEN element was introduced into yeast cells. After Cre-mediated excision of the ARS-CEN, the plasmid accumulated in mother cells and dramatically shortened RLS. Interestingly, this toxicity does not seem to be related to the rDNA sequence present in the ERC because the presence of an asymmetrically inherited, self-replicating plasmid without an rDNA sequence is sufficient to cause a similar premature senescence phenotype (Sinclair & Guarente 1997). The rDNA locus may be the source of the ill-fated episome simply because of the increased likelihood of ERC formation by homologous recombination, owing to the highly repetitive nature of the rDNA locus. There remains no compelling evidence that ERCs or episomes of any kind are a contributing factor to aging in other eukaryotic organisms.

Unlike mammalian cells, which often have multiple nucleoli dispersed throughout the nucleus, yeast cells contain only one nucleolus, which is separated from the rest of the nucleoplasm. Dispersion of this nucleolus into

USING YEAST TO STUDY AGE-RELATED DISEASES

S. cerevisiae is increasingly used to model age-related diseases. Two examples of diseases currently being modeled in yeast are cancer and neurodegenerative disorders.

Yeast and Cancer

One trait commonly seen during carcinogenesis is genomic instability. By studying inheritance patterns of genes from aging mother cells to daughter cells, investigators have demonstrated that yeast display age-associated genomic instability (MacMurray & Gottschling 2003). Work is currently under way to understand the mechanism of this instability.

Yeast and Neurodegeneration

Yeast models of two common neurodegenerative diseases, Huntington's and Parkinson's diseases, have been made. Huntington's disease is a polyglutamine disorder caused by an expansion of the polyglutamine tract in the huntingtin protein. Parkinson's disease can be caused by mutations in α-synuclein. In both cases, the mutant protein is associated with cellular toxicity. Both proteins aggregate into large inclusions in affected cells; however, whether these aggregates cause the cellular toxicity remains unclear. Work from the Lindquist lab has generated yeast strains expressing either mutant huntingtin or α-synuclein. These strains are being used to characterize the genetic factors leading to the aggregation and/or toxicity of the mutated proteins (Duennwald et al. 2006a,b; Ehrnhoefer et al. 2006; Willingham et al. 2003).

Superoxide dismutases (SODs): protect against oxidative damage by catalyzing the dismutation of superoxide into hydrogen peroxide

multiple fragments has been observed in aging mother cells (Sinclair et al. 1997). This is likely linked to the accumulation of ERCs; high-copy plasmids containing the rDNA locus cause similar fragmentation (Nierras et al. 1997). Fragmentation is unlikely to be required for yeast aging because ARS elements without rDNA repeats can also shorten life span (Sinclair & Guarente 1997). It is unlikely that these plasmids also cause nucleolar fragmentation, though this has not been formally tested.

Recessive mutations in the *WRN* locus, encoding a DNA helicase, cause Werner syndrome in humans (Yu et al. 1996). In this progeroid syndrome, affected individuals prematurely display many but not all of the phenotypes associated with normal aging (Epstein et al. 1966). The molecular basis of this disease remains unresolved, but increased DNA damage or defective repair in the absence of WRN remains a prominent candidate mechanism (Bohr 2005, Kudlow et al. 2007, Ozgenc & Loeb 2005). The yeast DNA helicase most similar to WRN is *SGS1* (Watt et al. 1996). Interestingly, *sgs1Δ* strains are short-lived owing to elevated rDNA recombination leading to ERC formation and elevated, age-independent arrest in mitosis that likely results from defective resolution of recombination intermediates (McVey et al. 2001, Sinclair & Guarente 1997).

ERCs are not the only factor that accumulates in aging mother cells; oxidative damage appears to do the same (Aguilaniu et al. 2003, Laun et al. 2001, Reverter-Branchat et al. 2004), as do protein aggregates (Erjavec et al. 2007). This observation is of particular interest, given the long-standing free-radical theory of aging, which posits that aging is caused by the accumulation of macromolecular damage caused by free radicals (Harman 1956). Whether ROS are a primary determining factor in aging in yeast or any other organism, however, remains to be conclusively established (Muller et al. 2007).

One indication that oxygen radicals may have an important role in yeast replicative aging comes from the observation that deletion of superoxide dismutases (SODs) can shorten life span (Kaeberlein et al. 2005b, Unlu & Koc 2007, Wawryn et al. 1999). Increased exposure to oxygen can also shorten life span (Nestelbacher et al. 2000). However, as discussed above, whether a short life span equates to accelerated aging is difficult to determine (Kaeberlein et al. 2005c).

Overexpressing SODs, in contrast, can confer a small extension of RLS. This extension is mild at best and sometimes results in a shorter life span, depending on the carbon source used for the aging assay (Harris et al. 2003, 2005). These overexpression assays were performed on media containing glycerol as a carbon source. Most life span assays have been performed on media containing 2% glucose. Yeast, being facultative anaerobes, generate energy primarily from fermentation when glucose is available and switch to a primarily respiratory growth state either when glucose is depleted or when they are grown on a nonfermentable carbon source such as glycerol (Gancedo & Serrano 1989). Kirchman & Botta (2007) have argued that yeast aging assays testing the importance of mitochondrial function should be performed on a glycerol medium because this pushes metabolic pathways generating energy into a mode more similar to that of mammalian cells. Under these conditions, copper supplementation is associated with life span extension, possibly through the upregulation of oxygen-radical defense mechanisms.

Mitochondria are one major source of ROS. Inefficient respiration and/or defective mitochondria may be major contributors to the enhanced generation of ROS found in aging organisms. However, the role of mitochondrial function in yeast replicative aging is enigmatic. For instance, yeast lacking mitochondrial DNA have varying RLSs depending on the strain background (Kaeberlein et al. 2005b, Kirchman et al. 1999). Whether life span extension by dietary restriction (DR) also requires enhanced respiration is also highly debated (discussed below) (Easlon et al. 2007, Kaeberlein et al. 2005a, Lin & Guarente 2006, Lin et al. 2002). Two groups have tested the effects of mitochondrial uncouplers on yeast replicative aging (**Figure 4**). Partial uncoupling by CCCP (carbonyl cyanide 3-chlorophenylhydrazone), a widely used uncoupler of oxidative phosphorylation, leads to enhanced ROS and shortened life span (Stockl et al. 2007), whereas dinitrophenol-mediated uncoupling results in reduced ROS and increased life span (Barros et al. 2004).

The end of the road for replicatively aging mother cells may be apoptosis, as initially suggested by findings that old mother cells are often TUNEL and annexin V positive (Laun et al. 2001). Apoptosis seems paradoxical for a single-

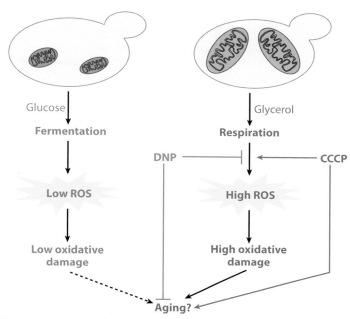

Figure 4

Mitochondria, reactive oxygen species (ROS) production, oxidative damage, and aging. Yeast cells produce energy via different pathways, depending on the carbon source. Pathways that promote aging are diagrammed in red; pathways that do not promote aging are diagrammed in blue. When in the presence of glucose, fermentation results in low levels of ROS production. However, in the presence of glycerol, respiration results in higher levels of ROS production. Elevated levels of ROS may lead to increased oxidative damage, which in turn may promote aging. The effects of two different mitochondrial uncouplers are also diagrammed: Carbonyl cyanide 3-chlorophenylhydrazone (CCCP) leads to increased ROS production and a shortened life span, whereas dinitrophenol (DNP) treatment results in decreased levels of ROS and enhanced life span.

celled organism but is induced under a variety of conditions (Buttner et al. 2006), including both chronological and replicative aging (Fabrizio et al. 2004a, Herker et al. 2004). Under these conditions, it is possible that a subset of cells dies for the benefit of the others, although this has not been formally demonstrated. Replicatively aged cells are likely to be a relatively small fraction of any growing colony of cells, so it is difficult to imagine apoptosis providing a benefit to other young cells. More likely, the cellular defects that accompany aging may tap into an apoptotic program that is beneficial in other settings where similar defects occur.

An early aging study by Müller et al. (1985) noted that aging yeast cells have a reduced

Dietary restriction (DR): the limitation of dietary intake short of nutrient deprivation

mating capacity. This phenotype is now well understood and involves an age-dependent relocalization of the SIR complex (Sir2, -3, and -4) (Kennedy et al. 1997, Smeal et al. 1996). In young cells, this protein complex transcriptionally represses two silent mating-type (*HM*) loci that serve as templates for mating-type switching in homothallic yeast strains (Hicks & Herskowitz 1977, Ivy et al. 1986, Rine & Herskowitz 1987). Unlike *HM* loci, the mating-specific genes at the *MAT* locus are expressed and dictate whether heterothallic haploid yeast strains are *MAT*α or *MAT***a**. In cells that have lost silencing at the *HM* loci, genes for both mating types are expressed, and cells enter a pseudodiploid state accompanied by sterility. Loss of SIR-dependent *HM* silencing occurs during replicative aging (Smeal et al. 1996), in addition to loss of telomere silencing at some chromosome ends (Kennedy et al. 1997, Kim et al. 1996). Expression of the *HM* loci in a haploid throughout the life span (e.g., in *sir3*Δ or *sir4*Δ strains) results in a slight decrease in mean RLS independently of ERCs (Kaeberlein et al. 1999). That expression of *HM* loci limits the life span of wild-type strains seems unlikely, given that increased expression would only occur approximately midway through the life span of a mother cell and that deletion fails to increase life span significantly (Kaeberlein et al. 1999).

Not all things change with aging. For instance, telomere length remains relatively constant throughout replicative aging, seemingly eliminating telomere shortening as a determinant of yeast aging (D'Mello & Jazwinski 1991). Nevertheless, it is clear that many more molecular changes occur and that a subset of these likely contributes to limiting the life span of mother cells.

A handful of attempts have been made to characterize the cellular changes that accompany aging in yeast by the use of microarrays to examine the global gene expression profiles of young and old cells. In one study, microarray analysis was carried out on "young" (0–1-generation-old) or "old" (7–8-generation-old) wild-type cells, which were obtained by magnetic sorting (Lin et al. 2001). From this analysis, it was concluded that gluconeogenesis and glucose storage increase as cells age, suggesting a metabolic shift away from glycolysis and toward gluconeogenesis. In a second study of this type, elutriation was used to obtain an aged population in which 75% of the cells were at least 15 generations old and 90% of the cells were more than 8 generations old (Lesur & Campbell 2004). Microarray analysis of aged cells relative to young cells suggested an increase in expression of enzymes associated with glucose storage and gluconeogenesis, consistent with the previous study (Lin et al. 2001). In addition, certain stress- and damage-responsive genes were also elevated in aged cells (Lesur & Campbell 2004).

Several hurdles associated with this type of approach have limited the utility of microarray studies of yeast aging. First, all these studies have faced the same technical difficulty—how to obtain sufficiently large numbers of relatively pure populations of aging cells (see section, Genetic Modulation of Yeast Replicative Life Span, above). Although enrichment of aged cells is feasible, there is always a detectable percentage of daughter cells present in any "old" population, and the resulting contamination in gene expression profile is hard to gauge. In addition, all the aging-related microarray experiments reported to date have been performed in liquid growth media—an environment quite different from that experienced by cells in the standard RLS assay. Finally, the "aged" populations used in studies published to date have generally been relatively young: between 8 and 15 generations. Because the median life span of most laboratory strains is between 21 and 25 generations, the "old" cells in these studies are not even middle-aged. In one case, an attempt was made to examine the gene expression profile of senescent cells obtained by elutriation (Laun et al. 2005). Approximately 30% of the resulting population were senescent and showed gene expression profiles consistent with cells undergoing an apoptosis-like response (Madeo et al. 1997).

DIETARY RESTRICTION AND YEAST REPLICATIVE AGING

Much of recent research on yeast replicative aging has focused on trying to determine the mechanism by which DR (also called calorie restriction) enhances longevity. The reasons for this obsession are obvious: DR is the only intervention that extends life span in all common model organisms for aging research. The mechanisms proposed to explain the effects of DR in yeast remain highly controversial. In this section, we discuss what is known about DR in yeast, including the generally agreed upon immediate signal transduction pathways downstream of DR and two nonexclusive possible targets of these pathways (**Figure 5**).

Dietary Restriction and Signal Transduction

In yeast, DR is generally invoked by reducing levels of glucose in the media during the life span experiment (Lin et al. 2000). A reduction of amino acid levels has also been reported to extend life span, but this form of DR has not been extensively studied (Jiang et al. 2000). Normal yeast growth media contains 2% glucose. This is well in excess of what is needed for rapid growth and has generally been employed to ensure that yeast reach high densities in liquid media for biochemical experimentation. Different labs favor different levels of glucose reduction for DR experiments, with glucose concentrations ranging from 0.5% to 0.005% (Kaeberlein et al. 2004, Lin et al. 2000). Ideally, a yeast strain should be analyzed at a series of reduced glucose concentrations to determine where the maximum increase in life span can be achieved. In fact, one commonly used strain (W303) may be totally unresponsive to DR, although this is controversial (Kaeberlein et al. 2006, Lamming et al. 2005). For the yeast ORF deletion strain background, maximum life span extension is achieved at 0.05% glucose (Kaeberlein et al. 2004). Although this seems to represent a drastic reduction of glucose levels (40-fold), yeast cells do not

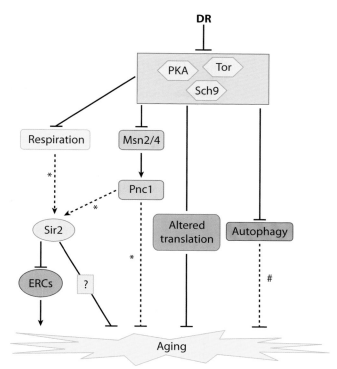

Figure 5

Model for the mechanism of dietary restriction (DR). In this proposed model, DR inhibits the three protein kinases Tor, protein kinase A (PKA), and Sch9. This inhibition results in increased levels of respiration and activation of the stress response proteins Msn2/4. Inhibition of Msn2/4 results in loss of activity of Pnc1, a nicotinamide deaminase. Both events lead to the activation of Sir2, which then affects aging by inhibiting ERC formation and by an unknown pathway. Inhibition of the three kinases may also result in altered translation levels as well as higher levels of autophagy. The cumulative effect of all events is the extension of life span. The asterisks indicate that the relevance of these branches of the pathway is in question among different research groups. The pound sign indicates where a role for autophagy in regulating yeast replicative life span is possible but not formally demonstrated. ERCs, extrachromosomal ribosomal DNA circles.

divide at dramatically lower rates under these conditions as long as glucose levels are held constant, which is the case for individual mother cells growing on solid media in the absense of neighboring cells during life span analysis (in contrast to liquid cultures, in which glucose is rapidly depleted by an increasing number of dividing cells, resulting in a drop in cell division rate upon glucose depletion) (V.L. MacKay, K. Steffen, M. Kaeberlein & B.K. Kennedy, unpublished). The reduction of growth rate that does exist is largely attributable to the slow first cell cycle of daughter cells; they must achieve a certain size before DNA replication ensues and the rate of cell growth is reduced (Hartwell & Unger 1977).

Several genetic mimetics of DR also lead to RLS extension. For instance, deletion of *HXK2*, which encodes the glycolytic enzyme hexokinase II (Hxk2) (Walsh et al. 1983), leads to life span extension (Lin et al. 2000). When glucose is abundant, Hxk2 is the major kinase that converts glucose to glucose-6-phosphate, leading to the entry of glucose into the glycolytic pathway. Two other glucose kinase genes, *HXK1* and *GLK1*, are not expressed at high levels in these conditions; however, they are induced in strains lacking *HXK2*, and it remains unclear to what extent glucose phosphorylation is reduced in this background (Rodriguez et al. 2001, Walsh et al. 1991). Hxk2 also acts in a signaling pathway important for maintaining glucose repression, and this activity may also be linked to longevity control (Ahuatzi et al. 2004).

Mutations leading to reduced activity of partially redundant nutrient-responsive signal transduction pathways [TOR and protein kinase A (PKA)] also lead to RLS extension (Fabrizio et al. 2004b, Kaeberlein et al. 2005c, Lin et al. 2000). The life spans of these mutants are not further extended by reducing the glucose levels in the media, consistent with a model in which these pathways directly mediate the longevity effects of DR. Yeast contain three different PKA catalytic subunits, which together are essential for cell viability. Two sensing pathways upstream of PKA mediate the induction of cAMP in yeast cells exposed to glucose, although the mechanisms by which these sensors are activated are unknown (Santangelo 2006). One sensing pathway leads to RAS activation, and the other is a G protein–coupled receptor system consisting of *GPA2* and *GPR1*. Deletion of either *GPA2* or *GPR1* leads to life span extension, and these mutants are often used to reduce PKA activity in life span experiments (Lin et al. 2000).

TOR signaling is regulated in an unknown fashion by glutamine levels, which in turn are determined by nitrogen availability (Carvalho & Zheng 2003, Crespo et al. 2002). Two TOR proteins, Tor1 and Tor2, exist in two Torc complexes (Dann & Thomas 2006). Torc2 is rapamycin insensitive and dynamically controls the actin cytoskeleton. Tor2 preferentially exists in Torc2 and is essential for viability, whereas Torc1 can contain either Tor1 or Tor2. Reduced TOR signaling, either in a *tor1Δ* strain or in the presence of the Tor inhibitors rapamycin or methionine sulfoximide, leads to life span extension in yeast (Kaeberlein et al. 2005c). DR of the *tor1Δ* mutant does not further increase life span, consistent with TOR signaling acting through a similar pathway as DR. Reduced TOR activity leads to life span extension in worms and flies as well (Jia et al. 2004, Kapahi et al. 2004, Vellai et al. 2003), indicating that links between this pathway and longevity are likely conserved in divergent eukaryotic species (see below).

Sch9 is a third nutrient-responsive kinase linked to yeast RLS. Deletion of *SCH9* leads to robust extension of both mean and maximum life span (Fabrizio et al. 2004b, Kaeberlein et al. 2005c). By sequence homology, *SCH9* is most similar to Akt, a central component in insulin signaling pathways (Burgering & Coffer 1995, Paradis & Ruvkun 1998). A formal insulin signaling pathway does not exist in yeast, however, and recent evidence suggests that Sch9 may be the functional ortholog of S6 kinase (Powers 2007, Urban et al. 2007), a substrate of TOR in multicellular eukaryotes and a central regulator of translation (Hay & Sonenberg 2004, Jorgensen et al. 2004). Whether yeast Sch9 plays roles carried out by both Akt and S6 kinase in multicellular eukaryotes remains to be determined. Interestingly, deletion of either Akt homologs or S6 kinase is sufficient to increase life span in worms (Hansen et al. 2007, Pan et al. 2007, Paradis & Ruvkun 1998).

There is general agreement that PKA, TOR, and Sch9 are responsive to nutrient deprivation, modulate longevity in evolutionarily divergent organisms, and mediate at least some of the health and longevity benefits associated with DR (Kennedy et al. 2007). An important unresolved question, however, is which downstream targets of these kinases are most important for the regulation of life span in yeast and other organisms. This question is not easily answered because these kinases have overlapping roles in regulating a number of cellular responses to nutrient exposure. In nutrient-replete conditions, high activity of these kinases drives ribosome biogenesis and cell growth while limiting stress response pathways and autophagy. As nutrients levels become limiting, reduced activity of these kinases leads to a reversal of these phenotypes, with emphasis placed on stress response pathways, including free-radical-scavenging enzymes and autophagy. Any of these cellular events could modulate longevity.

Two nonexclusive models have been proposed for how reduced TOR signaling could increase RLS in response to DR: activation of sirtuins and altered translational regulation (Kaeberlein et al. 2005c, Medvedik et al. 2007, Steffen et al. 2008). Both of these pathways are linked to longevity regulation in worms and flies, and therefore they may represent conserved pathways mediating DR. In the following subsections, we examine the evidence for and against both models, noting in advance that all evidence is not yet in and that further clarifying experiments are in high demand.

Sirtuins

In addition to Sir2, yeast have four other related class III deacetylases, Hst1–4. The distinguishing feature of class III deacetylases is their substrate requirement for NAD, which is metabolized during the deacetylation reaction to nicotinamide and O-acetyl-ADP-ribose (Imai et al. 2000, Landry et al. 2000, Smith et al. 2000). Recent reviews discuss the complex mechanisms by which this reaction occurs. Some Hsts have overlapping roles with Sir2 that both have and have not been reported to be relevant for RLS, and we discuss these Hsts in that context. The primary substrate of Sir2 in yeast appears to be acetyl-lysine residues in the N-terminal tails of histones H3 and H4 (Imai et al. 2000, Tanny & Moazed 2001, Xu et al. 2007), although the targets of Sir2 orthologs in worms, flies, and mammals are largely reported to be other transcription factors.

Sir2, when in complex with Sir3 and Sir4, is required for the establishment of silenced regions of chromatin in regions near telomeres and silent mating-type loci (Aparicio et al. 1991, Rine & Herskowitz 1987), and its deacetylase activity is required for silencing (Rusche et al. 2003). In addition, Sir2 can function independently of Sir3 and Sir4; it both silences PolII genes experimentally inserted in rDNA and suppresses rDNA recombination, thus inhibiting the formation of ERCs (Bryk et al. 1997, Defossez et al. 1999, Gottlieb & Esposito 1989, Smith & Boeke 1997). The Sir2/3/4 complex also localizes to rDNA in replicatively aged cells, reflective of a potential role for the complex at this locus as well (Kennedy et al. 1997). One possible mechanism for the effect of Sir2 on replicative aging is its repression of rDNA recombination (Sinclair & Guarente 1997); evidence for this comes from multiple experimental approaches, including the aforementioned decreased longevity that results from the generation of ERCs in young cells. Additional support for this model comes from analysis of $fob1\Delta$ strains. Fob1 is a replication fork barrier protein with activity specific for rDNA repeats, which leads to elevated recombination at that locus. Mutants lacking Fob1 have reduced rDNA recombination and thus low ERC levels; moreover, they are long-lived (Defossez et al. 1999). Fob1 also participates in a protein complex that recruits Sir2 to rDNA loci (Huang & Moazed 2003), raising the possibility that one effect of $fob1\Delta$ on longevity is caused by the relocalization of Sir2 to other loci. However, this has not been formally demonstrated.

There are likely other aging-specific functions of Sir2 that remain to be discovered. For example, $fob1\Delta$ mutants and $fob1\Delta$ $sir2\Delta$ double mutants behave differently for life span and ERC levels (Kaeberlein et al. 1999). The $sir2\Delta$ strain is short-lived and has elevated ERC levels, whereas the *fob1Δ* strain is long-lived and has reduced ERC levels. Loss of *FOB1* is epistatic to *SIR2* for rDNA recombination because the *fob1Δ* and *fob1Δ sir2Δ* strains both have very low ERC levels. However, the life span of the *fob1Δ sir2Δ* strain is shorter than that of the *fob1Δ* strain, a finding incongruous with ERC production being the sole downstream effect of Sir2 activity relevant to aging. One interpretation of this is that Sir2 has a second function important for mediating longevity that is not compensated for by loss of *FOB1*.

Sequestration of oxidized and aggregated proteins to mother cells may also relate to the life span functions of Sir2. However, the mechanism(s) by which Sir2 performs this function remains unknown. Moreover, this function may have contrasting effects on life span. With Sir2 allowing for the retention of damaged proteins in mother cells, the daughter cells are young and have full life span potential. However, this may simultaneously cause mother cells to accumulate damage more rapidly with age. The process is linked to RLS by the recent striking finding that overexpression of *HSP104*, a stress tolerance factor that acts along with chaperones on aggregated proteins, suppresses the short life span of *sir2Δ* (Erjavec et al. 2007). Increased Hsp104 activity also partially restores asymmetric distribution of damaged and aggregated proteins to mother cells in the *sir2Δ* mutant. This finding suggests that *sir2Δ* strains are not short-lived solely because of ERC accumulation, but possibly also because of missegregation of damaged proteins to daughters. An alternate possibility, that increased Hsp104 levels mitigate ERC toxicity, has not been examined.

Opinions over the importance of Sir2 and other sirtuins in the DR from many of the protagonists (including M.K. and B.K.K.) are already abundant in the literature, and the reader is referred to several papers (Chen & Guarente 2007, Kennedy et al. 2005, Longo & Kennedy 2006, Sinclair 2005). The goal in this section is to address the strengths and weaknesses of this model, with particular attention to recent findings. One issue still not fully resolved is whether DR enhances the activation of Sir2 in yeast.

Paradoxically, this is more clearly established in mice, for which several groups have reported that DR activates the *SIR2* ortholog, Sirt1 (Cohen et al. 2004, Nemoto et al. 2004, Picard et al. 2004). Whether Sirt1 is required for life span extension by DR in mice remains to be determined, a question complicated by the severe phenotype of *Sirt1*$^{-/-}$ mice. In yeast, however, DR enhances rDNA silencing in a Sir2-dependent manner and lowers rates of rDNA recombination (Lamming et al. 2005), although we have not observed any effect on telomere silencing (Kaeberlein et al. 2005a).

The mechanism by which DR may activate Sir2 in yeast is also a matter of debate. Two nonexclusive models are possible. First, DR in yeast may lead to enhanced respiration, which may increase NAD levels and lead to Sir2 activation (Lin et al. 2002). Consistent with this model, overexpression of *HAP4* leads to increased transcription of respiratory genes and extends RLS (Lin et al. 2004). However, we have found that DR extends life span in respiratory-deficient Rho0 strains, which lack mitochondrial DNA (Kaeberlein et al. 2005a). A recent study from Lin and colleagues has carefully studied respiration and replicative aging, finding that deletion of *LAT1*, a component of mitochondrial pyruvate dehydrogenase, blocks life span extension by DR and that overexpression of this gene extends life span (Easlon et al. 2007). Interestingly, life span extension by *LAT1* overexpression is independent of yeast sirtuins.

A second model by which DR may activate Sir2 is through increased Msn2/4-dependent transcription of *PNC1*, which encodes an enzyme that deaminates nicotinamide, a product of sirtuin catalysis that, if not catabolized, inhibits sirtuins. Deletion of *PNC1* either blocks (Anderson et al. 2003) or partially blocks life span extension by DR (Lin et al. 2004); furthermore, overexpression of *PNC1* extends life span (Anderson et al. 2003). Although we have found no evidence that sirtuins mediate life span extension by DR, our studies indicate that increased nicotinamide can block much of the life span extension by DR without inhibiting sirtuin activity, indicating that this metabolite may have other, undefined roles in the regulation of RLS (Tsuchiya et al. 2006). Msn2 and -4 are maintained in the cytoplasm during optimal growth conditions but translocate to the nucleus when either glucose levels or Tor signaling are reduced (Beck & Hall 1999, Gorner et al. 1998, Mayordomo et al. 2002). A recent study indicates that the life span extension conferred by rapamycin requires nuclear localization of Msn2/4 and increased transcription of *PNC1* (Medvedik et al. 2007). However, life span extension in the *tor1Δ* strain is independent of *SIR2* (Kaeberlein et al. 2005c). Whether Hst2 can also compensate for loss of *SIR2* under these conditions remains to be determined (see below).

It is agreed that genetic mimetics of DR do not extend life span in a *sir2Δ* strain (Kaeberlein et al. 2004, Lin et al. 2000) and that DR does extend life span in the *sir2Δ fob1Δ* strains (Kaeberlein et al. 2004, Lamming et al. 2005). These findings have led to two different interpretations, which hinge on an experiment in which different labs have reached discordant results. It has been suggested that DR works in the *sir2Δ fob1Δ* strain because other sirtuins (primarily Hst2) become activated by DR and inhibit rDNA recombination (Lamming et al. 2005, 2006). This finding has not been successfully repeated (Kaeberlein et al. 2004, Tsuchiya et al. 2006). Why Hst2 is apparently unable to compensate for the loss of *SIR2* in strains with functional Fob1 has also not been experimentally addressed.

In summary, the model proposed by Sinclair and colleagues (Sinclair 2005) posits that life span extension by DR results mainly from reduced rDNA recombination and ERC generation through the activation of sirtuins. One weakness of this model is that ERC-dependent aging appears to be specific to yeast. Thus, conserved longevity regulators (DR and/or increased *SIR2* expression) regulate yeast aging through a nonconserved mechanism. One possible resolution of this puzzle is the proposal that mammalian sirtuins extend life span through chromatin regulation, reducing DNA damage at other, more vulnerable sites in the mammalian genome. This would be consistent with the model discussed above.

On the basis of our data (Kaeberlein et al. 2004, 2006; Tsuchiya et al. 2006), we favor a model in which life span extension by increased *SIR2* expression is through a non-DR pathway. In this model, there are at least two pathways that enhance replicative aging in wild-type yeast. DR would fail to extend the short-lived *sir2Δ* because ERC levels are elevated; thus, all mother cells would die at an early age through an ERC-dependent mechanism. In the *sir2Δ fob1Δ* double mutant, however, ERC levels are low, and DR confers robust life span extension through the second pathway, which is more prominent when the influence of ERCs is muted. Data from our nonbiased genome screen have led us to favor a model whereby life span extension by DR is conferred through mechanisms leading to altered translational regulation in reduced nutrient environments.

Translational Regulation and Dietary Restriction

In addition to several deletions that are predicted to result in reduced TOR signaling, screening of the ORF deletion collection identified two *rplΔ* strains (*rpl31aΔ* and *rpl6bΔ*) as long-lived (Kaeberlein et al. 2005c). Mutations of four other *RP* genes (three in haploid cells, one in heterozygous diploid cells) have since been reported to have enhanced longevity (Chiocchetti et al. 2007), although not every *RP* deletion has this effect (Kaeberlein et al. 2005c). Although most ribosomal subunits are required for viability, yeast differs from other eukaryotes in that its ribosomal protein genes have been duplicated. This means that yeast strains lacking a gene encoding a ribosomal subunit are generally viable owing to the presence of the duplicated highly similar gene. This permits replicative analysis of most *rpΔ* strains, which result in reduction but not elimination of their respective subunit. Recently, we have reported the existence of 14 more *rpΔ*s that confer long life span, and surprisingly all the genes identified encode components of the ribosomal large subunit (Steffen et al. 2008). This specificity occurs at least in part because reduced 60S (and not 40S) subunit biogenesis leads paradoxically to enhanced translation of *GCN4* (Foiani et al. 1991, Steffen et al. 2008), a transcription factor induced in nutrient-deprived conditions (Yang et al. 2000). The transcriptional targets of Gcn4 that are important for longevity remain to be identified.

There is a well-established connection between the protein kinase Tor and ribosome biogenesis; decreased Tor signaling results in decreased levels of ribosomes (Jorgensen et al. 2004, Powers et al. 2004). Thus, altered translation may lie directly downstream of TOR and DR in longevity modulation.

Interestingly, this effect of loss of ribosomal proteins on life span does not seem to be restricted to yeast. RNAi screens for longevity genes in *C. elegans* have revealed both *rpl* and *rps* genes to be long-lived as well (Chen & Contreras 2007, Curran & Ruvkun 2007, Hansen et al. 2007, Pan et al. 2007). Unlike yeast, worm *RP* genes are not duplicated, and RNAi initiated in the embryo results in developmental lethality. Accordingly, in these screens, worms were not exposed to the RNAi bacteria until early adulthood. As such, it is not clear as to how much expression of the *RP* genes is knocked down, or why reduced expression of worm *rp* genes in adulthood allows for enhanced longevity. However, these results do suggest that life span extension by reduced ribosome biogenesis or function may be conserved in the eukaryotic lineage.

The mechanism for the effect of translation on extended life span is not yet known. One possibility is that reduced translation rates result in decreased accumulation of damaged proteins. Altered protein homeostasis may be one causal factor in aging and age-related disease, a theory supported by the finding that aggregated proteins accumulate aging yeast cells and in several mammalian neurodegenerative disorders. Reducing ribosomal protein expression in worms and yeast leads to decreased levels of translation, which may reduce the rate of accumulation of damaged proteins. This may allow better degradation or repair of existing damage with age. Alternatively (or in addition), we have recently shown that *rpl*Δ strains may lead to changes in the translation of specific messages linked to life span modulation. Whether this latter mechanism is conserved is unknown. Future research will be necessary to determine why reduced ribosome biogenesis can equate to long life.

CONCLUSIONS

Aging is not thought to be a programmed event but, rather, the inevitable consequence of an age-dependent decline in the forces of selection (Austad 2004, Kirkwood 2005). If this is the case, why should longevity pathways be conserved among disparate eukaryotic species with dramatically different reproductive strategies, life histories, and life spans? Now that genome-wide genetic approaches to longevity are feasible in more than one aging model organism, it has become possible to determine the levels of conservation that exist and to identify the specific genes and pathways with conserved effects. We have recently performed a genome-wide comparison between the genetic determinants of longevity in yeast and worms, finding that yeast orthologs of known worm aging genes are significantly more likely to modulate yeast aging than are genes chosen at random (Smith et al. 2008). In addition, these studies indicate that translational regulatory pathways are highly conserved for their effects on life span. It is our view that these pathways should be given specific attention in invertebrate studies because they have a higher likelihood of teaching us about processes that affect human life span and that the mammalian orthologs of conserved worm-yeast ortholog pairs may be of particular interest with regard to aging.

The state of yeast aging research is strong. In the past 15 years, the number of researchers in the field has grown exponentially, leading to unexpected discoveries and exciting new avenues of research. Although there is substantial controversy regarding key questions that need to be resolved, this is more a reflection of rapid progress than a cause for serious concern. Despite the identification in yeast and other organisms of numerous genetic modulators of aging and several molecular phenotypes accompanying aging, the key question remains unanswered: What are the fundamental causes of aging? Given the rate of recent progress, it does not seem overly optimistic to forecast that the puzzle pieces will fit together at some point in the near future. With this knowledge, opportunities to intervene pharmacologically in the aging process as a therapeutic avenue to age-related diseases will increase dramatically.

DISCLOSURE STATEMENT

The authors are not aware of any biases that might be perceived as affecting the objectivity of this review.

ACKNOWLEDGMENTS

Although we have tried to represent the ever-increasing sphere of investigation into yeast replicative aging, we apologize in advance that particular studies were not cited owing to space limitations. K.A.S. is funded by a postdoctoral fellowship from the Hereditary Disease Foundation. Aging research in the Kennedy and Kaeberlein labs is funded by a grant from the Ellison Medical Foundation, by an AFAR grant to M.K., and by an NIH grant to B.K.K.

LITERATURE CITED

Aguilaniu H, Gustafsson L, Rigoulet M, Nystrom T. 2003. Asymmetric inheritance of oxidatively damaged proteins during cytokinesis. *Science* 299:1751–53

Ahuatzi D, Herrero P, De la Cera T, Moreno F. 2004. The glucose-regulated nuclear localization of hexokinase 2 in *Saccharomyces cerevisiae* is Mig1-dependent. *J. Biol. Chem.* 279:14440–46

Anderson RM, Bitterman KJ, Wood JG, Medvedik O, Sinclair DA. 2003. Nicotinamide and *PNC1* govern lifespan extension by caloric restriction in *Saccharomyces cerevisiae*. *Nature* 423:181–85

Aparicio OM, Billington BL, Gottschling DE. 1991. Modifiers of position effect are shared between telomeric and silent mating-type loci in *S. cerevisiae*. *Cell* 66:1279–87

Ashrafi K, Sinclair D, Gordon JI, Guarente L. 1999. Passage through stationary phase advances replicative aging in *Saccharomyces cerevisiae*. *Proc. Natl. Acad. Sci. USA* 96:9100–5

Austad SN. 2004. Is aging programmed? *Aging Cell* 3:249–51

Austriaco NR Jr. 1996. *UTH1 and the genetic control of aging in the yeast*, Saccharomyces cerevisiae. PhD thesis. Mass. Inst. Technol., Cambridge, MA

Austriaco NR Jr, Guarente LP. 1997. Changes of telomere length cause reciprocal changes in the lifespan of mother cells in *Saccharomyces cerevisiae*. *Proc. Natl. Acad. Sci. USA* 94:9768–72

Bacon JS, Davidson ED, Jones D, Taylor IF. 1966. The location of chitin in the yeast cell wall. *Biochem. J.* 101:36C–38C

Bandara PD, Flattery-O'Brien JA, Grant CM, Dawes IW. 1998. Involvement of the *Saccharomyces cerevisiae* *UTH1* gene in the oxidative-stress response. *Curr. Genet.* 34:259–68

Barros MH, Bandy B, Tahara EB, Kowaltowski AJ. 2004. Higher respiratory activity decreases mitochondrial reactive oxygen release and increases life span in *Saccharomyces cerevisiae*. *J. Biol. Chem.* 279:49883–88

Bartke A. 2005. Minireview: role of the growth hormone/insulin-like growth factor system in mammalian aging. *Endocrinology* 146:3718–23

Barton AA. 1950. Some aspects of cell division in *Saccharomyces cerevisiae*. *J. Gen. Microbiol.* 4:84–86

Beck T, Hall MN. 1999. The TOR signalling pathway controls nuclear localization of nutrient-regulated transcription factors. *Nature* 402:689–92

Protein carbonyls and other oxidatively damaged proteins accumulate preferentially in mother cells in an actin-dependent manner.

Bohr VA. 2005. Deficient DNA repair in the human progeroid disorder, Werner syndrome. *Mutat. Res.* 577:252–59

Brachmann CB, Davies A, Cost GJ, Caputo E, Li J, et al. 1998. Designer deletion strains derived from *Saccharomyces cerevisiae* S288C: a useful set of strains and plasmids for PCR-mediated gene disruption and other applications. *Yeast* 14:115–32

Bryk M, Banerjee M, Murphy M, Knudsen KE, Garfinkel DJ, Curcio MJ. 1997. Transcriptional silencing of Ty1 elements in the *RDN1* locus of yeast. *Genes Dev.* 11:255–69

Burgering BM, Coffer PJ. 1995. Protein kinase B (c-Akt) in phosphatidylinositol-3-OH kinase signal transduction. *Nature* 376:599–602

Buttner S, Eisenberg T, Herker E, Carmona-Gutierrez D, Kroemer G, Madeo F. 2006. Why yeast cells can undergo apoptosis: death in times of peace, love, and war. *J. Cell Biol.* 175:521–25

Camougrand N, Grelaud-Coq A, Marza E, Priault M, Bessoule JJ, Manon S. 2003. The product of the UTH1 gene, required for Bax-induced cell death in yeast, is involved in the response to rapamycin. *Mol. Microbiol.* 47:495–506

Camougrand N, Kiššova I, Velours G, Manon S. 2004. Uth1p: a yeast mitochondrial protein at the crossroads of stress, degradation and cell death. *FEMS Yeast Res.* 5:133–40

Campisi J, d'Adda di Fagagna F. 2007. Cellular senescence: when bad things happen to good cells. *Nat. Rev. Mol. Cell Biol.* 8:729–40

Carvalho J, Zheng XF. 2003. Domains of Gln3p interacting with karyopherins, Ure2p, and the target of rapamycin protein. *J. Biol. Chem.* 278:16878–86

Chen C, Contreras R. 2007. Identifying genes that extend life span using a high-throughput screening system. *Methods Mol. Biol.* 371:237–48

Chen D, Guarente L. 2007. SIR2: a potential target for calorie restriction mimetics. *Trends Mol. Med.* 13:64–71

Chen JB, Sun J, Jazwinski SM. 1990. Prolongation of the yeast life span by the v-Ha-*RAS* oncogene. *Mol. Microbiol.* 4:2081–86

Chiocchetti A, Zhou J, Zhu H, Karl T, Haubenreisser O, et al. 2007. Ribosomal proteins Rpl10 and Rps6 are potent regulators of yeast replicative life span. *Exp. Gerontol.* 42:275–86

Cohen HY, Miller C, Bitterman KJ, Wall NR, Hekking B, et al. 2004. Calorie restriction promotes mammalian cell survival by inducing the SIRT1 deacetylase. *Science* 305:390–92

Crespo JL, Powers T, Fowler B, Hall MN. 2002. The TOR-controlled transcription activators GLN3, RTG1 and RTG3 are regulated in response to cellular levels of glutamine. *Proc. Natl. Acad. Sci. USA* 99:6784–89

Curran SP, Ruvkun G. 2007. Lifespan regulation by evolutionarily conserved genes essential for viability. *PLoS Genet.* 3:e56

D'Mello NP, Childress AM, Franklin DS, Kale SP, Pinswasdi C, Jazwinski SM. 1994. Cloning and characterization of LAG1, a longevity-assurance gene in yeast. *J. Biol. Chem.* 269:15451–59

D'Mello NP, Jazwinski SM. 1991. Telomere length constancy during aging of *Saccharomyces cerevisiae*. *J. Bacteriol.* 173:6709–13

Dann SG, Thomas G. 2006. The amino acid sensitive TOR pathway from yeast to mammals. *FEBS Lett.* 580:2821–29

Defossez PA, Prusty R, Kaeberlein M, Lin SJ, Ferrigno P, et al. 1999. Elimination of replication block protein Fob1 extends the life span of yeast mother cells. *Mol. Cell* 3:447–55

Dickson RC, Sumanasekera C, Lester RL. 2006. Functions and metabolism of sphingolipids in *Saccharomyces cerevisiae*. *Prog. Lipid Res.* 45:447–65

Duennwald ML, Jagadish S, Giorgini F, Muchowski PJ, Lindquist S. 2006a. A network of protein interactions determines polyglutamine toxicity. *Proc. Natl. Acad. Sci. USA* 103:11051–56

Duennwald ML, Jagadish S, Muchowski PJ, Lindquist S. 2006b. Flanking sequences profoundly alter polyglutamine toxicity in yeast. *Proc. Natl. Acad. Sci. USA* 103:11045–50

Easlon E, Tsang F, Dilova I, Wang C, Lu SP, et al. 2007. The dihydrolipoamide acetyltransferase is a novel metabolic longevity factor and is required for calorie restriction-mediated life span extension. *J. Biol. Chem.* 282:6161–71

Egilmez NK, Chen JB, Jazwinski SM. 1989. Specific alterations in transcript prevalence during the yeast life span. *J. Biol. Chem.* 264:14312–17

The first demonstration that genetic modification of yeast can alter its life span.

Egilmez NK, Jazwinski SM. 1989. Evidence for the involvement of a cytoplasmic factor in the aging of the yeast *Saccharomyces cerevisiae*. *J. Bacteriol.* 171:37–42

Ehrnhoefer DE, Duennwald M, Markovic P, Wacker JL, Engemann S, et al. 2006. Green tea (-)-epigallocatechin-gallate modulates early events in huntingtin misfolding and reduces toxicity in Huntington's disease models. *Hum. Mol. Genet.* 15:2743–51

Epstein CJ, Martin GM, Schultz AL, Motulsky AG. 1966. Werner's syndrome: a review of its symptomatology, natural history, pathologic features, genetics and relationship to the natural aging process. *Medicine* 45:177–222

Erjavec N, Larsson L, Grantham J, Nystrom T. 2007. Accelerated aging and failure to segregate damaged proteins in Sir2 mutants can be suppressed by overproducing the protein aggregation-remodeling factor Hsp104p. *Genes Dev.* 21:2410–21

Erjavec N, Nystrom T. 2007. Sir2p-dependent protein segregation gives rise to a superior reactive oxygen species management in the progeny of *Saccharomyces cerevisiae*. *Proc. Natl. Acad. Sci. USA* 104:10877–81

Fabrizio P, Battistella L, Vardavas R, Gattazzo C, Liou LL, et al. 2004a. Superoxide is a mediator of an altruistic aging program in *Saccharomyces cerevisiae*. *J. Cell Biol.* 166:1055–67

Fabrizio P, Longo VD. 2003. The chronological life span of *Saccharomyces cerevisiae*. *Aging Cell* 2:73–81

Fabrizio P, Pletcher SD, Minois N, Vaupel JW, Longo VD. 2004b. Chronological aging-independent replicative life span regulation by Msn2/Msn4 and Sod2 in *Saccharomyces cerevisiae*. *FEBS Lett.* 557:136–42

Foiani M, Cigan AM, Paddon CJ, Harashima S, Hinnebusch AG. 1991. GCD2, a translational repressor of the *GCN4* gene, has a general function in the initiation of protein synthesis in *Saccharomyces cerevisiae*. *Mol. Cell. Biol.* 11:3203–16

Gami MS, Wolkow CA. 2006. Studies of *Caenorhabditis elegans* DAF-2/insulin signaling reveal targets for pharmacological manipulation of lifespan. *Aging Cell* 5:31–37

Gancedo C, Serrano R. 1989. Energy-yielding metabolism. In *The Yeasts: Metabolism and Physiology of Yeasts*, ed. AH Rose, JS Harrison, pp. 205–59. London: Academic

Gillespie CS, Proctor CJ, Boys RJ, Shanley DP, Wilkinson DJ, Kirkwood TBL. 2004. A mathematical model of ageing in yeast. *J. Theor. Biol.* 229:189–96

Goldstrohm AC, Hook BA, Seay DJ, Wickens M. 2006. PUF proteins bind Pop2p to regulate messenger RNAs. *Nat. Struct. Mol. Biol.* 13:533–39

Goldstrohm AC, Seay DJ, Hook BA, Wickens M. 2007. PUF protein-mediated deadenylation is catalyzed by Ccr4p. *J. Biol. Chem.* 282:109–14

Gorner W, Durchschlag E, Martinez-Pastor MT, Estruch F, Ammerer G, et al. 1998. Nuclear localization of the C2H2 zinc finger protein Msn2p is regulated by stress and protein kinase A activity. *Genes Dev.* 12:586–97

Gottlieb S, Esposito RE. 1989. A new role for a yeast transcriptional silencer gene, *SIR2*, in regulation of recombination in ribosomal DNA. *Cell* 56:771–76

Gourlay CW, Carpp LN, Timpson P, Winder SJ, Ayscough KR. 2004. A role for the actin cytoskeleton in cell death and aging in yeast. *J. Cell Biol.* 164:803–9

Guillas I, Kirchman PA, Chuard R, Pfefferli M, Jiang JC, et al. 2001. C26-CoA-dependent ceramide synthesis of *Saccharomyces cerevisiae* is operated by Lag1p and Lac1p. *EMBO J.* 20:2655–65

Hamilton B, Dong Y, Shindo M, Liu W, Odell I, et al. 2005. A systematic RNAi screen for longevity genes in *C. elegans*. *Genes Dev.* 19:1544–55

Hansen M, Hsu AL, Dillin A, Kenyon C. 2005. New genes tied to endocrine, metabolic, and dietary regulation of lifespan from a *Caenorhabditis elegans* genomic RNAi screen. *PLoS Genet.* 1:119–28

Hansen M, Taubert S, Crawford D, Libina N, Lee SJ, Kenyon C. 2007. Lifespan extension by conditions that inhibit translation in *Caenorhabditis elegans*. *Aging Cell* 6:95–110

Harman D. 1956. Aging: a theory based on free radical and radiation chemistry. *J. Gerontol.* 11:298–300

Harris N, Bachler M, Costa V, Mollapour M, Moradas-Ferreira P, Piper PW. 2005. Overexpressed Sod1p acts either to reduce or to increase the lifespans and stress resistance of yeast, depending on whether it is Cu^{2+}-deficient or an active Cu,Zn-superoxide dismutase. *Aging Cell* 4:41–52

Harris N, Costa V, MacLean M, Mollapour M, Moradas-Ferreira P, Piper PW. 2003. Mnsod overexpression extends the yeast chronological (G_0) life span but acts independently of Sir2p histone deacetylase to shorten the replicative life span of dividing cells. *Free Radic. Biol. Med.* 34:1599–606

Accelerated aging of *sir2* mutants is suppressed by overexpressing Hsp104, indicating that Sir2's aging function may not be restricted to extrachromosomal rDNA circles.

Hartwell LH, Unger MW. 1977. Unequal division in *Saccharomyces cerevisiae* and its implications for the control of cell division. *J. Cell Biol.* 75:422–35

Hay N, Sonenberg N. 2004. Upstream and downstream of mTOR. *Genes Dev* 18:1926–45

Hayflick L. 1965. The limited in vitro lifetime of human diploid cell strains. *Exp. Cell Res.* 37:614–36

Helfand SL, Rogina B. 2003. Genetics of aging in the fruit fly, *Drosophila melanogaster*. *Annu. Rev. Genet.* 37:329–48

Herker E, Jungwirth H, Lehmann KA, Maldener C, Frohlich KU, et al. 2004. Chronological aging leads to apoptosis in yeast. *J. Cell Biol.* 164:501–7

Hicks JB, Herskowitz I. 1977. Interconversion of yeast mating types. II. Restoration of mating ability to sterile mutants in homothallic and heterothallic strains. *Genetics* 85:373–93

Hirsch HR. 1993. Accumulation of a senescence factor in yeast cells. *Exp. Gerontol.* 28:195–204

Hook BA, Goldstrohm AC, Seay DJ, Wickens M. 2007. Two yeast PUF proteins negatively regulate a single mRNA. *J. Biol. Chem.* 282:15430–38

Houthoofd K, Vanfleteren JR. 2007. Public and private mechanisms of life extension in *Caenorhabditis elegans*. *Mol. Genet. Genomics* 277:601–17

Huang J, Moazed D. 2003. Association of the RENT complex with nontranscribed and coding regions of rDNA and a regional requirement for the replication fork block protein Fob1 in rDNA silencing. *Genes Dev.* 17:2162–76

Imai S, Armstrong CM, Kaeberlein M, Guarente L. 2000. Transcriptional silencing and longevity protein Sir2 is an NAD-dependent histone deacetylase. *Nature* 403:795–800

Ivy JM, Klar AJ, Hicks JB. 1986. Cloning and characterization of four SIR genes of *Saccharomyces cerevisiae*. *Mol. Cell Biol.* 6:688–702

Jarolim S, Millen J, Heeren G, Laun P, Goldfarb DS, Breitenbach M. 2004. A novel assay for replicative lifespan in *Saccharomyces cerevisiae*. *FEMS Yeast Res.* 5:169–77

Jazwinski SM. 2005. Yeast longevity and aging: the mitochondrial connection. *Mech. Ageing Dev.* 126:243–48

Jazwinski SM, Egilmez NK, Chen JB. 1989. Replication control and cellular life span. *Exp. Gerontol.* 24:423–36

Jazwinski SM, Wawryn J. 2001. Profiles of random change during aging contain hidden information about longevity and the aging process. *J. Theor. Biol.* 213:599–608

Jia K, Chen D, Riddle DL. 2004. The TOR pathway interacts with the insulin signaling pathway to regulate *C. elegans* larval development, metabolism and life span. *Development* 131:3897–906

Jiang JC, Jaruga E, Repnevskaya MV, Jazwinski SM. 2000. An intervention resembling caloric restriction prolongs life span and retards aging in yeast. *FASEB J.* 14:2135–37

Jiang JC, Kirchman PA, Zagulski M, Hunt J, Jazwinski SM. 1998. Homologs of the yeast longevity gene LAG1 in *Caenorhabditis elegans* and human. *Genome. Res.* 8:1259–72

Johnston JR. 1966. Reproductive capacity and mode of death of yeast cells. *Antonie van Leeuwenhoek* 32:94–98

Jorgensen P, Rupes I, Sharom JR, Schneper L, Broach JR, Tyers M. 2004. A dynamic transcriptional network communicates growth potential to ribosome synthesis and critical cell size. *Genes Dev.* 18:2491–505

Kaeberlein M, Burtner CR, Kennedy BK. 2007. Recent developments in yeast aging. *PLoS Genet.* 3:655–60

Kaeberlein M, Guarente L. 2002. *Saccharomyces cerevisiae* MPT5 and SSD1 function in parallel pathways to promote cell wall integrity. *Genetics* 160:83–95

Kaeberlein M, Hu D, Kerr EO, Tsuchiya M, Westman EA, et al. 2005a. Increased life span due to calorie restriction in respiratory deficient yeast. *PLoS Genet.* 1:614–21

Kaeberlein M, Kirkland KT, Fields S, Kennedy BK. 2004. Sir2-independent life span extension by calorie restriction in yeast. *PLoS Biol.* 2:1381–87

Kaeberlein M, Kirkland KT, Fields S, Kennedy BK. 2005b. Genes determining yeast replicative life span in a long-lived genetic background. *Mech. Ageing Dev.* 126:491–504

Kaeberlein M, McVey M, Guarente L. 1999. The *SIR2/3/4* complex and *SIR2* alone promote longevity in *Saccharomyces cerevisiae* by two different mechanisms. *Genes Dev.* 13:2570–80

Kaeberlein M, Powers RW III, Steffen KK, Westman EA, Hu D, et al. 2005c. Regulation of yeast replicative life-span by TOR and Sch9 in response to nutrients. *Science* 310:1193–96

Kaeberlein M, Steffen KK, Hu D, Dang N, Kerr EO, et al. 2006. Comment on "*HST2* mediates *SIR2*-independent life-span extension by calorie restriction". *Science* 312:1312b

Dietary restriction does not extend the life span of yeast *sir2*Δ single mutants, although it does extend the life span of *sir2*Δ *fob1*Δ double mutants.

The only reported unbiased screen for mutants that extend replicative life span; 13 of 564 gene deletions resulted in extended life span, including a strain lacking *TOR1*.

Kapahi P, Zid BM, Harper T, Koslover D, Sapin V, Benzer S. 2004. Regulation of lifespan in *Drosophila* by modulation of genes in the TOR signaling pathway. *Curr. Biol.* 14:885–90

Kennedy BK, Austriaco NR Jr, Guarente L. 1994. Daughter cells of *Saccharomyces cerevisiae* from old mothers display a reduced life span. *J. Cell Biol.* 127:1985–93

Kennedy BK, Austriaco NR, Zhang J, Guarente L. 1995. Mutation in the silencing gene SIR4 can delay aging in *S. cerevisiae*. *Cell* 80:485–96

Kennedy BK, Gotta M, Sinclair DA, Mills K, McNabb DS, et al. 1997. Redistribution of silencing proteins from telomeres to the nucleolus is associated with extension of life span in *S. cerevisiae*. *Cell* 89:381–91

Kennedy BK, Smith ED, Kaeberlein M. 2005. The enigmatic role of Sir2 in aging. *Cell* 123:548–50

Kennedy BK, Steffen KK, Kaeberlein M. 2007. Ruminations on dietary restriction and aging. *Cell Mol. Life Sci.* 64:1323–28

Kim S, Villeponteau B, Jazwinski SM. 1996. Effect of replicative age on transcriptional silencing near telomeres in *Saccharomyces cerevisiae*. *Biochem. Biophys. Res. Commun.* 219:370–76

Kirchman PA, Botta G. 2007. Copper supplementation increases yeast life span under conditions requiring respiratory metabolism. *Mech. Ageing Dev.* 128:187–95

Kirchman PA, Kim S, Lai CY, Jazwinski SM. 1999. Interorganelle signaling is a determinant of longevity in *Saccharomyces cerevisiae*. *Genetics* 152:179–90

Kirkwood TB. 2005. Understanding the odd science of aging. *Cell* 120:437–47

Kissova I, Deffieu M, Manon S, Camougrand N. 2004. Uth1p is involved in the autophagic degradation of mitochondria. *J. Biol. Chem.* 279:39068–74

Kudlow BA, Kennedy BK, Monnat RJ Jr. 2007. Werner syndrome and Hutchinson-Gilford progeria: mechanistic basis of human progeroid syndromes. *Nat. Rev. Mol. Cell Biol.* 8:394–404

Lai CY, Jaruga E, Borghouts C, Jazwinski SM. 2002. A mutation in the *ATP2* gene abrogates the age asymmetry between mother and daughter cells of the yeast *Saccharomyces cerevisiae*. *Genetics* 162:73–87

Lamming DW, Latorre-Esteves M, Medvedik O, Wong SN, Tsang FA, et al. 2005. *HST2* mediates *SIR2*-independent life-span extension by calorie restriction. *Science* 309:1861–64

Lamming DW, Latorre-Esteves M, Medvedik O, Wong SN, Tsang FA, et al. 2006. Response to comment on "*HST2* mediates *SIR2*-independent life-span extension by calorie restriction." *Science* 312:1312c

Landry J, Slama JT, Sternglanz R. 2000. Role of NAD$^+$ in the deacetylase activity of the SIR2-like proteins. *Biochem. Biophys. Res. Commun.* 278:685–90

Laun P, Pichova A, Madeo F, Fuchs J, Ellinger A, et al. 2001. Aged mother cells of *Saccharomyces cerevisiae* show markers of oxidative stress and apoptosis. *Mol. Microbiol.* 39:1166–73

Laun P, Ramachandran L, Jarolim S, Herker E, Liang P, et al. 2005. A comparison of the aging and apoptotic transcriptome of *Saccharomyces cerevisiae*. *FEMS Yeast Res.* 5:1261–72

Laun P, Rinnerthaler M, Bogengruber E, Heeren G, Breitenbach M. 2006. Yeast as a model for chronological and reproductive aging: a comparison. *Exp. Gerontol.* 41:1208–12

Lee SS, Lee RY, Fraser AG, Kamath RS, Ahringer J, Ruvkun G. 2003. A systematic RNAi screen identifies a critical role for mitochondria in *C. elegans* longevity. *Nat. Genet.* 33:40–48

Lesur I, Campbell JL. 2004. The transcriptome of prematurely aging yeast cells is similar to that of telomerase deficient cells. *Mol. Biol. Cell* 15:1297–312

Lin SJ, Defossez PA, Guarente L. 2000. Requirement of NAD and SIR2 for life-span extension by calorie restriction in *Saccharomyces cerevisiae*. *Science* 289:2126–28

Lin SJ, Ford E, Haigis M, Liszt G, Guarente L. 2004. Calorie restriction extends yeast life span by lowering the level of NADH. *Genes Dev.* 18:12–16

Lin SJ, Guarente L. 2006. Increased life span due to calorie restriction in respiratory-deficient yeast. *PLoS Genet.* 2:e33

Lin SJ, Kaeberlein M, Andalis AA, Sturtz LA, Defossez PA, et al. 2002. Calorie restriction extends *Saccharomyces cerevisiae* lifespan by increasing respiration. *Nature* 418:344–48

Lin SS, Manchester JK, Gordon JI. 2001. Enhanced gluconeogenesis and increased energy storage as hallmarks of aging in *Saccharomyces cerevisiae*. *J. Biol. Chem.* 276:36000–7

Longo VD, Gralla EB, Valentine JS. 1996. Superoxide dismutase activity is essential for stationary phase survival in *Saccharomyces cerevisiae*. Mitochondrial production of toxic oxygen species in vivo. *J. Biol. Chem.* 271:12275–80

A screen for stress-resistant, long-lived mutants identifies the SIR complex as a key regulator of yeast aging.

Established both glucose limitation and genetic methods as means of achieving dietary restriction in yeast.

Longo VD, Kennedy BK. 2006. Sirtuins in aging and age-related disease. *Cell* 126:257–68

MacMurray MA, Gottschling DE. 2003. An age-induced switch to a hyper-recombinational state. *Science* 301:1908–11

Madeo F, Frohlich E, Frohlich KU. 1997. A yeast mutant showing diagnostic markers of early and late apoptosis. *J. Cell Biol.* 139:729–34

Martin DE, Hall MN. 2005. The expanding TOR signaling network. *Curr. Opin. Cell Biol.* 17:158–66

Mayordomo I, Estruch F, Sanz P. 2002. Convergence of the target of rapamycin and the Snf1 protein kinase pathways in the regulation of the subcellular localization of Msn2, a transcriptional activator of STRE (stress response element)-regulated genes. *J. Biol. Chem.* 277:35650–56

McVey M, Kaeberlein M, Tissenbaum HA, Guarente L. 2001. The short life span of *Saccharomyces cerevisiae sgs1* and *srs2* mutants is a composite of normal aging processes and mitotic arrest due to defective recombination. *Genetics* 157:1531–42

Medvedik O, Lamming DW, Kim KD, Sinclair DA. 2007. *MSN2* and *MSN4* link calorie restriction and TOR to sirtuin-mediated lifespan extension in *Saccharomyces cerevisiae*. *PLoS Biol.* 5:230–41

Melendez A, Talloczy Z, Seaman M, Eskelinen EL, Hall DH, Levine B. 2003. Autophagy genes are essential for dauer development and life-span extension in *C. elegans*. *Science* 301:1387–91

Mortimer RK, Johnston JR. 1959. Life span of individual yeast cells. *Nature* 183:1751–52

Muller FL, Lustgarten MS, Jang Y, Richardson A, Van Remmen H. 2007. Trends in oxidative aging theories. *Free Radic. Biol. Med.* 43:477–503

Müller I. 1985. Parental age and the life-span of zygotes of *Saccharomyces cerevisiae*. *Antonie van Leeuwenhoek* 51:1–10

Müller I, Zimmermann M, Becker D, Flomer M. 1980. Calendar life span versus budding life span of *Saccharomyces cerevisiae*. *Mech. Ageing Dev.* 12:47–52

Murray AW, Szostak JW. 1983. Pedigree analysis of plasmid segregation in yeast. *Cell* 34:961–70

Nemoto S, Fergusson MM, Finkel T. 2004. Nutrient availability regulates SIRT1 through a forkhead-dependent pathway. *Science* 306:2105–8

Nestelbacher R, Laun P, Vondrakova D, Pichova A, Schuller C, Breitenbach M. 2000. The influence of oxygen toxicity on yeast mother cell-specific aging. *Exp. Gerontol.* 35:63–70

Nierras CR, Liebman SW, Warner JR. 1997. Does *Saccharomyces* need an organized nucleolus? *Chromosoma* 108:444–51

Nyström T. 2005. Role of oxidative carbonylation in protein quality control and senescence. *EMBO J.* 24:1311–17

Obeid LM, Hannun YA. 2003. Ceramide, stress, and a "LAG" in aging. *Sci. Aging Knowl. Environ.* 2003:PE27

Olsen A, Vantipalli MC, Lithgow GJ. 2006. Using *Caenorhabditis elegans* as a model for aging and age-related diseases. *Ann. N.Y. Acad. Sci.* 1067:120–28

Ozgenc A, Loeb LA. 2005. Current advances in unraveling the function of the Werner syndrome protein. *Mutat. Res.* 577:237–51

Pan KZ, Palter JE, Rogers AN, Olsen A, Chen D, et al. 2007. Inhibition of mRNA translation extends lifespan in *Caenorhabditis elegans*. *Aging Cell* 6:111–19

Paradis S, Ruvkun G. 1998. *Caenorhabditis elegans* Akt/PKB transduces insulin receptor-like signals from AGE-1 PI3 kinase to the DAF-16 transcription factor. *Genes Dev.* 12:2488–98

Park PU, McVey M, Guarente L. 2002. Separation of mother and daughter cells. *Methods Enzymol.* 351:468–77

Pereira G, Tanaka TU, Nasmyth K, Schiebel E. 2001. Modes of spindle pole body inheritance and segregation of the Bfa1p-Bub2p checkpoint protein complex. *EMBO J.* 20:6359–70

Petes TD, Botstein D. 1977. Simple Mendelian inheritance of the reiterated ribosomal DNA of yeast. *Proc. Natl. Acad. Sci. USA* 74:5091–95

Philippsen P, Thomas M, Kramer RA, Davis RW. 1978. Unique arrangement of coding sequences for 5 S, 5.8 S, 18 S and 25 S ribosomal RNA in *Saccharomyces cerevisiae* as determined by R-loop and hybridization analysis. *J. Mol. Biol.* 123:387–404

Picard F, Kurtev M, Chung N, Topark-Ngarm A, Senawong T, et al. 2004. SirT1 promotes fat mobilization in white adipocytes by repressing PPARγ. *Nature* 429:771–76

Piper PW. 2006. Long-lived yeast as a model for ageing research. *Yeast* 23:215–26

Inhibition of Tor activity extends life span through a similar pathway as does dietary restriction.

This pioneering paper in yeast aging was the first to measure the replicative aging properties of yeast cells.

Powers T. 2007. TOR signaling and S6 kinase 1: Yeast catches up. *Cell Metab.* 6:1–2

Powers T, Dilova I, Chen CY, Wedaman K. 2004. Yeast TOR signaling: a mechanism for metabolic regulation. *Curr. Top. Microbiol. Immunol.* 279:39–51

Prinz S, Aldridge C, Ramsey SA, Taylor RJ, Galitski T. 2007. Control of signaling in a MAP-kinase pathway by an RNA-binding protein. *PLoS ONE* 2:e249

Reverter-Branchat G, Cabiscol E, Tamarit J, Ros J. 2004. Oxidative damage to specific proteins in replicative and chronological-aged *Saccharomyces cerevisiae*: common targets and prevention by calorie restriction. *J. Biol. Chem.* 279:31983–89

Rine J, Herskowitz I. 1987. Four genes responsible for a position effect on expression from HML and HMR in *Saccharomyces cerevisiae*. *Genetics* 116:9–22

Rodriguez A, De la Cera T, Herrero P, Moreno F. 2001. The hexokinase 2 protein regulates the expression of the *GLK1*, *HXK1* and *HXK2* genes of *Saccharomyces cerevisiae*. *Biochem. J.* 355:625–31

Rusche LN, Kirchmaier AL, Rine J. 2003. The establishment, inheritance, and function of silenced chromatin in *Saccharomyces cerevisiae*. *Annu. Rev. Biochem.* 72:481–516

Rustchenko EP, Sherman F. 1994. Physical constitution of ribosomal genes in common strains of *Saccharomyces cerevisiae*. *Yeast* 10:1157–71

Santangelo GM. 2006. Glucose signaling in *Saccharomyces cerevisiae*. *Microbiol. Mol. Biol. Rev.* 70:253–82

Schorling S, Vallee B, Barz WP, Riezman H, Oesterhelt D. 2001. Lag1p and Lac1p are essential for the acyl-CoA-dependent ceramide synthase reaction in *Saccharomyces cerevisiae*. *Mol. Biol. Cell* 12:3417–27

Seichertova O, Beran K, Holan Z, Pokorny V. 1973. The chitin-glucan complex of *Saccharomyces cerevisiae*. II. Location of the complex in the encircling region of the bud scar. *Folia Microbiol.* 18:207–11

Seo JG, Lai CY, Miceli MV, Jazwinski SM. 2007. A novel role of peroxin PEX6: suppression of aging defects in mitochondria. *Aging Cell* 6:405–13

Sinclair DA. 2005. Toward a unified theory of caloric restriction and longevity regulation. *Mech. Ageing Dev.* 126:987–1002

Sinclair DA, Guarente L. 1997. Extrachromosomal rDNA circles: a cause of aging in yeast. *Cell* 91:1033–42

Sinclair DA, Mills K, Guarente L. 1997. Accelerated aging and nucleolar fragmentation in yeast *sgs1* mutants. *Science* 277:1313–16

Smeal T, Claus J, Kennedy B, Cole F, Guarente L. 1996. Loss of transcriptional silencing causes sterility in old mother cells of *S. cerevisiae*. *Cell* 84:633–42

Smith ED, Tsuchiya M, Fox LA, Dang N, Hu D, et al. 2008. Quantitative evidence for conserved longevity pathways between divergent eukaryotic species. *Genome Res.* 18:564–70

Smith JS, Boeke JD. 1997. An unusual form of transcriptional silencing in yeast ribosomal DNA. *Genes Dev.* 11:241–54

Smith JS, Brachmann CB, Celic I, Kenna MA, Muhammad S, et al. 2000. A phylogenetically conserved NAD$^+$-dependent protein deacetylase activity in the Sir2 protein family. *Proc. Natl. Acad. Sci. USA* 97:6658–63

Spassieva S, Seo J-G, Jiang JC, Bielawski J, Alvarez-Vasquez F, et al. 2006. Necessary role for the Lag1 motif in (dihydro)ceramide synthase activity. *J. Biol. Chem.* 281:33931–38

Steffen KK, MacKay VL, Kerr EO, Tsuchiya M, Hu D, et al. 2008. Yeast life span extension by depletion of 60S ribosomal subunits is mediated by Gcn4. *Cell* 133:292–302

Stewart MS, Krause SA, McGhie J, Gray JV. 2007. Mpt5p, a stress tolerance- and lifespan-promoting PUF protein in *Saccharomyces cerevisiae*, acts upstream of the cell wall integrity pathway. *Eukaryot. Cell* 6:262–70

Stockl P, Zankl C, Hutter E, Unterluggauer H, Laun P, et al. 2007. Partial uncoupling of oxidative phosphorylation induces premature senescence in human fibroblasts and yeast mother cells. *Free Radic. Biol. Med.* 43:947–58

Sun J, Kale SP, Childress AM, Pinswasdi C, Jazwinski SM. 1994. Divergent roles for *RAS1* and *RAS2* in yeast longevity. *J. Biol. Chem.* 269:18638–45

Tanny JC, Moazed D. 2001. NAD breakdown by the yeast silencing protein Sir2: evidence for acetyl transfer from substrate to an NAD breakdown product. *Proc. Natl. Acad. Sci. USA* 98:415–20

Tsuchiya M, Dang N, Kerr EO, Hu D, Steffen KK, et al. 2006. Sirtuin-independent effects of nicotinamide on lifespan extension from calorie restriction in yeast. *Aging Cell* 5:505–14

Identified extrachromosomal rDNA circles as an aging factor in yeast.

Unlu ES, Koc A. 2007. Effects of deleting mitochondrial antioxidant genes on life span. *Ann. N.Y. Acad. Sci.* 1100:505–9

Urban J, Soulard A, Huber A, Lippman S, Mukhopadhyay D, et al. 2007. Sch9 is a major target of TORC1 in *Saccharomyces cerevisiae*. *Mol. Cell* 26:663–74

Vellai T, Takacs-Vellai K, Zhang Y, Kovacs AL, Orosz L, Muller F. 2003. Genetics: influence of TOR kinase on lifespan in *C. elegans*. *Nature* 426:620

Velours G, Boucheron C, Manon S, Camougrand N. 2002. Dual cell wall/mitochondria localization of the 'SUN' family proteins. *FEMS Microbiol. Lett.* 207:165–72

Walsh RB, Clifton D, Horak J, Fraenkel DG. 1991. *Saccharomyces cerevisiae* null mutants in glucose phosphorylation: metabolism and invertase expression. *Genetics* 128:521–27

Walsh RB, Kawasaki G, Fraenkel DG. 1983. Cloning of genes that complement yeast hexokinase and glucokinase mutants. *J. Bacteriol.* 154:1002–4

Watt PM, Hickson ID, Borts RH, Louis EJ. 1996. *SGS1*, a homologue of the Bloom's and Werner's syndrome genes, is required for maintenance of genome stability in *Saccharomyces cerevisiae*. *Genetics* 144:935–45

Wawryn J, Krzepilko A, Myszka A, Bilinski T. 1999. Deficiency in superoxide dismutase shortens life span of yeast cells. *Acta Biochim. Pol.* 46:249–53

Wharton RP, Aggarwal AK. 2006. mRNA regulation by Puf domain proteins. *Sci. STKE* 2006:pe37

Willingham S, Outeiro TF, DeVit MJ, Lindquist SL, Muchowski PJ. 2003. Yeast genes that enhance the toxicity of a mutant huntingtin fragment or alpha-synuclein. *Science* 302:1769–72

Winzeler EA, Shoemaker DD, Astromoff A, Liang H, Anderson K, et al. 1999. Functional characterization of the *S. cerevisiae* genome by gene deletion and parallel analysis. *Science* 285:901–6

Xu F, Zhang Q, Zhang K, Xie W, Grunstein M. 2007. Sir2 deacetylates histone H3 lysine 56 to regulate telomeric heterochromatin structure in yeast. *Mol. Cell* 27:890–900

Yang R, Wek SA, Wek RC. 2000. Glucose limitation induces *GCN4* translation by activation of Gcn2 protein kinase. *Mol. Cell. Biol.* 20:2706–17

Yu CE, Oshima J, Fu YH, Wijsman EM, Hisama F, et al. 1996. Positional cloning of the Werner's syndrome gene. *Science* 272:258–62

Provides evidence that Sch9 may be the functional ortholog of S6 kinase, a target of Tor, in yeast.

Auxin Receptors and Plant Development: A New Signaling Paradigm

Keithanne Mockaitis and Mark Estelle*

Department of Biology, Indiana University, Bloomington, Indiana 47405;
email: kmockait@indiana.edu, maestell@indiana.edu

Annu. Rev. Cell Dev. Biol. 2008. 24:55–80

First published online as a Review in Advance on July 16, 2008

The *Annual Review of Cell and Developmental Biology* is online at cellbio.annualreviews.org

This article's doi:
10.1146/annurev.cellbio.23.090506.123214

*Corresponding author.

Key Words

hormone receptor, plant development, SCF, gene transcription

Abstract

The plant hormone auxin, in particular indole-3-acetic acid (IAA), is a key regulator of virtually every aspect of plant growth and development. Auxin regulates transcription by rapidly modulating levels of Aux/IAA proteins throughout development. Recent studies demonstrate that auxin perception occurs through a novel mechanism. Auxin binds to TIR1, the F-box subunit of the ubiquitin ligase complex SCF^{TIR1}, and stabilizes the interaction between TIR1 and Aux/IAA substrates. This interaction results in Aux/IAA ubiquitination and subsequent degradation. Regulation of the Aux/IAA protein family by TIR1 and TIR1-like auxin receptors (AFBs) links auxin action to transcriptional regulation and provides a model by which the vast array of auxin influences on development may be understood. Moreover, auxin receptor function is the first example of small-molecule regulation of an SCF ubiquitin ligase and may have important implications for studies of regulated protein degradation in other species, including animals.

Contents

INTRODUCTION: AUXIN IS A MASTER REGULATOR OF GROWTH AND DEVELOPMENT

Two hundred and fifty years have passed since Henri-Louis Duhamel du Monceau reported that callus and roots formed above, but not below, the position of rings tightly clamped around young tree trunks (Duhamel 1758). He attributed this phenomenon to the accumulation of an organogenic sap that moved down from the leaves. The concept of plant hormones initially began to take shape in the nineteenth century as Julius von Sachs suggested that plant organ-forming substances move directionally within the plant, including a root-forming substance produced in leaves that moves downward (Sachs 1880). Charles Darwin likewise proposed that a mobile substance regulates the

bending of grass coleoptiles toward the sun (Darwin 1880). Subsequent attempts to purify and characterize substances responsible for each of these phenomena converged on a class of compounds called the auxins (Kögl & Smit 1931; Went 1926; Went & Thimann 1937, pp. 6–17), predominantly indole-3-acetic acid (IAA). These early observations, that auxin initiates processes as divergent as root formation and phototropic bending of stems, anticipated the breadth and complexity of the role(s) of auxin in plant development.

Much of plant growth depends on auxin-induced cell expansion and division, and numerous mutants deficient in auxin response exhibit overall dwarfism. Altered organ morphology is also commonly observed in auxin mutants owing to localized defects in growth.

The regulation of auxin distribution plays an essential role in many developmental processes. Recent excellent reviews describe the transport mechanisms that promote auxin movement from cell to cell during development and in response to environmental signals (Leyser 2006, Scheres & Xu 2006, Teale et al. 2006). Light regulates the orientation of shoot growth to optimize plant survival, a process termed phototropism, by promoting asymmetric auxin distribution in stems. This asymmetry produces a corresponding growth asymmetry resulting in organ bending. Originally proposed in the Cholodny-Went hypothesis, this mechanism explains Darwin's original observations of phototropism (Blancaflor & Masson 2003, Darwin 1880). In addition to light, other signals can influence auxin distribution. Recent studies indicate that brassinosteroid hormones influence development in part by affecting the distribution of auxin (Bao et al. 2004). Alterations in auxin localization can modify differential growth among cells within an organ, thus influencing organ shape, and can modify localized auxin-induced organogenesis, influencing overall plant architecture.

Auxin is required for the generation and maintenance of primary meristems as well as the formation of axillary meristems. The importance of auxin in both cell proliferation and meristem organization appears to contrast with its role in the expansion of already differentiated cells. Auxin is thought to be essential as early as the first zygotic division (Weijers & Jurgens 2005). During embryogenesis, auxin is necessary for specification of the initial cell of the root meristem and the vascular connectivity of all developing organs. As the plant matures, auxin reactivates differentiated cells to promote additional vascular tissue development and regulate lateral organ formation. Auxin also regulates organ polarity. Leaves and flowers that are severely auxin deficient or have reduced auxin response exhibit loss of asymmetry and develop as radial or funnel-shaped organs (Pekker et al. 2005).

Although a detailed understanding of the molecular basis for the complexity of auxin activity has not yet emerged, progress during the past 15 years has identified critical components of auxin signaling and provided a framework for addressing how auxin regulates diverse developmental processes. Perhaps the most dramatic development is the recent discoveries that the *Arabidopsis* F-box protein TIR1 is an auxin receptor and that auxin functions by directly regulating the ubiquitin (Ub) protein ligase SCF^{TIR1}. Here we provide an overview of current research describing this auxin receptor, the Ub cycle in which it functions, and the transcriptional regulators it targets.

AUXIN RAPIDLY REGULATES TRANSCRIPTION

Three decades of studies have explored the rapid effects of auxin on gene expression. Genome-wide studies indicate that the transcriptional response to auxin is rapid and broad, influencing the expression of a large and diverse set of genes within minutes (Goda et al. 2004, Nemhauser et al. 2006, Overvoorde et al. 2005, Tian et al. 2002; K. Mockaitis & M. Estelle, unpublished). Early work identified the *Aux/IAA* genes on the basis of their rapid transcriptional activation by auxin, and auxin response factors (ARFs) on the basis of their ability to bind auxin-responsive promoters and regulate transcription (Abel & Theologis 1996, Guilfoyle & Hagen 2007). Subsequent studies demonstrated that the Aux/IAA proteins are unstable transcriptional repressors that can interact with ARFs (Abel et al. 1995, Ainley et al. 1988, Conner et al. 1990, Guilfoyle et al. 1993, Theologis et al. 1985, Yamamoto et al. 1992). In *Arabidopsis* the ARF and Aux/IAA proteins are encoded by families of 23 and 29 members, respectively, and together remain the focal point of studies of auxin response.

The structures of the Aux/IAA and ARF proteins have been reviewed extensively (Guilfoyle & Hagen 2007, Reed 2001). ARFs are defined by their conserved N-terminal DNA-binding domain and an adjacent domain [middle region (MR)] that determines their effects on transcription. For 5 of the ARFs, this MR is a glutamine-rich domain that activates transcription either as part of an intact ARF protein or as an isolated domain. Up to 15 of the remaining ARF proteins may function as transcriptional repressors, whereas the activities of 3 more highly diverged ARFs remain unknown (Okushima et al. 2005, Tiwari et al. 2003, Ulmasov et al. 1999a).

Both ARF and Aux/IAA proteins contain conserved sequences near the C terminus termed domains III and IV. These domains mediate ARF-ARF, ARF-Aux/IAA, and Aux/IAA-Aux-IAA interactions in yeast two-hybrid tests. Recent quantitative assessments show that, for at least some ARF-Aux/IAA pairs, the heterodimer is more stable than either homodimer (Muto et al. 2006). Thus, ARF binding to Aux/IAA proteins may inhibit ARF-ARF dimer formation (Ulmasov et al. 1999b). Evidence exists, however, for an alternative or additional function of Aux/IAAs as active transcriptional repressors (Tiwari et al. 2001). A region in most Aux/IAA proteins, called domain I, contains a Leu-rich motif conserved among other families of transcriptional repressors. When fused to a DNA-binding domain, domain I effectively represses a heterologous transcriptional activator (VP16) and the activity of intact ARF proteins (Tiwari et al. 2004). Repression by domain I requires proximity to the activator on promoters, and domain I fails to act at a distance, consistent with the possibility that in some promoter complexes Aux/IAAs repress transcription through direct association with DNA-bound ARFs (Tiwari et al. 2004). Recently, Szemenyei et al. (2008) found that Aux/IAA proteins interact with a transcriptional corepressor called TOPLESS (TPL). During embryogenesis, TPL binds to domain I of the Aux/IAA protein BDL/IAA12 and represses MP/ARF5-dependent development. Thus, one function of Aux/IAAs appears to be the recruitment of corepressors.

Earlier studies showed that ARF activity varies with promoter context (Tiwari et al. 2003). Recent studies either have suggested (Nemhauser et al. 2004) or have demonstrated (Shin et al. 2007) that unrelated transcription factors act within or near ARF complexes. Whether Aux/IAAs function within such complexes or interact with ARFs prior to complex formation remains to be determined. Substantial sequence divergence in regions outside the conserved domains suggests that members of the Aux/IAA family may have diverse binding partners, perhaps explaining some of the complexity of auxin-mediated development. The identification of protein complexes that act on auxin-responsive promoters and the influence of Aux/IAAs on the assembly and/or activities of these complexes are important areas of ongoing investigation.

What is clear is that transcriptional and developmental responses to auxin are sensitive to the levels of Aux/IAA proteins (Dreher et al. 2006; Knox et al. 2003; Ouellet et al. 2001; Ramos et al. 2001; Tian et al. 2002; Timpte et al. 1994; Worley et al. 2000; Zenser et al. 2001, 2003). Multiple lines of evidence show that a small, conserved structure in the Aux/IAA proteins, called domain II, is essential for the degradation of these repressors and links their concentration directly to auxin levels. Developmental genetic screens conducted by several groups recovered dominant or semidominant gain-of-function mutations in a number of *Aux/IAA* genes (**Table 1**). In each line the mutation occurred within the conserved domain II sequence (GWPPV/I) (Reed 2001). Subsequent demonstration that domain II functions as an auxin-dependent degron suggested that the gain-of-function mutations stabilize the affected protein (Gray et al. 2001, Ramos et al. 2001). This was later confirmed for several of the *aux/iaa* mutants (Ouellet et al. 2001, Tian et al. 2003).

Plants harboring stabilized mutant forms of Aux/IAA proteins exhibit an array of developmental phenotypes, including aberrant embryonic patterning, seedling and mature organ development, tropic growth, maturation, and fertility (Liscum & Reed 2002). As expected, Aux/IAA stabilization in plants correlates with reduced auxin-regulated transcription. Studies of more recently available loss-of-function mutants in the *ARF* genes are beginning to

Table 1 Aux/IAA proteins in *Arabidopsis thaliana* and evidence for their roles in auxin-mediated development

Gene	Product	Function	Genetic evidence for role in auxin-mediated development	References
IAA1	IAA1	Auxin decreases protein half-life; *axr5-1* gain-of-function mutation is in degron	*axr5-1* degron mutation reduces multiple auxin responses	Abel et al. 1995; Park et al. 2002; Yang et al. 2004; Zenser et al. 2001, 2003
IAA2	IAA2	Contains domain II degron	Phylogenetic relationship	Abel et al. 1995, Liscum & Reed 2002
IAA3	SUPPRESSOR OF HY2 or SHORT HYPOCOTYL 2 (SHY2/IAA3)	*shy2-1*, *-2*, *-3*, *-6* mutations are in degron	*shy2-1*, *-2*, *-3*, *-6* degron mutations reduce multiple auxin responses	Abel et al. 1995, Kim et al. 1996, Reed 2001, Reed et al. 1998, Soh et al. 1999, Tian & Reed 1999, 2003
IAA4	IAA4	Pea ortholog shows rapid turnover in vivo	Phylogenetic relationship	Abel et al. 1994, 1995; Liscum & Reed 2002
IAA5	IAA5	Contains domain II degron	Phylogenetic relationship	Abel et al. 1995, Liscum & Reed 2002
IAA6	SUPPRESSOR OF HY1 (SHY1/IAA6)	Pea ortholog shows rapid turnover in vivo; *shy1-1* mutation is in degron	*shy1-1*-stabilizing mutation reduces multiple auxin responses	Abel et al. 1994, 1995; Kim et al. 1996; Ramos et al. 2001; Reed 2001
IAA7	AUXIN RESISTANT 2 (AXR2/IAA7)	Auxin decreases protein half-life; protein can interact with TIR1; *axr2-1* mutation is in degron; *axr2-1* mutation abolishes protein interaction with TIR1 and increases protein half-life	*axr2-1*-stabilizing mutations reduce multiple auxin responses	Abel et al. 1995, N. Dharmasiri et al. 2003, Gray et al. 2001, Nagpal et al. 2000, Timpte et al. 1994
IAA8	IAA8	Protein shows rapid turnover in vivo; contains domain II degron	Phylogenetic relationship	Abel et al. 1995, Dreher et al. 2006, Liscum & Reed 2002
IAA9	IAA9	Protein shows rapid turnover in vivo; contains domain II degron	RNAi-reduced levels in tomato increase sensitivity to auxin in multiple developmental processes	Abel et al. 1995, Dreher et al. 2006, Liscum & Reed 2002, Wang et al. 2005
IAA10	IAA10	Contains domain II degron	Phylogenetic relationship	Abel et al. 1995
IAA11	IAA11	Contains domain II degron	Phylogenetic relationship	Abel et al. 1995, Liscum & Reed 2002
IAA12	BODENLOS (BDL/IAA12)	*bdl* mutation is in degron	*bdl* degron mutation reduces multiple auxin responses	Abel et al. 1995; Hamann et al. 1999, 2002; Liscum & Reed 2002
IAA13	IAA13	Contains domain II degron	Degron mutant transgene impairs auxin-related development	Abel et al. 1995, Weijers et al. 2005
IAA14	SOLITARY ROOT (SLR/IAA14)	*slr-1* mutation is in degron	*slr-1* degron mutation reduces multiple auxin responses	Abel et al. 1995; Fukaki et al. 2002, 2005; Vanneste et al. 2005
IAA15	IAA15	Contains domain II degron	Phylogenetic relationship	Liscum & Reed 2002
IAA16	IAA16	Contains domain II degron	Phylogenetic relationship	Liscum & Reed 2002

(Continued)

Table 1 (*Continued*)

Gene	Product	Function	Genetic evidence for role in auxin-mediated development	References
IAA17	<u>AUX</u>IN <u>R</u>ESISTANT 3 (AXR3/IAA17)	Auxin decreases protein half-life; protein can interact with TIR1; *axr3* mutations are in degron and increase protein half-life	*axr3-1* and *-3* degron mutations reduce multiple auxin responses	N. Dharmasiri et al. 2003, Gray et al. 2001, Leyser et al. 1996, Ouellet et al. 2001, Overvoorde et al. 2005, Rouse et al. 1998
IAA18	IAA18	*iaa18-1* mutation is in degron	*iaa18-1* degron mutation reduces multiple auxin responses	Reed 2001
IAA19	MASSUGU 2 (MSG2/IAA19)	*msg2-1* to *-4* mutations are in degron	*msg2-1* to *-4* degron mutations reduce multiple auxin responses	Liscum & Reed 2002, Tatematsu et al. 2004
IAA26	Phytochrome interacting protein 1 (PAP1/IAA26)	Contains domain II degron	Phylogenetic relationship	Liscum & Reed 2002
IAA27	Phytochrome interacting protein 2 (PAP2/IAA27)	Contains domain II degron	Phylogenetic relationship	Liscum & Reed 2002
IAA28	IAA28	Auxin decreases protein half-life; *iaa28-1* mutation is in degron	*iaa28-1* degron mutations reduce multiple auxin responses	Dreher et al. 2006, Rogg et al. 2001
IAA29	IAA29	Contains domain II degron	Phylogenetic relationship	Liscum & Reed 2002
IAA31	IAA31	Auxin decreases protein half-life; imperfect conservation of domain II correlates with a half-life longer than that of other Aux/IAAs in vivo	Phylogenetic relationship	Dreher et al. 2006, Liscum & Reed 2002

contribute to our understanding of auxin-regulated transcription in development. Selected examples are described below. Similarities in the phenotypes conferred by loss-of-function *arf* mutations and stabilizing *aux/iaa* domain II mutations have led to recent functional pairing of some Aux/IAA and ARF proteins (Fukaki et al. 2006; Tatematsu et al. 2004; Weijers et al. 2005, 2006). In each case, yeast two-hybrid or other interaction assays have confirmed the potential for direct protein-protein interactions.

AUX/IAA AND ARF PROTEINS MEDIATE AUXIN ACTION IN VASCULAR DEVELOPMENT AND ORGANOGENESIS

Auxin plays a pivotal role in vascular tissue and organ initiation. Studies of these processes pro-vide the most detailed descriptions to date of the role of auxin in development. During embryogenesis auxin is required for normal organ formation, as evidenced by early developmental arrest in several auxin response mutants. Loss of ARF5 function in the *Arabidopsis* mutant *monopteros* (*mp*) completely prevents root formation (Berleth & Jurgens 1993, Hardtke & Berleth 1998, Weijers & Jurgens 2005). Identical effects are seen in the *bodenlos* (*bdl*) mutant, in which the Aux/IAA protein IAA12 is stabilized by a mutation in domain II (Hamann et al. 1999, 2002; Weijers & Jurgens 2005). Lack of root development in *mp* and *bdl* is due to impaired development of a single cell called the hypophysis, the founder cell of the basal meristem. In the apical portion of *mp* (and *bdl*) embryos, vascular tissue development is severely reduced, reflecting a general loss of normal cell proliferation. Smaller meristems, reduced cotyledon/leaf emergence, and defects in floral meristem formation in *mp* plants suggest that ARF5 acts early in promoting cell division prior to differentiation (Przemeck et al. 1996, Vidaurre et al. 2007).

The analysis of *arf5* hypomorphic lines indicates that this transcription factor also functions during postembryonic development to positively regulate vascular tissue formation (Hardtke et al. 2004). In leaves, as in embryos, expression of ARF5 precedes vascular development (Scarpella et al. 2006, Weijers et al. 2006, Wenzel et al. 2007). ARF5 expression in these contexts colocalizes with and precedes the expression of *PIN1*, which encodes a membrane protein that facilitates the movement of auxin from cell to cell and helps to establish gradients of auxin within developing organs. Extensive analyses show that PIN1 and related auxin carriers are asymmetrically localized within many cell types and that this distribution contributes to polar movement of auxin within tissues and organs. Aymmetric distribution of PIN1 is first observed at the embryonic 32-cell stage in provascular cells adjacent to the hypophysis (Friml et al. 2003) and in preprocambial cells of developing leaves (Scarpella et al. 2006). During formation of the embryonic root, expression of *ARF5* and *IAA12* is limited to embryonic cells directly adjacent to the hypophysis. Auxin movement into the hypophysis and provasculature of other organs appears to be essential for determining these cells' fates, implying that other auxin signaling proteins act in these cells to initiate auxin-regulated differentiation (Weijers et al. 2006). These findings add new validation to the hypothesis that auxin establishes and enhances its own transport during organogenesis, the time-honored developmental model termed canalization. Auxin-induced derepression of ARF5 transcriptional activity in one cell leads to the expression of PIN1, which promotes the movement of auxin into the adjacent cell, inducing additional transcriptional responses. Details of PIN-mediated mechanisms that establish cellular polarity and influence auxin allocation are described in another review in this volume (Kleine-Vehn & Friml 2008).

During the formation of lateral roots, auxin influences the reactivation of differentiated vascular cells in the primary root. The first anticlinal divisions during lateral root formation occur in pericycle cells adjacent to the xylem. As in embryogenesis, the division and differentiation of these cells require auxin (Casimiro et al. 2001, Himanen et al. 2002, Malamy & Benfey 1997). Mutations in several auxin response components cause defects in auxin-induced lateral root formation and reduce cell cycle activity in the xylem pole pericycle (Fukaki et al. 2006, Gray et al. 1999). One of these, a mutation in the degron motif of *SLR/IAA14*, stabilizes the IAA14 protein and completely blocks the early development of lateral roots (Fukaki et al. 2002). Targeted expression of the stabilized form of IAA14 indicates that the protein normally functions in xylem pole pericycle cells (Fukaki et al. 2005). Further studies suggest that IAA14-regulated transcription contributes to both cell cycle reactivation and subsequent regulation of cellular identity (Vanneste et al. 2005). Expression of *ARF7* and *ARF19* coincides with that of *SLR/IAA14* in lateral root initials, and the *arf7arf19* double mutant lacks lateral roots in the presence of auxin (Okushima et al. 2007), similar to *slr-1*. Results from two additional studies show that ARF7 and ARF19 can substitute for one another in activating some promoters (Li et al. 2006, Okushima et al. 2005).

AUXIN SIGNALING REQUIRES THE UBIQUITIN-PROTEASOME PATHWAY

As mentioned above, most of the *Aux/IAA* genes are transcriptionally regulated by auxin in an ARF- and Aux/IAA-dependent manner (Abel et al. 1995, Tatematsu et al. 2004, Tian et al. 2002). Auxin-regulated expression of these repressors serves as a rapid negative feedback mechanism in auxin signaling. The activity of the auxin receptor, described below, completes this regulatory loop by destabilizing the Aux/IAA proteins. As noted above, severe developmental consequences result when this loop is disrupted and the Aux/IAA repressors accumulate.

The Ub-proteasome pathway is responsible for the regulated degradation of diverse proteins in eukaryotes. Ub is attached to substrate proteins through a series of highly conserved enzymatic reactions, described below. Plants devote a remarkably large fraction of their genomes to this pathway, suggesting that protein degradation is particularly important for cellular regulation in plants (Smalle & Vierstra 2004).

The Ubiquitin-Conjugation Cycle

The Ub-protein conjugation pathway is initiated by an enzyme called the Ub-activating enzyme, or E1 (Hershko & Ciechanover 1998). This enzyme catalyzes an ATP-dependent reaction that activates a Ub monomer and transfers it to the second enzyme in the pathway, the Ub-conjugating enzyme (E2) (Hershko & Ciechanover 1998). A third protein or protein complex called the Ub-protein ligase (E3) interacts with both the Ub-E2 and specific substrate proteins, thus promoting the transfer of Ub to the substrate (Hershko & Ciechanover 1998, Pickart 2001). The SCF (Skp1-Cul1-F-box) protein complexes make up a major class of E3s in all eukaryotes and appear to be the most abundant type of E3 in plants (Moon et al. 2004, Smalle & Vierstra 2004). Each SCF contains a highly conserved central scaffold protein, called a cullin, that is associated with the adaptor protein Skp1 (a member of the ASK family in plants) (Petroski & Deshaies 2005, Smalle & Vierstra 2004). This adaptor protein provides the binding site for the F-box protein, which functions as the substrate-binding component of the SCF. The fourth subunit, variously called RBX1, ROC, or Hrt1, binds the Ub-E2 and promotes transfer of Ub to the F-box-protein-bound substrate. Ub-E2 docking to RBX1 is thought to allosterically promote the transfer of Ub, indicating that the purpose of SCF-complex architecture is to position

the protein substrate to receive the transferred Ub effectively (Petroski & Deshaies 2005). Indeed, the structure of the CUL1 subunit establishes a critical distance between the substrate protein and Ub-E2. Upon transfer by the E2, an isopeptide bond is formed between a lysyl ε-amino group on the substrate protein and the C-terminal glycyl residue of Ub (Petroski & Deshaies 2005).

Substrate marking for recognition by the 26S proteasome requires the addition of a chain of polymerized Ub (Petroski & Deshaies 2005). It is not clear if polyubiquitination occurs through the successive addition of single Ub molecules to SCF-bound substrate or by the attachment of a preformed Ub chain (Hochstrasser 2006). Members of a family of deubiquitinating enzymes (DUBs) assist in Ub recycling upon breakdown of polyubiquitinated substrates (Amerik & Hochstrasser 2004). Some DUBs may have additional roles in selectively reversing the ubiquitination of substrates, thereby preventing substrate degradation. Diversity among subunits of the proteasome may also contribute complexity to proteasome-substrate interactions (Brukhin et al. 2005, Demartino & Gillette 2007, Smalle et al. 2002, Ueda et al. 2004).

Regulation of SCF Assembly and Function

A number of factors that regulate SCF assembly and/or activity have been identified. These include the Ub-like protein RUB (or Nedd8 in animals) (Kerscher et al. 2006, Parry & Estelle 2004). RUB is conjugated to the cullin subunit of the SCF through a separate pathway consisting of dedicated E1 and E2 enzymes. The RUB molecule is removed from the cullin by the COP9 signalosome (CSN) complex (Kerscher et al. 2006, Wei & Deng 2003). RUB modification may be important for the recruitment of the Ub-E2 to the SCF (Kerscher et al. 2006). In addition, RUB appears to block binding of CUL by CAND1, a 120-kDa protein that sterically hinders the CUL-Skp1/ASK interaction. Several recent reviews have discussed in detail the role of these proteins in SCF assembly/disassembly (Petroski & Deshaies 2005, Wu et al. 2006).

Regulation of SCF-Substrate Recognition

The regulation of SCF-substrate recognition has now been characterized for many animal and fungal SCFs (Petroski & Deshaies 2005). In general the SCF-substrate interaction is regulated by posttranslational modification of the substrate. In almost all known cases, phosphorylation marks the substrate for SCF recognition. For example, the mammalian SCF^{Fbw7} promotes the degradation of a number of growth regulators, including cyclin E, c-Myc, c-Jun, Notch, Presenilin, and sterol regulatory element-binding proteins (SREBP) (Koepp et al. 2001, Minella & Clurman 2005, Nateri et al. 2004, Orlicky et al. 2003, Ye et al. 2004). Each of these proteins contains conserved Cdc4 phospho-degron (CPD) motifs. When a threonyl residue within the CPD is phosphorylated, the protein is recognized by SCF^{Fbw7}, ubiquitinated, and rapidly degraded. Phosphorylation also promotes degradation of the mammalian Cdk inhibitor p27^{Kip1} by SCF^{Skp2} (Nakayama & Nakayama 2005). In this case, however, an additional adaptor protein termed Cks1 is required for substrate recognition (Ganoth et al. 2001, Spruck et al. 2001, Xu et al. 2007). When p27^{Kip1} is phosphorylated at T187 by Cdk2–cyclin A, the phospho-threonyl motif interacts with Cks1 associated in the complex, whereas the F-box protein Skp2 interacts with another portion of the substrate to promote binding.

GENETIC STUDIES IN *ARABIDOPSIS* DEMONSTRATE THAT THE UBIQUITIN-PROTEASOME PATHWAY IS REQUIRED FOR AUXIN SIGNALING

The connection between auxin and the Ub pathway was established through a very simple screen for *Arabidopsis* mutants with altered auxin response (Walker & Estelle 1998). The roots of *Arabidopsis* seedlings are inhibited by low levels of auxin in the growth medium, making it relatively straightforward to isolate large numbers of auxin-resistant mutants. The first auxin-resistant mutant to be characterized in detail was called *axr1* (Leyser et al. 1993, Lincoln et al. 1990). The *AXR1* gene encodes a subunit of the heterodimeric RUB-E1 enzyme, the first enzyme in the RUB-conjugation pathway (del Pozo et al. 1998). Because RUB modification of CUL1 is important for SCF function, these results suggested that auxin response depends on the action of a cullin-containing E3 ligase. This idea was supported by later studies of another auxin-resistant mutant called *tir1* (Ruegger et al. 1998). The *TIR1* gene encodes a leucine-rich-repeat (LRR)-containing F-box protein that interacts with CUL1, ASK1 or ASK2, and RBX1 to form SCF^{TIR1} (Gray et al. 1999, Ruegger et al. 1998). Typically the biggest challenge in characterizing a newly discovered E3 ligase is identifying its substrates. In the case of SCF^{TIR1}, there were some obvious candidates because the Aux/IAA proteins were known to be unstable repressors of auxin-regulated transcription. Both genetic and biochemical studies confirmed that the Aux/IAAs are substrates of SCF^{TIR1} (Gray et al. 1999). Several members of the Aux/IAA family are stabilized in the *axr1* and *tir1* mutants, and both mutants exhibit reduced auxin-regulated gene expression (Gray et al. 1999; K. Mockaitis & M. Estelle, unpublished). Furthermore, in vitro studies demonstrated that Aux/IAA proteins interact with TIR1 and that auxin stimulates this interaction (Gray et al. 1999). Taken together, these results indicate that auxin acts by promoting the degradation of the Aux/IAAs through the action of SCF^{TIR1}, a model that is summarized in **Figure 1**.

Support for the model was provided by analyses of mutants that affect other proteins in the Ub pathway, including CUL1, ASK1, CAND1, and subunits of the CSN (Chuang et al. 2004; Gray et al. 2001, 2003; Hellmann et al. 2003; Moon et al. 2007; Quint et al. 2005; Schwechheimer et al. 2001) (**Table 2**).

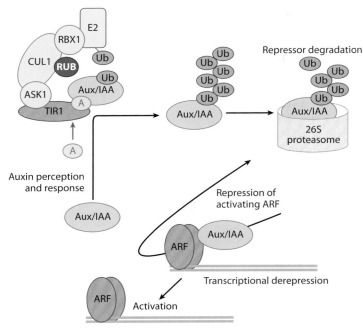

Figure 1

Auxin regulates transcription by promoting ubiquitin (Ub)-mediated degradation of Aux/IAA repressors. Auxin (A) binds to the F-box protein TIR1 in SCF^{TIR1} and stabilizes the interaction between TIR1 and an Aux/IAA substrate. The repressor is polyubiquitinated and degraded by the 26S proteasome. Loss of the Aux/IAA permits auxin response factor (ARF)-dependent transcription of auxin-regulated genes. E2, Ub-conjugating enzyme.

Additionally, investigators have isolated mutants that affect an AXR1-like enzyme (AXL), the partner of AXR1 required for RUB-E1 activity (ECR1), the RUB-E2 (RCE1), and other SCF regulators (Chuang et al. 2004, S. Dharmasiri et al. 2003, Dharmasiri et al. 2007, Walsh et al. 2006, Woodward et al. 2007). Like *axr1* and *tir1*, these mutants are deficient in auxin response and show a variety of auxin-related growth defects. For example, some *cul1* alleles (also called *axr6*) have a seedling lethal phenotype that is similar to the phenotypes of *mp/arf5* and *bdl/iaa12*, contributing to evidence that SCF-mediated degradation of IAA12 is required for formation of the embryonic root (Hellmann et al. 2003, Hobbie et al. 2000). Taken together, characterization of these mutants demonstrates that the regulation of SCF

function and the resulting Ub modification of Aux/IAA proteins are critical to auxin-regulated plant development.

Degradation of proteins other than the Aux/IAAs depends on many of the same Ub pathway regulators, and several newly described F-box proteins function in response to other plant hormones and environmental signals (Chini et al. 2007, Lechner et al. 2006, Moon et al. 2004, Thines et al. 2007). The observation that developmental defects in mutants of the Ub pathway, the CSN, and proteasome regulators often appear at least partially auxin related, mimicking phenotypes of Aux/IAA and ARF mutants, emphasizes the very early influences of auxin in plant developmental programs (Dohmann et al. 2005, Hellmann et al. 2003, Schwechheimer et al. 2001).

Auxin Perception through the SCF

The discovery that SCF^{TIR1} promotes the degradation of the Aux/IAA proteins was a major breakthrough in plant hormone signaling. However, there were many unresolved questions, including the identity of the auxin receptor and how TIR1-Aux/IAA recognition is regulated. On the basis of studies of SCFs in animals and fungi, it was assumed that Aux/IAA recognition would require a posttranslational modification, probably phosphorylation (Petroski & Deshaies 2005). However, in vitro studies strongly suggested that Aux/IAA modification was not required for recognition (N. Dharmasiri et al. 2003, Kepinski & Leyser 2004). For example, inhibitors of protein kinases and phosphatases do not affect the TIR1-Aux/IAA interaction (N. Dharmasiri et al. 2003, Kepinski & Leyser 2004). In addition, auxin promotes the interaction in membrane-depleted extracts, suggesting that the receptor and any intermediary components are not associated with cellular membranes (N. Dharmasiri et al. 2003).

Two important papers confirmed that auxin regulates SCF^{TIR1} through a novel mechanism (Dharmasiri et al. 2005a, Kepinski &

Table 2 Proteins involved in SCF assembly in *Arabidopsis thaliana* and evidence for their roles in auxin-mediated development

Gene	Product	Function	Genetic evidence for role in auxin-mediated development	References
ASK1	*Arabidopsis* SKP1	Orthologous to yeast Skp1; links F-box protein to CUL1	*ask1* loss-of-function mutations reduce multiple auxin responses	Gray et al. 1999
CUL1	CULLIN1/AUXIN RESISTANT 6 (AXR6/CUL1)	Scaffold protein of SCF complex	Several *cul1* loss-of-function mutations reduce multiple auxin responses	Hellmann et al. 2003, Moon et al. 2007, Shen et al. 2002
RBX1	RING-H2 finger protein	Orthologous to RBX/ROC/Hrt, SCF docking subunit for Ub-E2	Decreased expression or overexpression reduces multiple auxin responses	Gray et al. 2002
RUB1 and -2	RELATED TO UBIQUITIN 1 and 2	Orthologous to Nedd8	Reduced levels reduce multiple auxin responses; together *RUB1* and -2 are essential in development	Bostick et al. 2004
AXR1	AUXIN RESISTANT1	Subunit in RUB/Nedd8 activating enzyme	Loss-of-function mutations reduce multiple auxin responses and reduce RUB1 modification of CUL1	del Pozo & Estelle 1999, del Pozo et al. 2002, Leyser et al. 1993
AXL	AUXIN RESISTANT1-LIKE	Subunit in RUB/Nedd8 activating enzyme	Loss of function synergistically with *axr1* reduces multiple auxin responses	Dharmasiri et al. 2007
ECR1	RUB E1 enzyme subunit	With AXR1/AXL, activates RUB for transfer to RCE1	Loss-of-function mutation reduces multiple auxin responses	del Pozo & Estelle 1999, del Pozo et al. 2002, Woodward et al. 2007
RCE1	E2 enzyme for RUB conjugation	Interacts with RBX1 and SCF[TIR1]	Loss-of-function mutations reduce multiple auxin responses	del Pozo & Estelle 1999, S. Dharmasiri et al. 2003
CSN5	Component of COP9 signalosome	Interacts with SCF; removes RUB from CUL1; regulates SCF assembly	Loss-of-function mutations reduce multiple auxin responses	Dohmann et al. 2005, Peng et al. 2003, Schwechheimer et al. 2001
CAND1	Cullin-associated and neddylation-dissociated1	Orthologous to animal Cand1; interacts with CUL1; regulates SCF assembly	Loss-of-function mutations reduce multiple auxin responses	Alonso-Peral et al. 2006, Cheng et al. 2004, Chuang et al. 2004, Feng et al. 2004
SGT1b	Suppressor of G2 allele of skp1/ Enhancer of TIR1 auxin resistance ETA3	Yeast ortholog interacts with Skp1	Loss-of-function mutations reduce multiple auxin responses	Gray et al. 2003, Walsh et al. 2006

Leyser 2005). In these studies, partially purified SCF[TIR1] bound an Aux/IAA protein in an auxin-dependent manner, indicating that the receptor copurified with SCF[TIR1]. Furthermore, labeled auxin (^{3}H-IAA) bound specifically to SCF[TIR1], or a closely associated protein, signifying that an auxin receptor was present in the complex. One explanation for these results, something that previously seemed very unlikely, is that TIR1 is the auxin receptor.

That this is the case was strongly suggested by the discovery that TIR1 synthesized in insect cells or *Xenopus* embryos also binds recombinant Aux/IAA protein in the presence of auxin (Dharmasiri et al. 2005a, Kepinski & Leyser 2005). Because the only plant proteins in this assay are TIR1 and Aux/IAA, each synthesized in heterologous systems, the logical conclusion was that one of these two proteins binds auxin. Assays in vitro showed that Aux/IAA proteins do not bind auxin, leaving TIR1 as the best candidate.

AUXIN RECEPTOR ACTIVITY IS REVEALED

To address the mechanism of auxin perception, the structure of TIR1 in complex with ASK1 was determined in the presence of IAA and a peptide that includes the degron motif of IAA7/AXR2 (Tan et al. 2007). TIR1 is composed of the highly conserved F-box domain and 18 LRRs. The crystal structure reveals that the ASK1-TIR1 complex forms a mushroom-shaped structure, with ASK1 and the F-box domain forming the stem (**Figure 2a**). The cap

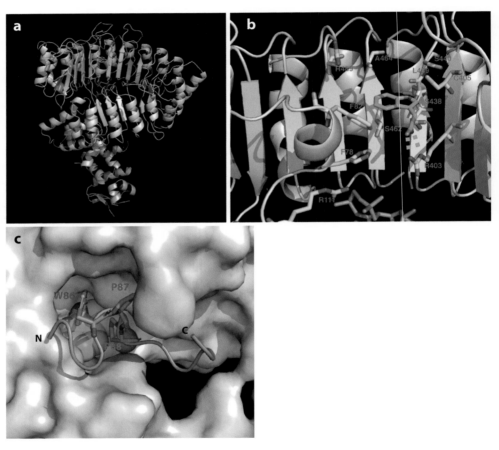

Figure 2

Auxin perception by the F-box protein TIR1. (*a*) Structure of TIR1 (*gray*) in complex with ASK1 (*dark blue*), indole-3-acetic acid (IAA) (*green*), Aux/IAA domain II peptide (*orange*), and inositol hexakisphosphate (*red*). (*b*) Close-up of the auxin-binding pocket occupied by IAA (*green*). Surrounding TIR1 residues are shown in yellow. Dashed pink lines indicate hydrogen bonds between the carboxyl group of IAA and conserved R403. (*c*) Surface view of TIR1 in complex with IAA (*green*) and domain II peptide (*orange*).

of the mushroom consists of the relatively long LRR domain that adopts a fold unique among known LRR domains (Tan et al. 2007). The TIR1 LRR domain forms a slightly twisted, incomplete ring-like structure of alternating solvent-facing alpha helices and core-lining beta strands. Auxin is bound within a mostly hydrophobic cavity (see below). Surprisingly, auxin binding does not induce major conformational changes in the receptor, indicating that the hormone does not act as an allosteric regulator. Instead, the auxin molecule fills the deepest portion of the cavity and provides an additional binding surface for the Aux/IAA degron. The Aux/IAA proteins appear to bind TIR1 in the absence of auxin, but with low affinity (Dharmasiri et al. 2005b, Kepinski & Leyser 2005, Tan et al. 2007). The auxin molecule acts as "molecular glue" between TIR1 and its substrate, binding both proteins and facilitating hydrophobic packing between TIR1 and its substrate. Once the TIR1-auxin-Aux/IAA complex is formed, the hormone is trapped within the auxin cavity, presumably until the ubiquitinated protein is released. Further biochemical studies are required to establish the precise requirements for auxin binding, but on the basis of the structure it is likely that high-affinity auxin binding requires both TIR1 and the Aux/IAA protein. If this is true, this may have important implications for the biological function of the auxin receptor (see below).

Importantly, a long-standing mystery regarding auxin activity is explained by the TIR1 structure. Over the years, a large number of synthetic auxins have been developed, mostly for use as herbicides. These compounds all have a planar ring and a free carboxyl group (Napier 2004, Napier et al. 2002, Sterling & Hall 2007). However, their ring structures vary greatly in size and substitution, leading to questions about how a single receptor can accommodate such different compounds. An examination of the auxin-binding pocket illustrates how this is achieved. The planar ring of the auxin molecule, indole in the case of IAA, fits into the generally hydrophobic cavity while the carboxyl

group forms a salt bridge with a key arginine (R403) (**Figure 2b**). Additional structural determinations were also performed with two different synthetic auxins, 1-NAA and 2,4-D. These compounds have a larger ring and smaller ring, respectively, than does IAA, and binding studies indicate that IAA has the highest affinity among these three compounds, followed by 1-NAA and 2,4-D (Dharmasiri et al. 2005a, Kepinski & Leyser 2005, Tan et al. 2007). Although the relatively spacious hydrophobic cavity accommodates the ring structure of all three molecules, the smaller size of the 2,4-D ring does not fill the cavity as well, and 2,4-D hence has the lowest affinity of the three compounds. IAA appears to bind more tightly than NAA because of electrostatic interactions involving the N on the indole ring (Dharmasiri et al. 2005a, Kepinski & Leyser 2005, Tan et al. 2007).

A recent theoretical analysis of auxin chemistry concluded that auxin activity may depend on the electron density of the ring, rather than its precise atomic composition (Ferro et al. 2006). This idea seems generally consistent with the similar shape-fitted binding of IAA, NAA, and 2,4-D into the TIR1 cavity.

The Auxin Receptor Structure Includes InsP$_6$

Another surprising feature of the TIR1 structure is the presence of a single inositol hexakisphosphate (InsP$_6$) molecule in the floor of the LRR domain (**Figure 2**). The position of InsP$_6$ appears to be critical for stabilizing the structure of the auxin-binding pocket. InsP$_6$ is found in all eukaryotes, and its putative role in a wide variety of cellular processes is beginning to be explored (Macbeth et al. 2005, Mulugu et al. 2007, Odom et al. 2000, Seeds & York 2007). In plants, InsP$_6$ (also called phyate) is an extremely abundant compound that has so far attracted attention primarily because of its animal antinutrient properties (Raboy 2007). Recent genetic studies suggest that it may have an important role in phosphate storage and signaling (Stevenson-Paulik et al. 2005). Currently it is not clear whether InsP$_6$ binding to TIR1 has a regulatory function or a structural function, although the abundance of InsP$_6$ in plant cells suggests the latter. Further studies are required to establish a role of InsP$_6$ in TIR1 function and auxin signaling.

A FAMILY OF AUXIN RECEPTORS IN PLANTS

The *Arabidopsis* genome encodes five F-box proteins exhibiting 50–70% sequence identity with TIR1. These proteins have been named auxin signaling F-box protein 1 to 5 (AFB1–AFB5) (**Table 3**). Genetic and biochemical studies have implicated these proteins in auxin signaling (Dharmasiri et al. 2005b, Walsh et al. 2006; A. Santner, S. Mooney & M. Estelle, unpublished). Moreover, binding of radiolabeled IAA is diminished in extracts from mutants lacking TIR1 and AFB1–3, confirming that these proteins are very likely to function as auxin receptors. As for the *tir1* mutants, single *afb* loss-of-function mutations do not cause dramatic developmental defects.

However, combining *tir1* and *afb1–3* mutations leads to a severely reduced auxin response and a variety of auxin-related developmental defects (Dharmasiri et al. 2005b). The most severely affected *tir1afb2afb3* and *tir1afb1afb2afb3* seedlings arrest as young seedlings, with a phenotype strikingly similar to the phenotypes of the *mp/arf5* and *bdl/iaa12* mutants described above. This similarity is explained by the fact that IAA12 accumulates in *tir1afb2afb3* seedlings, presumably because these plants are deficient in auxin-dependent degradation of IAA12 early in embryogenesis (Dharmasiri et al. 2005b). As with *bdl*, only a fraction of the triple and quadruple *afb* mutant seedlings fail to form roots. Compensatory mechanisms within an auxin feedback loop or other aspects of the developmental network may overcome the embryonic arrest in the fraction of seedlings that develop roots. These, however, continue to display a broad array of auxin response defects as they mature.

Although the available evidence suggests that TIR1 and AFB1–3 have similar functions

Table 3 Auxin receptors in *Arabidopsis thaliana*

Gene	Product	Function	Genetic evidence for role in auxin-mediated development	References
TIR1	Transport inhibitor response 1, TIR1 F-box protein	Interacts with ASK1; interacts with Aux/IAAs; auxin increases Aux/IAA affinity; crystal structure shows TIR1-auxin-Aux/IAA complex	Loss-of-function mutations reduce multiple auxin responses	N. Dharmasiri et al. 2003, Dharmasiri et al. 2005b, Gray et al. 1999, Kepinski & Leyser 2005, Ruegger et al. 1998, Tan et al. 2007
AFB1	Auxin F-box protein 1 (AFB1)	Member of TIR1/AFB family; auxin increases Aux/IAA affinity	Loss of function with *tir1*, *afb2*, *afb3* dramatically impairs development	Dharmasiri et al. 2005b
AFB2	Auxin F-box protein 2 (AFB2)	Member of TIR1/AFB family; auxin increases Aux/IAA affinity	Loss of function with *tir1* reduces multiple auxin responses	Dharmasiri et al. 2005b
AFB3	Auxin F-box protein 3 (AFB3)	Member of TIR1/AFB; auxin increases Aux/IAA affinity	Loss of function with *tir1* and *afb2* dramatically impairs development	Dharmasiri et al. 2005b
AFB4	Auxin F-box protein 4 (AFB4)	Member of TIR1/AFB family		Dharmasiri et al. 2005b
AFB5	Auxin F-box protein 5 (AFB5)	Member of TIR1/AFB family	Loss-of-function mutation confers resistance to auxin analogs	Dharmasiri et al. 2005b, Walsh et al. 2006

in development, it is likely that more detailed studies will reveal specific roles for one or more of these proteins. Such specific functions have already been demonstrated for AFB5. Genetic studies showed that loss of AFB5 results in resistance to the synthetic auxin picloram (Walsh et al. 2006). Because *afb5* plants are only slightly resistant to IAA and other auxins, AFB5 appears to have important chemical selectivity. It will be interesting to learn how the biological functions of these proteins relate to differences in the auxin-binding cavities or other elements of AFB4 and AFB5 structures.

Auxin Receptor Specificities

Most members of the Aux/IAA protein family contain the auxin degron, implying that these proteins are all substrates of $SCF^{TIR1/AFB}$. However, several studies demonstrate substantial differences in the rates of degradation among family members (Dreher et al. 2006, Gray et al. 2001, Hayashi et al. 2003, Ouellet et al. 2001). Because the structure of a complete Aux/IAA protein in complex with TIR1 has not been determined, it is not clear if there are contacts between the two proteins outside the degron. Interestingly, Dreher et al. (2006) showed that substitution of a conserved basic residue pair distant from the known degron motif increases the basal half-life of an IAA17-luciferase fusion protein in plants without affecting auxin-stimulated degradation. This site may participate in an electrostatic interaction between the LRR surface and the Aux/IAA that is needed for low-affinity substrate binding when auxin is not present. It is not known if $SCF^{TIR1/AFB}$ promotes Aux/IAA degradation in the absence of auxin.

A related question concerns the specificity of the TIR1/AFB-Aux/IAA interaction. In vitro experiments suggest that isolated TIR1 and AFB1–3 can interact with multiple members of the Aux/IAA family (Dharmasiri et al. 2005b, Yang et al. 2004). Further studies are required to determine the biological relevance of these interactions and in vivo functional specificities in auxin-mediated development.

JASMONIC ACID MAY BE PERCEIVED BY THE RELATED F-BOX PROTEIN COI1

TIR1 and AFB1–5 are part of a group of seven related F-box proteins. The last member of this group, a protein called COI1, is required for response to the hormone jasmonic acid (JA). Recent results demonstrate remarkable similarities between auxin and JA signaling. Like TIR1, COI1 promotes the degradation of transcriptional repressors in response to a hormone, in this case jasmonyl isoleucine (JA-Ile) (Chini et al. 2007, Thines et al. 2007). Stabilized versions of the repressors, the JAZ proteins, inhibit JA responses. On the basis of primary structure, the LRRs of COI1 should assume the same novel fold as does TIR1. The auxin-binding cavity is not present in COI1, but the $InsP_6$-binding pocket is conserved between the two proteins. On the basis of these similarities, it is tempting to speculate that COI1 functions as a JA-Ile receptor and that hormone binding stabilizes the interaction between COI1 and the JAZ proteins.

On the basis of the structural data, it is likely that both TIR1/AFB and the Aux/IAA protein are required for high-affinity binding of auxin. The mechanism of auxin binding offers an explanation for the failure to identify TIR1 in experiments designed to recover auxin-binding proteins (Napier 2004). Because the Aux/IAA proteins are rapidly ubiquitinated and degraded upon binding to TIR1, the TIR1-auxin-Aux/IAA complex is transient and present at low levels.

Auxin-Regulated Processes Are Sensitive to Levels of Both Auxin and Receptor

The abundance of auxin receptors may quantitatively modulate transcriptional responses to auxin and resulting developmental effects. The *tir1-1* mutation is semidominant (Ruegger et al. 1998), indicating that auxin response is sensitive to TIR1 levels, and loss of additional auxin receptor family members further impairs auxin-related development (Dharmasiri et al. 2005b).

Because the auxin signal does not appear to be amplified between hormone perception and gene regulation, transcription and its developmental consequences are expected to be acutely sensitive to the localized concentration of auxin in the cell. Indeed, numerous studies demonstrate that the transient regulation of auxin intercellular transport and intracellular homeostasis critically influences development (Leyser 2006, Tanaka 2006). The *tir1* phenotype is greatly exacerbated in the context of reduced cellular auxin levels. Dramatic hypermorphic phenotypes are apparent when the *tir1-1* mutation is combined with mutations in the *TAA1/TIR2* gene that reduce auxin levels (M. Yamada, P. Jensen & M. Estelle, unpublished). TAA1/TIR2 is an aminotransferase involved in auxin biosynthesis (Stepanova et al. 2008, Tao et al. 2008; M. Yamada, P. Jensen & M. Estelle, unpublished). Whereas *tir1* and *taa1/tir2* develop fully and show relatively mild auxin-related defects, root meristems of double-mutant seedlings are highly disorganized and underdeveloped (M. Yamada, P. Jensen & M. Estelle, unpublished). Because auxin levels are lower in *taa1/tir2* seedlings, they are sensitized to changes in the level of SCF^{TIR1}.

Consistent with these observations, mutants that are deficient in components of auxin response differ markedly from wild-type plants in their sensitivities to chemical or genetic inhibition of auxin transport. When the auxin transport inhibitor *N*-(1-naphthyl)phthalamic acid (NPA) is applied to floral meristems, auxin is depleted in that region to a level that minimally affects wild-type floral development (Nemhauser et al. 2000). In weak mutant alleles of *ett/arf3*, however, application of NPA leads to dramatic deformation of floral organs in a manner mimicking development in the strongest *ett/arf3* alleles (Nemhauser et al. 2000). In contrasting experiments, increasing localized auxin concentrations appears to compensate for a reduction in auxin receptor abundance. When NPA or other transport inhibitors are applied to seedlings, auxin accumulates in the root tip and stimulates excessive cell proliferation. The roots of *tir1* and other auxin response mutants are less sensitive to auxin transport inhibitors than are wild-type seedlings, and indeed this difference is the basis for the screen in which the *tir1* mutant was identified (Ruegger et al. 1997).

Regulation of AFB and ARF Levels

A variety of developmental and environmental cues may modulate development by regulating the local abundance of auxin receptors and other auxin response components. Experiments with promoter::GUS lines indicate that the *TIR1* and *AFB1–3* promoters are active throughout the life cycle of the plant, with particularly high activity in growing tissues. However, recent findings that the *TIR1*, *AFB2*, and *AFB3* transcripts are targets of the microRNA (miRNA) *miR393* add complexity to our understanding of the dynamics of auxin receptor action (Navarro et al. 2006). Studies indicate that *miR393* regulates growth and development during the plant response to bacterial pathogens. When *Arabidopsis* seedlings are treated with the pathogen *Pseudomonas syringae* or the bacterial elicitor flagellin, levels of *miR393* become elevated, leading to a reduction in *TIR1* transcript and TIR1 protein levels. Concomitant stabilization of AXR3/IAA17 and downregulation of auxin-activated transcription demonstrate that changes in TIR1 levels can very rapidly alter auxin response. Suppression of auxin signaling by *miR393* correlates with reduced growth of the pathogen, suggesting that regulation of auxin receptor abundance may serve as a disease resistance strategy (Navarro et al. 2006).

Levels and localization of auxin response components downstream of the receptors are also regulated by transcriptional and posttranscriptional mechanisms. A number of recent studies demonstrate that expression of ARF family members is subject to regulation by silencing RNAs. Transcripts of several ARFs are targeted by known miRNAs or *trans*-acting small interfering RNAs (siRNAs). Inhibiting miRNA-mediated cleavage of *ARF17* (Mallory et al. 2005) or *ARF10* (Liu et al. 2007) transcripts increases ARF accumulation and causes defects in development throughout the plant (Mallory et al. 2005). Blocking siRNA regulation of *ARF3* and *ARF4* drastically impairs normal development of leaves and flowers, in part owing to defects in cell differentiation and developmental timing (Fahlgren et al. 2006, Garcia et al. 2006, Hunter et al. 2006). In addition, regulation of translation initiation by upstream open reading frames (uORFs) modulates ARF3 and ARF5 levels during floral development, and a similar mechanism is predicted to influence nine additional *ARF* genes (Nishimura et al. 2005). Signals other than auxin promote proteasome-dependent degradation of ARF (Li et al. 2004) and ARF1 (Salmon et al. 2008) by as-yet-unknown mechanisms. Continued efforts to identify mechanisms by which the expression, localization, and association of auxin receptors and response components are regulated will add important insights to our understanding of how auxin signaling is integrated with the developmental network.

OTHER CELLULAR RESPONSES TO AUXIN MAY OCCUR INDEPENDENTLY OF THE TIR1/AFB RECEPTORS

Apart from the well-characterized transcriptional response, auxin affects cellular responses, such as ion transport through the plasma membrane, that are probably too rapid to be directly related to changes in transcription (Badescu & Napier 2006, Napier 2004, Yamagami et al. 2004). A variety of studies suggest that these responses may be mediated by a membrane-associated protein called AUXIN-BINDING PROTEIN1 (ABP1). This protein was isolated on the basis of its affinity for auxin compounds and is therefore considered a candidate auxin receptor (Napier 2004, Napier et al. 2002). Interestingly, loss of ABP1 function causes early embryo arrest as in *tir1afb2afb3*, *mp*, and *bdl* (above), but with a very different terminal phenotype (Chen et al. 2001). The *abp1* mutants exhibit pronounced defects in cell division, expansion, and arrest at the globular stage. ABP1 and the TIR1/AFBs are clearly not related, leaving open the possibility that ABP1 may serve an auxin perception role in cellular processes that are not yet well understood (David et al. 2007).

In addition, auxin regulates its own transport in part by inhibiting endocytosis of the auxin transporter protein PIN1 (Paciorek et al. 2005). This response does not appear to require transcription or the TIR1 auxin receptor, suggesting that it involves an independent signaling pathway. Whether this pathway includes ABP1 remains to be determined.

OTHER NATURAL AUXINS?

The structure of the auxin receptor explains for the first time how compounds with a variety of chemical structures can act as auxins. In addition, emerging evidence suggests that different members of the TIR1/AFB family may have distinct auxin specificities, at least with respect to synthetic auxins. These observations invite us to consider the possibility that natural auxins are also chemically diverse. IAA is generally thought to be the primary natural auxin, but very little is known regarding the possible existence of other auxins in plants. Compounds such as 4-chloroindole-3-acetic acid (4-Cl-IAA), indole-3-butyric acid (IBA), indole-3-pyruvic acid (IPA), and indole-3-acetonitrile (IAN), as well as phenylacetic acid (PPA) have been identified in plants and shown to have auxin-related effects (Ozga et al. 2002, Van Huizen et al. 1997, Woodward & Bartel 2005, Zolman et al. 2000). In some cases, such as IBA, the compound may be converted to IAA, whereas others may interact directly with the receptors. Because it is now possible to test this directly in the case of the TIR1/AFB proteins, we should have an answer to this question soon. If there are additional auxins present in the plant, it will be very interesting to explore their functions with regard to specific developmental processes (Campanoni & Nick 2005, Walsh et al. 2006).

DEVELOPMENTAL COMPLEXITY

As this review shows, auxin-dependent growth and development are sensitive to changes in the levels of auxin-regulated transcription complexes, auxin receptors, and local concentrations of auxin. Little is known regarding protein-protein interactions that contribute additional complexity to auxin response pathways. Plant responses to other intrinsic and environmental signals interact with auxin responses through a variety of mechanisms that continue to be uncovered. For example, the possibility that the photoreceptor phytochrome may directly regulate selected Aux/IAAs suggests that transcriptional outputs of auxin signaling vary with light conditions (Colon-Carmona et al. 2000). Indeed, some of the Aux/IAA proteins were originally identified in genetic screens assessing light responsiveness (Tian & Reed 1999). Interesting recent findings in the signaling of pathogens and other hormones have begun to broaden our view of how other factors modify auxin signaling. Because auxin response is dependent on the Ub-proteasome pathway, components of this pathway that function in developmental processes unrelated to auxin signaling may represent additional points of signal integration.

There are many outstanding questions regarding the cellular role of auxin in plant growth and development. Auxin receptor specificities are likely to explain important aspects of auxin-mediated development not yet understood. In addition, detailed knowledge of individual auxin target genes and the spatial and temporal controls governing the ARFs, Aux/IAAs, and other transcriptional regulators is required. These studies will reveal how such a small chemical signal has such a large impact on the progression of plant life.

SUMMARY POINTS

1. Plant development depends on auxin perception by newly identified receptors whose functions are integral to the ubiquitin-proteasome pathway of protein degradation. Auxin perception leads to the degradation of Aux/IAA transcriptional repressors and thereby rapidly alters gene expression.

2. The first auxin receptor structure reveals a novel mechanism of hormone-receptor and SCF-substrate interactions. Auxin is bound in a hydrophobic pocket within the F-box protein of the SCF. Auxin acts as a molecular glue to promote high-affinity binding of an Aux/IAA protein through its degron structure, allowing the substrate to be ubiquitinated without additional modification.

3. In *Arabidopsis* six auxin receptor F-box proteins appear to act similarly, and developmental specificities among these are being explored. Auxin receptor abundance is regulated through a variety of mechanisms, including RNA silencing. Localized availability of auxin to receptors is tightly regulated throughout development by the transcriptional output of auxin signaling as well as other signaling pathways.

FUTURE ISSUES

1. The selectivity of auxin receptors with substrate Aux/IAAs and the influence of different auxins on these interactions need to be determined. Such findings will contribute to our knowledge of auxin receptor specificities and/or biochemical redundancies.

2. Elucidating the role of phytate in auxin receptor structures may identify important physiological requirements for auxin signaling.

3. The identification of natural auxin-responsive promoters and higher-order ARF complexes will elaborate Aux/IAA functions and will better explain the role of the auxin receptor in regulating transcription.

4. Further elaborating mechanisms by which auxin receptors and their transcriptional effectors are spatially and temporally regulated will explain much of the complexity of the developmental progression and responses of plants to their environments.

DISCLOSURE STATEMENT

The authors are not aware of any biases that might be perceived as affecting the objectivity of this review.

LITERATURE CITED

Abel S, Nguyen MD, Theologis A. 1995. The PS-IAA4/5-like family of early auxin-inducible mRNAs in *Arabidopsis thaliana*. *J. Mol. Biol.* 251:533–49

Abel S, Oeller PW, Theologis A. 1994. Early auxin-induced genes encode short-lived nuclear proteins. *Proc. Natl. Acad. Sci. USA* 91:326–30

Abel S, Theologis A. 1996. Early genes and auxin action. *Plant Physiol.* 111:9–17

Ainley WM, Walker JC, Nagao RT, Key JL. 1988. Sequence and characterization of two auxin-regulated genes from soybean. *J. Biol. Chem.* 263:10658–66

Alonso-Peral MM, Candela H, del Pozo JC, Martínez-Laborda A, Ponce MR, Micol JL. 2006. The *HVE/CAND1* gene is required for the early patterning of leaf venation in *Arabidopsis*. *Development* 133:3755–66

Amerik AY, Hochstrasser M. 2004. Mechanism and function of deubiquitinating enzymes. *Biochim. Biophys. Acta* 1695:189–207

Badescu GO, Napier RM. 2006. Receptors for auxin: Will it all end in TIRs? *Trends Plant Sci.* 11:217–23

Bao F, Shen J, Brady SR, Muday GK, Asami T, Yang Z. 2004. Brassinosteroids interact with auxin to promote lateral root development in *Arabidopsis*. *Plant Physiol.* 134:1624–31

Berleth T, Jurgens G. 1993. The role of the *monopteros* gene in organising the basal body region of the *Arabidopsis* embryo. *Development* 118:575–87

Blancaflor EB, Masson PH. 2003. Plant gravitropism. Unraveling the ups and downs of a complex process. *Plant Physiol.* 133:1677–90

Bostick M, Lochhead SR, Honda A, Palmer S, Callis J. 2004. Related to ubiquitin 1 and 2 are redundant and essential and regulate vegetative growth, auxin signaling, and ethylene production in *Arabidopsis*. *Plant Cell* 16:2418–32

Brukhin V, Gheyselinck J, Gagliardini V, Genschik P, Grossniklaus U. 2005. The RPN1 subunit of the 26S proteasome in Arabidopsis is essential for embryogenesis. *Plant Cell* 17:2723–37

Campanoni P, Nick P. 2005. Auxin-dependent cell division and cell elongation. 1-Naphthaleneacetic acid and 2,4-dichlorophenoxyacetic acid activate different pathways. *Plant Physiol.* 137:939–48

Casimiro I, Marchant A, Bhalerao RP, Beeckman T, Dhooge S, et al. 2001. Auxin transport promotes *Arabidopsis* lateral root initiation. *Plant Cell* 13:843–52

Chen JG, Ullah H, Young JC, Sussman MR, Jones AM. 2001. ABP1 is required for organized cell elongation and division in *Arabidopsis* embryogenesis. *Genes Dev.* 15:902–11

Cheng Y, Dai X, Zhao Y. 2004. AtCAND1, a HEAT-repeat protein that participates in auxin signaling in *Arabidopsis*. *Plant Physiol.* 135:1020–26

Chini A, Fonseca S, Fernandez G, Adie B, Chico JM, et al. 2007. The JAZ family of repressors is the missing link in jasmonate signalling. *Nature* 448:666–71

Chuang HW, Zhang W, Gray WM. 2004. *Arabidopsis* ETA2, an apparent ortholog of the human cullin-interacting protein CAND1, is required for auxin responses mediated by the SCF^{TIR1} ubiquitin ligase. *Plant Cell* 16:1883–97

Colon-Carmona A, Chen DL, Yeh KC, Abel S. 2000. Aux/IAA proteins are phosphorylated by phytochrome in vitro. *Plant Physiol.* 124:1728–38

Conner TW, Goekjian VH, LaFayette PR, Key JL. 1990. Structure and expression of two auxin-inducible genes from *Arabidopsis*. *Plant Mol. Biol.* 15:623–32

Darwin C. 1880. *The Power of Movement in Plants*. London: John Murray. 592 pp.

David KM, Couch D, Braun N, Brown S, Grosclaude J, Perrot-Rechenmann C. 2007. The auxin-binding protein 1 is essential for the control of cell cycle. *Plant J.* 50:197–206

del Pozo JC, Dharmasiri S, Hellmann H, Walker L, Gray WM, Estelle M. 2002. AXR1-ECR1–dependent conjugation of RUB1 to the *Arabidopsis* cullin AtCUL1 is required for auxin response. *Plant Cell* 14:421–33

del Pozo JC, Estelle M. 1999. The *Arabidopsis* cullin AtCUL1 is modified by the ubiquitin-related protein RUB1. *Proc. Natl. Acad. Sci. USA* 96:15342–47

del Pozo JC, Timpte C, Tan S, Callis J, Estelle M. 1998. The ubiquitin-related protein RUB1 and auxin response in *Arabidopsis*. *Science* 280:1760–63

Demartino GN, Gillette TG. 2007. Proteasomes: machines for all reasons. *Cell* 129:659–62

Dharmasiri N, Dharmasiri S, Estelle M. 2005a. The F-box protein TIR1 is an auxin receptor. *Nature* 435:441–45

Dharmasiri N, Dharmasiri S, Jones AM, Estelle M. 2003. Auxin action in a cell-free system. *Curr. Biol.* 13:1418–22

Dharmasiri N, Dharmasiri S, Weijers D, Karunarathna N, Jurgens G, Estelle M. 2007. *AXL* and *AXR1* have redundant functions in RUB conjugation and growth and development in *Arabidopsis*. *Plant J.* 52:114–23

Dharmasiri N, Dharmasiri S, Weijers D, Lechner E, Yamada M, et al. 2005b. Plant development is regulated by a family of auxin receptor F box proteins. *Dev. Cell* 9:109–19

Dharmasiri S, Dharmasiri N, Hellmann H, Estelle M. 2003. The RUB/Nedd8 conjugation pathway is required for early development in *Arabidopsis*. *EMBO J.* 22:1762–70

Dohmann EM, Kuhnle C, Schwechheimer C. 2005. Loss of the CONSTITUTIVE PHOTOMORPHOGENIC9 signalosome subunit 5 is sufficient to cause the *cop/det/fus* mutant phenotype in *Arabidopsis*. *Plant Cell* 17:1967–78

Dreher KA, Brown J, Saw RE, Callis J. 2006. The *Arabidopsis* Aux/IAA protein family has diversified in degradation and auxin responsiveness. *Plant Cell* 18:699–714

Duhamel H-L. 1758. *La Physique des Arbres*. Paris: H-L Guerin & L-F Delatour. 306 pp.

Fahlgren N, Montgomery TA, Howell MD, Allen E, Dvorak SK, et al. 2006. Regulation of *AUXIN RESPONSE FACTOR3* by *TAS3* ta-siRNA affects developmental timing and patterning in *Arabidopsis*. *Curr. Biol.* 16:939–44

Feng S, Shen Y, Sullivan JA, Rubio V, Xiong Y, et al. 2004. *Arabidopsis* CAND1, an unmodified CUL1-interacting protein, is involved in multiple developmental pathways controlled by ubiquitin/proteasome-mediated protein degradation. *Plant Cell* 16:1870–82

Ferro N, Gallegos A, Bultinck P, Jacobsen HJ, Carbo-Dorca R, Reinard T. 2006. Coulomb and overlap self-similarities: a comparative selectivity analysis of structure-function relationships for auxin-like molecules. *J. Chem. Inf. Model.* 46:1751–62

Friml J, Vieten A, Sauer M, Weijers D, Schwarz H, et al. 2003. Efflux-dependent auxin gradients establish the apical-basal axis of *Arabidopsis*. *Nature* 426:147–53

Fukaki H, Nakao Y, Okushima Y, Theologis A, Tasaka M. 2005. Tissue-specific expression of stabilized SOLITARY-ROOT/IAA14 alters lateral root development in *Arabidopsis*. *Plant J.* 44:382–95

Fukaki H, Tameda S, Masuda H, Tasaka M. 2002. Lateral root formation is blocked by a gain-of-function mutation in the *SOLITARY-ROOT/IAA14* gene of *Arabidopsis*. *Plant J.* 29:153–68

Fukaki H, Taniguchi N, Tasaka M. 2006. PICKLE is required for SOLITARY-ROOT/IAA14-mediated repression of ARF7 and ARF19 activity during *Arabidopsis* lateral root initiation. *Plant J.* 48:380–89

Ganoth D, Bornstein G, Ko TK, Larsen B, Tyers M, et al. 2001. The cell-cycle regulatory protein Cks1 is required for SCF^{Skp2}-mediated ubiquitinylation of p27. *Nat. Cell Biol.* 3:321–24

Garcia D, Collier SA, Byrne ME, Martienssen RA. 2006. Specification of leaf polarity in *Arabidopsis* via the trans-acting siRNA pathway. *Curr. Biol.* 16:933–38

Goda H, Sawa S, Asami T, Fujioka S, Shimada Y, Yoshida S. 2004. Comprehensive comparison of auxin-regulated and brassinosteroid-regulated genes in *Arabidopsis*. *Plant Physiol.* 134:1555–73

Gray WM, del Pozo JC, Walker L, Hobbie L, Risseeuw E, et al. 1999. Identification of an SCF ubiquitin-ligase complex required for auxin response in *Arabidopsis thaliana*. *Genes Dev.* 13:1678–91

Gray WM, Hellmann H, Dharmsiri S, Estelle M. 2002. Role of the *Arabidopsis* RING-H2 finger protein RBX1 in RUB modification and SCF function. *Plant Cell* 14:2137–44

Gray WM, Kepinski S, Rouse D, Leyser O, Estelle M. 2001. Auxin regulates SCF^{TIR1}-dependent degradation of AUX/IAA proteins. *Nature* 414:271–76

Gray WM, Muskett PR, Chuang HW, Parker JE. 2003. *Arabidopsis* SGT1b is required for SCF^{TIR1}-mediated auxin response. *Plant Cell* 15:1310–19

Guilfoyle T, Hagen G, Li Y, Ulmasov T, Liu Z, et al. 1993. Auxin-regulated transcription. *Aust. J. Plant Physiol.* 20:489–502

Guilfoyle TJ, Hagen G. 2007. Auxin response factors. *Curr. Opin. Plant Biol.* 10:453–60

Hamann T, Benkova E, Baurle I, Kientz M, Jurgens G. 2002. The *Arabidopsis BODENLOS* gene encodes an auxin response protein inhibiting MONOPTEROS-mediated embryo patterning. *Genes Dev.* 16:1610–15

Hamann T, Mayer U, Jurgens G. 1999. The auxin-insensitive *bodenlos* mutation affects primary root formation and apical-basal patterning in the *Arabidopsis* embryo. *Development* 126:1387–95

Hardtke CS, Ckurshumova W, Vidaurre DP, Singh SA, Stamatiou G, et al. 2004. Overlapping and non-redundant functions of the *Arabidopsis* auxin response factors MONOPTEROS and NONPHOTOTROPIC HYPOCOTYL 4. *Development* 131:1089–100

Hardtke CS, Berleth T. 1998. The *Arabidopsis* gene *MONOPTEROS* encodes a transcription factor mediating embryo axis formation and vascular development. *EMBO J.* 17:1405–11

Hayashi K, Jones AM, Ogino K, Yamazoe A, Oono Y, et al. 2003. Yokonolide B, a novel inhibitor of auxin action, blocks degradation of AUX/IAA factors. *J. Biol. Chem.* 278:23797–806

Hellmann H, Hobbie L, Chapman A, Dharmasiri S, Dharmasiri N, et al. 2003. *Arabidopsis* AXR6 encodes CUL1 implicating SCF E3 ligases in auxin regulation of embryogenesis. *EMBO J.* 22:3314–25

Hershko A, Ciechanover A. 1998. The ubiquitin system. *Annu. Rev. Biochem.* 67:425–79

Himanen K, Boucheron E, Vanneste S, de Almeida Engler J, Inze D, Beeckman T. 2002. Auxin-mediated cell cycle activation during early lateral root initiation. *Plant Cell* 14:2339–51

Hobbie L, McGovern M, Hurwitz LR, Pierro A, Liu NY, et al. 2000. The *axr6* mutants of *Arabidopsis thaliana* define a gene involved in auxin response and early development. *Development* 127:23–32

Hochstrasser M. 2006. Lingering mysteries of ubiquitin-chain assembly. *Cell* 124:27–34

Hunter C, Willmann MR, Wu G, Yoshikawa M, de la Luz Gutierrez-Nava M, Poethig SR. 2006. Trans-acting siRNA-mediated repression of ETTIN and ARF4 regulates heteroblasty in *Arabidopsis. Development* 133:2973–81

Kepinski S, Leyser O. 2004. Auxin-induced SCF^{TIR1}-Aux/IAA interaction involves stable modification of the SCF^{TIR1} complex. *Proc. Natl. Acad. Sci. USA* 101:12381–86

Kepinski S, Leyser O. 2005. The *Arabidopsis* F-box protein TIR1 is an auxin receptor. *Nature* 435:446–51

Kerscher O, Felberbaum R, Hochstrasser M. 2006. Modification of proteins by ubiquitin and ubiquitin-like proteins. *Annu. Rev. Cell Dev. Biol.* 22:159–80

Kim BC, Soh MS, Kang BJ, Furuya M, Nam HG. 1996. Two dominant photomorphogenic mutations of *Arabidopsis thaliana* identified as suppressor mutations of *hy2. Plant J.* 9:441–56

Kleine-Vehn J, Friml J. 2008. Polar targeting and endocytic recycling in auxin-dependent plant development. *Annu. Rev. Cell Dev. Biol.* 24:447–73

Knox K, Grierson CS, Leyser O. 2003. AXR3 and SHY2 interact to regulate root hair development. *Development* 130:5769–77

Koepp DM, Schaefer LK, Ye X, Keyomarsi K, Chu C, et al. 2001. Phosphorylation-dependent ubiquitination of cyclin E by the SCF^{Fbw7} ubiquitin ligase. *Science* 294:173–77

Kögl F, Smit AJH. 1931. Über die Chemie des Wuchsstoffs. *Proc. Kon. Akad. Wetensch (Amsterdam)* 34:1411–16

Lechner E, Achard P, Vansiri A, Potuschak T, Genschik P. 2006. F-box proteins everywhere. *Curr. Opin. Plant Biol.* 9:631–38

Leyser HMO, Lincoln CA, Timpte C, Lammer D, Turner J, Estelle M. 1993. *Arabidopsis* auxin-resistance gene *AXR1* encodes a protein related to ubiquitin-activating enzyme E1. *Nature* 364:161–64

Leyser HMO, Pickett FB, Dharmasiri S, Estelle M. 1996. Mutations in the *AXR3* gene of *Arabidopsis* result in altered auxin response including ectopic expression from the *SAUR-AC1* promoter. *Plant J.* 10:403–13

Leyser O. 2006. Dynamic integration of auxin transport and signalling. *Curr. Biol.* 16:R424–33

Li H, Johnson P, Stepanova A, Alonso JM, Ecker JR. 2004. Convergence of signaling pathways in the control of differential cell growth in *Arabidopsis*. *Dev. Cell* 7:193–204

Li J, Dai X, Zhao Y. 2006. A role for auxin response factor 19 in auxin and ethylene signaling in *Arabidopsis*. *Plant Physiol.* 140:899–908

Lincoln C, Britton JH, Estelle M. 1990. Growth and development of the *axr1* mutants of *Arabidopsis*. *Plant Cell* 2:1071–80

Liscum E, Reed JW. 2002. Genetics of Aux/IAA and ARF action in plant growth and development. *Plant Mol. Biol.* 49:387–400

Liu PP, Montgomery TA, Fahlgren N, Kasschau KD, Nonogaki H, Carrington JC. 2007. Repression of *AUXIN RESPONSE FACTOR10* by microRNA160 is critical for seed germination and post-germination stages. *Plant J.* 52:133–46

Macbeth MR, Schubert HL, Vandemark AP, Lingam AT, Hill CP, Bass BL. 2005. Inositol hexakisphosphate is bound in the ADAR2 core and required for RNA editing. *Science* 309:1534–39

Malamy JE, Benfey PN. 1997. Organization and cell differentiation in lateral roots of *Arabidopsis thaliana*. *Development* 124:33–44

Mallory AC, Bartel DP, Bartel B. 2005. MicroRNA-directed regulation of *Arabidopsis AUXIN RESPONSE FACTOR17* is essential for proper development and modulates expression of early auxin response genes. *Plant Cell* 17:1360–75

Minella AC, Clurman BE. 2005. Mechanisms of tumor suppression by the SCF^{Fbw7}. *Cell Cycle* 4:1356–59

Moon J, Parry G, Estelle M. 2004. The ubiquitin-proteasome pathway and plant development. *Plant Cell* 16:3181–95

Moon J, Zhao Y, Dai X, Zhang W, Gray WM, et al. 2007. A new *CULLIN1* mutant has altered responses to hormones and light in *Arabidopsis*. *Plant Physiol.* 143:684–96

Mulugu S, Bai W, Fridy PC, Bastidas RJ, Otto JC, et al. 2007. A conserved family of enzymes that phosphorylate inositol hexakisphosphate. *Science* 316:106–9

Muto H, Nagao I, Demura T, Fukuda H, Kinjo M, Yamamoto KT. 2006. Fluorescence cross-correlation analyses of the molecular interaction between an Aux/IAA protein, MSG2/IAA19, and protein-protein interaction domains of auxin response factors of *Arabidopsis* expressed in HeLa cells. *Plant Cell Physiol.* 47:1095–101

Nagpal P, Walker LM, Young JC, Sonawala A, Timpte C, et al. 2000. *AXR2* encodes a member of the Aux/IAA protein family. *Plant Physiol.* 123:563–74

Nakayama KI, Nakayama K. 2005. Regulation of the cell cycle by SCF-type ubiquitin ligases. *Semin. Cell Dev. Biol.* 16:323–33

Napier R. 2004. Plant hormone binding sites. *Ann. Bot. (London)* 93:227–33

Napier RM, David KM, Perrot-Rechenmann C. 2002. A short history of auxin-binding proteins. *Plant Mol. Biol.* 49:339–48

Nateri AS, Riera-Sans L, Da Costa C, Behrens A. 2004. The ubiquitin ligase SCF^{Fbw7} antagonizes apoptotic JNK signaling. *Science* 303:1374–78

Navarro L, Dunoyer P, Jay F, Arnold B, Dharmasiri N, et al. 2006. A plant miRNA contributes to antibacterial resistance by repressing auxin signaling. *Science* 312:436–39

Nemhauser JL, Feldman LJ, Zambryski PC. 2000. Auxin and *ETTIN* in *Arabidopsis* gynoecium morphogenesis. *Development* 127:3877–88

Nemhauser JL, Hong F, Chory J. 2006. Different plant hormones regulate similar processes through largely nonoverlapping transcriptional responses. *Cell* 126:467–75

Nemhauser JL, Mockler TC, Chory J. 2004. Interdependency of brassinosteroid and auxin signaling in *Arabidopsis*. *PLoS Biol.* 2:E258

Nishimura T, Wada T, Yamamoto KT, Okada K. 2005. The *Arabidopsis* STV1 protein, responsible for translation reinitiation, is required for auxin-mediated gynoecium patterning. *Plant Cell* 17:2940–53

Odom AR, Stahlberg A, Wente SR, York JD. 2000. A role for nuclear inositol 1,4,5-trisphosphate kinase in transcriptional control. *Science* 287:2026–29

Okushima Y, Overvoorde PJ, Arima K, Alonso JM, Chan A, et al. 2005. Functional genomic analysis of the *AUXIN RESPONSE FACTOR* gene family members in *Arabidopsis thaliana*: unique and overlapping functions of *ARF*7 and *ARF19*. *Plant Cell* 17:444–63

Orlicky S, Tang X, Willems A, Tyers M, Sicheri F. 2003. Structural basis for phosphodependent substrate selection and orientation by the SCF^{Cdc4} ubiquitin ligase. *Cell* 112:243–56

Ouellet F, Overvoorde PJ, Theologis A. 2001. IAA17/AXR3. Biochemical insight into an auxin mutant phenotype. *Plant Cell* 13:829–42

Overvoorde PJ, Okushima Y, Alonso JM, Chan A, Chang C, et al. 2005. Functional genomic analysis of the *AUXIN/INDOLE-3-ACETIC ACID* gene family members in *Arabidopsis thaliana*. *Plant Cell* 17:3282–300

Ozga JA, van Huizen R, Reinecke DM. 2002. Hormone and seed-specific regulation of pea fruit growth. *Plant Physiol.* 128:1379–89

Paciorek T, Zazimalova E, Ruthardt N, Petrasek J, Stierhof YD, et al. 2005. Auxin inhibits endocytosis and promotes its own efflux from cells. *Nature* 435:1251–56

Park JY, Kim HJ, Kim J. 2002. Mutation in domain II of IAA1 confers diverse auxin-related phenotypes and represses auxin-activated expression of Aux/IAA genes in steroid regulator-inducible system. *Plant J.* 32:669–83

Parry G, Estelle M. 2004. Regulation of cullin-based ubiquitin ligases by the Nedd8/RUB ubiquitin-like proteins. *Semin. Cell Dev. Biol.* 15:221–29

Pekker I, Alvarez JP, Eshed Y. 2005. Auxin response factors mediate *Arabidopsis* organ asymmetry via modulation of KANADI activity. *Plant Cell* 17:2899–910

Peng Z, Shen Y, Feng S, Wang X, Chittetei BN, et al. 2003. Evidence for a physical association of the COP9 signalosome, the proteasome, and specific SCF E3 ligases *in vivo*. *Curr. Biol.* 13:R504–5

Petroski MD, Deshaies RJ. 2005. Function and regulation of cullin-RING ubiquitin ligases. *Nat. Rev. Mol. Cell Biol.* 6:9–20

Pickart CM. 2001. Mechanisms underlying ubiquitination. *Annu. Rev. Biochem.* 70:503–33

Przemeck GK, Mattsson J, Hardtke CS, Sung ZR, Berleth T. 1996. Studies on the role of the *Arabidopsis* gene *MONOPTEROS* in vascular development and plant cell axialization. *Planta* 200:229–37

Quint M, Ito H, Zhang W, Gray WM. 2005. Characterization of a novel temperature-sensitive allele of the CUL1/AXR6 subunit of SCF ubiquitin-ligases. *Plant J.* 43:371–83

Raboy V. 2007. The ABCs of low-phytate crops. *Nat. Biotechnol.* 25:874–75

Ramos JA, Zenser N, Leyser HM, Callis J. 2001. Rapid degradation of Aux/IAA proteins requires conserved amino acids of domain II and is proteasome-dependent. *Plant Cell* 13:2349–60

Reed JW. 2001. Roles and activities of Aux/IAA proteins in *Arabidopsis*. *Trends Plant Sci.* 6:420–25

Reed JW, Elumalai RP, Chory J. 1998. Suppressors of an *Arabidopsis thaliana phyB* mutation identify genes that control light signaling and hypocotyl elongation. *Genetics* 148:1295–310

Rogg LE, Lasswell J, Bartel B. 2001. A gain-of-function mutation in *IAA28* suppresses lateral root development. *Plant Cell* 13:465–80

Rouse D, Mackay P, Stirnberg P, Estelle M, Leyser O. 1998. Changes in auxin response from mutations in an *AUX/IAA* gene. *Science* 279:1371–73

Ruegger M, Dewey E, Gray WM, Hobbie L, Turner J, Estelle M. 1998. The TIR1 protein of *Arabidopsis* functions in auxin response and is related to human SKP2 and yeast Grr1p. *Genes Dev.* 12:198–207

Ruegger M, Dewey E, Hobbie L, Brown D, Bernasconi P, et al. 1997. Reduced naphthylphthalamic acid binding in the *tir3* mutant of *Arabidopsis* is associated with a reduction in polar auxin transport and diverse morphological defects. *Plant Cell* 9:745–57

Sachs J. 1880. Stoff und Form der Pflanzenorgane. *Arb. Bot. Inst. Würzburg* 2:452–88

Salmon J, Ramos J, Callis J. 2008. Degradation of the auxin response factor ARF1. *Plant J.* 54:118–28

Scarpella E, Marcos D, Friml J, Berleth T. 2006. Control of leaf vascular patterning by polar auxin transport. *Genes Dev.* 20:1015–27

Scheres B, Xu J. 2006. Polar auxin transport and patterning: grow with the flow. *Genes Dev.* 20:922–26

Schwechheimer C, Serino G, Callis J, Crosby WL, Lyapina S, et al. 2001. Interactions of the COP9 signalosome with the E3 ubiquitin ligase SCF^{TIR1} in mediating auxin response. *Science* 292:1379–82

Seeds AM, York JD. 2007. Inositol polyphosphate kinases: regulators of nuclear function. *Biochem. Soc. Symp.* 2007:183–97

Shen W-H, Parmentier Y, Hellmann, H, Lechner E, Dong A, et al. 2002. Null mutation of *AtCUL1* causes arrest in early embryogenesis in *Arabidopsis*. *Mol. Biol. Cell* 13:1916–28

Shin R, Burch AY, Huppert KA, Tiwari SB, Murphy AS, et al. 2007. The *Arabidopsis* transcription factor MYB77 modulates auxin signal transduction. *Plant Cell* 19:2440–53

Smalle J, Kurepa J, Yang P, Babiychuk E, Kushnir S, et al. 2002. Cytokinin growth responses in *Arabidopsis* involve the 26S proteasome subunit RPN12. *Plant Cell* 14:17–32

Smalle J, Vierstra RD. 2004. The ubiquitin 26S proteasome proteolytic pathway. *Annu. Rev. Plant Physiol. Plant Mol. Biol.* 55:555–90

Soh MS, Hong SH, Kim BC, Vizir I, Park DH, et al. 1999. Regulation of both light- and auxin-mediated development by the *Arabidopsis IAA3/SHY2* gene. *J. Plant Biol.* 42:239–46

Spruck C, Strohmaier H, Watson M, Smith AP, Ryan A, et al. 2001. A CDK-independent function of mammalian Cks1: targeting of SCF^{Skp2} to the CDK inhibitor p27^{Kip1}. *Mol. Cell* 7:639–50

Stepanova AN, Robertson-Hoyt J, Yun J, Benavente LM, Xie DY, et al. 2008. TAA1-mediated auxin biosynthesis is essential for hormone crosstalk and plant development. *Cell* 133:177–91

Sterling TM, Hall JC. 1997. Mechanism of action of natural auxins and the auxinic herbicide. In *Herbicide Activity: Toxicology, Biochemistry and Molecular Biology*, ed. MR Roe, RJ Kuhr, JD Burton, pp. 111–41. Amsterdam: IOP Press

Stevenson-Paulik J, Bastidas RJ, Chiou ST, Frye RA, York JD. 2005. Generation of phytate-free seeds in *Arabidopsis* through disruption of inositol polyphosphate kinases. *Proc. Natl. Acad. Sci. USA* 102:12612–17

Szemenyei H, Hannon M, Long JA. 2008. TOPLESS mediates auxin-dependent transcriptional repression during *Arabidopsis* embryogenesis. *Science* 319:1384–86

Tan X, Calderon-Villalobos LI, Sharon M, Zheng C, Robinson CV, et al. 2007. Mechanism of auxin perception by the TIR1 ubiquitin ligase. *Nature* 446:640–45

Tao Y, Ferrer JL, Ljung K, Pojer F, Hong F, et al. 2008. Rapid synthesis of auxin via a new tryptophan-dependent pathway is required for shade avoidance in plants. *Cell* 133:164–76

Tatematsu K, Kumagai S, Muto H, Sato A, Watahiki MK, et al. 2004. MASSUGU2 encodes Aux/IAA19, an auxin-regulated protein that functions together with the transcriptional activator NPH4/ARF7 to regulate differential growth responses of hypocotyl and formation of lateral roots in *Arabidopsis thaliana*. *Plant Cell* 16:379–93

Teale WD, Paponov IA, Palme K. 2006. Auxin in action: signalling, transport and the control of plant growth and development. *Nat. Rev. Mol. Cell Biol.* 7:847–59

Theologis A, Huynh TV, Davis RW. 1985. Rapid induction of specific mRNAs by auxin in pea epicotyl tissue. *J. Mol. Biol.* 183:53–68

Thines B, Katsir L, Melotto M, Niu Y, Mandaokar A, et al. 2007. JAZ repressor proteins are targets of the SCF^{COI1} complex during jasmonate signalling. *Nature* 448:661–65

Tian Q, Nagpal P, Reed JW. 2003. Regulation of *Arabidopsis* SHY2/IAA3 protein turnover. *Plant J.* 36:643–51

Tian Q, Reed JW. 1999. Control of auxin-regulated root development by the *Arabidopsis thaliana SHY2/IAA3* gene. *Development* 126:711–21

Tian Q, Uhlir NJ, Reed JW. 2002. *Arabidopsis* SHY2/IAA3 inhibits auxin-regulated gene expression. *Plant Cell* 14:301–19

Timpte C, Wilson AK, Estelle M. 1994. The *axr2-1* mutation of *Arabidopsis thaliana* is a gain-of-function mutation that disrupts an early step in auxin response. *Genetics* 138:1239–49

Tiwari SB, Hagen G, Guilfoyle T. 2003. The roles of auxin response factor domains in auxin-responsive transcription. *Plant Cell* 15:533–43

Tiwari SB, Hagen G, Guilfoyle TJ. 2004. Aux/IAA proteins contain a potent transcriptional repression domain. *Plant Cell* 16:533–43

Tiwari SB, Wang XJ, Hagen G, Guilfoyle TJ. 2001. AUX/IAA proteins are active repressors, and their stability and activity are modulated by auxin. *Plant Cell* 13:2809–22

Ueda M, Matsui K, Ishiguro S, Sano R, Wada T, et al. 2004. The *HALTED ROOT* gene encoding the 26S proteasome subunit RPT2a is essential for the maintenance of *Arabidopsis* meristems. *Development* 131:2101–11

Ulmasov T, Hagen G, Guilfoyle TJ. 1999a. Activation and repression of transcription by auxin-response factors. *Proc. Natl. Acad. Sci. USA* 96:5844–49

Ulmasov T, Hagen G, Guilfoyle TJ. 1999b. Dimerization and DNA binding of auxin response factors. *Plant J.* 19:309–19

Van Huizen R, Ozga JA, Reinecke DM. 1997. Seed and hormonal regulation of gibberellin 20-oxidase expression in pea pericarp. *Plant Physiol.* 115:123–28

Vanneste S, De Rybel B, Beemster GT, Ljung K, De Smet I, et al. 2005. Cell cycle progression in the pericycle is not sufficient for SOLITARY ROOT/IAA14-mediated lateral root initiation in *Arabidopsis thaliana*. *Plant Cell* 17:3035–50

Vidaurre DP, Ploense S, Krogan NT, Berleth T. 2007. *AMP1* and *MP* antagonistically regulate embryo and meristem development in *Arabidopsis*. *Development* 134:2561–67

Walker L, Estelle M. 1998. Molecular mechanisms of auxin action. *Curr. Opin. Plant Biol.* 1:434–39

Walsh TA, Neal R, Merlo AO, Honma M, Hicks GR, et al. 2006. Mutations in an auxin receptor homolog AFB5 and in SGT1b confer resistance to synthetic picolinate auxins and not to 2,4-dichlorophenoxyacetic acid or indole-3-acetic acid in *Arabidopsis*. *Plant Physiol.* 142:542–52

Wang H, Jones B, Li Z, Frasse P, Delalande C, et al. 2005. The tomato Aux/IAA transcription factor IAA9 is involved in fruit development and leaf morphogenesis. *Plant Cell* 17:2676–92

Wei N, Deng XW. 2003. The COP9 signalosome. *Annu. Rev. Cell Dev. Biol.* 19:261–86

Weijers D, Benkova E, Jager KE, Schlereth A, Hamann T, et al. 2005. Developmental specificity of auxin response by pairs of ARF and Aux/IAA transcriptional regulators. *EMBO J.* 24:1874–85

Weijers D, Jurgens G. 2005. Auxin and embryo axis formation: the ends in sight? *Curr. Opin. Plant Biol.* 8:32–37

Weijers D, Schlereth A, Ehrismann JS, Schwank G, Kientz M, Jurgens G. 2006. Auxin triggers transient local signaling for cell specification in *Arabidopsis* embryogenesis. *Dev. Cell* 10:265–70

Went FW. 1926. On growth-accelerating substances in the coleoptile of *Avena sativa*. *Proc. Kon. Akad. Wetensch (Amsterdam)* 30:10–19

Went FW, Thimann KV. 1937. *Phytohormones*. New York: Macmillan. 294 pp.

Wenzel CL, Schuetz M, Yu Q, Mattsson J. 2007. Dynamics of *MONOPTEROS* and *PIN-FORMED1* expression during leaf vein pattern formation in *Arabidopsis thaliana*. *Plant J.* 49:387–98

Woodward AW, Bartel B. 2005. Auxin: regulation, action, and interaction. *Ann. Bot. (London)* 95:707–35

Woodward AW, Ratzel SE, Woodward EE, Shamoo Y, Bartel B. 2007. Mutation of *E1-CONJUGATING ENZYME-RELATED1* decreases RELATED TO UBIQUITIN conjugation and alters auxin response and development. *Plant Physiol.* 144:976–87

Worley CK, Zenser N, Ramos J, Rouse D, Leyser O, et al. 2000. Degradation of Aux/IAA proteins is essential for normal auxin signalling. *Plant J.* 21:553–62

Wu JT, Chan YR, Chien CT. 2006. Protection of cullin-RING E3 ligases by CSN-UBP12. *Trends Cell Biol.* 16:362–69

Xu S, Abbasian M, Patel P, Jensen-Pergakes K, Lobardo CR, et al. 2007. Substrate recognition and ubiquitination of SCFSkp2/Cks1 ubiquitin-protein isopeptide ligase. *J. Biol. Chem.* 282:15462–70

Yamagami M, Haga K, Napier RM, Iino M. 2004. Two distinct signaling pathways participate in auxin-induced swelling of pea epidermal protoplasts. *Plant Physiol.* 134:735–47

Yamamoto KT, Mori H, Imaseki H. 1992. cDNA cloning of indole-3-acetic acid-regulated genes: Aux22 and SAUR from mung bean (*Vigna radiata*) hypocotyl tissue. *Plant Cell Physiol.* 33:93–97

Yang X, Lee S, So JH, Dharmasiri S, Dharmasiri N, et al. 2004. The IAA1 protein is encoded by *AXR5* and is a substrate of SCF^{TIR1}. *Plant J.* 40:772–82

Ye X, Nalepa G, Welcker M, Kessler BM, Spooner E, et al. 2004. Recognition of phosphodegron motifs in human cyclin E by the SCF^{Fbw7} ubiquitin ligase. *J. Biol. Chem.* 279:50110–19

Zenser N, Dreher KA, Edwards SR, Callis J. 2003. Acceleration of Aux/IAA proteolysis is specific for auxin and independent of AXR1. *Plant J.* 35:285–94

Zenser N, Ellsmore A, Leasure C, Callis J. 2001. Auxin modulates the degradation rate of Aux/IAA proteins. *Proc. Natl. Acad. Sci. USA* 98:11795–800

Zolman BK, Yoder A, Bartel B. 2000. Genetic analysis of indole-3-butyric acid responses in *Arabidopsis thaliana* reveals four mutant classes. *Genetics* 156:1323–37

REFERENCE ADDED IN PROOF

Okushima Y, Fukaki H, Onoda M, Theologis A, Tasaka M. 2007. ARF7 and ARF19 regulate lateral root formation via direct activation of *LBD/ASL* genes in *Arabidopsis*. *Plant Cell* 19:118–30

Systems Approaches to Identifying Gene Regulatory Networks in Plants

Terri A. Long,[1,2,*] Siobhan M. Brady,[1,2,*] and Philip N. Benfey[1,2]

[1]Department of Biology and [2]IGSP Center for Systems Biology, Duke University, Durham, North Carolina 27708; email: philip.benfey@duke.edu

Annu. Rev. Cell Dev. Biol. 2008. 24:81–103

First published online as a Review in Advance on July 10, 2008

The *Annual Review of Cell and Developmental Biology* is online at cellbio.annualreviews.org

This article's doi:
10.1146/annurev.cellbio.24.110707.175408

*These authors contributed equally to this work.

Key Words

systems biology, *Arabidopsis*, transcription factors, emergent properties, modeling, genomics

Abstract

Complex gene regulatory networks are composed of genes, noncoding RNAs, proteins, metabolites, and signaling components. The availability of genome-wide mutagenesis libraries; large-scale transcriptome, proteome, and metabalome data sets; and new high-throughput methods that uncover protein interactions underscores the need for mathematical modeling techniques that better enable scientists to synthesize these large amounts of information and to understand the properties of these biological systems. Systems biology approaches can allow researchers to move beyond a reductionist approach and to both integrate and comprehend the interactions of multiple components within these systems. Descriptive and mathematical models for gene regulatory networks can reveal emergent properties of these plant systems. This review highlights methods that researchers are using to obtain large-scale data sets, and examples of gene regulatory networks modeled with these data. Emergent properties revealed by the use of these network models and perspectives on the future of systems biology are discussed.

Contents

INTRODUCTION: SYSTEMS THEORY AND GENE REGULATORY NETWORKS

A plant's final form and ability to respond dynamically to the external environment are the outcome of many components interacting within complex gene regulatory networks. These networks exist at different scales: within a single cell, across multiple cells and cell types, and temporally in each of these contexts. Furthermore, it is these networks that are acted upon by evolutionary forces and whose modification gives rise to the vast diversity in morphological form among plant species. The emergence of high-throughput genomic technologies has resulted in an explosion of data, enabling the cataloging of genes, gene products, and their interactions. Plant biologists are now moving from analyzing the role of a small number of genes to monitoring the global dynamics of entire biological circuits.

Ideker et al. (2001) proposed a systems biology framework to integrate genome-wide measurements in an effort to understand the properties of biological systems. Systems theory studies the organization of variables and is based on the belief that only through understanding the interaction of these components can one identify emergent properties of a system. Emergent properties are those that cannot be identified by examining interactions between individual components alone. In a systems approach, first the components and their interactions that act within the network must be identified and defined (Ideker et al. 2001). To facilitate this approach, however, these components are most appropriately characterized in a global manner. The next step is to perturb the system and monitor its response. Ideally, the effects of perturbations are monitored with genome-scale measurements. Finally, these data are integrated, and the system is modeled. The observed experimental values are compared with the predictions of the model. Novel interactions between components can be inferred, and alternative hypotheses are devised to address discrepancies (Ideker et al. 2001). New experiments can then be undertaken to test these new hypotheses. Ideally, systems approaches can provide insights into complex, regulatory networks and provide a framework for biologists to understand the organization of life.

The plant community has embraced the use of systems approaches (Gutierrez et al. 2005) and produced vast amounts of genomic-scale data and a variety of databases and tools. The primary aim of this review is to describe examples of gene regulatory networks and, in particular, plant transcriptional regulatory networks, whose properties have been elucidated by systems approaches. We begin with a description of the various components that act within gene regulatory networks and of the high-throughput techniques that are being used to elucidate these components. With a list of components and their interactions in hand, gene regulatory networks can be inferred by the use of several different methods. We describe some of these methods, including examples of theoretical modeling and integration of genome-scale data sets. Each of these methods has advantages and disadvantages, but all the methods share the ability to provide a framework with predictive power. We also provide examples of how comparisons of simulations with observed experimental data have revealed gaps in our understanding of molecular interactions. These discrepancies have provided the rationale for predicting novel components or interactions that can reconcile these inconsistencies. Finally, as mentioned above, identifying emergent network properties is a primary goal of the systems approach. We describe some emergent properties identified in network descriptions generated from high-throughput data as well as from smaller network descriptions generated with various modeling approaches. Once we understand and can correctly simulate the dynamics of these gene regulatory networks, we will be able to understand how these complex regulatory networks give rise to a plant's form and function.

GENOME-SCALE DATA SETS: IDENTIFICATION OF COMPONENTS

Genes: Identification and Functional Characterization

A variety of methods have been developed in plants to identify components of plant regulatory networks in a high-throughput manner. Many of these methods have been described in other extensive reviews (Brady et al. 2006, Busch & Lohmann 2007, Jones-Rhoades et al. 2006, Willmann & Poethig 2007, Yazaki et al. 2007). Therefore, we highlight only a set that we feel will be essential for modeling the various molecular species that act to regulate gene expression.

Genome sequencing. Systems theory has been defined as the study of the nature of com-

plex systems (Bertalanffy 1973). The use of systems approaches has emerged only recently as a method to study, comprehend, and integrate large data sets generated during the genomics era. Although scientists have sequenced the genomes of a host of microbes and animals, to date only three plant genomes have been sequenced: *Arabidopsis* (The Arabidopsis Initiative 2000, Lin et al. 1999, Mayer et al. 1999, Theologis et al. 2000), rice (Int. Rice Genome Seq. Proj. 2005), and poplar (Tuskan et al. 2006). However, more than a dozen other plant species, including maize, potato, soybean, cassava, and grape, are in the sequencing pipeline (Pennisi 2007).

Mutant resources. Once the genome is sequenced and genes are predicted, the next goal is to determine the biological function of each gene. Systems biology is greatly facilitated by collections of sequence-indexed, genome-wide mutants (Alonso & Ecker 2006). This allows one to probe the function of genes, using reverse genetics approaches. These resources are integral to testing predictions made about gene regulatory networks. Although a range of methods can be used to generate collections of mutants, the preferred methods for generating sequence-indexed collections in plants include T-DNA and transposon insertional mutagenesis, TILLING (targeting-induced local lesions in genomes) of chemically induced mutants, ectopic expression, and gene silencing. The most extensive collections exist in *Arabidopsis*. Such collections include the Syngenta *Arabidopsis* Insertion Library (SAIL) lines, with insertions in the promoters and transcribed regions of ~15,000 to ~18,000 genes (Sessions et al. 2002); the SALK insertion collection, with insertions in more than 21,000 genes; and the GABI-KAT resource, which contains mutations in ~14,000 genes (Alonso et al. 2003, Rosso et al. 2003). Several groups have carried out, in rice and poplar, high-throughput T-DNA insertional mutagenesis and analysis of loci disrupted by these insertions (Chen et al. 2003, Groover et al. 2004, Hsing et al. 2007, Jeong et al. 2006, Sallaud et al. 2004, J. Zhang et al. 2006). Some of these lines allow functional characterization of target genes, easy detection of insertions using GUS fusions, and the possibility of obtaining ectopic expression of space- and time-specific genes (Groover et al. 2004, Hsing et al. 2007, J. Zhang et al. 2006).

However, insertional mutagenesis does have several disadvantages. Insertions can sometimes be biased toward intergenic regions (Hsing et al. 2007) and can cause dominant lethal mutations, which lead to incomplete saturation of the entire genome. To that end, scientists have begun TILLING plant populations after chemical mutagenesis (Till et al. 2004). This strategy begins with chemical mutagenesis of a population, followed by polymerase chain reaction (PCR) of target genes. Mutations are detected when the PCR products are denatured and reannealed, forming genetic lesions, which, when digested by a mismatch-specific endonuclease, are detectable by capillary gel electrophoresis. Although TILLING is labor intensive and therefore considerably more expensive than other methods, the advantages of TILLING are that it can be used in a high-throughput manner and that it produces heritable mutations in a genome independently of the genome size and of the plants' transformability, reproductive system, and generation time (Gilchrist & Haughn 2005). In addition, TILLING can generate allelic series that allow the study of essential genes, for which complete loss of function can be lethal. Suzuki et al. (2007) used this method in single zygotic rice cells to generate a population with mutations every 135 kb, which will soon be available to the research community. The Maize TILLING Project (MTP), funded by the National Science Foundation, is a national effort to identify point mutations in specific genes in mutant populations for two inbred lines, B73 and W22 (**http://genome.purdue.edu/maizetilling/**). TILLING efforts are also taking place in *Arabidopsis, Lotus,* rice, and *Brassica oleracea,* as well as in other plants (Gilchrist & Haughn 2005, Till et al. 2007).

Targeted mutagenesis can also be employed in a high-throughput manner. RNA interference (RNAi), a defense mechanism that evolved to protect against viruses and transposons in plants, has been exploited as a strategy to disrupt target gene expression. In this method, specific small interfering RNA (siRNA) molecules, which degrade target RNA species, are generated. Efforts are currently under way to generate 150 to 500 base-pair gene-specific targets (GSTs) for at least 21,500 genes in *Arabidopsis.* These GSTs have been used for microarray transcript profiling and cloned into bacterial plasmid vectors for targeted RNAi (Hilson et al. 2004).

Large-scale gene expression analysis. Microarray technology has revolutionized our ability to monitor the output of transcriptional regulation at the level of the whole genome. These expression analyses have been further refined by our ability to monitor expression, at high resolution, within individual cell types, tissues, and organs; at different developmental time points; in different mutant backgrounds; and in response to hormones and various stress conditions (Birnbaum et al. 2003, 2005; Brady et al. 2007; Dembinsky et al. 2007; Kilian et al. 2007; Nawy et al. 2005; Nelson et al. 2006). These large-scale experiments have demonstrated that to obtain accurate representations of gene expression, one must sample at sufficient resolution to differentiate the full complement of transcriptional programs occurring within a plant. To accomplish this, investigators have developed two technologies to identify gene expression in individual cell types or tissues within the plant. The first is the use of fluorescence-activated cell sorting to isolate cell-type-specific green fluorescent protein (GFP)-marked root populations, and the subsequent isolation of RNA from these populations for use in microarray analysis (Birnbaum et al. 2003, 2005). This technique has been used to obtain the most comprehensive microarray expression map of an organ and its component cell types (Brady et al. 2007). The second technique is the use of laser capture microdissection to isolate cell-type populations in maize and *Arabidopsis* (Dembinsky et al. 2007, Nakazono et al. 2003, Spencer et al. 2007, Woll et al. 2005). Cells isolated by this technology have also been used to characterize the cell-type-specific proteome (Dembinsky et al. 2007).

Phylogenetic conservation. Recent efforts in the field of comparative genomics have also contributed to our understanding of gene regulatory networks. Researchers have identified potential *cis*-regulatory sequences in many organisms by searching for evolutionary conservation (Harbison et al. 2004, Kheradpour et al. 2007, Pritsker et al. 2004). Furthermore, natural variation can be exploited to make correlations concerning sequence diversity and its functional consequences for phenotype. Genome-wide detection of polymorphisms among many wild strains (accessions) of *Arabidopsis* also provides a useful resource for detecting evolutionary similarities or differences that regulate transcriptional networks (Borevitz et al. 2007, Clark et al. 2007).

Epigenetic modification. It is now well documented that gene expression can be regulated in a nonheritable fashion, through epigenetic modifications. Methylation of cytosine has been mapped throughout the *Arabidopsis* genome, and most genes that are methylated within their transcribed regions are highly expressed and constitutively active (X. Zhang et al. 2006, Zilberman et al. 2007). Histone methylation, particularly trimethylation of lysine 27 of histone H3 (H3K27me3), plays an important role in regulating animal development. Tiling arrays used to map H3K27me3 methylation sites in the *Arabidopsis* genome revealed a surprising number of genes that were silenced in a manner largely independent of other epigenetic pathways (Zhang et al. 2007). The evidence suggests that a complex network of epigenetic mechanisms acts to regulate gene expression in *Arabidopsis* and, presumably, in other plant species.

Posttranscriptional processing. Small RNAs, particularly microRNAs (miRNAs),

are another component being investigated to understand the posttranscriptional control of gene regulatory networks (Schwab et al. 2005, Willmann & Poethig 2007, B. Zhang et al. 2006). Plant miRNAs are a large class of 20 to 24 base-pair noncoding RNAs. They bind to complementary sequences on target RNA and cause posttranscriptional gene silencing (PTGS) by cleaving or inhibiting translation of target mRNAs. miRNAs are a significant component of gene regulatory networks because they often modify the expression of transcription factors (Bartel 2004, Schwab et al. 2005). To date, more than 870 miRNAs have been identified in more than 70 plant species through genetic screens, cloning after isolation of small RNAs, and computational analyses (B. Zhang et al. 2006). Researchers are turning to several miRNA databases to identify and classify miRNAs. miRBase is a comprehensive repository for miRNAs and their predicted targets from 58 species (Griffiths-Jones et al. 2006). TarBase (Sethupathy et al. 2006) (**http://www.diana.pcbi.upenn.edu/tarbase. html**) is a collection of experimentally verified miRNA targets from human, mouse, fruit fly, worm, zebrafish, and plants. This database indicates whether an entry is a miRNA target protein–coding sequence or if it has tested negative for and is therefore unlikely to be a miRNA target. Related plant-specific databases include the *Arabidopsis* Small RNA Project (ASRP) (**http://asrp.cgrb.oregonstate.edu/**), which maintains a comprehensive database that seeks to functionally characterize all endogenous small RNAs, including miRNAs and siRNAs, in plants. Likewise, using high-throughput pyrosequencing, curators of the Cereal Small RNA Database (CSRDB) present a large data set of rice and maize small RNAs, along with their genomic location and predicted targets (Johnson et al. 2007).

Protein-DNA interactions. Proteins frequently interact with a large number of other gene products, and owing to the organization of the resulting complexes, genetic alterations in single genetic loci often do not yield phenotypes. Therefore, it is essential to understand how proteins interact to build gene regulatory networks. In a transcriptional regulatory network, proteins interact with *cis*-regulatory elements in target genes to control the expression of downstream targets. In plants, yeast-one-hybrid assays have identified interactions of several basic leucine zipper (bZIP) transcription factors with abscisic acid (ABA)-responsive elements (Kim et al. 1997, Uno et al. 2000). A Gateway™-compatible yeast-one-hybrid system that utilizes entire promoters has been developed in *Caenorhabditis elegans* (Deplancke et al. 2004), and this method should greatly facilitate the identification of protein-DNA interactions in plants.

Chromatin immunoprecipitation (ChIP) coupled with quantitative real-time PCR is another technique that plant researchers are increasingly employing. This technique allows one to isolate proteins bound to target chromatin (Orlando 2000). ChIP has been used to validate putative downstream targets of DELLA proteins, transcriptional regulators that control many aspects of signaling by the plant hormone gibberellin (Zentella et al. 2007). The technique has also been used to validate a physical interaction between TRICHOMELESS1, a MYB protein, and *cis* elements in the promoter of another MYB protein, GLABRA1 (GL1), which controls trichome formation (Wang et al. 2007), and to validate downstream targets of SHORTROOT, a protein essential for proper root development (Cui et al. 2007, Levesque et al. 2006). In a more systematic approach, researchers are also using ChIP in conjunction with high-density microarray platforms (ChIP-on-chip, or ChIP-chip, analyses). This allows global characterization of DNA associated with a target protein. For example, Thibaud-Nissen et al. (2006) used a whole-genome array as well as a high-density array with 2-kb promoter sequences for 27,166 putative *Arabidopsis* genes to determine the binding site for TGA2, a member of the TGA subclass of bZIP transcription factors, in salicylic acid–treated plants (Thibaud-Nissen et al. 2006). Charac-

terization of LONG HYPOCOTYL5 (HY5) interactions also used this strategy, revealing more than 3800 putative targets (Lee et al. 2007).

Protein-protein interactions. In addition to binding to chromatin, proteins involved in gene regulatory networks form complexes with other proteins to regulate target gene expression. Various proteomics options are available for the global study of plant protein content, form, and activity (Thelen & Peck 2007). However, the most commonly used methods for protein interaction are yeast-two-hybrid assays and affinity purification of tagged protein complexes followed by mass spectrometry (AP-MS). Tandem affinity purification (TAP) of tagged proteins coupled to mass spectrometry has been used to study the cell cycle interactome in *Arabidopsis* cell culture and protein kinase interactions in rice (Rohila et al. 2006, Van Leene et al. 2007). Protein microarrays can also identify protein-protein interactions in a high-throughput manner. Popescu et al. (2007) used a high-density protein array to detect interactions between *Arabidopsis* calmodulins and other plant proteins (Popescu et al. 2007). In addition, new techniques such as fluorescence resonance energy transfer (FRET) and bioluminescence resonance energy transfer (BRET) are being used in plants to visualize protein-protein interactions in vivo (Xu et al. 2007, Zelazny et al. 2007).

Metabolite profiling. Obtaining data from the transcriptome, its epigenetic modifications, and the proteome provides the pieces that can then be assembled into a model of transcriptional regulatory networks. However, researchers are assembling one other large data source that, in part, can represent the terminal output of transcriptional regulation. The identification of small-molecule metabolites can provide a direct link to a cell's physiology and, in some cases, signaling networks. In plants, a vast variety of metabolites are produced; their biosynthesis is the result of complex metabolic pathways. These metabolites are important in the differentiation of tissues and organs and in the responses of plants to the environment. In some cases, metabolites act in signaling cascades that influence transcriptional networks. Mass spectrometry–based and nuclear magnetic resonance–based methods have been applied to profile known metabolites within plants (Last et al. 2007, Ward et al. 2007). Moving from these metabolic fingerprints to high spatial and temporal resolution measurements of the dynamics of these metabolic pathways is a crucial next step and requires the measurement of metabolic flux, mathematical modeling, and the generation of dynamic biosensors (Lalonde et al. 2005, Morgenthal et al. 2006, Ratcliffe & Shachar-Hill 2006, Rios-Estepa & Lange 2007).

MODELING APPROACHES USED TO DESCRIBE GENE REGULATORY NETWORKS

To model regulatory networks, methods that describe nodes (genes) and their regulatory interactions (edges) are needed. Ideally, an edge will have support from multiple data sources. A number of methods commonly used to model transcriptional regulatory networks have been previously described (Brady & Benfey 2006) and are only briefly mentioned here. Many geneticists are familiar with one type of network model, diagram models, in which genetic interactions are indicated with a line between two nodes and the direction of the interaction is indicated by an arrowhead or a perpendicular line. These simple diagrams are further refined in circuit or wiring diagrams; a particularly elegant example is the sea urchin endomesoderm developmental regulatory network (Davidson et al. 2002). Relevance networks can use microarray expression data to infer gene interactions and to predict positive or negative interactions, using correlation and partial correlation methods (Ma et al. 2007). Boolean network models, one popular deterministic modeling approach, employ binary values (on/off states) and Boolean rules (e.g., AND, OR, NOR, etc.) to determine a target's Boolean state

(Price & Shmulevich 2007). The dynamics of the system can then be modeled by updating the Boolean functions either synchronously or asynchronously. In these cases a state is a binary representation of all variables' activity within the system at a particular time point. The system can then transition from state to state over time (Price & Shmulevich 2007). However, gene expression is often stochastic, and measurements of gene expression on a global scale often contain noise. This uncertainty can be further incorporated into probabilistic Boolean networks, which have been used in a number of systems (Price & Shmulevich 2007).

Bayesian networks offer another opportunity to incorporate statistical uncertainty. These networks provide a directed, acyclic, graphical representation of the joint probability distribution between random variables (Pe'er 2005). Dynamic Bayesian networks (DBNs) can be used to model networks that include the dimension of time. Standard Bayesian networks infer directed relationships and therefore cannot incorporate feedback control mechanisms (Zou & Conzen 2005). Kinetic models are particularly useful in the modeling of dynamic regulatory networks. In these models, the kinetics of a series of transcriptional regulatory mechanisms are described by the use of differential equations (Locke et al. 2005a). However, this requires knowledge of the rates of regulatory interactions, as well as parameters describing the activity or association and disassociation constants of transcription factors with their partners.

PLANT TRANSCRIPTIONAL REGULATORY NETWORKS: RECENT ADVANCES

Modeling Regulatory Networks: Theoretical Approaches

Theoretical approaches, often mathematical in nature, have long been used as a framework to conceptually understand regulatory interactions that give rise to organismal form and function. At the organismal level, Turing mathematically modeled the set of possible phyllotactic arrangements in vegetative plant growth, given available mechanical restraints (Saunders 1992). In vertebrates, Cooke and Zeeman (1976) presented the clock-wavefront hypothesis to explain the regular production of somites. Indeed, when the genes responsible for somitogenesis were elucidated, and their interaction characterized, they appeared to interact according to Cooke and Zeeman's hypothesis (Dequeant et al. 2006).

Recent studies have used these conceptual frameworks to try to understand the regulatory events underlying plant architecture. Mundermann et al. (2005) developed a model to capture quantitative aspects of *Arabidopsis* development. This model was intended to serve as a framework to identify the key attributes in plant form needed to specify observed growth and as a path for incremental development of mechanistic models of the whole plant (Mundermann et al. 2005). This study utilized imaging to capture data, including the size, shape, and growth rates in shoot organs from the seedling to the maturation stage of development. The input components included four types of modules—apices, internodes, leaves, and flowers. Each flower was further decomposed into modules representing individual floral organs and supporting tissue—the pedicel, sepals, petals, stamens, and carpel. Components were assembled into a three-dimensional structure, which, when simulated, described a growing plant and remarkably recapitulated *Arabidopsis* growth (Mundermann et al. 2005). An example of an emergent property revealed by modeling plant growth was the inverse correlation between the divergence angles of leaves and of the lateral inflorescences subtended by them. This inverse correlation suggested that the timing and positioning of primordia are interdependent, such that primordia that are initiated close together in time are positioned far apart in space.

In a similar manner, a conceptual framework presented to understand inflorescence architecture incorporated previously characterized genes into its regulatory framework. Although a variety of inflorescence architectures are theoretically possible, only three general inflorescence classes are observed (Prusinkiewicz & Lindenmayer 1990, Prusinkiewicz et al. 2007, Weberling 1992). Prusinkiewicz et al. (2007) proposed a single developmental model that incorporates theoretical and molecular genetic studies and that accounts for the restricted range of architectures observed. In nature, the three inflorescence architecture types are (*a*) panicles, in which a series of branching axes ends in terminal flowers; (*b*) racemes, in which axes bear flowers in lateral positions or in a lateral axis that reiterates the pattern; and (*c*) cymes, with an axis bearing a terminal flower in a lateral position, and a lateral axis that reiterates this pattern (**Figure 1**). Prusinkiewicz and others proposed that a meristem can give rise to shoots or flowers and that this decision is dependent on the vegetativeness (*veg*) variable (Prusinkiewicz et al. 2007). High levels of *veg* will produce shoot meristem identity, whereas low levels will produce flower meristem identity. A meristem can be in one of two internal states: *A*, which is characterized by a high level of *veg* at time T_A, or a transient state, *B*,

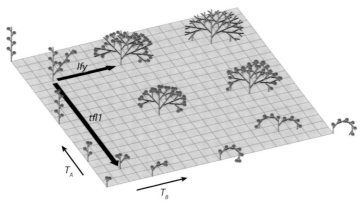

Figure 1

Morphospace for the transient model. Different phenotypes are generated by varying the times T_A and T_B at which flowers begin to form. Values along each axis range from 0 to 10 plastochrons. Black arrows, pointing away from the wild-type architecture of *Arabidopsis*, indicate the effect of *terminal flower1* (*tfl1*) and *leafy* (*lfy*) mutations (under inductive conditions). Inflorescences are shown at six plastochrons; a plastochron is a time interval during which a meristem may either switch to floral identity or continue to produce further meristems. From Prusinkiewicz et al. (2007). Reprinted with permission from AAAS.

which attains low levels of *veg* at time T_B. Every lateral meristem initially formed is in state B, during which the lateral meristem can proceed to one of two possible fates, each dependent on *veg* levels. If *veg* is low, the meristem will become a flower, whereas if *veg* is high, the meristem enters state A and produces a branch. This model can generate cymes, racemes, and panicles by changing the T_A and T_B parameters ($T_A < T_B$, $T_A > T_B$, and $T_A = T_B$ respectively) and has been represented in a single-parameter morphospace, that is, all possible morphologies given T_A and T_B parameters (Prusinkiewicz et al. 2007).

TERMINAL FLOWER1 (*TFL1*) and *LEAFY* (*LFY*) are two genes involved in regulating inflorescence architecture and proposed to increase and decrease *veg* levels, respectively. Wild-type inflorescence architecture results from high *TFL1*, low *LFY*, and therefore high *veg* in state A meristems, whereas high *LFY* and low *TFL1* activity results in low *veg* and flowers in state B meristems. These different architectures were correlated with their fitness and modeled in two-dimensional fitness landscapes (Prusinkiewicz et al. 2007). The ability of these architectures to generate adaptive solutions in response to variable season length and environmental conditions was further explored in an additional dimension within these fitness landscapes. The path to move between racemes and cymes within this morphospace is quite large, and this model therefore suggested that this move would require multiple genetic changes, which may represent why racemes and cymes are rarely found within the same genera (Prusinkiewicz et al. 2007). This theoretical framework can be used to provide a mechanism to explain how the evolution of inflorescence architecture can be constrained by the nature of the developmental genetic mechanisms involved and the interaction between organism and environment. Both of these examples of theoretical modeling of networks can serve as frameworks upon which gene interaction data can be superimposed and that can be used further to analyze properties of gene regulatory networks.

Integrating Data Sources to Elucidate Networks

A brief search of the literature will reveal an astounding amount of information about various components of plant regulatory networks. However, only when these components have been integrated in a cohesive manner can one begin to generate models that predict how a network functions. In a recent study, researchers used a systems approach to identify protein kinases that integrate transcriptional regulation with stress and signaling (Baena-Gonzalez et al. 2007). Baena-Gonzalez et al. (2007) initially found a set of dark-inducible genes that were repressed by protein kinase inhibitors. On the basis of these data, these investigators screened for protein kinases that may play a role in stress response and found two, KIN10 and KIN11. Characterization of the promoter of one of the dark-inducible genes, *DIN6*, revealed a G-box regulatory element in its promoter. Surprisingly, KIN10 and KIN11 act synergistically with C-group bZIP transcription factors to bind the G-box in these promoters and to transcriptionally activate genes in major catabolic pathways (Baena-Gonzalez et al. 2007). Although future efforts include elucidating the relationship between these protein kinases and transcriptional regulators, studies such as these are a first step toward more comprehensive efforts to integrate two types of components within a system.

In addition to integrating signaling and regulatory networks, researchers have also begun to combine their understanding of miRNAs with that of signaling networks. Zhou et al. (2007) developed a novel computational approach in which miRNA targets were predicted on the basis of upregulation of miRNA expression due to UV-B exposure, the presence of common *cis*-regulatory elements, and whether a miRNA target's expression was anticorrelated with expression of the target's miRNA (Zhou et al. 2007). On the basis of this analysis, Zhou et al. were able to identify 21 putative UV-B-responsive miRNAs as well as their targets, of which the majority were transcription factors involved in auxin signaling. This further validated the regulatory role of miRNAs in a host of important biological processes.

Several recent studies have also combined transcriptomics and metabalomics. Hirai et al. (2007) compared condition-independent expression profiles from 1388 microarray experiments with those generated under sulfur-deficiency conditions. Using Pearson correlation, these researchers were able to detect coexpressed gene clusters, one of which contained two uncharacterized MYB transcription factors, MYB28 and MYB29. Further analysis of these genes, using loss-of-function and gain-of-function mutants, revealed that MYB28 activates expression of the aliphatic glucosinolate biosynthetic gene, but not indole or aromatic glucosinolate biosynthetic genes. Hirai et al. (2007) hypothesized that MYB29 functions in the induction of aliphatic glucosinolate biosynthetic genes only in response to methyl jasmonate signaling.

Other labs have integrated numerous systems components to develop and test regulatory networks under other stress conditions. For example, Coruzzi's lab developed VirtualPlant, a multinetwork tool that integrates known and predicted information about *Arabidopsis* metabolic pathways as well as protein-protein, protein-DNA, and miRNA-target interactions (Gutierrez et al. 2007). After transcriptionally profiling *Arabidopsis* roots, using a systematic experimental space of carbon/nitrogen treatments, Coruzzi and coworkers applied these data to VirtualPlant (**http://virtualplant.bio.nyu.edu/cgi-bin/vpweb/virtualplant.cgi**). These investigators developed a qualitative multinetwork model for the carbon and nitrogen response, with 7635 nodes and more than 200,000 edges indicating putative regulatory interactions. In a subsequent study, Coruzzi and coworkers experimentally validated a subnetwork from this study, the proposed interaction between an miRNA, *miR167*, and its target, *ARF8*. Gifford et al. (2008) found that *ARF8* is up-regulated in pericycle cells that are precursors to lateral roots and that *miR167* is downregu-

lated in these same cells under nitrogen stress conditions. These data, along with the finding that overexpression of *miR176* results in complete loss of nitrogen-inducible lateral root emergence, led to the conclusion that *miR167* targets *ARF8* to control lateral root production (Gifford et al. 2008).

Emergent Properties: Utilization of High-Throughput Data

Above we describe components of plant regulatory networks and approaches for modeling these networks and show how researchers are beginning to integrate information about different systems components. As mentioned above, the goal of systems biology is the identification of emergent properties that arise from the interactions of different components within a system. Therefore, a comprehensive view of how each component interacts within a system is required. To that end we now describe recent efforts to generate gene regulatory network models from high-throughput data and emergent properties revealed by analysis of these networks.

In a comprehensive study, Cooper et al. (2003) integrated data from yeast-two-hybrid analysis, transcriptional profiling of different plant tissues under 11 different stress conditions, quantitative trait loci (QTL) analysis, and analysis of T-DNA insertion mutants to develop a comprehensive gene network of rice genes that play a role in stress responses. Through integration of these data sets, these researchers developed an interaction map that included protein-phosphatase interactions, transcription factor–target interactions, and interactions between signaling molecules such as 14-3-3 proteins and their targets. The modeling of this network allowed function to be ascribed to more than 200 genes, and five uncharacterized proteins were determined to play a role in disease resistance (Cooper et al. 2003).

Analyzing the NPR1-mediated gene regulatory network has revealed a complex set of regulatory interactions that influence systemic acquired resistance (SAR). Conditional induction of NPR1, a transcription cofactor that helps regulate SAR, in conjunction with microarray analysis, identified direct NPR1 targets (Wang et al. 2006). Of 64 putative targets, 8 were WRKY transcription factors. Pathogenicity analysis compared with microarray analyses of wild-type and *npr1*, single *wrky*, and double *wrky* mutants before and after SAR induction indicated that one of the factors, *WRKY18*, is a positive regulator of SAR, whereas another factor, *WRKY58*, is a negative regulator of spurious activation of SAR. Furthermore, a third factor, *WRKY70*, along with its functional homolog, appeared to negatively regulate SAR while positively mediating salicylic acid–mediated signaling (Wang et al. 2006). The emergent properties revealed by this study not only have enabled researchers to begin to understand the complex regulation of SAR but also can be used to identify further downstream SAR factors.

In addition to using high-throughput data to elucidate gene regulatory networks involved in stress response, investigators are also attempting to study plant developmental processes. A comprehensive plant protein-protein interaction map of more than 100 MADS box proteins in *Arabidopsis* revealed interactions between subgroups of MADS box proteins with similar biological functions. This study also revealed a surprising emergent property of floral development, namely, interactions between floral induction and floral organ identity proteins, suggesting feedback loops that regulate gene expression in these processes (de Folter et al. 2005).

High-resolution sampling and microarray expression analysis of developmental time points along the axis of the *Arabidopsis* root, in combination with the data from nearly all cell types in the *Arabidopsis* root, have yielded a large amount of spatiotemporal transcriptional information. Employing a computational pipeline that exploits methods used to identify strongly coexpressed groups of genes, Brady et al. (2007) obtained a set of distinct, dominant, transcriptional programs in both space and time. An example of an emergent property revealed by this systematic profiling of root development is a set of surprising expression patterns that underlie development. Nearly 50% of expression patterns fluctuate in developmental time, suggesting the need to separate biological processes along this temporal axis. Brady et al. (2007) used these high-resolution coexpression groups to infer a diverse set of transcriptional regulatory modules, one of which had direct support in experimental data. This suggests that, at least for the *Arabidopsis* root, we now have sufficient information to begin to elucidate transcriptional regulatory networks. These modules can be tested for their experimental validity and can then be used in modeling studies to understand higher-order properties of transcriptional regulatory networks.

Emergent Properties: Modeling Small Gene Regulatory Networks

A number of small gene regulatory networks, whose interactions have not necessarily been inferred by the use of high-throughput, genome-scale data, have greatly benefited from a systems biology framework. Modeling and testing of flower development, the circadian clock, and auxin flux regulatory networks have revealed a number of emergent network properties. These properties include novel regulatory component predictions and, strikingly, in all cases, the robustness of these networks in the face of stochastic biological fluctuations. These examples are intended to demonstrate the power of a systems approach as a framework to understand regulatory processes. As data obtained from genome-wide technologies are integrated, these model regulatory networks show how modeling can aid in elucidating the dynamics and properties of regulatory processes that give rise to plant form and function.

The logic of flower development. The *Arabidopsis* flower consists of four floral organs. From the outside of the flower to the inside, they include sepals, petals, stamens, and carpels, which are found in concentric whorls. In *Arabidopsis thaliana* and other plant species, the expression of overlapping transcription factors specifies floral organ development. The ABC model, which was one of the first plant gene regulatory networks modeled, described interactions among three classes of transcription factors that regulate floral pattern formation across plant species (Coen & Meyerowitz 1991). Additional studies identified genes that act prior to floral organ specification, in the vegetative-to-reproductive transition, as well as other modifiers of ABC transcription factor expression. These genes are involved in a variety of molecular processes from chromatin remodeling to signaling and protein turnover. Alvarez-Buylla and others have further modeled the genetic interactions controlling flower development, using Boolean logic (Espinosa-Soto et al. 2004, Mendoza & Alvarez-Buylla 1998, Mendoza et al. 1999). The main goal of their most recent model, which describes a small network of 15 genes, was to move beyond the ABC model to a dynamical explanation of how the steady-state pattern of gene expression characteristics in flowers is attained and maintained through the use of both ABC and non-ABC genes and logical rules in *Arabidopsis* and petunia (Espinosa-Soto et al. 2004). This analysis elucidated the robustness of the floral regulatory network and pointed to testable hypotheses concerning the existence of other regulators.

The directed interactions and logical rules were first assigned to 15 *Arabidopsis* nodes (genes) through the use of available experimental data. Eight nodes were assigned a binary activity state, that is, on or off, whereas seven nodes were assigned ternary activity states. In several cases, to maintain the coherence of the available experimental data, some interactions were inferred. One of the advantages of using a systems approach to understand network architecture or dynamics is that when a series of interactions is synthesized into a predictive model, gaps in available experimental data are revealed. One can use experimental data to predict the logical rules of these interactions, and these predictions can then be tested experimentally and incorporated into the model. Because the model describes the temporal dynamics of

floral development, an inflorescence state exists, and one should make rules that describe the activation of each gene upon floral induction. As an example, the three *SEPALLATA* genes (*SEP1–3*) are expressed after floral induction, but no known activator exists in the inflorescence state. In this model, *TFL1* was inferred to repress *SEP1–3* expression prior to floral induction. An additional gap in the current data included a factor responsible for maintaining expression of *PISTILLATA* (*PI*) in the inner three whorls of the flower.

Transcriptional regulatory networks are generally recognized for their properties of robustness or their ability to function nearly independently of biochemical parameters that tend to fluctuate from cell to cell (Alon 2007). Robustness of this floral network was tested by simulating alterations in outputs of the logical rule tables for randomly selected nodes. Only a very small number of alterations gave rise to a steady-state condition that was not observed in the wild type, demonstrating the robustness of the floral development network.

The evolution of the circadian clock model: from single to multiple loops. The circadian clock is an internal timing mechanism that allows the temporal synchronization of physiology with environment to ensure successful growth and development (Más 2005). Circadian timing mechanisms entrain to rhythmic cues of light and dark, and these rhythms are generated by gene expression acting in positive and negative feedback loops. Although a single feedback loop can generate an oscillatory expression pattern, mathematical modeling of the *Arabidopsis* circadian clock, using differential equations, has revealed that this clock is generated through multiple interconnecting loops (Locke et al. 2005a,b, 2006; Zeilinger et al. 2006). Modeling is usually an iterative process, and through both simulation and experimental validation of these models, novel components have been predicted, tested, and continuously incorporated, illuminating a complex set of interactions acting to generate this robust, internal timing mechanism.

A first-generation model in which the partially redundant *LATE ELONGATED HYPOCOTYL* (*LHY*) and *CIRCADIAN CLOCK ASSOCIATED1* (*CCA1*) genes repress expression of their activator, *TIMING OF CAB EXPRESSION1* (*TOC1*), in a single feedback loop was modeled through the use of seven coupled differential equations, Michaelis-Menten kinetics for protein degradation, Hill functions to describe transcriptional activation or repression, and gene product concentrations including mRNA, cytoplasmic, and nuclear protein species (**Figure 2a**) (Locke et al. 2005a). In cases in which experimental data were not available, an entire set of parameter values was analyzed and an optimal set selected that best accounted for clock characteristics (Locke et al. 2005a). Although this model was able to simulate robust oscillations over a 24-h period, it was not able to validate all available experimental data. The primary failures were in its inability to recapitulate experimental observations of an abrupt reduction in *TOC1* transcription after dusk during long-day conditions, a discrepancy in the accumulation of TOC1 protein at dawn when it should be activating *LHY* transcription maximally, and the inability of TOC1 to respond to photoperiod.

Because the observed experimental values did not match with those predicted by the model, the model was refined and novel components incorporated within this same mathematical framework (Locke et al. 2005b). Two hypothetical components, *X* and *Y*, were predicted also to act within this oscillator and to comprise interlocking feedback loops (**Figure 2b**). TOC1 protein would activate transcription of *X*, X protein would activate *LHY* transcription, and then LHY protein would repress *TOC1* transcription in a central loop. A second feedback loop would also exist: TOC1 protein would repress *Y* transcription, and Y protein would activate *TOC1* transcription. An additional light input was added, so that in addition to an acute light responsiveness of *LHY* transcription, light would also be able to activate *Y* transcription. This model was able to

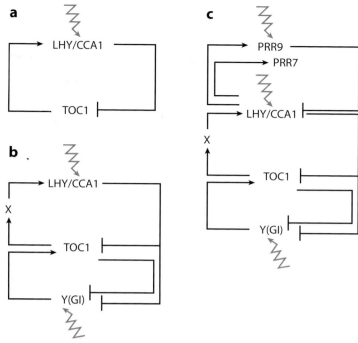

Figure 2

The *Arabidopsis* circadian clock has been elucidated by the use of systems approaches. In particular, modeling and iterative inclusion of novel parameters have revealed that the circadian clock is composed of three interconnecting loops. (*a*) The first-generation *Arabidopsis* circadian clock model. Light-activated (*orange line*) LHY/CCA1 (LATE ELONGATED HYPOCOTYL and CIRCADIAN CLOCK ASSOCIATED 1, respectively) repress the expression of their activator, *TIMING OF CAB EXPRESSION1* (*TOC1*), in a single feedback loop. (*b*) The second-generation circadian clock model. To resolve experimental observations, two hypothetical components X and Y were included. TOC1 protein activates transcription of *X*. X protein then activates *LHY/CCA1* transcription, and LHY/CCA1 protein represses *TOC1* transcription. In a second feedback loop, TOC1 protein represses *Y* transcription, and Y protein activates *TOC1* transcription. A second light input was added so that in addition to the acute light responsiveness of *LHY/CCA1* transcription, light is also able to activate *Y* transcription. *Y* is proposed to encode the GIGANTEA (GI) protein. (*c*) In the third-generation model, new network components, PSEUDO-RESPONSE REGULATOR 9 (PRR9) and PSEUDO-RESPONSE REGULATOR 7 (PRR7), were incorporated, resulting in a clock that can also sense the photoperiod. (Figure derived from Locke et al. 2005a,b, 2006; Zeilinger et al. 2006.)

account for a larger range of experimental data, primarily the appropriate timing of *TOC1* transcription and protein expression, than could the previous model. Predicted expression values of *Y* were used to query genes that affect the circadian clock for similar expression values in the correct time period of the clock.

GIGANTEA (*GI*) expression matched these predictions quite well, with a significant but transient light response in wild type and a strong light response in the *cca1;lhy* mutant. As postulated in a systems biology framework, modeling should inform further experiments. For example, if *GI* is the valid *Y* component within this system, and all components are accounted for, then a *gi;cca1;lhy* triple mutant should disrupt both oscillating loops.

On the basis of these predictions and further experiments that identified additional feedback regulators of *LHY/CCA1* expression, *PSEUDO-RESPONSE REGULATOR7* (*PRR7*) and *PSEUDO-RESPONSE REGULATOR9* (*PRR9*), new network components were incorporated within the circadian clock model, resulting in a clock that also contains a photoperiod sensing mechanism (**Figure 2c**) (Locke et al. 2006, Zeilinger et al. 2006). Two slightly different models were proposed, with both models composed of three loops—a core *LHY/CCA1-TOC1-X* loop that is coupled with an evening-expressed *TOC1-Y*(*GI*) loop, and a novel morning-expressed *PRR7/9-LHY/CCA1* loop. Of particular interest, Locke et al. (2006) biologically tested the identity of *GI* as the predicted *Y* component, using a *gi;cca1;lhy* triple mutant. These experimental observations performed very well compared with the model simulations, suggesting that *GI* is a good candidate for *Y*.

Locke et al. (2006) considered *PRR7* and *PRR9* as a single component; in contrast, on the basis of the partial redundancy of *PRR7* and *PRR9* in regulating *LHY/CCA1*, Zeilinger et al. (2006) incorporated *PRR7* and *PRR9* as separate components on the basis of their subtle transcriptional differences in response to light. This two-parameter inclusion revealed an emergent property of this network—that is, separate and distinct mechanisms of clock regulation. The magnitude of the *PRR9* response to light is much higher than that of *PRR7* and was accounted for by incorporating an acute light induction of *PRR9* by a component *P* that is both active and unstable in light. Zeilinger et al. (2006) found that the acute peak of *Y* expression

controls *TOC1* expression, whereas the circadian peak modulates the fine-tuning response to day length, suggesting two distinct mechanisms of clock regulation. Zeilinger et al. (2006) also used sensitivity analysis to capture areas of network robustness. Many parameters indicated low sensitivity, a reflection of the robust nature of this oscillatory network. However, parameters with high sensitivity were identified; these most likely indicate the need for further experimentation. As an example, CCA1/LHY parameters showed low sensitivity relative to TOC1-Y. However, experimentally, *cca1;lhy* mutants also show an extreme phenotype, and therefore further experimentation regarding *LHY/CCA1* regulation is needed.

Modeling auxin flux and regulatory networks in plant development. The plant hormone auxin is a potent regulatory molecule that acts in many aspects of plant growth and development. Auxin has been implicated as a morphogen, whereby its graded accumulation in cell types and tissues acts instructively to determine cell fate specification, division, and elongation. A systems approach has been used to model the dynamics of auxin flux in both the shoot and the root. Although the models we describe do not deal with gene regulatory networks directly, these modeling efforts describe how the flux of this hormone is established and maintained to generate complex patterns. Auxin gradients are dynamically and robustly controlled by the subcellular localization of auxin transporters, allowing auxin to act as a capacitor in morphogenesis. Dynamically controlled auxin flux is translated into gene regulatory networks, and therefore understanding the properties of auxin flux within the plant system is essential to comprehending auxin-mediated gene regulatory networks.

Modeling auxin flux in the shoot. Computer simulations of PIN-FORMED1 (PIN1), an auxin efflux facilitator, in the shoot apex were able to simulate successfully both a spiral and decussate phyllotaxis (de Reuille et al. 2005). These phyllotactic arrangements are dependent on the size of the central zone in the meristem. Surprisingly, however, these simulations also revealed an emergent property of this network—an auxin maximum that exists at the summit of the meristem (de Reuille et al. 2005). This was biologically tested, and indeed a free auxin maximum was found to exist in the center of the shoot apical meristem (SAM) (de Reuille et al. 2005). The simulations further predicted that this central auxin maximum is essential for the initiation of organ primordia but is not necessary for primordia maintenance, which remains to be experimentally tested. If biologically valid, this prediction suggests that the mechanisms by which primordia are maintained are remarkably robust.

The lab of Elliot Meyerowitz has established technology to collect time-lapse, single-cell, live images of key regulators of SAM formation (Reddy et al. 2004). This technology has revolutionized the ability to collect data on the dynamics of auxin flux and its role in establishing phyllotaxis and primordium development and has been used both to validate experimentally existing models and to infer novel models. One example of experimental validation involves models that describe floral primordium development. Live imaging of a developing inflorescence primordium confirmed model predictions that auxin accumulation and depletion are mediated by reversal of PIN1 localization in incipient primordia and that this reversal guides proper floral primordium development (Heisler et al. 2005). Genes known to be involved in floral primordium formation were analyzed to assess the temporal nature of this regulatory network in reference to this auxin flux. This regulatory network has also been analyzed by live-cell imaging during somatic embryogenesis (Gordon et al. 2007). Dynamic PIN1 concentrations were quantified and used to formulate a model based on the assumption that PIN1 polarity is regulated by relative auxin concentrations in neighboring cells within a two-dimensional space like the epidermis. This model also incorporated information regarding cellular growth and mechanics within the shoot apex (Jonsson et al. 2006). Simu-

lations correctly recapitulated observations on polarized auxin flow and phyllotactic patterning. Future directions entail assessing the robustness of this network regulating phyllotaxis in response to mechanical disturbance or stress.

Modeling auxin flux in the root. The *Arabidopsis* root is composed of different cell types arranged in concentric cylinders around the root's radial axis. Along the root's longitudinal axis, moving upward from the tip, all cell types are further organized in zones characterized by rapid cell division (meristematic), elongation, and, finally, maturation. An auxin response maximum is required for cell-type specification at the root tip. However, auxin is also required for cell division and expansion in the meristematic and elongation zones. The molecular mechanism by which auxin acts to regulate pattern formation, division, and elongation was previously unclear. Through a systems biology approach, two models have been developed to describe auxin distribution within the root and its regulation of root development (Grieneisen et al. 2007, Likhoshvai et al. 2007). Both models take into account root length and different cell types within the root, incorporate auxin derived from the shoot, and exclude auxin synthesis within the root. The model proposed by Grieneisen et al. (2007) additionally incorporated the cell-type and subcellular location and activity of auxin transporters, in addition to the shape and local neighborhood of different cell types. This modeling and experimental testing have revealed a minimum regulatory mechanism by which auxin can specify and maintain root patterning (Grieneisen et al. 2007, Likhoshvai et al. 2007).

In the Grieneisen et al. (2007) model, cells were characterized by appropriately scaled sizes and shapes to understand the interaction of local neighborhoods in auxin flux, and four generalized tissue types were considered—epidermal tissue, vascular tissue, a border tissue between the epidermal tissue and vascular tissue, and distal cap tissue. Furthermore, auxin diffusion and facilitated transport were considered as independent parameters, and auxin synthesis was

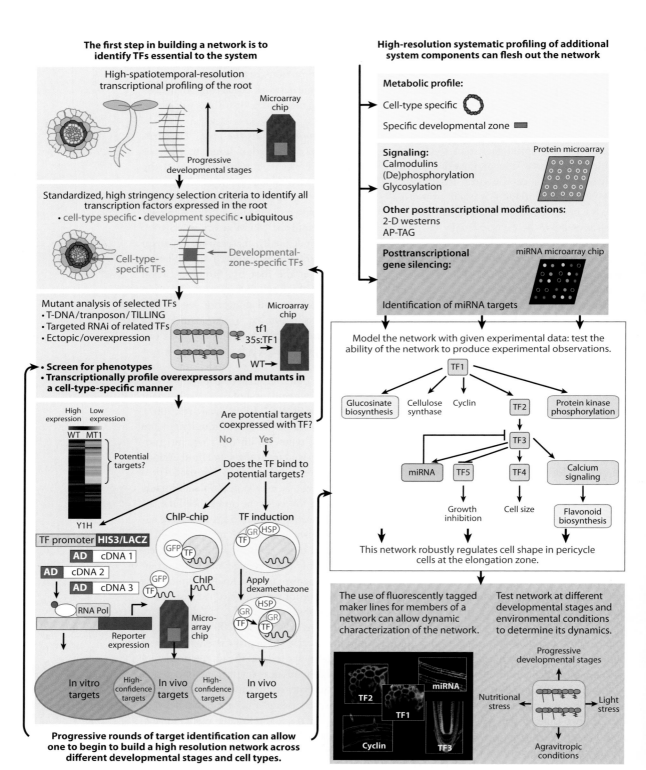

The first step in building a network is to identify TFs essential to the system

High-spatiotemporal-resolution transcriptional profiling of the root

Microarray chip

Progressive developmental stages

Standardized, high stringency selection criteria to identify all transcription factors expressed in the root
• cell-type specific • development specific • ubiquitous

Cell-type-specific TFs

Developmental-zone-specific TFs

Mutant analysis of selected TFs
• T-DNA/tranposon/TILLING
• Targeted RNAi of related TFs
• Ectopic/overexpression

Microarray chip

tf1
35s:TF1
WT

• **Screen for phenotypes**
• **Transcriptionally profile overexpressors and mutants in a cell-type-specific manner**

High expression Low expression

WT MT1

Potential targets?

Are potential targets coexpressed with TF?

No Yes

Does the TF bind to potential targets?

Y1H ChIP-chip TF induction

TF promoter **HIS3/LACZ**

AD cDNA 1
AD cDNA 2
AD cDNA 3

RNA Pol

Reporter expression

GFP TF

ChIP

GR HSP
TF

Micro-array chip

Apply dexamethazone

GR HSP
TF GR TF

In vitro targets High-confidence targets In vivo targets High-confidence targets In vivo targets

Progressive rounds of target identification can allow one to begin to build a high resolution network across different developmental stages and cell types.

High-resolution systematic profiling of additional system components can flesh out the network

Metabolic profile:

Cell-type specific

Specific developmental zone

Signaling:
Calmodulins
(De)phosphorylation
Glycosylation

Protein microarray

Other posttranscriptional modifications:
2-D westerns
AP-TAG

Posttranscriptional gene silencing:

miRNA microarray chip

Identification of miRNA targets

Model the network with given experimental data: test the ability of the network to produce experimental observations.

TF1

Glucosinate biosynthesis Cellulose synthase Cyclin TF2 Protein kinase phosphorylation

TF3

miRNA TF5 TF4 Calcium signaling

Growth inhibition Cell size Flavonoid biosynthesis

This network robustly regulates cell shape in pericycle cells at the elongation zone.

The use of fluorescently tagged maker lines for members of a network can allow dynamic characterization of the network.

Test network at different developmental stages and environmental conditions to determine its dynamics.

TF2 miRNA TF1 Cyclin TF3

Progressive developmental stages

Nutritional stress Light stress

Agravitropic conditions

not considered implicitly. The goal of modeling this aspect of auxin regulation was to determine if a minimal amount of information could provide an accurate estimate of auxin flux dynamics in cellular growth, and to provide testable hypotheses regarding the influence of each component on growth and the robustness of flux within the root.

First, the critical features of transport in this system were examined in a static growth phase (Grieneisen et al. 2007). Auxin was simulated as coming from the uppermost vascular region, and a steady state was quickly achieved with a local maximum in cells above the cap region. This steady state is quite robust and is insensitive to ubiquitous auxin synthesis or to the position of the auxin source. The root maximum can also be maintained for a relatively long period of time after removal of the shoot. This prediction of auxin capacitance was tested experimentally and validated. The most important parameter in establishing this maximum magnitude is the density of lateral auxin efflux transporters (PINs) in the border and epidermal files. This lateral density is critical in establishing reflux directed through the vascular tissues, as experimentally tested with mutations in three *PIN* loci. The model also predicts that the key parameter for determining the position of the auxin maximum is the efflux carriers in the root cap. Interestingly, the model predicted that stabilization of the auxin maximum–associated gradient takes much longer than formation of the maximum itself. This maintenance state was termed a quasi-steady state: Auxin levels increase, but the auxin distribution profile maintains its overall shape.

The model then incorporated root growth and explored the relationship between auxin dynamics and the different growth zones within a root (Grieneisen et al. 2007). A graded response function that was equal for all cells and that specified growth, division, or elongation was implemented. The auxin maximum was maintained in growing roots, and emerging zones that displayed meristematic and elongation properties were rapidly realized. In addition, the model predicted increased mitotic activity in vascular regions relative to other cell types, which has also been observed experimentally. These zones become sharper over time owing to feedback between cell growth dynamics and the auxin gradient. The model simulated a cut within the root and predicted a shift in the boundary between the meristematic and elongation zones, with a much longer elongation zone. This was experimentally validated with a localized application of an auxin transport inhibitor. These rounds of modeling and experimentation have demonstrated a further emergent property of the auxin-mediated regulatory network: that the formation of a meristematic zone and an elongation zone is due to the self-organizing property of the auxin response threshold that governs a variety of growth processes.

Figure 3

Systems approaches to studying root transcriptional regulatory networks regulating root development. Transcription factors (TFs) of interest are first identified by cell-type-specific and development-specific transcriptional profiling. Wild-type (WT) and mutants of cell-type-specific and development-specific TFs are analyzed and transcriptionally profiled to detect potential downstream targets of the initial TFs selected. One can validate physical interaction between the TFs and their potential targets first by determining that the TFs and their potential targets are coexpressed, using their transcriptional profile, then by in vitro tests such as yeast-one-hybrid (Y1H) assays, or in vivo by ChIP-chip or by conditional TF induction coupled with microarray analysis. High-confidence TF targets are validated by multiple methods of identification. Subsequently, those targets that are TFs themselves can be further analyzed to detect their targets. Subsequent rounds of TF/target identification can allow one to generate a model of a TF network. Other aspects of the network, such as the metabolic output, signaling, and posttranscriptional gene silencing, should also be characterized in a high-resolution, systematic manner. Combining all these results can allow researchers to generate a detailed, high-resolution, gene regulatory network model of root development. This model should then be tested experimentally to determine its ability to recapitulate experimental observations and for its robustness. The dynamics of these networks can then be monitored by measuring the expression of fluorescently tagged genes within the network and by testing the network under a range of conditions. Chip, microarray chip; ChIP, chromatin immunoprecipitation; GR, glucocorticoid receptor; HSP, heat shock protein.

CONCLUSIONS AND FUTURE DIRECTIONS

As we stand at the cusp of a major paradigm shift in how we approach science, some ask if we are really learning anything new. Initial indications are that moving from a reductionist to a systems approach can provide a clearer understanding of how biological systems are regulated, allowing one to predict their behavior. At the moment, plant biologists are collecting high-throughput data and identifying components acting in systems of interest. Researchers are using this information to model new gene regulatory networks and to expand upon older networks. However, when generating models that predict interactions between components, researchers are still testing models in a reductionist manner by perturbing a single component at a time in their respective network of interest. As we continue to use systems approaches, an open question is whether it is possible to test models in a nonreductionist manner. This will require the acquisition of dynamic, high-resolution, spatiotemporal expression and in-teraction data for all genes in a system. One area that seems tractable for this type of approach is transcriptional networks. Integration of expression data, interaction of transcription factors with DNA and with each other—in wild-type and mutant backgrounds, at the resolution of cell types and developmental stages, and in different environmental contexts—could generate high-confidence, dynamic gene regulatory models (**Figure 3**). However, this will require massive efforts from many labs. A potential problem is the temptation to focus on a few interactions for validation and further testing based on the current interests of a particular lab. However, the network would be expanded more rapidly if all targets were tested systematically. To address this issue, it may be possible to view systems biology endeavors as a group effort with two objectives: The first is to build a framework for understanding the inherent biology of plant systems of interest, and the second is to allow individual researchers to develop fine-tuned experiments that can elucidate missing aspects of a model.

DISCLOSURE STATEMENT

P.N.B. is a cofounder of a company, GrassRoots Biotechnology.

ACKNOWLEDGMENTS

Work in P.N.B.'s lab on systems biology is funded by grants from the NIH, NSF, and DARPA. T.A.L. is funded by an NSF Minority Postdoctoral Research Fellowship. S.M.B. is funded by an NSERC postdoctoral fellowship. We thank Jalean Petricka, Rosangela Sozzani, Anjali Iyer Pascuzzi, and Jee Jung for critical reading of the manuscript.

LITERATURE CITED

The Arabidopsis Initiative. 2000. Analysis of the genome sequence of the flowering plant *Arabidopsis thaliana*. *Nature* 408:796–815

Alon U. 2007. *An Introduction to Systems Biology: Design Principles of Biological Circuits*. Boca Raton, FL: Chapman and Hall/CRC

Alonso JM, Ecker JR. 2006. Moving forward in reverse: genetic technologies to enable genome-wide phenomic screens in *Arabidopsis*. *Nat. Rev. Genet.* 7:524–36

Alonso JM, Stepanova AN, Leisse TJ, Kim CJ, Chen H, et al. 2003. Genome-wide insertional mutagenesis of *Arabidopsis thaliana*. *Science* 301:653–57

Baena-Gonzalez E, Rolland F, Thevelein JM, Sheen J. 2007. A central integrator of transcription networks in plant stress and energy signalling. *Nature* 448:938–42

Bartel DP. 2004. MicroRNAs: genomics, biogenesis, mechanism, and function. *Cell* 116:281–97

Bertalanffy LV. 1973. *General Systems Theory*. Harmondsworth, UK: Penguin

Birnbaum K, Jung JW, Wang JY, Lambert GM, Hirst JA, et al. 2005. Cell type-specific expression profiling in plants via cell sorting of protoplasts from fluorescent reporter lines. *Nat. Methods* 2:615–19

Birnbaum K, Shasha DE, Wang JY, Jung JW, Lambert GM, et al. 2003. A gene expression map of the *Arabidopsis* root. *Science* 302:1956–60

Borevitz JO, Hazen SP, Michael TP, Morris GP, Baxter IR, et al. 2007. Genome-wide patterns of single-feature polymorphism in *Arabidopsis thaliana*. *Proc. Natl. Acad. Sci. USA* 104:12057–62

Brady SM, Benfey PN. 2006. A systems approach to understanding root development. *Can. J. Bot.* 84:695–701

Brady SM, Long TA, Benfey PN. 2006. Unraveling the dynamic transcriptome. *Plant Cell* 18:2101–11

Brady SM, Orlando DA, Lee J-Y, Wang JY, Koch J, et al. 2007. A high-resolution root spatiotemporal map reveals dominant expression patterns. *Science* 318:801–6

Busch W, Lohmann JU. 2007. Profiling a plant: expression analysis in *Arabidopsis*. *Curr. Opin. Plant Biol.* 10:136–41

Chen S, Jin W, Wang M, Zhang F, Zhou J, et al. 2003. Distribution and characterization of over 1000 T-DNA tags in rice genome. *Plant J.* 36:105–13

Clark RM, Schweikert G, Toomajian C, Ossowski S, Zeller G, et al. 2007. Common sequence polymorphisms shaping genetic diversity in *Arabidopsis thaliana*. *Science* 317:338–42

Coen ES, Meyerowitz EM. 1991. The war of the whorls: genetic interactions controlling flower development. *Nature* 353:31–37

Cooper B, Clarke JD, Budworth P, Kreps J, Hutchison D, et al. 2003. A network of rice genes associated with stress response and seed development. *Proc. Natl. Acad. Sci. USA* 100:4945–50

Cui H, Levesque MP, Vernoux T, Jung JW, Paquette AJ, et al. 2007. An evolutionarily conserved mechanism delimiting SHR movement defines a single layer of endodermis in plants. *Science* 316:421–25

Davidson EH, Rast JP, Oliveri P, Ransick A, Calestani C, et al. 2002. A genomic regulatory network for development. *Science* 295:1669–78

de Folter S, Immink RGH, Kieffer M, Parenicova L, Henz SR, et al. 2005. Comprehensive interaction map of the *Arabidopsis* MADS box transcription factors. *Plant Cell* 17:1424–33

de Reuille PB, Bohn-Courseau I, Ljung K, Morin H, Carraro N, et al. 2005. Computer simulations reveal properties of the cell-cell signaling network at the shoot apex in *Arabidopsis*. *Proc. Natl. Acad. Sci. USA* 103:1627–32

Dembinsky D, Woll K, Saleem M, Liu Y, Fu Y, et al. 2007. Transcriptomic and proteomic analyses of pericycle cells of the maize primary root. *Plant Physiol.* 145:575–88

Deplancke B, Dupuy D, Vidal M, Walhout AJM. 2004. A gateway-compatible yeast one-hybrid system. *Genome Res.* 14:2093–101

Dequeant M-L, Glynn E, Gaudenz K, Wahl M, Chen J, et al. 2006. A complex oscillating network of signaling genes underlies the mouse segmentation clock. *Science* 314:1595–98

Espinosa-Soto C, Padilla-Longoria P, Alvarez-Buylla ER. 2004. A gene regulatory network model for cell-fate determination during *Arabidopsis thaliana* flower development that is robust and recovers experimental gene expression profiles. *Plant Cell* 16:2923–39

Gifford ML, Dean A, Gutierrez RA, Coruzzi GM, Birnbaum KD. 2008. Cell-specific nitrogen responses mediate developmental plasticity. *Proc. Natl. Acad. Sci. USA* 105:803–8

Gilchrist EJ, Haughn GW. 2005. TILLING without a plough: a new method with applications for reverse genetics. *Curr. Opin. Plant Biol.* 8:211–15

Gordon SP, Heisler MG, Reddy GV, Ohno C, Das P, Meyerowitz EM. 2007. Pattern formation during de novo assembly of the *Arabidopsis* shoot meristem. *Development* 134:3539–48

Grieneisen VA, Xu J, Maree AFM, Hogeweg P, Scheres B. 2007. Auxin transport is sufficient to generate a maximum and gradient guiding root growth. *Nature* 449:1008–13

Griffiths-Jones S, Grocock RJ, van Dongen S, Bateman A, Enright AJ. 2006. miRBase: microRNA sequences, targets and gene nomenclature. *Nucleic Acids Res.* 34:D140–44

Groover A, Fontana JR, Dupper G, Ma C, Martienssen R, et al. 2004. Gene and enhancer trap tagging of vascular-expressed genes in poplar trees. *Plant Physiol.* 134:1742–51

Gutierrez R, Lejay L, Dean A, Chiaromonte F, Shasha D, Coruzzi G. 2007. Qualitative network models and genome-wide expression data define carbon/nitrogen-responsive molecular machines in *Arabidopsis*. *Genome Biol.* 8:R7

Gutierrez RA, Shasha DE, Coruzzi GM. 2005. Systems biology for the virtual plant. *Plant Physiol.* 138:550–54

Harbison CT, Gordon DB, Lee TI, Rinaldi NJ, Macisaac KD, et al. 2004. Transcriptional regulatory code of a eukaryotic genome. *Nature* 431:99–104

Heisler MG, Ohno C, Das P, Sieber P, Reddy GV, et al. 2005. Patterns of auxin transport and gene expression during primordium development revealed by live imaging of the *Arabidopsis* inflorescence meristem. *Curr. Biol.* 15:1899–911

Hilson P, Allemeersch J, Altmann T, Aubourg S, Avon A, et al. 2004. Versatile gene-specific sequence tags for *Arabidopsis* functional genomics: transcript profiling and reverse genetics applications. *Genome Res.* 14:2176–89

Hirai MY, Sugiyama K, Sawada Y, Tohge T, Obayashi T, et al. 2007. Omics-based identification of *Arabidopsis* Myb transcription factors regulating aliphatic glucosinolate biosynthesis. *Proc. Natl. Acad. Sci. USA* 104:6478–83

Hsing Y-I, Chern C-G, Fan M-J, Lu P-C, Chen K-T, et al. 2007. A rice gene activation/knockout mutant resource for high throughput functional genomics. *Plant Mol. Biol.* 63:351–64

Ideker T, Galitski T, Hood L. 2001. A new approach to decoding life: systems biology. *Annu. Rev. Genomics Hum. Genet.* 2:343–72

Jeong D-H, An S, Park S, Kang H-G, Park G-G, et al. 2006. Generation of a flanking sequence-tag database for activation-tagging lines in japonica rice. *Plant J.* 45:123–32

Johnson C, Bowman L, Adai AT, Vance V, Sundaresan V. 2007. CSRDB: a small RNA integrated database and browser resource for cereals. *Nucleic Acids Res.* 35:D829–33

Jones-Rhoades MW, Bartel DP, Bartel B. 2006. MicroRNAs and their regulatory roles in plants. *Annu. Rev. Plant Biol.* 57:19–53

Jonsson H, Heisler MG, Shapiro BE, Meyerowitz EM, Mjolsness E. 2006. An auxin-driven polarized transport model for phyllotaxis. *Proc. Natl. Acad. Sci. USA* 103:1633–38

Kheradpour P, Stark A, Roy S, Kellis M. 2007. Reliable prediction of regulator targets using 12 *Drosophila* genomes. *Genome Res.* 17:1919–31

Kilian J, Whitehead D, Horak J, Wanke D, Weinl S, et al. 2007. The AtGenExpress global stress expression data set: protocols, evaluation and model data analysis of UV-B light, drought and cold stress responses. *Plant J.* 50:347–63

Kim SY, Chung H-J, Thomas TL. 1997. Isolation of a novel class of bZIP transcription factors that interact with ABA-responsive and embryo-specification elements in the Dc3 promoter using a modified yeast one-hybrid system. *Plant J.* 11:1237–51

Lalonde S, Ehrhardt DW, Frommer WB. 2005. Shining light on signaling and metabolic networks by genetically encoded biosensors. *Curr. Opin. Plant Biol.* 8:574–81

Last RL, Jones AD, Shachar-Hill Y. 2007. Towards the plant metabolome and beyond. *Nat. Rev. Mol. Cell Biol.* 8:167–74

Lee J, He K, Stolc V, Lee H, Figueroa P, et al. 2007. Analysis of transcription factor HY5 genomic binding sites revealed its hierarchical role in light regulation of development. *Plant Cell* 19:731–49

Levesque MP, Vernoux T, Busch W, Cui H, Wang JY, et al. 2006. Whole-genome analysis of the SHORT-ROOT developmental pathway in *Arabidopsis*. *PLoS Biol.* 4:e143

Likhoshvai VA, Omel'yanchuk NA, Mironova VV, Fadeev SI, Mojolsness ED, Kolchanov NA. 2007. Mathematical model of auxin distribution in the plant root. *Russ. J. Dev. Biol.* 38:374–82

Lin X, Kaul S, Rounsley S, Shea TP, Benito M-I, et al. 1999. Sequence and analysis of chromosome 2 of the plant *Arabidopsis thaliana*. *Nature* 402:761–68

Locke JCW, Kozma-Bognár L, Gould PD, Fehér B, Kevei E, et al. 2006. Experimental validation of a predicted feedback loop in the multi-oscillator clock of *Arabidopsis thaliana*. *Mol. Syst. Biol.* 2:59

Locke JCW, Millar AJ, Turner MS. 2005a. Modelling genetic networks with noisy and varied experimental data: the circadian clock in *Arabidopsis thaliana*. *J. Theor. Biol.* 234:383–93

Locke JCW, Southern MM, Kozma-Bognár L, Hibberd V, Brown PE, et al. 2005b. Extension of a genetic network model by iterative experimentation and mathematical analysis. *Mol. Syst. Biol.* 1:2005.0013

Ma S, Gong Q, Bohnert HJ. 2007. An *Arabidopsis* gene network based on the graphical Gaussian model. *Genome Res.* 17:1614–25

Más P. 2005. Circadian clock signaling in *Arabidopsis thaliana*: from gene expression to physiology and development. *Int. J. Dev. Biol.* 49:491–500

Mayer K, Schuller C, Wambutt R, Murphy G, Volckaert G, et al. 1999. Sequence and analysis of chromosome 4 of the plant *Arabidopsis thaliana*. *Nature* 402:769–77

Mendoza L, Alvarez-Buylla ER. 1998. Dynamics of the genetic regulatory network for *Arabidopsis thaliana* flower morphogenesis. *J. Theor. Biol.* 193:307–19

Mendoza L, Thieffry D, Alvarez-Buylla ER. 1999. Genetic control of flower morphogenesis in *Arabidopsis thaliana*: a logical analysis. *Bioinformatics* 15:593–606

Morgenthal K, Weckwerth W, Steuer R. 2006. Metabolomic networks in plants: transitions from pattern recognition to biological interpretation. *Biosystems* 83:108–17

Mundermann L, Erasmus Y, Lane B, Coen E, Prusinkiewicz P. 2005. Quantitative modeling of *Arabidopsis* development. *Plant Physiol.* 139:960–68

Nakazono M, Qiu F, Borsuk LA, Schnable PS. 2003. Laser-capture microdissection, a tool for the global analysis of gene expression in specific plant cell types: identification of genes expressed differentially in epidermal cells or vascular tissues of maize. *Plant Cell* 15:583–96

Nawy T, Lee J-Y, Colinas J, Wang JY, Thongrod SC, et al. 2005. Transcriptional profile of the *Arabidopsis* root quiescent center. *Plant Cell* 17:1908–25

Nelson T, Tausta SL, Gandotra N, Liu T. 2006. Laser microdissection of plant tissue: What you see is what you get. *Annu. Rev. Plant Biol.* 57:181–201

Orlando V. 2000. Mapping chromosomal proteins in vivo by formaldehyde-crosslinked-chromatin immunoprecipitation. *Trends Biochem. Sci.* 25:99–104

Pe'er D. 2005. Bayesian network analysis of signaling networks: a primer. *Sci. STKE* 281:L4

Pennisi E. 2007. Genome sequencing: the greening of plant genomics. *Science* 317:317

Popescu SC, Popescu GV, Bachan S, Zhang Z, Seay M, et al. 2007. Differential binding of calmodulin-related proteins to their targets revealed through high-density *Arabidopsis* protein microarrays. *Proc. Natl. Acad. Sci. USA* 104:4730–35

Price ND, Shmulevich I. 2007. Biochemical and statistical network models for systems biology. *Curr. Opin. Biotechnol.* 18:365–70

Pritsker M, Liu Y-C, Beer MA, Tavazoie S. 2004. Whole-genome discovery of transcription factor binding sites by network-level conservation. *Genome Res.* 14:99–108

Prusinkiewicz P, Erasmus Y, Lane B, Harder LD, Coen E. 2007. Evolution and development of inflorescence architectures. *Science* 316:1452–56

Prusinkiewicz P, Lindenmayer A. 1990. *The Algorithmic Botany of Plants*. New York: Springer-Verlag

Ratcliffe RG, Shachar-Hill Y. 2006. Measuring multiple fluxes through plant metabolic networks. *Plant J.* 45:490–511

Reddy GV, Heisler MG, Ehrhardt DW, Meyerowitz EM. 2004. Real-time lineage analysis reveals oriented cell divisions associated with morphogenesis at the shoot apex of *Arabidopsis thaliana*. *Development* 131:4225–37

Rios-Estepa R, Lange BM. 2007. Experimental and mathematical approaches to modeling plant metabolic networks. *Phytochemistry* 68:2351–74

Rohila JS, Chen M, Chen S, Chen J, Cerny R, et al. 2006. Protein-protein interactions of tandem affinity purification-tagged protein kinases in rice. *Plant J.* 46:1–13

Rosso MG, Li Y, Strizhov N, Reiss B, Dekker K, Weisshaar B. 2003. An *Arabidopsis thaliana* T-DNA mutagenized population (GABI-Kat) for flanking sequence tag-based reverse genetics. *Plant Mol. Biol.* 53:247–59

Sallaud C, Gay C, Larmande P, Bes M, Piffanelli P, et al. 2004. High throughput T-DNA insertion mutagenesis in rice: a first step towards in silico reverse genetics. *Plant J.* 39:450–64

Saunders P, ed. 1992. *Collected Works of A.M. Turing: Morphogenesis*. Amsterdam: North-Holland

Schwab R, Palatnik JF, Riester M, Schommer C, Schmid M, Weigel D. 2005. Specific effects of microRNAs on the plant transcriptome. *Dev. Cell* 8:517–27

Int. Rice Genome Seq. Proj. 2005. The map-based sequence of the rice genome. *Nature* 436:793–800

Sessions A, Burke E, Presting G, Aux G, McElver J, et al. 2002. A high-throughput *Arabidopsis* reverse genetics system. *Plant Cell* 14:2985–94

Sethupathy P, Corda B, Hatzigeorgiou AG. 2006. TarBase: a comprehensive database of experimentally supported animal microRNA targets. *RNA* 12:192–97

Spencer MW, Casson SA, Lindsey K. 2007. Transcriptional profiling of the *Arabidopsis* embryo. *Plant Physiol.* 143:924–40

Suzuki T, Eiguchi M, Kumamaru T, Satoh H, Matsusaka H, et al. 2008. MNU-induced mutant pools and high performance TILLING enable finding of any gene mutation in rice. *Mol. Genet. Genomics* 279:213–23

Thelen JJ, Peck SC. 2007. Quantitative proteomics in plants: choices in abundance. *Plant Cell* 19:3339–46

Theologis A, Ecker JR, Palm CJ, Federspiel NA, Kaul S, et al. 2000. Sequence and analysis of chromosome 1 of the plant *Arabidopsis thaliana*. *Nature* 408:816–20

Thibaud-Nissen F, Wu H, Richmond T, Redman JC, Johnson C, et al. 2006. Development of *Arabidopsis* whole-genome microarrays and their application to the discovery of binding sites for the TGA2 transcription factor in salicylic acid-treated plants. *Plant J.* 47:152–62

Till B, Cooper J, Tai T, Colowit P, Greene E, et al. 2007. Discovery of chemically induced mutations in rice by TILLING. *BMC Plant Biol.* 7:19

Till B, Reynolds S, Weil C, Springer N, Burtner C, et al. 2004. Discovery of induced point mutations in maize genes by TILLING. *BMC Plant Biol.* 4:12

Tuskan GA, DiFazio S, Jansson S, Bohlmann J, Grigoriev I, et al. 2006. The genome of black cottonwood, *Populus trichocarpa* (Torr. & Gray). *Science* 313:1596–604

Uno Y, Furihata T, Abe H, Yoshida R, Shinozaki K, Yamaguchi-Shinozaki K. 2000. *Arabidopsis* basic leucine zipper transcription factors involved in an abscisic acid-dependent signal transduction pathway under drought and high-salinity conditions. *Proc. Natl. Acad. Sci. USA* 97:11632–37

Van Leene J, Stals H, Eeckhout D, Persiau G, Van De Slijke E, et al. 2007. A tandem affinity purification-based technology platform to study the cell cycle interactome in *Arabidopsis thaliana*. *Mol. Cell Proteomics* 6:1226–38

Wang D, Amornsiripanitch N, Dong X. 2006. A genomic approach to identify regulatory nodes in the transcriptional network of systemic acquired resistance in plants. *PLoS Pathog.* 2:e123

Wang S, Kwak S-H, Zeng Q, Ellis BE, Chen X-Y, et al. 2007. TRICHOMELESS1 regulates trichome patterning by suppressing GLABRA1 in *Arabidopsis*. *Development* 134:3873–82

Ward JL, Baker JM, Beale MH. 2007. Recent applications of NMR spectroscopy in plant metabolomics. *FEBS J.* 274:1126–31

Weberling F. 1992. *Morphology of Flowers and Inflorescences*. Cambridge, UK: Cambridge Univ. Press

Willmann MR, Poethig RS. 2007. Conservation and evolution of miRNA regulatory programs in plant development. *Curr. Opin. Plant Biol.* 10:503–11

Woll K, Borsuk LA, Stransky H, Nettleton D, Schnable PS, Hochholdinger F. 2005. Isolation, characterization, and pericycle-specific transcriptome analyses of the novel maize lateral and seminal root initiation mutant *rum1*. *Plant Physiol.* 139:1255–67

Xu X, Soutto M, Xie Q, Servick S, Subramanian C, et al. 2007. Imaging protein interactions with bioluminescence resonance energy transfer (BRET) in plant and mammalian cells and tissues. *Proc. Natl. Acad. Sci. USA* 104:10264–69

Yazaki J, Gregory BD, Ecker JR. 2007. Mapping the genome landscape using tiling array technology. *Curr. Opin. Plant Biol.* 10:534–42

Zeilinger MN, Farré EM, Taylor SR, Kay SA, Doyle FJ. 2006. A novel computational model of the circadian clock in *Arabidopsis* that incorporates PRR7 and PRR9. *Mol. Syst. Biol.* 2:58

Zelazny E, Borst JW, Muylaert M, Batoko H, Hemminga MA, Chaumont F. 2007. FRET imaging in living maize cells reveals that plasma membrane aquaporins interact to regulate their subcellular localization. *Proc. Natl. Acad. Sci. USA* 104:12359–64

Zentella R, Zhang Z-L, Park M, Thomas SG, Endo A, et al. 2007. Global analysis of DELLA direct targets in early gibberellin signaling in *Arabidopsis*. *Plant Cell* 19:3037–57

Zhang B, Pan X, Cobb GP, Anderson TA. 2006. Plant microRNA: a small regulatory molecule with big impact. *Dev. Biol.* 289:3–16

Zhang J, Li C, Wu C, Xiong L, Chen G, et al. 2006. RMD: a rice mutant database for functional analysis of the rice genome. *Nucleic Acids Res.* 34:D745–48

Zhang X, Clarenz O, Cokus S, Bernatavichute YV, Pellegrini M, et al. 2007. Whole-genome analysis of histone H3 lysine 27 trimethylation in *Arabidopsis*. *PLoS Biol.* 5:e129

Zhang X, Yazaki J, Sundaresan A, Cokus S, Chan SWL, et al. 2006. Genome-wide high-resolution mapping and functional analysis of DNA methylation in *Arabidopsis*. *Cell* 126:1189–201

Zhou X, Wang G, Zhang W. 2007. UV-B responsive microRNA genes in *Arabidopsis thaliana*. *Mol. Syst. Biol.* 3:103

Zilberman D, Gehring M, Tran RK, Ballinger T, Henikoff S. 2007. Genome-wide analysis of *Arabidopsis thaliana* DNA methylation uncovers an interdependence between methylation and transcription. *Nat. Genet.* 39:61–69

Zou M, Conzen SD. 2005. A new dynamic Bayesian network (DBN) approach for identifying gene regulatory networks from time course microarray data. *Bioinformatics* 21:71–79

REFERENCE ADDED IN PROOF

Cooke J, Zeeman EC. 1976. A clock and wavefront model for control of the number of repeated structures during animal morphogenesis. *J. Theor. Biol.* 58:455–76

Sister Chromatid Cohesion: A Simple Concept with a Complex Reality

Itay Onn,[1] Jill M. Heidinger-Pauli,[1,2]
Vincent Guacci,[1] Elçin Ünal,[3]
and Douglas E. Koshland[1,*]

[1] Howard Hughes Medical Institute, Carnegie Institution, Baltimore, Maryland 21218; email: onn@ciwemb.edu, heidinger@ciwemb.edu, guacci@ciwemb.edu, koshland@ciwemb.edu

[2] Department of Biology, Johns Hopkins University, Baltimore, Maryland 21218

[3] Department of Biology, Massachusetts Institute of Technology, Cambridge, Massachusetts 02139; email: elcin@mit.edu

Annu. Rev. Cell Dev. Biol. 2008. 24:105–29

First published online as a Review in Advance on July 10, 2008

The *Annual Review of Cell and Developmental Biology* is online at cellbio.annualreviews.org

This article's doi:
10.1146/annurev.cellbio.24.110707.175350

1081-0706/08/1110-0105$20.00

*Corresponding author.

Key Words

cohesin, chromosome segregation, DNA repair, genomic integrity, chromosome structure

Abstract

In eukaryotes, the process of sister chromatid cohesion holds the two sister chromatids (the replicated chromosomes) together from DNA replication to the onset of chromosome segregation. Cohesion is mediated by cohesin, a four-subunit SMC (structural maintenance of chromosome) complex. Cohesin and cohesion are required for proper chromosome segregation, DNA repair, and gene expression. To carry out these functions, cohesion is regulated by elaborate mechanisms involving a growing list of cohesin auxiliary factors. These factors control the timing and position of cohesin binding to chromatin, activate chromatin-bound cohesin to become cohesive, and orchestrate the orderly dissolution of cohesion. The 45-nm ringlike architecture of soluble cohesin is compatible with dramatically different mechanisms for both chromatin binding and cohesion generation. Solving the mechanism of cohesion and its complex regulation presents significant challenges but offers the potential to provide important insights into higher-order chromosome organization and chromosome biology.

Contents

INTRODUCTION

Sister chromatids: the two copies of each chromosome generated by DNA replication

Sister chromatid cohesion: the tethering together of sister chromatids

Cohesin regulatory factors: facilitate cohesin loading on chromatin, convert cohesin to the cohesive state, or control the maintenance or dissolution of cohesion

Cohesin: four-subunit complex consisting of Smc1, Smc3, Scc3, and Mcd1 (also named Rad21 or Scc1) that mediates tethering of sister chromatids

During a eukaryotic cell division, the two sister chromatids (the newly replicated chromosomes) are held together from the time of their synthesis in S phase through metaphase of mitosis. At the onset of anaphase this cohesion between sister chromatids is dissolved, allowing them to segregate to the opposite poles of the mitotic spindle. Initially, the mechanism of sister chromatid cohesion was thought to be a passive process mediated by the inherent stickiness of chromatin or by topological intertwines between sister DNA molecules. However, the characterization of two mutants in flies with specific defects in cohesion provided the first evidence that this process was mediated by dedicated cohesion factors (Kerrebrock et al. 1992, Miyazaki & Orr-Weaver 1992). Indeed, these fly mutants were the tip of the iceberg. Studies during the past decade and a half have revealed that sister chromatid cohesion is a complicated molecular process involving numerous cohesion proteins. Cohesion and its factors are important for diverse biological processes in-

cluding chromosome segregation, DNA repair, gene expression, and development.

The recent surge in the understanding of sister chromatid cohesion was initiated by the convergence of three different conceptual approaches. The visualization of sister chromatids by fluorescent in situ hybridization (FISH) in the simple budding yeast enabled a systematic cytogenetic approach to identify factors that mediate and regulate cohesion (Guacci et al. 1993, 1994, 1997; Yamamoto et al. 1996b). This approach was greatly augmented by the subsequent development of green fluorescent protein (GFP) tagging of chromosomes, which provided a direct visualization of the cohesion state of yeast sister chromatids (Straight et al. 1996). At the same time, extracts of *Xenopus laevis* egg were used to develop a systematic biochemical approach to identify and characterize components of mitotic chromosomes necessary for sister chromatid cohesion and condensation (Hirano & Mitchison 1994, Losada et al. 1998). Finally, these two bottom-up approaches were complemented by a top-down approach to understand the role of cohesion in the cell cycle, in particular the commitment to chromosome segregation at the metaphase-to-anaphase transition in mitosis (Irniger et al. 1995, Michaelis et al. 1997). These three approaches rapidly merged and were augmented by other approaches, leading to an explosion of observations from many different systems.

Summarizing these observations is a challenge. In principle, protein-based sister chromatid cohesion could be achieved by a very simple biochemical mechanism like the dimerization of two subunits, each with a canonical DNA binding domain. Instead, cohesion is mediated predominantly by cohesin, a four-subunit protein complex with complicated architecture and function. Despite great progress since the discovery of cohesin, many fundamental questions remain unanswered. How cohesin binds chromatin and how cohesin tethers two sister chromatids together remain controversial. Furthermore, cohesin is subjected to complex temporal and spatial regulation to ensure the proper establishment, maintenance, and dissolution of cohesion. Only partial skeletons of these regulatory pathways are known. Finally, elucidating the biological role of cohesion is complicated by the fact that cohesin factors are important for several distinct chromosomal processes. As a result of these complications, the field of cohesion is very much a work in progress and still evolving rapidly.

Because details are likely to change, this review emphasizes emerging concepts and outstanding questions in the field. We summarize the current understanding of the molecular mechanism of cohesion and its regulation. We then assess the biological function of cohesion in chromosome segregation and its emerging roles in other diverse biological processes. To limit the scope of the review, we present our analyses primarily in the context of mitotic cells but draw upon relevant meiotic results when pertinent. We also limit discussion of cohesin architecture, cohesion dissolution, and cohesion regulation in meiosis. For further information about these important and interesting

topics, the reader should see other excellent reviews (Nasmyth & Haering 2005, Watanabe 2005).

MOLECULAR MECHANISM OF SISTER CHROMATID COHESION

Cohesin Structure

Early studies of cohesin structure have had a tremendous impact on the field of cohesion and provide a framework for our ensuing discussion of the molecular and biological functions of cohesin. Cohesin is composed of four evolutionarily conserved subunits, a pair of SMC (structural maintenance of chromosomes) proteins called Smc1 and Smc3, a kleisin subunit called Mcd1 (also Scc1 or Rad21), and Scc3 (Guacci et al. 1997, Losada et al. 1998, Michaelis et al. 1997, Nasmyth & Haering 2005). Unfortunately, the conservation of the subunits did not manifest itself with conserved nomenclature (**Table 1**).

Smc: structural maintenance of chromosomes

Kleisin: an evolutionarily conserved subunit of Smc complexes, including Mcd1 of cohesin, that tethers together the head domains of the Smc dimer

Table 1   Cohesin subunits and regulatory proteins nomenclature[a]

	Saccharomyces cerevisiae	*Schizosacch-aromyces pombe*	*Drosophila melanogaster*	*Xenopus laevis*	**Human**
Cohesin subunits	SMC1	PSM1	SMC1	SMC1	SMC1
	SMC3	PSM3	SMC3	SMC3	SMC3
	MCD1 (SCC1)	RAD21	RAD21	RAD21	RAD21 (SCC1)
	IRR1 (SCC3)	PSC3	SA	SA1, SA2	SA1 (STAG1), SA2 (STAG2)
Loading	SCC2	MIS4	NIPBL	SCC2	NIPBL
	SCC4	SSL3	N/C	xSCC4	MAU2 (hSCC4)
Establishment	ECO1 (CTF7)	ESO1	San, Deco	XECO1, XECO2	EFO1 (ESCO1), EFO2 (ESCO2)
Maintenance	PDS5	PDS5	PDS5	PDS5A, PDS5B	PDS5A, PDS5B
	RAD61[*]	WPL1[*]	WAPL	N/C	WAPL
Dissolution	PDS1	CUT2	PIM	Securin	Securin (PTTG)
	ESP1	CUT1	Separase (SSE)	Separin	Separin (ESPL1)
	CDC5	PLO1	POLO	PLX1	PLK1
	SGO1[*]	SGO1, SGO2	SGO1 (Mei-S332)	Shugoshin-like 1 (xSGO1)	Shugoshin (hSGOl1)

[a]N/C denotes that a homologous gene has not been identified or annotated in this organism.
Asterisks indicate that homology has been inferred from sequence similarity but that either genes have not been characterized yet or function is not fully overlapping.

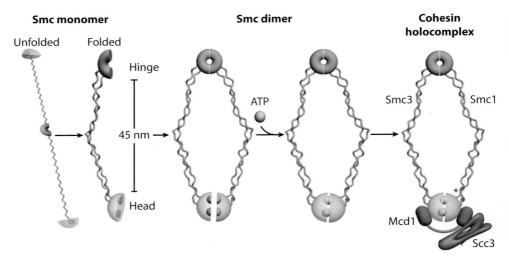

Smc monomer

Unfolded   Folded

Hinge

45 nm

Head

Smc dimer

ATP

Cohesin holocomplex

Smc3   Smc1

Mcd1

Scc3

Figure 1

Architecture of Smc proteins and cohesin. (*Left*) The folded Smc monomer contains hinge and head domains connected by a long coiled coil. (*Middle*) Smc dimers form by association of the hinges and ATP-dependent interaction of the heads. (*Right*) In cohesin, Mcd1 (kleisin subunit) cross-links the Smc heads and links Scc3 to the complex. This ringlike structure corresponds to the soluble, chromatin-free complex. The orange segment of the Smc1 coiled-coil (*asterisk*; *bottom right*), indicates the predicted location of loop 1 region.

For simplicity we use the official nomenclature in budding yeast for describing generic observations.

At the heart of the cohesin complex is a dimer of Smc1 and Smc3 (**Figure 1**). Smc1 and Smc3 share similarities in protein sequence and architecture with each other and with other SMC and Smc-like proteins conserved from bacteria to humans (Hirano 2005). Like Smc1 and Smc3, these other SMC proteins dimerize and associate with additional subunits to form structurally related Smc complexes. These Smc complexes also mediate higher-order changes in chromosome structure, presumably by tethering chromatin (for reviews, see Hirano 2006, Nasmyth & Haering 2005). Given these similarities, we use relevant knowledge from other SMC complexes to supplement our discussion of cohesin structure.

The remarkable architecture of Smc proteins provided an early indication that the process of cohesion is likely to be complicated. All Smc proteins contain globular domains at the N- and C-terminal ends that are connected by a long alpha helical structure. This alpha helical

structure is broken in the middle by a globular hinge domain (**Figure 1**). Folding at the hinge domain brings together the two halves of the alpha helix to form a long, antiparallel coiled-coil domain. Folding at the hinge also brings together the globular domains at the N and C termini to form the head domain (**Figure 1**, middle) (Haering et al. 2002, Melby et al. 1998). The head domain shares striking similarity with the half site of the ATP binding cassette (ABC), the ATPase domain found in ABC transporters and the Smc-like Rad50 protein (Haering et al. 2004, Hopfner et al. 2000). These ATPase domains contain three small highly conserved motifs called Walker A, Walker B, and signature motif (Hopfner et al. 2000, Saitoh et al. 1994, Walker et al. 1982). The final folded Smc forms an extended dumbbell with globular hinge and head domains separated by ~45 nm of coiled coil.

Soluble chromatin-free SMC proteins dimerize by a number of mechanisms (**Figure 1**). The most stable association occurs through the hydrophobic interactions of the hinge domain (Haering et al. 2002, 2004;

ABC: ATP binding cassette

Hirano et al. 2001). This dimerization generates large V-shaped structures visualized in the electron microscope (Anderson et al. 2002, Haering et al. 2002). Smc dimers also form closed rings through the additional association of their head domains (**Figure 1**). This association brings together the two half sites of the ABC-like ATPase domains, generating two functional ATPases. The association of the head domains depends in part on ATP binding because the ATP is coordinated simultaneously by the Walker A motif of one head and the signature motif of the other head (Haering et al. 2004, Jones & Sgouros 2001, Lowe et al. 2001). However, ATP-independent determinants for association of the heads apparently exist as well (Haering et al. 2002). Finally, the coiled coils of Smc1 and Smc3 provide another interface for potential interaction between Smc molecules. In some electron microscopy (EM) images the coiled-coil regions of the dimer are separate, whereas in others they are together (Anderson et al. 2002, Haering et al. 2002). In summary, the structure of the Smc dimer reveals multiple interaction surfaces and two ATPases, providing a potential energy-dependent mechanism to regulate those interactions.

Soluble chromatin-free cohesin complexes resemble the Smc dimers with the addition of the non-Smc subunits bound to the head domain (**Figure 1**). Of the non-Smc subunits, only the structure of the kleisin subunit, Mcd1, has been studied extensively. The N terminus of Mcd1 interacts with the Smc3 head domain, whereas the C terminus is the docking site for the Smc1 head domain (Haering et al. 2002). These two interactions allow the kleisin subunit to cross-link the head domains (**Figure 1**). Although both interactions occur at the bottom of the head near the ATP binding pockets of the Smc heads, only the Smc1-Mcd1 interaction is ATP dependent (Gruber et al. 2003; Haering et al. 2002, 2004). The proximity of Mcd1 to the ATPase active site and the ability of Mcd1 to cross-link heads make Mcd1 ideally suited to be a central regulator of cohesin function.

Independently of its interaction with the SMCs, Mcd1 also binds the fourth cohesin subunit, Scc3 (Haering et al. 2002). The sequence of this subunit lacks any defined motif other than HEAT repeats, loosely defined protein-protein interaction motifs. HEAT repeats are found in the cohesin-associated factor Pds5 (see subsection on Cohesion Maintenance and Dissolution, below), and the cohesin loading factor Scc2 (see subsection on Cohesin Binding to Chromatin, below). The structural/functional roles of Scc3 and its HEAT domains in cohesin remain a mystery.

The structure of the soluble chromatin-free cohesin inspired a number of models for the mechanism of cohesion (**Figure 2**). One of the first models proposed was the embrace model (Gruber et al. 2003). In this model the soluble chromatin-free ring structure is also the relevant structure for both chromatin binding and tethering. As originally postulated, this model proposed that ATP hydrolysis by the cohesin heads causes them to dissociate and the ring to open. Opening of the ring allows the two sister chromatids to enter the interior of the ring, either simultaneously or sequentially. The sister chromatids are entrapped when the ring reforms by the reassociation of the head domains through the binding of ATP and the kleisin subunit.

Alternative models for cohesin function begin with the premise that the single-ring structure of soluble cohesin is not the active form on chromatin (Huang et al. 2005, Milutinovich & Koshland 2003). Rather, the structure changes when cohesin binds to chromatin and actually tethers sister chromatids together (the cohesive state). One suggestion is that cohesins bind to each sister chromatid and then oligomerize to generate cohesion (**Figure 2**). In these models, oligomerization is achieved by exploiting one of the many interaction surfaces, like the coiled coils or hinge, to promote inter- rather than intracomplex association. Experiments to test the validity of the embrace and oligomerization models have resulted in important insights. However, active cohesin likely must undergo structural changes not anticipated by any model. These are discussed in detail below. Clearly, crystallographic and EM structures of

Cohesion generation: the step after cohesins bind chromatin, when cohesins become cohesive and actually tether sister chromatids together

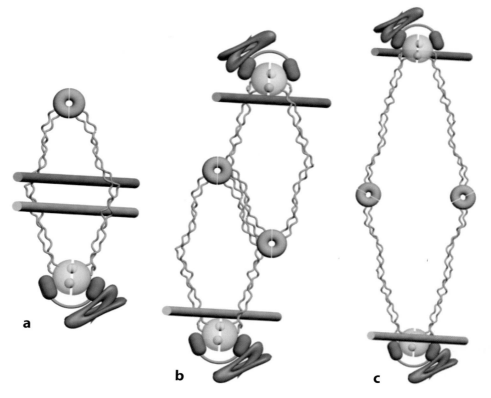

Figure 2

Models for cohesin chromosome tethering. In the ring model (*a*) soluble chromatin-free single cohesin topologically entraps sister chromatids inside the ring-shaped structure. Alternatively, the snap (*b*) and bracelet (*c*) models suggest that chromatin-bound cohesins form oligomers mediated by the coiled coils or hinges, respectively. In these models chromatids are held by a specific DNA-protein interaction inside or outside the complex. The actual molecular mechanism for chromosome tethering most likely is a hybrid of the models presented.

cohesin, both bound to chromatin and in the cohesive state, are critical steps toward unraveling the molecular basis of cohesion.

Cohesin Binding to Chromatin

Early studies revealed that the binding of cohesin to chromatin is highly regulated both spatially and temporally (**Figure 3*a***). Cohesins bind initially to DNA during the G1/S phase transition in budding yeast and during telophase of the preceding cell divsion in vertebrates. Cohesins then continue to bind until anaphase onset (Guacci et al. 1997, Losada et al. 2000, Michaelis et al. 1997, Sumara et al.

2000). This cell-cycle-regulated binding of cohesin occurs at high density in a large domain around each centromere (pericentric) and at lower density along chromosome arms. In budding and fission yeast, the low-density binding occurs on average at 15-kb intervals called cohesin-associated regions (CARs) (Blat & Kleckner 1999, Glynn et al. 2004, Laloraya et al. 2000, Lengronne et al. 2004). CARs tend to lie in AT-rich intergenic regions between divergently transcribed genes, but many exceptions to this distribution are found (Glynn et al. 2004, Laloraya et al. 2000, Lengronne et al. 2004). CARs span ~1 kb of DNA (Laloraya et al. 2000), but no specific sequence within any

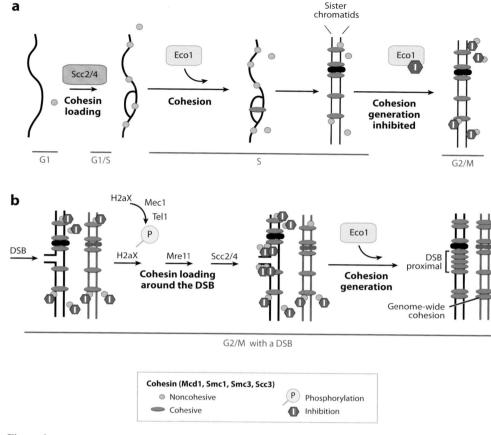

Figure 3

(*a*) In G1/S the Scc2/Scc4 complex begins loading cohesin onto chromosomes at cohesin-associated regions (CARs) and at pericentric regions. The chromatin-bound cohesin becomes cohesive in S, facilitated by the Eco1/Ctf7 factor. In G2/M cohesin continues to load at these regions but does not become cohesive because Eco1 activity is inhibited (indicated by I). (*b*) Upon a double-strand break (DSB), cohesin loading is directed to the DSB region through phosphorylation of H2AX (indicated by P) and binding of MRX to the break site. The inhibition of Eco1 is removed, allowing cohesion generation to occur at the DSB region and at CARs genome wide.

CAR has been demonstrated to be essential for cohesin binding. The large size of the CAR may reflect multiple interactions between a cohesin and the CAR, the binding of multiple cohesins to the CAR, or variable binding of a cohesin within the CAR.

Subsequent studies of cohesin revealed even greater regulation of its binding to chromatin. Cohesin binding is enriched at silent chromatin (Bernard et al. 2001, Chang et al. 2005, Nonaka et al. 2002). Cohesin also binds ex-tensively to chromatin surrounding a DNA double-strand break (DSB) to form a large cohesin domain (**Figure 3***b*) (J.S. Kim et al. 2002, Strom et al. 2004, Ünal et al. 2004). Finally, cohesins are even targeted to extra-chromosomal elements like the "selfish" 2-μ plasmid in budding yeast (Ghosh et al. 2006, Mehta et al. 2002). These diverse exam-ples of cohesin binding to chromatin raise two questions. What is the underlying mech-anism that allows cohesin to bind chromatin,

DSB: double-strand break

and how is this binding controlled spatially and temporarily?

A simple idea is that cohesin binds chromatin by binding DNA. In vitro biochemical studies indicate that the purified SMC dimers contain an intrinsic DNA binding activity and that cohesin can weakly bind to double-stranded and single-stranded DNA (Losada & Hirano 2001). Under these in vitro conditions, cohesin does not exhibit any preference to bind a specific DNA sequence but does exhibit some preference for secondary structure. However, the biological significance of these activities has not been established by mutations that block both DNA binding in vitro and chromatin binding in vivo.

The absence of a recognizable DNA binding motif in any of the cohesin subunits suggests a more complex method of binding. Indeed, genetic studies show that chromatin binding in vivo requires all the subunits of cohesin (Michaelis et al. 1997, Tóth et al. 1999). Moreover, cohesin binding to chromatin in vivo is abrogated by natural cleavage of the kleisin subunit or engineered cleavage of Smc3 (Hornig & Uhlmann 2004, Ivanov & Nasmyth 2005). These in vivo studies imply that the assembly of the entire cohesin complex is needed for its stable binding to chromatin.

More detailed structure/function studies reveal that cohesin association with chromatin requires motifs within Smc heads and the head-proximal region of the coiled coils. Mutations have been made in the Walker A and B motifs as well as in the signature motifs of the Smc1 and Smc3 heads to perturb ATP binding and hydrolysis, respectively (Arumugam et al. 2003, Weitzer et al. 2003). These mutations also block cohesin binding to chromatin. These ATP-dependent functions in cohesin binding are not to promote head dissociation, as postulated in the original embrace model, because cohesin binding and cohesion generation still occur when the head domains of Smc1 and Smc3 are tethered in vivo by artificial protein cross-links (Gruber et al. 2006). Intriguingly, an unbiased mutagenesis of Smc1 identified residues near the Loop1 region of the coiled coil of Smc1 as being critical for efficient cohesin binding (Milutinovich et al. 2007). Loop1 is defined as a predicted break in the coiled coil that is proximal to the head. These observations are consistent with a model in which the Smc head domains alter the coiled coil to facilitate chromatin binding.

The hinge also functions in cohesin binding to chromatin. Chromatin binding appears reduced when the hinge domains of Smc1 and Smc3 are tethered in vivo by artificial protein cross-links (see below) (Gruber et al. 2006). Furthermore, five-amino-acid insertions in the hinge are compatible with general chromatin binding but inhibit binding to CARs (Milutinovich et al. 2007). This observation extends the role of the hinge beyond general chromatin binding to the modulation of specific binding. The requirement for specific residues in the hinge, the head, and the head-proximal coiled coil for chromatin binding is fascinating given that the head and hinge lie at opposite ends of the cohesin complex, some 45 nm apart in the soluble structure. This requirement suggests that chromatin binding is achieved by a large energy-dependent change in cohesin conformation.

These observations are consistent with a modification of the original embrace model. In the revised model, cycles of ATP binding and hydrolysis of the head cause conformational changes in the Smc1 and Smc3 hinges, allowing sister chromatin strands to enter inside the ring and be entrapped (Gruber et al. 2006). The head may cause the dissociation of the hinge domains through a direct interaction. Indeed, several independent studies suggest head-hinge interactions for cohesin. A direct head-hinge interaction was implicated by FRET analysis of cohesin subunit interactions (Mc Intyre et al. 2007). In addition, atomic force microscopy of condensin, another Smc complex, reveals folded structures with the head and hinge in close proximity (Yoshimura et al. 2002). Finally, in the bacterial SMC complex, binding of DNA to the hinge stimulates the ATPase of the head in vitro (Hirano & Hirano 2006, Onn et al. 2007).

However, all these observations are also consistent with nontopological modes of DNA binding, like the DNA binding of histones or Mu transposase, in which DNA makes multiple contacts with multiple subunits (Chaconas 1999). DNA binding would be blocked by any mutation that prevents cohesin from assembling into the final active conformation. Indeed, tethering of the hinge domains has been interpreted solely to prevent hinge dissociation, but this tethering may also block any hinge structural change needed for nontopological chromatin binding. Furthermore, the bulky cross-linking method (engineered protein dimerization motifs) may simply preclude the hinge domains from binding another cohesin factor. Precedent that other proteins can bind to the hinge exists for Smc2 of condensin (Chen et al. 2004; Patel & Ghiselli 2005a,b).

The most compelling argument that cohesins binds chromatin by topologically entrapping DNA comes from studies of cohesin bound to purified circular minichromosomes. Cohesin can be released from the minichromosome by a single cleavage of the minichromosome DNA (Ivanov & Nasmyth 2005, 2007). However, this linearization also seems to perturb DNA binding of the centromere-specific nucleosome to a lesser but still significant extent (Ivanov & Nasmyth 2005). Perturbing the robust nucleosome/DNA interaction suggests that the linearization conditions may alter the minichromosome in additional ways beyond just modifying topology. Thus, although the current observations are consistent with a topological mechanism of cohesin binding to chromatin, its definitive demonstration awaits additional approaches, most importantly reconstitution in vitro by a biologically relevant assay.

The Scc2/4 complex is an evolutionarily conserved factor required for cohesin association with chromatin in vivo in all contexts (heterochromatin, CARs, centromeres, etc.) (Ciosk et al. 2000, Furuya et al. 1998, Tomonaga et al. 2000, Watrin et al. 2006). Virtually nothing is known about how Scc2/4 loads cohesin onto DNA. Studies of Scc2/Scc4 on the binding

of cohesin to DNA in vitro have not been reported. An early bioinformatic study suggested that the Scc2 protein may be a kinase (Jones & Sgouros 2001), and mutants in the Scc2 homolog in fission yeast have greatly reduced Mcd1 (Rad21) phosphorylation (Tomonaga et al. 2000). Yet, to our knowledge, the Scc2/4 complex has not been tested for kinase activity either. Even more enigmatic is the role of Scc4, which is only loosely conserved among eukaryotes. Given our current poor understanding of cohesin binding to chromatin, alternative functions for Scc2/4 may include an activator of Smc ATPase, a facilitator of hinge dimerization, a chromatin binding protein, or a chromatin remodeler.

However cohesin binds chromatin, this binding must be regulated to achieve the complicated spatial and temporal patterns of cohesin-chromosome association. Early studies suggested that the spatial pattern of cohesin binding could be attributed to a passive response to general chromosome properties and activities. As stated above, cohesins do not appear to recognize any specific DNA sequence. In addition, cohesin enrichment at CARs has been postulated to occur by a nonspecific process in which the cohesin ring is pushed along the chromatin by the transcription machinery (Lengronne et al. 2004). However, the notion of cohesin localization by such passive processes is becoming less and less attractive with the discovery of elaborate mechanisms to target cohesin to specific regions of chromosomes.

Underlying chromatin marks are required to target cohesin to many of its known chromosomal binding sites/regions. In fission yeast, histone H3 K9 methylation-dependent recruitment of the heterochromatin-associated protein Swi6 (HP1) directs the assembly of pericentromeric cohesin domain (Bernard et al. 2001, Hall et al. 2003, Nonaka et al. 2002, Partridge et al. 2002). Sir2, the histone deacetylase, is required for cohesin binding at HMR (Chang et al. 2005). Furthermore, damage-induced phosphorylation of the histone variant H2AX proximal to the DSB is important for the formation of damage-induced cohesin domains

Cohesion maintenance: the persistence of sister chromatid cohesion from its establishment in S phase until its dissolution at anaphase onset

(**Figure 3b**) (Ünal et al. 2004). In humans, cohesin is recruited to Alu repeats, and binding is influenced by DNA methylation (Hakimi et al. 2002). Finally, both Rsc and ISWI chromatin remodelers have been implicated in cohesin loading (Baetz et al. 2004, Hakimi et al. 2002, Huang et al. 2004, Yang et al. 2004). Thus, cohesin appears to be targeted to specific chromosomal regions by a code of evolutionarily conserved histone modifications and local chromosome structure. With this in mind, it will be interesting to revisit the mechanism that targets cohesin to CARs.

Cohesins also are recruited to specific chromosome addresses by distinct protein complexes. The cohesin domain assembled around a DSB requires the MRX complex bound to the broken end as well as the large domain of H2AX phosphorylation (Ünal et al. 2004). In budding yeast, conserved centromere proteins assemble on a 300-bp *CEN* sequence and then nucleate cohesin binding over a large pericentric domain (Weber et al. 2004). Thus, in these two contexts the MRX and *CEN* complexes nucleate cohesin binding at both proximal and distal chromatin sites. Another example is the Rep proteins, which recruit cohesin to the STB locus of the extrachromosomal 2-μ plasmid in yeast (Yang et al. 2004). Rep recruitment of cohesin may foreshadow how cohesin is recruited by other site-specific chromatin-binding proteins like transcription factors. This notion is attractive given the emerging role of cohesin in transcription regulation (Dorsett 2007). In summary, cells have elaborate mechanisms specifically dedicated to the temporal and spatial regulation of chromatin binding of cohesin. This complexity enables cohesin to perform diverse biological functions.

Generation of Cohesion: Making Chromatin-Bound Cohesins Become Cohesive

Once cohesin is chromatin bound, it must become cohesive, tethering together only sister chromatids. Numerous observations support the idea that cohesin can exist in two chromatin-bound states, cohesive and noncohesive. In most eukaryotes, cohesins bind to chromosomes prior to DNA replication at the G1/S transition or in telophase of the previous cell cycle (Guacci et al. 1997, Losada et al. 1998, Michaelis et al. 1997, Sumara et al. 2000, Tomonaga et al. 2000). Because in these phases of the cell cycle there is no sister chromatid, cohesins must be able to bind chromatin independently of being cohesive. Also, although cohesins generate cohesion when bound to CARs during DNA replication, they fail to generate cohesion when loaded onto CARs in G2/M (**Figure 3a**) (Haering et al. 2004, Lengronne et al. 2006, Strom et al. 2004, Uhlmann & Nasmyth 1998). Thus, cohesin binding to chromatin is not sufficient to generate cohesion even when sister chromatids are in close proximity. However, cohesins bound to chromatin in G2/M become cohesive when the cell suffers a DSB in one of its chromosomes (**Figure 3b**) (Strom et al. 2007, Ünal et al. 2007). These results suggest that cohesion requires two distinct steps. Cohesin first binds chromatin in a noncohesive state and then matures to a cohesive state. We define this second post-chromatin-binding step as cohesion generation. Cohesion generation is regulated by cell cycle progression and DNA damage.

Perhaps the most compelling evidence for a distinct step for cohesion generation came with the discovery and characterization of the evolutionarily conserved protein Eco1/Ctf7. Eco1 is not needed for chromatin binding of cohesin in S phase at pericentric regions, at CARs, or around a DSB (Milutinovich et al. 2007, Noble et al. 2006, Skibbens et al. 1999, Tóth et al. 1999). Eco1 is critical to generate cohesion in all cases (**Figure 3**), and inactivation of Eco1 in G2 does not abrogate cohesion once it is formed (Skibbens et al. 1999, Tóth et al. 1999). Thus, Eco1 acts after chromatin binding to help cohesin become cohesive but is dispensible for maintaining cohesion.

The activity of Eco1 responsible for cohesion generation remains to be elucidated. Eco1 contains a noncanonical C2H2 zinc finger (Ivanov et al. 2002). Eco1 also contains acetyl transferase activity. In vitro it can acetylate itself as well as Mcd1, Scc3, and Pds5, but not histones or PCNA (Ivanov et al. 2002). To date, mutations in these two domains of Eco1 are consistent with a model in which the acetyl transferase performs a regulatory function whereas the zinc-finger domain is responsible for cohesion generation, perhaps through direct interaction with cohesin (Brands & Skibbens 2005, Ivanov et al. 2002, Ünal et al. 2007).

However, this conclusion needs to be substantiated. First, Eco1 has not been localized to CARs or shown to bind to cohesin, as might be expected of a structural component. The evidence that the acetyl transferase has a regulatory function is based on phenotypic analysis of mutations that significantly reduce acetyl transferase activity of the recombinant protein in vitro (Ivanov et al. 2002). These *eco1* mutants do not impair the generation of cohesion in vivo during S phase but do block cohesion induction by a DSB (Ünal et al. 2007). However, if these acetyl transferase mutants retain some activity in vivo, then these results will not eliminate a critical role for acetylation in cohesion generation during S phase. This supports a model in which different levels of acetyl transferase activity are required for S phase and DSB-induced cohesion. If it turns out that the acetyl transferase activity is required for cohesion generation, then identifying the critical Eco1-acetylated residues of cohesin should be particularly insightful in understanding cohesion generation.

How might an activity(s) of Eco1 promote chromatin-bound cohesin to become cohesive? We can envision two types of models. In one, the initial chromatin-bound form of cohesin is primarily in the noncohesive state, and Eco1 helps promote its transition to the cohesive state. In the second, chromatin-bound cohesin reversibly switches between its noncohesive state and its cohesive state. Thus, cohesion is established but is maintained too transiently to be effective. Eco1 activity would change cohesin so that it is trapped in its cohesive state. The value of these models is that they make testable predictions and provide explanations to apparent dilemmas in the field.

One of the attractions of the embrace model is its inherent simplicity (**Figure 2**). Cohesion occurs by a single embrace of both sisters or by sequential embrace of first one and then the other sister chromatid. In either case, cohesion is the result of a single biochemical activity, chromatin binding by opening and closing the ring. However, the embrace model provides no explanation for either the existence or necessity of a second Eco1-dependent step after cohesin binds chromatin. In addition, the embrace model predicts that cohesin binding to chromatin in G2/M should topologically trap both sister chromatids (held in juxtaposition by cohesion generated in S phase) and generate additional cohesion. Yet cohesin binding in G2/M in an unperturbed cell fails to generate additional cohesion (Haering et al. 2004, Lengronne et al. 2006, Strom et al. 2004, Uhlmann & Nasmyth 1998), again implying the existence of an extra step not in the embrace model.

The essence of the embrace model can be salvaged if cohesin readily switches between embracing chromatids (the cohesive chromatin-bound state) and releasing chromatids (the noncohesive chromatin-free state). Eco1 would modify cohesin after embracing the two sister chromatids to lock it in the chromatin-bound cohesive state. If Eco1 activity were limiting in G2/M, cohesins would bind chromatin but be unable to be locked in the cohesive state. Indeed, Eco1 does appear to be limiting because its overexpression in G2/M allows cohesion even without a DSB (Ünal et al. 2007). This modified embrace model predicts that manipulating Eco1 activity should alter the off rate of cohesin from chromatin.

Oligomerization models posit that cohesion is generated when two or more chromatin-bound cohesins associate. Hence these models have an intrinsic requirement for a second step for cohesion after chromatin binding of cohesin that may be facilitated by Eco1 activity. A simple idea is that the coiled coils of cohesin undergo a conformation change to present interaction surfaces like the hinge or the coiled coils themselves for intercomplex association (**Figure 2**). Studies of other Smc and SMC-like complexes provide precedent for conformational changes in the coiled coil. In the Smc-like Rad50 complex, coiled coils undergo a dramatic conformation change upon binding to DNA, converting from a floppy rod to a rigid rod (Moreno-Herrero et al. 2005). Condensin may undergo significant changes in conformation, as evidenced by increased susceptibility of its Smc2 subunit to in vitro proteases upon ATP binding (Onn et al. 2007). In principle, Eco1 may either facilitate a conformational change in cohesin structure or stabilize dimerization after the conformational change has occurred.

The main criticism of oligomerization models for cohesion is the absence of evidence for biologically relevant cohesin oligomers. Although rare oligomers of purified Smc complexes can be observed either by microscopy or by biochemical methods (Haering et al. 2002, Hirano et al. 2001, Yoshimura et al. 2002), these oligomers can be attributed to artificial aggregation. However, the failure to recover soluble cohesin oligomers can easily be explained if they form only on chromatin as a way to ensure that cohesion occurs in the proper temporal/spatial context (see below). Chromatin binding may be a prerequisite for becoming cohesive by restricting Eco1 activity to chromatin-bound cohesin. If this is the case, manipulating Eco1 activity to make it active on the soluble complex may reveal changes in cohesin oligomerization that are otherwise difficult to detect.

Understanding the mechanism of cohesion generation does not explain how this cohesiveness is restricted to the relevant sister chromatin. In other words, given the global genome binding of cohesin, cohesins should tether any nearby chromatin, including unrelated chromosomes, and distant positions on the same chromatid. In the original version of the embrace model, cohesin embraces chromatin in G1, and DNA replication passes through the cohesin ring, ensuring the tethering of only sister chromatids (Haering et al. 2002). However, this replication-dependent model for specificity now seems unlikely because a DSB in G2/M in-duces sister chromatid cohesion without DNA replication (Strom et al. 2007, Ünal et al. 2007).

Alternatively, specificity can be achieved in S phase by the activation of chromatin-bound cohesin to become cohesive only near the replication fork (Milutinovich et al. 2007, Moldovan et al. 2006, Skibbens et al. 1999). The chromatin-bound cohesin(s) will preferentially tether the other sister chromatid by virtue of its proximity. In oligomerization models upon DNA replication, both newly synthesized CARs bind a cohesin(s). Fork-dependent activation of these cohesins would favor their oligomerization. Indeed, mutations in a number of replication factors exhibit partial cohesion defects, and direct physical and functional interactions between PCNA and Eco1 have been established (Bermudez et al. 2003; Kenna & Skibbens 2003; Moldovan et al. 2006; Skibbens et al. 1999, 2007). Whether Eco1 itself actually travels with the fork or might be activated by its passage is unclear. In a proximity model, DSB-induced cohesion in G2/M occurs between sister chromatids because their proximity is ensured by the preexisting cohesion established in S phase.

The mechanisms for generating sister chromatid cohesion remain major unsolved questions in the field. Above, we discuss observations in the context of the embrace and oligomerization models. However, these models are not mutually exclusive, and the real mechanism may well be a hybrid of the two (**Figure 2**). The ability to dissect cohesion generation would be greatly facilitated by the reconstitution of cohesion in vitro with purified components. With the knowledge that in vivo cohesion can be generated independently of DNA replication (Strom et al. 2007, Ünal et al. 2007), reconstitution of in vitro cohesion no longer requires in vitro DNA replication. Thus, developing cohesion in vitro should be feasible and represent an important future direction.

Although the cohesin-dependent mechanism is a major contributor to sister chromatid cohesion, it does not appear to be the sole source of cohesion. Inactivation of cohesin never causes complete dissolution of chromatid pairing, suggesting the existence of alternative cohesion pathways. Recent evidence suggests that condensin complexes, ORCs (origin recognition complexes), and centromere complexes mediate cohesion through cohesin-independent mechanisms (Lam et al. 2006, Monje-Casas et al. 2007, Shimada & Gasser 2007, Suter et al. 2004). In addition, DNA catenation may contribute to cohesion (Díaz-Martínez et al. 2006, Uemura et al. 1987). However, it is important to remember that topoisomerase II will catenate as well as decatenate any DNA molecules held in close juxtaposition in vitro. Therefore, the persistence of catenation until anaphase may be a consequence of cohesin-mediated cohesion rather than a mechanism to generate cohesion. Insight into the establishment, maintenance, and dissolution of cohesion by these alternative pathways would make important contributions to our understanding of chromosome transmission.

Cohesion Maintenance and Dissolution

The cohesion established in S phase must be maintained until anaphase onset. After every pair of sister chromatids achieves bipolar attachment, cohesion is dissolved, and sisters segregate. In principle, the maintenance of cohesion should require only that the cohesins remain stably bound and cohesive after S phase and that the trigger for cohesion dissolution be inactive until anaphase onset. However, studies in vertebrates reveal a process called prophase removal, exposing another layer of regulation (**Figure 4**) (Giménez-Abián et al. 2004, Losada et al. 2000, Sumara et al. 2000, Waizenegger et al. 2000). In early prophase, each pair of sister chromatids initially appears as a single unresolved rod, consistent with the extensive cohesion along the arms and around the centromere. During prophase, cohesins begin to disassociate from the arms so that by metaphase only a small fraction of cohesin remains bound. Concomitant with cohesin loss, the cohesion

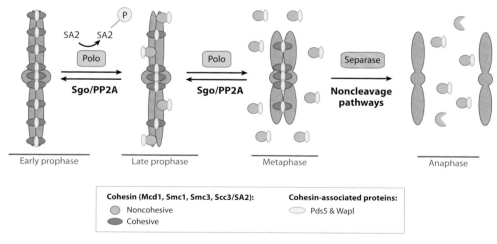

Figure 4

Early prophase chromosomes with cohesin in its cohesive state. For simplicity, we omit any chromatin-bound cohesins in the noncohesive state at early prophase, as depicted in **Figure 3**. During late prophase, Polo phosphorylation of SA2, the vertebrate isoform of Scc3, along with the action of Wapl convert most of the arm cohesins to the noncohesive form. These noncohesive cohesins ultimately dissociate from chromosomes by metaphase. Sgo and protein phosphatase 2A (PP2A) oppose Polo/Wapl, primarily at centromeric loci, to preserve the cohesive state and maintain cohesion at the centromeric loci. Complete dissolution of cohesion at anaphase onset is triggered by separase-mediated cleavage of the cohesin subunit Mcd1p in a subset of cohesins and potentially by other cleavage-independent mechanisms.

between the arms is reduced but not eliminated, as they now appear as closely associated parallel rods. The pericentric cohesin is protected from prophase removal, and cohesion around the centromere remains robust, maintaining the single-rod appearance. The spatial and temporal changes in cohesin/cohesion during prophase removal were the first hints that the maintenance of cohesion was a complex and highly regulated process.

Significant progress has been made in understanding the regulation of prophase removal from sister chromatid arms. Initial studies showed that vertebrate Polo-like kinase 1 (Plk1) is the primary kinase required for prophase removal (Losada et al. 2002, Sumara et al. 2002). Two vertebrate cohesin subunits, SA2 (a mammalian Scc3 isoform; see **Table 1**) and RAD21/MCD1, are Plk1 substrates, but SA2 is the key target for prophase removal (Hauf et al. 2005). SA2 phosphorylation occurs during mitosis, and cohesin driven from chromosomes during prophase removal contains phosphorylated SA2 (Hauf et al. 2005, Kueng et al. 2006). More definitively, cells expressing *SA2-12xA*, an allele that lacks Plk1 phosphorylation sites, are inhibited for prophase removal (Hauf et al. 2005). Consequently, these metaphase chromosomes now contain high levels of cohesin on the arms as well as pericentric regions and maintain arm cohesion after prolonged metaphase arrest. Prophase removal also requires an evolutionarily conserved protein called Wapl. In Wapl-depleted cells, prophase removal is blocked, and arm cohesion is stabilized (Gandhi et al. 2006, Kueng et al. 2006). In these cells phosphorylated SA2 remains bound to metaphase chromosomes (Kueng et al. 2006). Thus, SA2 phosphorylation is not sufficient for prophase removal but rather works either in conjunction with or upstream of Wapl.

If cohesins bound to pericentric regions and along the arms are structurally equivalent, why are pericentric cohesins not inactivated by prophase removal? The initial breakthrough came from *Drosophila* and then subsequent elegant meiotic studies in fission and budding yeast (Kerrebrock et al. 1995, Watanabe 2005).

The centromeric MEIS-322/Sgo1 family of proteins is required for centromeric cohesion during meiosis I and for cohesion in metaphase-arrested cells. Depletion of human SGO1 leads to the complete loss of both cohesin and cohesion along the entire length of the chromosomes during early mitosis (McGuinness et al. 2005, Salic et al. 2004). Sgo1p also localizes predominantly to centromeric regions, and when Sgo1p is mislocalized to chromosome arms by depletion of the Bub1p kinase, arm cohesion becomes more robust (Kitajima et al. 2005, Salic et al. 2004, Tang et al. 2004). Therefore, human Sgo1p preserves cohesin binding to chromosomes and sister cohesion wherever it localizes. Because the *SA2-12xA* allele suppresses the effects of SGO1 depletion, Sgo1 appears to act upstream of this phosphorylation (McGuinness et al. 2005).

On the basis of these results and additional meiotic studies, a simple model is emerging for the protection of pericentric cohesion in mitosis (**Figure 4**). Enrichment of Sgo1 and an associated phosphatase at the pericentric regions allows local removal of Polo-dependent phosphorylation of SA2, protecting cohesin from Wap1-dependent removal (Clarke & Orr-Weaver 2006, Kitajima et al. 2006, Riedel et al. 2006). This simple model will likely need additional modification to account for newly identified components like sororin, which appears to be important to protect prophase cohesion (Díaz-Martínez et al. 2007, Rankin et al. 2005, Schmitz et al. 2007). Moreover, recent evidence suggests that Wap1 contributes to the turnover of cohesin binding in interphase, indicating that this pathway may function outside the context of prophase (Kueng et al. 2006). Finally, budding and fission yeast cells defective for Sgo have only minor defects in cohesin maintenance during mitosis (Katis et al. 2004, Kitajima et al. 2004). This difference between yeasts and other eukaryotes underscores that it may not be possible to generate simple models that are valid for all organisms.

Although our understanding of prophase removal regulation has advanced significantly, the actual mechanism of prophase removal remains a mystery. A key to unlocking this mystery may be Pds5p, a protein conserved from yeast to humans (Hartman et al. 2000, Sumara et al. 2000, Tanaka et al. 2001, van Heemst et al. 1999). When Pds5p function is abrogated, cohesion is still established but cannot be maintained, despite the fact that cohesins remain chromatin bound (Dorsett et al. 2005, Hartman et al. 2000, Losada et al. 2005, Stead et al. 2003, Tanaka et al. 2001). Pds5p associates with cohesin, Wapl, Eco1, and sororin (Gandhi et al. 2006, Kueng et al. 2006, Noble et al. 2006, Rankin et al. 2005, Sumara et al. 2000). One possibility is that the common interaction of these factors with Pds5 coordinates their functions to toggle cohesin between cohesive (Eco1 and sororin) and noncohesive (Wapl) states. Validating these and other mechanisms for prophase removal will require a better understanding of the functional significance of the interactions between Pds5, Wapl, and sororin.

The cohesion protected from prophase removal must be completely dissolved at anaphase onset to enable sisters to segregate to opposite poles (**Figure 4**). An early insight into cohesion dissolution at anaphase came with the identification of Pds1p and Cut2, founding members of the securin family (Funabiki et al. 1996a, Yamamoto et al. 1996a). Securins inhibit cohesion dissolution and the metaphase-to-anaphase transition (Funabiki et al. 1996b, Yamamoto et al. 1996b). To initiate anaphase, the anaphase-promoting complex triggers the degradation of securin, releasing its binding partner separase, a caspase-like protease (Ciosk et al. 1998, Cohen-Fix et al. 1996, Funabiki et al. 1996b). Separase cleaves some fraction of Mcd1, which facilitates the inactivation of cohesin and dissolution of cohesion (Hauf et al. 2001, Tomonaga et al. 2000, Uhlmann et al. 1999, Waizenegger et al. 2000). Although separase is essential for cohesion inactivation, a number of observations suggest that separase is unlikely to act alone (Guacci 2007). The efficiency of these putative alternative pathways may explain the range of sister chromatid separation observed upon separase depletion in different organisms (Ciosk et al. 1998,

Funabiki et al. 1993, Giménez-Abían et al. 2005, Wirth et al. 2006). Indeed, given that the persistence of even a little cohesion causes defects in chromosome segregation, it is likely that the cell uses multiple mechanisms to ensure the complete inactivation of all cohesion (Guacci 2007).

THE BIOLOGICAL FUNCTION OF COHESION AND COHESIN

Chromosome Segregation

Early cytological observations suggested that sister chromatid cohesion was critical for proper chromosome segregation in mitosis. As new genetic and cell biological tools became available, this function of cohesion was the first to be tested and dissected. Indeed, the precocious separation of sister chromatids is induced by mutations that inactivate cohesin, cohesin regulators, or cohesion auxiliary factors (Guacci et al. 1997, Michaelis et al. 1997, Yamamoto et al. 1996a). In all cases, chromosome nondisjunction and aneuploidy ensue, consistent with a failure to achieve proper bipolar attachment of sister kinetochores to the mitotic spindle. Subsequently, a defect in bipolar attachment was demonstrated visually in cohesin mutants of budding yeast and *Xenopus* egg extracts depleted for cohesin function (Dewar et al. 2004, Tanaka et al. 2000). Taken together, these observations demonstrate an evolutionarily conserved role for cohesion in the bipolar attachment of sister kinetochores.

It is intriguing that chromosomes have a large pericentromeric domain with high-density cohesin binding, and mutations that lower this density cause elevated errors in chromosome disjunction (Bernard et al. 2001, Eckert et al. 2007). Pericentric cohesion appears to facilitate bipolar attachment of sister kinetochores, in part by sterically constraining the orientation of the sister kinetochores (Eckert et al. 2007). In addition, bipolar attachment of paired sister chromatids generates tension when microtubule-based forces move the sister kinetochores poleward.

Tension triggers a signal that stabilizes the microtubule-kinetochore interaction, locking in the bipolar attachment (Nicklas & Koch 1969, Pinsky & Biggins 2005). The pericentric cohesion may contribute to tension sensing of the kinetochore by increasing the resistance to poleward stretching.

Organisms with longer chromosomes have larger pericentric cohesin domains and tend to have kinetochores with increased numbers of microtubule attachments. The increase in pericentric cohesin is likely a necessity to respond to increases in tension or steric complexities associated with larger chromosomes. Even within an organism, individual chromosomes exhibit significant differences in the size of the pericentric cohesin domains, which may change the efficiency of generating a bipolar attachment and the spontaneous rate of chromosome aneuploidy (Weber et al. 2004). Thus, the size of the pericentric domain may contribute to the elevated frequency of aneuploidy for specific chromosomes in birth defects and cancer. With these intra- and interspecies differences in the size of pericentric cohesin domain, it will be interesting to use emerging tools to modulate systematically the size of the domain on an individual chromosome and monitor changes in chromosome transmission (Eckert et al. 2007).

Changes in cohesin and cohesion in meiosis I play a critical role in altering the pattern of chromosome segregation (Chelysheva et al. 2005, Klein et al. 1999, Parra et al. 2004, Watanabe & Nurse 1999). Meiotic cells express an additional cohesin complex in which Rec8, a meiotic-specific isoform of the kleisin subunit, replaces most, but not all, of the Mcd1. Meiotic (Rec8) cohesin along with other factors alter sister kinetochores such that they co-orient to form a monopolar rather than a bipolar attachment to the meiosis I spindle (Monje-Casas et al. 2007, Tóth et al. 2000, Watanabe & Nurse 1999). An intriguing idea is that in at least some organisms, meiotic cohesin causes a unique temporal or spatial juxtaposition of sister kinetochores, which promotes their maturation into a single unified structure (Yokobayashi & Watanabe 2005).

Changes in the dissolution of meiotic cohesion are also critical to ensure proper sister chromatid segregation in meiosis II. Unlike mitosis, in which all cohesion is dissolved in anaphase, pericentric cohesion is not dissolved in anaphase I, allowing such cohesion to persist until anaphase II (Klein et al. 1999, Watanabe & Nurse 1999). This cohesion ensures that sister chromatids make a bipolar attachment and segregate to opposite poles in the second meiotic division. MeiS322/Sgo1, which protects pericentric cohesion from the anaphase I dissolution machinery, mediates the persistence of pericentric cohesion (Katis et al. 2004, Kerrebrock et al. 1995, Watanabe 2005). Interestingly, the same master kinase, Aurora, controls these critical changes in meiotic cohesion (Monje-Casas et al. 2007, Yu & Koshland 2007).

DNA Repair

In principle, the segregation function of cohesion in mitosis could be mediated solely by the pericentric cohesion. Thus, the existence of arm cohesion led to the supposition that cohesion must be seen in processes other than chromosome segregation (Koshland & Guacci 2000). Indeed, additional functions for arm cohesion have been identified by the use of genetic and cell biological tools derived from cohesins and their regulators. Cohesin mutants are sensitive to different DNA-damaging agents, including gamma irradiation, camptothecin, and hydroxyurea (Birkenbihl & Subramani 1992, S.T. Kim et al. 2002, Schar et al. 2004). This sensitivity supported the idea that sister chromatids improve the efficiency of DNA repair by ensuring the close proximity of a template for homologous recombination (Kadyk & Hartwell 1992, Sjogren & Nasmyth 2001). It was initially thought that this proximity was generated by the repair-independent cohesion generated during S phase, the same cohesion that is critical for chromosome segregation.

However, it is now clear that at least the efficient postreplicative repair of DSBs requires additional cohesion generated via a specific and complex cellular response to damage (J.S. Kim et al. 2002, Strom et al. 2004, Ünal et al. 2004). In yeast, the master DNA damage regulators, Mec1 (ATM) and Tel1 (ATR), phosphorylate H2AX over a large domain around the DSB, making it permissive for cohesin loading (Ünal et al. 2004). MRX bound at the break site stimulates cohesin loading on the domain of H2AX phosphorylation. In G2/M, Mec1 and MRX act in a distinct process to promote cohesion generation around the break site and genome wide through the activation of Eco1 in G2 (Strom et al. 2007, Ünal et al. 2007). Why Eco1 is unable to generate cohesion in G2/M in undamaged cells remains to be elucidated. Cohesion around the break site apparently promotes efficient repair from the sister chromatid (Strom et al. 2004, Ünal et al. 2004, Xie et al. 2004). This restriction suppresses ectopic repair through recombination with the homolog or disperse repetitive sequences elsewhere in the genome. Importantly, suppression of ectopic recombination reduces loss of heterozygosity, translocation, and internal deletions.

Chromosome Morphogenesis

Phenotypes of cohesin mutants have also implicated cohesins in mitotic and meiotic chromosome morphogenesis. In budding and fission yeast, changing the levels of cohesins causes hypo- or hypercondensation (Ding et al. 2006, Guacci et al. 1997, Hartman et al. 2000). This has led to the idea that cohesin binding may define boundaries for the condensation machinery. Perturbing cohesin function in higher eukaryotic cells or *Xenopus* egg extracts appears to have subtler effects on chromosome condensation (Kueng et al. 2006, Losada et al. 2002, Sonoda et al. 2001). Thus, cohesion may not be an absolute requirement for condensation in larger eukaryotes. Indeed, cohesin-independent mechanisms for condensation have now been revealed in budding yeast as well (Lavoie et al. 2004). However, no experiment in any organism has yet shown that cohesin-independent condensation can support chromosome segregation. The amount of compaction in the absence of cohesins may be unchanged, but the quality of compaction may be less ordered, compromising segregation. Ultimately testing the contribution of cohesion to functional condensation in vivo awaits the identification of cohesin alleles that are defective only for condensation but not for cohesion.

In meiosis, the presence of chromatin-bound cohesins is essential to the assembly of the synaptonemal complex, a protein structure that forms between homologs and is critical for meiotic chromosome pairing, synapsis, and recombination (Klein et al. 1999). This observation sets a precedent for cohesins as a chromosomal platform for the assembly of other macromolecular complexes. In this light the large domain of cohesins bound around a DSB may be a platform for the assembly of an as-yet-undiscovered macro complex that modulates DNA repair.

Transcription

The functions of cohesins, as potential boundary elements and platforms for complex assembly, may be used to modulate transcription as well. The first studies to link a cohesin factor with gene expression came from studies in flies and yeast. The *Drosophila* Scc2 homolog, *Nipped-B*, is required for long-range activation of the homeobox genes (Rollins et al. 2004). In *Saccharomyces*, cohesins act as boundary elements to limit the spreading of transcriptional silencing at the silent mating cassette (Donze et al. 1999). In zebrafish, the functions of Rad21 and Smc3 are needed for proper expression of *runx3 runx1* genes in early embryonic development (Horsfield et al. 2007). In humans, the Scc3 homolog SA2 activates a multimeric NF-kappaB reporter construct and enhances the activity of the transactivation domain of p65/RelA (Lara-Pezzi et al. 2004). Elucidating the molecular mechanism for cohesin modulation of transcription is a critical new direction in cohesin biology. In particular, it will be important to determine whether the transcription functions of cohesin reflect novel activities distinct from its ability to tether chromatin.

CONCLUSION

The field of sister chromatid cohesion has exploded, revealing remarkable complexity in the mechanism and regulation of cohesion and in the range of biological functions for cohesin. At first blush this complexity is intimidating. Solving how cohesins bind chromatin or generate cohesion has already seemed daunting because of the sophisticated architecture of cohesins and their chromatin substrate. Answering these questions seems even more difficult now because the kleisin subunit and the domains of the Smc proteins each are likely to have multiple biochemical/structural activities. Furthermore, chromatin binding and/or cohesion generation are likely to involve a large change in the conformation of the complex. This structural change mandates that even previously simple hypotheses like the embrace or oligomerization models become more complex. Similarly, the complexity of the regulation and the diverse role of cohesion in chromosome biology complicate the interpretation of in vivo analyses. For example, a number of exciting studies have begun to associate defects in cohesion factors with human genetic disorders, including cancer and developmental diseases like Cornelia de Lange syndrome (Barber et al. 2008, Dorsett 2007). It is unclear whether these disorders arise from perturbing the transcription, chromatid cohesion, chromosome segregation, or DNA repair functions of cohesin.

However, the studies that revealed the mechanistic complexity of cohesion have also provided novel technical tools. For example, the fields of DNA replication and transcription were greatly advanced when they were studied in the specialized context of viruses. Similarly, studying the biochemical activities of cohesin in the specialized context of a DSB, on the 2-µ extrachromosomal element, or at homeobox promoters may provide easier readouts than does chromosome segregation to address mechanistic questions using both in vivo and in vitro approaches.

The emerging biological complexity may also inspire researchers to entertain new concepts to address previously perplexing observations. For example, initially it was thought that prophase removal in mitotic cells might act as a preemptive strike, reducing the amount of cohesin that must be inactivated at anaphase. However, mutant cells incapable of prophase removal undergo apparently normal anaphase (Gandhi et al. 2006, Hauf et al. 2005, Kueng et al. 2006). In the absence of a mitotic segregation function, the reason for prophase removal has been a mystery. The solution to this mystery may come from the newly discovered roles for cohesin in transcription and DNA repair. These processes may be inhibited by cohesion and may hence need cohesin removal to inactivate cohesion. Alternatively, these processes may need to generate cohesion at a new location in the genome. This new cohesion may form from a soluble cohesin pool that is generated by cohesin removal. The idea that cohesion is dynamic, remodeling to accommodate different chromosome biology, is consistent with the recent observation that cohesin removal is not limited to prophase (Kueng et al. 2006). Thus, in the end, the current biological and mechanistic complexities offer tremendous technical and conceptual tools that will lead to rapid clarification rather than confusion—so much so that much in this review will be soon obsolete.

SUMMARY POINTS

1. Sister chromatid cohesion is mediated by cohesin, a four-subunit SMC (structural maintenance of chromosome) complex, and a growing list of cohesin auxiliary factors.

2. Cohesion and its factors are essential for diverse biological processes including chromosome segregation, DNA repair, gene expression, and development.

3. Cohesin subunits can associate through multiple surfaces in the Smc subunits and non-Smc subunits that are potentially regulated through the Smc ATPase domains.

4. The complex architecture of cohesin has been used to generate dramatically different mechanisms for both chromatin binding and the generation of cohesion.

5. The chromatin binding of cohesin is regulated temporally and spatially by elaborate mechanisms to enable cohesin to perform diverse biological functions.

6. The chromatin-bound cohesin matures from a noncohesive state to a cohesive state. This conversion is regulated both during the cell cycle and in response to DNA damage.

7. The maintenance of cohesion is a dynamic process involving restricted dissolution along chromosome arms during prophase as well as de novo cohesion generation after DNA damage in G2/M.

8. Solving the mechanism of cohesion and its complex regulation presents significant challenges but offers the potential to provide important insights into higher-order chromosome organization and chromosome biology.

DISCLOSURE STATEMENT

The authors are not aware of any biases that might be perceived as affecting the objectivity of this review.

LITERATURE CITED

Anderson DE, Losada A, Erickson HP, Hirano T. 2002. Condensin and cohesin display different arm conformations with characteristic hinge angles. *J. Cell Biol.* 156:419–24

Arumugam P, Gruber S, Tanaka K, Haering CH, Mechtler K, Nasmyth K. 2003. ATP hydrolysis is required for cohesin's association with chromosomes. *Curr. Biol.* 13:1941–53

Baetz KK, Krogan NJ, Emili A, Greenblatt J, Hieter P. 2004. The *ctf13–30/CTF13* genomic haploinsufficiency modifier screen identifies the yeast chromatin remodeling complex RSC, which is required for the establishment of sister chromatid cohesion. *Mol. Cell Biol.* 24:1232–44

Barber T, McManus K, Ries M, Vogelstein B, Lengauer C, Hieter P. 2008. Chromatid cohesion defects may underlie chromosome instability in human colorectal cancers. *Proc. Natl. Acad. Sci. USA* 105:3443–48

Bermudez VP, Maniwa Y, Tappin I, Ozato K, Yokomori K, Hurwitz J. 2003. The alternative Ctf18-Dcc1-Ctf8-replication factor C complex required for sister chromatid cohesion loads proliferating cell nuclear antigen onto DNA. *Proc. Natl. Acad. Sci. USA* 100:10237–42

Bernard P, Maure JF, Partridge JF, Genier S, Javerzat JP, Allshire RC. 2001. Requirement of heterochromatin for cohesion at centromeres. *Science* 294:2539–42

Birkenbihl RP, Subramani S. 1992. Cloning and characterization of *rad21* an essential gene of *Schizosaccharomyces pombe* involved in DNA double-strand-break repair. *Nucleic Acids Res.* 20:6605–11

Blat Y, Kleckner N. 1999. Cohesins bind to preferential sites along yeast chromosome III, with differential regulation along arms versus the centric region. *Cell* 98:249–59

Brands A, Skibbens RV. 2005. Ctf7p/Eco1p exhibits acetyltransferase activity—but does it matter? *Curr. Biol.* 15:R50–51

Chaconas G. 1999. Studies on a "jumping gene machine": higher-order nucleoprotein complexes in Mu DNA transposition. *Biochem. Cell Biol.* 77:487–91

Chang CR, Wu CS, Hom Y, Gartenberg MR. 2005. Targeting of cohesin by transcriptionally silent chromatin. *Genes Dev.* 19:3031–42

Chelysheva L, Diallo S, Vezon D, Gendrot G, Vrielynck N, et al. 2005. AtREC8 and AtSCC3 are essential to the monopolar orientation of the kinetochores during meiosis. *J. Cell Sci.* 118:4621–32

Chen ES, Sutani T, Yanagida M. 2004. Cti1/C1D interacts with condensin SMC hinge and supports the DNA repair function of condensin. *Proc. Natl. Acad. Sci. USA* 101:8078–83

Ciosk R, Shirayama M, Shevchenko A, Tanaka T, Toth A, Nasmyth K. 2000. Cohesin's binding to chromosomes depends on a separate complex consisting of Scc2 and Scc4 proteins. *Mol. Cell* 5:243–54

Ciosk R, Zachariae W, Michaelis C, Shevchenko A, Mann M, Nasmyth K. 1998. An ESP1/PDS1 complex regulates loss of sister chromatid cohesion at the metaphase to anaphase transition in yeast. *Cell* 93:1067–76

Clarke A, Orr-Weaver TL. 2006. Sister chromatid cohesion at the centromere: confrontation between kinases and phosphatases? *Dev. Cell* 10:544–47

Cohen-Fix O, Peters JM, Kirschner MW, Koshland D. 1996. Anaphase initiation in *Saccharomyces cerevisiae* is controlled by the APC-dependent degradation of the anaphase inhibitor Pds1p. *Genes Dev.* 10:3081–93

Dewar H, Tanaka K, Nasmyth K, Tanaka TU. 2004. Tension between two kinetochores suffices for their bi-orientation on the mitotic spindle. *Nature* 428:93–97

Díaz-Martínez LA, Giménez-Abián JF, Azuma Y, Guacci V, Giménez-Martín G, et al. 2006. PIASγ is required for faithful chromosome segregation in human cells. *PLoS ONE* 1:e53

Díaz-Martínez LA, Gimenez-Abian JF, Clarke DJ. 2007. Regulation of centromeric cohesion by sororin independently of the APC/C. *Cell Cycle* 6:714–24

Ding DQ, Sakurai N, Katou Y, Itoh T, Shirahige K, et al. 2006. Meiotic cohesins modulate chromosome compaction during meiotic prophase in fission yeast. *J. Cell Biol.* 174:499–508

Donze D, Adams CR, Rine J, Kamakaka RT. 1999. The boundaries of the silenced HMR domain in *Saccharomyces cerevisiae*. *Genes Dev.* 13:698–708

Dorsett D. 2007. Roles of the sister chromatid cohesion apparatus in gene expression, development, and human syndromes. *Chromosoma* 116:1–13

Dorsett D, Eissenberg JC, Misulovin Z, Martens A, Redding B, McKim K. 2005. Effects of sister chromatid cohesion proteins on cut gene expression during wing development in *Drosophila*. *Development* 132:4743–53

Eckert CA, Gravdahl DJ, Megee PC. 2007. The enhancement of pericentromeric cohesin association by conserved kinetochore components promotes high-fidelity chromosome segregation and is sensitive to microtubule-based tension. *Genes Dev.* 21:278–91

Funabiki H, Hagan I, Uzawa S, Yanagida M. 1993. Cell cycle-dependent specific positioning and clustering of centromeres and telomeres in fission yeast. *J. Cell Biol.* 121:961–76

Funabiki H, Kumada K, Yanagida M. 1996a. Fission yeast Cut1 and Cut2 are essential for sister chromatid separation, concentrate along the metaphase spindle and form large complexes. *EMBO J.* 15:6617–28

Funabiki H, Yamano H, Kumada K, Nagao K, Hunt T, Yanagida M. 1996b. Cut2 proteolysis required for sister-chromatid separation in fission yeast. *Nature* 381:438–41

Furuya K, Takahashi K, Yanagida M. 1998. Faithful anaphase is ensured by Mis4, a sister chromatid cohesion molecule required in S phase and not destroyed in G1 phase. *Genes Dev.* 12:3408–18

Gandhi R, Gillespie PJ, Hirano T. 2006. Human Wapl is a cohesin-binding protein that promotes sister-chromatid resolution in mitotic prophase. *Curr. Biol.* 16:2406–17

Ghosh SK, Hajra S, Paek A, Jayaram M. 2006. Mechanisms for chromosome and plasmid segregation. *Annu. Rev. Biochem.* 75:211–41

Giménez-Abián JF, Díaz-Martínez LA, Waizenegger IC, Giménez-Martín G, Clarke DJ. 2005. Separase is required at multiple preanaphase cell cycle stages in human cells. *Cell Cycle* 4:1576–84

Giménez-Abián JF, Sumara I, Hirota T, Hauf S, Gerlich D, et al. 2004. Regulation of sister chromatid cohesion between chromosome arms. *Curr. Biol.* 14:1187–93

Glynn EF, Megee PC, Yu HG, Mistrot C, Ünal E, et al. 2004. Genome-wide mapping of the cohesin complex in the yeast *Saccharomyces cerevisiae*. *PLoS Biol.* 2:e259

Gruber S, Arumugam P, Katou Y, Kuglitsch D, Helmhart W, et al. 2006. Evidence that loading of cohesin onto chromosomes involves opening of its SMC hinge. *Cell* 127:523–37

Gruber S, Haering CH, Nasmyth K. 2003. Chromosomal cohesin forms a ring. *Cell* 112:765–77

Guacci V. 2007. Sister chromatid cohesion: The cohesin cleavage model does not ring true. *Genes Cells* 12:693–708

Guacci V, Hogan E, Koshland D. 1994. Chromosome condensation and sister chromatid pairing in budding yeast. *J. Cell Biol.* 125:517–30

Guacci V, Koshland D, Strunnikov A. 1997. A direct link between sister chromatid cohesion and chromosome condensation revealed through the analysis of MCD1 in *S. cerevisiae*. *Cell* 91:47–57

Guacci V, Yamamoto A, Strunnikov A, Kingsbury J, Hogan E, et al. 1993. Structure and function of chromosomes in mitosis of budding yeast. *Cold Spring Harb. Symp. Quant. Biol.* 58:677–85

Haering CH, Lowe J, Hochwagen A, Nasmyth K. 2002. Molecular architecture of SMC proteins and the yeast cohesin complex. *Mol. Cell* 9:773–88

Haering CH, Schoffnegger D, Nishino T, Helmhart W, Nasmyth K, Lowe J. 2004. Structure and stability of cohesin's Smc1-kleisin interaction. *Mol. Cell* 15:951–64

Hakimi MA, Bochar DA, Schmiesing JA, Dong Y, Barak OG, et al. 2002. A chromatin remodelling complex that loads cohesin onto human chromosomes. *Nature* 418:994–98

Hall IM, Noma K, Grewal SI. 2003. RNA interference machinery regulates chromosome dynamics during mitosis and meiosis in fission yeast. *Proc. Natl. Acad. Sci. USA* 100:193–98

Hartman T, Stead K, Koshland D, Guacci V. 2000. Pds5p is an essential chromosomal protein required for both sister chromatid cohesion and condensation in *Saccharomyces cerevisiae*. *J. Cell Biol.* 151:613–26

Hauf S, Roitinger E, Koch B, Dittrich CM, Mechtler K, Peters JM. 2005. Dissociation of cohesin from chromosome arms and loss of arm cohesion during early mitosis depends on phosphorylation of SA2. *PLoS Biol.* 3:e69

Hauf S, Waizenegger IC, Peters JM. 2001. Cohesin cleavage by separase required for anaphase and cytokinesis in human cells. *Science* 293:1320–23

Hirano M, Anderson DE, Erickson HP, Hirano T. 2001. Bimodal activation of SMC ATPase by intra- and intermolecular interactions. *EMBO J.* 20:3238–50

Hirano M, Hirano T. 2006. Opening closed arms: long-distance activation of SMC ATPase by hinge-DNA interactions. *Mol. Cell* 21:175–86

Hirano T. 2005. SMC proteins and chromosome mechanics: from bacteria to humans. *Philos. Trans. R. Soc. London Ser. B* 360:507–14

Hirano T. 2006. At the heart of the chromosome: SMC proteins in action. *Nat. Rev. Mol. Cell Biol.* 7:311–22

Hirano T, Mitchison TJ. 1994. A heterodimeric coiled-coil protein required for mitotic chromosome condensation in vitro. *Cell* 79:449–58

Hopfner KP, Karcher A, Shin DS, Craig L, Arthur LM, et al. 2000. Structural biology of Rad50 ATPase: ATP-driven conformational control in DNA double-strand break repair and the ABC-ATPase superfamily. *Cell* 101:789–800

Hornig NC, Uhlmann F. 2004. Preferential cleavage of chromatin-bound cohesin after targeted phosphorylation by Polo-like kinase. *EMBO J.* 23:3144–53

Horsfield JA, Anagnostou SH, Hu JK, Cho KH, Geisler R, et al. 2007. Cohesin-dependent regulation of Runx genes. *Development* 134:2639–49

Huang CE, Milutinovich M, Koshland D. 2005. Rings, bracelet or snaps: fashionable alternatives for Smc complexes. *Philos. Trans. R. Soc. London Ser. B* 360:537–42

Huang J, Hsu JM, Laurent BC. 2004. The RSC nucleosome-remodeling complex is required for cohesin's association with chromosome arms. *Mol. Cell* 13:739–50

Irniger S, Piatti S, Michaelis C, Nasmyth K. 1995. Genes involved in sister chromatid separation are needed for B-type cyclin proteolysis in budding yeast. *Cell* 81:269–78

Ivanov D, Nasmyth K. 2005. A topological interaction between cohesin rings and a circular minichromosome. *Cell* 122:849–60

Ivanov D, Nasmyth K. 2007. A physical assay for sister chromatid cohesion in vitro. *Mol. Cell* 27:300–10

Ivanov D, Schleiffer A, Eisenhaber F, Mechtler K, Haering CH, Nasmyth K. 2002. Eco1 is a novel acetyltransferase that can acetylate proteins involved in cohesion. *Curr. Biol.* 12:323–28

Jones S, Sgouros J. 2001. The cohesin complex: sequence homologies, interaction networks and shared motifs. *Genome Biol.* 2:RESEARCH0009

Kadyk LC, Hartwell LH. 1992. Sister chromatids are preferred over homologs as substrates for recombinational repair in *Saccharomyces cerevisiae*. *Genetics* 132:387–402

Katis VL, Galova M, Rabitsch KP, Gregan J, Nasmyth K. 2004. Maintenance of cohesin at centromeres after meiosis I in budding yeast requires a kinetochore-associated protein related to MEI-S332. *Curr. Biol.* 14:560–72

Kenna MA, Skibbens RV. 2003. Mechanical link between cohesion establishment and DNA replication: Ctf7p/Eco1p, a cohesion establishment factor, associates with three different replication factor C complexes. *Mol. Cell Biol.* 23:2999–3007

Kerrebrock A, Moore D, Wu J, Orr-Weaver T. 1995. Mei-S332, a *Drosophila* protein required for sister-chromatid cohesion, can localize to meiotic centromere regions. *Cell* 83:247–56

Kerrebrock AW, Miyazaki WY, Birnby D, Orr-Weaver TL. 1992. The *Drosophila mei-S332* gene promotes sister-chromatid cohesion in meiosis following kinetochore differentiation. *Genetics* 130:827–41

Kim JS, Krasieva TB, LaMorte V, Taylor AM, Yokomori K. 2002. Specific recruitment of human cohesin to laser-induced DNA damage. *J. Biol. Chem.* 277:45149–53

Kim ST, Xu B, Kastan MB. 2002. Involvement of the cohesin protein, Smc1, in Atm-dependent and independent responses to DNA damage. *Genes Dev.* 16:560–70

Kitajima TS, Hauf S, Ohsugi M, Yamamoto T, Watanabe Y. 2005. Human Bub1 defines the persistent cohesion site along the mitotic chromosome by affecting shugoshin localization. *Curr. Biol.* 15:353–59

Kitajima TS, Kawashima SA, Watanabe Y. 2004. The conserved kinetochore protein shugoshin protects centromeric cohesion during meiosis. *Nature* 427:510–17

Kitajima TS, Sakuno T, Ishiguro K, Iemura S, Natsume T, et al. 2006. Shugoshin collaborates with protein phosphatase 2A to protect cohesin. *Nature* 441:46–52

Klein F, Mahr P, Galova M, Buonomo SB, Michaelis C, et al. 1999. A central role for cohesins in sister chromatid cohesion, formation of axial elements, and recombination during yeast meiosis. *Cell* 98:91–103

Koshland DE, Guacci V. 2000. Sister chromatid cohesion: the beginning of a long and beautiful relationship. *Curr. Opin. Cell Biol.* 12:297–301

Kueng S, Hegemann B, Peters BH, Lipp JJ, Schleiffer A, et al. 2006. Wapl controls the dynamic association of cohesin with chromatin. *Cell* 127:955–67

Laloraya S, Guacci V, Koshland D. 2000. Chromosomal addresses of the cohesin component Mcd1p. *J. Cell Biol.* 151:1047–56

Lam WW, Peterson EA, Yeung M, Lavoie BD. 2006. Condensin is required for chromosome arm cohesion during mitosis. *Genes Dev.* 20:2973–84

Lara-Pezzi E, Pezzi N, Prieto I, Barthelemy I, Carreiro C, et al. 2004. Evidence of a transcriptional co-activator function of cohesin STAG/SA/Scc3. *J. Biol. Chem.* 279:6553–59

Lavoie BD, Hogan E, Koshland D. 2004. In vivo requirements for rDNA chromosome condensation reveal two cell-cycle-regulated pathways for mitotic chromosome folding. *Genes Dev.* 18:76–87

Lengronne A, Katou Y, Mori S, Yokobayashi S, Kelly GP, et al. 2004. Cohesin relocation from sites of chromosomal loading to places of convergent transcription. *Nature* 430:573–78

Lengronne A, McIntyre J, Katou Y, Kanoh Y, Hopfner KP, et al. 2006. Establishment of sister chromatid cohesion at the *S. cerevisiae* replication fork. *Mol. Cell* 23:787–99

Losada A, Hirano M, Hirano T. 1998. Identification of *Xenopus* SMC protein complexes required for sister chromatid cohesion. *Genes Dev.* 12:1986–97

Losada A, Hirano M, Hirano T. 2002. Cohesin release is required for sister chromatid resolution, but not for condensin-mediated compaction, at the onset of mitosis. *Genes Dev.* 16:3004–16

Losada A, Hirano T. 2001. Intermolecular DNA interactions stimulated by the cohesin complex in vitro: implications for sister chromatid cohesion. *Curr. Biol.* 11:268–72

Losada A, Yokochi T, Hirano T. 2005. Functional contribution of Pds5 to cohesin-mediated cohesion in human cells and *Xenopus* egg extracts. *J. Cell Sci.* 118:2133–41

Losada A, Yokochi T, Kobayashi R, Hirano T. 2000. Identification and characterization of SA/Scc3p subunits in the *Xenopus* and human cohesin complexes. *J. Cell Biol.* 150:405–16

Lowe J, Cordell SC, van den Ent F. 2001. Crystal structure of the SMC head domain: an ABC ATPase with 900 residues antiparallel coiled-coil inserted. *J. Mol. Biol.* 306:25–35

Mc Intyre J, Muller EG, Weitzer S, Snydsman BE, Davis TN, Uhlmann F. 2007. In vivo analysis of cohesin architecture using FRET in the budding yeast *Saccharomyces cerevisiae*. *EMBO J.* 26:3783–93

McGuinness BE, Hirota T, Kudo NR, Peters JM, Nasmyth K. 2005. Shugoshin prevents dissociation of cohesin from centromeres during mitosis in vertebrate cells. *PLoS Biol.* 3:e86

Mehta S, Yang XM, Chan CS, Dobson MJ, Jayaram M, Velmurugan S. 2002. The 2 micron plasmid purloins the yeast cohesin complex: a mechanism for coupling plasmid partitioning and chromosome segregation? *J. Cell Biol.* 158:625–37

Melby TE, Ciampaglio CN, Briscoe G, Erickson HP. 1998. The symmetrical structure of structural maintenance of chromosomes (SMC) and MukB proteins: long, antiparallel coiled coils, folded at a flexible hinge. *J. Cell Biol.* 142:1595–604

Michaelis C, Ciosk R, Nasmyth K. 1997. Cohesins: chromosomal proteins that prevent premature separation of sister chromatids. *Cell* 91:35–45

Milutinovich M, Koshland DE. 2003. Molecular biology. SMC complexes—wrapped up in controversy. *Science* 300:1101–2

Milutinovich M, Ünal E, Ward C, Skibbens RV, Koshland D. 2007. A multi-step pathway for the establishment of sister chromatid cohesion. *PLoS Genet.* 3:e12

Miyazaki WY, Orr-Weaver TL. 1992. Sister-chromatid misbehavior in *Drosophila ord* mutants. *Genetics* 132:1047–61

Moldovan GL, Pfander B, Jentsch S. 2006. PCNA controls establishment of sister chromatid cohesion during S phase. *Mol. Cell* 23:723–32

Monje-Casas F, Prabhu VR, Lee BH, Boselli M, Amon A. 2007. Kinetochore orientation during meiosis is controlled by Aurora B and the monopolin complex. *Cell* 128:477–90

Moreno-Herrero F, de Jager M, Dekker NH, Kanaar R, Wyman C, Dekker C. 2005. Mesoscale conformational changes in the DNA-repair complex Rad50/Mre11/Nbs1 upon binding DNA. *Nature* 437:440–43

Nasmyth K, Haering CH. 2005. The structure and function of SMC and kleisin complexes. *Annu. Rev. Biochem.* 74:595–648

Nicklas RB, Koch CA. 1969. Chromosome micromanipulation. III. Spindle fiber tension and the reorientation of mal-oriented chromosomes. *J. Cell Biol.* 43:40–50

Noble D, Kenna MA, Dix M, Skibbens RV, Ünal E, Guacci V. 2006. Intersection between the regulators of sister chromatid cohesion establishment and maintenance in budding yeast indicates a multi-step mechanism. *Cell Cycle* 5:2528–36

Nonaka N, Kitajima T, Yokobayashi S, Xiao G, Yamamoto M, et al. 2002. Recruitment of cohesin to heterochromatic regions by Swi6/HP1 in fission yeast. *Nat. Cell Biol.* 4:89–93

Onn I, Aono N, Hirano M, Hirano T. 2007. Reconstitution and subunit geometry of human condensin complexes. *EMBO J.* 26:1024–34

Parra MT, Viera A, Gomez R, Page J, Benavente R, et al. 2004. Involvement of the cohesin Rad21 and SCP3 in monopolar attachment of sister kinetochores during mouse meiosis I. *J. Cell Sci.* 117:1221–34

Partridge JF, Scott KS, Bannister AJ, Kouzarides T, Allshire RC. 2002. *cis*-acting DNA from fission yeast centromeres mediates histone H3 methylation and recruitment of silencing factors and cohesin to an ectopic site. *Curr. Biol.* 12:1652–60

Patel CA, Ghiselli G. 2005a. Hinderin, a five-domains protein including coiled-coil motifs that binds to SMC3. *BMC Cell Biol.* 6:3

Patel CA, Ghiselli G. 2005b. The RET finger protein interacts with the hinge region of SMC3. *Biochem. Biophys. Res. Commun.* 330:333–40

Pinsky BA, Biggins S. 2005. The spindle checkpoint: tension versus attachment. *Trends Cell Biol.* 15:486–93

Rankin S, Ayad NG, Kirschner MW. 2005. Sororin, a substrate of the anaphase-promoting complex, is required for sister chromatid cohesion in vertebrates. *Mol. Cell* 18:185–200

Riedel CG, Katis VL, Katou Y, Mori S, Itoh T, et al. 2006. Protein phosphatase 2A protects centromeric sister chromatid cohesion during meiosis I. *Nature* 441:53–61

Rollins RA, Korom M, Aulner N, Martens A, Dorsett D. 2004. *Drosophila* nipped-B protein supports sister chromatid cohesion and opposes the stromalin/Scc3 cohesion factor to facilitate long-range activation of the cut gene. *Mol. Cell. Biol.* 24:3100–11

Saitoh N, Goldberg IG, Wood ER, Earnshaw WC. 1994. ScII: An abundant chromosome scaffold protein is a member of a family of putative ATPases with an unusual predicted tertiary structure. *J. Cell Biol.* 127:303–18

Salic A, Waters JC, Mitchison TJ. 2004. Vertebrate shugoshin links sister centromere cohesion and kinetochore microtubule stability in mitosis. *Cell* 118:567–78

Schar P, Fasi M, Jessberger R. 2004. SMC1 coordinates DNA double-strand break repair pathways. *Nucleic Acids Res.* 32:3921–29

Schmitz J, Watrin E, Lenart P, Mechtler K, Peters JM. 2007. Sororin is required for stable binding of cohesin to chromatin and for sister chromatid cohesion in interphase. *Curr. Biol.* 17:630–36

Shimada K, Gasser SM. 2007. The origin recognition complex functions in sister-chromatid cohesion in *Saccharomyces cerevisiae. Cell* 128:85–99

Sjogren C, Nasmyth K. 2001. Sister chromatid cohesion is required for postreplicative double-strand break repair in *Saccharomyces cerevisiae. Curr. Biol.* 11:991–95

Skibbens RV, Corson LB, Koshland D, Hieter P. 1999. Ctf7p is essential for sister chromatid cohesion and links mitotic chromosome structure to the DNA replication machinery. *Genes Dev.* 13:307–19

Skibbens RV, Maradeo M, Eastman L. 2007. Fork it over: the cohesion establishment factor Ctf7p and DNA replication. *J. Cell Sci.* 120:2471–77

Sonoda E, Matsusaka T, Morrison C, Vagnarelli P, Hoshi O, et al. 2001. Scc1/Rad21/Mcd1 is required for sister chromatid cohesion and kinetochore function in vertebrate cells. *Dev. Cell* 1:759–70

Stead K, Aguilar C, Hartman T, Drexel M, Meluh P, Guacci V. 2003. Pds5p regulates the maintenance of sister chromatid cohesion and is sumoylated to promote the dissolution of cohesion. *J. Cell Biol.* 163:729–41

Straight AF, Belmont AS, Robinett CC, Murray AW. 1996. GFP tagging of budding yeast chromosomes reveals that protein-protein interactions can mediate sister chromatid cohesion. *Curr. Biol.* 6:1599–608

Strom L, Karlsson C, Lindroos HB, Wedahl S, Katou Y, et al. 2007. Postreplicative formation of cohesion is required for repair and induced by a single DNA break. *Science* 317:242–45

Strom L, Lindroos HB, Shirahige K, Sjogren C. 2004. Postreplicative recruitment of cohesin to double-strand breaks is required for DNA repair. *Mol. Cell* 16:1003–15

Sumara I, Vorlaufer E, Gieffers C, Peters BH, Peters JM. 2000. Characterization of vertebrate cohesin complexes and their regulation in prophase. *J. Cell Biol.* 151:749–62

Sumara I, Vorlaufer E, Stukenberg PT, Kelm O, Redemann N, et al. 2002. The dissociation of cohesin from chromosomes in prophase is regulated by Polo-like kinase. *Mol. Cell* 9:515–25

Suter B, Tong A, Chang M, Yu L, Brown GW, et al. 2004. The origin recognition complex links replication, sister chromatid cohesion and transcriptional silencing in *Saccharomyces cerevisiae. Genetics* 167:579–91

Tanaka K, Hao Z, Kai M, Okayama H. 2001. Establishment and maintenance of sister chromatid cohesion in fission yeast by a unique mechanism. *EMBO J.* 20:5779–90

Tanaka T, Fuchs J, Loidl J, Nasmyth K. 2000. Cohesin ensures bipolar attachment of microtubules to sister centromeres and resists their precocious separation. *Nat. Cell Biol.* 2:492–99

Tang Z, Sun Y, Harley SE, Zou H, Yu H. 2004. Human Bub1 protects centromeric sister-chromatid cohesion through shugoshin during mitosis. *Proc. Natl. Acad. Sci. USA* 101:18012–17

Tomonaga T, Nagao K, Kawasaki Y, Furuya K, Murakami A, et al. 2000. Characterization of fission yeast cohesin: essential anaphase proteolysis of Rad21 phosphorylated in the S phase. *Genes Dev.* 14:2757–70

Tóth A, Ciosk R, Uhlmann F, Galova M, Schleiffer A, Nasmyth K. 1999. Yeast cohesin complex requires a conserved protein, Eco1p(Ctf7), to establish cohesion between sister chromatids during DNA replication. *Genes Dev.* 13:320–33

Tóth A, Rabitsch KP, Galova M, Schleiffer A, Buonomo SB, Nasmyth K. 2000. Functional genomics identifies monopolin: a kinetochore protein required for segregation of homologs during meiosis I. *Cell* 103:1155–68

Uemura T, Ohkura H, Adachi Y, Morino K, Shiozaki K, Yanagida M. 1987. DNA topoisomerase II is required for condensation and separation of mitotic chromosomes in *S. pombe. Cell* 50:917–25

Uhlmann F, Lottspeich F, Nasmyth K. 1999. Sister-chromatid separation at anaphase onset is promoted by cleavage of the cohesin subunit Scc1. *Nature* 400:37–42

Uhlmann F, Nasmyth K. 1998. Cohesion between sister chromatids must be established during DNA replication. *Curr. Biol.* 8:1095–101

Ünal E, Arbel-Eden A, Sattler U, Shroff R, Lichten M, et al. 2004. DNA damage response pathway uses histone modification to assemble a double-strand break-specific cohesin domain. *Mol. Cell* 16:991–1002

Ünal E, Heidinger-Pauli JM, Koshland D. 2007. DNA double-strand breaks trigger genome-wide sister-chromatid cohesion through Eco1 (Ctf7). *Science* 317:245–48

van Heemst D, James F, Poggeler S, Berteaux-Lecellier V, Zickler D. 1999. Spo76p is a conserved chromosome morphogenesis protein that links the mitotic and meiotic programs. *Cell* 98:261–71

Waizenegger IC, Hauf S, Meinke A, Peters JM. 2000. Two distinct pathways remove mammalian cohesin from chromosome arms in prophase and from centromeres in anaphase. *Cell* 103:399–410

Walker JE, Saraste M, Runswick MJ, Gay NJ. 1982. Distantly related sequences in the alpha- and beta-subunits of ATP synthase, myosin, kinases and other ATP-requiring enzymes and a common nucleotide binding fold. *EMBO J.* 1:945–51

Watanabe Y. 2005. Sister chromatid cohesion along arms and at centromeres. *Trends Genet.* 21:405–12

Watanabe Y, Nurse P. 1999. Cohesin Rec8 is required for reductional chromosome segregation at meiosis. *Nature* 400:461–64

Watrin E, Schleiffer A, Tanaka K, Eisenhaber F, Nasmyth K, Peters JM. 2006. Human Scc4 is required for cohesin binding to chromatin, sister-chromatid cohesion, and mitotic progression. *Curr. Biol.* 16:863–74

Weber SA, Gerton JL, Polancic JE, DeRisi JL, Koshland D, Megee PC. 2004. The kinetochore is an enhancer of pericentric cohesin binding. *PLoS Biol.* 2:E260

Weitzer S, Lehane C, Uhlmann F. 2003. A model for ATP hydrolysis-dependent binding of cohesin to DNA. *Curr. Biol.* 13:1930–40

Wirth KG, Wutz G, Kudo NR, Desdouets C, Zetterberg A, et al. 2006. Separase: a universal trigger for sister chromatid disjunction but not chromosome cycle progression. *J. Cell Biol.* 172:847–60

Xie A, Puget N, Shim I, Odate S, Jarzyna I, et al. 2004. Control of sister chromatid recombination by histone H2AX. *Mol. Cell* 16:1017–25

Yamamoto A, Guacci V, Koshland D. 1996a. Pds1p is required for faithful execution of anaphase in the yeast, *Saccharomyces cerevisiae*. *J. Cell Biol.* 133:85–97

Yamamoto A, Guacci V, Koshland D. 1996b. Pds1p, an inhibitor of anaphase in budding yeast, plays a critical role in the APC and checkpoint pathway(s). *J. Cell Biol.* 133:99–110

Yang XM, Mehta S, Uzri D, Jayaram M, Velmurugan S. 2004. Mutations in a partitioning protein and altered chromatin structure at the partitioning locus prevent cohesin recruitment by the *Saccharomyces cerevisiae* plasmid and cause plasmid missegregation. *Mol. Cell Biol.* 24:5290–303

Yokobayashi S, Watanabe Y. 2005. The kinetochore protein Moa1 enables cohesion-mediated monopolar attachment at meiosis I. *Cell* 123:803–17

Yoshimura SH, Hizume K, Murakami A, Sutani T, Takeyasu K, Yanagida M. 2002. Condensin architecture and interaction with DNA: Regulatory non-SMC subunits bind to the head of SMC heterodimer. *Curr. Biol.* 12:508–13

Yu HG, Koshland D. 2007. The Aurora kinase Ipl1 maintains the centromeric localization of PP2A to protect cohesin during meiosis. *J. Cell Biol.* 176:911–18

The Epigenetics of rRNA Genes: From Molecular to Chromosome Biology

Brian McStay[1] and Ingrid Grummt[2]

[1] Biomedical Research Center, Ninewells Hospital, University of Dundee, Dundee DD1 9SY, United Kingdom; email: b.m.mcstay@dundee.ac.uk

[2] Molecular Biology of the Cell II, German Cancer Research Center, DKFZ-ZMBH Alliance, D-69120 Heidelberg, Germany; email: i.grummt@dkfz.de

Annu. Rev. Cell Dev. Biol. 2008. 24:131–57

First published online as a Review in Advance on July 10, 2008

The *Annual Review of Cell and Developmental Biology* is online at cellbio.annualreviews.org

This article's doi:
10.1146/annurev.cellbio.24.110707.175259

Key Words

NOR, nucleolus, rDNA, RNA polymerase I, NoRC, CSB, chromatin remodeling, histone modifications, DNA methylation, transcriptional silencing

Abstract

In eukaryotes, the genes encoding ribosomal RNAs (rDNA) exist in two distinct epigenetic states that can be distinguished by a specific chromatin structure that is maintained throughout the cell cycle and is inherited from one cell to another. The fact that even in proliferating cells with a high demand of protein synthesis a fraction of rDNA is silenced provides a unique possibility to decipher the mechanism underlying epigenetic regulation of rDNA. This chapter summarizes our knowledge of the molecular mechanisms that establish and propagate the epigenetic state of rRNA genes, unraveling a complex interplay of DNA methyltransferases and histone-modifying enzymes that act in concert with chromatin remodeling complexes and RNA-guided mechanisms to define the transcriptional state of rDNA. We also review the critical role of the RNA polymerase I transcription factor UBF in the formation of active nucleolar organizer regions (NORs) and maintenance of the euchromatic state of rRNA genes.

Contents

INTRODUCTION

Growing cells require continuous rRNA synthesis to ensure that subsequent generations contain the ribosome supply necessary for protein synthesis. Ribosome biogenesis is a major cellular undertaking that occurs in distinct nuclear compartments, the nucleoli. A nucleolus forms around clusters of repeated rRNA genes (rDNA) that encode rRNA, the scaffold and catalytic heart of the eukaryotic ribosome. The number of rDNA repeats varies greatly among organisms, ranging from fewer than 100 to more than 10,000. In growing cells, rRNA synthesis accounts for the majority of transcriptional activity to meet the demand for ribosome production and protein synthesis. Practically all signaling pathways that affect growth in response to nutrient and growth factor avail-

ability or during the cell cycle directly regulate rRNA synthesis, their downstream effectors converging at the RNA polymerase I (Pol I) transcription machinery. These topics have been reviewed in the past, and readers are referred to some recent articles for further reading (Grummt 2003, Mayer & Grummt 2005, Moss et al. 2007).

Each rRNA gene encodes a precursor transcript (45S pre-rRNA) that can be processed and posttranscriptionally modified to generate one molecule each of 18S, 5.8S, and 28S rRNA. Transcription of rDNA by Pol I requires the formation of a preinitiation complex on the promoter, including binding of UBF (upstream binding factor) and the promoter selectivity factor, termed SL1 in humans and TIF-IB in the mouse (Clos et al. 1986, Grummt 2003, Learned et al. 1986, Moss et al. 2007,

Paule & White 2000, Russell & Zomerdijk 2005). UBF affects Pol I transcription at multiple levels, functioning as a transcription activator (Bell et al. 1988, Panov et al. 2006), as an antirepressor (Kuhn & Grummt 1992, Pelletier et al. 2000), and as a regulator of transcription elongation (Stefanovsky et al. 2006), and it has been implicated in large-scale chromatin condensation (Chen et al. 2005, Mais et al. 2005, Wright et al. 2006). Promoter specificity is conferred by SL1/TIF-IB, a ~300-kDa protein complex that contains TBP (TATA box binding protein) and at least three Pol I–specific TBP-associated factors (TAF$_I$s), TAF$_I$110/95, TAF$_I$68, and TAF$_I$48 (Comai et al. 1992, Heix et al. 1997, Zomerdijk et al. 1994). Recently investigators have identified two more TAF$_I$s, TAF$_I$41 and TAF$_I$12, both of which are required for specific and efficient Pol I transcription initiation (Denissov et al. 2007, Gorski et al. 2007). TAF$_I$s perform important roles in transcription complex assembly, mediating specific interactions between the rDNA promoter and Pol I. They interact with UBF and recruit Pol I to rDNA by binding to TIF-IA, a basal regulatory factor that is associated with the initiation-competent subpopulation of Pol I (Pol Iβ). The interaction of SL1/TIF-IB with TIF-IA, the mammalian homolog of yeast Rrn3 that mediates growth-dependent control of rDNA transcription (Bodem et al. 2000, Miller et al. 2001, Yuan et al. 2002), drives the assembly of productive transcription initiation complexes.

Given the repetitive nature of rRNA genes, two strategies for regulating rRNA synthesis are conceivable. Pol I transcription may be controlled either by changing the rate of transcription from each active gene or by adjusting the number of genes that are involved in transcription. Although there is evidence for both options, the majority of short-term regulation affects the rDNA transcription cycle, e.g., preinitiation complex assembly, initiation, promoter escape, and transcription elongation or termination (for review, see Russell & Zomerdijk 2005). Moreover, posttranslational modifications influence the activity and func-

tional interplay of transcription factors, adding further complexity and fine-tuning to transcriptional regulation in response to external signals that affect cell growth and proliferation (for review, see Grummt 2003, Russell & Zomerdijk 2005).

The number of active rRNA genes varies between different cell types, indicating that the fraction of active gene copies changes during development and differentiation (Haaf et al. 1991). Thus, long-term changes in rDNA transcription can be achieved by regulating the number of rRNA genes that are transcriptionally active. Some recent reviews summarize our current knowledge of the epigenetic mechanisms that mediate silencing and epigenetic control of rDNA (Grummt 2007, Grummt & Pikaard 2003, Lawrence & Pikaard 2004, McStay 2006). This review provides an update on recent advances in the epigenetic mechanisms that regulate the balance between active and inactive rDNA repeats in mammalian cells. In general, we restrict our review to work concerning mammalian rRNA genes; however, key experiments from other systems are discussed where appropriate.

ORGANIZATION OF MAMMALIAN rRNA GENES

Structure of Mammalian rDNA Transcription Units

Mammalian rDNA transcription units are large, comprising ~43 kb in humans and ~45 kb in mice (Gonzalez & Sylvester 1995, Grozdanov et al. 2003, Sylvester et al. 2004). Sequences encoding pre-rRNA (13–14 kb) are separated by long intergenic spacers (IGSs) of approximately 30 kb. Regulatory elements, including gene promoters, spacer promoters, repetitive enhancer elements, and transcription terminators, are located in the IGS (**Figure 1**). The rDNA promoter has a bipartite structure, consisting of a core promoter element adjacent to the transcription start site and an upstream control element (UCE) approximately 100 nucleotides further upstream (Haltiner

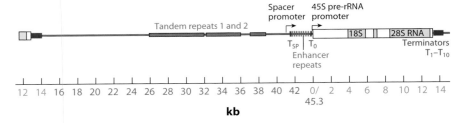

Figure 1

Structural organization of mouse rRNA gene. Graphic of mouse rRNA genes is derived from Genbank accession number BK000964. The sites of transcription initiation of the 45S pre-rRNA and transcripts from the intergenic spacer promoter are indicated by arrows. Scale bars (in kb) are shown below; 0 kb indicates the 5' end of the pre-rRNA. Terminator elements located downstream of the transcription unit (T_1–T_{10}), downstream of the spacer promoter (T_{SP}), and upstream of the gene promoter (T_0) are marked by red bars. Repetitive enhancer elements (*purple*) located between the spacer promoter and major gene promoter of the mouse gene promoter are also indicated.

et al. 1986, Learned et al. 1986). Mammalian rDNA transcription units are flanked at their 5' and 3' ends by one or more terminator elements that are recognized by TTF-I (transcription termination factor), a specific DNA binding protein that stops elongating Pol I and serves an important role in epigenetic regulation of rRNA genes (Grummt et al. 1985, 1986a; Henderson & Sollner 1986; McStay & Reeder 1986). The major part of the IGS appears to be devoid of regulatory elements, comprising a high density of simple sequence repeats and transposable elements (for review, see Sylvester et al. 2004).

Tissue-Specific Expression of rRNA Gene Variants

The current concept is that arrays of mammalian rRNA genes are composed of identical repetitive transcription units that are clustered on specific chromosomal loci. So far, only one complete mouse rDNA transcription unit has been sequenced (Grozdanov et al. 2003), and therefore rDNA loci constitute major gaps in the human and mouse genome. Contrary to the notion that all rDNA repeats are identical, early cytogenetic studies have documented that individual chromosomal rDNA loci are not equally active in different human cells (de Capoa et al. 1985). Consistent with the exis-

tence of sequence polymorphism and cell-type-specific regulation of rDNA variants, mouse cells contain seven mouse rDNA variant types (v-rDNA) that vary in the length of the IGS and exhibit sequence polymorphism both in the variable region of 28S rRNA and in the 5'-terminal part of the transcription unit (Tseng 2006, Tseng et al. 2008, S. Zhang et al. 2007). Analysis of the copy numbers, expression profiles, and methylation pattern in multiple mouse tissues revealed that v-rDNAs are not regulated in concert, but independently and, in some cases, in a tissue-specific manner. Three v-rDNA types were expressed in all tissues (constitutively active), two were expressed in some tissues (selectively active), and two were not expressed (silent). The finding that rDNA exist in genetically distinct subdomains, which can be regulated individually in different tissues, suggests a heretofore-unappreciated complexity in mammalian rDNA structure and regulation.

In multicellular organisms, cells differ in their requirements for rRNA. The developing mouse oocyte, for example, doubles the activity of Pol I to accumulate rRNA without amplifying the number of rRNA genes. Instead, these cells use basonuclin, a transcriptional regulator that is expressed in highly proliferative cells and tissues, e.g., in keratinocytes and reproductive germ cells, to enhance rDNA transcription (Iuchi & Green 1999, Tian et al. 2001, Tseng &

Green 1992, Tseng et al. 1999, S. Zhang et al. 2007). Another cell-type-specific regulator of rRNA synthesis is Runx2, a factor that controls bone lineage commitment and cell proliferation (Young et al. 2007). Both basonuclin and Runx2 localize in nucleoli, are associated with rDNA throughout the cell cycle, and affect Pol I transcription, basonuclin acting as an activator of Pol I transcription and Runx2 as a transcriptional repressor. These results indicate that tissue-specific factors may regulate a subset of rDNA variants and suggest that a one-size-fits-all model for regulation of rDNA expression is probably an oversimplification.

Nucleolar Organizer Regions

In situ hybridization experiments have revealed that clusters of rDNA repeats, termed nucleolar organizer regions (NORs), are located on the short arms of the five human acrocentric chromosomes, chromosomes 13, 14, 15, 21, and 22, in a telomere-to-centromere orientation (Henderson et al. 1972). In the mouse, NORs are on chromosomes 12, 15, 16, 17, 18, and 19 (**Figure 2a**) (Dev et al. 1977). The positioning of NORs on the short arms of acrocentric chromosomes isolates them from genes transcribed by Pol II and Pol III. This isolation is further reinforced by adjacent heterochromatic repetitive satellite DNA. The repetitive nature of both rDNA and adjacent sequences has precluded sequencing of mouse and human NORs. Despite this drawback, other techniques have uncovered interesting and unexpected features of human NORs. For example, pulse-field gel electrophoresis of genomic DNA digested with enzymes that do not cut human rDNA, such as EcoRV and Sse83871, revealed a major rDNA band of 3 Mb as well as several minor bands of 1 and 2 Mb (Sakai et al. 1995). This implies that most human NORs are composed of ~70 copies of rDNA repeats and demonstrates that NORs contain solely rDNA rather than other sequences.

Concerted evolution of rDNA clusters is mediated by interchromosomal recombination between NORs on different chromosomes.

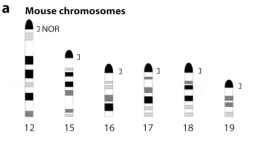

Mouse chromosomes

12 15 16 17 18 19

Human chromosomes

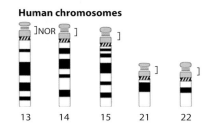

13 14 15 21 22

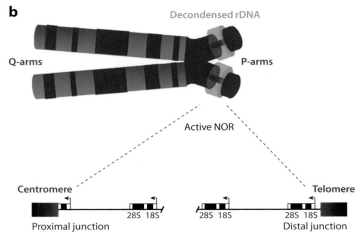

Decondensed rDNA

Q-arms   P-arms

Active NOR

Centromere   Telomere

28S 18S   28S 18S   28S 18S

Proximal junction   Distal junction

Figure 2

Positioning and organization of nucleolar organizer regions (NORs). (*a*) The positions of NORs on ideograms of mouse and human chromosomes are indicated by brackets. Ideograms were obtained from the homepage of the University of Washington, Department of Pathology (**http://www.pathology.washington.edu/research/cytopages**). Chromosome identities are indicated below each ideogram. (*b*) A diagram depicting DAPI-stained human chromosome 15. Decondensed rDNA (*red*) is shown around the NOR of each sister chromatid. The organization of rDNA within the NOR is shown below (see text for further details).

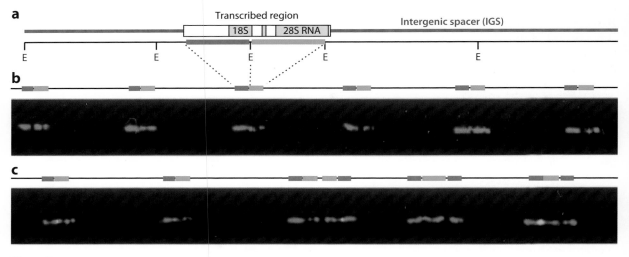

Figure 3

Analysis of the human rDNA locus by molecular combing. (*a*) Scheme depicting the localization of molecular probes used to identify rDNA transcription units on combed human DNA by two-color hybridization. The red probe (detected with Texas Red) hybridizes to the 5′ part of the pre-rRNA coding region; the green probe (detected with FITC) hybridizes to the 3′ part of the pre-rRNA coding region. (*b*) The image displays canonical rDNA units in tandem, each composed of a dual fluorescent signal and the adjacent intergenic spacer (IGS). (*c*) The image displays a region containing two canonical units (*left*), followed by three palindromic units, each half joined by its 3′ region and separated by short IGS sequences. The arrangement of the transcription units and the position of EcoRI restriction sites (E) is illustrated in the schemes above the individual images (adapted from Caburet et al. 2005 with permission from Cold Spring Harbor Laboratory Press).

Such interchromosomal crossover events also result in conservation of sequences distal to the rDNA cluster, a prediction based on the finding that sequences abutting rDNA on the distal end of the NOR are conserved among all five acrocentric chromosomes (Gonzalez & Sylvester 1997, Worton et al. 1988). Moreover, a most surprising observation relates to the organization of rDNA repeats within the NORs. Until recently rRNA genes were thought to be organized as a uniform head-to-tail tandem array, although this hypothesis was unproven owing to difficulties in cloning and sequencing of repetitive DNA. Single-DNA-molecule analysis by molecular combing, however, has revealed that NORs comprise a mosaic of canonical and noncanonical rDNA repeats (Caburet et al. 2005). As many as one-third of rDNA repeats are noncanonical, apparently forming palindromic structures (**Figure 3**). One would predict that these noncanonical repeats are nonfunctional and that the cell has to silence noncanonical re-

peats to avoid the possibility of base pairing of antisense transcripts to pre-rRNA, which could seriously compromise ribosome biogenesis.

Active and Silent Nucleolar Organizer Regions

Active NORs remain undercondensed during mitosis and have a distinct chromatin structure that is evident as secondary constriction on metaphase chromosomes (**Figure 2b**). rDNA in active NORs is approximately tenfold less condensed than the adjacent satellite DNA (Heliot et al. 1997). This undercondensation results in reduced dye binding when chromosomes are stained, giving rise to an apparent gap in the chromosome. Often, an axis of condensed AT-rich DNA is found within the secondary constriction; the identity of these sequences is uncertain (Saitoh & Laemmli 1994). The most persuasive evidence that secondary constrictions correlate with the transcriptional

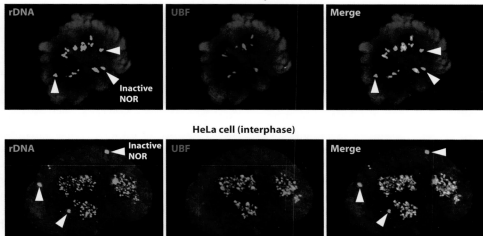

HeLa cell (metaphase)

rDNA | UBF | Merge

Inactive NOR

HeLa cell (interphase)

rDNA | Inactive NOR | UBF | Merge

Figure 4

A fraction of nucleolar organizer regions (NORs) are silent throughout the cell cycle. HeLa cells in metaphase (*upper panels*) and interphase (*lower panels*) were subjected to combined immunostaining and fluorescent immunohybridization (immuno-FISH) to show the localization of rDNA and the Pol I–specific upstream binding factor (UBF). rDNA was visualized by hybridization to a probe from the intergenic spacer (*green*), and UBF was visualized with antibodies coupled to rhodamine (*red*). Inactive NORs, devoid of UBF, are indicated by arrowheads. Chromosomes and nuclei were visualized by DAPI staining (*blue*).

competence of rDNA is that Pol I together with Pol I–specific transcription factors, such as UBF, SL1/TIF-IB, and TTF-I, remain associated with NORs on mitotic chromosomes (Roussel et al. 1993, 1996). Because components of the Pol I transcription machinery contain acidic/argyophilic domains, this also explains why metaphase NORs can be easily visualized by silver nitrate (McClintock 1934).

On inactive NORs, rDNA appears to be packaged in a form that is indistinguishable from the surrounding heterochromatin. Silent NORs can be visualized as condensed foci of rDNA that lack associated Pol I and Pol I–specific factors and the secondary constriction that characterizes the decondensed, open state of rDNA (see **Figure 4**). Thus, it appears that in organisms containing multiple NORs, there are mechanisms that silence entire NORs, thereby maintaining this specific epigenetic state throughout the cell cycle and propagating it from one cell generation to the next.

Psoralen Cross-Linking Identifies Active rDNA Repeats

The proportion of rRNA genes that are actively transcribed can be identified by their susceptibility to the DNA cross-linking agent psoralen (Sogo & Thoma 2004). Psoralen is a drug that intercalates in double-stranded DNA and generates covalent interstrand links upon UV irradiation. Chromatin of active, euchromatic genes is accessible to psoralen cross-linking, whereas silent genes exhibit a compact heterochromatic structure that is not cross-linked by psoralen. Because cross-linked DNA migrates more slowly than non-cross-linked DNA in agarose gels, psoralen cross-linking can discriminate between nucleosomal and nonnucleosomal chromatin conformations. Psoralen cross-linking assays in a variety of organisms have shown that two classes of rRNA genes coexist in growing cells. Active genes are free of regularly spaced nucleosomes and are associated with nascent pre-rRNA (Conconi et al. 1989). Inactive gene copies are inaccessible to psoralen, display regularly spaced nucleosomes, and are not associated with transcription factors and Pol I. The IGS is constitutively nucleosomal in both active and silent gene copies (Conconi et al. 1989, Dammann et al. 1993). In mouse cells, psoralen-accessible and -inaccessible rRNA genes are typically found in similar proportions; approximately half of rDNA repeats are active, and the other half are transcriptionally silent. The ratio of psoralen-accessible to psoralen-inaccessible rRNA genes is tissue-specific and stably propagated through the cell cycle (Conconi et al. 1989). Because more than 50% of NORs in most mammalian cells are active, both active and inactive rRNA genes likely associate with each other to form three-dimensional, higher-order structures within nucleoli.

With regard to the chromatin structure of active genes, electron microscopic studies and psoralen cross-linking experiments suggested that transcribed genes are devoid of nucleosomes in the pre-rRNA coding sequences (Sogo & Thoma 2004). However, recent studies have demonstrated that histones and chromatin remodeling activities are associated with transcriptionally active rRNA genes, indicating that Pol I is capable of elongating through chromatin (Jones et al. 2007, Tongaonkar et al. 2005, Yuan et al. 2007). However, it is unknown whether the nucleosome density is similar at transcribed and nontranscribed rDNA sequences and whether canonical histone octamers are present within the pre-rRNA coding region.

ACTIVE AND SILENT rRNA GENES EXIST IN DISTINCT EPIGENETIC STATES

DNA Methylation

DNA methylation at cytosine residues located 5′ to a guanosine in a CpG dinucleotide is an epigenetic mark associated with gene silencing. Specific DNA methylation is mediated by DNA methyltransferases DNMT1, DNMT3a, and DNMT3b, and proper propagation of the

respective CpG methylation through cell division is critical for development and differentiation (Klose & Bird 2006, Meehan et al. 2001).

Regulatory elements and transcribed sequences in vertebrate rDNA are unusual in that they are both rich in CpG dinucleotides and densely methylated. Initial studies used methylation-sensitive and -insensitive restriction enzymes, such as HpaII and MspI, to determine the methylation status of CpGs within the sequence CCGG of mouse or rat rDNA (Bird et al. 1981, Santoro & Grummt 2001). These studies revealed an intriguing correlation between the proportion of active and inactive versus unmethylated and methylated rRNA genes, the fraction of methylated sequences corresponding to silent repeats (**Figure 5**). Moreover, cross-linking experiments demonstrated that methylated sites are predominantly present in the promoter and enhancer of inactive genes (Stancheva et al. 1997). Consistent with the results of psoralen cross-linking assays, ~40% of rRNA genes were resistant to cleavage with HpaII both in mouse liver and NIH3T3 cells. The intriguing correlation between promoter methylation and transcriptional silencing was further strengthened by the finding that treatment of cells with 5-aza-2′-deoxycytidine (aza-dC), a nucleotide analog that inhibits cytosine methylation, stimulated rDNA transcription, suggesting that lack of DNA methylation alleviates transcriptional repression of rDNA (Santoro & Grummt 2001). Importantly, methylation did not impair transcription on naked rDNA templates. However, when assembled into chromatin, methylated templates were not transcribed, indicating a mechanistic link between DNA methylation and chromatin-based processes. Analysis of wild-type and mutant templates in both transfection and in vitro transcription experiments revealed that methylation of one CpG dinucleotide at position −133 is sufficient to impair binding of UBF to nucleosomal rDNA, thereby preventing transcription complex assembly on preassembled chromatin templates. This finding suggests that cytosine −133 is exposed on the surface of the positioned

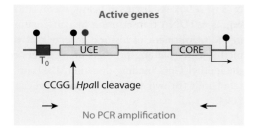
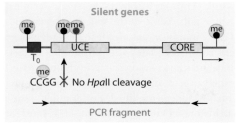

Figure 5

Active (*left*) and silent (*right*) rRNA genes can be distinguished by cleavage with methylation-sensitive restriction enzymes. The scheme illustrates the organization of the murine rDNA promoter, highlighting the position of the upstream terminator T_0, the upstream control element (UCE), and the core promoter element (CORE). The transcription start site is marked by an arrow. The lollypops indicate the position of CpG residues at nucleotides −167, −143, −133, and +8; the critical cytosine at −133 (see text for details) is colored red. If the CpG residues are unmethylated, the CCGG sequence at −143 is sensitive to *Hpa*II digestion and cannot be amplified by PCR using a primer pair that covers sequences from −160/−140 (forward) and −21/−1 (reverse). On silent genes, the CpG residues are methylated and resistant to *Hpa*II cleavage.

nucleosome and that the addition of a methyl group may represent an unfavorable sterical hinderance for UBF binding. These results imply that transcriptional silencing in mammals can be mediated or reinforced through an effect of DNA methylation on essential protein-DNA interactions that are needed for transcription initiation complex formation.

In human cells, the methylation status of rDNA, with 25 CpGs residing within the promoter, is more complex. Usually, human rDNA promoters exhibit a mosaic methylation pattern; i.e., they are neither completely methylated nor unmethylated but show methylation of a few to most CpGs (Ghoshal et al. 2004). Analysis of the methylation profile of human hepatocellular carcinomas or the colon cancer cell line HCT116 showed significant hypomethylation of the rDNA promoter in tumors compared with matched normal tissues, consistent with the elevated rRNA synthetic activity of rapidly proliferating cells (Ghoshal et al. 2004, Majumder et al. 2006). Importantly, hypomethylation of rRNA genes correlates with decreased genomic stability, suggesting that silencing entails the assembly of a generally repressive chromatin domain that is less accessible to the cellular recombination machinery.

Bisulfite sequencing of rDNA recovered from chromatin immunoprecipitations (ChIPs) using antibodies directed against components of the Pol I transcription machinery revealed two classes of hypomethylated rDNA promoters. The first is an active fraction that is unmethylated over the entire promoter and is associated with both UBF and Pol I. In the other fraction, only the core promoter is unmethylated, and this fraction is associated with UBF but not with Pol I (Brown & Szyf 2007). Apparently, marking individual rDNA transcription units by specific methylation contributes to the stable propagation of a subset of active genes during cell proliferation and differentiation. Finally, the finding that in human cells approximately one-third of rDNA repeats exhibit a noncanonical arrangement (Caburet et al. 2005 and **Figure 3**) raises the possibility that noncanonical repeats may constitute a major fraction of methylated rRNA genes.

Histone Modifications Distinguish Active from Inactive rDNA Repeats

Modification of histones has become a key issue in our understanding of gene regulation. The core histones that make up the nucleosome are subject to numerous posttranslational modifications, including acetylation, methylation, phosphorylation, ubiquitination, and SUMOylation. Most modifications localize at specific positions within the N- and C-terminal histone tails. Some of the functional outcomes of these modifications are clear. Whereas lysine acetylation correlates with chromatin accessibility and transcriptional activity, lysine methylation can have different effects, depending on which residue is modified. For example, lysine 4 in histone H3 is trimethylated (H3K4me3) at the 5' ends of active genes, whereas trimethylation of H3K9 and H3K27 marks the promoter of heterochromatic, transcriptionally silent genes (for review, see Wang et al. 2007). These key modifications distinguish silent heterochromatin from permissive euchromatin and correlate with the activity status of rDNA repeats.

The ChIP technique has provided valuable insights into specific histone modifications associated with active and silent rDNA repeats. This technique, combined with the digestion of precipitated DNA with methylation-sensitive restriction enzymes, can be used to link particular histone modifications with transcriptional activity. Hypomethylated, active genes are associated with acetylated histones H4 and H3 as well as with H3K4me3 (Earley et al. 2006, Lawrence et al. 2004, Santoro & Grummt 2005, Santoro et al. 2002, Zhou et al. 2002). The promoter of hypermethylated, silent genes, in contrast, is associated with methylated H3K9, H3K20, and H3K27. As we discuss below, there is not always a strict division between active and repressive modifications, as for example for H3K9me3, indicating that the function of specific chromatin marks is more complex than previously thought. The current view is that histone modifications lay down positive- or negative-acting marks that recruit effector proteins such as heterochromatin protein 1 (HP1), causing structural changes to chromatin that affect the transcriptional outcome. Likewise, DNA methylation recruits repressors that specifically bind sites containing methylated CpG dinucleotides. DNMTs and DNA binding proteins that specifically recognize methylated cytosine residues interact with histone deacetylase corepressors and histone methyltransferases (for review, see Klose

& Bird 2006). As discussed below, methylation represses rDNA transcription by participating in the recruitment of histone deacetylases via methyl-CpG binding proteins or members of the methyl-CpG binding domain (MBD) protein family (Brown & Szyf 2007, Ghoshal et al. 2004).

TTF-I BOUND TO THE PROMOTER-PROXIMAL TERMINATOR RECRUITS CHROMATIN MODIFIERS TO rDNA

During replication, chromatin is erased and the epigenetic state has to be reestablished on the newly replicated daughter strands. This raises the question how the active state and the silent state of rRNA genes are established and maintained throughout cell division. A key player in the establishment and inheritance of a given epigenetic state at specific subsets of rDNA repeats is TTF-I (Bartsch et al. 1988, Grummt et al. 1986b). TTF-I is a multifunctional protein that binds to specific terminator elements downstream of the rDNA transcription unit and mediates transcription termination and replication fork arrest (Gerber et al. 1997, Grummt et al. 1986b). A similar terminator element, termed T_0 in mammals and T3 in frogs (Reeder 1999), is also present upstream of the transcription start site (**Figure 1**). The conservation of a binding site for a Pol I transcription terminator protein adjacent to the gene promoter suggested that TTF-I may also exert some essential function in transcription initiation. Indeed, binding of TTF-I (or the frog homolog Rib2) to the promoter-proximal terminator stimulates Pol I transcription in vivo (Henderson & Sollner 1986, McStay & Reeder 1990). Subsequent in vitro studies showed that TTF-I binding to the upstream terminator triggered structural alterations of the chromatin on preassembled nucleosomal templates, and these changes in chromatin structure correlated with activation of Pol I transcription in vitro (Langst et al. 1997, 1998). These results indicate that in the vicinity of the promoter, TTF-I influences nucleosome positioning in such a way that allows transcription initiation to proceed. Furthermore, these findings suggest that TTF-I may recruit chromatin remodeling activities to rDNA that modify the promoter-bound nucleosome, thereby facilitating the access of transcription factors and Pol I.

COCKAYNE SYNDROME PROTEIN B: A CHROMATIN REMODELER THAT PROMOTES rDNA TRANSCRIPTION

Given that both TTF-I binding to the upstream terminator and nucleosome remodeling are required for activation of Pol I transcription on chromatin templates, it is reasonable to predict that TTF-I recruits a remodeling complex(es) and coactivators that establish euchromatic features at active rDNA repeats. A candidate for such a chromatin remodeler is CSB (Cockayne syndrome protein B), a DNA-dependent ATPase that is capable of chromatin remodeling and of disrupting protein-DNA interactions at the expense of ATP hydrolysis (Beerens et al. 2005, Citterio et al. 2000). Defects in CSB lead to the genetic disorder Cockayne syndrome (Laine & Egly 2006, Venema et al. 1990), and transcription is markedly reduced in cells from Cockayne syndrome patients in whom the CSB protein is mutated (Balajee et al. 1997, Dianov et al. 1997). CSB localizes in the nucleolus at sites of active rDNA transcription (**Figure 6**) and is part of a protein complex that contains Pol I, TFIIH, and basal Pol I transcription initiation factors (Bradsher et al. 2002). CSB interacts with TTF-I, a finding that suggests that TTF-I targets CSB to active rRNA genes. In support of CSB activating transcription on chromatin templates, overexpression of CSB stimulates rDNA transcription, whereas siRNA-mediated depletion of CSB impairs the assembly of transcription complexes and inhibits pre-rRNA synthesis (Yuan et al. 2007). Activation of Pol I transcription requires the ATPase activity of CSB, indicating that the chromatin remodeling activity of CSB promotes transcription through chromatin. Sig-

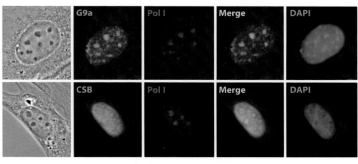

Figure 6

CSB (Cockayne syndrome protein B), G9a, and RNA polymerase I (Pol I) colocalize within nucleoli. The indirect immunofluorescence images show the localization of G9a, CSB, and Pol I in NIH3T3 cells. Phase contrast images are shown at the left. This figure is reproduced from Yuan et al. (2007) with permission from Elsevier.

nificantly, transcription activation by CSB depends on binding of TTF-I to the promoter-proximal terminator T_0, a finding that demonstrates the synergism of TTF-I and CSB in chromatin-mediated processes and underscores the functional relevance of TTF-I in targeting positive-acting chromatin modifiers to rDNA.

Importantly, CSB-mediated activation of rDNA transcription requires association with G9a, a histone methyltransferase that is responsible for mono- and dimethylation of H3K9, and facilitates binding of heterochromatin protein 1γ (HP1γ), a protein containing a chromodomain that recognizes H3K9 methylation (Tachibana et al. 2002). Methylation of histone H3 at lysine 9 and HP1 association have well-established roles in heterochromatin formation (Bannister et al. 2001, Lachner et al. 2001, Peters et al. 2003, Rice et al. 2003). Therefore, the finding that G9a is associated with CSB and is required for Pol I transcription suggested additional surprising functions for H3K9 methylation and HP1γ recruitment in chromatin-based processes. Notably, H3K9me2 and HP1γ are present within the transcribed region of active rDNA repeats, and both H3K9 methylation and association of HP1γ with rDNA are dependent on ongoing Pol I transcription (Yuan et al. 2007). This demonstrates that components of heterochromatin, such as

H3K9me2 and HP1γ, play additional dynamic roles in establishing a chromatin structure that characterizes actively transcribed genes. This notion is in accord with recent studies that reveal novel roles for H3K9 methylation and HP1γ in transcription activation. H3K9 di- and trimethylation occur in the transcribed region of all active mammalian Pol II genes examined. H3K9 methylation and HP1γ binding are dynamic and require active transcription, increasing during transcription activation and being rapidly removed upon gene repression (Hediger & Gasser 2006, Piacentini et al. 2003, Vakoc et al. 2005). This finding demonstrates that the function of these chromatin marks is more complex than previously thought and suggests that these marks may serve distinct functions in transcription, depending on the context of other posttranslational histone modifications.

Important questions are how the active state of rRNA genes is maintained and how demethylated promoters may coexist with hypermethylated transcribed regions; such coexistence has been frequently observed in tumors (Yan et al. 2000). An interesting possibility is the involvement of specific proteins that either protect the promoters from methylation or target them for demethylation. A protein that may serve this function(s) is MBD3, a member of the MBD proteins, which bind to methylated DNA. MBD3 has two amino acid substitutions in the MBD domain that abolish binding to methylated DNA. Interestingly, MBD3 is associated with the rDNA promoter, and bisulfite mapping revealed that the fraction of rDNA bound to MBD3 is unmethylated (Ghoshal et al. 2004). Overexpression of MBD3 decreased methylation of the rDNA promoter, whereas knockdown of MBD3 increased methylation and decreased pre-rRNA synthesis (Brown & Szyf 2007). These results suggest that MBD3 plays an important role in maintaining rDNA promoters in an unmethylated state. In addition, silent rDNA repeats may be converted into active ones by demethylation. DNA demethylation can occur either by a passive mechanism owing to progressive loss of methylated cytosines with each round of replication or by a process that actively removes the methyl group from CpG residues. An expression screen for an active demethylase has identified Gadd45a, an 18-kDa histone-fold protein that is involved in regulating proliferation, genomic stability, DNA repair, cell cycle, and apoptosis (Barreto et al. 2007). Overexpression of Gadd45a activates transcription of methylation-silenced reporter genes and induces global DNA hypomethylation in mammalian cells. Strikingly, Gadd45a also triggers demethylation of the rDNA promoter (K.-M. Schmitz, N. Schmitt, A. Schäfer, C. Niehrs, I. Grummt & C. Mayer, unpublished data). Preliminary results have shown that Gadd45a is associated with active rDNA copies and that DNA damage induces Gadd45a recruitment to rDNA, resulting in hypomethylation of the rDNA promoter and transient increase of Pol I levels. Conversely, depletion of Gadd45a or XPG, a component of the NER (nucleotide excision repair) machinery, leads to hypermethylation of rDNA and transient transcription silencing. Notably, rDNA demethylation depends on active Pol I transcription, emphasizing the importance of Gadd45a in maintaining the active state of rDNA.

Together, the available experimental evidence reveals a complex and coordinated interplay of the chromatin remodeler CSB, the histone methyltransferase G9a, and the methylation-sensitive proteins MBD3 and Gadd45a in the establishment of an epigenetically active, euchromatic structure at the rDNA promoter. CSB and G9a may promote Pol I transcription elongation by depositing a specific histone modification pattern that is recognized by other chromatin-modifying activities or by elongation factors that are required for transcription through chromatin. MBD3 and Gadd45a, in contrast, may protect the promoter from de novo methylation by DNMTs and therefore may be the key players that maintain the unmethylated state of rDNA.

NoRC: A CHROMATIN REMODELING COMPLEX THAT SILENCES rDNA

NoRC Establishes Heterochromatic Features at a Subset of rDNA Repeats

A yeast two-hybrid screen searching for TTF-I-interacting proteins that have the potential to alter the chromatin structure of the rDNA promoter has identified a chromatin remodeling complex, termed NoRC (nucleolar remodeling complex), which induces nucleosome sliding in an ATP-dependent and a histone H4 tail–dependent fashion (Strohner et al. 2001). NoRC is composed of two subunits, the ATPase SNF2h and a 205-kDa protein termed TIP5 (TTF-I-interacting protein 5). TIP5 shares a number of important protein domains with the large subunits of human SNF2-containing chromatin remodeling complexes ACF, WCRF, CHRAC, and WICH (Bochar et al. 2000, Bozhenok et al. 2002, Ito et al. 1999, LeRoy et al. 1998, Poot et al. 2000). Such shared domains include AT hooks; BAZ1, BAZ2, and WAKZ motifs; a C-terminal PHD (plant homeodomain); and a bromo-domain (**Figure 7**). The bromodomain and an adjacent PHD finger form a cooperative unit that has been found in several transcriptional corepressors (Schultz et al. 2001). Consistent with a repressor function, NoRC inhibits Pol I transcription on preassembled chromatin templates in vitro (Strohner et al. 2004), and overexpression of TIP5 in human and mouse cells repressed rDNA transcription in a concentration-dependent manner (Santoro et al. 2002). Transcriptional repression did not occur in the presence of inhibitors of DNMTs and histone deacetylases, such as aza-dC and TSA, implicating NoRC in repressing rDNA transcription by inducing DNA methylation and histone deacetylation. Indeed, subsequent biochemical studies have demonstrated that NoRC physically interacts with DNMT1 and DNMT3 as well as with the Sin3 corepressor complex, which contains the histone deacetylases HDAC1 and HDAC2 (Santoro et al. 2002, Zhou et al. 2002). As a consequence of NoRC interacting with DNMTs and specific corepressors, a subset of rDNA repeats is silenced, and specific epigenetic marks are propagated throughout cell divisions. This indicates that

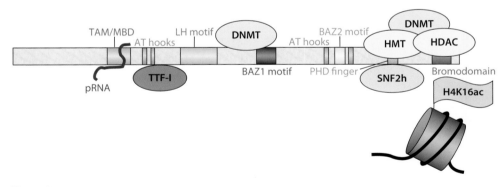

Figure 7

Modular organization and domains of TIP5 (TTF-I-interacting protein 5). Scheme illustrating the modular organization and localization of sequence motifs in TIP5 that have been associated with functions in chromatin structure and function. The domains of TIP5 (*colored boxes*) that interact with proteins involved in the epigenetic control of gene expression are illustrated. The C-terminal part of TIP5 contains a PHD (plant homeodomain) finger that interacts with SNF2h and with histone methyltransferases (HMTs) and a bromodomain that interacts with histone deacetylases (HDAC1 and -2) and with histone H4 acetylated at lysine 16 (H4K16ac). DNA methyltransferases (DNMTs) interact with both the internal and the C-terminal part of TIP5. The MBD (methyl-CpG binding domain)-like TAM (TIP5/ARBD/MBD) domain is required for association with small intergenic transcripts (pRNA) that are required for nucleolar remodeling complex (NoRC)-mediated heterochromatin formation.

NoRC serves as a scaffold, coordinating the activities of macromolecular complexes that modify histones, methylate DNA, and establish a closed heterochromatic chromatin state.

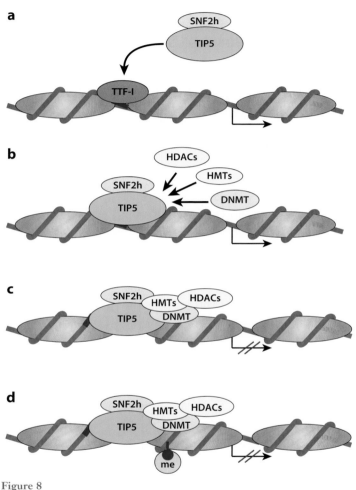

Figure 8

Model depicting individual steps of rDNA silencing. (*a*) First, NoRC is recruited to the rDNA promoter by TTF-I bound to the promoter-proximal terminator T_0. (*b*) In a subsequent step, NoRC interacts with the Sin3 corepressor complex, leading to deacetylation of histones H3 and H4 and with histone methyltransferases (HMTs) that methylate H3K9, H3K20, and H3K27. (*c*) These heterochromatic histone modifications may act as a signal for the ATPase SNF2h to shift the promoter-bound nucleosome 25 nt further downstream into a translational position that is unfavorable for preinitiation complex formation. (*d*) The action of SNF2h may either relieve a steric constraint or expose CpG at –133 to methylation by DNA methyltransferases (DNMTs). Methylation of CpG at –133 in the context of chromatin impairs UBF binding and preinitiation complex assembly.

Figure 8 illustrates a model depicting the current view of the individual steps and the complex interplay of multiple protein complexes in the formation of the epigenetically silent state of rRNA genes. As a first step, TTF-I bound to the promoter-proximal terminator T_0 interacts with TIP5, and this interaction targets NoRC to the rDNA promoter. NoRC in turn recruits histone modifiers and DNMTs to rDNA, leading to repressive histone modifications and specific methylation of the promoter. The resulting modifications alter the nucleosome surfaces, which then may recruit other regulatory proteins, for example, HP1, leading to spreading of heterochromatic marks into the body of the gene. Moreover, methylation of a critical CpG residue within the rDNA promoter (at position –133) prevents binding of the basal transcription factor UBF to chromatin, which leads to impaired preinitiation complex formation and repression of Pol I transcription (Santoro & Grummt 2001, Santoro et al. 2002). Although attractive, this model is probably an oversimplification because of the interdependence and functional interplay of different epigenetic layers affecting the transcriptional output. In addition to requiring histone deacetylation and DNA methylation, repression of previously active rDNA repeats would be predicted to require a histone H3K4 demethylase activity. Indeed, recent work has demonstrated that the histone demethylase JHDM1B is located in the nucleolus and triggers H3K4 demethylation and transcriptional repression (Frescas et al. 2007). As yet there are no clues to how JHDM1B is targeted to rDNA or to how it relates to NoRC-mediated silencing.

NoRC Alters the Translational Position of Nucleosomes at the rDNA Promoter

Active and silent rDNA copies are characterized both by distinct epigenetic marks and by different nucleosome positions. At potentially active genes, a nucleosome occupies sequences from –157 to the transcription start site, whereas at silent genes the nucleosome covers sequences from −132 to +22, indicating that specific nucleosome positions determine the transcriptional readout of rRNA genes (Li et al. 2006). This is consistent with several studies demonstrating the importance of nucleosome positioning in the organization of nucleoprotein complexes at promoters and regulatory elements (Simpson 1991). Positioned nucleosomes may either occlude or facilitate binding of basal transcription factors to chromatin, thereby repressing or activating transcription. In some cases, nucleosomes are positioned as a consequence of specific factor binding, whereas in other cases certain DNA sequences can position nucleosomes in vitro (Rando & Ahmad 2007). However, most of the sequences identified in vitro fail to precisely position nucleosomes in vivo, suggesting that in addition to DNA structure and flexibility, other mechanisms define nucleosome positioning in cellular chromatin.

With regard to silent rDNA copies, NoRC is the remodeling complex that shifts the promoter-bound nucleosome into the silent position (Li et al. 2006). In the silent position (covering sequences from −132 to +22), both the UBF binding site and the functionally important CpG residue at nucleotide −133 are placed into the nucleosomal linker region. The core element, in contrast, has been moved inside the nucleosome, and the relative alignment of the DNA element with respect to the histone octamer surface has been changed. As a consequence, the core promoter is less accessible for binding of transcription factors. Thus, whereas at active genes the nucleosome juxtaposes the core promoter and the UCE, both sequence elements are separated at silent genes, prohibiting the cooperative binding of UBF and SL1/TIF-IB, the factors that nucleate preinitiation complex assembly. The identification of NoRC as the major determinant of the silent nucleosome position suggests that remodeling complexes are the major determinants of chromatin dynamics and are capable of defining a specific chromatin structure. This dual function may also explain

why remodeling complexes are so diverse and abundant in the cell. Differential gene regulation by specifically positioned nucleosomes is an attractive mechanism that would allow the cell to keep a high signal-to-noise ratio of DNA-dependent processes and to reduce the complexity of regulation by establishing chromatin structures that allow or prevent binding of transcription factors to regulatory sequences. NoRC—the key player in epigenetic silencing of rDNA—coordinates several enzymatic processes, including histone deacetylation and methylation, ATP-dependent chromatin remodeling, and DNA methylation, to establish a closed chromatin structure and block initiation complex formation.

INTERGENIC RNA IS REQUIRED FOR rDNA SILENCING

Recent analyses of mammalian transcriptomes have revealed that the majority of the genomes of mammals and other complex organisms are transcribed into noncoding (nc)RNAs. ncRNAs have an important role in the epigenetic control and in the modulation of gene expression, tissue-specific patterning, and cell fate specification. To date, siRNAs and miRNAs have received the broadest attention owing to their universal applicability in regulating gene expression. However, there is increasing evidence that intergenic and antisense transcripts control gene expression via sequence-specific interactions with regulatory proteins. In mouse cells, transcripts originating from a promoter within the IGS that is located ~2 kb upstream of the pre-rRNA transcription start site have been shown to play an important role in heterochromatin formation and rDNA silencing (Mayer et al. 2006, Moss et al. 1980). Transcripts from the IGS are synthesized from a subfraction of rDNA repeats by Pol I (R. Santoro & I. Grummt, unpublished results) and usually do not accumulate in vivo (Kuhn & Grummt 1987, Morgan et al. 1983, Paalman et al. 1995). Presumably, these <2-kb transcripts are processed into shorter intermediates that are either rapidly degraded or shielded from further

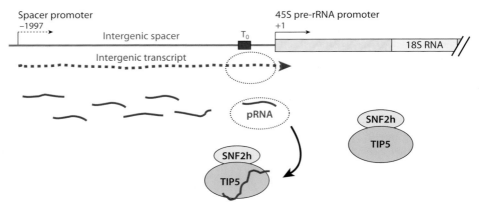

Figure 9

Model depicting the role of promoter-associated RNA (pRNA) in rDNA silencing. Intergenic transcripts (*dotted line*) are synthesized from a spacer promoter located ~2 kb upstream of the major 45S pre-rRNA promoter. The primary intergenic transcripts are degraded or processed by an as-yet-unknown mechanism. Transcripts of 150–300 nt that match the rDNA promoter (pRNA) bind to TIP5 (TTF-I-interacting protein 5) via the MBD (methyl-CpG binding domain)-like TAM (TIP5/ARBD/MBD) domain. Association with pRNA is required for NoRC-mediated heterochromatin formation.

degradation by binding to NoRC. In support of this, a population of processed 150–300-nt IGS transcripts, whose sequence matches the rDNA promoter and therefore have been dubbed pRNA (promoter-associated RNA), is stabilized by binding to TIP5, the large subunit of NoRC. RNase treatment and RNA replenishment experiments have demonstrated that pRNA is an important determinant for NoRC function because it is indispensable for heterochromatin formation and rDNA silencing (**Figure 9**).

The interaction of NoRC with RNA is mediated by the TAM (TIP5/ARBD/MBD) domain of TIP5, a motif that exhibits sequence homology to the MBD in proteins that recognize methyl-CpG. Mutations in the TAM domain abrogate the interaction of TIP5 with RNA, impair NoRC binding to chromatin, and prevent heterochromatin formation. Surprisingly, however, mutant TIP5 can still recruit DNMTs, leading to de novo CpG methylation and transcriptional silencing. This finding demonstrates that DNA methylation rather than repressive chromatin modifications causes silencing. Moreover, it indicates that the establishment of repressive histone marks and transcriptional silencing can be uncoupled.

Regarding the function of pRNA in rDNA silencing, depletion of pRNA by antisense LNA/DNA oligonucleotides had several severe consequences, leading to displacement of NoRC from nucleoli, decreased rDNA methylation, and enhanced pre-rRNA synthesis (Mayer et al. 2006). Moreover, recent results indicate that pRNA has an architectural capacity, playing a role either as a scaffold or an allosteric effector of NoRC in the epigenetic control of rDNA transcription. pRNA folds into a phylogenetically conserved secondary structure that is recognized by TIP5 and is required for both localizing NoRC to nucleoli and for rDNA silencing. Mutations that disrupt the stem-loop structure impair binding of NoRC to pRNA and abolish targeting of NoRC to nucleoli, whereas the introduction of compensatory base changes restores the interaction with TIP5 (Mayer et al. 2008). Thus, NoRC recognizes a specific secondary or tertiary RNA conformation rather than specific sequence information. These results reveal an RNA-dependent mechanism that targets NoRC to chromatin and facilitates the interaction with corepressors that promote heterochromatin formation and silencing. RNase footprinting and protease sensitivity experiments suggest that TIP5 binds pRNA in an induced-fit mechanism, resulting in structural changes that may facilitate NoRC function. Another possibility that must be considered is that NoRC, by virtue of its MBD-like domain, may aid in guiding pRNA to recruit chromatin-modifying enzymes that silence the rDNA locus. In this scenario, pRNA would direct chromatin modifications by base pairing with complementary DNA sequences.

Future studies will show whether the role of intergenic RNA is restricted to NoRC-dependent silencing or whether RNA cooperates with TTF-I to target transcription activators, such as CSB or WSTF (Percipalle et al. 2006), to rDNA. As TTF-I recruits both NoRC and CSB to the rDNA promoter, this factor is the key player triggering the chain of events by which the active or silent state of rRNA genes is established (**Figure 10**). Whether the epigenetic state is spread into adjacent genes is unknown. Given that the epigenetic balance between active and silent rRNA genes is crucial not only for rRNA synthesis but also for genomic stability, it is probable that the interaction of TTF-I with NoRC and CSB (and possibly other factors) is efficiently regulated to avoid cellular transformation and malignancy.

THE ROLE OF UBF IN MAINTAINING A SPECIFIC CHROMATIN STRUCTURE

As discussed above, active rRNA genes display a specialized decondensed chromatin structure that is associated with the presence of a secondary constriction at active NORs in most or all eukaryotes (McStay 2006). This decondensed chromatin retains the Pol I transcription machinery during mitosis, thereby facilitating the rapid resumption of ribosome

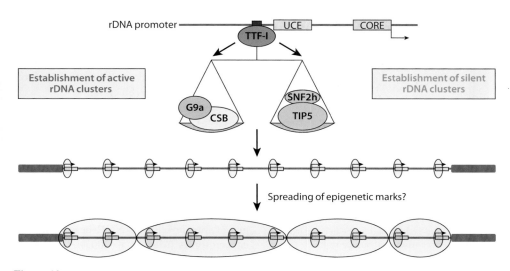

Figure 10

Cockayne syndrome B protein (CSB) and nucleolar remodeling complex (NoRC) establish the balance of active and silent clusters of rRNA genes. TTF-I bound to its target site T_0 upstream of the gene promoter (*red box*) interacts with either CSB or TIP5 (TTF-I-interacting protein 5), thereby recruiting CSB—together with associated G9a—or NoRC to rDNA. The balance of CSB and NoRC association with rRNA genes determines the ratio of euchromatic active (*blue*) to heterochromatic silent (*orange*) genes. Once the epigenetic state is established at the 5′-terminal part of the transcription unit, the respective chromatin structure is propagated throughout the rDNA repeats by an as-yet-unknown spreading mechanism. CORE, core promoter element; UCE, upstream control element.

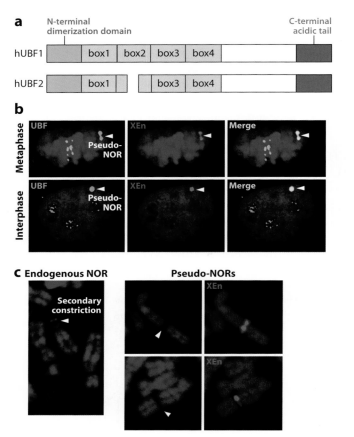

a

N-terminal
dimerization domain

C-terminal
acidic tail

hUBF1 | box1 | box2 | box3 | box4

hUBF2 | box1 | | box3 | box4

b

Metaphase

UBF | Pseudo-NOR | XEn | Merge

Interphase

UBF | Pseudo-NOR | XEn | Merge

c Endogenous NOR

Secondary
constriction

Pseudo-NORs

XEn

XEn

Figure 11

Extensive upstream binding factor (UBF) binding underpins rDNA undercondensation at active NORs. (*a*) Depiction of human UBF1 and -2 (hUBF1 and hUBF2, respectively) showing HMG (high mobility group) boxes 1–4, which mediate DNA binding; the N-terminal dimerization domain (*green*); and the C-terminal acidic tail (*red*). (*b*) Pseudo-NORs are bound by UBF throughout the cell cycle. A human cell line (3D-1) containing a 1.4-Mb array of a heterologous UBF binding sequence, *Xenopus* enhancer (XEn), on chromosome 10, was subjected to combined immuno-FISH. XEn DNA was visualized by hybridization with a spectrum-red-labeled probe derived from the intergenic spacer. UBF was visualized with antibodies coupled to FITC (*green*). Upper panels show a cell in metaphase, and lower panels a cell in interphase. Nuclei were visualized by DAPI staining (*blue*). For details, see Mais et al. (2005). (*c*) Pseudo-NORs are ectopic UBF binding site arrays that appear as novel secondary constrictions during metaphase. Chromosome spreads from the above cell line were probed with XEn DNA (*red*) and stained with DAPI. Note the lack of staining (secondary constrictions, indicated by *arrowheads*) observed over XEn sequences in the panels on the right. For comparison, a single panel on the left shows an acrocentric chromosome with a secondary constriction.

biogenesis as cells enter the G1 phase of the cell cycle. Apparently, the association of Pol I and transcription factors, such as UBF, gives active repeats a unique conformation that resists condensation to the same degree as do adjacent chromosomal regions (Prieto & McStay 2007).

UBF is an abundant protein that persists at NORs throughout metaphase and is absent from transcriptionally silent NORs (Roussel et al. 1993, Wright et al. 2006). UBF is a member of HMG (high mobility group) proteins, containing six HMG box DNA binding motifs, at least four of which are involved in DNA binding (**Figure 11***a*) (Jantzen et al. 1990, 1992; McStay et al. 1991; Reeder et al. 1995). A characteristic feature of the HMG box DNA binding motif is its ability to bend DNA. Multiple HMG boxes present in a dimer of UBF can organize naked, i.e., nucleosome-free, DNA into a 360° loop, establishing a structure that resembles the core nucleosome in both mass and DNA content (Bazett-Jones et al. 1994, Putnam et al. 1994). In vitro DNA binding assays have failed to identify a consensus other than a preference for binding to GC-rich sequences (Copenhaver et al. 1994). This apparent lack of sequence specificity contrasts greatly with its highly specific targeting to rDNA repeats throughout the cell cycle.

UBF binds throughout the IGS and the pre-rRNA coding region, suggesting that UBF plays an important structural and functional role on active NORs (O'Sullivan et al. 2002). This hypothesis has been supported by the demonstration that arrays of heterologous binding sites for UBF trigger the formation of ectopic secondary constrictions when integrated into novel, non-NOR-bearing human chromosomes (Mais et al. 2005). The largest of these arrays were ~2 Mb in length, approximating the size of endogenous NORs. These ectopic UBF binding sites, termed pseudo-NORs, were associated with UBF throughout the cell cycle and adopted the key morphological features of active NORs during metaphase; i.e., they were undercondensed, appearing as achromatic regions on DAPI-stained chromosomes (**Figure 11***b,c*). Notably, pseudo-NORs were transcriptionally inert but positive in silver staining. Thus, the appearance of secondary constrictions at NORs on metaphase chromosomes is not due to rDNA transcription or certain structural features impeding chromosome condensation, but rather to binding of argyophilic proteins to rDNA. In accord with this finding, depletion of UBF by siRNA led to loss of secondary constrictions and silver staining at pseudo-NORs (Prieto & McStay 2007). Thus, besides its role in Pol I transcription, UBF plays an important role in promoting undercondensation of active NORs and maintaining the active chromatin structure through cell divisions. Strikingly, although pseudo-NORs do not contain rDNA promoters and do not support transcription, they can recruit the entire Pol I transcription machinery and components of the pre-rRNA processing machinery (Mais et al. 2005, Prieto & McStay 2007). These results suggest that UBF binding establishes a chromatin structure that facilitates the rapid reformation of nucleoli around active NORs as cells exit mitosis.

That UBF occupancy is observed across the entire rDNA repeat raises the question as to whether UBF binding and the presence of nucleosomes are compatible. Clearly, the resolution of ChIP experiments is not sufficient to distinguish whether UBF binds to nucleosomal DNA or whether cooperative binding of UBF loops DNA into a structure, termed enhancesome, that is free of nucleosomes (Stefanovsky et al. 2001). However, several lines of evidence support the view that UBF binds to nucleosomal DNA in vivo. First, a positioned nucleosome that encompasses the UBF binding sequence is located on active promoters (Langst et al. 1998, Li et al. 2006). Second, the UBF binding sequences that form pseudo-NORs yield a classical nucleosomal ladder when digested with micrococcal nuclease (Wright et al. 2006). Moreover, pseudo-NORs can be readily visualized when cells are stained with antibodies against acetylated histone H4, consistent with pseudo-NORs exhibiting a euchromatic structure (J. Wright & B. McStay, unpublished observation).

Regarding the mechanism by which the secondary constriction characteristic for active NORs is generated, there is evidence that UBF competes with histone H1, leading to chromatin decompaction. The interaction of the linker histone H1 with nucleosomes stabilizes compact higher-order chromatin structures and impedes the access of regulatory factors (for review, see Catez et al. 2006). UBF can displace histone H1 from histone octamers in vitro, thereby promoting decompaction of chromatin (Kermekchiev et al. 1997). In support of this, RNAi-mediated depletion of UBF increases the level of histone H1 on rDNA and decreases the fraction of rDNA that is accessible to psoralen cross-linking (E. Sanij & R. Hannan, personal communication). These results indicate that UBF binds to rDNA on the surface of nucleosomes, similar to what has been proposed for the HMG box protein HMGB (Travers 2003). UBF binding to chromatin leads to a less compact chromatin structure that is accessible to Pol I and transcription factors, suggesting that UBF can maintain rDNA in a euchromatic, transcriptionally active state throughout the cell cycle. Because UBF does not bind to methylated rDNA repeats and silent NORs, it is not likely to be directly involved in the decision process that determines whether or not a given cluster of rRNA genes can be transcribed.

HETEROCHROMATIN IS IMPORTANT FOR NUCLEOLAR STRUCTURE

Heterochromatin plays an essential role in nuclear organization and chromosome structure. For example, centromeric heterochromatin on different chromosomes can fuse to form chromocenters during interphase (Hsu et al. 1971), indicating the involvement of centromeric heterochromatin in chromosome segregation (Bernard & Allshire 2002). Heterochromatin also plays a role in maintaining the structure of nucleoli and the integrity of rDNA repeats. Typically, nucleoli stain poorly with the fluorescent dye DAPI but are surrounded by a shell of intensely stained heterochromatin. This so-called perinucleolar heterochromatin is composed of satellite DNA that surrounds NORs and silent rDNA clusters located on either active or silent NORs (Sullivan et al. 2001). A link between heterochromatin formation and the nucleolus is further strengthened by the observations that heterochromatin from non-NOR-bearing chromosomes associates with nucleoli (Manuelidis & Borden 1988) and that the inactive X chromosome requires transient association with nucleoli to facilitate heterochromatin formation (Zhang et al. 2007).

It is surprising that—despite its tight association with silent heterochromatin—the nucleolus is the transcriptionally most active cellular organelle. This apparent paradox suggests that heterochromatin serves an important role in nucleolar function. Indeed, there is evidence that heterochromatin prevents homologous recombination between rDNA repeats, thereby preserving nucleolar structure and rDNA stability. Loss of silencing correlates with rDNA instability, nucleolar disintegration, and cellu-

lar senescence. Among the key players that ensure rDNA stability are the NAD^+-dependent histone deacetylase Sir2 (Silent information regulator 2) and the histone methyltransferase Su(var)3-9 (Suppressor of variegation 3-9). In *Drosophila*, inhibition of H3K9 methylation by mutation of *Su(var)3-9* destabilizes rDNA, leading to the excision of rDNA repeats and the generation of extrachromosomal rDNA circles (Peng & Karpen 2007). Likewise, mutations in yeast *Sir2* lead to increased rDNA instability and shortening of replicative life span (Sinclair & Guarente 1997). Finally, somatic knockout of DNMT1 in human cells leads to severe rDNA demethylation, which is accompanied by enhanced binding of the Pol I transcription machinery to rDNA and profound disorganization of the nucleolus (Espada et al. 2007). These results underscore the functional relevance of specific heterochromatic histone modifications and DNA methylation in deciding which rDNA copies are to be transcribed, and reveal a mechanism that determines how local chromatin structure can regulate genome stability.

SUMMARY POINTS

1. Mammalian genomes contain hundreds of rRNA gene (rDNA) repeats that are located at several nucleolar organizer regions (NORs). Active NORs form secondary constrictions on metaphase chromosomes.

2. Eukaryotic cells contain two epigenetically distinct classes of rRNA genes, one that exhibits euchromatic features and is permissive to transcription and another that has a heterochromatic conformation and is transcriptionally refractive.

3. Active and silent rDNA clusters can be distinguished by their pattern of DNA methylation, specific histone modifications, and distinct nucleosome positions.

4. The transcription termination factor TTF-I bound to the promoter-proximal terminator T_0 is the key player in establishing the epigenetically active or silent state of rDNA, recruiting either an activating [Cockayne syndrome protein B (CSB)] or a repressive (NoRC) chromatin remodeling complex.

5. CSB interacts with the histone methyltransferase G9a and HP1γ, thereby triggering the chain of events that establish or maintain the active state of rDNA.

6. Interaction with TIP5 (TTF-I-interacting protein 5), the large subunit of the nucleolar remodeling complex NoRC, mediates heterochromatin formation and silencing by recruiting histone-modifying and DNA-methylating activities and shifting the promoter-bound nucleosome into a silent position. The fine-tuned balance between

the activating chromatin remodeler CSB and the repressive NoRC complex establishes the ratio of active to silent rDNA repeats.

7. Binding of UBF across rDNA repeats is essential for maintaining the active chromatin state throughout the cell cycle and is responsible for the formation of secondary constrictions on metaphase chromosomes.

8. Heterochromatin formation and transcriptional silencing play an important role in maintaining the structural integrity of nucleoli and genetic stability of rDNA repeats.

FUTURE ISSUES

1. Why do eukaryotes contain more rRNA genes than are needed in proliferative cells?

2. What are the mechanisms that determine CSB and NoRC recruitment and hence decide between silencing or transcriptional competence?

3. Do CSB and NoRC regulate individual rRNA genes or entire NORs?

4. Which pathways regulate the level and/or the activity of CSB and NoRC and therefore control the epigenetic state and copy usage of rDNA?

5. How is a given epigenetic state inherited, and which mechanisms are involved in spreading specific histone modifications and DNA methylation patterns across clusters of rRNA genes?

6. What is the functional impact of keeping a certain ratio of active to silent rDNA repeats throughout cell division, and how is this ratio altered during cell differentiation, senescence, and cancer?

7. How are variant and noncanonical rDNA repeats distributed among NORs, and which cell-type-specific processes select a subtype of rDNA to be transcribed?

8. How does UBF promote chromatin decondensation and the formation of secondary constriction at metaphase chromosomes?

9. Does the chromosomal context play a role in regulating the activity of individual NORs?

DISCLOSURE STATEMENT

The authors are not aware of any biases that might be perceived as affecting the objectivity of this review.

ACKNOWLEDGMENTS

We thank Hung Tseng and Ross Hannan for communication of unpublished data. B.M.'s work is funded by the MRC UK. I.G.'s work is funded by the Deutsche Forschungsgemeinschaft (SFB/Transregio 5, SP, Epigenetics) and the EU-Network Epigenome.

LITERATURE CITED

Balajee AS, May A, Dianov GL, Friedberg EC, Bohr VA. 1997. Reduced RNA polymerase II transcription in intact and permeabilized Cockayne syndrome group B cells. *Proc. Natl. Acad. Sci. USA* 94:4306–11

Bannister AJ, Zegerman P, Partridge JF, Miska EA, Thomas JO, et al. 2001. Selective recognition of methylated lysine 9 on histone H3 by the HP1 chromo domain. *Nature* 410:120–24

Barreto G, Schafer A, Marhold J, Stach D, Swaminathan SK, et al. 2007. Gadd45a promotes epigenetic gene activation by repair-mediated DNA demethylation. *Nature* 445:671–75

Bartsch I, Schoneberg C, Grummt I. 1988. Purification and characterization of TTFI, a factor that mediates termination of mouse ribosomal DNA transcription. *Mol. Cell. Biol.* 8:3891–97

Bazett-Jones DP, Leblanc B, Herfort M, Moss T. 1994. Short-range DNA looping by the *Xenopus* HMG-box transcription factor, xUBF. *Science* 264:1134–37

Beerens N, Hoeijmakers JH, Kanaar R, Vermeulen W, Wyman C. 2005. The CSB protein actively wraps DNA. *J. Biol. Chem.* 280:4722–29

Bell SP, Learned RM, Jantzen HM, Tjian R. 1988. Functional cooperativity between transcription factors UBF1 and SL1 mediates human ribosomal RNA synthesis. *Science* 241:1192–97

Bernard P, Allshire R. 2002. Centromeres become unstuck without heterochromatin. *Trends Cell Biol.* 12:419–24

Bird AP, Taggart MH, Gehring CA. 1981. Methylated and unmethylated ribosomal RNA genes in the mouse. *J. Mol. Biol.* 152:1–17

Bochar DA, Savard J, Wang W, Lafleur DW, Moore P, et al. 2000. A family of chromatin remodeling factors related to Williams syndrome transcription factor. *Proc. Natl. Acad. Sci. USA* 97:1038–43

Bodem J, Dobreva G, Hoffmann-Rohrer U, Iben S, Zentgraf H, et al. 2000. TIF-IA, the factor mediating growth-dependent control of ribosomal RNA synthesis, is the mammalian homolog of yeast Rrn3p. *EMBO Rep.* 1:171–75

Bozhenok L, Wade PA, Varga-Weisz P. 2002. WSTF-ISWI chromatin remodeling complex targets heterochromatic replication foci. *EMBO J.* 21:2231–41

Bradsher J, Auriol J, Proietti de Santis L, Iben S, Vonesch JL, et al. 2002. CSB is a component of RNA pol I transcription. *Mol. Cell* 10:819–29

Brown SE, Szyf M. 2007. Epigenetic programming of the rRNA promoter by MBD3. *Mol. Cell. Biol.* 27:4938–52

Caburet S, Conti C, Schurra C, Lebofsky R, Edelstein SJ, Bensimon A. 2005. Human ribosomal RNA gene arrays display a broad range of palindromic structures. *Genome Res.* 15:1079–85

Catez F, Ueda T, Bustin M. 2006. Determinants of histone H1 mobility and chromatin binding in living cells. *Nat. Struct. Mol. Biol.* 13:305–10

Chen D, Dundr M, Wang C, Leung A, Lamond A, et al. 2005. Condensed mitotic chromatin is accessible to transcription factors and chromatin structural proteins. *J. Cell Biol.* 168:41–54

Citterio E, Van Den Boom V, Schnitzler G, Kanaar R, Bonte E, et al. 2000. ATP-dependent chromatin remodeling by the Cockayne syndrome B DNA repair-transcription-coupling factor. *Mol. Cell. Biol.* 20:7643–53

Clos J, Buttgereit D, Grummt I. 1986. A purified transcription factor (TIF-IB) binds to essential sequences of the mouse rDNA promoter. *Proc. Natl. Acad. Sci. USA* 83:604–8

Comai L, Tanese N, Tjian R. 1992. The TATA-binding protein and associated factors are integral components of the RNA polymerase I transcription factor, SL1. *Cell* 68:965–76

Conconi A, Widmer RM, Koller T, Sogo JM. 1989. Two different chromatin structures coexist in ribosomal RNA genes throughout the cell cycle. *Cell* 57:753–61

Copenhaver GP, Putnam CD, Denton ML, Pikaard CS. 1994. The RNA polymerase I transcription factor UBF is a sequence-tolerant HMG-box protein that can recognize structured nucleic acids. *Nucleic Acids Res.* 22:2651–57

Dammann R, Lucchini R, Koller T, Sogo JM. 1993. Chromatin structures and transcription of rDNA in yeast *Saccharomyces cerevisiae*. *Nucleic Acids Res.* 21:2331–38

de Capoa A, Marlekaj P, Baldini A, Rocchi M, Archidiacono N. 1985. Cytologic demonstration of differential activity of rRNA gene clusters in different human cells. *Hum. Genet.* 69:212–17

Denissov S, van Driel M, Voit R, Hekkelman M, Hulsen T, et al. 2007. Identification of novel functional TBP-binding sites and general factor repertoires. *EMBO J.* 26:944–54

Dev VG, Tantravahi R, Miller DA, Miller OJ. 1977. Nucleolus organizers in *Mus musculus* subspecies and in the RAG mouse cell line. *Genetics* 86:389–98

Dianov GL, Houle JF, Iyer N, Bohr VA, Friedberg EC. 1997. Reduced RNA polymerase II transcription in extracts of Cockayne syndrome and Xeroderma pigmentosum/Cockayne syndrome cells. *Nucleic Acids Res.* 25:3636–42

Earley K, Lawrence RJ, Pontes O, Reuther R, Enciso AJ, et al. 2006. Erasure of histone acetylation by *Arabidopsis* HDA6 mediates large-scale gene silencing in nucleolar dominance. *Genes Dev.* 20:1283–93

Espada J, Ballestar E, Santoro R, Fraga MF, Villar-Garea A, et al. 2007. Epigenetic disruption of ribosomal RNA genes and nucleolar architecture in DNA methyltransferase 1 (Dnmt1) deficient cells. *Nucleic Acids Res.* 35:2191–98

Frescas D, Guardavaccaro D, Bassermann F, Koyama-Nasu R, Pagano M. 2007. JHDM1B/FBXL10 is a nucleolar protein that represses transcription of ribosomal RNA genes. *Nature* 450:309–13

Gerber JK, Gogel E, Berger C, Wallisch M, Muller F, et al. 1997. Termination of mammalian rDNA replication: polar arrest of replication fork movement by transcription termination factor TTF-I. *Cell* 90:559–67

Ghoshal K, Majumder S, Datta J, Motiwala T, Bai S, et al. 2004. Role of human ribosomal RNA (rRNA) promoter methylation and of methyl-CpG-binding protein MBD2 in the suppression of rRNA gene expression. *J. Biol. Chem.* 279:6783–93

Gonzalez IL, Sylvester JE. 1995. Complete sequence of the 43-kb human ribosomal DNA repeat: analysis of the intergenic spacer. *Genomics* 27:320–28

Gonzalez IL, Sylvester JE. 1997. Beyond ribosomal DNA: on towards the telomere. *Chromosoma* 105:431–37

Gorski JJ, Pathak S, Panov K, Kasciukovic T, Panova T, et al. 2007. A novel TBP-associated factor of SL1 functions in RNA polymerase I transcription. *EMBO J.* 26:1560–68

Grozdanov P, Georgiev O, Karagyozov L. 2003. Complete sequence of the 45-kb mouse ribosomal DNA repeat: analysis of the intergenic spacer. *Genomics* 82:637–43

Grummt I. 2003. Life on a planet of its own: regulation of RNA polymerase I transcription in the nucleolus. *Genes Dev.* 17:1691–702

Grummt I. 2007. Different epigenetic layers engage in complex crosstalk to define the epigenetic state of mammalian rRNA genes. *Hum. Mol. Genet.* 16(R1):R21–27

Grummt I, Kuhn A, Bartsch I, Rosenbauer H. 1986a. A transcription terminator located upstream of the mouse rDNA initiation site affects rRNA synthesis. *Cell* 47:901–11

Grummt I, Maier U, Öhrlein A, Hassouna N, Bachellerie JP. 1985. Transcription of mouse rDNA terminates downstream of the 3′ end of 28S RNA and involves interaction of factors with repeated sequences in the 3′ spacer. *Cell* 43:801–10

Grummt I, Pikaard CS. 2003. Epigenetic silencing of RNA polymerase I transcription. *Nat. Rev. Mol. Cell Biol.* 4:641–49

Grummt I, Rosenbauer H, Niedermeyer I, Maier U, Öhrlein A. 1986b. A repeated 18 bp sequence motif in the mouse rDNA spacer mediates binding of a nuclear factor and transcription termination. *Cell* 45:837–46

Haaf T, Hayman DL, Schmid M. 1991. Quantitative determination of rDNA transcription units in vertebrate cells. *Exp. Cell Res.* 193:78–86

Haltiner MM, Smale ST, Tjian R. 1986. Two distinct promoter elements in the human rRNA gene identified by linker scanning mutagenesis. *Mol. Cell. Biol.* 6:227–35

Hediger F, Gasser SM. 2006. Heterochromatin protein 1: Don't judge the book by its cover! *Curr. Opin. Genet. Dev.* 16:143–50

Heix J, Zomerdijk JC, Ravanpay A, Tjian R, Grummt I. 1997. Cloning of murine RNA polymerase I-specific TAF factors: conserved interactions between the subunits of the species-specific transcription initiation factor TIF-IB/SL1. *Proc. Natl. Acad. Sci. USA* 94:1733–38

Heliot L, Kaplan H, Lucas L, Klein C, Beorchia A, et al. 1997. Electron tomography of metaphase nucleolar organizer regions: evidence for a twisted-loop organization. *Mol. Biol. Cell* 8:2199–216

Henderson AS, Warburton D, Atwood KC. 1972. Location of ribosomal DNA in the human chromosome complement. *Proc. Natl. Acad. Sci. USA* 69:3394–98

Henderson S, Sollner WB. 1986. A transcriptional terminator is a novel element of the promoter of the mouse ribosomal RNA gene. *Cell* 47:891–900

Hsu TC, Cooper JE, Mace ML Jr, Brinkley BR. 1971. Arrangement of centromeres in mouse cells. *Chromosoma* 34:73–87

Ito T, Levenstein ME, Fyodorov DV, Kutach AK, Kobayashi R, Kadonaga JT. 1999. ACF consists of two subunits, Acf1 and ISWI, that function cooperatively in the ATP-dependent catalysis of chromatin assembly. *Genes Dev.* 13:1529–39

Iuchi S, Green H. 1999. Basonuclin, a zinc finger protein of keratinocytes and reproductive germ cells, binds to the rRNA gene promoter. *Proc. Natl. Acad. Sci. USA* 96:9628–32

Jantzen HM, Admon A, Bell SP, Tjian R. 1990. Nucleolar transcription factor hUBF contains a DNA-binding motif with homology to HMG proteins. *Nature* 344:830–36

Jantzen HM, Chow AM, King DS, Tjian R. 1992. Multiple domains of the RNA polymerase I activator hUBF interact with the TATA-binding protein complex hSL1 to mediate transcription. *Genes Dev.* 6:1950–63

Jones HS, Kawauchi J, Braglia P, Alen CM, Kent NA, Proudfoot NJ. 2007. RNA polymerase I in yeast transcribes dynamic nucleosomal rDNA. *Nat. Struct. Mol. Biol.* 14:123–30

Kermekchiev M, Workman JL, Pikaard CS. 1997. Nucleosome binding by the polymerase I transactivator upstream binding factor displaces linker histone H1. *Mol. Cell. Biol.* 17:5833–42

Klose RJ, Bird AP. 2006. Genomic DNA methylation: the mark and its mediators. *Trends Biochem. Sci.* 31:89–97

Kuhn A, Grummt I. 1987. A novel promoter in the mouse rDNA spacer is active in vivo and in vitro. *EMBO J.* 6:3487–92

Kuhn A, Grummt I. 1992. Dual role of the nucleolar transcription factor UBF: trans-activator and antirepressor. *Proc. Natl. Acad. Sci. USA* 89:7340–44

Lachner M, O'Carroll D, Rea S, Mechtler K, Jenuwein T. 2001. Methylation of histone H3 lysine 9 creates a binding site for HP1 proteins. *Nature* 410:116–20

Laine JP, Egly JM. 2006. When transcription and repair meet: a complex system. *Trends Genet.* 22:430–36

Langst G, Becker PB, Grummt I. 1998. TTF-I determines the chromatin architecture of the active rDNA promoter. *EMBO J.* 17:3135–45

Langst G, Blank TA, Becker PB, Grummt I. 1997. RNA polymerase I transcription on nucleosomal templates: The transcription termination factor TTF-I induces chromatin remodeling and relieves transcriptional repression. *EMBO J.* 16:760–68

Lawrence RJ, Earley K, Pontes O, Silva M, Chen ZJ, et al. 2004. A concerted DNA methylation/histone methylation switch regulates rRNA gene dosage control and nucleolar dominance. *Mol. Cell* 13:599–609

Lawrence RJ, Pikaard CS. 2004. Chromatin turn ons and turn offs of ribosomal RNA genes. *Cell Cycle* 3:880–83

Learned RM, Learned TK, Haltiner MM, Tjian RT. 1986. Human rRNA transcription is modulated by the coordinate binding of two factors to an upstream control element. *Cell* 45:847–57

LeRoy G, Orphanides G, Lane WS, Reinberg D. 1998. Requirement of RSF and FACT for transcription of chromatin templates in vitro. *Science* 282:1900–4

Li J, Langst G, Grummt I. 2006. NoRC-dependent nucleosome positioning silences rRNA genes. *EMBO J.* 25:5735–41

Mais C, Wright JE, Prieto JL, Raggett SL, McStay B. 2005. UBF-binding site arrays form pseudo-NORs and sequester the RNA polymerase I transcription machinery. *Genes Dev.* 19:50–64

Majumder S, Ghoshal K, Datta J, Smith DS, Bai S, Jacob ST. 2006. Role of DNA methyltransferases in regulation of human ribosomal RNA gene transcription. *J. Biol. Chem.* 281:22062–72

Manuelidis L, Borden J. 1988. Reproducible compartmentalization of individual chromosome domains in human CNS cells revealed by in situ hybridization and three-dimensional reconstruction. *Chromosoma* 96:397–410

Mayer C, Grummt I. 2005. Cellular stress and nucleolar function. *Cell Cycle* 4:1036–38

Mayer C, Neubert M, Grummt I. 2008. Specific interaction of a chromatin remodeling complex with a conserved structure within a small non-coding RNA. *EMBO Rep.* In press

Mayer C, Schmitz KM, Li J, Grummt I, Santoro R. 2006. Intergenic transcripts regulate the epigenetic state of rRNA genes. *Mol. Cell* 22:351–61

McClintock B. 1934. The relationship of a particular chromosomal element to the development of the nucleoli in *Zea mays*. *Zeit. Zellforsch. Mik. Anat.* 21:294–328

McStay B. 2006. Nucleolar dominance: a model for rRNA gene silencing. *Genes Dev.* 20:1207–14

McStay B, Frazier MW, Reeder RH. 1991. xUBF contains a novel dimerization domain essential for RNA polymerase I transcription. *Genes Dev.* 5:1957–68

McStay B, Reeder RH. 1986. A termination site for *Xenopus* RNA polymerase I also acts as an element of an adjacent promoter. *Cell* 47:913–20

McStay B, Reeder RH. 1990. An RNA polymerase I termination site can stimulate the adjacent ribosomal gene promoter by two distinct mechanisms in *Xenopus laevis*. *Genes Dev.* 4:1240–51

Meehan RR, Pennings S, Stancheva I. 2001. Lashings of DNA methylation, forkfuls of chromatin remodeling. *Genes Dev.* 15:3231–36

Miller G, Panov KI, Friedrich JK, Trinkle-Mulcahy L, Lamond AI, Zomerdijk JC. 2001. hRRN3 is essential in the SL1-mediated recruitment of RNA Polymerase I to rRNA gene promoters. *EMBO J.* 20:1373–82

Morgan GT, Reeder RH, Bakken AH. 1983. Transcription in cloned spacers of *Xenopus laevis* ribosomal DNA. *Proc. Natl. Acad. Sci. USA* 80:6490–94

Moss T, Boseley PG, Birnstiel ML. 1980. More ribosomal spacer sequences from *Xenopus laevis*. *Nucleic Acids Res.* 8:467–85

Moss T, Langlois F, Gagnon-Kugler T, Stefanovsky V. 2007. A housekeeper with power of attorney: the rRNA genes in ribosome biogenesis. *Cell Mol. Life Sci.* 64:29–49

O'Sullivan AC, Sullivan GJ, McStay B. 2002. UBF binding in vivo is not restricted to regulatory sequences within the vertebrate ribosomal DNA repeat. *Mol. Cell. Biol.* 22:657–68

Paalman MH, Henderson SL, Sollner-Webb B. 1995. Stimulation of the mouse rRNA gene promoter by a distal spacer promoter. *Mol. Cell. Biol.* 15:4648–56

Panov KI, Friedrich JK, Russell J, Zomerdijk JC. 2006. UBF activates RNA polymerase I transcription by stimulating promoter escape. *EMBO J.* 25:3310–22

Paule MR, White RJ. 2000. Survey and summary: transcription by RNA polymerases I and III. *Nucleic Acids Res.* 28:1283–98

Pelletier G, Stefanovsky VY, Faubladier M, Hirschler-Laszkiewicz I, Savard J, et al. 2000. Competitive recruitment of CBP and Rb-HDAC regulates UBF acetylation and ribosomal transcription. *Mol. Cell* 6:1059–66

Peng JC, Karpen GH. 2007. H3K9 methylation and RNA interference regulate nucleolar organization and repeated DNA stability. *Nat. Cell Biol.* 9:25–35

Percipalle P, Fomproix N, Cavellàn E, Voit R, Reimer G, et al. 2006. Nuclear myosin 1 and WSTF-ISWI chromatin remodeling complex binds to rDNA to promote rRNA transcription. *EMBO Rep.* 7:525–30

Peters AH, Kubicek S, Mechtler K, O'Sullivan RJ, Derijck AA, et al. 2003. Partitioning and plasticity of repressive histone methylation states in mammalian chromatin. *Mol. Cell* 12:1577–89

Piacentini L, Fanti L, Berloco M, Perrini B, Pimpinelli S. 2003. Heterochromatin protein 1 (HP1) is associated with induced gene expression in *Drosophila* euchromatin. *J. Cell Biol.* 161:707–14

Poot RA, Dellaire G, Hulsmann BB, Grimaldi MA, Corona DF, et al. 2000. HuCHRAC, a human ISWI chromatin remodelling complex contains hACF1 and two novel histone-fold proteins. *EMBO J.* 19:3377–87

Prieto JL, McStay B. 2007. Recruitment of factors linking transcription and processing of pre-rRNA to NOR chromatin is UBF-dependent and occurs independent of transcription in human cells. *Genes Dev.* 21:2041–54

Putnam CD, Copenhaver GP, Denton ML, Pikaard CS. 1994. The RNA polymerase I transactivator upstream binding factor requires its dimerization domain and high-mobility-group (HMG) box 1 to bend, wrap, and positively supercoil enhancer DNA. *Mol. Cell. Biol.* 14:6476–88

Rando OJ, Ahmad K. 2007. Rules and regulation in the primary structure of chromatin. *Curr. Opin. Cell Biol.* 19:250–56

Reeder RH. 1999. Regulation of RNA polymerase I transcription in yeast and vertebrates. *Prog. Nucleic Acid Res. Mol. Biol.* 62:293–327

Reeder RH, Pikaard CS, McStay B. 1995. UBF, an architectural element for RNA polymerase I promoters. In *Nucleic Acids and Molecular Biology*, ed. F Eckstein, DMJ Lilley, pp. 251–63. Berlin/Heidelberg: Springer-Verlag

Rice JC, Briggs SD, Ueberheide B, Barber CM, Shabanowitz J, et al. 2003. Histone methyltransferases direct different degrees of methylation to define distinct chromatin domains. *Mol. Cell* 12:1591–98

Roussel P, Andre C, Comai L, Hernandez-Verdun D. 1996. The rDNA transcription machinery is assembled during mitosis in active NORs and absent in inactive NORs. *J. Cell Biol.* 133:235–46

Roussel P, Andre C, Masson C, Geraud G, Hernandez VD. 1993. Localization of the RNA polymerase I transcription factor hUBF during the cell cycle. *J. Cell Sci.* 104:327–37

Russell J, Zomerdijk JC. 2005. RNA-polymerase-I-directed rDNA transcription, life and works. *Trends Biochem. Sci.* 30:87–96

Saitoh Y, Laemmli UK. 1994. Metaphase chromosome structure: Bands arise from a differential folding path of the highly AT-rich scaffold. *Cell* 76:609–22

Sakai K, Ohta T, Minoshima S, Kudoh J, Wang Y, et al. 1995. Human ribosomal RNA gene cluster: identification of the proximal end containing a novel tandem repeat sequence. *Genomics* 26:521–26

Santoro R, Grummt I. 2001. Molecular mechanisms mediating methylation-dependent silencing of ribosomal gene transcription. *Mol. Cell* 8:719–25

Santoro R, Grummt I. 2005. Epigenetic mechanism of rRNA gene silencing: temporal order of NoRC-mediated histone modification, chromatin remodeling, and DNA methylation. *Mol. Cell. Biol.* 25:2539–46

Santoro R, Li J, Grummt I. 2002. The nucleolar remodeling complex NoRC mediates heterochromatin formation and silencing of ribosomal gene transcription. *Nat. Genet.* 32:393–96

Schultz DC, Friedman JR, Rauscher FJ 3rd. 2001. Targeting histone deacetylase complexes via KRAB-zinc finger proteins: The PHD and bromodomains of KAP-1 form a cooperative unit that recruits a novel isoform of the Mi-2α subunit of NuRD. *Genes Dev.* 15:428–43

Simpson RT. 1991. Nucleosome positioning: occurrence, mechanisms, and functional consequences. *Prog. Nucleic Acid Res. Mol. Biol.* 40:143–84

Sinclair DA, Guarente L. 1997. Extrachromosomal rDNA circles: a cause of aging in yeast. *Cell* 91:1033–42

Sogo JM, Thoma F. 2004. The structure of rDNA chromatin. In *The Nucleolus*, ed. MO Olson, pp. 73–87. New York: Kluwer Acad./Plenum

Stancheva I, Lucchini R, Koller T, Sogo JM. 1997. Chromatin structure and methylation of rat rRNA genes studied by formaldehyde fixation and psoralen cross-linking. *Nucleic Acids Res.* 25:1727–35

Stefanovsky V, Langlois F, Gagnon-Kugler T, Rothblum LI, Moss T. 2006. Growth factor signaling regulates elongation of RNA polymerase I transcription in mammals via UBF phosphorylation and r-chromatin remodeling. *Mol. Cell* 21:629–39

Stefanovsky VY, Pelletier G, Bazett-Jones DP, Crane-Robinson C, Moss T. 2001. DNA looping in the RNA polymerase I enhancesome is the result of noncooperative in-phase bending by two UBF molecules. *Nucleic Acids Res.* 29:3241–47

Strohner R, Nemeth A, Jansa P, Hofmann-Rohrer U, Santoro R, et al. 2001. NoRC—a novel member of mammalian ISWI-containing chromatin remodeling machines. *EMBO J.* 20:4892–900

Strohner R, Nemeth A, Nightingale KP, Grummt I, Becker PB, Langst G. 2004. Recruitment of the nucleolar remodeling complex NoRC establishes ribosomal DNA silencing in chromatin. *Mol. Cell. Biol.* 24:1791–98

Sullivan GJ, Bridger JM, Cuthbert AP, Newbold RF, Bickmore WA, McStay B. 2001. Human acrocentric chromosomes with transcriptionally silent nucleolar organizer regions associate with nucleoli. *EMBO J.* 20:2867–74

Sylvester JE, Gonzales IL, Mougey EB. 2004. Structure and organisation of vertebrate ribosomal DNA. In *The Nucleolus*, ed. MO Olson, pp. 58–72. New York: Kluwer Acad./Plenum

Tachibana M, Sugimoto K, Nozaki M, Ueda J, Ohta T, et al. 2002. G9a histone methyltransferase plays a dominant role in euchromatic histone H3 lysine 9 methylation and is essential for early embryogenesis. *Genes Dev.* 16:1779–91

Tian Q, Kopf GS, Brown RS, Tseng H. 2001. Function of basonuclin in increasing transcription of the ribosomal RNA genes during mouse oogenesis. *Development* 128:407–16

Tongaonkar P, French SL, Oakes ML, Vu L, Schneider DA, et al. 2005. Histones are required for transcription of yeast rRNA genes by RNA polymerase I. *Proc. Natl. Acad. Sci. USA* 102:10129–34

Travers AA. 2003. Priming the nucleosome: a role for HMGB proteins? *EMBO Rep.* 4:131–36

Tseng H. 2006. Cell-type-specific regulation of RNA polymerase I transcription: a new frontier. *Bioessays* 28:719–25

Tseng H, Biegel JA, Brown RS. 1999. Basonuclin is associated with the ribosomal RNA genes on human keratinocyte mitotic chromosomes. *J. Cell Sci.* 112(Pt. 18):3039–47

Tseng H, Chou W, Wang W, Zhang X, Zhanh S, Schultz RM. 2008. Mouse ribosomal RNA genes contain multiple differentially regulated variants. *PLoS ONE* 3:e1843

Tseng H, Green H. 1992. Basonuclin: a keratinocyte protein with multiple paired zinc fingers. *Proc. Natl. Acad. Sci. USA* 89:10311–15

Vakoc CR, Mandat SA, Olenchock BA, Blobel GA. 2005. Histone H3 lysine 9 methylation and HP1γ are associated with transcription elongation through mammalian chromatin. *Mol. Cell* 19:381–91

Venema J, Mullenders LH, Natarajan AT, van Zeeland AA, Mayne LV. 1990. The genetic defect in Cockayne syndrome is associated with a defect in repair of UV-induced DNA damage in transcriptionally active DNA. *Proc. Natl. Acad. Sci. USA* 87:4707–11

Wang GG, Allis CD, Chi P. 2007. Chromatin remodeling and cancer, part I: Covalent histone modifications. *Trends Mol. Med.* 13:363–72

Worton RG, Sutherland J, Sylvester JE, Willard HF, Bodrug S, et al. 1988. Human ribosomal RNA genes: orientation of the tandem array and conservation of the 5′ end. *Science* 239:64–68

Wright JE, Mais C, Prieto JL, McStay B. 2006. A role for upstream binding factor in organizing ribosomal gene chromatin. *Biochem. Soc. Symp.* 73:77–84

Yan PS, Rodriguez FJ, Laux DE, Perry MR, Standiford SB, Huang TH. 2000. Hypermethylation of ribosomal DNA in human breast carcinoma. *Br. J. Cancer* 82:514–17

Young DW, Hassan MQ, Pratap J, Galindo M, Zaidi SK, et al. 2007. Mitotic occupancy and lineage-specific transcriptional control of rRNA genes by Runx2. *Nature* 445:442–46

Yuan X, Feng W, Imhof A, Grummt I, Zhou Y. 2007. Activation of RNA polymerase I transcription by Cockayne syndrome group B protein and histone methyltransferase G9a. *Mol. Cell* 27:585–95

Yuan X, Zhao J, Zentgraf H, Hoffmann-Rohrer U, Grummt I. 2002. Multiple interactions between RNA polymerase I, TIF-IA and TAF$_I$ subunits regulate preinitiation complex assembly at the ribosomal gene promoter. *EMBO Rep.* 3:1082–87

Zhang LF, Huynh KD, Lee JT. 2007. Perinucleolar targeting of the inactive X during S phase: evidence for a role in the maintenance of silencing. *Cell* 129:693–706

Zhang S, Wang J, Tseng H. 2007. Basonuclin regulates a subset of ribosomal RNA genes in HaCaT cells. *PLoS ONE* 2:e902

Zhou Y, Santoro R, Grummt I. 2002. The chromatin remodeling complex NoRC targets HDAC1 to the ribosomal gene promoter and represses RNA polymerase I transcription. *EMBO J.* 21:4632–40

Zomerdijk JC, Beckmann H, Comai L, Tjian R. 1994. Assembly of transcriptionally active RNA polymerase I initiation factor SL1 from recombinant subunits. *Science* 266:2015–18

The Evolution, Regulation, and Function of Placenta-Specific Genes

Saara M. Rawn and James C. Cross

Department of Comparative Biology & Experimental Medicine, Faculty of Veterinary Medicine, and the Graduate Program in Biochemistry & Molecular Biology, University of Calgary, Calgary, Alberta T2N 4N1, Canada; email: srawn@ucalgary.ca, jcross@ucalgary.ca

Annu. Rev. Cell Dev. Biol. 2008. 24:159–81

First published online as a Review in Advance on July 10, 2008

The *Annual Review of Cell and Developmental Biology* is online at cellbio.annualreviews.org

This article's doi:
10.1146/annurev.cellbio.24.110707.175418

Key Words

tissue-specific genes, trophoblast, hormone, transcription factor

Abstract

A number of placenta-specific genes (e.g., *Tpbp*, *Plac1*, *Syncytin*, and retrotransposon-associated genes such as *Peg10*, *Rtl1*, *Endothelin B receptor*, *Insl4*, *Leptin*, *Midline1*, and *Pleiotrophin*), enhancer elements (e.g., glycoprotein hormone α-subunit) and gene isoforms (e.g., *3βHSD*, *Cyp19*), as well as placenta-specific members of gene families (e.g., *Gcm1*, *Mash2*, *Rhox*, *Esx1*, *Cathepsin*, *PAG*, *TKDP*, *Psg*, *Siglec*) have been identified. This review summarizes their evolution, regulation, and biochemical functions and discusses their significance for placental development and function. Strikingly, the number of unique, truly placenta-specific genes that have been discovered to date is very small. The vast majority of placenta-specific gene products have resulted from one of three mechanisms: evolution of placenta-specific promoters, evolution of large gene families with several placenta-specific members, or adoption of functions associated with endogenous retroviruses and retroelements. Interestingly, nearly all the examples of placenta-specific genes that have been discovered to date are not present in all placental mammals.

Contents

INTRODUCTION

The placenta is a complex organ that facilitates nutrient and gas exchange between the mother and fetus and also serves as a barrier to protect the fetus from the maternal immune system. Placental mammals originated more than 100 million years ago (mya) (Springer et al. 2003) and therefore are relatively recent in terms of vertebrate evolution. Interestingly, though, placentas are quite diverse among mammalian species; differences exist in structure, cell types, and endocrine function. For example, the placentas of the most well-studied species—human, rodent, and ruminants such as sheep and cattle—are quite dissimilar in terms of morphology owing to their unique evolutionary histories (**Figure 1**). In general, the evolution of the feto-placental unit was not associated with the invention of an entirely new set of genes because existing housekeeping genes and signaling pathways underlying placental devel-

opment are, for the most part, conserved with pathways underlying the development of other organs (Cross et al. 2003). In some cases, the placenta uses genes for the same function as in other organ systems, as in the use of fibroblast growth factor (FGF) signaling in epithelial branching morphogenesis (Xu et al. 1998), or coopts existing genes to assume a new function, as in the use of *Hand1* for development of the placenta, heart, and blood vessels (Riley et al. 1998) and *Dlx3* for the development of the placenta, neural crest, epidermis, and limbs (Beanan & Sargent 2000).

There are some important examples, however, in which the genome has evolved in concert with placental development, leading to the appearance of a few truly placenta-specific genes. In other cases, some placenta-specific gene products have arisen with the use of alternative promoters as well as the expression of retroviral genes to assume placenta-specific functions. Additionally, multigene families produced as a result of gene duplication events have provided novel genetic material for placental development and function in some species. What is curious is that these examples of placenta-specific genes tend to be isolated to a few species and are not conserved across all Mammalia. As such, unique compositions of placenta-specific genes are found among the mammalian species. The diverse nature of placenta-specific genes may explain species differences in the structure, cell types, and endocrine functions of the placenta and may help to accommodate differences in the physiology of pregnancy such as the number of fetuses per pregnancy, fetal size, and length of gestation. We review here the recent genomic evidence for the diversification of placenta-specific genes and discuss its functional significance.

PLACENTA-SPECIFIC GENES

Expression of only a very limited number of genes is truly restricted to the placenta (Cross et al. 2003). Mouse *trophoblast-specific protein* (*Tpbp*) *a* and *b* (Kawai et al. 2001) and the related rat gene, *SSP* (*spongiotrophoblast-specific protein*) (Iwatsuki et al. 2000), are exclusively expressed in the placenta. *Tpbpa* (initially called *4311*) is expressed very early in a subset of cells in the ectoplacental cone of the mouse, as well as later in undifferentiated and differentiated spongiotrophoblast cells of the mature placenta (Calzonetti et al. 1995), whereas *SSP* is expressed only in the latter half of pregnancy (Iwatsuki et al. 2000). These genes have been found only in rodents and are novel, with the exception of short stretches (<125 nt) of sequence similarity to cathepsin genes. This may reflect their evolutionary origin because the *Tpbpa* and *Tpbpb* genes map to chromosome 13 at the end of a locus of placenta-specific cathepsin genes (see below). The *Tpbp* gene encodes a truncated protein with homology to cathepsin propeptides due to a stop codon (Deussing et al. 2002, Mason 2008). Cathepsin propeptides typically function by inhibiting mature cathepsins (Wiederanders et al. 2003), and therefore the Tpbps may function as inhibitors of cathepsin proteases. Rat SSP is a secreted protein and can serve as the core of a unique chondroitin sulfate proteoglycan (Achur et al. 2006). Chondroitin sulfate proteoglycans are also expressed in human placentas, albeit with a different core protein. Such proteoglycans are often associated with the extracellular matrix or cell surface and may help to mobilize nutrients, hormones, cytokines, and growth factors for fetal development (Achur et al. 2006). Another gene, *placental-specific protein 1* (*PLAC1*), has traditionally been considered to be placenta-specific, although recent findings indicate that besides being expressed in the placenta, it may also be transcribed in the testis in humans (Silva et al. 2007). The *PLAC1* gene is annotated in the cow, rat, mouse, and human. In humans, *PLAC1* is X-linked, and the protein is expressed in cytotrophoblasts and also localizes to the apical border of syncytiotrophoblast cells (Fant et al. 2007). *PLAC1* expression is constant throughout gestation in the human, but the murine ortholog, or closely related family member (*Plac1*), is restricted to embryonic days (E) 7.5–14.5 and is expressed in all cells of trophoblast lineage (Cocchia et al. 2000, Massabbal et al.

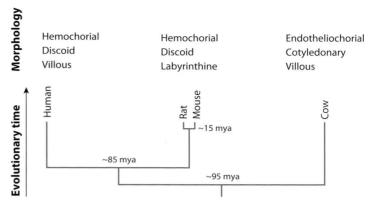

Figure 1

Diverse placental morphologies in different mammalian species. The phylogenetic tree shows divergence between humans, rodents, and ruminants in millions of years. Features describing the type of placental interface (hemochorial versus endotheliochorial), the shape of the feto-placental unit (discoid versus cotyledonary), and the kind of interdigitation between fetal and maternal tissues (villous versus labyrinthine) are indicated for each species. mya denotes million years ago. Based on information from Wildman et al. (2006) and Springer et al. (2003).

2005). The cellular function of PLAC1 is not known, but it is thought to be membrane associated and has been linked to trophoblast differentiation (Fant et al. 2007) and FGF7 signaling (Massabbal et al. 2005). Interestingly, *PLAC1* expression is elevated in various cancers and lung tumors (Silva et al. 2007). Although *PLAC1* may have begun as a placenta-specific gene, its function may have been coopted by cancer cells. In summary, investigators have identified very few genes with placenta-specific expression that either are not derived from retroviruses or are members of large gene families with placenta-specific members. Much work is still required to elucidate the functional significance of placenta-specific genes such as *Tpbpa*, *Tpbpb*, and *Plac1*.

GENE FAMILIES WITH PLACENTA-SPECIFIC MEMBERS

Gene duplication is a powerful method of creating new genetic material that can drive evolution (Ohno 1970). Once copied in the genome, the duplicate gene has a number of possible fates: It can be lost or deleted, assume a

Syncytiotrophoblast: a multinucleated barrier that separates fetal and maternal blood spaces; formed by the fusion of postmitotic trophoblast cells

Retrovirus: a virus that replicates with host DNA. Consists of long terminal repeats and *gag* (group-specific antigen), *pol* (polymerase), and *env* (envelope) genes

nonoverlapping or novel function via sequence divergence, assume a complementary function that often encompasses an aspect of the parental gene's function, or gain regulatory elements that can enhance its level of transcrip- tion or expand its boundaries by changing its spatial and temporal expression (Louis 2007). Species-specific gene duplication events have arisen multiple times during placental evolution (**Table 1**) and represent a large pool of genetic

Table 1 Placental expression of gene family members in different species

| Gene family | Species | Number of genes | | | Type |
		Told	Placenta-specific	Placenta and other tissues	
Siglec (CD33r)	Human	9		1	Enzymes
	Mouse	5			
	Bovine	?			
CG-β	Human	6	6		Hormones
	Mouse	0			
	Bovine	0			
Growth Hormone	Human	5	4		
	Mouse	1			
	Bovine	1			
Interferon-τ	Human	0			
	Mouse	0			
	Bovine	3	3		
Prolactin	Human	1			
	Mouse	23	22		
	Bovine	11	10		
Cysteine Cathepsins	Human	11		11	Proteases
	Mouse	18	8	3	
	Bovine	?			
PAG	Human	?			
	Mouse	1		1	
	Bovine	21	21		
Psg	Human	11	11		
	Mouse	17	17		
	Bovine	0			
TKDP	Human	0			Protease inhibitors
	Mouse	0			
	Bovine	5	5		
Gcm	Human	2		1	Transcription factors
	Mouse	2		1	
	Bovine	2		1	
Mash	Human	2		1	
	Mouse	2		1	
	Bovine	2	1		
Rhox	Human	3			
	Mouse	~30[a]		19	
	Bovine	0			

[a]Annotation of the murine *Rhox* locus is ongoing.

material for the development of new functions or specializations (Soares et al. 2007). The functional significance of these genes is explored below in the context of placental evolution.

Transcription Factors

As with other organs, several tissue-specific transcription factors play key roles in the development and function of the placenta. They have arisen by a variety of means.

Gcm1 and Mash2. The *glial cells missing* (*Gcm*) gene was first identified in *Drosophila* as a mutant that interfered with development of both glial cells in the nervous system as well as macrophage-like cells in the immune system (Hosoya et al. 1995, Jones et al. 1995). Vertebrates have two orthologs, *Gcm1/Gcm-a* and *Gcm2/Gcm-b*, neither of which is implicated in glial cell development. The *Gcm2* gene is essential for parathyroid gland development (Gunther et al. 2000). In mice, *Gcm1* expression during development is limited primarily to the placenta (Basyuk et al. 1999), although transcripts have been detected by PCR in the embryo proper (Kim et al. 1998). *Gcm1* mutant mice die at midgestation owing to failure to

develop the labyrinth layer of the placenta (Anson-Cartwright et al. 2000). Rescue of the placental phenotype by the tetraploid complementation technique (Rossant & Cross 2001) results in liveborn *Gcm1* null mice that have no obvious abnormalities (S. Grisaru, C. Geary-Joo & J. Cross, in preparation). Expression has been reported in the kidney and thymus postnatally (Hashemolhosseini et al. 2002), but its functional significance is unclear. Like *Gcm1*, the *Mash2* transcription factor gene is homologous to genes first described in *Drosophila*, the achaete-scute genes, and in vertebrates *Mash2* has a single sister gene called *Mash1*. *Mash1* plays a critical role in neurogenesis (Guillemot 1995), whereas *Mash2* is required for spongiotrophoblast development in the placenta (Guillemot et al. 1994).

Rhox and Esx1. The reproductive homeobox X-linked (*Rhox*) gene family was identified through genome annotation (Maclean et al. 2005). Humans have 3 *Rhox* family members, but none of them are expressed in the placenta, whereas mice have 32 members that are all expressed in multiple reproductive tissues (**Figure 2**) (MacLean et al. 2006, Wang & Zhang 2006, Wayne et al. 2002). *Rhox4, -5, -6,*

Gene family: a set of paralogous genes that evolved from a common ancestral gene via gene duplication

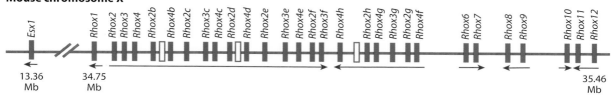

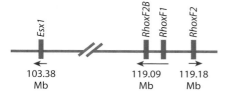

Figure 2

Maps of the reproductive homeobox X-linked (*Rhox*) gene locus and *Esx1* gene in mouse and human. The *Rhox* and *Esx1* homeobox genes are located on the X chromosome in both species. The *Rhox* locus map is still under construction, and the exact location of *Rhox5* is not yet available in genome sequences. Solid boxes indicate putative genes, whereas open boxes indicate pseudogenes. Arrows indicate the direction of transcription. The depiction of the murine locus is based on data from Wang & Zhang (2006).

and -9 are all expressed in the placenta in mice. Mice mutant for *Rhox5* (Pitman et al. 1998) and *Rhox9* (Takasaki et al. 2001) have no obvious reproductive defects, potentially owing to redundancy within the cluster. Of the 32 *Rhox* genes in mice, 20 represent a mouse-specific expansion that arose from repeated duplications of 3 genes, *Rhox2, -3*, and *-4* (**Figure 2**) (MacLean et al. 2006). So far, 7 members of this expansion have been shown to have placental expression (MacLean et al. 2006). *Rhox4* (previously *Ehox*) regulates early stages of embryonic stem cell differentiation (Jackson et al. 2002) and is also expressed in trophoblast stem cells, thus supporting the idea that this gene has a role in the placental stem cell population as well (Jackson et al. 2003). Because humans appear to lack an orthologous *Rhox* gene expansion, the *Rhox2/3/4* genes may help to explain the differences in characteristics of embryonic stem cells between mice and humans (Jackson et al. 2006). Interestingly, *Esx1* is also a homeobox gene located on the X chromosome, 21 Mb from the *Rhox* locus, but is not formally part of the Rhox family (**Figure 2**). Notably, *Esx1* mutant mice have defects in the development of the labyrinth layer of the placenta, and pups show intrauterine growth restriction (Li & Behringer 1998).

Hormones

The placenta is a rich source of hormones that are thought to mediate a range of local and systemic changes in the mother during pregnancy. The placenta-specific hormones have arisen by a variety of evolutionary means.

Chorionic gonadotropin. Chorionic gonadotropin (CG) is a member of the glycoprotein hormone family that consists of three other members: luteinizing hormone (LH), follicle-stimulating hormone (FSH), and thyroid-stimulating hormone (TSH) (Pierce & Parsons 1981). They are dimeric protein hormones; the α-subunit is shared among all glycoprotein hormones, and the different β-subunits are encoded by separate genes. LH, FSH, and TSH are expressed in the pituitary, whereas CG is produced by the placenta, although only in primates and horses. In these species, the glycoprotein hormone α-subunit is expressed in both the pituitary and placenta, whereas expression of CGβ is restricted to the placenta (Jameson et al. 1986, Nilson et al. 1991). The *CGβ* gene arose from duplication of the *LH* β-subunit gene, and in humans, six *CGβ* genes are found together with the *LHβ* gene on chromosome 19 (Policastro et al. 1986). Human CG is expressed in the cytotrophoblast early in pregnancy and at later stages is expressed in the syncytiotrophoblast (Braunstein et al. 1980, Maruo et al. 1992). The primary role of CG is to maintain, through its LH-like effects, the production of progesterone from the corpus luteum to sustain pregnancy (Huhtaniemi & Tena-Sempere 1999). CG also has direct effects on the uterine endometrium, preparing it for pregnancy (Cameo et al. 2004).

Interferon-τ. The *interferon-τ* (*IFNT*) gene arose via duplication from type I interferon (α and β) genes ~36 mya, roughly coinciding with the emergence of ruminants (Roberts 2007). Within the past six million years, *IFNT* has undergone multiple duplication events to produce 3 paralogs in cattle and more than 20 in sheep. The IFNT proteins are produced by trophoblast cells of the peri-implantation conceptus and act on the uterus to suppress the production of a luteolytic signal to maintain progesterone production from the corpus luteum during early pregnancy. Although the sites of action are different, this function is therefore somewhat analogous to that of chorionic gonadotrophin. Therefore, multiple, seemingly disparate genes have evolved comparable functions as an example of convergent evolution. Although IFNT has taken on its reproductive function, the IFNT proteins work through typical type I interferon receptors and have potent antiviral activity, similar to other type I interferons (Roberts 2007). Therefore, *IFNT* is an excellent example of a gene that has had its temporal and spatial expression pattern altered in the process of duplication to facilitate a novel role in the placenta.

Growth hormone and prolactin. The pituitary hormones growth hormone (GH) and prolactin (Prl) stem from the same ancestral gene (Forsyth & Wallis 2002, Niall et al. 1971). Each gene has in turn been duplicated to take on different functions in the placenta, although there are significant differences among species in the extent of the subsequent evolution of the

gene families. The *GH* gene is single copy in rodents and ruminants but contains 5 members in humans. In humans, expression of 1 *GH* gene is restricted to the pituitary, whereas the other 4 *GH* genes are expressed exclusively in the placenta (Su et al. 2000). By contrast, the *Prl* gene is single copy in humans but contains 23 members in mice (**Figure 3**) (Wiemers et al. 2003), 24 in rats (Alam et al. 2006), and 11 in cattle (Ushizawa & Hashizume 2006), with all but the ancestral gene expressed exclusively in

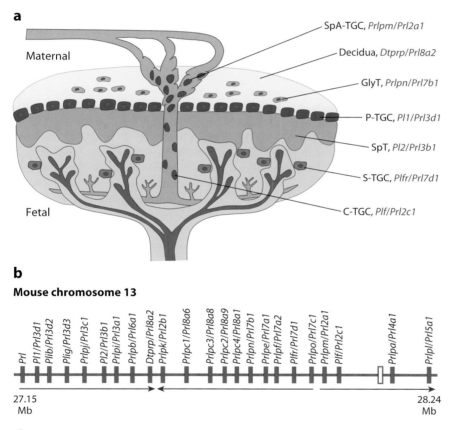

Figure 3

Cell-type-specific expression of the prolactin (Prl)/placental lactogen gene family in the murine placenta. (*a*) Most trophoblast cell subtypes in the placenta express at least one Prl family member; a unique Prl family gene is identified for each cell type shown. Some expression information is from D. Simmons, S. Rawn & J. Cross (submitted). SpA-TGC, spiral artery trophoblast giant cell; GlyT, glycogen trophoblast; P-TGC, parietal trophoblast giant cell; SpT, spongiotrophoblast; S-TGC, sinusoidal trophoblast giant cell; C-TGC, canal trophoblast giant cell. The placental diagram is adapted from Watson et al. (2005). (*b*) Map of the Prl/placental lactogen family locus on mouse chromosome 13. Both old and new gene nomenclature is provided. Solid boxes indicate genes, whereas the open box indicates a pseudogene. Arrows indicate the direction of transcription.

the placenta. Detailed analysis of gene expression has shown that the 23 genes in mice each have unique spatial and temporal expression patterns (D. Simmons, S. Rawn & J.C. Cross, submitted), and many serve as trophoblast cell subtype–specific markers (**Figure 3**). Although *GH* and *Prl* stem from the same ancestral gene, even the pituitary forms have distinct functions, and indeed each form has a vast range of biological activities (Nicoll & Bern 1972, Waters et al. 2006). Some evidence suggests that the placenta-specific forms of GH and Prl may have functions that are distinct from the pituitary-derived forms. Human GH-V is secreted into the maternal bloodstream and has both growth-promoting and lactogenic activities (Alsat et al. 1998, Goodman et al. 1991, MacLeod et al. 1991). Similar effects are associated with classical members of the Prl family in rodents that can stimulate the Prl receptor such as placental lactogen I and II (Soares et al. 2007). GH-V also promotes blood flow to the placenta by decreasing uterine and peripheral arterial resistance (Schiessl et al. 2007), an activity that has not been observed for any of the Prl family members (Soares et al. 2007).

The vast majority of the rodent Prl family members do not act through the Prl receptor and are thought to have diverse functions in promoting maternal adaptations to pregnancy, including effects on vessel development, blood cell production, and activity of immune cells (Soares et al. 2007). The ruminant Prl-related genes are also thought to mediate similar pregnancy-related adaptations (Soares et al. 2007). Because these genes are limited to rodents and ruminants, how are feto-maternal interactions mediated in other species? One hypothesis is that these genes do not have essential normal functions but are only required to cope with physiological stress. For example, it is thought that PLP-A facilitates vascular remodeling under duress. *Prlpa* mutant mice are unable to adapt to hypoxic conditions (Ain et al. 2004), whereas they have no phenotype under normal physiological conditions. However, there may be redundant PLP-A-like hormones encoded within the locus, and mutating only

one of them at a time may be insufficient to cause a phenotype. To test this idea, it would be feasible to make mutations that delete several or all of the family members at once, because *Prl* and its 22 related genes are all present within a single locus in mice, without any intervening genes (**Figure 3**).

Proteases and Protease Inhibitors

Proteases have been extensively studied in the context of the placenta, initially of interest for their ability to regulate trophoblast cell invasion. However, it is clear that putative protease and protease inhibitor genes have rapidly evolved in placental mammals.

Cathepsin. The cathepsin family of cysteine proteases contains several members in humans (Varanou et al. 2006) and rodents (Sol-Church et al. 2002). In ruminants, the so-called pregnancy-associated glycoproteins (PAGs) represent a distantly related gene family (Szafranska et al. 2006). In humans, there are 11 cathepsin genes that are expressed in multiple tissues in the body, but all are also expressed in the placenta (Varanou et al. 2006). Mice have orthologs to these genes, and at least some of them (*Ctsz*, *Ctsl*, *Ctsb*) show placental expression. Mice that are mutant for *Ctsl* (Roth et al. 2000) or *Ctsb* (Deussing et al. 1998) do not have placental defects, perhaps indicating redundancy in function. Mice have eight additional cathepsin genes that are in a single locus on chromosome 13 adjacent to the *Tpbp* genes (Sol-Church et al. 2002). There are limited functional data for these genes. However, the cell-type-specific expression of human cathepsins and mouse placenta–specific cathepsins (Ishida et al. 2004, Nakajima et al. 2000), when known, indicates that family members are differentially expressed in the placenta. For example, human *CTSB* is expressed in the syncytiotrophoblast, whereas human *CTSL* and mouse *Cts7* and *Cts8* are expressed in trophoblast cells that invade the maternal decidua (Hemberger 2007, Varanou et al. 2006). These data suggest, therefore, that different cathepsins have different functions, if not different substrates, in vivo. Overall, much work is required to determine the targets of these proteases during pregnancy to appreciate their exact functions.

Pregnancy-associated glycoproteins. The PAGs, present in both vertebrates and nonvertebrates, belong to the aspartyl protease superfamily (Szafranska et al. 2006). They have undergone species-specific gene duplications in pigs and ruminants such that there are thought to be ~100 members in cattle and sheep (Xie et al. 1997). PAGs are expressed in the ruminant placenta by cells with invasive properties (trophoblast binucleate cells) and in the syncytium, which is formed by the fusion of binucleate cells with uterine epithelial cells (Hughes et al. 2000, Szafranska et al. 2006). Binucleate cells store PAGs in cytoplasmic granules and, upon fusion with the maternal epithelial cells, deliver the PAGs into the maternal bloodstream (Wooding 1992). Investigators have predicted that the protease activity has not been functionally conserved in many PAG family members (Guruprasad et al. 1996, Xie et al. 1997). Recently, it has been demonstrated that the types of glycosylation groups attached to PAGs change throughout pregnancy, supporting the hypothesis that the function of PAGs may be related more to their associated carbohydrate groups than to the core protein (Klisch et al. 2008), similar to what has been described above for the rat SSP protein.

Trophoblast Kunitz domain serine protease inhibitors. In addition to protease-like gene families, ruminants also have a family of Kunitz-type serine protease inhibitors, called the trophoblast Kunitz domain proteins (TKDPs), which are expressed in the placenta (Chakrabarty et al. 2006a). These proteins are evolving very rapidly and have an intriguing expression pattern in which they are abundantly expressed in the trophoblast only around the time of implantation (Chakrabarty et al. 2006b). So far, the function of TKDPs in placental de-

velopment is speculative, and experiments indicate that some members have lost their ability to inhibit proteases. TKDPs may modulate ion channels (MacLean et al. 2004).

Immunoglobulin Superfamily

The immunoglobulin domain is found in a wide variety of transmembrane and secreted proteins. Several novel proteins are expressed in the placenta.

Pregnancy-specific glycoproteins. The immunoglobulin superfamily contains the carcinoembryonic antigen (CEA) family, which includes CEA-related cell adhesion molecules (CEACAMs) and the pregnancy-specific glycoproteins (PSGs) (Brummendorf & Rathjen 1994). The CEACAM/PSG primordial gene is thought to be common to both primates and rodents, but subsequent gene duplications may have arisen independently in both organisms (Rudert et al. 1989). The human PSG locus consists of 11 genes clustered on chromosome 19 (Teglund et al. 1994, Thompson et al. 1990), whereas the mouse Psg family consists of 17 genes located on chromosome 7 (McLellan et al. 2005). PSGs are produced by the syncytiotrophoblast of humans (Lei et al. 1992) and by spongiotrophoblast and trophoblast giant cells in the murine placenta (Kromer et al. 1996, Rebstock et al. 1993) and appear in the maternal bloodstream during pregnancy (Lin et al. 1974). Mouse *Psg16* is also expressed in the brain (Chen et al. 1995), and *Psg18* is expressed in the follicle-associated epithelium in the gut, where it may modulate the immune response with the mucosa-associated lymphoid tissues (Kawano et al. 2007). PSGs contain an N-terminal domain encoding an integrin-binding motif that is thought to mediate interactions with the extracellular matrix (Rooney et al. 1988, Ruoslahti et al. 1986) and immune cells (Rutherfurd et al. 1995). The exact physiological functions of the PSGs are not known. Given that the PSGs are heavily glycosylated and the protein sequences are evolving rapidly, it is possible that PSGs function

Transposition:
process whereby a
segment of one
chromosome is
transferred to a new
position on the same
or another
chromosome

Retrotransposon: a
transposable element
consisting of long
terminal repeats and
gag (group-specific
antigen) and *pol*
(polymerase) coding
regions

similarly as do the ruminant PAGs. Indeed, the glycosylated PAG (Klisch et al. 2008, Szafranska et al. 2006) and PSG (McLellan et al. 2005, Wynne et al. 2006) proteins are both implicated in immunological roles.

Siglec

Siglec-6 is a sialic acid–binding lectin that is expressed only in the placenta of humans, not even in the closely related great apes (Brinkman-Van der Linden et al. 2007). The *Siglec* gene family is rapidly evolving in multiple taxa, and changes to the sequence of the regulatory region of human *Siglec-6* likely explain its placental expression (Brinkman-Van der Linden et al. 2007). Functionally, siglec-6 binds to multiple sialylated ligands, including the hormone leptin, which is also expressed in the human placenta. Other siglecs regulate the activity of cells in the innate and adaptive immune system (Crocker et al. 2007). Expression of *Siglec-6* increases during labor and so is thought to regulate signaling events that initiate parturition (Brinkman-Van der Linden et al. 2007).

COOPTED RETROELEMENTS

The genome is constantly changing. However, in evolutionary terms, mutagenesis is relatively slow, and therefore most novel sequences are acquired through recombination and transposition (Lower et al. 1996). Many genes that are expressed in the placenta are derived from retroelements such as retrotransposons and endogenous retroviruses. In fact, transposed long terminal repeat (LTR) elements account for 8% and 10% of the human and murine genomes, respectively (Lander et al. 2001, Waterston et al. 2002). Retrotransposons typically consist of LTR, *gag* (group-specific antigen gene), and *pol* (polymerase) coding regions, whereas retroviruses also have an *env* (envelope gene) (**Figure 4**) (Lower et al. 1996). The prevalent expression of retrotransposons and endogenous retroviruses in the placenta may be due to the fact that global DNA methylation is lower in the placenta compared with other tissues, and DNA

methylation often represses transposon activity (Kudaka et al. 2007). Strikingly, the endogenous retroviral elements that are associated with and thought to drive the placental expression of the genes encoding endothelin receptor B, pleiotrophin, and midline 1 (see below) are selectively unmethylated in the placenta but heavily methylated in blood cells (Reiss et al. 2007).

Ty3/Gypsy Retrotransposon–Derived Genes

Ty3/gypsy retrotransposons have undergone positive selection in the mammalian genome and, over time, have acquired distinct functions within their hosts in a process called exaptation (Youngson et al. 2005). Thus far, researchers have identified 11 sushi-ichi-class, Ty3/gypsy retrotranspon–derived genes that are conserved in eutherian mammals (Sekita et al. 2008). Two members of this class, *Paternally expressed gene 10 (Peg10)* and *Retrotransposon-like 1 (Rtl1*, also called *Peg 11)*, are located on different chromosomes and have recently been demonstrated to be essential for mammalian placental development (Ono et al. 2006, Sekita et al. 2008). Of the nine remaining sushi-ichi-class genes, a few others show placental expression (Sekita et al. 2008).

Peg10 is thought to be conserved in all mammalian species (Ono et al. 2006). It has two overlapping open reading frames (ORFs), with one ORF transcribed via high-efficiency 1 frameshifting. ORF1 encodes a gag-like protein, and ORF1/2 contains a gag-pol-like protein (Clark et al. 2007, Lux et al. 2005). *Peg10* is a maternally imprinted gene that is predominantly expressed in the placenta of both human and mouse. Mutation of *Peg10* in mice results in early embryonic lethality owing to a lack of the spongiotrophoblast and labyrinth layers (Ono et al. 2006). In humans, *PEG10* expression becomes elevated at approximately 11–12 weeks of pregnancy, reinforcing the idea that *PEG10* plays an important role in placental development (Smallwood et al. 2003). Interestingly, *PEG10* expression is also associated

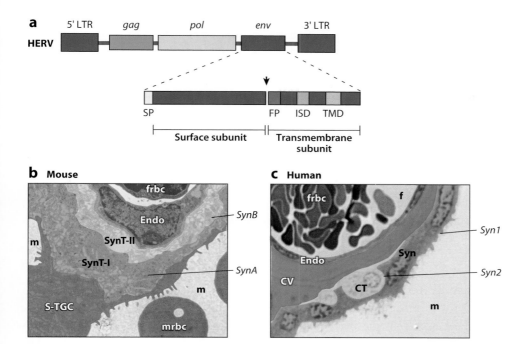

Figure 4

Syncytins are retroviral envelope genes that display trophoblast-cell-type-specific expression in the placenta. (*a*) Generic structure of a human endogenous retrovirus (HERV) and its encoded proteins. HERVs are typically composed of 5′ and 3′ long terminal repeats (LTRs), *gag* (group-specific antigen gene), *pol* (polymerase), and *env* (envelope gene). Syncytins are encoded by the *env* gene and encode a protein product composed of surface and transmembrane subunits. The arrowhead represents a consensus furin cleavage site. SP, signal peptide; FP, fusion peptide; ISD, putative immunosuppressive domain; TMD, transmembrane domain. Schematic of retroviral protein subunits and corresponding domains is adapted from Mangeney et al. (2007). (*b*) Cell-type-specific expression of *Syncytin A* (*SynA*) and *Syncytin B* (*SynB*) in the murine placenta. Colorized electron micrograph of the mouse labyrinth layer of the placenta showing three layers of fetal trophoblast cells that separate the maternal blood space (m) and fetal blood space in the mature placenta. *SynA* is restricted to syncytiotrophoblast layer I (SynT-I) and *SynB* to syncytiotrophoblast layer II (SynT-II). Endo, fetal endothelium; frbc, fetal red blood cell; mrbc, maternal red blood cell; S-TGC, sinusoidal trophoblast giant cell. (*c*) Cell-type-specific expression of *Syncytin 1* (*Syn1*) and *Syncytin 2* (*Syn2*) in the human placenta. Colorized semithin section of a third-trimester villus depicting fetal cell layers separating the maternal blood space (m) and fetal blood space (f). Note that the human placenta has only a single syncytial layer. *Syn1* is predominantly expressed in the syncytiotrophoblast, whereas *Syn2* is expressed in the villous cytotrophoblast (CT) cells. CV, chorionic villi; Endo, fetal endothelium; frbc, fetal red blood cells.

with the differentiation of adipocytes (Hishida et al. 2007). The PEG10 ORF1 protein, but not ORF1/2, interacts with activin receptor–like kinase 1 (ALK1), a member of the transforming growth factor-β (TGF-β) superfamily of receptors. Coexpression of Peg10-ORF1 and ALK1 promotes spreading in transfected cells, suggesting a role for PEG10 in cell migration (Lux et al. 2005).

Rtl1/Peg11 contains the *gag* and *pol* domains in the same ORF (Youngson et al. 2005). *Rtl1* is expressed in the labyrinth zone, specifically around the nuclei of capillary endothelial cells, in later pregnancy. Deletion of *Rtl1/Peg11* results in placental malfunction owing to damage in the cellular architecture, but not in active transport between the maternal and fetal blood spaces in the labyrinth. Overexpression of

Rtl1/Peg11 results in an expansion of the inner spaces of the fetal capillaries. Therefore, both overproduction and loss of *Rtl1/Peg11* cause late fetal or neonatal lethality in mice owing to abnormalities in the placental capillaries (Sekita et al. 2008). In humans, *RTL1* is also expressed in the placenta and is located in an imprinted region of chromosome 14 (Kagami et al. 2008). A gain-of-function mutation of *RTL1* is associated with facial abnormality and a bell-shaped thorax (Kagami et al. 2005), whereas loss of function leads to pre- and postnatal growth failure (Kotzot 2004). Because the ORF1/2 protein contains both *gag* and *pol* domains, it will be intriguing to determine which domains are required for function.

Endogenous Retrovirus–Derived Genes

Throughout evolution, the majority of endogenous retroviruses have undergone genetic degradation via the introduction of in-frame stop codons or mutations that prevent transcription. However, multiple endogenous retroviruses have intact ORFs and are actively transcribed (Okahara et al. 2004, Rote et al. 2004). *HERV-Fb1* and *H7/F(XA34)* transcripts localize to the cytoplasm of trophoblast cells, whereas *HML6-c14* transcripts are uniquely expressed within the nuclei of the syncytiotrophoblast (Kudaka et al. 2007). Of the human endogenous retroviruses expressed in the placenta, ORFs exist in *gag*, *pol*, and *env* elements. Of these, the best characterized are the actively transcribed *env* genes, such as the syncytins and *ERV-3*. The *env* genes have been ascribed different roles in the placenta, such as mediating cell-cell fusion to form the syncytiotrophoblast, suppressing the maternal immune response, and preventing infection by exogenous viruses (Ponferrada et al. 2003, Rote et al. 2004). Of note, ERV-3 has been ruled out as a fusogenic protein, despite its expression in the syncytiotrophoblast. Rather, ERV-3 has been implicated in trophoblast differentiation because it is associated with increased expression of

human chorionic gonadotropin (hCG) and cell cycle arrest prior to syncytiotrophoblast formation (Rote et al. 2004).

The human *Syncytin* genes, *Syncytin 1/HERV-W* and *Syncytin 2/HERV-FRD*, are actively transcribed, placenta-specific *env* genes of endogenous retroviruses (**Figure 4**). They have fusogenic activity in promoting the formation of the multinucleated syncytiotrophoblast cells in the placenta (Prudhomme et al. 2005, Rote et al. 2004, Taruscio & Mantovani 2004). *Syncytin 1* is expressed throughout gestation (Mi et al. 2000, Okahara et al. 2004) in syncytiotrophoblast cells (Kudaka et al. 2007, Malassine et al. 2005). It is a target gene of the GCM1 transcription factor, which is itself downstream of cAMP-regulated protein kinase A (Chang et al. 2005, Knerr et al. 2005, Yu et al. 2002). Syncytin 1 binds to its receptor, the RD114/mammalian type D retrovirus receptor, which is expressed in adjacent cells (Blaise et al. 2003, Malassine et al. 2005). The syncytin 2 protein, although having fusogenic activity and sequence similarity, differs from syncytin 1 in several respects. First, syncytin 2 does not bind RD114, although the identity of the syncytin 2 receptor is unclear. Second, syncytin 2 has an immunosuppressive domain not found in syncytin 1 that may play a role in protecting the fetus from the maternal immune system (Blaise et al. 2003). Third, syncytin 2 is expressed in villous cytotrophoblast cells, specifically lining the membranes of a subset of cells bordering the syncytiotrophoblast, but not in the syncytiotrophoblast itself (Kudaka et al. 2007, Malassine et al. 2007). Finally, in contrast to syncytin 1 expression, syncytin 2 expression decreases as pregnancy progresses (Kudaka et al. 2007).

When the human syncytins were first identified, investigators believed that mice did not have homologous genes, given a lack of obvious sequence similarities (Knerr et al. 2004). However, mice have independently acquired retroviral envelope proteins of their own from a different endogenous retrovirus family; these proteins have been designated syncytin A and B

(Dupressoir et al. 2005). Similar to the primate syncytins, the mouse *Syncytin A* and *B* genes are specifically expressed in the placenta and can trigger cell-cell fusion in vitro (Dupressoir et al. 2005). Their expression is predominantly in the syncytiotrophoblast-containing labyrinth layer of the mouse placenta (Dupressoir et al. 2005). However, in contrast to the human, two distinct layers of syncytiotrophoblast are present in mice. Detailed in situ hybridization studies have revealed that *Syncytin A* mRNA specifically localizes to syncytiotrophoblast layer I, which is closer to the maternal blood space, and *Syncytin B* mRNA is detected exclusively in syncytiotrophoblast layer II, which is closest to the fetal capillaries (**Figure 4**) (D. Simmons, S. Rawn & J.C. Cross, submitted).

Recent structure-function studies on mouse syncytin A have provided some insight into how it mediates cell-cell fusion and have identified it as a Class I viral fusion protein (Peng et al. 2007). The potential functional differences between syncytin 1 and 2 in humans and syncytin A and B in rodents support the notion that pairs of syncytins are conserved for a reason. For example, syncytin 2 and syncytin B have retained their ancient ability to be immunosuppressive, whereas syncytin 1 and syncytin A lack immunosuppression activity but retain fusogenic activity (Mangeney et al. 2007).

The *endogenous Jaagsiekte sheep retrovirus* (*enJSRV*) *env* gene in sheep is another example of an *env* gene expressed in trophoblast, although it has yet to be detected in cattle (Dunlap et al. 2005, Morozov et al. 2007). The *enJSRV env* is first expressed in the trophectoderm of the ovine placenta at day 12, when mononuclear trophectoderm cells begin proliferating in the process of blastocyst elongation. Hyaluronidase 2 (HYAL2) has been identified as the cellular receptor for the enJSRV env protein and is located in association with binucleate cells and the syncytiotrophoblast (Dunlap et al. 2005). Morpholinos against the *enJSRV env* gene result in retarded trophectoderm outgrowth and binucleate cell differentiation, leading to pregnancy loss (Dunlap et al. 2006).

PLACENTA-SPECIFIC TRANSCRIPTS

Some genes that are expressed in various organs in the body have evolved an isoform that is exclusively expressed in the placenta via the adoption of a novel promoter. These placenta-specific promoters have evolved independently in different mammalian species. Some genes that are expressed in the placenta have gained placental expression via alterations to their regulatory regions. A handful of other genes have placenta-specific isoforms as a result of insertion of retroviral elements in proximity to their regulatory regions. Examples of each of these cases are outlined below.

Placenta-Specific Promoters and Enhancers

As mentioned above, the glycoprotein hormone α-subunit has both pituitary and placental expression (Fiddes & Talmadge 1984). Its tissue-specific expression is coordinated by different *cis*-acting sequences within the same promoter. For example, a cyclic AMP response element (CRE) drives placental but not pituitary expression in humans (Bokar et al. 1989). Interestingly, humans have two CRE elements in tandem in their regulatory region, whereas bovine and rodent sequences have only one (Bokar et al. 1989). The CRE likely does not drive placental expression of the gene in rodents and cattle because they display a C-to-T transition in the CRE sequence that significantly lowers its binding affinity for the CREB (cyclic AMP response element–binding) transcription factor (Bokar et al. 1989). This notion is further supported by the fact that the human α-subunit promoter is active in both the pituitary and the placenta of transgenic mice, whereas a transgene with the bovine promoter is active only in the pituitary (Bokar et al. 1989). These data indicate that mice have all the transcription factors in the placenta to drive expression of the glycoprotein hormone α-subunit gene and therefore that the lack of placental expression of the endogenous gene is due to changes in regulatory sequences.

The human *3-β-hydroxysteroid dehydrogenase type I* (*3βHSD1*) gene is expressed in trophoblast cells of the placenta, as well as skin and mammary gland. The placenta-specific promoter/enhancer that defines its placental expression contains binding sites for TEF-5 and GATA-like transcription factors (Peng et al. 2004). Interestingly, transcription of the mouse ortholog, *Hsd3b6*, is driven by the AP-2γ and Dlx3 transcription factors (Peng & Payne 2002). These binding sites are conserved in the regulatory region of human *3βHSD1*, but they are not involved in its placental expression (Peng et al. 2004). This indicates that the transcription factors responsible for placental expression of related genes need not be conserved even if the sequences of the *cis* elements are. Interestingly, AP-2γ regulates both *Hsd3b6*, the enzyme that converts pregnalone to progesterone, as well as *P450scc*, the enzyme that produces pregnalone from cholesterol (Ben-Zimra et al. 2002, Peng et al. 2004). *3βHSD* is also expressed in bovine and ovine placentas (Anderson et al. 1975, Conley et al. 1992). In humans, it is thought that placental progesterone production by 3βHSD1 is required to maintain pregnancy past the first trimester, but a similar role has not been demonstrated in mice (Peng et al. 2004).

The *Cyp19* gene encoding another steroidogenic enzyme, aromatase, is expressed in multiple tissues in the body. The general function of aromatase is to convert androgens to estrogens (Simpson et al. 1994), which regulate uterine and placental growth and differentiation and also play a role in preparation for parturition (Furbass et al. 2008). The *Cyp19* gene also has a placenta-specific isoform in cattle, sheep, and humans, but not in rodents (Kamat & Mendelson 2001, Vanselow et al. 1999). The *Cyp19* gene has evolved multiple promoters to expand its expression into different tissues, and for example, the human *CYP19* gene has at least 10 promoters overall (Bulun et al. 2004). Interestingly, the bovine, ovine, and human *CYP19* genes have each evolved a distinct placenta-specific promoter (**Figure 5**) (Kamat & Mendelson 2001, Vanselow et al. 1999). The placenta-specific promoter of human *CYP19* has been identified as an endogenous long terminal repeat (LTR) (van de Lagemaat et al. 2003). Ruminant placental isoforms of *Cyp19* show differential expression in the preterm and term placenta (Vanselow et al. 2004) and are likely localized in trophoblast giant cells of the placental cotyledons (Schuler et al. 2006). In comparison, human *CYP19* is highly expressed in the syncytiotrophoblast (Fournet-Dulguerov et al. 1987). Similar to the case involving the glycoprotein hormone α-subunit gene, the human *CYP19* placenta-specific promoter is active in transgenic mice, indicating that all the necessary transcription factors exist in mice (Kamat et al. 2005).

Endogenous Retrovirus Regulation and Placental Expression

In addition to *Cyp19*, at least five other genes are specifically expressed in the placenta owing to the insertion of retroviral elements into their regulatory regions (Prudhomme et al. 2005, Taruscio & Mantovani 2004), such as those encoding the *Endothelin B receptor* (Landry & Mager 2003), *Early placenta insulin-like peptide*, *INSL4* (Bièche et al. 2003), *Leptin* (Bi et al. 1997), *Midline1* (Landry et al. 2002), and *Pleiotrophin* (Schulte et al. 1996). Essentially, these retroviral sequences contain an enhancer region(s) and/or a promoter that directs transcription in placental cells. Interestingly, all five genes identified to date are found exclusively in humans and New World monkeys. The evolution of the primate hemochorial placenta may have been affected by ancient retroviral infection and may have resulted in the primate placenta's particularly invasive growth phenotype (Bièche et al. 2003, Cohen & Bischof 2007). Recent studies support this hypothesis: EDNRB has antiapoptotic effects (Cervar-Zivkovic et al. 2007), INSL4 acts in some cancer cells to enhance their invasiveness and motility (Brandt et al. 2005), leptin

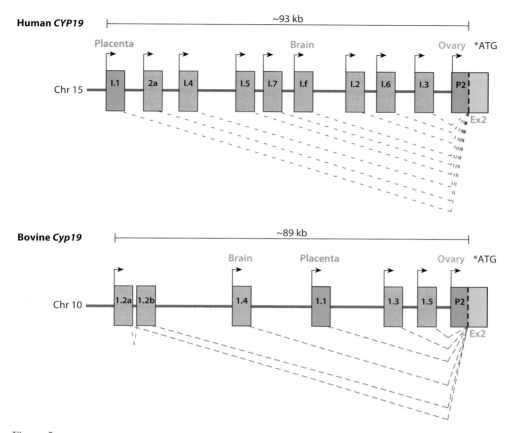

Figure 5

Different placental specific promoters in the human *CYP19* and bovine *Cyp19* genes. The human *CYP19* and bovine *Cyp19* genes display multiple tissue-specific promoters. The major placental, brain, and ovarian promoters are highlighted. For both species, the translated protein products are the same in all tissues owing to a common splice acceptor site in exon 2 (Ex2) that also contains the translation initiation codon denoted by ATG. Boxes represent exons, and arrows indicate transcription start sites. Angled broken lines connect potential splice donors and acceptors. Chr denotes chromosome. The human *CYP19* upstream region is based on information from Bulun et al. (2003). The bovine *Cyp19* upstream region is based on information from Vanselow et al. (2004). Diagrams are not to scale.

promotes cell proliferation and survival in trophoblast cells (Magarinos et al. 2007), midline1 associates with translation factor complexes associated with the cytoskeleton (Aranda-Orgilles et al. 2008), and pleiotrophin can induce the migration of epithelial progenitors (Heiss et al. 2007). Interestingly, *Leptin*, *EDNRB*, and *Pleiotrophin* have orthologs that are expressed in the placentas of rodents not as a result of retroviral insertions. The conservation of their expression is suggestive that

these genes have conserved placental functions (Fan et al. 2000, Henson & Castracane 2006, Thaete et al. 2007).

CONCLUSIONS

We are only beginning to appreciate the extensive contribution of placenta-specific genes to the development of the placenta. A large fraction of these genes apparently evolved to fulfill basic aspects of placental physiology; many of them seem to have functionally equivalent counterparts in other species. However, for the most part, direct biochemical and genetic evidence that establishes functions in different species is lacking. In fact, there have been very few genetic manipulations of placenta-specific genes to test their consequences. Mouse mutants that have been generated are encouraging because they indicate that these genes can affect different stages and processes in development by altering placental structure, cell-type differentiation and function, and endocrine functions involved in maternal adaptation to pregnancy.

SUMMARY POINTS

1. A major limitation to determining the function of placenta-specific genes or isoforms is that many of them are species-specific.

2. Multiple placenta-specific factors appear to have functionally orthologous counterparts in other mammalian species but are encoded by diverse genes, supporting the notion of convergent evolution.

3. It is likely that placenta-specific genes, gene family members, or isoforms that are unique to some species confer a specialized function particular to that species. For the most part, the large, placenta-specific gene families that are species-specific encode hormones or factors that regulate the immune system. This may reflect the difference in physiological interactions that occur between mother and fetus during pregnancy. The exception is the *Rhox* gene family and the closely related *Esx1* gene found only in mice. These genes may bestow a unique property to certain stem cell populations in that organism. Additionally, members of the TKDP gene family are found only in ruminants. Although their precise cellular function is not known, they are expressed only during implantation and may contribute to the shallow invasion phenotype typical of the ruminant placenta.

4. Some genes are conserved between species and yet are expressed only in the placenta of certain species (glycoprotein hormone α-subunit, *Cyp19*). In these cases, the limitation lies not in the lack of expression of the appropriate cell-type-specific transcription factors but rather in subtle differences in promoter sequences.

5. The number of truly placenta-specific genes is quite modest. Therefore, the functions of placenta-specific genes cannot account for the apparent diversity among mammalian species. Much more work is required to explain the diversity in placental form and function among eutherian mammals.

DISCLOSURE STATEMENT

The authors are not aware of any biases that might be perceived as affecting the objectivity of this review.

ACKNOWLEDGMENTS

We thank Dr. Berthold Huppertz for graciously providing the photo of a semithin section of human placental villus. The work is supported by grants from the Canadian Institutes of Health Research (CIHR) and the Alberta Heritage Foundation for Medical Research (AHFMR). S.M.R. is supported by a Studentship from the AHFMR, and J.C.C. is a Scientist of the AHFMR. The authors apologize to those whose work has not been cited owing to space limitations.

LITERATURE CITED

Achur RN, Agbor-Enoh ST, Gowda DC. 2006. Rat spongiotrophoblast-specific protein is predominantly a unique low sulfated chondroitin sulfate proteoglycan. *J. Biol. Chem.* 281:32327–34

Ain R, Dai G, Dunmore JH, Godwin AR, Soares MJ. 2004. A prolactin family paralog regulates reproductive adaptations to a physiological stressor. *Proc. Natl. Acad. Sci. USA* 101:16543–48

Alam SM, Ain R, Konno T, Ho-Chen JK, Soares MJ. 2006. The rat prolactin gene family locus: species-specific gene family expansion. *Mamm. Genome* 17:858–77

Alsat E, Guibourdenche J, Couturier A, Evain-Brion D. 1998. Physiological role of human placental growth hormone. *Mol. Cell Endocrinol.* 140:121–27

Anderson AB, Flint AP, Turnbull AC. 1975. Mechanism of action of glucocorticoids in induction of ovine parturition: effect on placental steroid metabolism. *J. Endocrinol.* 66:61–70

Anson-Cartwright L, Dawson K, Holmyard D, Fisher SJ, Lazzarini RA, Cross JC. 2000. The glial cells missing-1 protein is essential for branching morphogenesis in the chorioallantoic placenta. *Nat. Genet.* 25:311–14

Aranda-Orgilles B, Trockenbacher A, Winter J, Aigner J, Köhler A, et al. 2008. The Opitz syndrome gene product MID1 assembles a microtubule-associated ribonucleoprotein complex. *Hum. Genet.* 123:163–76

Basyuk E, Cross JC, Corbin J, Nakayama H, Hunter P, et al. 1999. Murine *Gcm1* gene is expressed in a subset of placental trophoblast cells. *Dev. Dyn.* 214:303–11

Beanan MJ, Sargent TD. 2000. Regulation and function of Dlx3 in vertebrate development. *Dev. Dyn.* 218:545–53

Ben-Zimra M, Koler M, Orly J. 2002. Transcription of cholesterol side-chain cleavage cytochrome P450 in the placenta: Activating protein-2 assumes the role of steroidogenic factor-1 by binding to an overlapping promoter element. *Mol. Endocrinol.* 16:1864–80

Bi S, Gavrilova O, Gong DW, Mason MM, Reitman M. 1997. Identification of a placental enhancer for the human leptin gene. *J. Biol. Chem.* 272:30583–88

Bièche I, Laurent A, Laurendeau I, Duret L, Giovangrandi Y, et al. 2003. Placenta-specific *INSL4* expression is mediated by a human endogenous retrovirus element. *Biol. Reprod.* 68:1422–29

Blaise S, de Parseval N, Benit L, Heidmann T. 2003. Genomewide screening for fusogenic human endogenous retrovirus envelopes identifies syncytin 2, a gene conserved on primate evolution. *Proc. Natl. Acad. Sci. USA* 100:13013–18

Bokar JA, Keri RA, Farmerie TA, Fenstermaker RA, Andersen B, et al. 1989. Expression of the glycoprotein hormone α-subunit gene in the placenta requires a functional cyclic AMP response element, whereas a different *cis*-acting element mediates pituitary-specific expression. *Mol. Cell. Biol.* 9:5113–22

Brandt B, Kemming D, Packeisen J, Simon R, Helms M, et al. 2005. Expression of early placenta insulin-like growth factor in breast cancer cells provides an autocrine loop that predominantly enhances invasiveness and motility. *Endocr. Relat. Cancer* 12:823–37

Braunstein GD, Rasor JL, Engvall E, Wade ME. 1980. Interrelationships of human chorionic gonadotropin, human placental lactogen, and pregnancy-specific β1-glycoprotein throughout normal human gestation. *Am. J. Obstet. Gynecol.* 138:1205–13

Brinkman-Van der Linden EC, Hurtado-Ziola N, Hayakawa T, Wiggleton L, Benirschke K, et al. 2007. Human-specific expression of Siglec-6 in the placenta. *Glycobiology* 17:922–31

Brummendorf T, Rathjen FG. 1994. Cell adhesion molecules. 1. Immunoglobulin superfamily. *Protein Profile* 1:951–1058

Bulun SE, Sebastian S, Takayama K, Suzuki T, Sasano H, Shozu M. 2003. The human *CYP19* (aromatase P450) gene: update on physiologic roles and genomic organization of promoters. *J. Steroid Biochem. Mol. Biol.* 86:219–24

Bulun SE, Takayama K, Suzuki T, Sasano H, Yilmaz B, Sebastian S. 2004. Organization of the human aromatase p450 (*CYP19*) gene. *Semin. Reprod. Med.* 22:5–9

Calzonetti T, Stevenson L, Rossant J. 1995. A novel regulatory region is required for trophoblast-specific transcription in transgenic mice. *Dev. Biol.* 171:615–26

Cameo P, Srisuparp S, Strakova Z, Fazleabas AT. 2004. Chorionic gonadotropin and uterine dialogue in the primate. *Reprod. Biol. Endocrinol.* 2:50

Posits an evolutionary consequence for placental genes mediated by endogenous retroviral elements.

Cervar-Zivkovic M, Hu C, Barton A, Sadovsky Y, Desoye G, et al. 2007. Endothelin-1 attenuates apoptosis in cultured trophoblasts from term human placentas. *Reprod. Sci.* 14:430–39

Chakrabarty A, Green JA, Roberts RM. 2006a. Origin and evolution of the *TKDP* gene family. *Gene* 373:35–43

Chakrabarty A, MacLean JA 2nd, Hughes AL, Roberts RM, Green JA. 2006b. Rapid evolution of the trophoblast kunitz domain proteins (TKDPs): a multigene family in ruminant ungulates. *J. Mol. Evol.* 63:274–82

Chang CW, Chuang HC, Yu C, Yao TP, Chen H. 2005. Stimulation of GCMa transcriptional activity by cyclic AMP/protein kinase A signaling is attributed to CBP-mediated acetylation of GCMa. *Mol. Cell. Biol.* 25:8401–14

Chen DS, Asanaka M, Yokomori K, Wang F, Hwang SB, et al. 1995. A pregnancy-specific glycoprotein is expressed in the brain and serves as a receptor for mouse hepatitis virus. *Proc. Natl. Acad. Sci. USA* 92:12095–99

Clark MB, Janicke M, Gottesbuhren U, Kleffmann T, Legge M, et al. 2007. Mammalian gene *PEG10* expresses two reading frames by high efficiency 1 frameshifting in embryonic-associated tissues. *J. Biol. Chem.* 282:37359–69

Cocchia M, Huber R, Pantano S, Chen EY, Ma P, et al. 2000. *PLAC1*, an Xq26 gene with placenta-specific expression. *Genomics* 68:305–12

Cohen M, Bischof P. 2007. Factors regulating trophoblast invasion. *Gynecol. Obstet. Investig.* 64:126–30

Conley AJ, Head JR, Stirling DT, Mason JI. 1992. Expression of steroidogenic enzymes in the bovine placenta and fetal adrenal glands throughout gestation. *Endocrinology* 130:2641–50

Crocker PR, Paulson JC, Varki A. 2007. Siglecs and their roles in the immune system. *Nat. Rev. Immunol.* 7:255–66

Cross JC, Baczyk D, Dobric N, Hemberger M, Hughes M, et al. 2003. Genes, development and evolution of the placenta. *Placenta* 24:123–30

Deussing J, Kouadio M, Rehman S, Werber I, Schwinde A, Peters C. 2002. Identification and characterization of a dense cluster of placenta-specific cysteine peptidase genes and related genes on mouse chromosome 13. *Genomics* 79:225–40

Deussing J, Roth W, Saftig P, Peters C, Ploegh HL, Villadangos JA. 1998. Cathepsins B and D are dispensable for major histocompatibility complex class II–mediated antigen presentation. *Proc. Natl. Acad. Sci. USA* 95:4516–21

Dunlap KA, Palmarini M, Adelson DL, Spencer TE. 2005. Sheep endogenous betaretroviruses (enJSRVs) and the hyaluronidase 2 (HYAL2) receptor in the ovine uterus and conceptus. *Biol. Reprod.* 73:271–79

Dunlap KA, Palmarini M, Varela M, Burghardt RC, Hayashi K, et al. 2006. Endogenous retroviruses regulate periimplantation placental growth and differentiation. *Proc. Natl. Acad. Sci. USA* 103:14390–95

Dupressoir A, Marceau G, Vernochet C, Benit L, Kanellopoulos C, et al. 2005. Syncytin-A and syncytin-B, two fusogenic placenta-specific murine envelope genes of retroviral origin conserved in Muridae. *Proc. Natl. Acad. Sci. USA* 102:725–30

Fan QW, Muramatsu T, Kadomatsu K. 2000. Distinct expression of midkine and pleiotrophin in the spinal cord and placental tissues during early mouse development. *Dev. Growth Differ.* 42:113–19

Fant M, Barerra-Saldana H, Dubinsky W, Poindexter B, Bick R. 2007. The PLAC1 protein localizes to membranous compartments in the apical region of the syncytiotrophoblast. *Mol. Reprod. Dev.* 74:922–29

Fiddes JC, Talmadge K. 1984. Structure, expression, and evolution of the genes for the human glycoprotein hormones. *Recent Prog. Horm. Res.* 40:43–78

Forsyth IA, Wallis M. 2002. Growth hormone and prolactin—molecular and functional evolution. *J. Mammary Gland Biol. Neoplasia* 7:291–312

Fournet-Dulguerov N, MacLusky NJ, Leranth CZ, Todd R, Mendelson CR, et al. 1987. Immunohistochemical localization of aromatase cytochrome P-450 and estradiol dehydrogenase in the syncytiotrophoblast of the human placenta. *J. Clin. Endocrinol. Metab.* 65:757–64

Furbass R, Selimyan R, Vanselow J. 2008. DNA methylation and chromatin accessibility of the proximal *Cyp19* promoter region 1.5/2 correlate with expression levels in sheep placentomes. *Mol. Reprod. Dev.* 75:1–7

Goodman HM, Tai LR, Ray J, Cooke NE, Liebhaber SA. 1991. Human growth hormone variant produces insulin-like and lipolytic responses in rat adipose tissue. *Endocrinology* 129:1779–83

This review provides an excellent framework for comparing genes from different species involved in placental development.

Guillemot F. 1995. Analysis of the role of basic-helix-loop-helix transcription factors in the development of neural lineages in the mouse. *Biol. Cell* 84:3–6

Guillemot F, Nagy A, Auerbach A, Rossant J, Joyner AL. 1994. Essential role of Mash-2 in extraembryonic development. *Nature* 371:333–36

Gunther T, Chen ZF, Kim J, Priemel M, Rueger JM, et al. 2000. Genetic ablation of parathyroid glands reveals another source of parathyroid hormone. *Nature* 406:199–203

Guruprasad K, Blundell TL, Xie S, Green J, Szafranska B, et al. 1996. Comparative modelling and analysis of amino acid substitutions suggests that the family of pregnancy-associated glycoproteins includes both active and inactive aspartic proteinases. *Protein Eng.* 9:849–56

Hashemolhosseini S, Hadjihannas M, Stolt CC, Haas CS, Amann K, Wegner M. 2002. Restricted expression of mouse GCMa/Gcm1 in kidney and thymus. *Mech. Dev.* 118:175–78

Heiss C, Wong ML, Block VI, Lao D, Real WM, et al. 2007. Pleiotrophin induces nitric oxide dependent migration of endothelial progenitor cells. *J. Cell Physiol.* 215:366–73

Hemberger M. 2007. Epigenetic landscape required for placental development. *Cell. Mol. Life Sci.* 64:2422–36

Henson MC, Castracane VD. 2006. Leptin in pregnancy: an update. *Biol. Reprod.* 74:218–29

Hishida T, Naito K, Osada S, Nishizuka M, Imagawa M. 2007. *peg10*, an imprinted gene, plays a crucial role in adipocyte differentiation. *FEBS Lett.* 581:4272–78

Hosoya T, Takizawa K, Nitta K, Hotta Y. 1995. *glial cells missing*: a binary switch between neuronal and glial determination in *Drosophila*. *Cell* 82:1025–36

Hughes AL, Green JA, Garbayo JM, Roberts RM. 2000. Adaptive diversification within a large family of recently duplicated, placentally expressed genes. *Proc. Natl. Acad. Sci. USA* 97:3319–23

Huhtaniemi IT, Tena-Sempere M. 1999. *Gonadotropin Receptors*. New York: Parthenon. 165 pp.

Ishida M, Ono K, Taguchi S, Ohashi S, Naito J, et al. 2004. Cathepsin gene expression in mouse placenta during the latter half of pregnancy. *J. Reprod. Dev.* 50:515–23

Iwatsuki K, Shinozaki M, Sun W, Yagi S, Tanaka S, Shiota K. 2000. A novel secretory protein produced by rat spongiotrophoblast. *Biol. Reprod.* 62:1352–59

Jackson M, Baird JW, Cambray N, Ansell JD, Forrester LM, Graham GJ. 2002. Cloning and characterization of *Ehox*, a novel homeobox gene essential for embryonic stem cell differentiation. *J. Biol. Chem.* 277:38683–92

Jackson M, Baird JW, Nichols J, Wilkie R, Ansell JD, et al. 2003. Expression of a novel homeobox gene *Ehox* in trophoblast stem cells and pharyngeal pouch endoderm. *Dev. Dyn.* 228:740–44

Jackson M, Watt AJ, Gautier P, Gilchrist D, Driehaus J, et al. 2006. A murine specific expansion of the Rhox cluster involved in embryonic stem cell biology is under natural selection. *BMC Genomics* 7:212

Jameson JL, Lindell CM, Habener JF. 1986. Evolution of different transcriptional start sites in the human luteinizing hormone and chorionic gonadotropin β-subunit genes. *DNA* 5:227–34

Jones BW, Fetter RD, Tear G, Goodman CS. 1995. *glial cells missing*: a genetic switch that controls glial versus neuronal fate. *Cell* 82:1013–23

Kagami M, Nishimura G, Okuyama T, Hayashidani M, Takeuchi T, et al. 2005. Segmental and full paternal isodisomy for chromosome 14 in three patients: narrowing the critical region and implication for the clinical features. *Am. J. Med. Genet. A* 138:127–32

Kagami M, Sekita Y, Nishimura G, Irie M, Kato F, et al. 2008. Deletions and epimutations affecting the human 14q32.2 imprinted region in individuals with paternal and maternal upd(14)-like phenotypes. *Nat. Genet.* 40:237–42

Kamat A, Mendelson CR. 2001. Identification of the regulatory regions of the human aromatase P450 (*CYP19*) gene involved in placenta-specific expression. *J. Steroid Biochem. Mol. Biol.* 79:173–80

Kamat A, Smith ME, Shelton JM, Richardson JA, Mendelson CR. 2005. Genomic regions that mediate placental cell-specific and developmental regulation of human *Cyp19* (aromatase) gene expression in transgenic mice. *Endocrinology* 146:2481–88

Kawai J, Shinagawa A, Shibata K, Yoshino M, Itoh M, et al. 2001. Functional annotation of a full-length mouse cDNA collection. *Nature* 409:685–90

Kawano K, Ebisawa M, Hase K, Fukuda S, Hijikata A, et al. 2007. Psg18 is specifically expressed in follicle-associated epithelium. *Cell Struct. Funct.* 32:115–26

Kim J, Jones BW, Zock C, Chen Z, Wang H, et al. 1998. Isolation and characterization of mammalian homologs of the *Drosophila* gene *glial cells missing*. *Proc. Natl. Acad. Sci. USA* 95:12364–69

Klisch K, Jeanrond E, Pang PC, Pich A, Schuler G, et al. 2008. A tetraantennary glycan with bisecting *N*-acetylglucosamine and the Sd[a] antigen is the predominant *N*-glycan on bovine pregnancy-associated glycoproteins. *Glycobiology* 18:42–52

Demonstrates an additional layer of complexity when discerning function of placental glycoproteins.

Knerr I, Huppertz B, Weigel C, Dotsch J, Wich C, et al. 2004. Endogenous retroviral syncytin: compilation of experimental research on syncytin and its possible role in normal and disturbed human placentogenesis. *Mol. Hum. Reprod.* 10:581–88

Knerr I, Schubert SW, Wich C, Amann K, Aigner T, et al. 2005. Stimulation of GCMa and syncytin via cAMP mediated PKA signaling in human trophoblastic cells under normoxic and hypoxic conditions. *FEBS Lett.* 579:3991–98

Kotzot D. 2004. Maternal uniparental disomy 14 dissection of the phenotype with respect to rare autosomal recessively inherited traits, trisomy mosaicism, and genomic imprinting. *Ann. Genet.* 47:251–60

Kromer B, Finkenzeller D, Wessels J, Dveksler G, Thompson J, Zimmermann W. 1996. Coordinate expression of splice variants of the murine pregnancy-specific glycoprotein (PSG) gene family during placental development. *Eur. J. Biochem.* 242:280–87

Kudaka W, Oda T, Jinno Y, Yoshimi N, Aoki Y. 2007. Cellular localization of placenta-specific human endogenous retrovirus (HERV) transcripts and their possible implication in pregnancy-induced hypertension. *Placenta* 29:282–89

Lander ES, Linton LM, Birren B, Nusbaum C, Zody MC, et al. 2001. Initial sequencing and analysis of the human genome. *Nature* 409:860–921

Landry JR, Mager DL. 2003. Functional analysis of the endogenous retroviral promoter of the human endothelin B receptor gene. *J. Virol.* 77:7459–66

Landry JR, Rouhi A, Medstrand P, Mager DL. 2002. The Opitz syndrome gene *Mid1* is transcribed from a human endogenous retroviral promoter. *Mol. Biol. Evol.* 19:1934–42

Lei KJ, Sartwell AD, Pan CJ, Chou JY. 1992. Cloning and expression of genes encoding human pregnancy-specific glycoproteins. *J. Biol. Chem.* 267:16371–78

Li Y, Behringer RR. 1998. *Esx1* is an X-chromosome-imprinted regulator of placental development and fetal growth. *Nat. Genet.* 20:309–11

Lin TM, Halbert SP, Spellacy WN. 1974. Measurement of pregnancy-associated plasma proteins during human gestation. *J. Clin. Investig.* 54:576–82

Louis EJ. 2007. Evolutionary genetics: making the most of redundancy. *Nature* 449:673–74

Provides insight into how gene duplication leads to new genetic material.

Lower R, Lower J, Kurth R. 1996. The viruses in all of us: characteristics and biological significance of human endogenous retrovirus sequences. *Proc. Natl. Acad. Sci. USA* 93:5177–84

Lux A, Beil C, Majety M, Barron S, Gallione CJ, et al. 2005. Human retroviral gag- and gag-pol-like proteins interact with the transforming growth factor-β receptor activin receptor-like kinase 1. *J. Biol. Chem.* 280:8482–93

Maclean JA 2nd, Chen MA, Wayne CM, Bruce SR, Rao M, et al. 2005. *Rhox*: a new homeobox gene cluster. *Cell* 120:369–82

MacLean JA 2nd, Lorenzetti D, Hu Z, Salerno WJ, Miller J, Wilkinson MF. 2006. *Rhox* homeobox gene cluster: recent duplication of three family members. *Genesis* 44:122–29

MacLean JA 2nd, Roberts RM, Green JA. 2004. Atypical Kunitz-type serine proteinase inhibitors produced by the ruminant placenta. *Biol. Reprod.* 71:455–63

MacLeod JN, Worsley I, Ray J, Friesen HG, Liebhaber SA, Cooke NE. 1991. Human growth hormone-variant is a biologically active somatogen and lactogen. *Endocrinology* 128:1298–302

Magarinos MP, Sanchez-Margalet V, Kotler M, Calvo JC, Varone CL. 2007. Leptin promotes cell proliferation and survival of trophoblastic cells. *Biol. Reprod.* 76:203–10

Malassine A, Blaise S, Handschuh K, Lalucque H, Dupressoir A, et al. 2007. Expression of the fusogenic HERV-FRD Env glycoprotein (syncytin 2) in human placenta is restricted to villous cytotrophoblastic cells. *Placenta* 28:185–91

Malassine A, Handschuh K, Tsatsaris V, Gerbaud P, Cheynet V, et al. 2005. Expression of HERV-W Env glycoprotein (syncytin) in the extravillous trophoblast of first trimester human placenta. *Placenta* 26:556–62

Mangeney M, Renard M, Schlecht-Louf G, Bouallaga I, Heidmann O, et al. 2007. Placental syncytins: genetic disjunction between the fusogenic and immunosuppressive activity of retroviral envelope proteins. *Proc. Natl. Acad. Sci. USA* 104:20534–39

Maruo T, Ladines-Llave CA, Matsuo H, Manalo AS, Mochizuki M. 1992. A novel change in cytologic localization of human chorionic gonadotropin and human placental lactogen in first-trimester placenta in the course of gestation. *Am. J. Obstet. Gynecol.* 167:217–22

Mason RW. 2008. Emerging functions of placental cathepsins. *Placenta* 29:385–90

Massabbal E, Parveen S, Weisoly DL, Nelson DM, Smith SD, Fant M. 2005. *PLAC1* expression increases during trophoblast differentiation: evidence for regulatory interactions with the fibroblast growth factor-7 (FGF-7) axis. *Mol. Reprod. Dev.* 71:299–304

McLellan AS, Fischer B, Dveksler G, Hori T, Wynne F, et al. 2005. Structure and evolution of the mouse pregnancy-specific glycoprotein (*Psg*) gene locus. *BMC Genomics* 6:4

Mi S, Lee X, Li X, Veldman GM, Finnerty H, et al. 2000. Syncytin is a captive retroviral envelope protein involved in human placental morphogenesis. *Nature* 403:785–89

Morozov VA, Morozov AV, Lagaye S. 2007. Endogenous JSRV-like proviruses in domestic cattle: analysis of sequences and transcripts. *Virology* 367:59–70

Nakajima A, Kataoka K, Takata Y, Huh NH. 2000. Cathepsin-6, a novel cysteine proteinase showing homology with and colocalized expression with cathepsin J/P in the labyrinthine layer of mouse placenta. *Biochem. J.* 349(Pt. 3):689–92

Niall HD, Hogan ML, Sauer R, Rosenblum IY, Greenwood FC. 1971. Sequences of pituitary and placental lactogenic and growth hormones: evolution from a primordial peptide by gene reduplication. *Proc. Natl. Acad. Sci. USA* 68:866–70

Nicoll CS, Bern HA. 1972. *On the Action of Prolactin among the Vertebrates: Is There a Common Denominator?* London: Churchill-Livingstone. 299 pp.

Nilson JH, Bokar JA, Clay CM, Farmerie TA, Fenstermaker RA, et al. 1991. Different combinations of regulatory elements may explain why placenta-specific expression of the glycoprotein hormone α-subunit gene occurs only in primates and horses. *Biol. Reprod.* 44:231–37

Ohno S. 1970. *Evolution by Gene Duplication.* New York: Springer-Verlag. 160 pp.

Okahara G, Matsubara S, Oda T, Sugimoto J, Jinno Y, Kanaya F. 2004. Expression analyses of human endogenous retroviruses (HERVs): tissue-specific and developmental stage-dependent expression of HERVs. *Genomics* 84:982–90

Ono R, Nakamura K, Inoue K, Naruse M, Usami T, et al. 2006. Deletion of *Peg10*, an imprinted gene acquired from a retrotransposon, causes early embryonic lethality. *Nat. Genet.* 38:101–6

Peng L, Huang Y, Jin F, Jiang SW, Payne AH. 2004. Transcription enhancer factor-5 and a GATA-like protein determine placental-specific expression of the type I human 3β-hydroxysteroid dehydrogenase gene, *HSD3B1*. *Mol. Endocrinol.* 18:2049–60

Peng L, Payne AH. 2002. AP-2γ and the homeodomain protein distal-less 3 are required for placental-specific expression of the murine 3β-hydroxysteroid dehydrogenase VI gene, *Hsd3b6*. *J. Biol. Chem.* 277:7945–54

Peng X, Pan J, Gong R, Liu Y, Kang S, et al. 2007. Functional characterization of syncytin-A, a newly murine endogenous virus envelope protein. Implication for its fusion mechanism. *J. Biol. Chem.* 282:381–89

Pierce JG, Parsons TF. 1981. Glycoprotein hormones: structure and function. *Annu. Rev. Biochem.* 50:465–95

Pitman JL, Lin TP, Kleeman JE, Erickson GF, MacLeod CL. 1998. Normal reproductive and macrophage function in Pem homeobox gene-deficient mice. *Dev. Biol.* 202:196–214

Policastro PF, Daniels-McQueen S, Carle G, Boime I. 1986. A map of the hCGβ-LHβ gene cluster. *J. Biol. Chem.* 261:5907–16

Ponferrada VG, Mauck BS, Wooley DP. 2003. The envelope glycoprotein of human endogenous retrovirus HERV-W induces cellular resistance to spleen necrosis virus. *Arch. Virol.* 148:659–75

Prudhomme S, Bonnaud B, Mallet F. 2005. Endogenous retroviruses and animal reproduction. *Cytogenet. Genome Res.* 110:353–64

Rebstock S, Lucas K, Weiss M, Thompson J, Zimmermann W. 1993. Spatiotemporal expression of pregnancy-specific glycoprotein gene *rnCGM1* in rat placenta. *Dev. Dyn.* 198:171–81

Reiss D, Zhang Y, Mager DL. 2007. Widely variable endogenous retroviral methylation levels in human placenta. *Nucleic Acids Res.* 35:4743–54

Riley P, Anson-Cartwright L, Cross JC. 1998. The Hand1 bHLH transcription factor is essential for placentation and cardiac morphogenesis. *Nat. Genet.* 18:271–75

Roberts RM. 2007. Interferon-τ, a Type 1 interferon involved in maternal recognition of pregnancy. *Cytokine Growth Factor Rev.* 18:403–8

Rooney BC, Horne CH, Hardman N. 1988. Molecular cloning of a cDNA for human pregnancy-specific β1-glycoprotein: homology with human carcinoembryonic antigen and related proteins. *Gene* 71:439–49

Rossant J, Cross JC. 2001. Placental development: lessons from mouse mutants. *Nat. Rev. Genet.* 2:538–48

Rote NS, Chakrabarti S, Stetzer BP. 2004. The role of human endogenous retroviruses in trophoblast differentiation and placental development. *Placenta* 25:673–83

Roth W, Deussing J, Botchkarev VA, Pauly-Evers M, Saftig P, et al. 2000. Cathepsin L deficiency as molecular defect of furless: hyperproliferation of keratinocytes and pertubation of hair follicle cycling. *FASEB J.* 14:2075–86

Rudert F, Zimmermann W, Thompson JA. 1989. Intraspecies and interspecies analyses of the carcinoembryonic antigen (CEA) gene family reveal independent evolution in primates and rodents. *J. Mol. Evol.* 29:126–34

Ruoslahti E, Bourdon M, Krusius T. 1986. Molecular cloning of proteoglycan core proteins. *Ciba Found. Symp.* 124:260–71

Rutherfurd KJ, Chou JY, Mansfield BC. 1995. A motif in PSG11s mediates binding to a receptor on the surface of the promonocyte cell line THP-1. *Mol. Endocrinol.* 9:1297–305

Schiessl B, Strasburger CJ, Bidlingmeier M, Gutt B, Kirk SE, et al. 2007. Role of placental growth hormone in the alteration of maternal arterial resistance in pregnancy. *J. Reprod. Med.* 52:313–16

Schuler G, Ozalp GR, Hoffmann B, Harada N, Browne P, Conley AJ. 2006. Reciprocal expression of 17α-hydroxylase-C17,20-lyase and aromatase cytochrome P450 during bovine trophoblast differentiation: A two-cell system drives placental oestrogen synthesis. *Reproduction* 131:669–79

Schulte AM, Lai S, Kurtz A, Czubayko F, Riegel AT, Wellstein A. 1996. Human trophoblast and choriocarcinoma expression of the growth factor pleiotrophin attributable to germ-line insertion of an endogenous retrovirus. *Proc. Natl. Acad. Sci. USA* 93:14759–64

Sekita Y, Wagatsuma H, Nakamura K, Ono R, Kagami M, et al. 2008. Role of retrotransposon-derived imprinted gene, *Rtl1*, in the feto-maternal interface of mouse placenta. *Nat. Genet.* 40:243–48

Silva WA Jr, Gnjatic S, Ritter E, Chua R, Cohen T, et al. 2007. PLAC1, a trophoblast-specific cell surface protein, is expressed in a range of human tumors and elicits spontaneous antibody responses. *Cancer Immun.* 7:18

Simpson ER, Mahendroo MS, Means GD, Kilgore MW, Hinshelwood MM, et al. 1994. Aromatase cytochrome P450, the enzyme responsible for estrogen biosynthesis. *Endocr. Rev.* 15:342–55

Smallwood A, Papageorghiou A, Nicolaides K, Alley MK, Jim A, et al. 2003. Temporal regulation of the expression of syncytin (HERV-W), maternally imprinted PEG10, and SGCE in human placenta. *Biol. Reprod.* 69:286–93

Soares MJ, Konno T, Alam SM. 2007. The prolactin family: effectors of pregnancy-dependent adaptations. *Trends Endocrinol. Metab.* 18:114–21

Sol-Church K, Picerno GN, Stabley DL, Frenck J, Xing S, et al. 2002. Evolution of placentally expressed cathepsins. *Biochem. Biophys. Res. Commun.* 293:23–29

Springer MS, Murphy WJ, Eizirik E, O'Brien SJ. 2003. Placental mammal diversification and the Cretaceous-Tertiary boundary. *Proc. Natl. Acad. Sci. USA* 100:1056–61

Su Y, Liebhaber SA, Cooke NE. 2000. The human growth hormone gene cluster locus control region supports position-independent pituitary- and placenta-specific expression in the transgenic mouse. *J. Biol. Chem.* 275:7902–9

Szafranska B, Panasiewicz G, Majewska M. 2006. Biodiversity of multiple Pregnancy-Associated Glycoprotein (PAG) family: gene cloning and chorionic protein purification in domestic and wild eutherians (Placentalia)—a review. *Reprod. Nutr. Dev.* 46:481–502

Takasaki N, Rankin T, Dean J. 2001. Normal gonadal development in mice lacking GPBOX, a homeobox protein expressed in germ cells at the onset of sexual dimorphism. *Mol. Cell. Biol.* 21:8197–202

Taruscio D, Mantovani A. 2004. Factors regulating endogenous retroviral sequences in human and mouse. *Cytogenet. Genome Res.* 105:351–62

Demonstrates a novel placental function for retrotransposon-derived genes.

Provides insight into the evolutionary significance of a placenta-specific gene family.

Teglund S, Olsen A, Khan WN, Frangsmyr L, Hammarström S. 1994. The pregnancy-specific glycoprotein (PSG) gene cluster on human chromosome 19: fine structure of the 11 PSG genes and identification of 6 new genes forming a third subgroup within the carcinoembryonic antigen (CEA) family. *Genomics* 23:669–84

Thaete LG, Jilling T, Synowiec S, Khan S, Neerhof MG. 2007. Expression of endothelin 1 and its receptors in the hypoxic pregnant rat. *Biol. Reprod.* 77:526–32

Thompson J, Koumari R, Wagner K, Barnert S, Schleussner C, et al. 1990. The human pregnancy-specific glycoprotein genes are tightly linked on the long arm of chromosome 19 and are coordinately expressed. *Biochem. Biophys. Res. Commun.* 167:848–59

Ushizawa K, Hashizume K. 2006. Biology of the prolactin family in bovine placenta. II. Bovine prolactin-related proteins: their expression, structure and proposed roles. *Anim. Sci. J.* 77:18–27

van de Lagemaat LN, Landry JR, Mager DL, Medstrand P. 2003. Transposable elements in mammals promote regulatory variation and diversification of genes with specialized functions. *Trends Genet.* 19:530–36

Vanselow J, Furbass R, Rehbock F, Klautschek G, Schwerin M. 2004. Cattle and sheep use different promoters to direct the expression of the aromatase cytochrome P450 encoding gene, *Cyp19*, during pregnancy. *Domest. Anim. Endocrinol.* 27:99–114

Vanselow J, Zsolnai A, Fesus L, Furbass R, Schwerin M. 1999. Placenta-specific transcripts of the aromatase encoding gene include different untranslated first exons in sheep and cattle. *Eur. J. Biochem.* 265:318–24

Varanou A, Withington SL, Lakasing L, Williamson C, Burton GJ, Hemberger M. 2006. The importance of cysteine cathepsin proteases for placental development. *J. Mol. Med.* 84:305–17

Wang X, Zhang J. 2006. Remarkable expansions of an X-linked reproductive homeobox gene cluster in rodent evolution. *Genomics* 88:34–43

Waters MJ, Hoang HN, Fairlie DP, Pelekanos RA, Brown RJ. 2006. New insights into growth hormone action. *J. Mol. Endocrinol.* 36:1–7

Waterston RH, Lindblad-Toh K, Birney E, Rogers J, Abril JF, et al. 2002. Initial sequencing and comparative analysis of the mouse genome. *Nature* 420:520–62

Watson ED, Cross JC. 2005. Development of structures and transport functions in the mouse placenta. *Physiology* 20:180–93

Wayne CM, MacLean JA, Cornwall G, Wilkinson MF. 2002. Two novel human X-linked homeobox genes, *hPEPP1* and *hPEPP2*, selectively expressed in the testis. *Gene* 301:1–11

Wiederanders B, Kaulmann G, Schilling K. 2003. Functions of propeptide parts in cysteine proteases. *Curr. Protein Pept. Sci.* 4:309–26

Wiemers DO, Shao LJ, Ain R, Dai G, Soares MJ. 2003. The mouse prolactin gene family locus. *Endocrinology* 144:313–25

Wildman DE, Chen C, Erez O, Grossman LI, Goodman M, Romero R. 2006. Evolution of the mammalian placenta revealed by phylogenetic analysis. *Proc. Natl. Acad. Sci USA* 103:3203–8

Wooding FB. 1992. The synepitheliochorial placenta of ruminants: binucleate cell fusions and hormone production. *Placenta* 13:101–13

Wynne F, Ball M, McLellan AS, Dockery P, Zimmermann W, Moore T. 2006. Mouse pregnancy-specific glycoproteins: tissue-specific expression and evidence of association with maternal vasculature. *Reproduction* 131:721–32

Xie S, Green J, Bixby JB, Szafranska B, DeMartini JC, et al. 1997. The diversity and evolutionary relationships of the pregnancy-associated glycoproteins, an aspartic proteinase subfamily consisting of many trophoblast-expressed genes. *Proc. Natl. Acad. Sci. USA* 94:12809–16

Xu X, Weinstein M, Li C, Naski M, Cohen RI, et al. 1998. Fibroblast growth factor receptor 2 (FGFR2)-mediated reciprocal regulation loop between FGF8 and FGF10 is essential for limb induction. *Development* 125:753–65

Youngson NA, Kocialkowski S, Peel N, Ferguson-Smith AC. 2005. A small family of sushi-class retrotransposon-derived genes in mammals and their relation to genomic imprinting. *J. Mol. Evol.* 61:481–90

Yu C, Shen K, Lin M, Chen P, Lin C, et al. 2002. GCMa regulates the syncytin-mediated trophoblastic fusion. *J. Biol. Chem.* 277:50062–68

Shows that sequence similarity between orthologous genes in different species may not indicate conserved function on the basis of gene expression data.

Communication Between the Synapse and the Nucleus in Neuronal Development, Plasticity, and Disease

Sonia Cohen[1,2] and Michael E. Greenberg[1,*]

[1]F.M. Kirby Neurobiology Center, Children's Hospital Boston and Departments of Neurology and Neurobiology, and [2]Program in Biological and Biomedical Sciences, Harvard Medical School, Boston, Massachusetts 02115; email: cohen@fas.harvard.edu, Michael.Greenberg@childrens.harvard.edu

Annu. Rev. Cell Dev. Biol. 2008. 24:183–209

First published online as a Review in Advance on July 10, 2008

The *Annual Review of Cell and Developmental Biology* is online at cellbio.annualreviews.org

This article's doi: 10.1146/annurev.cellbio.24.110707.175235

*Corresponding author.

Key Words

activity-dependent transcription, calcium, CREB, MEF2, MeCP2, Bdnf

Abstract

Sensory experience is critical for the proper development and plasticity of the brain throughout life. Successful adaptation to the environment is necessary for the survival of an organism, and this process requires the translation of specific sensory stimuli into changes in the structure and function of relevant neural circuits. Sensory-evoked activity drives synaptic input onto neurons within these behavioral circuits, initiating membrane depolarization and calcium influx into the cytoplasm. Calcium signaling triggers the molecular mechanisms underlying neuronal adaptation, including the activity-dependent transcriptional programs that drive the synthesis of the effector molecules required for long-term changes in neuronal function. Insight into the signaling pathways between the synapse and the nucleus that translate specific stimuli into altered patterns of connectivity within a circuit provides clues as to how activity-dependent programs of gene expression are coordinated and how disruptions in this process may contribute to disorders of cognitive function.

Contents

EXPERIENCE SHAPES THE NERVOUS SYSTEM

Amblyopia: poor vision through an eye that is otherwise healthy due to disruption of transmission of the visual image to the brain

Synapses: specialized chemical junctions between neurons that transmit electrical activity from the presynaptic to the postsynaptic cell via neurotransmitter release

Development of the brain throughout life occurs in concert with exposure to the environment. The perturbation of sensory or psychosocial experience during early childhood may result in the impairment of cognitive function or behavior, as in cases of amblyopia due to congenital cataracts or intellectual impairment following early deprivation. Interventions that limit exposure to impoverished environments and promote exposure to enriched environments can prevent or even reverse the long-term consequences of deprivation on brain development (Maurer et al. 1999, Nelson et al. 2007). Why is early experience so important to cognition? During embryonic development of the central nervous system (CNS), genetically

programmed molecular cues control the proliferation, migration, and maturation of neurons, leading to the widespread formation of connections between neurons and the establishment of rudimentary neuronal circuits. Although neuronal activity is not strictly required for the early development of synaptic connections (Verhage et al. 2000), spontaneous activity within the nascent circuits provides modulatory information about the appropriateness of the synapses formed (Katz & Shatz 1996). As the CNS starts to receive and interpret environmental stimuli, sensory cues begin to drive synaptic activity. The discovery that blocking visual experience by monocular deprivation in cats during the critical period disrupts the development of ocular dominance columns in the visual cortex (Wiesel & Hubel 1963) suggested that this sensory-evoked neuronal activity may play a crucial role in CNS development. Since then, researchers have shown that experience modulates the cellular mechanisms that underlie the strengthening and stabilization of useful synapses and the weakening or elimination of those that are unnecessary during both postnatal development and in the adult. Thus, following an initial program of widespread synaptogenesis, neuronal activity leads to the refinement of CNS circuitry, reflecting postnatal experience and allowing continued adaptation to the environment.

Synaptic and Nuclear Roles of Activity in Neuronal Development

The initial formation of an excitatory synapse in the CNS depends on contact between the presynaptic axon and the postsynaptic dendrite, the recruitment of pre- and postsynaptic proteins to the site of contact, and stabilization of the axodendritic interaction to initiate the assembly of a functional synapse. A major class of ionotropic glutamate receptors in the CNS, the NMDA (N-methyl-D-aspartate) receptor, is recruited early on to the postsynaptic membrane of the nascent synapse (McAllister 2007). Coincident binding of glutamate to the NMDA receptor and postsynaptic membrane depolarization activate the channel, allowing calcium influx to initiate signals that modulate the maturation of the synapse. An important local effect of calcium influx through the NMDA receptor is to regulate the recruitment of a second major class of ionotropic glutamate receptor to the postsynaptic membrane, the AMPA (α-amino-3-hydroxy-5-methylisoxazole-4-propionic acid) receptor (Petralia et al. 1999, Shi et al. 1999). AMPA receptors mediate fast excitatory neurotransmission in the brain, and the number of AMPA receptors at a synapse correlates with the size and maturity of the synapse, determining the relative strength of the synaptic response to glutamate stimulation (Bourne & Harris 2008). The majority of mature glutamatergic synapses in the cortex occur on dendritic spines, actin-rich protrusions from the dendritic shaft that serve to compartmentalize postsynaptic calcium influx in response to synaptic stimulation (Alvarez & Sabatini 2007). Early postnatal development is characterized by an experience-dependent widespread net loss of spines, or pruning, that depends on NMDA receptor activation and local regulation of spine dynamics to maintain the spines of productive synapses, leading to appropriate maturation of cortical circuits (Grutzendler et al. 2002). A major determinant of synapse formation and the integration of neurons into a circuit is the pattern of dendritic arborization receiving the afferent input. As with dendritic spines, development of dendritic morphology depends on sensory-evoked neuronal activation of glutamate receptors to establish and stabilize the precise connections between pre- and postsynaptic neurons (Parrish et al. 2007).

Synaptic activation and subsequent calcium influx into the postsynaptic neuron regulate dendritic branching and outgrowth not only by acting locally at the site of calcium entry but also by inducing changes in transcription within the nucleus. Calcium influx through the NMDA receptor or voltage-sensitive calcium channels (VSCCs) during the development of dendritic arbors can activate a number of signaling pathways, including the calcium/calmodulin-dependent protein kinases (CaMKs), a diverse group of calcium-sensitive signaling enzymes implicated in neuronal function. Activated CaMKII plays an important local role in mediating AMPA receptor number and conductivity at the synapse and in regulating dendritic growth by inducing changes in the actin cytoskeleton (Dillon & Goda 2005). Calcium-dependent CaMK activity in cultured neurons also initiates signaling to the nucleus, where activation of the cAMP response element binding protein (CREB) transcription factor and the induction of gene expression contribute to activity-dependent dendritic development (Redmond et al. 2002, Wayman et al. 2006). Mice lacking the calcium-responsive transcriptional coactivator CREST have reduced growth and branching of cortical and hippocampal

Critical period: a time window during development in which experience provides information that is essential for normal brain function

Ocular dominance columns: functional columns within primary visual cortex in which neurons respond predominantly to visual inputs from one eye or the other

Glutamate: the primary neurotransmitter released at excitatory synapses in the brain

NMDA: N-methyl-D-aspartate

AMPA: α-amino-3-hydroxy-5-methylisoxazole-4-propionic acid

VSCC: voltage-sensitive calcium channel

CREB: cAMP response element binding protein

dendrites and overall smaller brains, likely as a result of a specific deficit in calcium-dependent induction of dendritic arborization (Aizawa et al. 2004). Thus, both in vitro and in vivo, neuronal development depends on activity to modulate dendritic growth and morphology by local effects at the synapse and by regulation of nuclear programs of gene expression.

Synaptic and Nuclear Roles of Activity in Neuronal Plasticity

As in development, activity-induced calcium influx into mature neurons affects synaptic function by acting both at the synapse and within the nucleus. Changes in the strength of individual synapses are thought to enable information storage within neuronal circuits and to represent a cellular correlate of learning and memory. The long-term potentiation (LTP) and long-term depression (LTD) of synaptic efficacy

elicited by a short period of synaptic stimulation are partially mediated by local effects at the stimulated synapse, including the incorporation or removal of AMPA receptors to modulate synaptic strength (Derkach et al. 2007) and the regulation of dendritic spine turnover (Alvarez & Sabatini 2007). This contributes to the first, immediate phase of LTP, which depends on the rapid modification of synaptic proteins and the actin cytoskeleton and results in alterations of synaptic strength that are of relatively short duration. Lasting changes in synaptic strength in late-LTP involve activity-dependent changes in gene transcription and the synthesis of effector proteins that stably alter neuronal function. These activity-dependent changes in gene expression rely on the faithful report of synaptic activity to the nucleus, coordinated control of transcription within the nucleus, and ultimately the stable alteration of synapses by the newly synthesized gene products.

THE IDENTIFICATION OF c-*fos*, CREB, AND ACTIVITY-DEPENDENT TRANSCRIPTIONAL REGULATION

The realization that extracellular stimuli trigger rapid changes in gene expression to influence cellular behavior came initially from studies of quiescent fibroblasts stimulated with growth factors to reenter the cell cycle, and subsequent studies of calcium influx into neuronal cell lines (Sheng & Greenberg 1990). Induction of the c-*fos* proto-oncogene, rapidly and without new protein synthesis, has come to define the immediate early genes (IEGs). The discovery that sensory-evoked stimuli induce c-*fos* in the CNS suggested that activity-dependent gene products may mediate adaptation of neuronal function (Hunt et al. 1987, Rusak et al. 1990), and *fos*-deficient animals indeed display deficits in synaptic plasticity and behavioral adaptations (Brown et al. 1996, Fleischmann et al. 2003, Hiroi et al. 1997). Identification of a *cis*-acting regulatory element in the c-*fos* promoter, the cAMP response element (CRE), and the transcription factor, CREB, involved in the induction of CRE-dependent transcription has led to the characterization of a prototypical signaling pathway that has yielded great insight into the mechanisms by which extracellular stimuli are transformed into changes in activity-dependent gene expression (Sheng & Greenberg 1990; Sheng et al. 1990, 1991).

Role of Activity-Dependent Gene Expression

For experience to shape the CNS, an individual neuron must process thousands of synaptic inputs and translate them into the appropriate changes in function. Synaptic activity initiates calcium-dependent signaling events that regulate the expression of a group of genes involved in various aspects of neuronal function from metabolism to synaptic function, the modulation of which allows the cell to respond to extracellular stimuli (**Figure 1**). In-depth study of several such genes in the CNS, including c-*fos* (see side bar) and *brain derived neurotrophic factor* (*bdnf*) (see below), has yielded insight into the signaling pathways, transcriptional effectors, and activity-dependent gene products important for experience-dependent neuronal development and plasticity. As the mechanisms underlying neuronal adaptation have become better understood, mutations in many of the molecules involved in activity-dependent gene regulation have been implicated in human disorders of cognitive function. Behaviors that require environmental input for development, such as verbal communication, or that depend on environmental adaptation, such as learning, are often disrupted in neurodevelopmental and psychiatric disorders, suggesting that dysregulation of experience-dependent neuronal adaptation may contribute to the pathogenesis of these human diseases. Understanding how the synapse and nucleus communicate with one another to coordinate activity-dependent gene expression may thus provide insight into both normal development and plasticity of the brain, as well as the etiology of disorders of cognitive function.

Figure 1

Bidirectional communication between the synapse and the nucleus mediates neuronal development and plasticity. Calcium influx into the postsynaptic cell in response to sensory experience modulates neuronal function both by direct actions at the activated synapse and through communication to the nucleus to affect activity-dependent transcriptional programs. (*a*) Synaptic activity induces glutamate release into the synaptic cleft and activation of the postsynaptic NMDA receptor (NMDAR). Calcium influx into the dendritic spine through the NMDA receptor regulates dendritic patterning and synapse morphology through local effects on the actin cytoskeleton. NMDA receptor activation also regulates the recruitment of AMPA receptors to the synapse in processes important for synaptic maturation and plasticity. (*b*) Synaptic activity is communicated to the nucleus to regulate activity-dependent gene expression. Calcium influx through both NMDA receptors and L-type voltage-sensitive calcium channels (L-VSCCs) acts as a second messenger in the cytoplasm to initiate signaling to the nucleus, where the modulation of transcription factors results in activity-dependent changes in gene expression. (*c*) The mRNA and protein products of activity-dependent genes regulate a range of neuronal functions in response to extracellular stimuli. During processes important for neuronal development and plasticity, the activity of these gene products throughout the cell provides a mechanism by which the nucleus is able to communicate to the synapse the functional changes required for adaptive response.

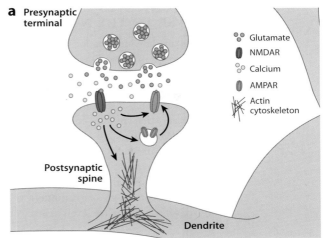

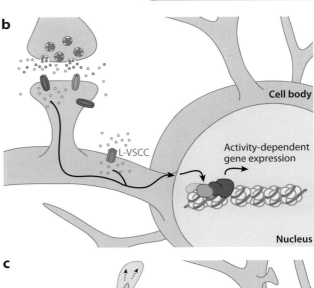

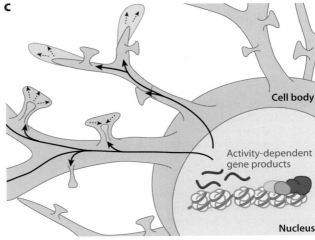

COMMUNICATION FROM THE SYNAPSE TO THE NUCLEUS

Because an individual neuron must process a diverse array of extracellular stimuli, received by hundreds of individual synapses, and coordinate a functional response, neuronal adaptation presents a significant signaling challenge. Since the discovery that stimulus-induced calcium influx into neuronal cell lines is required for the induction of immediate early gene (IEG) expression, the role of calcium in the biochemical transduction of signals from the synapse to the nucleus has been a topic of great interest. Neurons actively maintain low levels of intracellular

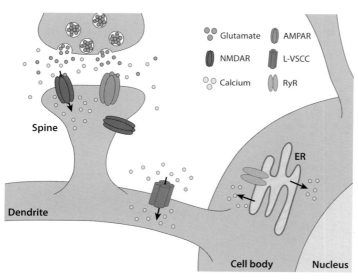

Figure 2

Mechanisms to increase calcium levels in the postsynaptic cell. Calcium plays a well-defined role in the biochemical transduction of signals from the synapse to the nucleus. In response to synaptic activity and neurotransmitter release, extracellular calcium flows into the postsynaptic cell through synaptic and extrasynaptic ligand- and voltage-gated calcium channels. Major routes of entry with well-established effects on nuclear gene expression are the NMDA receptor (NMDAR) and the L-type voltage-sensitive calcium channel (L-VSCC). Calcium-permeable AMPA receptors (AMPAR) may play a role at developing synapses or after the induction of synaptic plasticity. Calcium signals can also be amplified by calcium-induced release of calcium from intracellular stores, triggered by activation of ryanodine receptors (RyR). Calcium at the mouth of the channel, in the cytoplasm, or within the nucleus can signal to activity-dependent transcription factors. Alterations in calcium influx into the postsynaptic cell during development or as a result of mutation modulate the induction of gene expression in response to neuronal activity. ER denotes endoplasmic reticulum.

calcium through the uptake of calcium into internal stores and the extrusion of calcium into the extracellular space. By thus limiting baseline calcium noise, the cell can quickly sense and respond to calcium influx. There are several possible routes of calcium entry into the cytoplasm of the postsynaptic neuron: Extracellular calcium can enter through the NMDA or AMPA glutamate receptors or through VSCCs, or calcium can be released from intracellular stores (**Figure 2**).

The AMPA Receptor: Calcium Signaling in Synaptic Development or Plasticity?

Recent evidence suggests that AMPA receptors may play a direct role in calcium signaling to the nucleus during CNS development and synaptic plasticity. Early in development cortical pyramidal neurons express calcium-permeable, GluR2 subunit–lacking AMPA receptors. During postnatal development these neurons undergo a switch in the subunit composition of AMPA receptors, expressing instead GluR2-containing, calcium-impermeable AMPA receptors (Kumar et al. 2002). However, even at the mature synapse, the initiation of LTP can induce the rapid and transient incorporation of GluR2-lacking AMPA receptors into activated synapses, allowing a brief period of calcium flux through the AMPA receptor before the calcium-permeable channels are replaced (Liu & Cull-Candy 2000, Plant et al. 2006). Thus, both early in development and during synaptic plasticity, calcium influx through AMPA receptors may regulate activity-dependent gene expression. Although AMPA receptors may initiate signals to the nucleus (Perkinton et al. 1999, Rao et al. 2006), whether the regulated expression of calcium-permeable AMPA receptors can drive activity-dependent changes in gene expression remains an outstanding question.

As the result of the developmental switch in AMPA receptor subunit expression, mature glutamatergic synapses in the CNS primarily express calcium-impermeable AMPA receptors

(Derkach et al. 2007), and AMPA receptor activation at these synapses contributes to calcium signaling by mediating the postsynaptic membrane depolarization that is required to activate the NMDA receptor and VSCC. Thus, studies of the induction of activity-dependent gene expression have largely focused on calcium influx through the NMDA receptor and the VSCC.

The NMDA Receptor: Local and Transcriptional Responses to Activity

Calcium influx through the NMDA receptor and the subsequent initiation of signaling pathways have a well-established role in activity-dependent neuronal development and plasticity. Activation of NMDA receptors within an individual dendritic spine by glutamate and postsynaptic membrane depolarization leads to rapid, restricted accumulation of calcium within the spine, allowing for synapse-specific induction of signaling. NMDA receptors are heteromeric channels composed of NR1 and NR2 subunits, with alternative splicing of the NR1 subunit, multiple NR2 isoforms, and developmental regulation of subunit incorporation providing complex regulation of channel composition (Lau & Zukin 2007). Regulation of NMDA receptor subunit incorporation affects the kinetics of calcium influx through the channel and the cytoplasmic coupling to downstream effectors, influencing both the local and transcriptional consequences of NMDA receptor activation.

Over the course of cortical development, NR2B-containing NMDA receptors are replaced by NR2A-containing receptors that have a shortened duration of calcium influx (Carmignoto & Vicini 1992). This developmental regulation of NMDA receptor expression may have implications for synaptic adaptation to activity. Recent work suggests that early in development the presence of NR2B-containing NMDA receptors may inhibit synaptic AMPA receptor accumulation, whereas the activation of mature, NR2A-containing synapses recruits AMPA receptors to the postsynaptic membrane (Hall et al. 2007).

Activity-dependent signaling to the nucleus may also be affected by the developmental regulation of the NMDA receptor subunit composition. Sensory experience in visual cortex drives age-specific programs of gene expression (Majdan & Shatz 2006), and NMDA receptor–dependent alterations in both synaptic function and calcium signaling may mediate the developmental regulation of specific activity-dependent transcriptional programs. In support of this idea, the ability of the NMDA receptor to activate the transcription factor CREB by phosphorylation of CREB at serine-133 (discussed below) depends on the age of the hippocampal neurons. Whereas NMDA stimulation in immature neurons initiates a lasting phosphorylation of CREB serine-133, stimulation of more mature cultures induces only a transient phosphorylation as the result of coincident activation of a CREB phosphatase (Sala et al. 2000). This developmental effect on CREB regulation is unique to NMDA receptor–dependent signaling; depolarization of postsynaptic membranes to induce VSCC activation does not result in such a developmental transition.

Studies of Eph receptor tyrosine kinase modulation of NMDA channel function provide further support for the conclusion that alterations in calcium influx through the NMDA receptor can directly affect activity-dependent gene expression. The EphB subfamily of receptor tyrosine kinases has been implicated in dendritic spine development both in vitro and in vivo (Pasquale 2005). During synaptic maturation in cultured cortical neurons, activation of EphB in the postsynaptic membrane by its presynaptic ligand, ephrinB, induces the extracellular association of EphB with the NR1 subunit of the NMDA receptor, promoting rapid clustering of the NMDA receptor with EphB and inducing synapse formation (Dalva et al. 2000). In the adult brain, the NR1-interacting extracellular domain of EphB is required for NMDA receptor–dependent induction of LTP and LTD, suggesting that EphB may regulate the NMDA receptor during synaptic plasticity as well as in synaptic development (Grunwald et al. 2001, Henderson et al. 2001). Although the EphB kinase domain is not required for the interaction of EphB with the NMDA receptor (Dalva et al. 2000, Grunwald et al. 2001, Henderson et al. 2001), ephrinB stimulation of EphB induces the activity of the nonreceptor tyrosine kinase Src (Grunwald et al. 2001, Takasu et al. 2002). Src-dependent tyrosine phosphorylation of the NR2B subunit of the NMDA receptor increases calcium influx through the NMDA receptor in response to glutamate activation and, as a result, leads to the upregulation of activity-dependent gene expression (Takasu et al. 2002). Although it remains possible that ephrinB/EphB-dependent phosphorylation of the NMDA receptor also regulates its association with downstream signaling molecules, these findings suggest that changes in the magnitude of NMDA receptor–dependent calcium influx are able to modulate nuclear gene expression.

The VSCC: Activity-Dependent Regulation of Gene Expression

In neurons the dihydropyridine-sensitive L-type VSCCs (L-VSCCs), $Ca_v1.2$ and $Ca_v1.3$, are concentrated in the basal dendrites and cell soma, where they are well-positioned to respond to the cumulative activation of many synapses and transduce calcium-regulated signaling events to the nucleus (Westenbroek et al. 1998). Indeed, although pharmacological blockade of the L-VSCCs has a relatively minor effect on the rise in cytoplasmic calcium in response to synaptic activity, blockade of L-VSCCs results in a disproportionate disruption of IEG induction (Murphy et al. 1991), consistent with a key role for the L-VSCC in the communication of synaptic activity to the nucleus (Bading et al. 1993). Mice with specific deletion of $Ca_v1.2$ L-type channels in the hippocampus and cortex display deficits in protein synthesis–dependent LTP and spatial learning tasks (Moosmang et al. 2005), suggesting a requirement for L-VSCC-dependent calcium influx in cellular and behavioral adaptation to experience.

As with the NMDA receptor, precise regulation of calcium influx through the voltage-gated calcium channel is required for appropriate CNS development and function. This is illustrated by mutations in an alternatively spliced exon of $Ca_v1.2$ that give rise to Timothy syndrome, a disorder characterized by severe cardiac arrhythmias and generalized cognitive dysfunction with autistic features (Splawski et al. 2004). The tissues affected express a $Ca_v1.2$ splice variant containing exon 8A, which has a relatively limited expression pattern in the brain. Mutation of $Ca_v1.2$ exon 8A in Timothy syndrome results in inappropriately sustained calcium currents upon channel opening and, despite its limited expression, gives rise to the phenotypes described above (Barrett & Tsien 2008, Erxleben et al. 2006, Splawski et al. 2004). A mutation affecting the same amino acid in the pore of the more widely expressed $Ca_v1.2$ exon 8 splice variant, and thus predicted to give rise to sustained calcium currents throughout the brain, was identified in individuals with severe mental retardation (Splawski et al. 2005), supporting the correlation between the expression of the dysfunctional channel and cognitive impairment. Similar mutations in the $Ca_v1.4$ pore–forming subunit of an L-type channel associated with congenital stationary night blindness also disrupt channel inactivation, giving rise to sustained calcium currents upon activation, and are likewise associated with intellectual impairment (Hemara-Wahanui et al. 2005, Hope et al. 2005, Splawski et al. 2006). That these abnormalities result from defects in the regulation of calcium influx through voltage-gated calcium channels, rather than a loss of channel expression, suggests that dysregulated activation of downstream activity-dependent gene expression may contribute to the pathogenesis of these disorders.

Input-Specific Calcium Signaling to the Nucleus

As illustrated by studies of the NMDA receptor and L-VSCC, the downstream consequences of synaptic activity are dependent on the precise regulation of calcium influx through the various channels. Moreover, the specific route of calcium entry into the postsynaptic neuron, whether through the NMDA receptor or the VSCC, can determine the effect on activity-dependent transcriptional regulation (Bading et al. 1993). How is such input-specific translation of synaptic activity accomplished? Although localized microdomains of high calcium concentration arise near the mouths of open calcium channels, neuronal activity can also trigger more widespread calcium transients throughout the neuronal cytoplasm and nucleus via the spread of membrane depolarization and the triggered release of calcium from intracellular stores.

Experimental evidence confirms that submembranous calcium, cytoplasmic calcium, and nuclear calcium are each capable of regulating gene expression. However, the study of calcium channel–associated complexes suggests that the physical association of signaling molecules with calcium channels is particularly important in coupling calcium influx to activity-dependent transcriptional changes. The use of calcium chelators that specifically inhibit the signaling capacities of either submembranous or cytoplasmic calcium demonstrates that local calcium influx restricted to the channel mouth can be sufficient to induce signaling to the nucleus (Deisseroth et al. 1996, Hardingham et al. 2001). As calcium ions flow through the channel into the postsynaptic cell, they encounter a complex of calcium sensors and signaling enzymes physically associated with the cytoplasmic portion of the calcium channel. The identity of the molecules within this complex determines the functional consequences of channel activation.

The cytoplasmic protein complex associated with the NMDA receptor determines both the local synaptic effects of NMDA receptor activation as well as the consequences for changes in activity-dependent gene expression. Association of the NR2 subunit of the NMDA receptor with members of the MAGUK family of scaffolding proteins localizes the receptor to the postsynaptic density (PSD) of glutamatergic synapses (Sheng & Hoogenraad 2007). Clustered within the PSD are hundreds of proteins involved in functions as diverse as neurotransmission, cell adhesion, intracellular signaling, and cytoskeletal rearrangements. The NMDA receptor associates directly or indirectly with a number of these effector molecules, many of which, such as CaMKII, are activated upon calcium influx through the NMDA receptor. As a result, the protein composition of the PSD can determine the signaling properties of the channel.

The subunit composition of the NMDA receptor itself also contributes to downstream signaling by determining which proteins can interact with the NMDA receptor cytoplasmic domain. Mice lacking the cytoplasmic C terminus of the NR2B subunit die perinatally, whereas in vivo loss of the NR2A C terminus results in deficits of synaptic function and behavioral defects in learning and memory (Sprengel et al. 1998), suggesting unique roles for the cytoplasmic portion of the various NR2 subunits in mediating NMDA receptor function. Likewise, alternative splicing of the NR1 subunit regulates the expression of the C1 C-terminal domain, resulting in differential effects on gene expression without altering calcium current through the channel (Bradley et al. 2006).

Regulated association with distinct signaling complexes, for instance, during CNS development or in the mature nervous system in response to sensory experience, may allow the NMDA receptor to activate specific programs of gene expression and mediate particular biological responses. Recent evidence suggests that NMDA receptor context indeed determines the transcriptional response elicited by calcium influx. The NMDA receptor moves laterally in and out of the synapse (Groc et al. 2004, Tovar & Westbrook 2002), raising the possibility that extrasynaptic NMDA receptors may not associate with the synaptic PSD protein complex and may therefore initiate distinct signaling. Stimulation paradigms designed to specifically activate either synaptic or extrasynaptic NMDA receptors are able to induce transcriptional programs with opposite effects on neuronal survival (Hardingham et al. 2002, Zhang

Calcium microdomain: a cytoplasmic region limited to the immediate vicinity of a calcium channel in which the concentration of calcium can rise dramatically

et al. 2007). This finding may be explained by altered subunit composition in synaptic versus extrasynaptic NMDA receptors (Groc et al. 2006) or by differential association with distinct cytoplasmic signaling complexes. Although further work is required to elucidate the underlying mechanisms, it is clear that NMDA receptor context can have a significant effect on the transcriptional consequences of NMDA receptor activation.

Like the NMDA receptor, the L-type channel associates with scaffolding proteins that cluster signaling molecules in close proximity to one another. A theme emerging from the study of these anchored signaling complexes is that calcium plays a dual role, regulating both L-type channel function and nuclear signaling. Activation of the calcium sensor calmodulin (CaM), which is bound to the L-type channel via the L-VSCC C-terminal IQ domain, can initiate Ras/MAPK signaling to the nucleus, leading to the induction of activity-dependent gene expression (Dolmetsch et al. 2001). In addition, the stable association of CaM with the L-type channel mediates both facilitation and inactivation of the L-type channel, resulting in feedback autoregulation of the channel that alters calcium influx and thereby has consequences for subsequent activity-dependent changes in gene expression (Peterson et al. 1999, Zuhlke et al. 1999). Likewise, the cAMP-dependent protein kinase (PKA), which phosphorylates the L-type channel to facilitate calcium influx, is present at the mouth of the channel in association with other activating or inhibitory signaling molecules such as G protein–coupled receptors and protein phosphatases (Davare et al. 2001). A-kinase anchoring proteins (AKAPs) often anchor PKA to its targets, and one such AKAP, AKAP79/150, mediates the effect of calcium influx through the L-VSCC by recruiting both PKA and calcineurin, a protein phosphatase that antagonizes PKA facilitation (Oliveria et al. 2007). Importantly, AKAP79/150 is required for L-type channel–dependent activation of the transcription factor NFAT (nuclear factor of activated T cells), an activity-dependent transcriptional regulator that has recently been implicated in the pathogenesis of Down syndrome (DS) (discussed below). Thus, the establishment of signaling microdomains, through direct interaction of proteins with calcium channels or via localization of the channels within larger scaffolding complexes, allows for input-specific control of channel function, local modification of synaptic components, and nuclear signaling.

ACTIVITY-DEPENDENT TRANSCRIPTIONAL REGULATION

Integration of the calcium-regulated signaling networks at the synapse, within the cytoplasm, and in the nucleus allows for the coordinated regulation of nuclear transcription factors in response to a variety of extracellular stimuli. In the nucleus, calcium-regulated transcription factors cooperate to control the expression of hundreds of activity-dependent genes, orchestrating the experience-dependent development and plasticity of neuronal function. The mechanisms underlying these activity-dependent transcriptional events, and the nature of the gene expression programs they induce, have been the subject of intense investigation and have led to the identification of a number of activity-regulated transcription factors. Studies of a subset of these factors have begun to yield insight into the role of experience in CNS development and human disorders of cognition.

CREB-Dependent Transcription and Cognitive Function

The transcription factor CREB often serves as the prototype for calcium-dependent regulators of transcription. A reporter gene that contains multiple CREB binding sites (CREs) within its promoter is driven by stimuli that induce cortical plasticity during postnatal development, by LTP, and by hippocampus-dependent learning and memory, suggesting that CREB can regulate experience-dependent gene expression (Lonze & Ginty 2002). A diverse array of extracellular stimuli are converted into changes in gene expression via the regulation of CREB activity, and insight into the mechanisms by which a single stimulus-inducible factor such as CREB can coordinate the expression of specific activity-dependent genes in response to a host of signaling cues has begun to emerge.

CREB was initially identified as a factor that bound to (a) the CRE within the *somatostatin* proximal promoter responsible for cAMP-dependent induction of *somatostatin* gene expression (Montminy & Bilezikjian 1987) and (b) the calcium response element (CaRE) required for calcium-dependent c-*fos* activation (Sheng et al. 1990). The identification of a cAMP- and calcium-inducible phosphorylation event at CREB serine-133 that is required for CRE/CaRE-dependent transcriptional activation (Dash et al. 1991, Gonzalez & Montminy 1989, Sheng et al. 1991), and the ability to identify the kinases that trigger CREB activation using a phospho-specific antibody to CREB phosphorylated at serine-133 (Ginty et al. 1993), enabled the identification of the upstream signaling pathways that promote CREB-dependent transcriptional activation. A number of signal transduction cascades initiated by either cytoplasmic or nuclear calcium have since been shown to mediate CREB serine-133 phosphorylation in various neuronal cell lines and primary neuronal cultures. These pathways ultimately result in the activation of CREB kinases such as the CaMKs (Dash et al. 1991, Kang et al. 2001, Sheng et al. 1991, West et al. 2001) and the Ras/ERK-dependent kinases ribosomal S6 kinases (RSKs) and mitogen- and stress-activated protein kinases (MSKs) (Ginty et al. 1994, Impey et al. 1998, Rosen et al. 1994, Xing et al. 1996) (Figure 3).

The prevailing view of CREB-dependent transcriptional activation proposes that in the unstimulated cell, CREB binds CREs within the promoters of CREB-regulated genes and recruits components of the basal transcriptional machinery. In the absence of extracellular stimuli, the presence of transcriptional repressors and a relatively condensed chromatin confor-

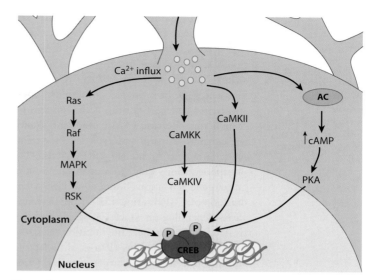

Figure 3

Model of calcium-dependent phosphorylation of CREB (cAMP response element binding protein). Phosphorylation of CREB at serine-133 in response to a diverse array of extracellular stimuli results in CREB transcriptional activation. The signal transduction cascades initiated by these stimuli ultimately result in the activation of a CREB kinase, including protein kinase A (PKA), calcium/calmodulin-dependent kinases II and IV (CaMKII and CaMKIV), and Ras/ERK-dependent kinases such as RSK. Activation of CREB-dependent transcription at particular target genes depends on additional events including other sites of CREB phosphorylation and the recruitment of transcriptional cofactors. CaMKK, CaMK kinase.

mation result in low levels of CRE-driven transcription from these promoters. Cellular stimuli that result in the phosphorylation of CREB at serine-133 recruit CREB-binding protein (CBP) or its paralog p300, multifunctional proteins that increase the transcriptional activity of the CREB transcriptional complex (Chrivia et al. 1993). CBP possesses endogenous histone acetyltransferase (HAT) activity and catalyzes the acetylation of promoter-associated histones, disrupting the histone-DNA interactions and making the chromatin surrounding the transcriptional start site accessible to the transcriptional machinery (Bannister & Kouzarides 1996). CBP may also promote transcription by binding and stabilizing the preinitiation complex that forms at the promoters of CREB target genes (Kwok et al. 1994).

CREB serine-133 phosphorylation is a reasonable correlate for CREB activation and has

Chromatin: a complex of DNA, histones, and nonhistone proteins that controls the accessibility of the DNA to the transcriptional machinery

HAT: histone acetyltransferase

Circadian
entrainment: the
synchronization of
physiology and
behavior to
extracellular cues by a
clock mechanism in
the suprachiasmatic
nucleus of the brain

proven useful in identifying CREB kinases and transcriptional coactivators. However, clues that CREB phosphorylation and transcriptional activation are not a simple ON-OFF switch came from studies of the relationship between CREB serine-133 phosphorylation and target gene expression. Although various stimuli that increase cAMP or calcium, such as neurotransmission and growth factor treatment, are able to induce CREB serine-133 phosphorylation, they do not always induce target gene activation (Bonni et al. 1995). The duration of CREB serine-133 phosphorylation varies depending on which CREB kinase is activated, and may reflect the duration or nature of the synaptic stimulus (Wu et al. 2001). In addition, the timing of target gene induction does not necessarily coincide with the onset or duration of CREB serine-133 phosphorylation, suggesting that additional modifications are required for CREB activation or that CREB cooperates with other regulatory factors at some target genes (Tao et al. 1998). Studies have since demonstrated that, depending on the nature of the stimulus and the cell type, CREB-dependent transcription is regulated by a number of additional mechanisms. These include additional CREB phosphorylation sites (Gau et al. 2002, Kornhauser et al. 2002, Parker et al. 1998), stimulus-dependent CREB dephosphorylation (Bito et al. 1996, Hardingham et al. 2002, Sala et al. 2000), inducible binding of CREB to the regulatory elements of target genes (Riccio et al. 2006), and the association of CREB with novel transcriptional coactivators (Conkright et al. 2003, Iourgenko et al. 2003). Each of these mechanisms is likely involved in the regulation of only a subset of CREB targets, suggesting that a number of signaling pathways may converge to promote a stimulus-specific transcriptional outcome.

The phosphorylation of CREB at serine-142 and -143, in addition to serine-133, is required for maximal, calcium-specific CREB-dependent gene expression in cortical neurons (Kornhauser et al. 2002). Surprisingly, these additional phosphorylation sites prevent CREB-CBP interactions, implying that CREB may be able to initiate gene expression without recruiting CBP (Kornhauser et al. 2002, Parker et al. 1998). Both CREB serine-142 phosphorylation and serine-133 phosphorylation are induced in the brain in response to light stimulation (Gau et al. 2002, Ginty et al. 1993). Mutation of CREB serine-142 to alanine in mice prevents calcium-specific phosphorylation at this site in response to visual experience, resulting in impaired activity-dependent gene induction in the suprachiasmatic nucleus and a consequent behavioral defect in circadian entrainment (Gau et al. 2002). Together these findings suggest that CBP-independent CREB function is required for stimulus-dependent behavioral adaptations under some circumstances.

A better understanding of the context in which CREB-CBP interactions are required may reveal how this aspect of CREB function determines the induction of target genes and specific biological outcomes, and may yield insight into the etiology of some human cognitive disorders that affect the activity-dependent signaling pathways important for CREB-dependent gene expression. Mutations of the CREB kinase, RSK2, have been identified in Coffin-Lowry syndrome (CLS), a severe mental retardation disorder (Trivier et al. 1996), and mutations in CBP and p300 cause the neurodevelopmental disorder Rubenstein-Taybi syndrome (RTS) (Petrij et al. 1995, Roelfsema et al. 2005). Although disruption of CREB function may play a role in the etiology of RTS and CLS, mutations in RSK2 and CBP do not conclusively implicate CREB in these disorders. RSK2 likely has other activity-dependent functions in neurons and may play a role in the phosphorylation of histone H3 as part of the modification of chromatin structure thought to contribute to the activation of the promoters of inducible genes (Sassone-Corsi et al. 1999). Although CREB and CBP cooperate to regulate certain target genes, each likely functions independently of the other as well. CBP itself is posttranslationally modified in response to extracellular stimuli (Impey et al. 2002, Xu et al. 2001) and can interact with sequence-specific transcription factors other than CREB. Thus, CLS and RTS are likely the consequence of disruption of signaling involving a number of transcription factors, including CREB. Nevertheless, elucidation of the mechanisms underlying stimulus-dependent CREB activation has begun to identify the complex interplay among signaling pathways, transcription factors, and the chromatin structure required for the coordinated regulation of activity-dependent programs of gene expression. The fact that CREB, together with its transcriptional coactivator CBP and its upstream regulatory pathways, may play a role in synaptic development, plasticity, and the pathogenesis of human disorders suggests that regulation of these activity-dependent genes underlies cognitive development and function.

MEF2-Dependent Transcription Mediates Activity-Dependent Synaptic Remodeling

Like CREB, the myocyte enhancer factor 2 (MEF2) family of transcription factors is regulated by a number of extracellular stimuli, including those that can induce calcium-dependent signaling pathways. As with CREB, activation of the transcriptional targets of MEF2 likely depends on the coordinate regulation of chromatin structure and transcription factor function. Calcium-dependent modulation of MEF2 function in myocytes has been well-characterized, and similar mechanisms likely play a role in neuronal cells in which MEF2 controls the activity-dependent regulation of synapse number (Flavell et al. 2006, Shalizi et al. 2006).

The MEF2 proteins appear to be constitutively bound to target genes and to act as either transcriptional activators or repressors, depending on their posttranslational modification state (**Figure 4**). In the unstimulated cell, MEF2 is phosphorylated at serine-408, is sumoylated at lysine-403 (Flavell et al. 2006, Shalizi et al. 2006), and associates with the class II histone deacetylases (HDACs) (McKinsey et al. 2000), resulting in repression of MEF2-dependent transcription at target promoters.

In response to calcium influx, calcineurin, a protein phosphatase, dephosphorylates MEF2 at serine-408, lysine-403 is desumoylated and subsequently acetylated, and the association of MEF2 with the class II HDACs is disrupted. The resultant activation of MEF2-dependent transcription restricts synapse number in developing neuronal cultures (Flavell et al. 2006, Shalizi et al. 2006).

Although the in vivo role of MEF2 in the nervous system is not known, its function in primary neurons in vitro, together with the finding that activity controls MEF2-dependent transcription, suggests that MEF2 family members may mediate experience-dependent neuronal development and plasticity. In support of this hypothesis, the stimulus-dependent nuclear export of the class II HDACs, a process correlated with MEF2 activation, has recently been implicated in behavioral adaptation to cocaine and stress (Renthal et al. 2007).

The Control of NFAT-Dependent Transcription and Down Syndrome

Studies in other cell types raise the possibility that in neurons MEF2 may interact with additional transcription factors to control activity-dependent synapse development. Consistent with this hypothesis, activation of calcineurin in neurons not only dephosphorylates MEF2 but also dephosphorylates and activates nuclear factor of activated T cells (NFAT) (Graef et al. 1999) (**Figure 5**). Prior to synaptic activity, NFAT transcription factors are maintained in the cytoplasm by kinases that phosphorylate a series of NFAT residues. The subsequent dephosphorylation of NFAT induces a conformational change in the transcription factor that exposes its nuclear localization signal (NLS) and leads to NFAT transport into the nucleus. Once in the nucleus, NFAT proteins require the cooperative binding of a nuclear factor to initiate transcription, and MEF2 is one of many transcription factors that can serve this function in nonneuronal cells (Olson & Williams 2000). One possibility is that NFAT activates MEF2 target genes by bringing calcineurin in

HDAC: histone deacetylase

close proximity to MEF2, promoting MEF2 dephosphorylation and transcriptional activation. Within the nucleus, NFAT is subject to regulation by kinases, such as glycogen synthase kinase-3 (GSK-3) (Graef et al. 1999), that promote the export of NFAT back into the cytoplasm, thereby inhibiting the transcription of NFAT target genes.

Although NFAT is known to regulate neuronal survival and axonal outgrowth (Benedito et al. 2005, Graef et al. 2003), NFAT's role in experience-dependent synaptic development and plasticity is largely unexplored. However, recent work suggests that the dysregulation of calcium-dependent NFAT signaling may be involved in the etiology of Down syndrome (DS), a neurodevelopmental disorder caused by trisomy of chromosome 21 and characterized by cognitive impairment. Mice with a homozygous deletion in the genes for two NFAT family members, *Nfat2* and *Nfat4*, have characteristic craniofacial skeletal structure reminiscent of previous DS mouse models, and abnormalities in social- and anxiety-related behaviors

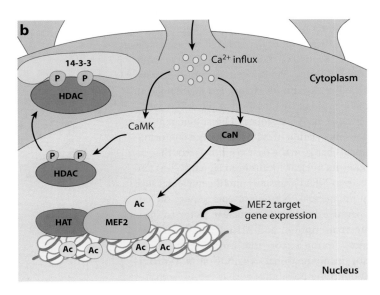

Figure 4

Model of calcium-dependent regulation of myocyte enhancer factor 2 (MEF2) transcriptional activity. MEF2 proteins bound to their target genes can act as either transcriptional activators or repressors, depending on the stimulation state of the cell. (*a*) In the unstimulated cell, the class II histone deacetylases (HDACs), which repress transcription by removing acetyl groups from histones and transcription factors, associate with MEF2. Under these conditions, MEF2 is also phosphorylated at a number of sites. Both basal phosphorylation of MEF2 at serine-408 and its association with HDACs contribute to MEF2 transcriptional repression, in part by promoting the sumoylation (Su) of MEF2 at lysine-403, a modification that represses MEF2-dependent transcription. (*b*) In response to synaptic activity, two calcium-dependent signaling pathways convert MEF2 from a repressor to an activator of transcription. Calcium/calmodulin-dependent protein kinase (CaMK) activation leads to the phosphorylation of the class II HDACs, initiating their binding to the 14-3-3 chaperone proteins and subsequent nuclear export. As a result, MEF2 is able to interact with the transcription-activating histone acetyltransferases (HATs), which likely increases histone acetylation at MEF2 target genes, promoting transcription, and may also contribute to the acetylation of MEF2 itself. In addition, activation of calcineurin (CaN), a calcium-dependent protein phosphatase, dephosphorylates MEF2 at serine-408. Serine-408 dephosphorylation of MEF2 promotes the desumoylation and subsequent acetylation of MEF2 lysine-403, contributing to MEF2 transcriptional activation.

consistent with a DS-like phenotype (Arron et al. 2006). This observation, and findings from a screen for upstream regulators of calcium-dependent NFAT translocation in *Drosophila* (Gwack et al. 2006), led to the identification of gene products encoded by the human Down syndrome critical region (DSCR) as negative regulators of NFAT transcriptional activity. These include DSCR1, an inhibitor of calcineurin (Arron et al. 2006, Rothermel et al. 2000), and DYRK1A [dual-specificity tyrosine (Y) phosphorylation–regulated kinase 1A], a serine/threonine kinase that primes substrates for phosphorylation by GSK-3 (Arron et al. 2006, Gwack et al. 2006). Duplication of the DSCR in DS results in overexpression of DSCR1 and DYRK1A, both of which are predicted to prevent NFAT activation in response to calcium (**Figure 5**), supporting a model whereby increased gene dosage of two negative regulators of NFAT in the DSCR decreases calcium-dependent NFAT activation. Experimental disruption of NFAT signaling during CNS development and postnatal plasticity may shed light on the nature of the intellectual impairment that characterizes DS, and the identification of NFAT transcriptional targets may provide new insight into experience-dependent gene programs in neuronal development.

Activity-Dependent Regulation of MeCP2 and Rett Syndrome

Although studies of activity-dependent transcriptional regulation have focused on transcription factors, such as CREB and MEF2, that bind specific sequences within target promoters, available evidence suggests that stimulus-dependent gene expression relies on the coordinated control of a range of transcriptional effectors that form regulated complexes at the promoters of target genes. It is now becoming clear that many nuclear proteins once thought to bind statically to DNA in neurons are actually dynamically regulated by extracellular stimuli and contribute to the activity-dependent programs of gene expression relevant to synaptic development and plasticity.

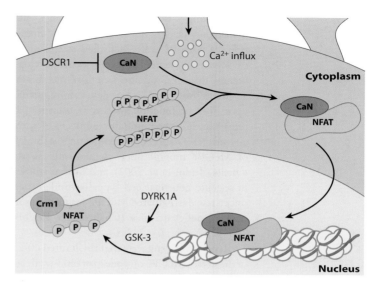

Figure 5

Model of calcium-dependent nuclear factor of activated T cells (NFAT) activation. In the unstimulated cell, NFAT transcription factors are maintained in the cytoplasm by kinases that phosphorylate a number of NFAT phosphorylation sites. Calcineurin (CaN) docking and the subsequent dephosphorylation of NFAT induce a conformational change in the transcription factor that exposes its nuclear localization signal (NLS) and leads to NFAT transport into the nucleus. Within the nucleus, NFAT is subject to regulation by kinases that promote the export of NFAT back into the cytoplasm, thereby resulting in the shutoff of NFAT target genes. The exportin protein Crm1 shuttles NFAT back into the cytoplasm and interacts with the same region of NFAT as does calcineurin, competing with calcineurin for binding to NFAT. Nuclear NFAT kinases that phosphorylate NFAT, such as glycogen synthase kinase-3 (GSK-3), may trigger the release of calcineurin from NFAT to promote NFAT export from the nucleus. When overexpressed in Down syndrome as the result of duplication of the Down syndrome critical region (DSCR), both DSCR1 and DYRK1A [dual-specificity tyrosine (Y) phosphorylation–regulated kinase 1A] are predicted to prevent NFAT activation in response to calcium. Increased DSCR1 activity may block calcineurin-dependent NFAT dephosphorylation and translocation to the nucleus, whereas overexpression of DYRK1A may promote premature GSK3-dependent export of NFAT from the nucleus, inhibiting NFAT transcriptional activity.

One such protein is the methyl-CpG-binding protein 2 (MeCP2), a transcriptional regulator initially identified on the basis of its ability to bind singly methylated CpGs in the genome (Meehan et al. 1992). MeCP2 is thought to play a role in the structural conformation of stably repressed chromatin. Once bound to methylated DNA, MeCP2 recruits a complex of chromatin-remodeling enzymes that help to condense and silence the DNA surrounding the MeCP2 binding site (Chahrour & Zoghbi 2007). When mutations in MeCP2 were identified as the cause of Rett syndrome, a severe neurodevelopmental disorder, significant effort was aimed at identifying the target genes upregulated upon loss of function of this transcriptional repressor. However, initial attempts to identify altered gene expression profiles in the brains of MeCP2 mutant mice yielded only subtle defects (Tudor et al. 2002), and further studies in specific neuronal cell types have identified only a few dysregulated MeCP2 target genes in MeCP2-deficient mice (Chahrour & Zoghbi 2007).

Recent work suggests that the limited effect of the loss of MeCP2 on gene expression reflects additional, unknown functions for MeCP2. A clue regarding these uncharacterized functions of MeCP2 came from experiments demonstrating that synaptic activity, both in cultured neurons and in the brain, induces the phosphorylation of MeCP2 at serine-421 (Chen et al. 2003a, Zhou et al. 2006). Phosphorylation of MeCP2 serine-421 occurs with a time course that suggests that this phosphorylation event may play a role in activity-dependent transcription, and MeCP2 binds to the promoter of *Bdnf*, an activity-regulated gene important for neuronal development and plasticity (Chen et al. 2003a, Martinowich et al. 2003). MeCP2 serine-421 phosphorylation appears to be required for activity-dependent *Bdnf* transcription: Mutation of MeCP2 serine-421 to alanine blocks serine-421 phosphorylation and disrupts *Bdnf* induction in response to membrane depolarization (Zhou et al. 2006). Importantly, phosphorylation of MeCP2 serine-421 is enriched in the brain relative to other tissues and regulates dendritic branching and spine development, providing insight into how mutations in MeCP2 that prevent its role in activity-dependent gene regulation may contribute to neuronal dysfunction and therefore may be relevant to Rett syndrome.

Rett syndrome is an autism spectrum disorder characterized by relatively normal development during the first year of life, followed by a period of regression accompanied by the loss of acquired skills and cognitive impairment (Chahrour & Zoghbi 2007). Although CNS development in Rett syndrome is grossly normal, small neuronal soma size (Chen et al. 2001, Guy et al. 2001), simplified cortical dendritic morphology (Kishi & Macklis 2004), and deficits in glutamatergic function (Chao et al. 2007, Dani et al. 2005, Nelson et al. 2006) occur.

These findings and other lines of evidence suggest that Rett syndrome may be a disorder of experience-dependent synaptic maturation and plasticity. MeCP2 levels increase in the CNS throughout neuronal development (Kishi & Macklis 2004), and mutation of MeCP2 results in a predominantly neurological phenotype despite the fact that MeCP2 is expressed in most tissues. Rett syndrome–like symptoms manifest during postnatal development in both humans and mice (Chahrour & Zoghbi 2007), and the phenotypes and synaptic deficits in MeCP2-null mice can be rescued by the reintroduction of MeCP2 in animals that have already begun to display severe neurological symptoms (Guy et al. 2007). These data suggest that MeCP2 has a critical role in regulating mature neuronal function rather than in survival or early development. Insight into the activity-dependent transcriptional functions of MeCP2 may reveal mechanisms by which disruptions in experience-dependent neuronal adaptation contribute to the pathogenesis of Rett syndrome and other cognitive disorders.

COMMUNICATION FROM THE NUCLEUS TO THE SYNAPSE

Although stimulus-dependent transcription factors are now known to control specific cellular responses to synaptic activity, the genetic programs that they regulate in response to sensory experience are still poorly defined. Some progress has been made in the identification of the direct transcriptional targets of CREB in neuronal cell lines (Impey et al. 2004). However, genome-wide characterization of the transcriptional targets that are induced by activity-regulated transcription factors in addition to

CREB (e.g., MEF2, NFAT, MeCP2, CREST, and others) will be necessary to understand how these transcriptional regulators coordinate context-dependent neuronal function. To date much effort has been made toward elucidating the mechanisms by which individual CREB target genes, such as c-*fos* and *Bdnf*, and an MEF2 target gene, *Arc* (*activity-regulated cytoskeletal-associated protein*), are regulated in a coordinated manner downstream of particular stimuli. Studies of the functions of these target genes suggest that the induction of activity-dependent programs of gene expression in response to synaptic activity allows the nucleus to communicate instructions for functional change back to the synapse (**Figure 1**).

Coordinated Activity-Dependent Regulation of *Bdnf*

One of the best-studied activity-regulated genes encodes BDNF, a neurotrophin that plays a key role in nervous system development and plasticity. The *Bdnf* gene is composed of at least nine distinct exons, many with unique promoters that drive the synthesis of mRNA transcripts containing distinct 5′ untranslated regions (UTRs), a common coding exon, and either of two distinct 3′ UTRs that differ in length because of the presence of two distinct sites of polyadenylation (Aid et al. 2007). This complex locus gives rise to the production of at least 18 distinct *Bdnf* transcripts that all encode an identical protein (Aid et al. 2007, Timmusk et al. 1993). Synaptic activity and calcium influx into the postsynaptic neuron lead to the induction of *Bdnf* transcription (Ghosh et al. 1994, Tao et al. 1998, Timmusk et al. 1993, Zafra et al. 1990), and which *Bdnf* transcripts are produced depends on the nature of the stimulus and the signaling pathways that are activated.

Investigation of the mechanisms by which activity induces promoter-specific transcription of the *Bdnf* gene has led to the identification of distinct signaling mechanisms that regulate the different *Bdnf* promoters. The regulation of two of the *Bdnf* promoters, I and IV, both of which are transcribed in a calcium-dependent

manner, has been relatively well-characterized. Deletion analysis identified two CaREs in *Bdnf* promoter I and three CaREs in *Bdnf* promoter IV that contribute to the activity dependence of these promoters. CREB and upstream stimulatory factors (USFs) mediate the activity-dependent regulation of both *Bdnf* promoters I and IV (Chen et al. 2003b, Shieh et al. 1998, Tabuchi et al. 2002, Tao et al. 1998). Regulation of promoter IV is also dependent on additional transcription factors that are involved in the activity-dependent transcriptional response, including a novel transcription factor, calcium response factor (CaRF) (Tao et al. 2002), and MeCP2 (Chen et al. 2003a, Zhou et al. 2006). Consistent with the idea that transcriptional activation requires the coordinate regulation of transcription factors and chromatin structure at the promoters of activity-dependent genes, changes in synaptic activity and experience affect not only the activity of transcription factors but also the modification of the histones at the activity-dependent promoters of *Bdnf* (Chen et al. 2003a, Martinowich et al. 2003). Perturbations in the level of BDNF expression have been associated with human psychiatric disorders, and recent reports of altered patterns of *Bdnf* chromatin modifications in mouse models of depression and stress suggest that dysregulation of *Bdnf* transcription plays a role in these disorders of neuronal adaptation (Tsankova et al. 2007).

Although the transcriptional regulation of *Bdnf* in response to experience has been partially characterized, how the different *Bdnf* transcripts relate to the different functions of the BDNF protein remains poorly understood. The production of distinct *Bdnf* transcripts suggests that transcriptional initiation from a particular promoter, or inclusion of a particular UTR in the transcript produced, may determine the localization or translational fate of a *Bdnf* transcript and, as a consequence, the function of the BDNF protein produced from that mRNA transcript. Alternatively, specific stimuli or signaling cascades may drive transcription from particular promoters, regulating the stimulus dependence and amount of BDNF

BDNF: brain derived neurotrophic factor

produced. At the present time, our understanding of the consequences of this type of regulation is rudimentary. Additional work is required to reveal how regulated transcripts initiated at different promoters contribute to the specificity of BDNF function.

Bdnf in Synapse Development and Plasticity

Bdnf mRNA transcripts initiated at any of the BDNF promoters are translated into an identical BDNF precursor, proBDNF, that is packaged into vesicles of the constitutive and regulated secretory pathways. Proteolytic cleavage of proBDNF and the secretion of mature BDNF occur in an activity-dependent manner in response to calcium influx (Hartmann et al. 2001). Once released, BDNF binds the tyrosine kinase receptor B (trkB), a neurotrophin receptor located both pre- and postsynaptically. Because of the regulated processing and secretion of BDNF, its functional roles have been difficult to ascertain in vitro, but experiments using bath application of BDNF have implicated BDNF in the regulation of dendritic arborization; the growth of dendritic spines; and the potentiation of activated synapses, as in LTP (Horch et al. 1999, McAllister et al. 1995, Patterson et al. 1996).

In vivo, BDNF is involved in the experience-dependent maturation and maintenance of cortical circuits. Forebrain-specific deletion of BDNF using a conditional knockout mouse revealed that the initial dendritic formation and branching of cortical neurons occur normally through the first few weeks of postnatal development (Gorski et al. 2003). However, BDNF-deficient cortical neurons exhibit reductions in dendritic complexity and soma size by five weeks of age. In addition, mice heterozygous for deletion of the BDNF gene were unable to appropriately modify the number and morphology of dendritic spines in the somatosensory barrel cortex in response to whisker stimulation (Genoud et al. 2004). Another mouse model, with an accelerated increase in postnatal BDNF levels, undergoes premature closure of the critical period for ocular dominance plasticity in the visual cortex (Huang et al. 1999). These in vivo consequences of the disruption of BDNF expression likely result from defective experience-dependent modulation of neuronal circuits, supporting the conclusion that BDNF plays a role in this aspect of activity-dependent synaptic development and plasticity.

In humans, a common single-nucleotide polymorphism (SNP) in the *Bdnf* gene results in the substitution of methionine for valine at codon 66 (Val66Met) in the BDNF prodomain. The presence of this SNP correlates with poor performance on memory tasks and may contribute to the pathogenesis of depression and anxiety disorders (Bath & Lee 2006, Egan et al. 2003). Mice harboring the Val66Met mutation show normal constitutive secretion of BDNF, but activity-regulated secretion of BDNF is perturbed (Chen et al. 2006, Egan et al. 2003). This defect in the regulated secretion of BDNF may reflect a role for the prodomain of BDNF in interactions with sortilin, a protein that is involved in sorting BDNF into the regulated secretory pathway (Chen et al. 2005). Val66Met mice show dendritic arborization defects in the hippocampus and reduced hippocampal volume similar to those seen in mice heterozygous for BDNF. These anatomical defects in mice are consistent with the reduced hippocampal volume observed in human subjects with the Val66Met SNP (Bath & Lee 2006, Chen et al. 2006). Importantly, the Val66Met mice display defects in learning and memory tasks as well as anxiety-related behaviors, suggesting that abnormalities in activity-dependent secretion of BDNF may underlie some aspects of the human disorders associated with the Val66Met SNP.

Targeting of Activity-Dependent Gene Products to the Synapse

The changes in synaptic weight that underlie neuronal adaptation are input specific and are typically limited spatially to the vicinity of the activated synapse (Harvey & Svoboda 2007). However, early experiments demonstrated that the regulation of transcription (and the subsequent synthesis of activity-induced gene products) is required for long-term changes in synaptic function. Late-LTP induction is prevented when hippocampal dendrites are severed from the neuronal cell body, suggesting a requirement for new gene expression (Frey et al. 1989). Late-LTP also requires protein synthesis: An initial, strong, late-LTP-inducing stimulus at one set of inputs allows the subsequent weak stimulation of a separate synapse—one that, if given on its own, would normally not induce late-LTP—to induce late-LTP at the second synapse (Frey & Morris 1997). This reduction of the LTP threshold for the weak second stimulation requires protein synthesis within a 2–3-h time window surrounding the first stimulation, implying that activity-dependent transcription and protein synthesis in the cell body initiated by the first synaptic stimulus may function in the potentiation of the second synapse.

Elucidating the mechanism by which the correct synapses are modulated in response to nuclear gene expression has been the subject of major effort. One clue comes from a transgenic mouse model expressing a constitutively active form of CREB (VP16-CREB) in the hippocampus under the control of an inducible promoter (Barco et al. 2002). In this mouse model, transcription of VP16-CREB target genes was sufficient to reduce the stimulus threshold required for the induction of late-LTP, much in the same way that an earlier LTP-inducing stimulus elsewhere on a neuron reduces the LTP threshold. Analysis of gene expression in the hippocampus of this VP16 transgenic mouse demonstrated that several genes, including *Bdnf*, are upregulated with VP16-CREB induction (Barco et al. 2005). Further analysis of late-LTP in the VP16-CREB mouse as well as in the *Bdnf* heterozygous mice confirmed a role for BDNF in promoting LTP through both pre- and postsynaptic actions (Barco et al. 2005). Thus, synaptic activity induces the transcription of genes, such as *Bdnf*, whose mRNA or protein products are produced and trafficked to synapses throughout the cell, where they are able to modulate neuronal function in response to subsequent stimuli. Once secreted from the dendrite, BDNF is believed to act both pre- and postsynaptically, facilitating presynaptic neurotransmitter release and increasing the local translation of proteins required within the postsynaptic dendrite (Kang & Schuman 1995, 1996).

Arc in Activity-Dependent Synaptic Plasticity

Some of the best evidence for the role of activity-dependent genes in synaptic function comes from the study of *Arc*, an activity-dependent MEF2 target gene (Flavell et al. 2006) that encodes a cytoskeleton-interacting protein found in the PSD of glutamatergic neurons. A variety of different external stimuli, including visual stimulation, induce *Arc* transcription in the brain (Steward & Worley 2001b, Tagawa et al. 2005, Wang et al. 2006). During development, *Arc* expression is first detected postnatally at day 12 and increases to a maximal and stable level at postnatal day 21 (Lyford et al. 1995), consistent with a role in experience-dependent synaptic plasticity. Animals lacking *Arc* show no gross abnormalities in neuronal development but show impaired late-LTP, impaired long-term memory in behavioral tasks, and a disruption of experience-dependent development of orientation selectivity in the visual cortex (Plath et al. 2006, Wang et al. 2006). Recent experiments have implicated Arc in the postsynaptic endocytosis of the AMPA receptor through interactions with the endocytic machinery (Chowdhury et al. 2006, Rial Verde et al. 2006, Shepherd et al. 2006), suggesting a direct function for Arc in the modulation of synaptic strength.

Arc transcripts are produced in the nucleus and trafficked specifically to active synapses, where the *Arc* mRNA is translated (Steward et al. 1998). NMDA receptor activation can induce the transcription of *Arc* within 2 min of synaptic stimulation, the processed *Arc* mRNA is exported to the cell body within 15 min, and the synaptically localized *Arc* mRNA is translated within 30 min (Guzowski et al. 1999).

Studies using electroconvulsive shock (ECS), a nonphysiological inducer of massive glutamate release at synapses, confirmed that newly synthesized *Arc* mRNA is transported throughout the dendritic tree of activated neurons. Subsequent synaptic activation of a specific set of inputs initiates the redistribution of *Arc* message specifically to the stimulated inputs, suggesting that active synapses can recruit activity-dependent effector proteins (Steward & Worley 2001a,b).

This regulation of activity-dependent gene products suggests a model for communication from the nucleus to the synapse. Synaptic activity induces the transcription of genes such as *Arc* or *Bdnf* in the nucleus, and the mRNA transcripts and/or proteins that are produced are trafficked into the dendritic arbor of the neuron. The presence of these activity-dependent gene products allows the synapse to respond differently to subsequent stimulation events by modifying synaptic function. For instance, Arc protein produced within the dendritic tree may interact with other activity-dependent gene products and local signaling molecules to mediate AMPA receptor expression at the synapse. Through this type of mechanism, activity-dependent gene expression in the nucleus can influence adaptive changes at the appropriate synapses. The full complement of synaptic effectors that, like *Arc* and *Bdnf*, may contribute to processes of neuronal development and plasticity remains to be defined and is the subject of ongoing research.

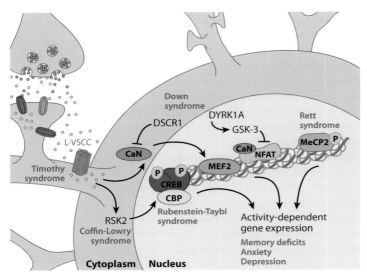

Figure 6

Human diseases of cognitive function disrupt communication between the synapse and the nucleus. The signaling mechanisms that operate within neurons to relay the effect of synaptic stimulation to the nucleus, and the gene products produced as a result, allow communication between the synapse and the nucleus. Mutations in components of these activity-dependent signaling networks have been identified and shown to disrupt experience-dependent neuronal development and plasticity. These include mutations in the L-VSCC in Timothy syndrome, RSK2 in Coffin-Lowry syndrome, CBP in Rubenstein-Taybi syndrome, and MeCP2 in Rett syndrome. Duplications in DSCR1 and DYRK1A may contribute to the etiology of Down syndrome. Disruptions of the activity-dependent genes and their products may contribute to disorders of adaptive behavior, including depression, anxiety, and addiction. These and other mutations suggest that further insight into the programs of activity-dependent gene expression and their regulation may aid in our understanding of CNS development and function as well as of human disorders of cognitive function. Abbreviations used: CaN, calcineurin; CREB, cAMP response element binding protein; CBP, CREB-binding protein; DSCR1, Down syndrome critical region 1; DYRK1A, dual-specificity tyrosine (Y) phosphorylation–regulated kinase 1A; GSK-3, glycogen synthase kinase-3; L-VSCC, L-type voltage-sensitive calcium channel; NFAT, nuclear factor of activated T cells; MeCP2, methyl-CpG-binding protein 2; MEF2, myocyte enhancer factor 2; RSK2, ribosomal S6 kinase 2.

CONCLUSION

The ability to adapt to and learn from the environment requires long-term changes in brain function in response to input from the environment. Sensory experience drives activity within neuronal circuits, and as the individual neurons within these circuits receive and respond to extracellular cues, cellular changes that modulate the strength of synaptic connections drive changes in circuit function. Synaptic activity is required for many aspects of postnatal neuronal development, including dendritic patterning, synapse formation, and synapse elimination, and plays a major role in synaptic plasticity in the adult. The signaling mechanisms that operate within neurons to relay the effect of synaptic stimulation to the nucleus, and the gene products produced as a result, allow the synapse and the nucleus to communicate with one another. Integration of these pathways at the synapse, within the cytoplasm, and in the nucleus allows the neuron to coordinate adaptive responses to a wide range of extracellular cues. Mutations that affect components of the activity-regulated signaling network have been identified and shown to result in deregulation of communication between the synapse and the nucleus and therefore to contribute to the disruption of experience-dependent development and plasticity in human disorders of cognitive function (**Figure 6**).

As we learn more about the individual molecules involved in the bidirectional signaling between the synapse and the nucleus, many unanswered questions arise. Particular patterns of sensory experience induce synaptic activity in only a subset of neurons within a circuit—each individual neuron must then interpret hundreds of synaptic inputs to generate an appropriate response. How is this specificity of signaling accomplished? Future studies of the regulation and function of activity-dependent gene expression will be required to reveal more fully the mechanisms by which synaptic activity generates structural and functional changes in neural circuits, the importance of experience in shaping brain function, and how disruption in these processes gives rise to human cognitive disorders.

DISCLOSURE STATEMENT

The authors are not aware of any biases that might be perceived as affecting the objectivity of this review.

ACKNOWLEDGMENTS

We thank current and past members of the Greenberg lab for critical reading of the manuscript and J. Zieg for assistance with figures. We apologize to our colleagues whose work is not discussed or cited here because of length restrictions. Work on this subject in our laboratory is supported by the F.M. Kirby Foundation, the Nancy Lurie Marks Family Foundation, Autism Speaks, Cure Autism Now, and Mental Retardation Developmental Disabilities Research Center grant HD18655 and NIH grant NS048276.

LITERATURE CITED

Aid T, Kazantseva A, Piirsoo M, Palm K, Timmusk T. 2007. Mouse and rat BDNF gene structure and expression revisited. *J. Neurosci. Res.* 85:525–35

Aizawa H, Hu SC, Bobb K, Balakrishnan K, Ince G, et al. 2004. Dendrite development regulated by CREST, a calcium-regulated transcriptional activator. *Science* 303:197–202

Alvarez VA, Sabatini BL. 2007. Anatomical and physiological plasticity of dendritic spines. *Annu. Rev. Neurosci.* 30:79–97

Arron JR, Winslow MM, Polleri A, Chang CP, Wu H, et al. 2006. NFAT dysregulation by increased dosage of DSCR1 and DYRK1A on chromosome 21. *Nature* 441:595–600

Bading H, Ginty DD, Greenberg ME. 1993. Regulation of gene expression in hippocampal neurons by distinct calcium signaling pathways. *Science* 260:181–86

Bannister AJ, Kouzarides T. 1996. The CBP coactivator is a histone acetyltransferase. *Nature* 384:641–43

Barco A, Alarcon JM, Kandel ER. 2002. Expression of constitutively active CREB protein facilitates the late phase of long-term potentiation by enhancing synaptic capture. *Cell* 108:689–703

Barco A, Patterson S, Alarcon JM, Gromova P, Mata-Roig M, et al. 2005. Gene expression profiling of facilitated L-LTP in VP16-CREB mice reveals that BDNF is critical for the maintenance of LTP and its synaptic capture. *Neuron* 48:123–37

Barrett CF, Tsien RW. 2008. The Timothy syndrome mutation differentially affects voltage- and calcium-dependent inactivation of CaV1.2 liters-type calcium channels. *Proc. Natl. Acad. Sci. USA* 105:2157–62

Bath KG, Lee FS. 2006. Variant BDNF (Val66Met) impact on brain structure and function. *Cogn. Affect. Behav. Neurosci.* 6:79–85

Benedito AB, Lehtinen M, Massol R, Lopes UG, Kirchhausen T, et al. 2005. The transcription factor NFAT3 mediates neuronal survival. *J. Biol. Chem.* 280:2818–25

Bito H, Deisseroth K, Tsien RW. 1996. CREB phosphorylation and dephosphorylation: a Ca^{2+}- and stimulus duration-dependent switch for hippocampal gene expression. *Cell* 87:1203–14

Bonni A, Ginty DD, Dudek H, Greenberg ME. 1995. Serine 133-phosphorylated CREB induces transcription via a cooperative mechanism that may confer specificity to neurotrophin signals. *Mol. Cell Neurosci.* 6:168–83

Bourne JN, Harris KM. 2008. Balancing structure and function at hippocampal dendritic spines. *Annu. Rev. Neurosci.* 31:47–67

Bradley J, Carter SR, Rao VR, Wang J, Finkbeiner S. 2006. Splice variants of the NR1 subunit differentially induce NMDA receptor-dependent gene expression. *J. Neurosci.* 26:1065–76

Brown JR, Ye H, Bronson RT, Dikkes P, Greenberg ME. 1996. A defect in nurturing in mice lacking the immediate early gene *fosB*. *Cell* 86:297–309

Carmignoto G, Vicini S. 1992. Activity-dependent decrease in NMDA receptor responses during development of the visual cortex. *Science* 258:1007–11

Chahrour M, Zoghbi HY. 2007. The story of Rett syndrome: from clinic to neurobiology. *Neuron* 56:422–37

Chao HT, Zoghbi HY, Rosenmund C. 2007. MeCP2 controls excitatory synaptic strength by regulating glutamatergic synapse number. *Neuron* 56:58–65

Chen RZ, Akbarian S, Tudor M, Jaenisch R. 2001. Deficiency of methyl-CpG binding protein-2 in CNS neurons results in a Rett-like phenotype in mice. *Nat. Genet.* 27:327–31

Chen WG, Chang Q, Lin Y, Meissner A, West AE, et al. 2003a. Derepression of BDNF transcription involves calcium-dependent phosphorylation of MeCP2. *Science* 302:885–89

Chen WG, West AE, Tao X, Corfas G, Szentirmay MN, et al. 2003b. Upstream stimulatory factors are mediators of Ca^{2+}-responsive transcription in neurons. *J. Neurosci.* 23:2572–81

Chen ZY, Ieraci A, Teng H, Dall H, Meng CX, et al. 2005. Sortilin controls intracellular sorting of brain-derived neurotrophic factor to the regulated secretory pathway. *J. Neurosci.* 25:6156–66

Chen ZY, Jing D, Bath KG, Ieraci A, Khan T, et al. 2006. Genetic variant BDNF (Val66Met) polymorphism alters anxiety-related behavior. *Science* 314:140–43

Chowdhury S, Shepherd JD, Okuno H, Lyford G, Petralia RS, et al. 2006. Arc/Arg3.1 interacts with the endocytic machinery to regulate AMPA receptor trafficking. *Neuron* 52:445–59

Chrivia JC, Kwok RP, Lamb N, Hagiwara M, Montminy MR, Goodman RH. 1993. Phosphorylated CREB binds specifically to the nuclear protein CBP. *Nature* 365:855–59

Conkright MD, Canettieri G, Screaton R, Guzman E, Miraglia L, et al. 2003. TORCs: transducers of regulated CREB activity. *Mol. Cell* 12:413–23

Dalva MB, Takasu MA, Lin MZ, Shamah SM, Hu L, et al. 2000. EphB receptors interact with NMDA receptors and regulate excitatory synapse formation. *Cell* 103:945–56

Dani VS, Chang Q, Maffei A, Turrigiano GG, Jaenisch R, Nelson SB. 2005. Reduced cortical activity due to a shift in the balance between excitation and inhibition in a mouse model of Rett syndrome. *Proc. Natl. Acad. Sci. USA* 102:12560–65

Dash PK, Karl KA, Colicos MA, Prywes R, Kandel ER. 1991. cAMP response element-binding protein is activated by Ca^{2+}/calmodulin- as well as cAMP-dependent protein kinase. *Proc. Natl. Acad. Sci. USA* 88:5061–65

Davare MA, Avdonin V, Hall DD, Peden EM, Burette A, et al. 2001. A β_2 adrenergic receptor signaling complex assembled with the Ca^{2+} channel $Ca_v1.2$. *Science* 293:98–101

Deisseroth K, Bito H, Tsien RW. 1996. Signaling from synapse to nucleus: postsynaptic CREB phosphorylation during multiple forms of hippocampal synaptic plasticity. *Neuron* 16:89–101

Derkach VA, Oh MC, Guire ES, Soderling TR. 2007. Regulatory mechanisms of AMPA receptors in synaptic plasticity. *Nat. Rev. Neurosci.* 8:101–13

Dillon C, Goda Y. 2005. The actin cytoskeleton: integrating form and function at the synapse. *Annu. Rev. Neurosci.* 28:25–55

Dolmetsch RE, Pajvani U, Fife K, Spotts JM, Greenberg ME. 2001. Signaling to the nucleus by an L-type calcium channel-calmodulin complex through the MAP kinase pathway. *Science* 294:333–39

Egan MF, Kojima M, Callicott JH, Goldberg TE, Kolachana BS, et al. 2003. The BDNF val66met polymorphism affects activity-dependent secretion of BDNF and human memory and hippocampal function. *Cell* 112:257–69

Erxleben C, Liao Y, Gentile S, Chin D, Gomez-Alegria C, et al. 2006. Cyclosporin and Timothy syndrome increase mode 2 gating of Ca$_V$1.2 calcium channels through aberrant phosphorylation of S6 helices. *Proc. Natl. Acad. Sci. USA* 103:3932–37

Flavell SW, Cowan CW, Kim TK, Greer PL, Lin Y, et al. 2006. Activity-dependent regulation of MEF2 transcription factors suppresses excitatory synapse number. *Science* 311:1008–12

Fleischmann A, Hvalby O, Jensen V, Strekalova T, Zacher C, et al. 2003. Impaired long-term memory and NR2A-type NMDA receptor-dependent synaptic plasticity in mice lacking c-Fos in the CNS. *J. Neurosci.* 23:9116–22

Frey U, Krug M, Brodemann R, Reymann K, Matthies H. 1989. Long-term potentiation induced in dendrites separated from rat's CA1 pyramidal somata does not establish a late phase. *Neurosci. Lett.* 97:135–39

Frey U, Morris RG. 1997. Synaptic tagging and long-term potentiation. *Nature* 385:533–36

Gau D, Lemberger T, von Gall C, Kretz O, Le Minh N, et al. 2002. Phosphorylation of CREB Ser142 regulates light-induced phase shifts of the circadian clock. *Neuron* 34:245–53

Genoud C, Knott GW, Sakata K, Lu B, Welker E. 2004. Altered synapse formation in the adult somatosensory cortex of brain-derived neurotrophic factor heterozygote mice. *J. Neurosci.* 24:2394–400

Ghosh A, Carnahan J, Greenberg ME. 1994. Requirement for BDNF in activity-dependent survival of cortical neurons. *Science* 263:1618–23

Ginty DD, Bonni A, Greenberg ME. 1994. Nerve growth factor activates a Ras-dependent protein kinase that stimulates c-*fos* transcription via phosphorylation of CREB. *Cell* 77:713–25

Ginty DD, Kornhauser JM, Thompson MA, Bading H, Mayo KE, et al. 1993. Regulation of CREB phosphorylation in the suprachiasmatic nucleus by light and a circadian clock. *Science* 260:238–41

Gonzalez GA, Montminy MR. 1989. Cyclic AMP stimulates somatostatin gene transcription by phosphorylation of CREB at serine 133. *Cell* 59:675–80

Gorski JA, Zeiler SR, Tamowski S, Jones KR. 2003. Brain-derived neurotrophic factor is required for the maintenance of cortical dendrites. *J. Neurosci.* 23:6856–65

Graef IA, Mermelstein PG, Stankunas K, Neilson JR, Deisseroth K, et al. 1999. L-type calcium channels and GSK-3 regulate the activity of NF-ATc4 in hippocampal neurons. *Nature* 401:703–8

Graef IA, Wang F, Charron F, Chen L, Neilson J, et al. 2003. Neurotrophins and netrins require calcineurin/NFAT signaling to stimulate outgrowth of embryonic axons. *Cell* 113:657–70

Groc L, Heine M, Cognet L, Brickley K, Stephenson FA, et al. 2004. Differential activity-dependent regulation of the lateral mobilities of AMPA and NMDA receptors. *Nat. Neurosci.* 7:695–96

Groc L, Heine M, Cousins SL, Stephenson FA, Lounis B, et al. 2006. NMDA receptor surface mobility depends on NR2A-2B subunits. *Proc. Natl. Acad. Sci. USA* 103:18769–74

Grunwald IC, Korte M, Wolfer D, Wilkinson GA, Unsicker K, et al. 2001. Kinase-independent requirement of EphB2 receptors in hippocampal synaptic plasticity. *Neuron* 32:1027–40

Grutzendler J, Kasthuri N, Gan WB. 2002. Long-term dendritic spine stability in the adult cortex. *Nature* 420:812–16

Guy J, Gan J, Selfridge J, Cobb S, Bird A. 2007. Reversal of neurological defects in a mouse model of Rett syndrome. *Science* 315:1143–47

Guy J, Hendrich B, Holmes M, Martin JE, Bird A. 2001. A mouse *Mecp2*-null mutation causes neurological symptoms that mimic Rett syndrome. *Nat. Genet.* 27:322–26

Guzowski JF, McNaughton BL, Barnes CA, Worley PF. 1999. Environment-specific expression of the immediate-early gene *Arc* in hippocampal neuronal ensembles. *Nat. Neurosci.* 2:1120–24

Gwack Y, Sharma S, Nardone J, Tanasa B, Iuga A, et al. 2006. A genome-wide *Drosophila* RNAi screen identifies DYRK-family kinases as regulators of NFAT. *Nature* 441:646–50

Hall BJ, Ripley B, Ghosh A. 2007. NR2B signaling regulates the development of synaptic AMPA receptor current. *J. Neurosci.* 27:13446–56

Hardingham GE, Arnold FJ, Bading H. 2001. A calcium microdomain near NMDA receptors: on switch for ERK-dependent synapse-to-nucleus communication. *Nat. Neurosci.* 4:565–66

Hardingham GE, Fukunaga Y, Bading H. 2002. Extrasynaptic NMDARs oppose synaptic NMDARs by triggering CREB shut-off and cell death pathways. *Nat. Neurosci.* 5:405–14

Hartmann M, Heumann R, Lessmann V. 2001. Synaptic secretion of BDNF after high-frequency stimulation of glutamatergic synapses. *EMBO J.* 20:5887–97

Harvey CD, Svoboda K. 2007. Locally dynamic synaptic learning rules in pyramidal neuron dendrites. *Nature* 450:1195–200

Hemara-Wahanui A, Berjukow S, Hope CI, Dearden PK, Wu SB, et al. 2005. A *CACNA1F* mutation identified in an X-linked retinal disorder shifts the voltage dependence of $Ca_v1.4$ channel activation. *Proc. Natl. Acad. Sci. USA* 102:7553–58

Henderson JT, Georgiou J, Jia Z, Robertson J, Elowe S, et al. 2001. The receptor tyrosine kinase EphB2 regulates NMDA-dependent synaptic function. *Neuron* 32:1041–56

Hiroi N, Brown JR, Haile CN, Ye H, Greenberg ME, Nestler EJ. 1997. *Fos*B mutant mice: loss of chronic cocaine induction of Fos-related proteins and heightened sensitivity to cocaine's psychomotor and rewarding effects. *Proc. Natl. Acad. Sci. USA* 94:10397–402

Hope CI, Sharp DM, Hemara-Wahanui A, Sissingh JI, Lundon P, et al. 2005. Clinical manifestations of a unique X-linked retinal disorder in a large New Zealand family with a novel mutation in *CACNA1F*, the gene responsible for CSNB2. *Clin. Experiment Ophthalmol.* 33:129–36

Horch HW, Kruttgen A, Portbury SD, Katz LC. 1999. Destabilization of cortical dendrites and spines by BDNF. *Neuron* 23:353–64

Huang ZJ, Kirkwood A, Pizzorusso T, Porciatti V, Morales B, et al. 1999. BDNF regulates the maturation of inhibition and the critical period of plasticity in mouse visual cortex. *Cell* 98:739–55

Hunt SP, Pini A, Evan G. 1987. Induction of c-*fos*-like protein in spinal cord neurons following sensory stimulation. *Nature* 328:632–34

Impey S, Fong AL, Wang Y, Cardinaux JR, Fass DM, et al. 2002. Phosphorylation of CBP mediates transcriptional activation by neural activity and CaM kinase IV. *Neuron* 34:235–44

Impey S, McCorkle SR, Cha-Molstad H, Dwyer JM, Yochum GS, et al. 2004. Defining the CREB regulon: a genome-wide analysis of transcription factor regulatory regions. *Cell* 119:1041–54

Impey S, Obrietan K, Wong ST, Poser S, Yano S, et al. 1998. Cross talk between ERK and PKA is required for Ca^{2+} stimulation of CREB-dependent transcription and ERK nuclear translocation. *Neuron* 21:869–83

Iourgenko V, Zhang W, Mickanin C, Daly I, Jiang C, et al. 2003. Identification of a family of cAMP response element-binding protein coactivators by genome-scale functional analysis in mammalian cells. *Proc. Natl. Acad. Sci. USA* 100:12147–52

Kang H, Schuman EM. 1995. Long-lasting neurotrophin-induced enhancement of synaptic transmission in the adult hippocampus. *Science* 267:1658–62

Kang H, Schuman EM. 1996. A requirement for local protein synthesis in neurotrophin-induced hippocampal synaptic plasticity. *Science* 273:1402–6

Kang H, Sun LD, Atkins CM, Soderling TR, Wilson MA, Tonegawa S. 2001. An important role of neural activity-dependent CaMKIV signaling in the consolidation of long-term memory. *Cell* 106:771–83

Katz LC, Shatz CJ. 1996. Synaptic activity and the construction of cortical circuits. *Science* 274:1133–38

Kishi N, Macklis JD. 2004. MECP2 is progressively expressed in postmigratory neurons and is involved in neuronal maturation rather than cell fate decisions. *Mol. Cell Neurosci.* 27:306–21

Kornhauser JM, Cowan CW, Shaywitz AJ, Dolmetsch RE, Griffith EC, et al. 2002. CREB transcriptional activity in neurons is regulated by multiple, calcium-specific phosphorylation events. *Neuron* 34:221–33

Kumar SS, Bacci A, Kharazia V, Huguenard JR. 2002. A developmental switch of AMPA receptor subunits in neocortical pyramidal neurons. *J. Neurosci.* 22:3005–15

Kwok RP, Lundblad JR, Chrivia JC, Richards JP, Bachinger HP, et al. 1994. Nuclear protein CBP is a coactivator for the transcription factor CREB. *Nature* 370:223–36

Lau CG, Zukin RS. 2007. NMDA receptor trafficking in synaptic plasticity and neuropsychiatric disorders. *Nat. Rev. Neurosci.* 8:413–26

Liu SQ, Cull-Candy SG. 2000. Synaptic activity at calcium-permeable AMPA receptors induces a switch in receptor subtype. *Nature* 405:454–58

Lonze BE, Ginty DD. 2002. Function and regulation of CREB family transcription factors in the nervous system. *Neuron* 35:605–23

Lyford GL, Yamagata K, Kaufmann WE, Barnes CA, Sanders LK, et al. 1995. *Arc*, a growth factor and activity-regulated gene, encodes a novel cytoskeleton-associated protein that is enriched in neuronal dendrites. *Neuron* 14:433–45

Majdan M, Shatz CJ. 2006. Effects of visual experience on activity-dependent gene regulation in cortex. *Nat. Neurosci.* 9:650–59

Martinowich K, Hattori D, Wu H, Fouse S, He F, et al. 2003. DNA methylation-related chromatin remodeling in activity-dependent BDNF gene regulation. *Science* 302:890–93

Maurer D, Lewis TL, Brent HP, Levin AV. 1999. Rapid improvement in the acuity of infants after visual input. *Science* 286:108–10

McAllister AK. 2007. Dynamic aspects of CNS synapse formation. *Annu. Rev. Neurosci.* 30:425–50

McAllister AK, Lo DC, Katz LC. 1995. Neurotrophins regulate dendritic growth in developing visual cortex. *Neuron* 15:791–803

McKinsey TA, Zhang CL, Lu J, Olson EN. 2000. Signal-dependent nuclear export of a histone deacetylase regulates muscle differentiation. *Nature* 408:106–11

Meehan RR, Lewis JD, Bird AP. 1992. Characterization of MeCP2, a vertebrate DNA binding protein with affinity for methylated DNA. *Nucleic Acids Res.* 20:5085–92

Montminy MR, Bilezikjian LM. 1987. Binding of a nuclear protein to the cyclic-AMP response element of the somatostatin gene. *Nature* 328:175–78

Moosmang S, Haider N, Klugbauer N, Adelsberger H, Langwieser N, et al. 2005. Role of hippocampal $Ca_v1.2$ Ca^{2+} channels in NMDA receptor-independent synaptic plasticity and spatial memory. *J. Neurosci.* 25:9883–92

Murphy TH, Worley PF, Baraban JM. 1991. L-type voltage-sensitive calcium channels mediate synaptic activation of immediate early genes. *Neuron* 7:625–35

Nelson CA 3rd, Zeanah CH, Fox NA, Marshall PJ, Smyke AT, Guthrie D. 2007. Cognitive recovery in socially deprived young children: the Bucharest Early Intervention Project. *Science* 318:1937–40

Nelson ED, Kavalali ET, Monteggia LM. 2006. MeCP2-dependent transcriptional repression regulates excitatory neurotransmission. *Curr. Biol.* 16:710–16

Oliveria SF, Dell'Acqua ML, Sather WA. 2007. AKAP79/150 anchoring of calcineurin controls neuronal L-type Ca^{2+} channel activity and nuclear signaling. *Neuron* 55:261–75

Olson EN, Williams RS. 2000. Remodeling muscles with calcineurin. *Bioessays* 22:510–19

Parker D, Jhala US, Radhakrishnan I, Yaffe MB, Reyes C, et al. 1998. Analysis of an activator:coactivator complex reveals an essential role for secondary structure in transcriptional activation. *Mol. Cell* 2:353–59

Parrish JZ, Emoto K, Kim MD, Jan YN. 2007. Mechanisms that regulate establishment, maintenance, and remodeling of dendritic fields. *Annu. Rev. Neurosci.* 30:399–423

Pasquale EB. 2005. Eph receptor signalling casts a wide net on cell behaviour. *Nat. Rev. Mol. Cell Biol.* 6:462–75

Patterson SL, Abel T, Deuel TA, Martin KC, Rose JC, Kandel ER. 1996. Recombinant BDNF rescues deficits in basal synaptic transmission and hippocampal LTP in BDNF knockout mice. *Neuron* 16:1137–45

Perkinton MS, Sihra TS, Williams RJ. 1999. Ca^{2+}-permeable AMPA receptors induce phosphorylation of cAMP response element-binding protein through a phosphatidylinositol 3-kinase-dependent stimulation of the mitogen-activated protein kinase signaling cascade in neurons. *J. Neurosci.* 19:5861–74

Peterson BZ, DeMaria CD, Adelman JP, Yue DT. 1999. Calmodulin is the Ca^{2+} sensor for Ca^{2+}-dependent inactivation of L-type calcium channels. *Neuron* 22:549–58

Petralia RS, Esteban JA, Wang YX, Partridge JG, Zhao HM, et al. 1999. Selective acquisition of AMPA receptors over postnatal development suggests a molecular basis for silent synapses. *Nat. Neurosci.* 2:31–36

Petrij F, Giles RH, Dauwerse HG, Saris JJ, Hennekam RC, et al. 1995. Rubinstein-Taybi syndrome caused by mutations in the transcriptional coactivator CBP. *Nature* 376:348–51

Plant K, Pelkey KA, Bortolotto ZA, Morita D, Terashima A, et al. 2006. Transient incorporation of native GluR2-lacking AMPA receptors during hippocampal long-term potentiation. *Nat. Neurosci.* 9:602–4

Plath N, Ohana O, Dammermann B, Errington ML, Schmitz D, et al. 2006. Arc/Arg3.1 is essential for the consolidation of synaptic plasticity and memories. *Neuron* 52:437–44

Rao VR, Pintchovski SA, Chin J, Peebles CL, Mitra S, Finkbeiner S. 2006. AMPA receptors regulate transcription of the plasticity-related immediate-early gene *Arc*. *Nat. Neurosci.* 9:887–95

Redmond L, Kashani AH, Ghosh A. 2002. Calcium regulation of dendritic growth via CaM kinase IV and CREB-mediated transcription. *Neuron* 34:999–1010

Renthal W, Maze I, Krishnan V, Covington HE 3rd, Xiao G, et al. 2007. Histone deacetylase 5 epigenetically controls behavioral adaptations to chronic emotional stimuli. *Neuron* 56:517–29

Rial Verde EM, Lee-Osbourne J, Worley PF, Malinow R, Cline HT. 2006. Increased expression of the immediate-early gene *arc/arg3.1* reduces AMPA receptor-mediated synaptic transmission. *Neuron* 52:461–74

Riccio A, Alvania RS, Lonze BE, Ramanan N, Kim T, et al. 2006. A nitric oxide signaling pathway controls CREB-mediated gene expression in neurons. *Mol. Cell* 21:283–94

Roelfsema JH, White SJ, Ariyurek Y, Bartholdi D, Niedrist D, et al. 2005. Genetic heterogeneity in Rubinstein-Taybi syndrome: mutations in both the *CBP* and *EP300* genes cause disease. *Am. J. Hum. Genet.* 76:572–80

Rosen LB, Ginty DD, Weber MJ, Greenberg ME. 1994. Membrane depolarization and calcium influx stimulate MEK and MAP kinase via activation of Ras. *Neuron* 12:1207–21

Rothermel B, Vega RB, Yang J, Wu H, Bassel-Duby R, Williams RS. 2000. A protein encoded within the Down syndrome critical region is enriched in striated muscles and inhibits calcineurin signaling. *J. Biol. Chem.* 275:8719–25

Rusak B, Robertson HA, Wisden W, Hunt SP. 1990. Light pulses that shift rhythms induce gene expression in the suprachiasmatic nucleus. *Science* 248:1237–40

Sala C, Rudolph-Correia S, Sheng M. 2000. Developmentally regulated NMDA receptor-dependent dephosphorylation of cAMP response element-binding protein (CREB) in hippocampal neurons. *J. Neurosci.* 20:3529–36

Sassone-Corsi P, Mizzen CA, Cheung P, Crosio C, Monaco L, et al. 1999. Requirement of Rsk-2 for epidermal growth factor-activated phosphorylation of histone H3. *Science* 285:886–91

Shalizi A, Gaudilliere B, Yuan Z, Stegmuller J, Shirogane T, et al. 2006. A calcium-regulated MEF2 sumoylation switch controls postsynaptic differentiation. *Science* 311:1012–17

Sheng M, Greenberg ME. 1990. The regulation and function of c-*fos* and other immediate early genes in the nervous system. *Neuron* 4:477–85

Sheng M, Hoogenraad CC. 2007. The postsynaptic architecture of excitatory synapses: a more quantitative view. *Annu. Rev. Biochem.* 76:823–47

Sheng M, McFadden G, Greenberg ME. 1990. Membrane depolarization and calcium induce c-*fos* transcription via phosphorylation of transcription factor CREB. *Neuron* 4:571–82

Sheng M, Thompson MA, Greenberg ME. 1991. CREB: a Ca^{2+}-regulated transcription factor phosphorylated by calmodulin-dependent kinases. *Science* 252:1427–30

Shepherd JD, Rumbaugh G, Wu J, Chowdhury S, Plath N, et al. 2006. Arc/Arg3.1 mediates homeostatic synaptic scaling of AMPA receptors. *Neuron* 52:475–84

Shi SH, Hayashi Y, Petralia RS, Zaman SH, Wenthold RJ, et al. 1999. Rapid spine delivery and redistribution of AMPA receptors after synaptic NMDA receptor activation. *Science* 284:1811–16

Shieh PB, Hu SC, Bobb K, Timmusk T, Ghosh A. 1998. Identification of a signaling pathway involved in calcium regulation of BDNF expression. *Neuron* 20:727–40

Splawski I, Timothy KW, Decher N, Kumar P, Sachse FB, et al. 2005. Severe arrhythmia disorder caused by cardiac L-type calcium channel mutations. *Proc. Natl. Acad. Sci. USA* 102:8089–96

Splawski I, Timothy KW, Sharpe LM, Decher N, Kumar P, et al. 2004. $Ca_V 1.2$ calcium channel dysfunction causes a multisystem disorder including arrhythmia and autism. *Cell* 119:19–31

Splawski I, Yoo DS, Stotz SC, Cherry A, Clapham DE, Keating MT. 2006. *CACNA1H* mutations in autism spectrum disorders. *J. Biol. Chem.* 281:22085–91

Sprengel R, Suchanek B, Amico C, Brusa R, Burnashev N, et al. 1998. Importance of the intracellular domain of NR2 subunits for NMDA receptor function in vivo. *Cell* 92:279–89

Steward O, Wallace CS, Lyford GL, Worley PF. 1998. Synaptic activation causes the mRNA for the IEG Arc to localize selectively near activated postsynaptic sites on dendrites. *Neuron* 21:741–51

Steward O, Worley PF. 2001a. A cellular mechanism for targeting newly synthesized mRNAs to synaptic sites on dendrites. *Proc. Natl. Acad. Sci. USA* 98:7062–68

Steward O, Worley PF. 2001b. Selective targeting of newly synthesized Arc mRNA to active synapses requires NMDA receptor activation. *Neuron* 30:227–40

Tabuchi A, Sakaya H, Kisukeda T, Fushiki H, Tsuda M. 2002. Involvement of an upstream stimulatory factor as well as cAMP-responsive element-binding protein in the activation of brain-derived neurotrophic factor gene promoter I. *J. Biol. Chem.* 277:35920–31

Tagawa Y, Kanold PO, Majdan M, Shatz CJ. 2005. Multiple periods of functional ocular dominance plasticity in mouse visual cortex. *Nat. Neurosci.* 8:380–38

Takasu MA, Dalva MB, Zigmond RE, Greenberg ME. 2002. Modulation of NMDA receptor-dependent calcium influx and gene expression through EphB receptors. *Science* 295:491–95

Tao X, Finkbeiner S, Arnold DB, Shaywitz AJ, Greenberg ME. 1998. Ca^{2+} influx regulates BDNF transcription by a CREB family transcription factor-dependent mechanism. *Neuron* 20:709–26

Tao X, West AE, Chen WG, Corfas G, Greenberg ME. 2002. A calcium-responsive transcription factor, CaRF, that regulates neuronal activity-dependent expression of BDNF. *Neuron* 33:383–95

Timmusk T, Palm K, Metsis M, Reintam T, Paalme V, et al. 1993. Multiple promoters direct tissue-specific expression of the rat BDNF gene. *Neuron* 10:475–89

Tovar KR, Westbrook GL. 2002. Mobile NMDA receptors at hippocampal synapses. *Neuron* 34:255–64

Trivier E, De Cesare D, Jacquot S, Pannetier S, Zackai E, et al. 1996. Mutations in the kinase Rsk-2 associated with Coffin-Lowry syndrome. *Nature* 384:567–70

Tsankova N, Renthal W, Kumar A, Nestler EJ. 2007. Epigenetic regulation in psychiatric disorders. *Nat. Rev. Neurosci.* 8:355–67

Tudor M, Akbarian S, Chen RZ, Jaenisch R. 2002. Transcriptional profiling of a mouse model for Rett syndrome reveals subtle transcriptional changes in the brain. *Proc. Natl. Acad. Sci. USA* 99:15536–41

Verhage M, Maia AS, Plomp JJ, Brussaard AB, Heeroma JH, et al. 2000. Synaptic assembly of the brain in the absence of neurotransmitter secretion. *Science* 287:864–69

Wang KH, Majewska A, Schummers J, Farley B, Hu C, et al. 2006. In vivo two-photon imaging reveals a role of Arc in enhancing orientation specificity in visual cortex. *Cell* 126:389–402

Wayman GA, Impey S, Marks D, Saneyoshi T, Grant WF, et al. 2006. Activity-dependent dendritic arborization mediated by CaM-kinase I activation and enhanced CREB-dependent transcription of Wnt-2. *Neuron* 50:897–909

West AE, Chen WG, Dalva MB, Dolmetsch RE, Kornhauser JM, et al. 2001. Calcium regulation of neuronal gene expression. *Proc. Natl. Acad. Sci. USA* 98:11024–31

Westenbroek RE, Hoskins L, Catterall WA. 1998. Localization of Ca^{2+} channel subtypes on rat spinal motor neurons, interneurons, and nerve terminals. *J. Neurosci.* 18:6319–30

Wiesel TN, Hubel DH. 1963. Single-cell responses in striate cortex of kittens deprived of vision in one eye. *J. Neurophysiol.* 26:1003–17

Wu GY, Deisseroth K, Tsien RW. 2001. Activity-dependent CREB phosphorylation: convergence of a fast, sensitive calmodulin kinase pathway and a slow, less sensitive mitogen-activated protein kinase pathway. *Proc. Natl. Acad. Sci. USA* 98:2808–13

Xing J, Ginty DD, Greenberg ME. 1996. Coupling of the RAS-MAPK pathway to gene activation by RSK2, a growth factor-regulated CREB kinase. *Science* 273:959–63

Xu W, Chen H, Du K, Asahara H, Tini M, et al. 2001. A transcriptional switch mediated by cofactor methylation. *Science* 294:2507–11

Zafra F, Hengerer B, Leibrock J, Thoenen H, Lindholm D. 1990. Activity dependent regulation of BDNF and NGF mRNAs in the rat hippocampus is mediated by non-NMDA glutamate receptors. *EMBO J.* 9:3545–50

Zhang SJ, Steijaert MN, Lau D, Schutz G, Delucinge-Vivier C, et al. 2007. Decoding NMDA receptor signaling: identification of genomic programs specifying neuronal survival and death. *Neuron* 53:549–62

Zhou Z, Hong EJ, Cohen S, Zhao WN, Ho HY, et al. 2006. Brain-specific phosphorylation of MeCP2 regulates activity-dependent *Bdnf* transcription, dendritic growth, and spine maturation. *Neuron* 52:255–69

Zuhlke RD, Pitt GS, Deisseroth K, Tsien RW, Reuter H. 1999. Calmodulin supports both inactivation and facilitation of L-type calcium channels. *Nature* 399:159–62

Disulfide-Linked Protein Folding Pathways

Bharath S. Mamathambika[1,3]
and James C. Bardwell[2,3,*]

[1]Biophysics Graduate Program, [2]Department of Molecular, Cellular, and Developmental Biology, [3]Howard Hughes Medical Institute, University of Michigan, Ann Arbor, Michigan 48109; email: bharath@umich.edu, jbardwel@umich.edu

Annu. Rev. Cell Dev. Biol. 2008. 24:211–35

First published online as a Review in Advance on June 26, 2008

The *Annual Review of Cell and Developmental Biology* is online at cellbio.annualreviews.org

This article's doi:
10.1146/annurev.cellbio.24.110707.175333

1081-0706/08/1110-0211$20.00

*Corresponding author.

Key Words

thiol-disulfide exchange, oxidative folding, RNAse A, BPTI, hirudin, oxidoreductase

Abstract

Determining the mechanism by which proteins attain their native structure is an important but difficult problem in basic biology. The study of protein folding is difficult because it involves the identification and characterization of folding intermediates that are only very transiently present. Disulfide bond formation is thermodynamically linked to protein folding. The availability of thiol trapping reagents and the relatively slow kinetics of disulfide bond formation have facilitated the isolation, purification, and characterization of disulfide-linked folding intermediates. As a result, the folding pathways of several disulfide-rich proteins are among the best known of any protein. This review discusses disulfide bond formation and its relationship to protein folding in vitro and in vivo.

Contents

INTRODUCTION

Proteins are synthesized as linear polypeptide chains. Following synthesis on ribosomes, the polypeptide chains are rapidly folded into their unique three-dimensional structures. Proper folding is necessary for the biological functioning of all proteins. Most purified proteins can spontaneously fold in vitro under suitable conditions. Thus, the information needed to specify the three-dimensional structure is contained within the protein's primary structure. The kinetic processes or pathways by which proteins adopt the native structure have been extensively investigated over the past few decades. To this end, the focus of protein folding has been the identification and characterization of the initial, final, and intermediate conformational states as well as the determination of the steps by which they are interconverted. Most protein folding intermediates are only transiently present, making difficult their isolation and characterization by commonly used spectroscopic techniques. However, most secretory proteins have an important covalent modification: disulfide bonds. Disulfide bonds are one of the few posttranslational covalent modifications that occur during protein folding. Disulfide bond formation in proteins is required not only for folding but also for stability and function. Failure to form the correct disulfide bonds is likely to cause protein aggregation and subsequent degradation by cellular proteases.

Disulfide bonds are formed because of the reduction-oxidation chemistry of the covalent interaction between two thiol groups. The relatively slow kinetics of formation of the disulfide bond and the availability of thiol trapping reagents that rapidly quench disulfide bond formation have facilitated the isolation, purification, and characterization of folding intermediates. These trapped intermediates have been used to determine the pathways of several disulfide rich proteins in vitro. Knowledge of these disulfide-linked folding pathways has furthered our understanding of protein structure-function relationships.

Disulfide bonds can be formed spontaneously by molecular oxygen. For instance, under aerobic conditions, a thin layer of cysteine is generated at the air-liquid interface when a cysteine solution is left exposed to air. However, this type of spontaneous, random air-oxidation reaction is very slow and cannot account for the rapid rates of disulfide bond formation needed by the cell. This discrepancy led Anfinsen to the discovery of the first catalyst for disulfide bond formation, the eukaryotic protein disulfide isomerase (PDI). PDI is a part of the complex machinery responsible for the formation and isomerization of disulfide bonds in the eukaryotic endoplasmic reticulum (ER) (Sevier & Kaiser 2002, 2006). In the prokaryotic periplasm, the same function is carried out by the Dsb family of proteins (Kadokura et al. 2003, Nakamoto & Bardwell 2004).

In this review, we discuss the central role of disulfide bonds in protein folding. The characterization of in vitro disulfide-linked protein folding pathways is studied with the help of small disulfide-linked proteins. In addition, we attempt to point out the role of important protein folding catalysts in catalyzing the in vitro protein folding of these model proteins. A discussion of the methodology of oxidative folding is also included.

DISULFIDE BONDS AS A MEASURE OF PROTEIN FOLDING

During in vitro oxidative folding, disulfide bonds in proteins are formed by two thiol-disulfide exchange reactions with a redox reagent. During the first reaction, a mixed disulfide is formed between the protein and the redox reagent (**Figure 1a**). This reaction is followed by an intramolecular attack on the mixed disulfide bond in which a second cysteine thiol displaces the mixed disulfide (**Figure 1b**). Disulfide bonds can also be formed intramolecularly wherein the thiolate of a cysteine may attack a disulfide bond of the same protein. This process that leads to the rearrangement of disulfide bonds within the protein is called disulfide reshuffling.

Factors That Influence Disulfide Bond Formation in Proteins

Disulfide bond formation is influenced by four major factors: the concentration of thiolate an-

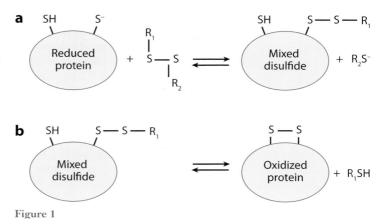

Figure 1

Thiol-disulfide exchange reaction between a protein and a redox reagent. Disulfide bonds in proteins are formed by two thiol-disulfide exchange reactions. (*a*) In the first step, a thiolate anion (S$^-$), which is formed by deprotonation of a free thiol, displaces a sulfur atom of the redox reagent. This leads to the formation of a mixed disulfide bond between the protein and redox reagent. (*b*) In the second step, the remaining thiol anion attacks the mixed disulfide, leading to the formation of the oxidized protein.

ions and the accessibility, proximity, and reactivities of the thiol groups and disulfide bonds. During thiol-disulfide exchange, a nucleophilic thiolate group (S$^-$) attacks a sulfur atom of a disulfide bond (-S-S-). The original disulfide bond is broken, and a new disulfide bond forms between the attacking thiolate and the original sulfur atom. The ionized, thiolate form (S$^-$) is capable of forming the disulfide bond, whereas the protonated thiol (SH) form is unreactive. Thiol-disulfide exchange is dependent on the concentration of the reactive thiolate anion relative to that of the unreactive thiol group, both of which in turn are strongly dependent on solution pH. Thus, one of the most important conditions that influences oxidative folding is the pH of the refolding buffer (Scheraga & Wedemeyer 2001). The pK$_a$ of a residue is the pH at which it is 50% ionized. The amount of reactive thiolate ion decreases tenfold for each pH unit below the pK$_a$ of the thiol. The pK$_a$ of cysteines in denatured proteins is usually approximately 8.7. Therefore, rapid oxidative folding reactions tend to occur when the pH is above 9, and oxidative folding becomes progressively slower at solution pH values below the pK$_a$ of the thiols involved. In vivo folding environments are not as flexible in terms of pH as in vitro reactions. One way in which organisms get around this limitation is by decreasing the pK_a of the reactive thiol groups in disulfide oxidoreductases so that these thiol groups remain ionized and reactive at physiological pH. Because thiol-disulfide exchange is affected by the reactivities of the thiolate groups and the disulfide bond, any change in the electrostatic environment of the reactive group (i.e., in the pH or pK_a of the thiol group) will influence disulfide bond formation (Arolas et al. 2006, Wedemeyer et al. 2000).

Thiol-disulfide exchange reactions can occur only when a thiolate and a disulfide bond come in contact. Therefore, burial of reactive groups in the protective tertiary structure of a protein will inhibit disulfide bond reactions. The rate of disulfide bond formation is also influenced by the proximity of the two reactive thiol groups. Thus, disulfide bond formation in proteins is influenced by multiple factors and is not a simple chemical reaction.

Disulfide Bonds and Stability of Proteins

Most disulfide bonds serve to stabilize protein structure. It is generally accepted that protein disulfide bonds stabilize the native conformation of a protein by destabilizing the denatured form; i.e., they decrease the entropy of the unfolded form, making it less favorable compared with the folded form (Thornton 1981). According to theoretical studies, the increase in the stability of the native structure due to the formation of a particular disulfide bond is directly proportional to the number of residues between the linked cysteines: the larger the number of residues between the disulfide, the greater is the stability imparted to the native structure (Flory 1953, Pace et al. 1988). The kinetics of protein folding are greatly affected by the location of the disulfide bond relative to the folding nucleus. Disulfide bonds introduced in or near the folding nucleus accelerate protein folding, whereas disulfide bonds introduced elsewhere can decelerate folding by up to three or-

ders of magnitude (Abkevich & Shakhnovich 2000).

The overall equilibrium constant K_{eq} for a thiol-disulfide exchange reaction is a measure of the stability of the protein disulfide bond. The K_{eq} value can be as high as 10^5 in folded proteins and as low as 10^{-3} in unfolded proteins (Darby & Creighton 1993). The formation of disulfide bonds is thermodynamically coupled to the process of protein folding. The folded conformation stabilizes the disulfide bond to the same extent that the conformation is stabilized by the formation of that particular disulfide bond (**Figure 2**) (Creighton 1990).

In general, most disulfide bonds stabilize proteins and affect the rate of protein folding. However, a minor population of the disulfide bonds also serves a functional role. Functional disulfides can be further classified into catalytic disulfides and allosteric disulfides. Catalytic disulfides are typically found at the active site of enzymes that mediate thiol-disulfide exchange (oxidoreductases). These dithiols/disulfides are transferred to a protein substrate, resulting in the formation, reduction, or isomerization of disulfide bonds. Allosteric disulfides regulate function in a nonenzymatic way by mediating changes in the protein structure (Hogg 2003, Schmidt et al. 2006).

OXIDATIVE PROTEIN FOLDING TECHNIQUES

Oxidative protein folding is a composite process in which a reduced, unfolded protein not only forms its native set of disulfide bonds but also undergoes conformational folding, leading to the formation of a native and biologically active form (Narayan et al. 2000). In a typical oxidative folding study, proteins are initially fully reduced and denatured (Creighton 1986). The reducing and denaturing agents are removed, and the protein is refolded in the presence of suitable buffers containing redox agents. At various intervals, a reagent is added; this reagent quenches disulfide bond formation and thus serves to halt the oxidative folding process. The trapped folding intermediates are then separated, identified, and quantified. We now discuss the various factors that have to be considered for the oxidative folding of proteins.

Choice of Redox Reagent

Typically, oxidizing agents such as glutathione disulfide (GSSG) and oxidized dithiothreitol (DTT^{ox}) are used to form disulfide bonds, and reducing agents such as the reduced form of these reagents (GSH and DTT^{red}, respectively) are used to reduce and reshuffle disulfide bonds. Normally, a redox buffer composed of a mixture of oxidized and reduced reagents is used during in vitro folding experiments. Two classes of redox reagents are commonly used in oxidative folding: cyclic redox reagents (e.g., DTT^{ox}/DTT^{red}) and linear redox reagents (e.g., GSSG/GSH). Cyclic redox reagents are powerful reducing agents in part because the close proximity of the two thiols in these reagents leads to rapid resolution of the mixed disulfides between the reagents and the proteins. This greatly simplifies interpretation of oxidative folding experiments (Scheraga & Wedemeyer 2001, Wedemeyer et al. 2000). The vast majority of thiol-disulfide oxidoreductases present in nature also contain two thiols in a CXXC motif and thus function as cyclic redox reagents. Linear redox reagents such as GSSG are better oxidizing agents than are small-molecule cyclic redox agents owing to the more oxidizing redox potential of the former. However, with linear disulfide reagents, the mixed disulfide species are much more stable than with cyclic disulfide reagents and can be problematic because they can accumulate significantly during folding reactions. High concentrations of linear redox reagents can even block all the free thiols, interrupting oxidative folding.

The composition of the redox buffer can drastically affect the rate of in vitro oxidative protein folding. For example, hirudin, a protein with three disulfides, can be refolded within seconds in a buffer of optimal redox composition, whereas refolding can take as long as 24 h in a buffer containing only catalytic amounts

of a thiol (Chang 1994, Chatrenet & Chang 1993).

Efforts have been made to develop novel redox reagents. Some of them include redox-active cyclic bis(cysteinyl)peptides (Cabrele et al. 2002); *ortho*- and *meta*-substituted aromatic thiols (Gough et al. 2006); selenoglutathione (GSeSeG), an analog of glutathione that contains a diselenide bond in place of the natural disulfide (Beld et al. 2007); and

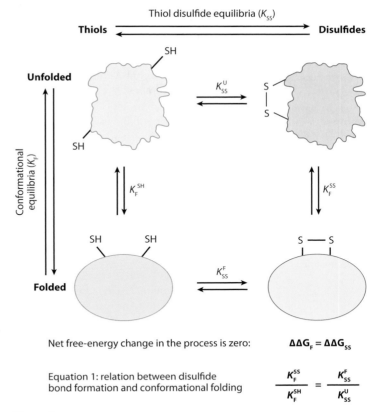

Figure 2

Relationship between disulfide bond formation and conformational folding of a protein. A protein with two cysteine residues is shown in its unfolded and folded conformations. The stability conferred by the disulfide bond and the conformation is given by the equilibrium constants K_{SS} and K_F, respectively. The equilibrium constants for folding with and without the disulfide bond are given by K_F^F and K_F^{SH}, respectively. The stability of the disulfide bond in the folded and unfolded states is given by K_{SS}^F and K_{SS}^U, respectively. The net free-energy change around the cycle should be zero, and therefore the equilibrium constants are linked (Equation 1). Thus, the folded conformation affects the stability of the disulfide bond to the same extent to which the disulfide bond affects the stability of the conformation (Creighton 1990).

GSSG: glutathione disulfide/oxidized glutathione

DTT: dithiothreitol

GSH: reduced glutathione

the dithiol (±)-*trans*-1,2-bis(2-mercaptoaceta-mido)cyclohexane (BMC), which acts as a small-molecule mimic of PDI (Woycechowsky et al. 1999).

Oxidative folding through nonredox chemistry has been explored recently. Curcumin, an antioxidant and an anticancer chemotherapeutic, was successfully used to accelerate oxidative folding of bovine pancreatic ribonuclease A (RNase A) (Gomez et al. 2007). Oxidized BMC, when used in combination with nonredox-active molecules [trimethylamine-*N*-oxide (TMAO) and trifluoroethanol (TFE)], accelerated the oxidative folding rate of RNase A as compared with that achieved by oxidized BMC alone (Fink et al. 2008). In both cases, the increase in the oxidative folding rate was attributed to the ability of nonredox-active molecules (curcumin, TMAO, TFE) to induce native-like elements in the reduced protein and stabilize key folding intermediates that have properties of the native protein.

The optimal redox buffer for in vitro protein folding is empirical for each protein and may reflect unknown differences between the in vivo and in vitro conditions, different in vivo folding environments, or the fact that every protein has a unique folding pathway. Not surprisingly, optimal folding is generally observed under redox conditions in which the conformational and oxidative kinetic traps (such as mixed disulfides leading to the formation of dead-end intermediates) are kept to a minimum (Kibria & Lees 2008).

Quenching Methods

By the use of appropriate thiol quenching reagents, disulfide bond formation can be stopped, and disulfide intermediates can then be isolated, enabling the detailed study of protein folding pathways. An ideal quenching method, according to Wedemeyer et al. (2000), should (*a*) completely quench free thiols, (*b*) impose a long-term block on disulfide reshuffling to allow for efficient fractionation, (*c*) aid in the separation and isolation of disulfide intermediates, (*d*) be reversible so that refolding of interme-

diates can be resumed following their isolation, and (*e*) prevent unfolding of structured disulfide intermediates.

Quenching is usually achieved by one of four methods: acid quenching, blocking with maleimides, blocking with alkyl halides, or blocking with aminomethylthiosulfonate (AEMTS). Acid quenching is fast and reversible, and the protein does not undergo any covalent modification. This method also has the advantage that it denatures proteins, which simultaneously allows access to all thiol groups and also destroys any special reactivities by bringing all thiol pK_as into the normal range. However, this first method just greatly slows thiol reactions, by tenfold for each pH unit of the buffer below that of the pK_as of the reactive thiols; it does not completely stop thiol-disulfide exchange. Blocking with maleimides such as *N*-ethylmaleimide (NEM) or 4-acetamido-4′-maleimidylstilbene-2,2′-disulfonic acid (AMS) is rapid and very specific for cysteine residues (Zander et al. 1998). Maleimides, however, block irreversibly and do not always gain access to all free thiols. Iodoacetate and iodoacetamide are the commonly used alkyl halides. When used at low-millimolar concentrations, alkyl halides often block too slowly to completely prevent disulfide reshuffling. At higher concentrations, alkyl halides can modify other residues of the protein (Scheraga & Wedemeyer 2001). Blocking by AEMTS is reversible and rapid [five orders of magnitude faster than iodoacetate (Rothwarf & Scheraga 1991)], and this compound adds a positively charged cysteamine group for every blocked thiol. Acid quenching and AEMTS blocking have the disadvantage that they usually perturb the conformational structure of folding intermediates. Thus, no single quenching method meets all of Wedemeyer et al.'s (2000) criteria. The use of different reagents can generate very different results. For instance, the slow reaction rate of alkyl halides is thought to be one of the chief reasons behind fundamental disagreements between Creighton and Kim (Creighton 1988, 1990; Weissman & Kim 1991) on the nature of the intermediates in the bovine pancreatic trypsin inhibitor (BPTI) folding pathway. One approach is to use a combination quench methodology, an initial quench using acid, to exploit its ability to quench rapidly and denature proteins, followed by dilution into a buffer containing a chemical quench reagent such as a maleimide (Zander et al. 1998).

Isolation of Disulfide Intermediates

Disulfide intermediates trapped during oxidative folding can be fractionated and characterized to determine the number of free thiols and disulfides (Weissman & Kim 1991). This is the first step in determining disulfide connectivity for each of these folding intermediates, which can lead to a detailed study of the folding pathway. Separation of intermediates becomes an increasing problem as the number of disulfide bonds increases. A protein with three disulfides in its mature form has 15 possible one-disulfide intermediates, a protein with four disulfides has 28, and a protein with five has 45. This explosion in the number of intermediates as the number of disulfides increases has limited the detailed analysis of folding pathways for proteins with more than three disulfide bonds.

The intermediates of acid quenching must be analyzed at low pH, which eliminates many separation techniques. Disulfide-linked folding intermediates trapped by acid quenching can in some cases be separated by reversed-phase high-performance liquid chromatography at low pH. However, not all proteins can be acid quenched owing to stability issues, and for many proteins, not all intermediates can be separated from each other. Intermediates blocked with AMS or polyethylene-maleimide can be separated by SDS-PAGE because of the large mass of the modification group added. Intermediates blocked with biotin polyethylene glycol-maleimide can be isolated on avidin columns. Intermediates blocked with iodoacetate have the thiols in the form of *S*-carboxymethylcysteine and the disulfides in the form of cysteine. These intermediates can be separated by chromatography, and the fraction of the free thiols and disulfides can be determined by amino acid analysis (Chang & Knecht 1991). Intermediates blocked with AEMTS have a positively charged 2-aminoethanethiol group for every free thiol present on the protein, and therefore ion exchange chromatography can be used to separate these intermediates. In general, a wide variety of analytical techniques, such as gel filtration, capillary electrophoresis, and 2-D gel electrophoresis, can be applied to separate the quenched intermediates.

Characterization of Disulfide Intermediates

The ensemble of intermediates and the disulfide bonds formed at various steps along the folding pathways of bovine pancreatic RNase A and three-fingered toxins have been characterized by mass spectrometry (Ruoppolo et al. 1996a,b). Electrospray mass spectrometry (ESMS) can be used to determine the number of disulfides on the basis of the increase in molecular weight by the addition of a blocking reagent for each of the thiol groups. The relative abundance of different intermediates can also be determined, facilitating kinetic analysis of the intermediates. To assign the correct disulfide pairings, ESMS analysis can be followed by disulfide mapping of proteolytically digested intermediates through the use of matrix-assisted laser desorption and ionization mass spectrometry (MALDIMS) or liquid chromatography ESMS (Ruoppolo et al. 2005).

A multitude of other biophysical techniques can be used to characterize the structure, activity, and role of the intermediates in the folding pathway. For example, fluorescent resonance energy transfer and nuclear Overhauser effects (NOEs) of nuclear magnetic resonance (NMR) spectroscopy can be used to measure inter-residue distances to understand how the structure of the protein changes as it folds to its native structure (Elisha 2005, Roques et al. 1980). Structural characterization of disulfide intermediates has been used to understand the oxidative folding pathway of some disulfide-rich proteins such as RNase A and BPTI (Weissman & Kim 1991). The high-resolution

BPTI: bovine pancreatic trypsin inhibitor

ESMS: electrospray mass spectrometry

MALDIMS: matrix-assisted laser desorption and ionization mass spectrometry

structure of those rare intermediates that are kinetically stable has occasionally been determined with X-ray crystallography (Pearson et al. 1998) and NMR (Laity et al. 1997, van Mierlo et al. 1994).

The role of particular disulfides in the folding and stability of particular proteins can be studied by site-specific mutagenesis experiments that replace the corresponding cysteines with serines or alanines. In some cases, these experiments can generate stable analogs of folding intermediates, which can then be structurally characterized.

Kinetic analysis of the regeneration process can be carried out by modeling the concentrations of various disulfide intermediates. Detailed kinetic analysis has been carried out for the regeneration of RNase A (Rothwarf et al. 1998a) and hirudin variant 1 (rHV1) (Thannhauser et al. 1997) by the method developed by Konishi and colleagues (Konishi et al. 1982, Rothwarf & Scheraga 1993a, Scheraga et al. 1987). In this method, the relative concentrations of the various intermediate species are determined as a function of time and redox conditions. These data are then modeled to a folding pathway consistent with the regeneration kinetics (Konishi et al. 1982). This approach can be used to determine the rate constant for the regeneration of native protein as well as the rate constants for the formation and reduction of disulfide bonds at different stages of regeneration (Rothwarf et al. 1998a, Thannhauser et al. 1997).

OXIDATIVE FOLDING OF MODEL DISULFIDE-BONDED PROTEINS

The oxidative folding pathway of several small disulfide-rich proteins has been determined. Here, we discuss the pathway of folding of three of the most extensively characterized proteins: RNase A, BPTI, and hirudin. The known pathways of oxidative folding exhibit a high degree of diversity, as revealed by the disulfide heterogeneity of folding intermediates, the predominance of native disulfide bonds in intermediates, and the level of accumulation of fully

oxidized but scrambled isomers as intermediates (Chang 2004). Nevertheless, the pathways of oxidative folding can be classified broadly into two major types on the basis of the nature of the folding intermediates (Narayan et al. 2000). First, an oxidative folding pathway in which the intermediates are unstructured is called a des_U pathway (des refers to the disulfide species or ensemble that possess all but one of the native disulfide bonds). The rate-determining step in a des_U pathway is the formation of the native protein N by oxidation and conformational folding of the disulfide intermediates. Second, a pathway in which the des species are structured is called a des_N pathway. The native disulfide bonds in des_N species are buried in the stable tertiary structure, but the free thiol groups are kept readily accessible to form the native protein. The rate-determining step in such des_N pathways is the formation of the structured des species by disulfide reshuffling and conformational folding of the unstructured precursors.

Bovine Pancreatic Ribonuclease A

RNase A is a single-domain protein with four native disulfide bonds (26-84, 40-95, 58-110, and 65-72). Over the years, a multitude of physical and chemical methods have been used to gain insight into the folding of RNase A. Both the NMR and crystal structures of the fully folded protein have been determined (Santoro et al. 1993, Wlodaver et al. 1988). One structural complication is that Pro93 and Pro114 in RNase A adopt the less common *cis* conformation in the folded state, making *cis-trans* proline isomerization an important part of the folding process. This problem, along with difficulties in expressing RNase A at high levels in bacterial hosts, has complicated detailed analysis of its folding pathway. Nevertheless, RNase A is one of the best-studied models for disulfide-linked folding; for reviews, see Narayan et al. 2000, Scheraga & Wedemeyer 2001, and Wedemeyer et al. 2000.

Scheraga and coworkers have extensively characterized the process of sequential formation of its disulfide bonds and the acquisition of native structure in fully reduced RNase A. Reoxidation in the presence of a redox agent (DTT^{ox}) resulted in the formation of heterogeneous disulfide-bonded intermediates (scrambled RNase A). According to this model (**Figure 3a**) (Iwaoka et al. 1998; Rothwarf et al. 1998a,b; Scheraga & Wedemeyer 2001; Wedemeyer et al. 2000; Xu & Scheraga 1998), RNase A folds through two stages at 25°C.

During the first prefolding stage, reduced RNase A undergoes sequential oxidation, resulting in the formation of four unstructured disulfide ensembles containing 1–4 disulfide bonds (ensembles 1S, 2S, 3S, and 4S). The composition of the disulfide bonds among 1S and 2S intermediates is nonrandom (Volles et al. 1999, Wedemeyer et al. 2002, Xu et al. 1996). The intermediate that contains a disulfide between cysteines 65 and 72 (called here the [65-72] intermediate) is the most populated species, accounting for 40% of the 1S ensemble. The representation of all other individual 1S intermediates is less than 10%. The preference for the [65-72] intermediate is due not only to entropic stabilization but also presumably to the significant enthalpic stabilization offered by the formation of a β-turn-like structure in residues 65–68. This β-turn is also observed in the native protein (Laity et al. 1997, Wlodaver et al. 1988) and in the NMR structure of the mutant (C40A, C95A) of RNase A (Laity et al. 1997). Because this β-turn structure is present in the fully folded protein, it may serve as a chain-folding initiation site. The [65-72] disulfide intermediate is also predominant among the 2S intermediates. Thus, the [65-72] disulfide bond may act to accelerate protein folding by decreasing the conformational space that has to be scanned for RNase A to attain native structure (Volles et al. 1999).

In the second stage, structured disulfide intermediates form and are subsequently converted to the native form. In RNase A, the rate-determining step in the regeneration of native protein is the formation of two disulfide species with native-like structure, des[40-95]

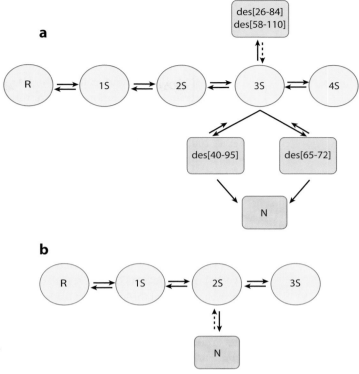

Figure 3

The folding pathways of wild-type RNAse A and its three-disulfide mutants. R represents the reduced protein, and nS represents the ensemble of species with n disulfide bonds. des[ ] represents a disulfide species with native disulfide bonds but lacking the disulfide bond in the brackets, and N represents the native protein. (*a*) Wild-type RNAse A follows a *des$_N$* type of pathway. The rate-limiting step in the formation of RNAse A at 25°C is the formation of two des species, [40-95] and [65-72], from the 3S ensemble. At 15°C, two other des species, [26-84] and [58-110], are formed; these reshuffle slowly to des[40-95] and des[65-72] via the 3S ensemble (Iwaoka et al. 1998; Rothwarf et al. 1998a,b; Scheraga & Wedemeyer 2001). (*b*) The three-disulfide mutants of RNase A follow a *des$_U$* pathway. The rate-limiting step is the formation of the two native proteins by oxidation and conformational folding of the unstructured 2S ensemble (Scheraga & Wedemeyer 2001).

and des[65-72]. These two species are formed from the 3S ensemble by disulfide reshuffling (**Figure 3a**). Upon the formation of these species, RNase A mainly attains a locked-in conformation wherein the three native disulfide bonds are protected from further reduction/reshuffling. However, the two remaining thiol groups still remain largely accessible to the solvent, thus allowing them to undergo rapid oxidation to the native protein.

Conformational stability of the des species is critical for oxidative folding in RNase A. Conditions that destabilize the structure of the des species (e.g., high temperatures) greatly hinder the regeneration of RNase A (Rothwarf & Scheraga 1993b, Rothwarf et al. 1998b). However, the rate of regeneration can be restored by anions that restabilize the conformational structure (e.g., phosphate, fluoride) (Lawrence et al. 2000, Low et al. 2002). Thus, the native-like conformation conferred by the des species is important for the oxidative folding of RNase A, in part because the conformational structure of the intermediates protects the native disulfides from rearrangement (Narayan et al. 2000).

Oxidative folding studies of the mutants of RNase A having only three disulfides, [C40A, C95A] and [C65S, C72S], reveal that native protein is formed through direct oxidation and conformational folding of the 2S ensemble. The des species (the 2S ensemble) have very little structure, and therefore these three-disulfide mutants of RNase A follow the des_U pathway (**Figure 3b**).

Native RNase A can also be generated through the oxidation of two other des species, des[26-84] and des[58-110] (**Figure 3a**). But these two species have a stable conformation only in the presence of stabilizing salts [phosphate (Low et al. 2002)] or at low temperatures [≤15°C (Welker et al. 1999)]. Even at low temperatures, des[26-84] and des[58-110] are metastable intermediates that reshuffle preferentially to the 3S ensemble rather than directly oxidize to form the native protein (Welker et al. 2001). The burial of their free thiol groups in their hydrophobic cores of a native-like structure presumably inhibits any redox reactions of these thiols in these intermediates.

Bovine Pancreatic Trypsin Inhibitor

BPTI is a member of the serine protease family of inhibitors; it is a very small globular protein, 58 amino acid residues in length in its mature form. BPTI adopts a tertiary fold compris-

ing two strands of antiparallel β-sheet and two short segments of α-helix. It contains three stabilizing disulfide bonds in its structure: between cysteines 5 and 55, 14 and 38, and 30 and 51.

The oxidative folding of BPTI was one of the first protein folding pathways to be studied and remains among the best characterized. Historically, there have been two models of BPTI folding, which differ greatly in the role played by nonnative intermediates in the folding pathway.

Early studies on the oxidative folding of BPTI were carried out by trapping the disulfide bond folding intermediates with the use of alkyl halides (Creighton 1988, 1990; Creighton et al. 1996). Using this approach, Creighton and colleagues found a heterogeneous population of unfolded molecules that fold by a distinct pathway via disulfide reshuffling of one-disulfide intermediates (**Figure 4a**). The native-like [30-51] intermediate composed 60% of the one-disulfide molecules, the nonnative [5-30] intermediate composed another 30% of the one-disulfide molecules, and the remaining possible 13 disulfide species accounted for the rest of the one-disulfide molecules (BPTI can form 15 unique 1S intermediates). The one-disulfide intermediates appear to be in an equilibrium state prior to folding. The [30-51] intermediate is kinetically significant for the folding of BPTI, and all further intermediates retain this disulfide bond. In native BPTI, the [30-51] disulfide links a major α-helix to a β-sheet, and the interaction between these secondary structure elements can stabilize the protein. The other native disulfide, [5-55], appeared in only 3% of the one-disulfide intermediates, whereas the [14-38] disulfide was not present at detectable levels in the 1S and 2S ensembles. According to this model, the rate-limiting step in BPTI refolding is the formation of the quasi-native two-disulfide intermediate [30-51, 5-55]. Once this native-like intermediate is formed, the third native disulfide, [14-38], is rapidly formed; its thiols are held in proximity on the molecule surface.

In a subsequent study, using acid trapping followed by high-performance liquid

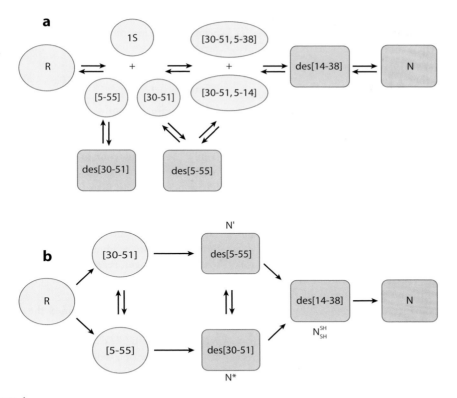

Figure 4

Pathways of folding of BPTI. *n*S represents the ensemble of species with *n* disulfide bonds. (*a*) The reduced protein (R) folds by forming both native and nonnative disulfide bonds. The major intermediates are indicated by the brackets. According to the model, the rate-limiting step in the regeneration of native (N) BPTI is the formation of the quasi-native species des[14-38]. The one-disulfide species, [5-55], leads to the formation of a dead-end intermediate, des[30-51] (Creighton 1990). (*b*) As per this model, native BPTI is formed mainly by intermediates that contain native disulfide bonds. The rate-limiting step is the formation of the des[14-38] species from two kinetic traps, N' and N* (Weissman & Kim 1991).

chromatography separation, Weissman & Kim (1991) reexamined the folding pathway of BPTI and proposed a revised model of folding. Unlike the earlier model of Creighton and colleagues, Weissman & Kim found that nonnative intermediates are not populated significantly during folding. Only six well-populated native disulfide species were isolated in their experiments (**Figure 4*b***). Upon oxidation, reduced BPTI rapidly forms one-disulfide intermediates that then rearrange rapidly to form either of two native intermediates, [30-51] or [5-55]. Both of these intermediates presumably have substantial native-like structure. The thiols of cysteines 14 and 38 are solvent exposed and read-

ily form the [14-38] disulfide bond to generate two two-disulfide species: [30-51; 14-38] (designated N') and [5-55; 14-38] (designated N*). The two-disulfide species serve as kinetic traps for BPTI folding. The N* intermediate is very stable and does not undergo significant rearrangement. The other intermediate, N', is highly stable and rearranges slowly to form either N_{SH}^{SH} or N*. NMR spectra of native BPTI and the N' intermediate indicate that N' is very native-like in configuration, burying the thiols of cysteines 5 and 55, thereby inhibiting the direct oxidation to native protein and explaining the observed slow disulfide rearrangement within N'. The rearrangement of N' to either

N_{SH}^{SH} or N^* occurs via the formation of non-native intermediates [30-51; 5-14] and [30-51; 5-38]. Upon the formation of N_{SH}^{SH}, the protein is rapidly oxidized to form the third native disulfide bond, [14-38].

During oxidative folding of BPTI, only half of the molecules form native BPTI. The remaining molecules stay kinetically trapped in the form of the stable intermediate N^*. Although N^* lacks the native [30-51] disulfide, NMR and crystallographic studies reveal that it has a structure similar to that of native BPTI. This native structure buries cysteines 30 and 51, rendering them inaccessible to oxidizing agents. Consequently, N^* is a dead-end intermediate that can persist for weeks.

Weissman & Kim (1995) explained the preference of N' to undergo rearrangement to form N_{SH}^{SH} and then N over direct oxidation to form the third native disulfide [5-55] by measuring the rate of direct oxidation of N'. The thiols in N' are buried and constrained by the structure of this intermediate, preventing any direct oxidation. As a result, any formation of native protein from N' requires substantial unfolding, and N' unfolds and rearranges its disulfide bonds before forming N_{SH}^{SH}. Unlike N^*, which leads to a nonproductive pathway, the rearrangement of N' to N_{SH}^{SH} leads to the productive folding of BPTI. Very recently, Kibria & Lees (2008) reexamined the folding pathway of BPTI, using optimized concentrations of glutathione (5 mM GSSG and 5 mM GSH). Under these conditions, the N^* intermediate was decreased in concentration, leading to substantially faster BPTI folding (Kibria & Lees 2008).

BPTI is initially synthesized as a pre-pro form containing a signal sequence required for the secretion of BPTI into the ER. This sequence is cleaved following secretion. BPTI also has a pro sequence that greatly influences the folding of BPTI in part because it contains a cysteine residue that is involved in disulfide isomerization reactions, with cysteines present on the mature portion of BPTI (Weissman & Kim 1992). This pro region is cleaved off of BPTI following maturation. Unfortunately, the vast majority of the work on BPTI folding has been with the less physiologically relevant mature protein.

Hirudin

Hirudins are a family of thrombin-specific protease inhibitors isolated from the medicinal leech *Hirudo medicinalis*. Members of this family of proteins contain approximately 65 residues and share three highly conserved disulfide bonds: C6-C14, C16-C28, and C22-C39. Hirudin contains an N-terminal globular domain (residues 1–49) that binds to the catalytic site of thrombin and a disordered, acidic C-terminal domain (residues 50–65) that interacts with the fibrinogen recognition site of the enzyme (Chang 1983, Grutter et al. 1990, Rydel et al. 1990).

Investigators have determined the in vitro oxidative folding pathway of a recombinant variant of hirudin (rHV1) in both the presence and the absence of a redox reagent (Chatrenet & Chang 1992, 1993; Thannhauser et al. 1997). Two similar models of oxidative folding for hirudin have been proposed on the basis of these experiments.

Chatrenet & Chang (1992) proposed the trial-and-error mechanism of folding for hirudin on the basis of refolding experiments in the absence of a redox couple such as GSSG/GSH or DTT^{ox}/DTT^{red}. Oxidation was achieved by dissolved atmospheric O_2, and a reductant (β-mercaptoethanol/GSH) was used to achieve full regeneration of native hirudin from the mixture of nonnative three-disulfide hirudin intermediates (scrambled hirudin). According to this model, all cysteines of hirudin participate in disulfide shuffling throughout the folding process, and the folding proceeds via a mechanism of trial and error without preferred pathways (Chatrenet & Chang 1992).

In a similar study, using a fragment of rHV1 (residues 1–49), Chatrenet & Chang (1993) proposed a sequential biphasic pathway for the folding of hirudin. Unlike BPTI and RNase A, the folding intermediates revealed an exceedingly high heterogeneity among the disulfide isomers. Of the 60 theoretically possible one- and two-disulfide intermediates, at least 30 fractions have been identified. Among the 14 possible three-disulfide scrambled isomers, 11 are present as folding intermediates and have been characterized. Hirudin spontaneously and sequentially flows from fully reduced protein to one-disulfide isomers to two-disulfide isomers to three-disulfide isomers (**Figure 5a**). The first stage of folding involves the packing of the polypeptide chain driven mostly by hydrophobic collapse. Starting with the reduced and unfolded hirudin, disulfides are randomly paired sequentially and irreversibly to form one-, two-, and finally three-disulfide intermediates (scrambled hirudin). During the second stage, the native protein is formed by disulfide reshuffling of the scrambled three-disulfide intermediates (β-mercaptoethanol was used as a reductant). This process is driven by noncovalent specific interactions that stabilize the native protein. Taken together, the proposal suggests that refolding of hirudin is dependent on the consolidation (disulfide rearrangement) of a heterogeneous scrambled population of three-disulfide species without any preferred pathway.

Thannhauser et al. (1997) studied the kinetics of folding of rHV1 under anaerobic conditions in the presence of DTT^{ox} and DTT^{red}. According to their kinetic model (**Figure 5b**), the reduced protein and the disulfide bond intermediates (1S, 2S, and 3S) rapidly approach a pre-equilibrium steady state during refolding. Unlike the earlier model of Chatrenet & Chang (1992, 1993), in which the 3S scrambled species is directly converted to native species, the 2S ensemble undergoes oxidation to form a 3S* ensemble that presumably has the same disulfide bonds as does the native protein, but may possess a different conformation. The 3S* ensemble folds rapidly to the native state. The rate of regeneration of the native protein was dependent on both the concentration of the 2S ensemble and the DTT^{ox} concentration. Therefore, Thannhauser et al. (1997) suggested that the rate-determining step in the regen-

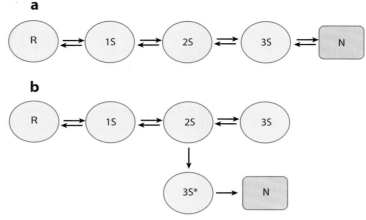

Figure 5

Oxidative folding of two variants of recombinant hirudin (rHV1). (*a*) The pathway of folding of a fragment of rHV1 (1–49 residues) follows a *des_U* type of pathway. The reduced protein (R) undergoes successive oxidation to form a mixture of highly heterogeneous intermediates (1S, 2S, and 3S, where *n*S represents the ensemble of species with *n* disulfide bonds). This process of formation of intermediates is driven by hydrophobic collapse. The rate-limiting step is the reshuffling of the scrambled 3S species to form the native protein (N) (Chatrenet & Chang 1992, 1993). (*b*) The pathway of folding of rHV1 determined by kinetic fitting. The reduced protein (R) undergoes successive oxidation to form the intermediates (1S, 2S, and 3S). The rate-limiting step is the irreversible formation of a 3S* species by the oxidation of the 2S ensemble and is dependent on the concentrations of the 2S intermediate and the redox reagent (Thannhauser et al. 1997).

eration of rHV1 is the oxidation of one or more species of the 2S ensemble to form 3S*. Moreover, these researchers postulated that the 2S species should contain at least two native disulfide bonds ([6-14; 16-28], [6-14; 22-39], or [16-28; 22-39]), raising the possibility of the existence of three distinct regeneration pathways. However, this analysis could not determine the specific composition of the 2S disulfide ensemble that is involved in the rate-limiting step.

The different model proteins and techniques used to derive data led to differences in these two models of hirudin folding. Unlike Thannhauser et al. (1997), who used rHV1 and a redox couple to oxidize rHV1, Chatrenet & Chang (1992) used a truncated rHV1 (1–49 residues) and dissolved atmospheric O_2 in their experiments. rHV1(1–49) regenerates native structures at a different rate than does rHV1. The importance of 3S scrambled species in the earlier model may be because of the use of highly oxidizing agents that caused the reduction of the 3S ensemble to become rate-limiting in the regeneration process.

Taken together, the data suggest that oxidative folding of hirudin is characterized by the presence of heterogeneous folding intermediates, indicating that the protein follows a des_U-type folding pathway. The prominence of scrambled isomers along the folding pathway contradicts the conventional wisdom that they are off-pathway or dead-end intermediates.

ROLE OF PROTEIN FOLDING FACTORS IN CATALYZING PROTEIN FOLDING

Disulfide-bonded proteins can be folded in vitro with the help of redox reagents that assist the process of thiol-disulfide exchange. In vivo, proteins are aided by molecular chaperones that protect them from forming insoluble aggregates. Disulfide bond formation is one of the major rate-limiting steps in protein folding in vivo. Therefore, in addition to the molecular chaperones, catalysts that can catalyze the thiol-disulfide exchange at rates comparable to in vivo protein folding rates are required. This section reviews the disulfide folding catalysts found in bacteria and eukaryotes and the role of these catalysts in catalyzing protein folding and directing folding pathways in vitro.

Disulfide Bond Formation in Bacteria

The process of disulfide bond formation in the bacterial periplasm has been extensively studied over the past decade. In *Escherichia coli*, disulfide bonds are introduced in the periplasm by the Dsb (disulfide bond formation) family of proteins. The family includes DsbA and DsbB, which are involved in forming disulfide bonds, and DsbC and DsbD, which are involved in isomerizing disulfide bonds.

Disulfide bond formation: DsbA and DsbB.

DsbA, a 21-kDa soluble protein, is the immediate donor of disulfide bonds to proteins secreted into the *E. coli* periplasm (Bardwell et al. 1991). In the absence of DsbA, most of the periplasmic proteins have their thiols in the reduced form. DsbA consists of a thioredoxin-like fold and a CXXC motif as its active site. For DsbA to be active, its two cysteines must be in the oxidized state. In general, disulfide bonds stabilize proteins. However, oxidized DsbA is unstable compared with reduced DsbA and reacts rapidly with unfolded proteins (Zapun et al. 1993). This instability of the oxidized protein, along with the instability of the mixed disulfide intermediate with a target protein, provides a thermodynamic driving force for the transfer of disulfide bonds from DsbA to the target protein (**Figure 6**). The transfer of disulfides by DsbA can be thought of as a thiol-disulfide exchange reaction of a protein with a redox reagent. This transfer reaction has two steps. First, an unstable mixed disulfide is formed between DsbA and a target protein. Then, another thiol group in the target protein attacks the mixed disulfide. This results in the formation of a disulfide bond in the target protein and the eventual reduction of the active-site cysteines of DsbA.

DsbA is one of the most oxidizing thiol-disulfide oxidoreductases known, with a redox potential of -120 mV. The oxidizing power is attributed to unusual electrostatic properties of the CXXC motif, particularly the unusually low pK_a of the most N-terminal cysteine in this active site, Cys30. Cys30 has a pK_a of ≈ 3, whereas the pK_a of most cysteine residues is between 8 and 9 (Grauschopf et al. 1995). Owing to its low pK_a, Cys30 is almost entirely in the thiolate anion state at physiological pH. The thiolate anion is also stabilized by hydrogen bonds, electrostatic interactions, and helix dipole interactions; an electrostatic interaction between His32 and Cys30 is thought to be the most important stabilizing influence (Guddat et al. 1997, Martin et al. 1993). Mutations that alter His32 greatly decrease the oxidizing power of DsbA by altering the pK_a of Cys30 (Grauschopf et al. 1995). Other residues that are located near the active disulfide, such as Pro31, also contribute to the oxidizing power of DsbA but

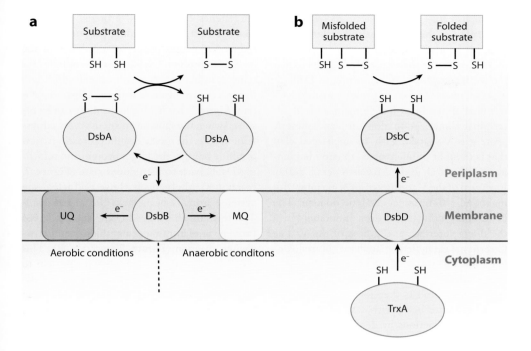

Figure 6

Disulfide bond formation and isomerization in the *Escherichia coli* periplasm (Pan & Bardwell 2006). (*a*) DsbA introduces disulfides into newly secreted proteins. The inner-membrane protein DsbB reoxidizes the active site of DsbA. Under aerobic conditions, the electrons from DsbB are passed to ubiquinone (UQ), and under anaerobic conditions they are passed to menaquinone (MQ). The electrons eventually flow to molecular oxygen via the electron transport chain. (*b*) Nonnative disulfide bonds are reshuffled by DsbC. DsbC is kept reduced by another inner-membrane protein, DsbD, which receives its electrons from the periplasmic thioredoxin (TrxA) system.

are less important. DsbA, in addition to being strongly oxidizing thermodynamically, also oxidizes proteins with very fast kinetics. Investigators have solved the three-dimensional structure of DsbA both in the oxidized and reduced states (Guddat et al. 1998, Martin et al. 1993), revealing a helical domain embedded into a thioredoxin domain. A rotational motion occurs between the two domains upon substrate binding.

Following transfer of its disulfide bond to the target protein, DsbA is reduced. To regain its ability to transfer disulfide bonds, DsbA must be reoxidized by DsbB (**Figure 6**). DsbB removes electrons from DsbA and transfers them to the respiratory chain. In aerobic conditions, the electrons are passed on to ubiquinone and ultimately to molecular oxygen. However, in anaerobic conditions, electrons are accepted by menaquinone, which transfers them to nitrate, nitrite, and fumarate (Bader et al. 1999, 2000; Kobayashi et al. 1997; Xie et al. 2002). Therefore, DsbA is reactivated via thiol-disulfide exchange reactions between the active sites of DsbA and DsbB (Inaba et al. 2006).

Disulfide bond reshuffling: DsbC and DsbD. DsbA is a very strong oxidase and introduces disulfide bonds into proteins relatively nonspecifically. Therefore, DsbA can introduce nonnative disulfides into proteins with multiple cysteines (Rietsch et al. 1996). Formation of the native set of disulfide bonds is essential for attaining the proper folded conformation. To accomplish this, an enzyme or redox reagent that catalyzes the reduction and reshuffling of disulfide bonds is required.

In *E. coli*, a protein called DsbC acts to isomerize incorrectly oxidized proteins. DsbC is a two-domain 23.5-kDa protein. It has a C-terminal thioredoxin-like domain and an N-terminal dimerization domain. The dimeric protein is V-shaped, with an uncharged cleft that is thought to be involved in peptide binding (Collet et al. 2002, McCarthy et al. 2000). Each arm of the V consists of an N-terminal domain and a C-terminal catalytic domain. The N-terminal domains of each monomer form the dimer interface at the base of the V. The C-terminal catalytic domain has a thioredoxin-like fold. The sulfur of the first cysteine of the active-site CXXC motif (Cys98) is partially solvent exposed and is therefore able to form a mixed disulfide bond with a substrate. DsbC presumably functions by detecting hydropho-bic patches on misfolded proteins via its uncharged cleft. Upon binding proteins, DsbC's reduced cysteines probe for disulfides in the misfolded protein. Cys98, the nucleophilic cysteine in DsbC, attacks a substrate disulfide and forms a mixed disulfide with the substrate protein (**Figure 7**). The mixed disulfide can be resolved when the substrate protein's reduced cysteine attacks the mixed disulfide, creating a new disulfide bond in the target protein and returning DsbC back to its reduced state (**Figure 7**, reaction A). Alternatively, the second active-site cysteine from DsbC attacks the mixed disulfide, forming an oxidized DsbC and a reduced protein via an intramolecular thiol-disulfide exchange reaction (**Figure 7**, reaction B). This process causes the target substrate protein to become reduced and allows DsbA to reoxidize that protein to the correct conformation (**Figure 6**).

DsbC must be kept reduced in the periplasm to stay active as an isomerase. The inner-membrane protein DsbD carries out the reduction of DsbC (**Figure 6**) and another protein, DsbG, whose function is yet to be determined.

Disulfide Bond Formation in Eukaryotes

In eukaryotic cells, disulfide bonds are formed in the lumen of the ER, which is a specialized compartment for protein folding and assembly. Two proteins are primarily responsible for controlling the process of oxidative folding: protein disulfide isomerase (PDI) and Ero1p.

PDI, a 57-kDa soluble protein, was one of the first identified thiol-disulfide oxidoreductases (Goldberger et al. 1963) and has been well characterized. Depending on the redox environment and the nature of the substrates, PDI can catalyze the formation, reduction, and isomerization of disulfide bonds (Gilbert 1994). Tian et al. (2006) recently determined the crystal structure of yeast PDI. The protein has two thioredoxin domains (a and a′) as its active site, with the sequence Cys-Gly-His-Cys. The redox potentials of the a and a′ domains are −188 mV and −152 mV, respectively. Ero1p

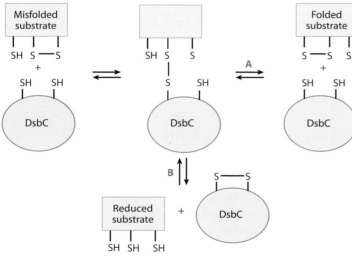

Figure 7

DsbC isomerizes wrongly formed disulfide bonds (Nakamoto & Bardwell 2004). Reduced DsbC attacks an incorrect disulfide bond of a substrate protein, forming an intermolecular disulfide intermediate. The intermolecular disulfide is exchanged for the correct intramolecular disulfide in the substrate protein, releasing DsbC in a reduced state (reaction A). Alternatively, the intermolecular disulfide between the substrate protein and DsbC is exchanged for an intramolecular disulfide within DsbC, releasing the substrate protein in a reduced state and DsbC in an oxidized state (reaction B). The reduced protein can then be oxidized by DsbA, and DsbC is regenerated by DsbD (not shown).

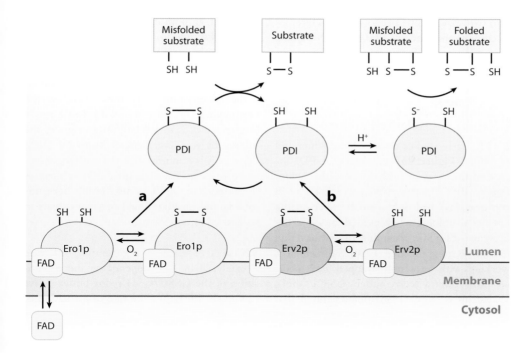

Figure 8

Disulfide bond formation in the lumen of the endoplasmic reticulum (ER) (Kersteen & Raines 2003, Sevier & Kaiser 2002). There are two pathways for disulfide bond formation in the ER. In the first pathway (*a*), oxidizing equivalents are transferred to protein disulfide isomerase (PDI) from the membrane-associated Ero1p-FAD (flavin adenine dinucleotide) complex. PDI transfers the oxidizing equivalents to the reduced substrate. In the second pathway (*b*), oxidizing equivalents can be transferred by another membrane-associated protein, Erv2p. Misfolded substrates are isomerized by the thiolate form of the reduced PDI. For simplicity, only one of the two active sites of Ero1p, Erv2p, and PDI is shown.

is a 65-kDa, membrane-bound, flavin adenine dinucleotide (FAD)-containing oxidase that acts on PDI (Frand & Kaiser 1998, Pollard et al. 1998, Sevier et al. 2001, Tu et al. 2000).

There are two pathways for disulfide bond formation in *Saccharomyces cerevisiae* (**Figure 8**). In the first pathway, oxidizing equivalents are transferred from Ero1p to PDI, which in turn oxidizes substrate proteins. The flow of oxidizing equivalents in this pathway occurs through a series of thiol-disulfide exchange reactions (Frand & Kaiser 1998, Tu et al. 2000). The second pathway involves the protein Erv2p. Erv2p transfers oxidizing equivalents from molecular oxygen to PDI via the FAD cofactor to form disulfide bonds (Sevier & Kaiser 2002). Therefore, in eukaryotic disulfide bond forma-

tion electrons appear to flow from the protein to PDI to Ero1p (or Erv2p) and ultimately to an electron acceptor. The second pathway has been observed only in the absence of Ero1p and in the presence of a plasmid overproducing Erv2p. The normal role of Erv2p is unknown.

CATALYSIS OF OXIDATIVE PROTEIN FOLDING BY PROTEIN FOLDING FACTORS IN VITRO

To determine how disulfide bond formation occurs in the cell, extensive investigation has been conducted on the in vitro refolding of model proteins by protein folding factors. Knowledge from these studies can be used to determine how oxidative folding occurs in vivo. Here, we discuss the influence of PDI and DsbA/DsbC on the in vitro oxidative folding pathways, using BPTI, RNase A, and hirudin as model proteins.

Catalysis of Oxidative Folding by PDI

BPTI. Early studies on BPTI unfolding and refolding (**Figure 4***b*) indicated that PDI increased the rates of oxidation and the reduction of BPTI in the presence of DTT^{ox}. In contrast, PDI had only a small effect on the kinetics of folding when used alone or in the presence of GSSG, cystamine, or hydroxyethyl disulfide (Creighton et al. 1980). Subsequently, working with reversibly trapped intermediates and using a redox buffer (GSSG/GSH), Weissman & Kim (1993) demonstrated that PDI dramatically increased both the yield and rate of formation of native BPTI. PDI showed a modest increase in the rate of formation of the two kinetically trapped intermediates and N*. However, PDI dramatically accelerated the formation of native protein (N) from the kinetic traps N′ and N* (accelerations of 3500- and 6000-fold, respectively). The effect of PDI on the reduced protein and the one-disulfide intermediates [30-51] and [5-55] was negligible, indicating that the effects of PDI are specific to the kinetically trapped intermediates.

Recently, Satoh et al. (2005) reexamined the catalysis of BPTI folding by PDI. They used acid quenching to trap the folding intermediates and determined the influence of PDI on each of the intermediates. PDI efficiently catalyzed the folding reaction from the fully reduced form to the native form (N). PDI readily converted N′ to N and partially to N*, indicating that PDI catalyzed the reduction of the [14-38] disulfide bond and the formation of the [5-55] disulfide bond and then recreated the [14-38] disulfide bond. PDI also converted N* to N, demonstrating that PDI catalyzed the reduction of the [14-38] disulfide bond and the formation of the [30-51] disulfide bond, followed by the recreation of the [14-38] disul-

fide bond. In both cases, the reduction of the [14-38] disulfide bond preceded the disulfide bond formation. The structure of intermediate N′ is very similar to that of the native protein, and the free thiols are presumably buried in the conformational structure. Therefore, the intermediate N′ must be unfolded to form N (Weissman & Kim 1991). PDI accelerates the folding by rearrangement of N′ to N*, N$_{SH}^{SH}$. Because it is important for the rearrangement of N′ to N to lose structure, PDI accelerates the folding of BPTI by promoting both unfolding and disulfide bond rearrangements in structured intermediates.

RNase A. The rate of regeneration of RNase A catalyzed by PDI depends on the composition of the GSSG/GSH redox buffer (Lyles & Gilbert 1991a,b). The rate of formation of native RNase A with DTT^{ox}/DTT^{red} as a redox agent markedly increases in the presence of PDI (9-fold at 15°C, 6-fold at 25°C, and 62-fold at 37°C). Although major changes were observed in the distribution of some disulfide intermediates with the rapid accumulation of the des species [65-72] and [40-95], PDI did not alter the two major pathways of RNase A regeneration (**Figure 3***a*) (Shin & Scheraga 1999). A subsequent study on the regeneration of RNase A at 25°C confirmed that PDI accelerates the formation of RNase A by catalyzing each of the intermediate steps without changing the folding mechanism (Shin & Scheraga 2000).

During the regeneration of RNase A, four possible three-disulfide intermediates can form: des[65-72], des[40-95], des[26-84], and des[58-110] (**Figure 3***a*). As discussed above, at 25°C, the majority of the three-disulfide intermediates are made up of des[65-72] and des[40-95], which regenerate native RNase A (Rothwarf et al. 1998a). However, at 15°C, des[26-84] and des[58-110] accumulate (Welker et al. 1999) as long-lived kinetic traps that slowly reshuffle back to the 3S ensemble (Welker et al. 2001). Shin et al. (2002) regenerated RNase A in the presence of catalytically active and inactive PDI to determine the effects of PDI as an oxidase and as a chaperone. Both forms of PDI increased the rate constant for the formation of RNase A when compared with the rate constant for the case involving the redox reagent alone (~17-fold and 2-fold for catalytically active and inactive PDI, respectively). In the presence of catalytically active PDI, the populations of des[40-95], des[26-84], and des[58-110] decreased as the reaction proceeded, making the des[65-72] species the prominent des species responsible for the regeneration of native protein. Shin et al. (2002) also determined that the catalytically inactive PDI did not affect the populations of des[65-72], des[26-84], and des[58-110], indicating that noncatalytic binding of the enzyme has no effect on the conformation of these des species. However, the concentration of only des[40-95] was significantly reduced, with a corresponding formation of the native protein, indicating that the noncatalytic binding of PDI induced a conformational change that led to the formation of the fourth disulfide in des[40-95]. Both disulfide bonds [26-84] and [58-110] are buried in the native protein; therefore, the 26 and 84 thiol groups in des[58-110] and the 58 and 110 thiol groups in des[26-84] must be exposed before direct oxidation takes place. The concentration of the species was similar in the presence and absence of catalytically inactive PDI and the redox agent DTT^{ox}, making direct oxidation of these des species unlikely. This finding suggests that noncatalytic binding of PDI to the substrates induces the exposure of thiol groups in the des[26-84] and des[58-110] species. Therefore, PDI converts the kinetically trapped des[26-84] and des[58-110] species into des[40-95] by disulfide rearrangement through the 3S ensemble (**Figure 3*a***). Thus, PDI plays a dual role as an oxidase/isomerase and a chaperone in the regeneration of RNase A.

Hirudin. The role of PDI in hirudin folding is to promote the process of disulfide rearrangement in the scrambled species (consolidation) (Chang 1994). PDI alone has no effect on the consolidation process. However, in the presence of free thiols (cysteines), PDI dis-

plays an additive effect in reshuffling the scrambled species. By optimizing the mixture of PDI and the redox reagent (Cys/Cys-Cys), PDI can complete the folding of hirudin within 30 s. Therefore, the in vitro efficiency of hirudin refolding is comparable to the scale of in vivo protein folding. PDI thus can accelerate the speed of hirudin folding in vitro. In general, PDI can accelerate the oxidation and isomerization of disulfide bonds but does not greatly alter folding pathways.

Recently, Chang et al. (2006) studied oxidative folding of hirudin in human serum. Consistent with earlier studies on hirudin (Chatrenet & Chang 1993), Chang et al. (2006) reported that the major rate-limiting step for the regeneration of native protein is the disulfide shuffling of the scrambled three-disulfide intermediates, which requires a reductant as the initiator. Native hirudin was completely regenerated in undiluted human serum (in a period of 48 h) without any redox supplement, indicating that human serum may contain unidentified oxidases like PDI that can catalyze disulfide bond formation.

Catalysis of Oxidative Folding by DsbA and DsbC

BPTI. Zapun & Creighton (1994) examined the influence of DsbA on the folding of BPTI in the presence of GSSG/GSH as the redox agent. DsbA differs significantly from PDI in its effect on the refolding of BPTI. Unlike PDI, DsbA induced a marginal increase in the rate of formation of native BPTI. The marginal increase was attributed to the direct oxidation of BPTI by DsbA, as indicated by the disappearance of the reduced protein. However, DsbA was unable to catalyze intramolecular disulfide bond rearrangements in the two-disulfide intermediates [30-51, 14-38] and [5-55, 14-38], whereas PDI had a dramatic effect on these two reactions. Thus, DsbA can rapidly oxidize BPTI but is unable to eliminate the kinetic traps in the folding pathway (Zapun & Creighton 1994). Disulfide bond rearrangements using DsbA were albeit observed when folding was carried out at low pH, at which the rate of thiol-disulfide exchange using redox buffers with normal pK_a values is very slow. This activity of DsbA is likely due to the very low pK_a of its active-site cysteine and the consequential high reactivity at low pH. However, stoichiometric amounts of DsbA are required, and folding occurs on the hour timescale.

DsbC has no influence on the rate of oxidation of reduced BPTI and therefore does not appear to catalyze disulfide bond formation. However, DsbC exhibits a marked effect on the rate of appearance of native BPTI. DsbC can catalyze rearrangements in [30-51, 14-38] and [5-55, 14-38] intermediates forming the native protein. The efficiency of DsbC in rearranging the disulfide bonds of BPTI is greater than that of DsbA but less than that of PDI (Zapun et al. 1995).

RNase A. DsbA stimulates oxidation of reduced RNase A in the presence of GSSG/GSH as the redox buffer but is very inefficient in promoting isomerization (Akiyama et al. 1992). In later studies, by using the reconstituted DsbA-DsbB system in vitro with DsbB as the redox agent, Bader et al. (2000) showed that DsbA was able to oxidize RNase A to the point at which no free thiols were detectable; however, RNase A gained negligible activity, indicating that the bulk of the protein had not been folded properly, presumably owing to misoxidation of thiols by DsbA. But with the addition of reduced DsbC, the reactivation of RNase A increased dramatically, suggesting that DsbC acts as an isomerase on a misoxidized 4S ensemble.

Hirudin. Catalytic amounts of DsbA accelerate the overall folding of native hirudin and decrease its half time of formation by two- to threefold in a GSSG/GSH redox buffer (pH 8.7) without changing the relative distribution of intermediates. At acidic pH, substoichiometric quantities of DsbA were able to catalyze hirudin folding, indicating that DsbA is required for the formation of disulfide bonds when bacteria are exposed to acidic pH (Wunderlich et al. 1993, 1995).

CONCLUSION AND FUTURE PERSPECTIVES

Disulfide bonds are critical posttranslational modifications of proteins. They not only stabilize protein structures but also are required for the proper folding and biological activity of several proteins. Because the formation of disulfide bonds is tightly linked to the conformational folding of the protein, the problem of protein folding can be addressed by investigating disulfide-linked protein folding. Several in vitro studies on small disulfide-rich proteins have helped elucidate the mechanism of disulfide-linked protein folding. However, protein folding in the cell is not spontaneous and requires the presence of protein folding catalysts. The discovery and characterization of the oxidative folding machinery in both prokaryotes and eukaryotes have opened up avenues to exploit the system for folding disulfide-rich proteins in the cell. Future research now can probably be aimed at utilizing this knowledge to engineer efficient systems for the expression of pharmacologically important proteins. How proteins fold in vivo is one of the key unsolved problems in basic biology. The vast majority of detailed folding studies have not been done in vivo but rather in vitro, simply because most of the techniques that are used to follow folding, such as circular dichroism, fluorescence, and hydrogen/deuterium (H/D) exchange, work well only in isolated systems. There are, however, big differences between the in vivo and in vitro environments. The presence of folding factors is the most obvious difference, but factors such as molecular crowding may be equally important. Fortunately, thiol trapping is one technique by which folding can be monitored and that can be used almost as well in vivo as in vitro. Future studies are expected to investigate in vivo folding pathways, perhaps by using some of the same tools that have been used so successfully to analyze disulfide-linked folding pathways in vitro.

SUMMARY POINTS

1. Disulfide bonds are formed in proteins by two thiol-disulfide exchange reactions with a redox reagent or another protein.

2. Disulfide bond formation is intimately linked to the conformational folding of a protein. The folded conformation stabilizes a disulfide bond to the same extent to which the disulfide bond is stabilized by that particular conformation.

3. The technique of direct oxidative folding can be used to study the in vitro disulfide-linked folding pathway of proteins. Reduced proteins are folded in the presence of a suitable redox reagent, and the intermediates are trapped by a suitable quenching method. The intermediates are then isolated and characterized by the use of biochemical and structural techniques.

4. Protein folding catalysts called oxidoreductases are required to form disulfide bonds in vivo. Oxidoreductases accelerate oxidative folding by eliminating kinetic traps in protein folding.

DISCLOSURE STATEMENT

The authors are not aware of any biases that might be perceived as affecting the objectivity of this review.

LITERATURE CITED

Abkevich VI, Shakhnovich EI. 2000. What can disulfide bonds tell us about protein energetics, function and folding: simulations and bioninformatics analysis. *J. Mol. Biol.* 300:975–85

Akiyama Y, Kamitani S, Kusukawa N, Ito K. 1992. In vitro catalysis of oxidative folding of disulfide-bonded proteins by the *Escherichia coli* dsbA (ppfA) gene product. *J. Biol. Chem.* 267:22440–45

Arolas JL, Aviles FX, Chang J-Y, Ventura S. 2006. Folding of small disulfide-rich proteins: clarifying the puzzle. *Trends Biochem. Sci.* 31:292–301

Bader M, Muse W, Ballou DP, Gassner C, Bardwell JCA. 1999. Oxidative protein folding is driven by the electron transport system. *Cell* 98:217–27

Bader MW, Xie T, Yu C-A, Bardwell JCA. 2000. Disulfide bonds are generated by quinone reduction. *J. Biol. Chem.* 275:26082–88

Bardwell JCA, McGovern K, Beckwith J. 1991. Identification of a protein required for disulfide bond formation in vivo. *Cell* 67:581–89

Beld J, Woycechowsky KJ, Hilvert D. 2007. Selenoglutathione: efficient oxidative protein folding by a diselenide. *Biochemistry* 46:5382–90

Cabrele C, Fiori S, Pegoraro S, Moroder L. 2002. Redox-active cyclic bis(cysteinyl)peptides as catalysts for in vitro oxidative protein folding. *Chem. Biol.* 9:731–40

Chang J-Y. 1983. The functional domain of hirudin, a thrombin-specific inhibitor. *FEBS Lett.* 164:307–13

Chang J-Y, Knecht R. 1991. Direct analysis of the disulfide content of proteins: methods for monitoring the stability and refolding process of cystine-containing proteins. *Anal. Biochem.* 197:52–58

Chang J-Y, Lu B-Y, Lai P-H. 2006. Oxidative folding of hirudin in human serum. *Biochem. J.* 394:249–57

Chang JY. 1994. Controlling the speed of hirudin folding. *Biochem. J.* 300(Pt. 3):643–50

Chang JY. 2004. Evidence for the underlying cause of diversity of the disulfide folding pathway. *Biochemistry* 43:4522–29

Chatrenet B, Chang JY. 1992. The folding of hirudin adopts a mechanism of trial and error. *J. Biol. Chem.* 267:3038–43

Chatrenet B, Chang JY. 1993. The disulfide folding pathway of hirudin elucidated by stop/go folding experiments. *J. Biol. Chem.* 268:20988–96

Collet J-F, Riemer J, Bader MW, Bardwell JCA. 2002. Reconstitution of a disulfide isomerization system. *J. Biol. Chem.* 277:26886–92

Creighton TE. 1986. Disulfide bonds as probes of protein folding pathways. In *Methods in Enzymology*, ed. CHW Hirs, SN Timasheff, 131:83–106. San Diego: Academic

Creighton TE. 1988. On the relevance of nonrandom polypeptide conformations for protein folding. *Biophys. Chem.* 31:155–62

Creighton TE. 1990. Protein folding. *Biochem. J.* 270:1–16

Creighton TE, Darby NJ, Kemmink J. 1996. The roles of partly folded intermediates in protein folding. *FASEB J.* 10:110–18

Creighton TE, Hillson DA, Freedman RB. 1980. Catalysis by protein-disulfide isomerase of the unfolding and refolding of proteins with disulphide bonds. *J. Mol. Biol.* 142:43–62

Darby NJ, Creighton TE. 1993. Dissecting the disulphide-coupled folding pathway of bovine pancreatic trypsin inhibitor: forming the first disulfide bonds in analogues of the reduced protein. *J. Mol. Biol.* 232:873–96

Elisha H. 2005. The study of protein folding and dynamics by determination of intramolecular distance distributions and their fluctuations using ensemble and single-molecule FRET measurements. *Chem. Phys. Chem.* 6:858–70

Fink M, Nieves P, Chang S, Narayan M. 2008. Non-redox-active small-molecules can accelerate oxidative protein folding by novel mechanisms. *Biophys. Chem.* 132:104–9

Flory P. 1953. *Principles of Polymer Chemistry*. Ithaca: Cornell Univ. Press

Frand AR, Kaiser CA. 1998. The *ERO1* gene of yeast is required for oxidation of protein dithiols in the endoplasmic reticulum. *Mol. Cell* 1:161–70

Gilbert HF. 1994. The formation of disulfide bonds. In *Mechanisms of Protein Folding*, ed. RH Pain, pp. 104–35. Oxford, UK: Oxford Univ. Press

Goldberger RF, Epstein CJ, Anfinsen CB. 1963. Acceleration of reactivation of reduced bovine pancreatic ribonuclease by a microsomal system from rat liver. *J. Biol. Chem.* 238:628–35

Gomez G, Mansouraty G, Gardea J, Narayan M. 2007. Acceleration of oxidative protein folding by curcumin through novel nonredox chemistry. *Biochem. Biophys. Res. Commun.* 364:561–66

Gough JD, Barrett EJ, Silva Y, Lees WJ. 2006. *ortho*- and *meta*-substituted aromatic thiols are efficient redox buffers that increase the folding rate of a disulfide-containing protein. *J. Biotechnol.* 125:39–47

Grauschopf U, Winther JR, Korber P, Zander T, Dallinger P, Bardwell JCA. 1995. Why is DsbA such an oxidizing disulfide catalyst? *Cell* 83:947–55

Grutter MG, Priestle JP, Rahuel J, Grossenbacher H, Bode W, et al. 1990. Crystal structure of the thrombin-hirudin complex: a novel mode of serine protease inhibition. *EMBO J.* 9:2361–65

Guddat LW, Bardwell JCA, Glockshuber R, Huber-Wunderlich M, Zander T, Martin JL. 1997. Structural analysis of three His32 mutants of DsbA: support for an electrostatic role of His32 in DsbA stability. *Protein Sci.* 6:1893–900

Guddat LW, Bardwell JCA, Martin JL. 1998. Crystal structures of reduced and oxidized DsbA: investigation of domain motion and thiolate stabilization. *Structure* 6:757–67

Hogg PJ. 2003. Disulfide bonds as switches for protein function. *Trends Biochem. Sci.* 28:210–14

Inaba K, Murakami S, Suzuki M, Nakagawa A, Yamashita E, et al. 2006. Crystal structure of the DsbB-DsbA complex reveals a mechanism of disulfide bond generation. *Cell* 127:789–801

Iwaoka M, Juminaga D, Scheraga HA. 1998. Regeneration of three-disulfide mutants of bovine pancreatic ribonuclease A missing the 65-72 disulfide bond: characterization of a minor folding pathway of ribonuclease A and kinetic roles of Cys65 and Cys72. *Biochemistry* 37:4490–501

Kadokura H. 2006. Oxidative protein folding: many different ways to introduce disulfide bonds. *Antioxid. Redox Signal.* 8:731–33

Kersteen EA, Raines RT. 2003. Catalysis of protein folding by protein disulfide isomerase and small-molecule mimics. *Antioxid. Redox Signal.* 5:413–24

Kibria FM, Lees WJ. 2008. Balancing conformational and oxidative kinetic traps during the folding of bovine pancreatic trypsin inhibitor (BPTI) with glutathione and glutathione disulfide. *J. Am. Chem. Soc.* 130:796–97

Kobayashi T, Kishigami S, Sone M, Inokuchi H, Mogi T, Ito K. 1997. Respiratory chain is required to maintain oxidized states of the DsbA-DsbB disulfide bond formation system in aerobically growing *Escherichia coli* cells. *Proc. Natl. Acad. Sci. USA* 94:11857–62

Konishi Y, Ooi T, Scheraga HA. 1982. Regeneration of ribonuclease A from the reduced protein. Rate-limiting steps. *Biochemistry* 21:4734–40

Laity JH, Lester CC, Shimotakahara S, Zimmerman DE, Montelione GT, Scheraga HA. 1997. Structural characterization of an analog of the major rate-determining disulfide folding intermediate of bovine pancreatic ribonuclease A. *Biochemistry* 36:12683–99

Lawrence KL, Hang-Cheol S, Mahesh N, William JW, Harold AS. 2000. Acceleration of oxidative folding of bovine pancreatic ribonuclease A by anion-induced stabilization and formation of structured native-like intermediates. *FEBS Lett.* 472:67–72

Low LK, Shin H-C, Scheraga HA. 2002. Oxidative folding of bovine pancreatic ribonuclease A: insight into the overall catalysis of the refolding pathway by phosphate. *J. Protein Chem.* 21:19–27

Lyles MM, Gilbert HF. 1991a. Catalysis of the oxidative folding of ribonuclease A by protein disulfide isomerase: dependence of the rate on the composition of the redox buffer. *Biochemistry* 30:613–19

Lyles MM, Gilbert HF. 1991b. Catalysis of the oxidative folding of ribonuclease A by protein disulfide isomerase: presteady-state kinetics and the utilization of the oxidizing equivalents of the isomerase. *Biochemistry* 30:619–25

Martin JL, Bardwell JCA, Kuriyan J. 1993. Crystal structure of the DsbA protein required for disulphide bond formation in vivo. *Nature* 365:464–68

McCarthy AA, Haebel PW, Torronen A, Rybin V, Baker EN, Metcalf P. 2000. Crystal structure of the protein disulfide bond isomerase, DsbC, from *Escherichia coli*. *Nat. Struct. Biol.* 7:196–99

Nakamoto H, Bardwell JCA. 2004. Catalysis of disulfide bond formation and isomerization in the *Escherichia coli* periplasm. *Biochim. Biophys. Acta Mol. Cell Res.* 1694:111–19

Narayan M, Welker E, Wedemeyer WJ, Scheraga HA. 2000. Oxidative folding of proteins. *Acc. Chem. Res.* 33:805–12

Pace CN, Grimsley GR, Thomson JA, Barnett BJ. 1988. Conformational stability and activity of ribonuclease T1 with zero, one, and two intact disulfide bonds. *J. Biol. Chem.* 263:11820–25

Pan JL, Bardwell JCA. 2006. The origami of thioredoxin-like folds. *Protein Sci.* 15:2217–27

Pearson MA, Karplus PA, Dodge RW, Laity JH, Scheraga HA. 1998. Crystal structures of two mutants that have implications for the folding of bovine pancreatic ribonuclease A. *Protein Sci.* 7:1255–58

Pollard MG, Travers KJ, Weissman JS. 1998. Ero1p: a novel and ubiquitous protein with an essential role in oxidative protein folding in the endoplasmic reticulum. *Mol. Cell* 1:171–82

Rietsch A, Belin D, Martin N, Beckwith J. 1996. An in vivo pathway for disulfide bond isomerization in *Escherichia coli*. *Proc. Natl. Acad. Sci. USA* 93:13048–53

Roques BP, Rao R, Marion D. 1980. Use of nuclear Overhauser effect in the study of peptides and proteins. *Biochimie* 62:753–73

Rothwarf DM, Li YJ, Scheraga HA. 1998a. Regeneration of bovine pancreatic ribonuclease A: detailed kinetic analysis of two independent folding pathways. *Biochemistry* 37:3767–76

Rothwarf DM, Li YJ, Scheraga HA. 1998b. Regeneration of bovine pancreatic ribonuclease A: identification of two nativelike three-disulfide intermediates involved in separate pathways. *Biochemistry* 37:3760–66

Rothwarf DM, Scheraga HA. 1991. Regeneration and reduction of native bovine pancreatic ribonuclease A with oxidized and reduced dithiothreitol. *J. Am. Chem. Soc.* 113:6293–94

Rothwarf DM, Scheraga HA. 1993a. Regeneration of bovine pancreatic ribonuclease A. 2. Kinetics of regeneration. *Biochemistry* 32:2680–89

Rothwarf DM, Scheraga HA. 1993b. Regeneration of bovine pancreatic ribonuclease A. 4. Temperature dependence of the regeneration rate. *Biochemistry* 32:2698–703

Ruoppolo M, Freedman RB, Pucci P, Marino G. 1996a. Glutathione-dependent pathways of refolding of RNase T1 by oxidation and disulfide isomerization: catalysis by protein disulfide isomerase. *Biochemistry* 35:13636–46

Ruoppolo M, Pucci P, Marino G. 2005. Folding and disulfide formation. In *Protein Folding Handbook*, ed. T Kiefhaber, J Buchner, pp. 946–64. Weinheim, Ger.: Wiley

Ruoppolo M, Torella C, Kanda F, Panico M, Pucci P, et al. 1996b. Identification of disulphide bonds in the refolding of bovine pancreatic RNase A. *Fold. Des.* 1:381–90

Rydel TJ, Ravichandran KG, Tulinsky A, Bode W, Huber R, et al. 1990. The structure of a complex of recombinant hirudin and human alpha-thrombin. *Science* 249:277–80

Santoro J, Gonzalez C, Bruix M, Neira JL, Nieto JL, et al. 1993. High-resolution three-dimensional structure of ribonuclease A in solution by nuclear magnetic resonance spectroscopy. *J. Mol. Biol.* 229:722–34

Satoh M, Shimada A, Kashiwai A, Saga S, Hosokawa M. 2005. Differential cooperative enzymatic activities of protein disulfide isomerase family in protein folding. *Cell Stress Chaperones* 10:211–20

Scheraga HA, Konishi Y, Rothwarf DM, Mui PW. 1987. Toward an understanding of the folding of ribonuclease A. *Proc. Natl. Acad. Sci. USA* 84:5740–44

Scheraga HA, Wedemeyer WJ. 2001. Bovine pancreatic ribonuclease A: oxidative and conformational folding studies. In *Methods in Enzymology*, ed. AW Nicholson, 341:189–221. San Diego: Academic

Schmidt B, Ho L, Hogg PJ. 2006. Allosteric disulfide bonds. *Biochemistry* 45:7429–33

Sevier CS, Cuozzo JW, Vala A, Aslund F, Kaiser CA. 2001. A flavoprotein oxidase defines a new endoplasmic reticulum pathway for biosynthetic disulphide bond formation. *Nat. Cell Biol.* 3:874–82

Sevier CS, Kaiser CA. 2002. Formation and transfer of disulphide bonds in living cells. *Nat. Rev. Mol. Cell Biol.* 3:836–47

Sevier CS, Kaiser CA. 2006. Conservation and diversity of cellular disulfide bond formation pathways. *Antioxid. Redox Signal.* 8:797–811

Shin H-C, Scheraga HA. 1999. Effect of protein disulfide isomerase on the regeneration of bovine ribonuclease A with dithiothreitol. *FEBS Lett.* 456:143–45

Shin H-C, Scheraga HA. 2000. Catalysis of the oxidative folding of bovine pancreatic ribonuclease A by protein disulfide isomerase. *J. Mol. Biol.* 300:995–1003

Shin H-C, Song M-C, Scheraga HA. 2002. Effect of protein disulfide isomerase on the rate-determining steps of the folding of bovine pancreatic ribonuclease A. *FEBS Lett.* 521:77–80

Thannhauser TW, Rothwarf DM, Scheraga HA. 1997. Kinetic studies of the regeneration of recombinant hirudin variant 1 with oxidized and reduced dithiothreitol. *Biochemistry* 36:2154–65

Thornton JM. 1981. Disulphide bridges in globular proteins. *J. Mol. Biol.* 151:261–87

Tian G, Xiang S, Noiva R, Lennarz WJ, Schindelin H. 2006. The crystal structure of yeast protein disulfide isomerase suggests cooperativity between its active sites. *Cell* 124:61–73

Tu BP, Ho-Schleyer SC, Travers KJ, Weissman JS. 2000. Biochemical basis of oxidative protein folding in the endoplasmic reticulum. *Science* 290:1571–74

van Mierlo CP, Kemmink J, Neuhaus D, Darby NJ, Creighton TE. 1994. 1H NMR analysis of the partly-folded non-native two-disulphide intermediates (30-51,5-14) and (30-51,5-38) in the folding pathway of bovine pancreatic trypsin inhibitor. *J Mol Biol* 235:1044–61

Volles MJ, Xu X, Scheraga HA. 1999. Distribution of disulfide bonds in the two-disulfide intermediates in the regeneration of bovine pancreatic ribonuclease A: further insights into the folding process. *Biochemistry* 38:7284–93

Wedemeyer WJ, Welker E, Narayan M, Scheraga HA. 2000. Disulfide bonds and protein folding. *Biochemistry* 39:4207–16

Wedemeyer WJ, Xu X, Welker E, Scheraga HA. 2002. Conformational propensities of protein folding intermediates: Distribution of species in the 1S, 2S, and 3S ensembles of the [C40A,C95A] mutant of bovine pancreatic ribonuclease A. *Biochem.* 41:1483–91

Weissman JS, Kim PS. 1991. Reexamination of the folding of BPTI: predominance of native intermediates. *Science* 253:1386–93

Weissman JS, Kim PS. 1992. The pro region of BPTI facilitates folding. *Cell* 71:841–51

Weissman JS, Kim PS. 1993. Efficient catalysis of disulphide bond rearrangements by protein disulphide isomerase. *Nature* 365:185–88

Weissman JS, Kim PS. 1995. A kinetic explanation for the rearrangement pathway of BPTI folding. *Nat. Struct. Mol. Biol.* 2:1123–30

Welker E, Narayan M, Volles MJ, Scheraga HA. 1999. Two new structured intermediates in the oxidative folding of RNase A. *FEBS Lett.* 460:477–79

Welker E, Narayan M, Wedemeyer WJ, Scheraga HA. 2001. Structural determinants of oxidative folding in proteins. *Proc. Natl. Acad. Sci. USA* 98:2312–16

Wlodaver LAS, Sjöin L, Gilliland GL. 1988. Structure of phosphate-free ribonuclease A refined at 1.26 Å. *Biochemistry* 27:2705–17

Woycechowsky KJ, Wittrup KD, Raines RT. 1999. A small-molecule catalyst of protein folding in vitro and in vivo. *Chem. Biol.* 6:871–79

Wunderlich M, Otto A, Maskos K, Mu M, Seckler R, Glockshuber R. 1995. Efficient catalysis of disulfide formation during protein folding with a single active-site cysteine. *J. Mol. Biol.* 247:28–33

Wunderlich M, Otto A, Seckler R, Glockshuber R. 1993. Bacterial protein disulfide isomerase: efficient catalysis of oxidative protein folding at acidic pH. *Biochemistry* 32:12251–56

Xie T, Yu L, Bader MW, Bardwell JCA, Yu C-A. 2002. Identification of the ubiquinone-binding domain in the disulfide catalyst disulfide bond protein B. *J. Biol. Chem.* 277:1649–52

Xu X, Rothwarf DM, Scheraga HA. 1996. Nonrandom distribution of the one-disulfide intermediates in the regeneration of ribonuclease A. *Biochemistry* 35:6406–17

Xu X, Scheraga HA. 1998. Kinetic folding pathway of a three-disulfide mutant of bovine pancreatic ribonuclease A missing the [40-95] disulfide bond. *Biochemistry* 37:7561–71

Zander T, Phadke ND, Bardwell JCA. 1998. Disulfide bond catalysts in *Escherichia coli*. In *Methods in Enzymology*, ed. GH Lorimer, TO Baldwin, 290:59–74. San Diego: Academic

Zapun A, Bardwell JCA, Creighton TE. 1993. The reactive and destabilizing disulfide bond of DsbA, a protein required for protein disulfide bond formation in vivo. *Biochemistry* 32:5083–92

Zapun A, Creighton TE. 1994. Effects of DsbA on the disulfide folding of bovine pancreatic trypsin inhibitor and α-lactalbumin. *Biochemistry* 33:5202–11

Zapun A, Missiakas D, Raina S, Creighton TE. 1995. Structural and functional characterization of DsbC, a protein involved in disulfide bond formation in *Escherichia coli*. *Biochemistry* 34:5075–89

Molecular Mechanisms of Presynaptic Differentiation

Yishi Jin[1] and Craig C. Garner[2]

[1] Division of Biological Sciences, Section of Neurobiology, Howard Hughes Medical Institute, University of California, San Diego, La Jolla, California 92093; email: yijin@ucsd.edu

[2] Department of Psychiatry and Behavioral Science, Nancy Pritzker Laboratory, Stanford University, Stanford, California 94304; email: cgarner@stanford.edu

Annu. Rev. Cell Dev. Biol. 2008. 24:237–62

First published online as a Review in Advance on June 26, 2008

The *Annual Review of Cell and Developmental Biology* is online at cellbio.annualreviews.org

This article's doi: 10.1146/annurev.cellbio.23.090506.123417

Key Words

synapse, active zone, presynaptic cytomatrix, transport, development, axon, ubiquitination

Abstract

Information processing in the nervous system relies on properly localized and organized synaptic structures at the correct locations. The formation of synapses is a long and intricate process involving multiple interrelated steps. Decades of research have identified a large number of molecular components of the presynaptic compartment. In addition to neurotransmitter-containing synaptic vesicles, presynaptic terminals are defined by cytoskeletal and membrane specializations that allow highly regulated exo- and endocytosis of synaptic vesicles and that maintain precise registration with postsynaptic targets. Functional studies at multiple levels have revealed complex interactions between the transport of vesicular intermediates, the presynaptic cytoskeleton, growth cone navigation, and synaptic targets. With the advent of finer anatomical, physiological, and molecular tools, great insights have been gained toward the mechanistic dissection of functionally redundant processes controlling the specificity and dynamics of synapses. This review highlights the recent findings pertaining to the cellular and molecular regulation of presynaptic differentiation.

Contents

INTRODUCTION

Presynaptic differentiation begins after axon formation and culminates with the assembly of synapses. A presynaptic terminal is defined as a specialized region of the axon, either at the ends of the axon (*boutons terminaux*) or along the axon shaft (*boutons en passant*), where synaptic vesicles cluster around a specialized region at the membrane. This presynaptic specialization, referred to as the active zone, is defined physiologically as the site of regulated synaptic vesicle fusion and neurotransmitter release (Couteaux 1963).

The cellular process concerning presynaptic differentiation has three continuous and interrelated stages: biogenesis and transport, trapping and stabilization, and maturation and growth. Progress in the past decade has greatly advanced our knowledge of the genes involved in the delivery of synaptic components and assembly of the presynaptic terminals. Dynamic imaging of cellular transport and trapping of synaptic components have further revealed previously unsuspected properties of axons. This review examines axonal dynamics and the molecular regulatory themes underlying presynaptic differentiation. Owing to space limitations, several relevant areas, such as axon formation, motor proteins, target recognition, and synaptic adhesion, are not discussed. Apologies are also offered for many excellent studies and the original research articles that are inevitably omitted. Readers are advised to consult outstanding reviews covering these related topics (e.g., Bonanomi et al. 2006, McAllister 2007, Piechotta et al. 2006, Waites et al. 2005, Wiggin et al. 2005, Zhai & Bellen 2004).

MORPHOLOGICAL AND MOLECULAR ORGANIZATION OF PRESYNAPTIC BOUTONS

The seminal ultrastructural imaging of synaptic junctions and vesicles in the 1950s (De Robertis & Bennett 1955, Palade & Palay 1954) provoked endless questions as to the composition and action of synaptic vesicles, the nature of the electron-dense specializations associated with the plasma membrane, and the interplay between different subcompartments at the synapse. A molecular understanding of synapses began with biochemical purification of synapse-associated proteins. The ingenious invention of the synaptosome preparation by Victor Whittaker and coworkers was instrumental in the inception of decades of synaptic biochemistry (Nagy et al. 1976). With the power of modern proteomic analysis, several hundred distinct presynaptic proteins have been identified (Südhof 2004). A recent major proteomic dissection in combination with elegant informatic analyses listed 410 proteins associated with synaptic vesicles and presynaptic membranes (Takamori et al. 2006).

The appearance of an electron-dense matrix associated with patches of the axonal plasma membrane and surrounded by small clusters of vesicles, as assessed by electron microscopy (EM), has been taken as the morphological landmark of a presynaptic terminal (Couteaux 1963, Vaughn 1989). These presynaptic specializations, or active zones, are almost invariably juxtaposed to a second electron-dense specialization present in the postsynaptic membrane, the postsynaptic density (PSD). Unfortunately, the proteins that compose the presynaptic density are in general insoluble in the biochemical purifications, resulting in a lag in their identification. Moreover, some presynaptic proteins may be present in selective types of synapses or transiently associate with synapses. Although major progress in the past decade has been made toward defining the molecular components of the cytomatrix assembled at the presynaptic active zone (CAZ), it is expected that many more proteins remain to be identified. Currently, known CAZ proteins are usually categorized as adaptor or scaffold because they have multiple protein-protein binding domains, and catalytic domains are relatively scarce (Schoch & Gundelfinger 2006). These proteins are capable of homomeric interactions and often physically associate with other CAZ proteins, or the synaptic plasma membrane, components of the synaptic cytoskeleton, and the synaptic vesicle recycling machinery. **Figure 1a** summarizes the best-characterized CAZ components, and detailed descriptions of the genes can be found in the online **Supplemental Text** (to access, follow the **Supplemental Material link** from the Annual Reviews home page at **http://www.annualreviews.org**). **Figure 1b** illustrates some of the protein interactions known to date. Below, we briefly convey recent observations of the molecular organizations of presynaptic terminals and then touch upon the

cellular biogenesis and delivery of presynaptic components.

Classic ultrastructural examination of samples fixed with different chemicals revealed stereotypic morphologies of the presynaptic specializations in different types of synapses (Akert et al. 1971, Couteaux 1963, Gray & Willis 1970, Pfenninger 1971). These observations led to the notion that the presynaptic specialization is structured to tether the synaptic vesicles in a regular pattern. Recent three-dimensional EM tomography studies on samples fixed by high-pressure freezing procedure have validated this view and have further revealed additional fine filamentous elements (**Figure 2**). In the frog neuromuscular synapses, the presynaptic active zone is composed of repeated electron-dense units that are flanked by docked synaptic vesicles (Harlow et al. 2001). Organized filaments project across the cytoplasm and toward the plasma membrane, connecting, possibly via voltage-gated Ca^{2+} channels, to the docked synaptic vesicles and the release machinery (**Figure 2b,c**). In central excitatory synapses, filaments emerge from the density at the plasma membrane and connect synaptic vesicles in an electron-dense network (Siksou et al. 2007) (**Figure 2d–f**). In the ribbon synapses of hair cells, filaments also tether synaptic vesicles to the ribbon and to the plasma membrane (Lenzi et al. 1999). The composition of such filaments remains elusive, but they may contain proteins like RIM1a, which decorates the surface of ribbons and directly binds the synaptic vesicle protein Rab3a (Dick et al. 2001, tom Dieck et al. 2005, Wang et al. 2001).

The organized nature of presynaptic architecture suggests that the presynaptic molecular scaffold must exert spatial constraints on the distribution of synaptic vesicles (SVs) and on the connection of SVs with the plasma membrane. Indeed, immuno-EM studies of the presynaptic CAZ proteins in several types of synapses have depicted a highly ordered spatial distribution (please refer to **Supplemental Text** for the CAZ proteins). In vertebrate CNS glutamatergic synapses, Bassoon, one of the

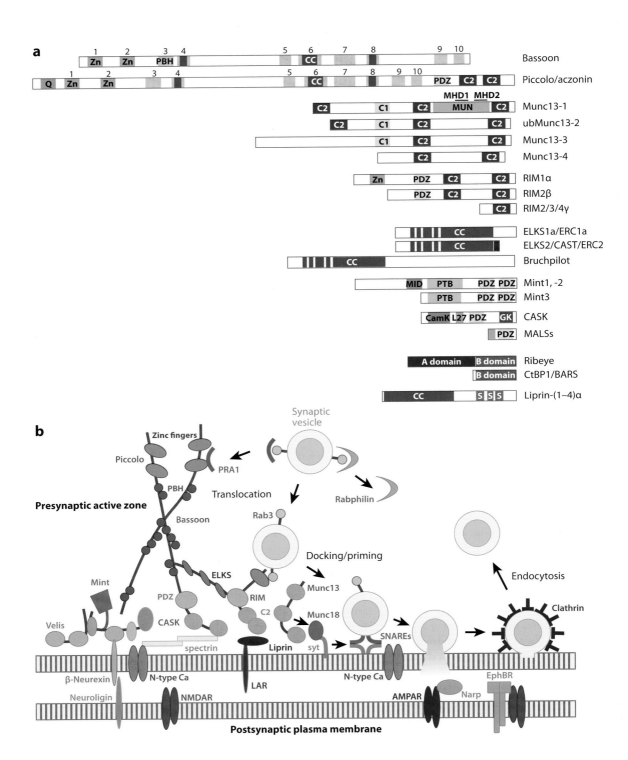

first known CAZ proteins, resides approximately ~70 nm away from the active zone and above filaments emanating from the plasma membrane at the active zone, whereas ELKS (or CAST) resides at focal points, ~30 nm next to the active zone (Siksou et al. 2007). In *Caenorhabditis elegans* neurons, which have a simple plaque-shaped dense projection, Liprin-α SYD-2 is restricted to the base of the dense projections; UNC-13 and Rim are further away (Weimer et al. 2006, Yeh et al. 2005). The mammalian photoreceptor ribbon synapse has two subcompartments: a dense projection from the plasma membrane and a ribbon extending from the SV release site into the presynaptic cytoplasm (Gray & Pease 1971) (**Figure 3a**). The ribbon is an electron-dense band of large surface area covered with synaptic vesicles. Ribeye and Piccolo are associated with the ribbon; Rim, Munc13, and ELKS are present at the density at the plasma membrane, whereas Bassoon localizes at the border between the two subcompartments (tom Dieck et al. 2005) (**Figure 3a**).

Besides the traditional immuno-EM methodology, a major advance in studying synapse proteins in situ has been the development of high-resolution microscopy that overcomes the light diffraction limit. For example, the stimulated emission depletion (STED) fluorescence microscopy revealed that the *Drosophila* Bruchpilot, a homolog of CAST/ELKS, is localized in donut-shaped structures centered at the T-bar of neuromuscular junctions (NMJs) (Kittel et al. 2006) (**Figure 3b**). Similarly, extended high-resolution structured-illumination microscopy showed that a presynaptic ankyrin molecule forms a lattice-like structure in *Drosophila* NMJs (Pielage et al. 2008). Such an orderly arrangement of presynaptic matrix proteins is consistent with the functional studies of these proteins described above and indicates that presynaptic assembly is a finely orchestrated process.

BIOGENESIS AND DELIVERY OF PRESYNAPTIC PROTEINS

Neuronal axons are microtubule-filled information highways. Synaptic components are constitutively generated in the cell soma and transported along the length of axons. Combinatorial studies using biochemical, anatomical, and imaging methods have established that most synaptic proteins are carried by vesicular intermediates derived from the trans-Golgi network (Ahmari et al. 2000, Shapira et al. 2003, Zhai et al. 2001). These transport intermediates have been variably described as dense core vesicles, pleomorphic vesicles, or vesicular-tubular structures. In fact, in early studies in mouse dorsal root ganglion neuron axons in which axonal

---

Figure 1

Molecular components of the presynaptic cytomatrix at the active zone (CAZ). (*a*) Protein domain illustration of a select group of presynaptic CAZ proteins (modified with permission from Schoch & Gundelfinger 2006). Only representative isoforms of a given protein family are shown and their relevant domains labeled; the size of the domains is approximate. (*b*) A schematic diagram of a subset of proteins found at presynaptic active zones of vertebrate synapses that are involved in defining the active-zone plasma membrane as the site of synaptic vesicle (SV) recycling. This cycle begins with the translocation of SVs from the reserve pool to the readily releasable pool docked at the plasma membrane. Docking occurs via the interactions of SV proteins, such as Rab3a with RIM. In preparation for calcium-triggered SV fusion, SVs are primed by RIM, Munc13, and Munc18 to enter into the SNARE fusion complex. Following fusion, SV proteins are captured and reused by the clathrin endocytic machinery. Many are structural molecules that define the active zone, including Piccolo, Bassoon, Rim, CASK, Velis, Mints, ELKS, and Liprins, which are composed of modular domain structures that make them suitable for their putative scaffolding functions. The relationships between the molecules shown are derived primarily from in vitro binding data. Dark lines represent the backbone of the molecule, and the colored elliptical objects represent individual domains, such as zinc fingers (*red*), C2 (*orange*), PDZ (*aqua*), and PBH (*blue*). Other proteins are named and represented as a single object, e.g., neurexin, neuroligin, and clathrin. (For a more detailed description, see Ziv & Garner 2004.)

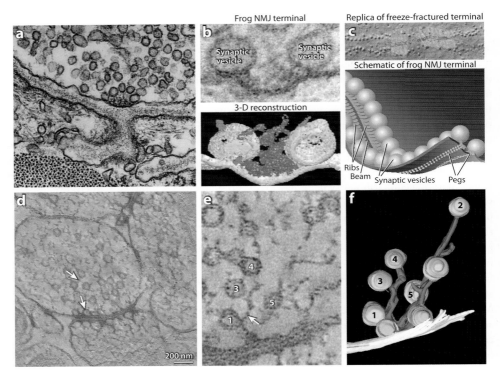

Frog NMJ terminal

Synaptic vesicle · Synaptic vesicle

3-D reconstruction

Replica of freeze-fractured terminal

Schematic of frog NMJ terminal

Ribs · Beam · Synaptic vesicles · Pegs

200 nm

Figure 2

Ultrastructure of synapses by traditional electron miscroscopy and tomography. (*a*) An electron micrograph of a frog neuromuscular junction (NMJ) taken by Dr. John Heuser. Electron-dense proteinaceous material associated with the cytoplasmic face of the active zone is associated with presynaptic synaptic vesicle (SV) clusters and is juxtaposed to postsynaptic membrane invaginations. (*b*) Tomographic image of a cross section of an active zone showing SVs docked at the plasma membrane and interacting with a fine filamentous projection. The bottom panel shows a 3-D reconstruction of the frog active zone shown in the top panel. (*c*) (*Upper panel*) Replica from a freeze-fractured frog NMJ showing the presence of parallel rows of bumps (possibly Ca^{2+} channels). Ribs (*green*) and beams (*blue*) (*bottom panel*) reflect the relationship of the presynaptic cytoskeletal matrix assembled at the active zone and these bumps. The bottom panel shows a schematic diagram of SVs organized into two parallel rows and tethered to the active zone via ribs, beams, and pegs at the frog NMJ (reproduced from Harlow et al. 2001). (*d–f*) Ultrastructural features of the presynaptic active zone from a hippocampal CA1 synapse visualized by electron tomography (reproduced with permission from Siksou et al. 2007). (*d*) A section from the tomographic reconstruction of a CNS synapse, using high-pressure freezing protocol; scale bar, 200 nm. The black arrow marks the docked vesicles, and the white arrow marks the filaments between the SVs; scale bar, 100 nm. (*e*) Example of a filament (*arrow*) contacting several SVs as numbered and a filament projecting from the cytoplasmic face of the active-zone membrane and extending several hundred nanometers into the interior of the bouton making contact with SVs. (*f*) A model drawing of a presynaptic active zone (shown in *e*) illustrating how fibers link synaptic vesicles to the presynaptic active zone. The numbers in panels *e* and *f* represent individual SVs.

transport was blocked by local cooling, typical mature SVs were rarely present (Tsukita & Ishikawa 1980). This result indicated that the generation of mature synaptic vesicles of uniform size and shape occurs after transport (see below). The CAZ proteins Bassoon, Pic-colo, and CtBP1 colocalize with trans-Golgi components and coassemble into a primordial vesicular form before transport to synapses (Dresbach et al. 2006). The vesicular packets containing cytomatrix proteins are frequently closely associated with vesicles transporting synaptic vesicle components but are not necessarily in the same package (Tao-Cheng 2007). The rarity of all these vesicular intermediates makes it difficult to determine their full molecular composition.

The kinesin-3 family of motor proteins, which includes KIF1A and UNC-104, is specifically responsible for transporting synaptic vesicle prescursors (Hall & Hedgecock 1991, Okada et al. 1995, Pack-Chung et al. 2007), whereas multiple motors appear to be involved in the delivery of vesicular intermediates carrying CAZ proteins. Mammalian Liprin-α binds the Unc104/KIF1A motor (Shin et al. 2003), and Drosophila Liprin-α binds conventional kinesin-1 (Miller et al. 2005). However, disrupting either motor in the C. elegans or Drosophila nervous systems only mildly perturbs the localization of the CAZ proteins (Deken et al. 2005, Miller et al. 2005, Pack-Chung et al. 2007, Yeh et al. 2005), indicating that each motor partially contributes to the transport of Liprin-α and other CAZ proteins. In mammalian neurons, kinesin-1 KIF5B motor and its adaptor syntabulin copurify with Bassoon and Piccolo and with syntaxin (Cai et al. 2007). Inhibiting syntabulin causes retention of Bassoon in cell bodies and reduces the formation of new synapses. This dependency of CAZ proteins on multiple motors is consistent with the heterogeneous nature of the transport intermediates destined for the presynaptic cytomatrix.

VESICULAR CONVERSION AND FUNCTION AT NASCENT SYNAPSES

A widespread view of synapse formation is that contact between presynaptic axons and postsynaptic partners, such as muscles and dendrites, triggers the assembly of synapses from transport vesicles. However, it has long been known that developing axons can form rudimentary synapses capable of releasing neurotransmitter in the absence of contacts from postsynaptic cells (Hume et al. 1983, Young & Poo 1983). In vivo, morphologically normal presynaptic terminals, or hemisynapses, can also form in the absence of postsynaptic targets or onto improper cells (Henrikson & Vaughn 1974, Prokop et al. 1996). Thus, synapse assembly is an intrinsic property of axons.

At nascent synapses, vesicles assume a less uniform shape, described as tubular or pleomorphic, although small 80-nm dense core vesicles are also more abundant (Vaughn 1989). Such nascent synapses undergo active exo- and endocytosis and display release properties distinct from those of mature synapses. In mature synapses, neurotransmitter release depends on P/Q-type Ca^{2+} channels and is primarily mediated by the SNARE VAMP2 (Murthy & De Camilli 2003, Südhof 2004). Tetanus toxin cleaves VAMP2 and blocks neurotransmitter release at mature synapses (Montecucco et al. 1996). Moreover, replenishment of synaptic vesicles in mature synapses requires dynamin and adaptor complex 2 (AP2)-mediated endocytosis. In contrast, at nascent synapses, neurotransmitter release depends on L-type Ca^{2+} channels and is insensitive to tetanus toxin, implying the utilization of a different v-SNARE in the fusion of immature synaptic vesicles (Coco et al. 1998, Verderio et al. 1999, Zakharenko et al. 1999). The fungal chemical brefeldin A (BFA) acts as a noncompetitive inhibitor for ADP ribosylation factor (ARF) GTPase activation and has been used to distinguish vesicular biogenesis originated in the Golgi, as opposed to the plasma membrane (Zeghouf et al. 2005). Neurotransmitter release at nascent synapses is sensitive to BFA treatment. In neurons treated with BFA, synaptophysin I is redistributed to tubular structures, whereas other SV proteins, such as synaptotagmin, synaptobrevin, and Rab3A, maintain a vesicular distribution (Mundigl et al. 1993). These observations have led to a long-standing proposal that transporting vesicular precursors undergo multiple cycles of exo- and endocytosis along the axon and that specialized domains along the axonal membrane may play a role in the morphological and functional maturation of SVs (Bonanomi et al. 2006, Matteoli et al. 2004). The transient nature of vesicular conversion imposes technical challenges on dissecting

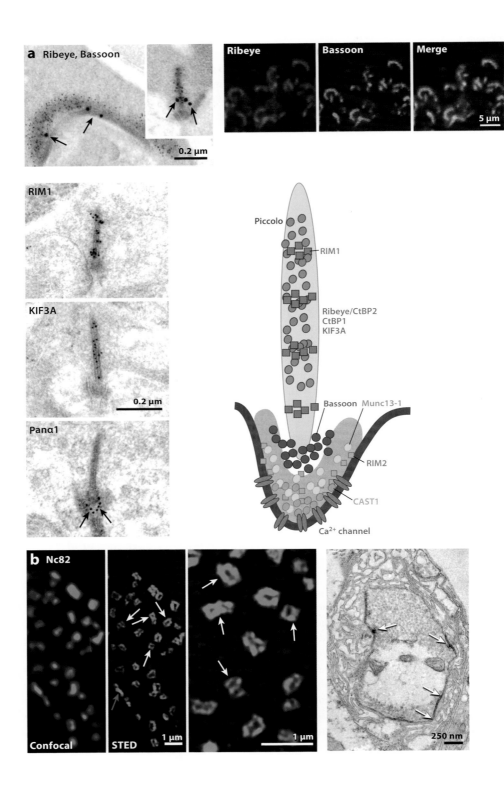

the molecular pathways underlying SV maturation. Nonetheless, recent studies have implicated several routes operating in the transition from nascent synapses to maturation.

AP3 and Synaptic Vesicle Genesis

One type of SV genesis that requires ARF and is sensitive to BFA involves the adaptor complex 3 (AP3). AP3 has both ubiquitous and neuronal isoforms and is primarily associated with endosomes (Newell-Litwa et al. 2007). Several cargos of AP3 are present in synaptic vesicles, leading to the hypothesis that AP3 may be involved in sorting synaptic membrane proteins and may contribute to the maturation of synaptic vesicles. A series of in vitro reconstitution experiments in the 1990s demonstrated ARF1-AP3-mediated synaptic vesicle biogenesis from endosomes isolated from PC12 cells (Faundez et al. 1998, Salem et al. 1998). Mutant mice that lack the ubiquitous isoform of AP3, known as *mocha*, show neurological defects (Kantheti et al. 1998) and increased sustained transmission during prolonged high-frequency stimulation, resembling normal synapses treated with BFA (Voglmaier et al. 2006). However, initial analysis of SV populations in *mocha* mice did not reveal gross abnormalities (Kantheti et al. 1998), suggesting that this ARF-dependent and AP3-mediated SV biogenesis was not essential for SV production. Only recently have several studies revealed a context-dependent, compensatory function of AP3 in the genesis of SVs in selected synapses. Mice lacking a particular neuronal form of AP3B exhibit spontaneous epileptic seizures; in such mutants the SVs of GABA-inhibitory synapses are less uniform in size and have reduced vesicular GABA transporter levels (Nakatsu et al. 2004). In *mocha* mice, several AP3 cargos, such as chloride channel 3, zinc transporter 3 (ZnT3), and VAMP7 (also known as TI-VAMP, a tetanus-toxin-resistant form of VAMP), all of which are SV membrane proteins, are mistargeted in different types of neurons (Salazar et al. 2004a,b; Scheuber et al. 2006). At CNS glutamatergic excitatory synapses, the vesicular transporter VGLUT1 is normally internalized through the AP2 pathway by binding to endophilin (Voglmaier et al. 2006). Blocking this binding results in VGLUT1 recycling through a slow pathway involving AP3. These observations show that AP3-mediated SV genesis plays a compensatory role in a synapse-specific manner and revitalize the hypothesis that such a process may regulate SV maturation at nascent synapses.

Exocyst and Nascent Synapse Sites

Certain trans-Golgi-derived vesicles may define the sites of nascent synapses in developing axons. The exocyst is a protein complex composed of eight proteins, including Sec3p, Sec5p, Sec6p, Sec8p, Sec10p, Sec15p, Exo70p,

Figure 3

Spatial distribution of presynaptic cytomatrix proteins. (*a*) Localization of Bassoon, Ribeye, and others in ribbon synapses (reproduced with permission from tom Dieck et al. 2005). (*Top left*) Immuno-EM images of Bassoon (large particles) and Ribeye (small particles), showing that, whereas Ribeye is present all over the surface of the ribbon, Bassoon localizes to the interface between ribbons and the archiform density. Scale bar, 0.2 µm. (*Top right*) Confocal images of coimmunostaining of Bassoon and Ribeye. Scale bar, 5 µm. (*Bottom left*) Immuno-EM images of RIM1α, KIF3A, and Ca^{2+} channel, showing the association of RIM1α and KIF3A with the synaptic ribbons at Ca^{2+} channels and with the archiform density/active zone. (*Bottom right*) Illustration of the relative distributions of known cytomatrix proteins at and along photoreceptor cell ribbon synapses. (*b*) Localization of *Drosophila* Bruchpilot seen with stimulated emission depletion (STED) microscopy. (*Left*) Images of immunostaining against Bruchpilot, using confocal and STED microscopy. STED images show that Bruchpilot is localized in a donut shape, likely surrounding the T-platform. White arrows point to individual rings, and the red arrow indicates a synapse viewed parallel to the synaptic plane. Scale bars, 1 µm. (*Right*) The T-bar structures (*arrows*) in a *Drosophila* neuromuscular junction by transmission electron microscopy. Reproduced with permission from Kittel et al. (2006).

and Exo84p, that was originally identified in yeast for its roles in targeting secretory vesicles to the specific domains of the plasma membrane (TerBush et al. 1996). The exocyst complex is present in neuronal growth cones (Hazuka et al. 1999, Hsu et al. 1996). Functional studies in *Drosophila* support a role for the exocyst in the fusion of membrane vesicles with the plasma membrane in neurite outgrowth. In mosaic flies lacking the *Sec5* gene, newly synthesized membrane vesicles fail to stay at the tips of neurites, and neurons are arrested at the neurite outgrowth stage of development (Murthy et al. 2003). Similarly, in *Sec15* mutant photoreceptors several cell adhesion membrane proteins are mistargeted, and photoreceptor axons display targeting defects (Mehta et al. 2005). In mammals, exocyst components cluster at the plasma membrane at periodic intervals and colocalize with SV markers in the developing CNS axons but disappear from the axons upon stable synapse formation (Hazuka et al. 1999). Recently, time-lapse observations of VAMP2-labeled synaptic transporting vesicles (STVs) in cultured young cortical axons revealed that STVs exhibit saltatory movement and repeated pausing at predefined sites in the absence of contacts to postsynaptic dendrites (Sabo et al. 2006). Such STV pausing sites are preferentially associated with Sec6. But Sec6 localization is independent of STVs. These observations imply that the exocyst may contribute to the specialization of regions of the axonal membrane and facilitate an enrichment of Golgi-derived immature synaptic components.

NCAM and Maturation of Nascent Synapses

The cell adhesion molecule NCAM is also associated with trans-Golgi-derived vesicles (Sytnyk et al. 2002). Complete elimination of NCAM function does not block neurite outgrowth or the formation of normal synapses (Moscoso et al. 1998). However, neuromuscular synapses exhibit an immature release pattern that is dependent on L-type Ca^{2+} channels and is sensitive to BFA (Polo-Parada et al.

2001). Stimulus-dependent SV exocytosis and endocytosis occur along the entire presynaptic axon, including regions that are not in direct contact with muscles, indicating that lack of NCAM blocks the conversion of immature synapses to mature synapses. NCAM has three isoforms: NCAM140, NCAM180, and NCAM120. Time-lapse studies in cultured hippocampal neurons, and in chick developing motor axons, show that NCAM180 and NCAM140 are associated with trans-Golgi-derived SV precursors at nascent synapses along the axons (Hata et al. 2007, Sytnyk et al. 2002). The NCAM puncta take up styryl dyes (FM4-64 or FM1-43), a process that is sensitive to treatment with BFA or nifedipine, an L-type-channel antagonist (Hata et al. 2007). Upon contact with myotubes, axonal NCAM puncta disappear, and SV cycling along the axons is downregulated. NCAM140 and NCAM180 are then selectively targeted to the synaptic terminals. Interestingly, targeting of NCAM180 to mature synaptic terminals does not depend on postsynaptic NCAM. In mice lacking the NCAM180 isoform alone, release from immature synapses is downregulated normally, but mature synapses express immature features (Polo-Parada et al. 2004). These findings indicate that there is a consolidation of nascent synapses upon the formation of mature synapses at the correct site and that contacts with postsynaptic sites trigger multiple independent events in presynaptic neurons.

Actin-Spectrin Cytoskeleton and Nascent Synapse Stabilization

The actin-spectrin cytoskeleton is abundant in both developing and mature synapses and has many roles in synapse dynamics (Dillon & Goda 2005). Spectrins interact with Munc13 and presynaptic voltage-gated Ca^{2+} channels (Sakaguchi et al. 1998, Sunderland et al. 2000). Perturbing the F-actin cytoskeleton has more pronounced effects in nascent synapses than in mature synapses (Zhang & Benson 2001). In developing cortical neurons, treatment with latrunculin A did not abolish the STV pausing sites but greatly increased the duration of STV pausing (Sabo et al. 2006). In *Drosophila* NMJs, specific elimination of spectrin from presynaptic terminals destabilizes synapses (Pielage et al. 2005). The NCAM180 cytoplasmic domain binds spectrin and interacts with actin-myosin (Polo-Parada et al. 2005, Sytnyk et al. 2002). These studies indicate that the transition of nascent synapses to functional synapses involves a cohort of events from vesicular recycling at the axonal membrane to remodeling of local cytoskeleton. However, the observation that eliminating NCAM or exocyst functions (see above) does not lead to a major failure in synapse formation suggests that each event is regulated by redundant pathways.

Nascent Synapses and Axon Arbor Formation

Nascent synapses may carry out functions in addition to SV maturation. Using in vivo time-lapse imaging of synaptic GFP markers, investigators have observed a remarkable correlation between nascent synapse sites and axon arbor formation in several types of neurons. In *Xenopus* tadpoles and zebrafish, retinal axons arborize through a process of extensive interstitial axon branching, preceding dendritic contacts. Stable synaptic GFP-VAMP2 puncta demarcate the sites where stable axon arbor branches form, and the branches formed from sites lacking synaptic GFP-VAMP2 puncta tend to retract or be eliminated (Meyer & Smith 2006, Ruthazer et al. 2006). Nascent synapses of *Xenopus* retinal axons also express ephrin-B (Lim et al. 2008). Activation of ephrin-B-mediated reverse signaling increases the efficacy of transmitter release and stabilizes retinal axon arbors. The development of motor neuron axons in *Xenopus* and zebrafish exhibits similar correlations with nascent synapses (Javaherian & Cline 2005, Panzer et al. 2006). STV pausing sites in cultured mammalian cortical neurons highly correlate with sites of axon-dendrite stabilization (Sabo et al. 2006). In vivo imaging of axon elongation in intact brains also shows stereotypical patterns specific to neuron types (Portera-Cailliau et al. 2005). These studies suggest that many aspects of presynaptic differentiation reflect the intrinsic properties of the axon type. Understanding how such intrinsic properties are regulated remains a major question in the field.

REGULATION OF SYNAPSE DYNAMICS AT MATURE SYNAPSES

Classic morphological studies of synapses have etched in the minds of many the concept of synapses as static structures that, once formed, are stable and unchanging. With the advent of live fluorescent imaging of synapses, this view is giving way to the realization that nearly all aspects of synapse structure and function are in a constant state of flux (Bresler et al. 2004, Okabe et al. 2001, Trachtenberg et al. 2002, Tsuriel et al. 2006). With regard to presynaptic function, these changes occur on three timescales. The fastest (milliseconds to seconds) is tightly linked to activity-dependent events that are associated with the recycling of SVs and the release of neurotransmitter. The second (minutes to hours) is coupled to the stability/turnover of different classes of presynaptic proteins, and the third (minutes to days) is associated with the life span of individual boutons/synapses.

Three types of events are coupled to the dynamics of neurotransmitter release. The first is linked to the Ca^{2+}-dependent fusion of SVs docked at the active zone. This event is very fast, occurring on a timescale of tens of milliseconds (Neher & Sakaba 2001), and is thought to involve a set of conformational changes in the docking and fusion machinery that trigger SV fusion upon the influx of Ca^{2+} (Südhof 2004). The second event is associated with refilling this readily releasable pool of vesicles by SVs present in the reserve pool. This event is also fast occurring, on the timescale of tens to hundreds of milliseconds (Neher & Sakaba 2001). Emerging data reveal that this second event involves many macromolecular events, including the uncoupling of SVs from synapsin and the actin cytoskeleton and the physical movement of SVs toward the active-zone plasma membrane (Dillon & Goda 2005, Greengard et al. 1993). The third event is associated with the recapture of SV proteins through clathrin-mediated endocytosis (Moskowitz et al. 2005). This is a relatively slow event with a time constant of tens of seconds (Balaji & Ryan 2007).

A fundamental question raised by these observations is how these extremely dynamic processes affect other aspects of presynaptic function. For example, are there erosive forces associated with the docking, fusion, and recycling of SVs that negatively affect the structural/functional integrity of synapses? This concept is tightly linked to both the general stability and the turnover of synaptic proteins and how synapses retain functionality over long periods of time. Time-lapse imaging of GFP-tagged synaptic proteins is beginning to resolve these questions. For example, in vivo studies in zebrafish, *Xenopus*, and mouse have shown that synapse life is somewhat age dependent: Nascent synapses exhibit relatively short life spans from 15 min to a few hours, whereas synapses in the mature brain can be maintained for weeks to months (reviewed in Meyer et al. 2003). These latter studies indicate that synapses have mechanisms to maintain their structure over long periods of time, but how? One possibility is that core structural proteins of the synapse have very long life/residency times at the synapse that are directly coupled to synapse life. Alternatively, synaptic proteins may be in a constant state of exchange, such that synapse life is determined by the on/off exchange kinetics of protein subsets. The regulation of molecular kinetics, or dynamics, has been most thoroughly studied for postsynaptic proteins. Here, most core PSD proteins have half-lives in neuronal cells from 2 to 15 h (Ehlers 2003) and dynamics regulated in part by the ubiquitin/proteasome system (Yi & Ehlers 2005) (see below). However, the exchange kinetics of individual postsynaptic proteins occur on much faster timescales of a few minutes to a couple of hours (Bresler et al. 2004, Nakagawa et al. 2004, Okabe et al. 2001, Sharma et al. 2006, Tsuriel et al. 2006, Yao et al. 2003). These data suggest that most synaptic proteins are in a constant state of flux and that other mechanisms, such as the overall on/off kinetics of the system, control synapse life. Similar results have been described for presynaptic proteins such as synapsin, SV2, actin, and Munc13 (Gaffield et al. 2006, Kalla et al. 2006, Sankaranarayanan et al. 2003, Shtrahman et al. 2005, Tsuriel et al. 2006), indicating that mechanisms regulating postsynaptic protein turnover also apply to the dynamics of presynaptic proteins.

In the past couple of years, research has yielded two types of cellular and molecular mechanisms that appear to control the stability and thus the life of synapses. The first mechanism relates to the fate of synaptic proteins following activity-dependent events. A number of studies have shown that axons contain significant extrasynaptic pools of synaptic proteins that directly contribute to, for example, the rapid and efficient recapture and recycling of SV proteins (Fernandez-Alfonso et al. 2006, Tsuriel et al. 2006). Intriguingly, these extrasynaptic pools are stocked by both de novo–synthesized somatic proteins (Tsuriel et al. 2006) as well as proteins and vesicular membranes that transiently disperse out of individual boutons following a train of action potentials (Fernandez-Alfonso et al. 2006, Tsuriel et al. 2006). Importantly, these dispersing proteins and vesicles are free to associate with and contribute to the release of neurotransmitter from adjacent boutons (Darcy et al. 2006, Tsuriel et al. 2006).

The second mechanism relates to a collection of E3 ubiquitin ligases that target subsets of pre- and postsynaptic proteins for proteasome-mediated degradation (Varshavsky 2005, Yi & Ehlers 2005). With regard to presynaptic function, some of the most studied are members of the PHR protein family, which regulate several aspects of presynaptic differentiation (see below). In addition, several E3 ligases, including the anaphase-promoting complex (APC), Siah, Staring, and Scrapper, selectively target specific presynaptic proteins for degradation, such as synaptophysin, syntaxin, Liprin-α, and RIM1α, respectively (see **Figure 4a** for

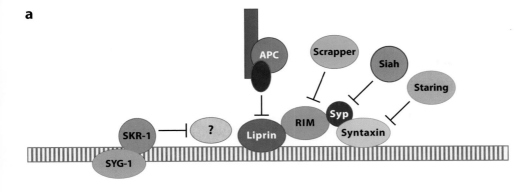

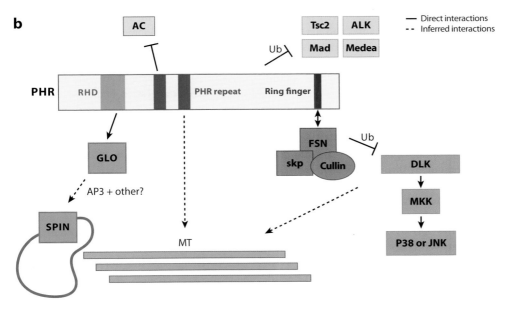

Figure 4

Ubiquitination in presynaptic development. (*a*) Multiple types of regulation involving ubiquitination regulate presynaptic active-zone assembly and dynamics in development and mature synapses. Liprin-αs are substrates of anaphase-promoting-complex (APC) (Hoogenraad et al. 2007, van Roessel et al. 2004), and RIM1α is a substrate of Scrapper (Yao et al. 2007); both APC and Scrapper may regulate synapse stability or plasticity, respectively. Similarly, the synaptic vesicle proteins synaptophysin (Syp) and the t-SNARE syntaxin are substrates for the E3 ligases Siah and Staring, respectively, potentially providing a mechanism to regulate synaptic vesicle fusion locally (Chin et al. 2002, Wheeler et al. 2002). Additionally, studies in *C. elegans* reveal that the stabilization of HSN synapses by SYG-1 requires the inhibition of an E3 ligase (Ding et al. 2007). (*b*) PHR (Pam/Highwire/RPM-1) proteins are conserved E3 ligases. They target DLK for degradation in multiple types of synapses and neurons (Collins et al. 2006, Lewcock et al. 2007, Nakata et al. 2005) and may also have other ligase targets, such as TSC2, Smad, and ALK (Liao et al. 2004, McCabe et al. 2004, Murthy et al. 2004). PHR may positively regulate the endolysosomal compartment at synapses or axon endings through the GLO and AP3 (adaptor complex 3) pathway or other unknown players (Grill et al. 2007, Sweeney & Davis 2002). PHR can also inhibit adenylate cyclase (AC) (Scholich et al. 2001). The red box denotes a ring finger, and the blue boxes represent PHR repeats. Other abbreviations used: DLK, dual-leucine-zipper-bearing MAPK kinase kinase; HSN, hermaphrodite-specific neuron; MT, microtubule; RHD, RCC1 homology domain; SPIN, spinster/benchwarmer; Ub, ubiquitin.

a description) (Chin et al. 2002, Hoogenraad et al. 2007, van Roessel et al. 2004, Wheeler et al. 2002, Yao et al. 2007). These data indicate that ubiquitination and the proteasome system can play rather subtle roles within nerve terminals, including the activity-dependent regulation of synaptic plasticity.

MULTIFACETED FUNCTION OF PHR PROTEINS IN AXON DYNAMICS AND SYNAPSE FORMATION

The PHR proteins are conserved large proteins with E3 ligase activities and have gained attention for their roles in multiple aspects of presynaptic differentiation. This protein family includes human Pam (protein associated with Myc), mouse Phr1, zebrafish Esrom, *Drosophila* Highwire, and *C. elegans* RPM-1, collectively called PHR (for Pam/Highwire/RPM-1) proteins. PHR proteins are unusually large, averaging 4000 amino acids or more, and exhibit extensive homology throughout the protein. The N terminus of a PHR protein contains an RCC1 homology domain that may be a guanine nucleotide exchange factor (GEF), whereas the C terminus has a ring-finger E3 ubiquitin ligase domain (**Figure 4*b***). The founding member, human Pam, was identified on the basis of expression cloning for proteins binding to the Myc oncogene (Guo et al. 1998). Subsequently, analyses of mutations disrupting *C. elegans* RPM-1 and *Drosophila* Highwire revealed that PHR proteins have key roles in synapse formation and axon patterning (Schaefer et al. 2000, Wan et al. 2000, Zhen et al. 2000). Recently, researchers have described mutations in zebrafish Esrom and mouse Phr1 (Bloom et al. 2007, Burgess et al. 2004, D'Souza et al. 2005, Lewcock et al. 2007). PHR proteins are widely expressed, with highest expression in the developing nervous systems. The phenotypic consequences of loss of PHR function vary from organism to organism and from neuron to neuron. The emerging consensus is that PHR proteins use both conserved and divergent signaling pathways to reg-

ulate axonal dynamics in a context-dependent, and possibly a stage-specific, manner.

C. elegans neurons form synapses *en passant* along axons. In *rpm-1* mutants, motor and sensory neurons form fewer synapses, and those synapses formed have fewer SVs and display disorganization of synaptic architecture (Schaefer et al. 2000, Zhen et al. 2000). Lack of RPM-1 does not affect overall axonal guidance, but some neurons overshoot beyond their normal termination points. In *Drosophila* larval NMJs, motor neurons elaborate stereotypical terminal branches on the muscle surface and form synaptic boutons in a characteristic pattern. During larval development the motor terminals undergo regulated bouton addition, or synaptic growth, to match the increase in muscle surface. In *highwire* mutants, the motor terminals exhibit excessive branching, doubling the synaptic bouton number, a phenotype described as synaptic overgrowth (Wan et al. 2000). However, individual boutons are smaller than those of the wild type, and the quantal size and content of the mutant synapses are also reduced. Both RPM-1 and Highwire are localized in presynaptic terminals and function in a cell-autonomous manner (Schaefer et al. 2000, Wan et al. 2000, Zhen et al. 2000).

Complete loss of function in mouse *phr1* results in early lethality, limiting the ability to examine the effects on synapses in many neurons. An early study on a compound mutant mouse lacking *phr1* revealed that the peripheral motor nerve innervating the diaphragm muscles has normal axon projection and termination onto normal-appearing muscle endplates but that the axon terminals frequently extend extrasynaptic varicosities (Burgess et al. 2004). A recent targeted deletion of *phr1* in motor axons has confirmed these observations and further demonstrated a cell-autonomous requirement of *phr1* in NMJ formation (Bloom et al. 2007). A tour-de-force forward genetic screen for mutants displaying embryonic motor axon guidance defects produced two loss-of-function mutations of *phr1*, known as Magellan mice (Lewcock et al. 2007). In *Magellan* (*phr1*) mutant embryos, developing motor and sensory axons wander or stall at a critical choice point, despite their normal sensitivity to axon guidance cues. In the cortex, targeted deletion of *phr1* causes major disruption in multiple cortical axon tracts (Bloom et al. 2007). Surprisingly, some of the cortical axon projection defects are due to a non-cell-autonomous function of *phr1*. Zebrafish *esrom* mutants were isolated in a retinal topographic mapping screen (Karlstrom et al. 1996). The retinal axons show segregation and fasciculation defects and fail to map onto the tectum; another type of axon, the habenula commissural axon, also fails to cross the midline (Hendricks et al. 2008, Le Guyader et al. 2005). Together, these studies reveal an axon- and neuron-type-specific requirement of the vertebrate PHR proteins in synapse formation and axon patterning.

The dissection of signaling pathways involving PHR proteins has been greatly advanced by parallel genetic approaches in *C. elegans* and *Drosophila*. The genetic interaction between Highwire and a deubiquitinating enzyme provided the initial hint that PHR proteins function in ubiquitin-mediated protein degradation (DiAntonio et al. 2001). The identification of a conserved F-box protein FSN-1 as a functional partner of RPM-1 provides the definitive proof that PHR proteins constitute a functional E3 ubiquitin ligase (Liao et al. 2004, Wu et al. 2007). The use of genetic modifier screens demonstrated that *C. elegans* DLK-1 and *Drosophila* Wallenda, members of the dual-leucine-zipper-bearing MAPK kinase kinases (DLKs), are substrates of the RPM-1/FSN-1 and Hiw/dFsn ubiquitin ligases, respectively (Collins et al. 2006, Nakata et al. 2005, Wu et al. 2007). Recent studies of mouse Phr1 and DLK show that this interaction is conserved in the embryonic motor axon projection (Lewcock et al. 2007). Cellular analyses further show that the negative regulation of DLK by PHR proteins restricts DLK signaling to a small region of the axon or the growth cone. In *C. elegans* and *Drosophila* synapses, both RPM-1 and Highwire display restricted localization to subcompartments near the presynaptic termi-

nal (Abrams et al. 2008, Wu et al. 2005). In *rpm-1* and *highwire* mutants, DLK expression at synapses is upregulated (Collins et al. 2006, Nakata et al. 2005). In mouse embryonic motor axons, DLK is localized to the tip of the growth cone, and Phr1 is present in axon shaft and is excluded from the growth cone. In *phr1* mutant axons, DLK levels increase, and DLK spreads into the axonal shaft (Lewcock et al. 2007). DLK activates a p38 MAPK cascade in *C. elegans* and mouse, whereas in *Drosophila* the terminal MAPK is JNK (Collins et al. 2006, Lewcock et al. 2007, Nakata et al. 2005). The output of these MAPK cascades is likely to be partly via nuclear transcription (Collins et al. 2006). The DLK pathway is well positioned to provide retrograde signals between (*a*) growth cones and/or presynaptic terminals and (*b*) the cell soma in controlling the overall maturation state of the axon and synapses.

Examination of the growth cone dynamics in *phr1* mutant axons has revealed that PHR proteins and DLK can regulate microtubule stability (Lewcock et al. 2007). Phr1 is associated with a stable microtubule cytoskeleton in the axon shaft. When grown in culture, normal motor axons display a leading growth cone that is filled with F-actin and reduced numbers of microtubules, especially in growth cone lamellipodia and filopodia (Burnette et al. 2007, Suter & Forscher 2000). In contrast, Phr1 mutant axons extend several growth cone–like structures that retain microtubules and are not oriented in the direction of axon growth (Lewcock et al. 2007). Stabilization of microtubules by taxol rescues these growth cone defects. *Drosophila* DLK/Wallenda has recently been implicated in kinesin-1-mediated axonal transport (Horiuchi et al. 2007). Activation of DLK/Wallenda may cause kinesin-1 to dissociate from microtubules. It is generally thought that microtubules are absent from mature synapses. However, early work depicted different forms of microtubules associated with different types of synapses (Gray et al. 1982). In *Drosophila* NMJs, where synapses form at the ends of axons, microtubules are associated with synaptic cytoskeletal loop structures (Roos et al.

2000). Disrupting the function of the MAP-1B protein Futsch causes a reduction of synaptic bouton numbers, and the boutons exhibit abnormal architecture. In synapses formed along the axon shaft, the relationship between microtubules and synapses is less well understood. In general, microtubules are not seen to invade synapse boutons, but run as tracks along one side of the presynaptic varicosities that are packed with SV clusters, presumably allowing microtubule-dependent transport to more distal synapses. Thus, the regulation of microtubule stability must be balanced for synapses to form and grow. PHR proteins may restrict the action of DLK in the growth cone tip or synaptic region. Furthermore, MAPK signaling may affect the transport of cargos and the local assembly of the cytoskeleton, which are necessary for growth cone movement and the stabilization of nascent synapses.

The identification of a RabGEF, GLO-4, as a functional partner of *C. elegans* RPM-1 provides an unexpected link between PHR proteins and the endolysosomal vesicular pathway (Grill et al. 2007). GLO-4 acts through a Rab protein, GLO-1, to intersect with the AP3 pathway. Loss of this vesicular regulation causes penetrant defects in axon termination and a mild alteration in synapses. The GLO-AP3 pathway was discovered by virtue of its role in the formation of lysosome-related organelles in intestinal epithelial cells (Hermann et al. 2005). In *rpm-1* and *glo* mutants, late-endosomal markers in motor neuron synapses exhibited a disorganized pattern (Grill et al. 2007). In *Drosophila* mutants for the late-endosomal protein Spinster, also known as Benchwarmer, motor terminals display a synaptic overgrowth phenotype resembling that of *highwire* (Dermaut et al. 2005, Sweeney & Davis 2002). Zebrafish Esrom also regulates the pigment color of retinal neurons, which involves lysosome-related organelles (Le Guyader et al. 2005). In the vertebrate developing axons, organelles bearing features of late-endolysosomal components are present at the axon branching points and at the growing tips (Arantes & Andrews 2006, Overly & Hollenbeck 1996).

Lysosomal-membrane proteins such as LAMP1 are present in synaptic membranes (Arantes & Andrews 2006, Takamori et al. 2006). TI-VAMP and phosphatidylinositol-4-kinase IIα, two known AP3 cargos, are associated with SVs (Guo et al. 2003, Salazar et al. 2005, Martinez-Arca et al. 2003). Lysosomal organelles can undergo Ca^{2+}-dependent exocytosis and fusion with the plasma membrane (Arantes & Andrews 2006, Rao et al. 2004). As mentioned above, murine *phr1* has a nonautonomous function that does not involve DLK (Bloom et al. 2007). Such a nonautonomous function of Phr1 may be mediated through regulated secretion. The identification of the signals from Phr1-expressing neurons should clarify the underlying mechanism.

In summary, PHR proteins have conserved roles in the coordination of synaptic and axon growth. However, their precise roles vary considerably depending on the cell type and the organism. Nonetheless, it is tempting to speculate that a unifying theme for PHR proteins is that they sculpt microdomains within the axon by regulating the interactions between the axonal microtubule cytoskeleton and transport vesicles. Distinct, and likely transient, vesicular organelles that bear late-endolysosomal features likely play active roles in vesicular membrane conversions necessary for membrane exchange and precursor maturation. The giant size of PHR proteins predicts that they function through multiple pathways. Indeed, in addition to the above-discussed conserved pathways, investigators have reported several other binding partners for PHR proteins, ranging from the nuclear proteins Myc and Smad (Guo et al. 1998, McCabe et al. 2004) to adenylate cyclase (Scholich et al. 2001), ALK receptor tyrosine kinase (Liao et al. 2004), and Tuberin TSC2 (Murthy et al. 2004). *highwire* exhibits dose-dependent interactions with TSC2 (Murthy et al. 2004). In *esrom* mutant axons, phosphorylated TSC2 is upregulated (D'Souza et al. 2005). A major challenge is to define the qualitative and quantitative contributions of different signaling pathways regulated by PHR proteins in a context-specific and dynamic environment.

MOLECULAR MECHANISMS FOR SYNAPSE STABILIZATION, EXCLUSION, AND ELIMINATION

The discussions above suggest that de novo synapse formation occurs frequently as a result of the intrinsic properties of axons and transporting vesicular intermediates. Live-imaging studies show that contact from the postsynaptic targets per se does not necessarily result in the stable formation of synapses (Meyer & Smith 2006, Sabo et al. 2006). Moreover, developing neurons form numerous synapses, many of which are later eliminated in the mature nervous system. Therefore, active mechanisms exist to stabilize synapses selectively, to eliminate unwanted synapses, or to exclude synapse formation. Intense studies in the past decade have identified a plethora of molecules that are capable of inducing or stabilizing synapses. These molecules function in a highly redundant manner, and the stabilization of nascent synapses at the correct locations and the subsequent growth of synapses involve multiple steps mediated by diverse molecular pathways. A comprehensive description of all molecules identified to date is beyond the scope of this review. Readers are directed to other articles (Fox & Umemori 2006, Piechotta et al. 2006). Here, we highlight a few recent examples that demonstrate the diverse regulatory themes in the regulation of presynaptic differentiation and synapse maturation.

In the complex environment of the intact brain, guidepost cells have been proposed to provide spatial information for synapse positioning (Sanes & Yamagata 1999, Super et al. 1998). Recent genetic studies in *C. elegans* neurons have uncovered two pathways by which epidermal or neuronal guide cells can position synapses. The HSN neurons form *en passant* synapses on vulval muscles, well after their axon guidance and the development of postsynaptic targets. Initially, numerous synapses appear in places around the vulva, but only the synapses formed onto two sets of postsynaptic targets are stabilized (Ding et al. 2007). The vulval epithelium provides instructive signals to localize HSN synapses (Shen & Bargmann 2003).

The immunoglobulin (Ig) domain–containing membrane protein SYG-2, a member of the Nephrin family of ligands, is produced from vulval epithelial cells and binds to SYG-1, another Ig domain protein and a member of the NEPH receptors, in the HSN neurons (Shen & Bargmann 2003, Shen et al. 2004). This interaction triggers a series of active recruitment orchestrated by two key cytomatrix proteins, SYD-1 rhoGAP and SYD-2 Liprin-α (Dai et al. 2006, Patel et al. 2006). In addition, the SYG-1 and SYG-2 interaction also actively inhibits a proteasome-mediated synapse elimination (Ding et al. 2007). One binding partner of SYG-1 is a homolog of Skp1, SKR-1, a component of the ubiquitin E3 ligase. The binding of SYG-1 to SKR-1 inhibits the E3 ligase activity at the primary synapse site, allowing synapses to be stabilized, whereas the SKR-1 E3 ligase is active in surrounding regions to degrade secondary synapses. A similar kind of synapse regulation by surrounding cells also occurs in the synapses formed between two interneurons, AIY and RIA. Netrin/UNC-6 is produced locally from the supporting sheath cells and acts via the receptor UNC-40/DCC in the presynaptic AIY neuron to position synapse assembly (Colon-Ramos et al. 2007). These findings begin to unravel the molecular mechanisms underlying the guidepost-mediated synapse positioning.

Classically defined morphogens such as Wnt, BMP, and FGF are emerging as critical organizers of synapse formation. In mouse cerebellum, locally produced Wnt7 induces axonal terminal remodeling in the mossy fibers and acts through Dishevelled (Dvl) to regulate presynaptic differentiation in two steps (Ahmad-Annuar et al. 2006, Ciani et al. 2004, Hall et al. 2000). One is to increase the formation of presynaptic boutons, and the other is to promote functional maturation of the synapses. Dvl is tightly associated with stable microtubules and regulates microtubule stability (Ciani et al. 2004, Krylova et al. 2000). In *C. elegans*, the motor neuron DA9 resides in the tail of the animal and forms synapses in a restricted segment of the axon. Wnt morphogens pattern the *C. elegans* tail and determine the region of the DA9 axon that is capable of forming presynaptic terminals (Klassen & Shen 2007). Loss of Wnt function causes an expansion of the axonal presynaptic domains, whereas over-expression of Wnt inhibits synapse formation. This effect of Wnt also involves a Dvl homolog. In *Drosophila* NMJs, both Wnt signaling and TGF signaling influence the formation and addition of motor synaptic boutons in larvae (Marques 2005). Distinct Wnts exert either inductive or inhibitory effects on motor terminals (Speese & Budnik 2007). One target of Wnt signaling appears to be the MAP1B molecule Futsch (Franco et al. 2004). These studies illustrate the complex interactions between secreted molecules and axonal cytoskeleton dynamics.

The mechanisms underlying the formation of the vertebrate NMJs are the best characterized (Sanes & Lichtman 1999). Bidirectional interactions between the motor terminal and myotubes stabilize the presynaptic terminals and promote synapse growth and maintenance. As mentioned above, nascent synapses are present in ingrowing motor axons and disappear upon contacting final targets. NCAM is involved in the downregulation of these nascent axonal synapses (Piechotta et al. 2006, Polo-Parada et al. 2001). The dramatic expansion of synaptic terminals at the motor axon endings requires several sequential signalings. FGFs secreted from the muscle targets act through the FGF2 receptor in the presynaptic terminal to stimulate local growth and the stabilization of synaptic terminals in embryos (Fox et al. 2007, Umemori et al. 2004). FGF signaling is downregulated postnatally. The extracellular matrix protein laminin $\beta2$ is required for postnatal presynaptic differentiation. Furthermore, as NMJs form, several forms of collagens accumulate at the synaptic cleft. Developmental expression of different isoforms of collagen contributes in a sequential manner to embryonic and postnatal NMJ growth (Fox et al. 2007). Such combinatorial regulation ensures the precise maturation and proper function of a synapse throughout different phases of a neuron.

The cell-culture-based search for synaptogenic molecules in the 1990s led to the identification of numerous cell surface receptors and ligands, such as neurexin and neuroligin, SynCAM, EphR kinases, and thrombospondin (Biederer & Scheiffele 2007, Piechotta et al. 2006, Scheiffele et al. 2000). Recent functional studies reveal the general theme that, although such cell adhesion molecules are able to induce presynaptic terminal differentiation in the synapse-induction assay, their effects in vivo are predominantly to promote functional maturation of synapses. For example, neuroligin can induce clustering of presynaptic components, yet genetic elimination of all neuroligins has little effect on overall synaptic architecture and number. Instead, neuroligins mediate the functional maturation of synapses in an activity-dependent manner (Varoqueaux et al. 2006). In this respect, neuroligins in the CNS may resemble the roles of NCAM in NMJs. Moreover, differential tissue and temporal expression of these synaptic adhesive and inductive molecules in intact animals appears to contribute greatly to the diversification of synapse types and function, such as inhibitory versus excitatory synapses (Budreck & Scheiffele 2007, Chubykin et al. 2007, Graf et al. 2004, Tabuchi et al. 2007; reviewed in Craig & Kang 2007).

In most neurons, more numerous synapses are formed in the developing stage than in mature stages. Synapse elimination is an obligatory step in wiring the functional neuronal circuit and involves many signaling pathways (Goda & Davis 2003, Waites et al. 2005). A new finding reveals an active mechanism in CNS synapse elimination that involves a complement cascade traditionally known for its roles in the innate immune system. Factors of the classical complement are preferentially associated with immature synapses in the developing retina and are downregulated in the mature CNS (Stevens et al. 2007). In mice deficient in complement proteins, lateral geniculate nucleus (LGN) neurons exhibit multi-innervation and a failure in retinal synapse refinement. Such studies emphasize many unsuspected players that play important functions at synapses.

In short, these studies exemplify the multi-step regulations of presynaptic differentiation. They further depict a high degree of functional redundancy among members of the same molecular family and combinatorial interactions between different signaling modes. These findings strengthen the notion that synapse formation is a long process involving multiple organizers, each having a distinct role.

CONCLUSIONS AND PERSPECTIVES

Presynaptic differentiation is an ongoing process throughout a neuron's life. Synapse formation begins as an intrinsic aspect of axonal differentiation. The role of extrinsic signals is largely to modulate, maintain, or refine this intrinsic synaptogenic activity. The mere presence of SV clusters at the membrane does not ensure the proper formation and function of synapses. Even in mature neurons, synaptic clusters possessing mature release properties, known as orphan vesicles, are present without postsynaptic partners (Krueger et al. 2003). The function of such orphan vesicle clusters remains unknown.

In the future, understanding the basis of synapse formation will require analysis at many levels. In terms of cell biology, studies of presynaptic vesicular intermediates will be important to shed light on the critical events in the initiation of synapse assembly and will depend on the ability to trap or enrich for such transient structures. At the genetic level, have the forward genetic screens for mutants with synaptic defects in *C. elegans* and *Drosophila* been saturated? The answer is no. Such screens may be biased against genes with other essential functions. Moreover, genetic interaction studies often show a high degree of redundancy in synaptogenic pathways. The biochemical basis for this redundancy is still unclear, yet it suggests that the effects of eliminating single synaptogenic proteins are often very subtle. More refined second-generation screens using sensitized backgrounds and new markers will likely yield additional genetic insights. For example, a split-GFP-based method, GRASP (GFP reconstitution across synaptic partners), using synaptic membrane proteins can precisely identify the synaptic partners in *C. elegans* neurons (Feinberg et al. 2008). The broad use of this labeling method in combination with genetics and in vivo imaging will offer exciting findings regarding our understanding of neuronal connectivity in the near future. Although much progress has been made in what may be thought of as the core synaptogenesis pathways, such pathways are susceptible to a high degree of modulation to yield the structural and functional diversity of synapses known from classical ultrastructural and physiological work. Another major future goal will be to understand what makes synapses different as well as what they have in common.

DISCLOSURE STATEMENT

The authors are not aware of any biases that might be perceived as affecting the objectivity of this review.

ACKNOWLEDGMENTS

We are indebted to S. Schoch, E. Gundelfinger, S. Marty, S. Sigrist, J. Heuser, and U. McMahan for their permission for the beautiful images and figures. We thank A. Chisholm, G. Gallegos, H. van Epps, and members of the Jin and Garner labs for comments and discussions. Funding from NINDS (NS35546 to Y.J. and NS39471 and NS353862 to C.C.G.) supported research in our labs. Y.J. is an investigator of HHMI. C.C.G. is supported by the Nancy Pritzker family.

LITERATURE CITED

Abrams B, Grill B, Huang X, Jin Y. 2008. Cellular and molecular determinants targeting the *Caenorhabditis elegans* PHR protein RPM-1 to perisynaptic regions. *Dev. Dyn.* 237:630–39

Ahmad-Annuar A, Ciani L, Simeonidis I, Herreros J, Fredj NB, et al. 2006. Signaling across the synapse: a role for Wnt and Dishevelled in presynaptic assembly and neurotransmitter release. *J. Cell Biol.* 174:127–39

Ahmari SE, Buchanan J, Smith SJ. 2000. Assembly of presynaptic active zones from cytoplasmic transport packets. *Nat. Neurosci.* 3:445–51

Akert K, Moor H, Pfenninger K. 1971. Synaptic fine structure. *Adv. Cytopharmacol.* 1:273–90

Arantes RM, Andrews NW. 2006. A role for synaptotagmin VII-regulated exocytosis of lysosomes in neurite outgrowth from primary sympathetic neurons. *J. Neurosci.* 26:4630–37

Balaji I, Ryan TA. 2007. Single-vesicle imaging reveals that synaptic vesicle exocytosis and endocytosis are coupled by a single stochastic mode. *Proc. Natl. Acad. Sci. USA* 104:20576–81

Biederer T, Scheiffele P. 2007. Mixed-culture assays for analyzing neuronal synapse formation. *Nat. Protoc.* 2:670–76

Bloom AJ, Miller BR, Sanes JR, DiAntonio A. 2007. The requirement for Phr1 in CNS axon tract formation reveals the corticostriatal boundary as a choice point for cortical axons. *Genes Dev.* 21:2593–606

Bonanomi D, Benfenati F, Valtorta F. 2006. Protein sorting in the synaptic vesicle life cycle. *Prog. Neurobiol.* 80:177–x217

Bresler T, Shapira M, Boeckers T, Dresbach T, Futter M, et al. 2004. Postsynaptic density assembly is fundamentally different from presynaptic active zone assembly. *J. Neurosci.* 24:1507–20

Budreck EC, Scheiffele P. 2007. Neuroligin-3 is a neuronal adhesion protein at GABAergic and glutamatergic synapses. *Eur. J. Neurosci.* 26:1738–48

Burgess RW, Peterson KA, Johnson MJ, Roix JJ, Welsh IC, O'Brien TP. 2004. Evidence for a conserved function in synapse formation reveals *Phr1* as a candidate gene for respiratory failure in newborn mice. *Mol. Cell Biol.* 24:1096–105

Burnette DT, Schaefer AW, Ji L, Danuser G, Forscher P. 2007. Filopodial actin bundles are not necessary for microtubule advance into the peripheral domain of Aplysia neuronal growth cones. *Nat. Cell Biol.* 9:1360–69

Cai Q, Pan YP, Sheng HZ. 2007. Syntabulin-kinesin-1 family member 5B-mediated axonal transport contributes to activity-dependent presynaptic assembly. *J. Neurosci.* 27:7284–96

Chin LS, Vavalle JP, Li L. 2002. Staring, a novel E3 ubiquitin-protein ligase that targets syntaxin 1 for degradation. *J. Biol. Chem.* 277:35071–79

Chubykin AA, Atasoy D, Etherton RM, Brose N, Kavalali TE, et al. 2007. Activity-dependent validation of excitatory versus inhibitory synapses by neuroligin-1 versus neuroligin-2. *Neuron* 54:919–31

Ciani L, Krylova O, Smalley JM, Dale CT, Salinas CP. 2004. A divergent canonical WNT-signaling pathway regulates microtubule dynamics: Dishevelled signals locally to stabilize microtubules. *J. Cell Biol.* 164:243–53

Coco S, Verderio C, De Camilli P, Matteoli M. 1998. Calcium dependence of synaptic vesicle recycling before and after synaptogenesis. *J. Neurochem.* 71:1987–92

Collins CA, Wairkar PY, Johnson LS, DiAntonio A. 2006. Highwire restrains synaptic growth by attenuating a MAP kinase signal. *Neuron* 51:57–69

Colon-Ramos DA, Margeta AM, Shen K. 2007. Glia promote local synaptogenesis through UNC-6 (netrin) signaling in *C. elegans*. *Science* 318:103–6

Couteaux R. 1963. The differentiation of synaptic areas. *Proc. R. Soc. London Ser. B* 158:457–80

Craig AM, Kang Y. 2007. Neurexin-neuroligin signaling in synapse development. *Curr. Opin. Neurobiol.* 17:43–52

D'Souza J, Hendricks M, Le Guyader S, Subburaju S, Grunewald B, et al. 2005. Formation of the retinotectal projection requires Esrom, an ortholog of PAM (protein associated with Myc). *Development* 132:247–56

Dai Y, Taru H, Deken LS, Grill B, Ackley B, et al. 2006. SYD-2 Liprin-α organizes presynaptic active zone formation through ELKS. *Nat. Neurosci.* 9:1479–87

Darcy KJ, Staras K, Collinson LM, Goda Y. 2006. Constitutive sharing of recycling synaptic vesicles between presynaptic boutons. *Nat. Neurosci.* 9:315–21

De Robertis ED, Bennett SH. 1955. Some features of the submicroscopic morphology of synapses in frog and earthworm. *J. Biophys. Biochem. Cytol.* 1:47–58

Deken SL, Vincent R, Hadwiger G, Liu Q, Wang WZ, Nonet LM. 2005. Redundant localization mechanisms of RIM and ELKS in *Caenorhabditis elegans. J. Neurosci.* 25:5975–83

Dermaut B, Norga KK, Kania A, Verstreken P, Pan H, et al. 2005. Aberrant lysosomal carbohydrate storage accompanies endocytic defects and neurodegeneration in *Drosophila* benchwarmer. *J. Cell Biol.* 170:127–39

DiAntonio A, Haghighi PA, Portman LS, Lee DJ, Amaranto MA, Goodman SC. 2001. Ubiquitination-dependent mechanisms regulate synaptic growth and function. *Nature* 412:449–52

Dick O, Hack I, Altrock DW, Garner CC, Gundelfinger DE, Brandstatter HJ. 2001. Localization of the presynaptic cytomatrix protein Piccolo at ribbon and conventional synapses in the rat retina: comparison with Bassoon. *J. Comp. Neurol.* 439:224–34

Dillon C, Goda Y. 2005. The actin cytoskeleton: integrating form and function at the synapse. *Annu. Rev. Neurosci.* 28:25–55

Ding M, Chao D, Wang G, Shen K. 2007. Spatial regulation of an E3 ubiquitin ligase directs selective synapse elimination. *Science* 317:947–51

Dresbach T, Torres V, Wittenmayer N, Altrock DW, Zamorano P, et al. 2006. Assembly of active zone precursor vesicles: obligatory trafficking of presynaptic cytomatrix proteins Bassoon and Piccolo via a trans-Golgi compartment. *J. Biol. Chem.* 281:6038–47

Ehlers MD. 2003. Activity level controls postsynaptic composition and signaling via the ubiquitin-proteasome system. *Nat. Neurosci.* 6:231–42

Faundez V, Horng TJ, Kelly BR. 1998. A function for the AP3 coat complex in synaptic vesicle formation from endosomes. *Cell* 93:423–32

Feinberg EH, Vanhoven MK, Bendesky A, Wang G, Fetter RD, et al. 2008. GFP reconstitution across synaptic partners (GRASP) defines cell contacts and synapses in living nervous systems. *Neuron* 57:353–63

Fernandez-Alfonso T, Kwan R, Ryan TA. 2006. Synaptic vesicles interchange their membrane proteins with a large surface reservoir during recycling. *Neuron* 51:179–86

Fox MA, Sanes RJ, Borza BD, Eswarakumar PV, Fassler R, et al. 2007. Distinct target-derived signals organize formation, maturation, and maintenance of motor nerve terminals. *Cell* 129:179–93

Fox MA, Umemori H. 2006. Seeking long-term relationship: Axon and target communicate to organize synaptic differentiation. *J. Neurochem.* 97:1215–31

Franco B, Bogdanik L, Bobinnec Y, Debec A, Bockaert J, et al. 2004. Shaggy, the homolog of glycogen synthase kinase 3, controls neuromuscular junction growth in *Drosophila. J. Neurosci.* 24:6573–77

Gaffield MA, Rizzoli SO, Betz WJ. 2006. Mobility of synaptic vesicles in different pools in resting and stimulated frog motor nerve terminals. *Neuron* 51:317–25

Goda Y, Davis WG. 2003. Mechanisms of synapse assembly and disassembly. *Neuron* 40:243–64

Graf ER, Zhang X, Jin XS, Linhoff WM, Craig MA. 2004. Neurexins induce differentiation of GABA and glutamate postsynaptic specializations via neuroligins. *Cell* 119:1013–26

Greengard P, Valtorta F, Czernik AJ, Benfenati F. 1993. Synaptic vesicle phosphoproteins and regulation of synaptic function. *Science* 259:780–85

Gray EG, Burgoyne DR, Westrum EL, Cumming R, Barron J. 1982. The enigma of microtubule coils in brain synaptosomes. *Proc. R. Soc. London Ser. B* 216:385–96

Gray EG, Pease LH. 1971. On understanding the organisation of the retinal receptor synapses. *Brain Res.* 35:1–15

Grill B, Bienvenut VW, Brown MH, Ackley DB, Quadroni M, Jin Y. 2007. *C. elegans* RPM-1 regulates axon termination and synaptogenesis through the Rab GEF GLO-4 and the Rab GTPase GLO-1. *Neuron* 55:587–601

Guo J, Wenk RM, Pellegrini L, Onofri F, Benfenati F, De Camilli P. 2003. Phosphatidylinositol 4-kinase type IIα is responsible for the phosphatidylinositol 4-kinase activity associated with synaptic vesicles. *Proc. Natl. Acad. Sci. USA* 100:3995–4000

Guo Q, Xie J, Dang VC, Liu TE, Bishop MJ. 1998. Identification of a large Myc-binding protein that contains RCC1-like repeats. *Proc. Natl. Acad. Sci. USA* 95:9172–77

Hall AC, Lucas RF, Salinas CP. 2000. Axonal remodeling and synaptic differentiation in the cerebellum is regulated by WNT-7a signaling. *Cell* 100:525–35

Hall DH, Hedgecock ME. 1991. Kinesin-related gene *unc-104* is required for axonal transport of synaptic vesicles in *C. elegans*. *Cell* 65:837–47

Harlow M, Ress D, Stoschek A, Marshall MR, McMahan JU. 2001. The architecture of active zone material at the frog's neuromuscular junction. *Nature* 409:479–84

Hata K, Polo-Parada L, Landmesser TL. 2007. Selective targeting of different neural cell adhesion molecule isoforms during motoneuron myotube synapse formation in culture and the switch from an immature to mature form of synaptic vesicle cycling. *J. Neurosci.* 27:14481–93

Hazuka CD, Foletti LD, Hsu CS, Kee Y, Hopf WF, Scheller HR. 1999. The sec6/8 complex is located at neurite outgrowth and axonal synapse-assembly domains. *J. Neurosci.* 19:1324–34

Hendricks M, Mathuru SA, Wang H, Silander O, Kee ZM, Jesuthasan S. 2008. Disruption of Esrom and Ryk identifies the roof plate boundary as an intermediate target for commissure formation. *Mol. Cell Neurosci.* 37:271–83

Henrikson CK, Vaughn EJ. 1974. Fine structural relationships between neurites and radial glial processes in developing mouse spinal cord. *J. Neurocytol.* 3:659–75

Hermann GJ, Schroeder KL, Hieb AC, Kershner MA, Rabbitts MB, et al. 2005. Genetic analysis of lysosomal trafficking in *Caenorhabditis elegans*. *Mol. Biol. Cell.* 16:3273–88

Hoogenraad CC, Feliu-Mojer MI, Spangler AS, Milstein DA, Dunah WA, et al. 2007. Liprinα1 degradation by calcium/calmodulin-dependent protein kinase II regulates LAR receptor tyrosine phosphatase distribution and dendrite development. *Dev. Cell* 12:587–602

Horiuchi D, Collins AC, Bhat P, Barkus VR, Diantonio A, Saxton MW. 2007. Control of a kinesin-cargo linkage mechanism by JNK pathway kinases. *Curr. Biol.* 17:1313–17

Hsu SC, Ting EA, Hazuka DC, Davanger S, Kenny WJ, et al. 1996. The mammalian brain rsec6/8 complex. *Neuron* 17:1209–19

Hume RI, Role WL, Fischbach DG. 1983. Acetylcholine release from growth cones detected with patches of acetylcholine receptor-rich membranes. *Nature* 305:632–34

Javaherian A, Cline TH. 2005. Coordinated motor neuron axon growth and neuromuscular synaptogenesis are promoted by CPG15 in vivo. *Neuron* 45:505–12

Kalla S, Stern M, Basu J, Varoqueaux F, Reim K, et al. 2006. Molecular dynamics of a presynaptic active zone protein studied in Munc13-1-enhanced yellow fluorescent protein knock-in mutant mice. *J. Neurosci.* 26:13054–66

Kantheti P, Qiao X, Diaz EM, Peden AA, Meyer EG, et al. 1998. Mutation in AP-3δ in the *mocha* mouse links endosomal transport to storage deficiency in platelets, melanosomes, and synaptic vesicles. *Neuron* 21:111–22

Karlstrom RO, Trowe T, Klostermann S, Baier H, Brand M, et al. 1996. Zebrafish mutations affecting retinotectal axon pathfinding. *Development* 123:427–38

Kittel RJ, Wichmann C, Rasse MT, Fouquet W, Schmidt M, et al. 2006. Bruchpilot promotes active zone assembly, Ca^{2+} channel clustering, and vesicle release. *Science* 312:1051–54

Klassen MP, Shen K. 2007. Wnt signaling positions neuromuscular connectivity by inhibiting synapse formation in *C. elegans*. *Cell* 130:704–16

Krueger SR, Kolar A, Fitzsimonds MR. 2003. The presynaptic release apparatus is functional in the absence of dendritic contact and highly mobile within isolated axons. *Neuron* 40:945–57

Krylova O, Messenger JM, Salinas CP. 2000. Dishevelled-1 regulates microtubule stability: a new function mediated by glycogen synthase kinase-3β. *J. Cell Biol.* 151:83–94

Le Guyader S, Maier J, Jesuthasan S. 2005. Esrom, an ortholog of PAM (protein associated with c-myc), regulates pteridine synthesis in the zebrafish. *Dev. Biol.* 277:378–86

Lenzi D, Runyeon JW, Crum J, Ellisman MH, Roberts WM. 1999. Synaptic vesicle populations in saccular hair cells reconstructed by electron tomography. *J. Neurosci.* 19:119–32

Lewcock JW, Genoud N, Lettieri K, Pfaff LS. 2007. The ubiquitin ligase Phr1 regulates axon outgrowth through modulation of microtubule dynamics. *Neuron* 56:604–20

Liao EH, Hung W, Abrams B, Zhen M. 2004. An SCF-like ubiquitin ligase complex that controls presynaptic differentiation. *Nature* 430:345–50

Lim BK, Matsuda N, Poo MM. 2008. Ephrin-B reverse signaling promotes structural and functional synaptic maturation in vivo. *Nat. Neurosci.* 11:160–69

Marques G. 2005. Morphogens and synaptogenesis in *Drosophila*. *J. Neurobiol.* 64:417–34

Martinez-Arca S, Rudge R, Vacca M, Raposo G, Camonis J, et al. 2003. A dual mechanism controlling the localization and function of exocytic v-SNAREs. *Proc. Natl. Acad. Sci. USA* 100:9011–16

Matteoli M, Coco S, Schenk U, Verderio C. 2004. Vesicle turnover in developing neurons: how to build a presynaptic terminal. *Trends Cell Biol.* 14:133–40

McAllister AK. 2007. Dynamic aspects of CNS synapse formation. *Annu. Rev. Neurosci.* 30:425–50

McCabe BD, Hom S, Aberle H, Fetter DR, Marques G, et al. 2004. Highwire regulates presynaptic BMP signaling essential for synaptic growth. *Neuron* 41:891–905

Mehta SQ, Hiesinger RP, Beronja S, Zhai GR, Schulze LK, et al. 2005. Mutations in *Drosophila* sec15 reveal a function in neuronal targeting for a subset of exocyst components. *Neuron* 46:219–32

Meyer MP, Niell CM, Smith SJ. 2003. Brain imaging: How stable are synaptic connections? *Curr. Biol.* 13:R180–82

Meyer MP, Smith JS. 2006. Evidence from in vivo imaging that synaptogenesis guides the growth and branching of axonal arbors by two distinct mechanisms. *J. Neurosci.* 26:3604–14

Miller KE, DeProto J, Kaufmann N, Patel NB, Duckworth A, Van Vactor D. 2005. Direct observation demonstrates that Liprin-α is required for trafficking of synaptic vesicles. *Curr. Biol.* 15:684–89

Montecucco C, Schiavo G, Rossetto O. 1996. The mechanism of action of tetanus and botulinum neurotoxins. *Arch. Toxicol. Suppl.* 18:342–54

Moscoso LM, Cremer H, Sanes JR. 1998. Organization and reorganization of neuromuscular junctions in mice lacking neural cell adhesion molecule, tenascin-C, or fibroblast growth factor-5. *J. Neurosci.* 18:1465–77

Moskowitz HS, Yokoyama CT, Ryan TA. 2005. Highly cooperative control of endocytosis by clathrin. *Mol. Biol. Cell* 16:1769–76

Mundigl O, Matteoli M, Daniell L, Thomas-Reetz A, Metcalf A, et al. 1993. Synaptic vesicle proteins and early endosomes in cultured hippocampal neurons: differential effects of Brefeldin A in axon and dendrites. *J. Cell Biol.* 122:1207–21

Murthy M, Garza D, Scheller HR, Schwarz LT. 2003. Mutations in the exocyst component Sec5 disrupt neuronal membrane traffic, but neurotransmitter release persists. *Neuron* 37:433–47

Murthy V, Han S, Beauchamp LR, Smith N, Haddad AL, et al. 2004. Pam and its ortholog highwire interact with and may negatively regulate the TSC1·TSC2 complex. *J. Biol. Chem.* 279:1351–58

Murthy VN, De Camilli P. 2003. Cell biology of the presynaptic terminal. *Annu. Rev. Neurosci.* 26:701–28

Nagy A, Baker RR, Morris JS, Whittaker PV. 1976. The preparation and characterization of synaptic vesicles of high purity. *Brain Res.* 109:285–309

Nakagawa T, Engler JA, Sheng M. 2004. The dynamic turnover and functional roles of α-actinin in dendritic spines. *Neuropharmacology* 47:734–45

Nakata K, Abrams B, Grill B, Goncharov A, Huang X, et al. 2005. Regulation of a DLK-1 and p38 MAP kinase pathway by the ubiquitin ligase RPM-1 is required for presynaptic development. *Cell* 120:407–20

Nakatsu F, Okada M, Mori F, Kumazawa N, Iwasa H, et al. 2004. Defective function of GABA-containing synaptic vesicles in mice lacking the AP-3B clathrin adaptor. *J. Cell Biol.* 167:293–302

Neher E, Sakaba T. 2001. Estimating transmitter release rates from postsynaptic current fluctuations. *J. Neurosci.* 21:9638–54

Newell-Litwa K, Seong E, Burmeister M, Faundez V. 2007. Neuronal and non-neuronal functions of the AP-3 sorting machinery. *J. Cell Sci.* 120:531–41

Okabe S, Urushido T, Konno D, Okado H, Sobue K. 2001. Rapid redistribution of the postsynaptic density protein PSD-Zip45 (Homer 1c) and its differential regulation by NMDA receptors and calcium channels. *J. Neurosci.* 21:9561–71

Okada Y, Yamazaki H, Sekine-Aizawa Y, Hirokawa N. 1995. The neuron-specific kinesin superfamily protein KIF1A is a unique monomeric motor for anterograde axonal transport of synaptic vesicle precursors. *Cell* 81:769–80

Overly CC, Hollenbeck JP. 1996. Dynamic organization of endocytic pathways in axons of cultured sympathetic neurons. *J. Neurosci.* 16:6056–64

Pack-Chung E, Kurshan TP, Dickman KD, Schwarz LT. 2007. A *Drosophila* kinesin required for synaptic bouton formation and synaptic vesicle transport. *Nat. Neurosci.* 10:980–89

Palade GE, Palay LS. 1954. Electron microscope observations of interneuronal and neuromuscular synapses. *Anat. Rec.* 118:335–36

Panzer JA, Song Y, Balice-Gordon RJ. 2006. In vivo imaging of preferential motor axon outgrowth to and synaptogenesis at prepatterned acetylcholine receptor clusters in embryonic zebrafish skeletal muscle. *J. Neurosci.* 26:934–47

Patel MR, Lehrman KE, Poon YV, Crump GJ, Zhen M, et al. 2006. Hierarchical assembly of presynaptic components in defined *C. elegans* synapses. *Nat. Neurosci.* 9:1488–98

Pfenninger KH. 1971. The cytochemistry of synaptic densities. I. An analysis of the bismuth iodide impregnation method. *J. Ultrastruct. Res.* 34:103–22

Piechotta K, Dudanova I, Missler M. 2006. The resilient synapse: insights from genetic interference of synaptic cell adhesion molecules. *Cell Tissue Res.* 326:617–42

Pielage J, Fetter DR, Davis WG. 2005. Presynaptic spectrin is essential for synapse stabilization. *Curr. Biol.* 15:918–28

Pielage J, Cheng L, Fetter RD, Carlton PM, Sedat JW, Davis GW. 2008. A presynaptic giant ankyrin stabilizes the NMJ through regulation of presynaptic microtubules and transsynaptic cell adhesion. *Neuron* 58:195–209

Polo-Parada L, Bose MC, Landmesser TL. 2001. Alterations in transmission, vesicle dynamics, and transmitter release machinery at NCAM-deficient neuromuscular junctions. *Neuron* 32:815–28

Polo-Parada L, Bose MC, Plattner F, Landmesser TL. 2004. Distinct roles of different neural cell adhesion molecule (NCAM) isoforms in synaptic maturation revealed by analysis of NCAM 180 kDa isoform-deficient mice. *J. Neurosci.* 24:1852–64

Polo-Parada L, Plattner F, Bose C, Landmesser TL. 2005. NCAM 180 acting via a conserved C-terminal domain and MLCK is essential for effective transmission with repetitive stimulation. *Neuron* 46:917–31

Portera-Cailliau C, Weimer MR, De Paola V, Caroni P, Svoboda K. 2005. Diverse modes of axon elaboration in the developing neocortex. *PLoS Biol.* 3:e272

Prokop A, Landgraf M, Rushton E, Broadie K, Bate M. 1996. Presynaptic development at the *Drosophila* neuromuscular junction: assembly and localization of presynaptic active zones. *Neuron* 17:617–26

Rao SK, Huynh C, Proux-Gillardeaux V, Galli T, Andrews WN. 2004. Identification of SNAREs involved in synaptotagmin VII-regulated lysosomal exocytosis. *J. Biol. Chem.* 279:20471–79

Roos J, Hummel T, Ng N, Klambt C, Davis WG. 2000. *Drosophila* Futsch regulates synaptic microtubule organization and is necessary for synaptic growth. *Neuron* 26:371–82

Ruthazer ES, Li J, Cline TH. 2006. Stabilization of axon branch dynamics by synaptic maturation. *J. Neurosci.* 26:3594–603

Sabo SL, Gomes AR, McAllister KA. 2006. Formation of presynaptic terminals at predefined sites along axons. *J. Neurosci.* 26:10813–25

Sakaguchi G, Orita S, Naito A, Maeda M, Igarashi H, et al. 1998. A novel brain-specific isoform of β spectrin: isolation and its interaction with Munc13. *Biochem. Biophys. Res. Commun.* 248:846–51

Salazar G, Craige B, Wainer HB, Guo J, De Camilli P, Faundez V. 2005. Phosphatidylinositol-4-kinase type IIα is a component of adaptor protein-3-derived vesicles. *Mol. Biol. Cell* 16:3692–704

Salazar G, Love R, Styers LM, Werner E, Peden A, et al. 2004a. AP-3-dependent mechanisms control the targeting of a chloride channel (ClC-3) in neuronal and non-neuronal cells. *J. Biol. Chem.* 279:25430–39

Salazar G, Love R, Werner E, Doucette MM, Cheng S, et al. 2004b. The zinc transporter ZnT3 interacts with AP-3 and it is preferentially targeted to a distinct synaptic vesicle subpopulation. *Mol. Biol. Cell.* 15:575–87

Salem N, Faundez V, Horng TJ, Kelly BR. 1998. A v-SNARE participates in synaptic vesicle formation mediated by the AP3 adaptor complex. *Nat. Neurosci.* 1:551–56

Sanes JR, Lichtman WJ. 1999. Development of the vertebrate neuromuscular junction. *Annu. Rev. Neurosci.* 22:389–442

Sanes JR, Yamagata M. 1999. Formation of lamina-specific synaptic connections. *Curr. Opin. Neurobiol.* 9:79–87

Sankaranarayanan S, Atluri PP, Ryan TA. 2003. Actin has a molecular scaffolding, not propulsive, role in presynaptic function. *Nat. Neurosci.* 6:127–35

Schaefer AM, Hadwiger DG, Nonet LM. 2000. *rpm-1*, a conserved neuronal gene that regulates targeting and synaptogenesis in *C. elegans*. *Neuron* 26:345–56

Scheiffele P, Fan J, Choih J, Fetter R, Serafini T. 2000. Neuroligin expressed in nonneuronal cells triggers presynaptic development in contacting axons. *Cell* 101:657–69

Scheuber A, Rudge R, Danglot L, Raposo G, Binz T, et al. 2006. Loss of AP-3 function affects spontaneous and evoked release at hippocampal mossy fiber synapses. *Proc. Natl. Acad. Sci. USA* 103:16562–67

Schoch S, Gundelfinger DE. 2006. Molecular organization of the presynaptic active zone. *Cell Tissue Res.* 326:379–91

Scholich K, Pierre S, Patel BT. 2001. Protein associated with Myc (PAM) is a potent inhibitor of adenylyl cyclases. *J. Biol. Chem.* 276:47583–89

Shapira M, Zhai GR, Dresbach T, Bresler T, Torres IV, et al. 2003. Unitary assembly of presynaptic active zones from Piccolo-Bassoon transport vesicles. *Neuron* 38:237–52

Sharma K, Fong DK, Craig AM. 2006. Postsynaptic protein mobility in dendritic spines: long-term regulation by synaptic NMDA receptor activation. *Mol. Cell Neurosci.* 31:702–12

Shen K, Bargmann IC. 2003. The immunoglobulin superfamily protein SYG-1 determines the location of specific synapses in *C. elegans*. *Cell* 112:619–30

Shen K, Fetter DR, Bargmann IC. 2004. Synaptic specificity is generated by the synaptic guidepost protein SYG-2 and its receptor, SYG-1. *Cell* 116:869–81

Shin H, Wyszynski M, Huh KH, Valtschanoff JG, Lee JR, et al. 2003. Association of the kinesin motor KIF1A with the multimodular protein liprin-α. *J. Biol. Chem.* 278:11393–401

Shtrahman M, Yeung C, Nauen DW, Bi GQ, Wu XL. 2005. Probing vesicle dynamics in single hippocampal synapses. *Biophys. J.* 89:3615–27

Siksou L, Rostaing P, Lechaire PJ, Boudier T, Ohtsuka T, et al. 2007. Three-dimensional architecture of presynaptic terminal cytomatrix. *J. Neurosci.* 27:6868–77

Speese SD, Budnik V. 2007. Wnts: up-and-coming at the synapse. *Trends Neurosci.* 30:268–75

Stevens B, Allen JN, Vazquez EL, Howell RG, Christopherson SK, et al. 2007. The classical complement cascade mediates CNS synapse elimination. *Cell* 131:1164–78

Südhof TC. 2004. The synaptic vesicle cycle. *Annu. Rev. Neurosci.* 27:509–47

Sunderland WJ, Son JY, Miner HJ, Sanes RJ, Carlson SS. 2000. The presynaptic calcium channel is part of a transmembrane complex linking a synaptic laminin (α4β2γ1) with nonerythroid spectrin. *J. Neurosci.* 20:1009–19

Super H, Martinez A, Del Rio JA, Soriano E. 1998. Involvement of distinct pioneer neurons in the formation of layer-specific connections in the hippocampus. *J. Neurosci.* 18:4616–26

Suter DM, Forscher P. 2000. Substrate-cytoskeletal coupling as a mechanism for the regulation of growth cone motility and guidance. *J. Neurobiol.* 44:97–113

Sweeney ST, Davis WG. 2002. Unrestricted synaptic growth in *spinster*—a late endosomal protein implicated in TGF-β-mediated synaptic growth regulation. *Neuron* 36:403–16

Sytnyk V, Leshchyns'ka I, Delling M, Dityateva G, Dityatev A, Schachner M. 2002. Neural cell adhesion molecule promotes accumulation of TGN organelles at sites of neuron-to-neuron contacts. *J. Cell Biol.* 159:649–61

Tabuchi K, Blundell J, Etherton RM, Hammer ER, Liu X, et al. 2007. A neuroligin-3 mutation implicated in autism increases inhibitory synaptic transmission in mice. *Science* 318:71–76

Takamori S, Holt M, Stenius K, Lemke AE, Gronborg M, et al. 2006. Molecular anatomy of a trafficking organelle. *Cell* 127:831–46

Tao-Cheng JH. 2007. Ultrastructural localization of active zone and synaptic vesicle proteins in a preassembled multi-vesicle transport aggregate. *Neuroscience* 150:575–84

TerBush DR, Maurice T, Roth D, Novick P. 1996. The exocyst is a multiprotein complex required for exocytosis in *Saccharomyces cerevisiae*. *EMBO J.* 15:6483–94

tom Dieck S, Altrock DW, Kessels MM, Qualmann B, Regus H, et al. 2005. Molecular dissection of the photoreceptor ribbon synapse: Physical interaction of Bassoon and RIBEYE is essential for the assembly of the ribbon complex. *J. Cell Biol.* 168:825–36

Tsukita S, Ishikawa H. 1980. The movement of membranous organelles in axons. Electron microscopic identification of anterogradely and retrogradely transported organelles. *J. Cell Biol.* 84:513–30

Tsuriel S, Geva R, Zamorano P, Dresbach T, Boeckers T, et al. 2006. Local sharing as a predominant determinant of synaptic matrix molecular dynamics. *PLoS Biol.* 4:e271

Trachtenberg JT, Chen BE, Knott GW, Feng G, Sanes JR, et al. 2002. Long-term in vivo imaging of experience-dependent synaptic plasticity in adult cortex. *Nature* 420:788–94

Umemori H, Linhoff WM, Ornitz MD, Sanes RJ. 2004. FGF22 and its close relatives are presynaptic organizing molecules in the mammalian brain. *Cell* 118:257–70

van Roessel P, Elliott AD, Robinson MI, Prokop A, Brand HA. 2004. Independent regulation of synaptic size and activity by the anaphase-promoting complex. *Cell* 119:707–18

Varoqueaux F, Aramuni G, Rawson LR, Mohrmann R, Missler M, et al. 2006. Neuroligins determine synapse maturation and function. *Neuron* 51:741–54

Varshavsky A. 2005. Regulated protein degradation. *Trends Biochem. Sci.* 30:283–86

Vaughn JE. 1989. Fine structure of synaptogenesis in the vertebrate central nervous system. *Synapse* 3:255–85

Verderio C, Coco S, Bacci A, Rossetto O, De Camilli P, et al. 1999. Tetanus toxin blocks the exocytosis of synaptic vesicles clustered at synapses but not of synaptic vesicles in isolated axons. *J. Neurosci.* 19:6723–32

Voglmaier SM, Kam K, Yang H, Fortin LD, Hua Z, et al. 2006. Distinct endocytic pathways control the rate and extent of synaptic vesicle protein recycling. *Neuron* 51:71–84

Waites CL, Craig MA, Garner CC. 2005. Mechanisms of vertebrate synaptogenesis. *Annu. Rev. Neurosci.* 28:251–74

Wan HI, DiAntonio A, Fetter DR, Bergstrom K, Strauss R, Goodman SC. 2000. Highwire regulates synaptic growth in *Drosophila*. *Neuron* 26:313–29

Wang X, Hu B, Zimmermann B, Kilimann WM. 2001. Rim1 and rabphilin-3 bind Rab3-GTP by composite determinants partially related through N-terminal α-helix motifs. *J. Biol. Chem.* 276:32480–88

Weimer RM, Gracheva OE, Meyrignac O, Miller GK, Richmond EJ, Bessereau LJ. 2006. UNC-13 and UNC-10/rim localize synaptic vesicles to specific membrane domains. *J. Neurosci.* 26:8040–47

Wheeler TC, Chin LS, Li Y, Roudabush FL, Li L. 2002. Regulation of synaptophysin degradation by mammalian homologues of *Seven in Absentia*. *J. Biol. Chem.* 277:10273–82

Wiggin GR, Fawcett PJ, Pawson T. 2005. Polarity proteins in axon specification and synaptogenesis. *Dev. Cell* 8:803–16

Wu C, Daniels WR, Diantonio A. 2007. DFsn collaborates with Highwire to down-regulate the Wallenda/DLK kinase and restrain synaptic terminal growth. *Neural Dev.* 2:16

Wu C, Wairkar PY, Collins AC, DiAntonio A. 2005. Highwire function at the *Drosophila* neuromuscular junction: spatial, structural, and temporal requirements. *J. Neurosci.* 25:9557–66

Yao I, Iida J, Nishimura W, Hata Y. 2003. Synaptic localization of SAPAP1, a synaptic membrane-associated protein. *Genes Cells* 8:121–29

Yao I, Takagi H, Ageta H, Kahyo T, Sato S, et al. 2007. SCRAPPER-dependent ubiquitination of active zone protein RIM1 regulates synaptic vesicle release. *Cell* 130:943–57

Yeh E, Kawano T, Weimer MR, Bessereau LJ, Zhen M. 2005. Identification of genes involved in synaptogenesis using a fluorescent active zone marker in *Caenorhabditis elegans*. *J. Neurosci.* 25:3833–41

Yi JJ, Ehlers MD. 2005. Ubiquitin and protein turnover in synapse function. *Neuron* 47:629–32

Young SH, Poo MM. 1983. Spontaneous release of transmitter from growth cones of embryonic neurones. *Nature* 305:634–37

Zakharenko S, Chang S, O'Donoghue M, Popov VS. 1999. Neurotransmitter secretion along growing nerve processes: comparison with synaptic vesicle exocytosis. *J. Cell Biol.* 144:507–18

Zeghouf M, Guibert B, Zeeh CJ, Cherfils J. 2005. Arf, Sec7 and Brefeldin A: a model towards the therapeutic inhibition of guanine nucleotide-exchange factors. *Biochem. Soc. Trans.* 33:1265–68

Zhai RG, Bellen JH. 2004. The architecture of the active zone in the presynaptic nerve terminal. *Physiology (Bethesda)* 19:262–70

Zhai RG, Vardinon-Friedman H, Cases-Langhoff C, Becker B, Gundelfinger DE, et al. 2001. Assembling the presynaptic active zone: a characterization of an active one precursor vesicle. *Neuron* 29:131–43

Zhang W, Benson LD. 2001. Stages of synapse development defined by dependence on F-actin. *J. Neurosci.* 21:5169–81

Zhen M, Huang X, Bamber B, Jin Y. 2000. Regulation of presynaptic terminal organization by *C. elegans* RPM-1, a putative guanine nucleotide exchanger with a RING-H2 finger domain. *Neuron* 26:331–43

Ziv NE, Garner CC. 2004. Cellular and molecular mechanisms of presynaptic assembly. *Nat. Rev. Neurosci.* 5:385–99

Regulation of Spermatogonial Stem Cell Self-Renewal in Mammals

Jon M. Oatley[1,*] and Ralph L. Brinster[2]

[1] Department of Animal Sciences, Center for Reproductive Biology and Health, College of Agricultural Sciences, Pennsylvania State University, University Park, Pennsylvania 16802; email: jmo15@psu.edu

[2] Department of Animal Biology, School of Veterinary Medicine, University of Pennsylvania, Philadelphia, Pennsylvania 19104; email: cpope@vet.upenn.edu

Annu. Rev. Cell Dev. Biol. 2008. 24:263–86

First published online as a Review in Advance on June 26, 2008

The *Annual Review of Cell and Developmental Biology* is online at cellbio.annualreviews.org

This article's doi: 10.1146/annurev.cellbio.24.110707.175355

1081-0706/08/1110-0263$20.00

*Corresponding author.

Key Words

rodent, stem cell niche, testis, GDNF, transcription factor

Abstract

Mammalian spermatogenesis is a classic adult stem cell–dependent process, supported by self-renewal and differentiation of spermatogonial stem cells (SSCs). Studying SSCs provides a model to better understand adult stem cell biology, and deciphering the mechanisms that control SSC functions may lead to treatment of male infertility and an understanding of the etiology of testicular germ cell tumor formation. Self-renewal of rodent SSCs is greatly influenced by the niche factor glial cell line–derived neurotrophic factor (GDNF). In mouse SSCs, GDNF activation upregulates expression of the transcription factor–encoding genes *bcl6b*, *etv5*, and *lhx1*, which influence SSC self-renewal. Additionally, the non-GDNF-stimulated transcription factors Plzf and Taf4b have been implicated in regulating SSC functions. Together, these molecules are part of a robust gene network controlling SSC fate decisions that may parallel the regulatory networks in other adult stem cell populations.

Contents

INTRODUCTION

Spermatogenesis is the intricate and coordinated process by which thousands of spermatozoa are produced daily within the male gonad or testis (Russell et al. 1990). Morphogenesis of the mammalian testis begins shortly after birth and continues until puberty, at which time the first round of spermatogenesis is completed. This period also establishes the framework for all successive spermatozoa production, which continues until old age in males. In addition to being the site of spermatozoa production, the testis also serves as an endocrine organ, producing the high levels of testosterone needed for normal spermatogenesis and male phenotypic characteristics. Spermatogenesis

is highly coordinated and complex, consisting of three distinct phases (Sharpe 1994). First, in the proliferative phase, spermatogonia undergo a series of mitotic amplifying divisions and differentiate into primary spermatocytes (Clermont 1962) that enter the second phase, or meiotic phase, in which meiosis and genetic recombination occur, resulting in the formation of haploid spermatids (Stern 1993). The third phase, termed spermiogenesis, involves the rearrangement of cytoskeletal structure, transforming round germ cells to specialized spermatozoa (Clermont et al. 1993). Spermatozoa are the vehicle by which male genetic information or germplasm is transmitted to successive generations. Thus,

Spermatogenesis: the process by which mature male gametes or spermatozoa are generated, beginning with the differentiation of spermatogonial stem cells

normal spermatogenesis is essential for species preservation and genetic diversity. The entire developmental process from spermatogonia to spermatozoa occurs within seminiferous tubules and is supported by close interaction of the germ cells with somatic Sertoli cells. This interaction forms a complex three-dimensional architecture referred to as the seminiferous epithelium, which is supported by a basement membrane generated from contributions of both Sertoli and outlying peritubular myoid cells (Clermont 1972, Russell 1993). The seminiferous epithelium is divided into a basal compartment, exposed to many lymph- and blood-borne substances, and an adluminal compartment, to which blood-borne substances have limited direct access. These compartments are established by the tight junctions formed between adjacent Sertoli cells, which also provide a major component of the blood-testis barrier. Late-meiotic-stage germ cells, postmeiotic spermatids, and spermatazoa are located in the adluminal compartment, which must, therefore, be an immune-privileged site.

Following puberty, spermatogenesis is one of the most productive cell-producing systems in adult animals, generating approximately 100 million spermatozoa each day in adult men and as many as 1.6 billion sperm per day in male pigs (Sharpe 1994). Approximately 1000 spermatozoa are produced with every heart beat in men. Thus, spermatogenesis is a process in which terminally differentiated cells are continually produced and lost. Like other adult self-renewing tissues whose function relies on the replenishment of differentiated cells at a constant rate or more rapidly after toxic injury, continual spermatogenesis is dependent on an adult tissue–specific stem cell population termed spermatogonial stem cells (SSCs).

SPERMATOGONIAL STEM CELLS

SSCs are the adult stem cell population of the testis, and their biological activities provide a foundation for the high productivity of spermatogenesis. These cells arise postnatally and persist throughout the lifetime of a male. SSCs are rare, with an estimated concentration of 1 in 3000 cells in the adult mouse testis (Tegelenbosch & de Rooij 1993). Thus, little is known of their phenotypic characteristics or mechanisms regulating their functions. Similar to other adult stem cells, SSCs maintain prolonged tissue homeostasis by undergoing both self-renewal and differentiation, which are regulated by extrinsic niche stimuli and intrinsic gene expression.

Origin of SSCs

Postnatally, SSCs arise from more undifferentiated precursors termed gonocytes, which derive from primordial germ cells (PGCs) that migrate from the embryonic ectoderm to the urogenital ridges and take part in formation of the embryonic gonad (Clermont & Perey 1957, Sapsford 1962, McLaren 2003). Upon formation of seminiferous cords during embryogenesis, PGCs become known as gonocytes, which persist until shortly after birth. Transformation of gonocytes into SSCs occurs between 0 and 6 days postpartum (dpp) in male mice (Huckins & Clermont 1968, Bellve et al. 1977, de Rooij & Russell 2000), with the first appearance of biologically active SSCs occurring at approximately 3–4 dpp (McLean et al. 2003). In other species, the transition period of gonocytes into SSCs is largely undefined and may occur over a period of several months in livestock animals or years in humans and other primates. Several studies in mice suggest that two different populations of gonocytes are present in the neonatal mouse testis, in which one subpopulation progresses directly into differentiating spermatogonia and completes the first round of postnatal spermatogenesis without undergoing self-renewal, whereas a second subpopulation transforms into SSCs that then provide the basis for all subsequent rounds of spermatogenesis (de Rooij 1998, de Rooij & Russell 2000, Yoshida et al. 2006). Whether this process is conserved in males of other mammals is currently unknown.

Stem cells: cells capable of continual self-renewal and generation of progeny committed to differentiation into particular cell type(s). Generally classified as two types: embryonic and adult

Spermatogonial stem cell (SSC): the adult tissue–specific stem cell population of postnatal mammalian testes. Self-renewal and differentiation of SSCs provide the foundation for spermatogenesis

Self-renewal: the unique ability of stem cells to replicate themselves continually without committing to differentiation

Gonocyte: precursor germ cell of spermatogonial stem cells in the postnatal mammalian testis. Derived from primordial germ cells of the embryonic gonad, which have very similar characteristics

PGC: primordial germ cell

SSC Biological Activities

Similar to other adult stem cell populations, SSCs are capable of undergoing both self-renewal and differentiation (**Figure 1a**). Whether SSC division is a symmetric process or an asymmetric process (**Figure 1b**) in mammals is currently unknown and a topic of debate. Regardless of the symmetry, self-renewal is thought to be an infinite process that results in maintenance of a stem cell pool, allowing for continual spermatogenesis throughout the majority of a male's life span. There are up to nine different spermatogonia populations in mouse and rat, of which there are three major subclasses: type A, intermediate, and type B spermatogonia (Huckins 1978). The type A spermatogonia population consists of A_{single} (A_s), A_{paired} (A_{pr}), $A_{aligned}$ (A_{al}), A_1, A_2, A_3, and A_4 spermatogonia. SSCs are often considered the A_s spermatogonia; this type is the most primitive and does not contain intercellular bridges. As depicted in **Figure 1c**, initiation of spermatogenesis occurs when SSC differentiation results in the production of daughter progeny, the A_{pr} spermatogonia, which are committed to further development into spermatozoa rather than self-renewal (Huckins 1971, Oakberg 1971, de Rooij & Russell 2000). The A_{pr} spermatogonia then undergo a series of mitotic cell divisions to become $A_{al(4)}$, $A_{al(8)}$, and $A_{al(16)}$ spermatogonia, which transform into A_1 spermatogonia, a process that does not include a mitotic division. A series of proliferative divisions then results in the formation of A_2, A_3, and A_4 spermatogonia. At this point A_4 spermatogonia mature into intermediate and type B spermatogonia that subsequently enter meiosis to become primary and secondary spermatocytes, leading eventually to the production of haploid spermatids, which undergo a transformation into spermatozoa (Russell et al. 1990). In this model, all spermatogonia more advanced than SSCs (A_s) are considered differentiating spermatogonia (Russell et al. 1990, de Rooij & Russell 2000).

The balance between SSC self-renewal and differentiation is regulated by both extrinsic

---

Figure 1

Characteristics of mammalian spermatogonial stem cell (SSC) functions and their associated niche microenvironment. (*a*) Two possible SSC fate decisions. Stem cells are defined by their ability to produce both more stem cells (self-renewal) and differentiating progeny (differentiation). In the mammalian testis, SSCs undergo either self-renewal, to maintain a pool of SSCs that support fertility for the majority of a male's life span, or differentiation, resulting in the formation of A_{pr} spermatogonia, which are committed to the terminal pathway of spermatozoa production. (*b*) Possible division pathways of SSCs. Symmetrical division dictates that an SSC divides to produce either two new SSCs (self-renewal) or A_{pr} spermatogonia (differentiation) with an interconnecting cytoplasmic bridge; A_{pr} spermatogonia are destined for differentiation into spermatozoa. The asymmetrical theory suggests that SSC division produces two daughter cells: one new SSC (self-renewal) and one committed differentiating cell that produces A_{pr} spermatogonia upon its next division. It is currently unknown whether one or both of these pathways occur in mammalian testes. (*c*) Differentiation and proliferation of the spermatogonia population in rodent testes. Spermatogenesis is the sum of all germ cell divisions and transformations beginning with SSC differentiation and ending with the generation of spermatozoa. Following SSC differentiation is the formation of A_{pr} spermatogonia, which mitotically divide to produce $A_{al(4)}$ spermatogonia followed by $A_{al(8)}$ and $A_{al(16)}$ spermatogonia. More mature spermatogonia are then formed and undergo another series of mitotic amplifying divisions, beginning with A_1 spermatogonia and ending with type B spermatogonia. This stage is followed by meiosis and the formation of haploid spermatozoa. (*d*) Postulated SSC niche microenvironment in mammalian testes. SSCs reside in the basal compartment of the seminiferous tubule, surrounded by Sertoli cells but below their tight junctions, which separate the seminiferous epithelium into basal and adluminal compartments. Stem cell niches are formed on the basis of both architectural support and specific growth factors produced by so-called niche cells. In the mammalian testis, only Sertoli cells have currently been identified as a niche cell that produces growth factors influencing SSC functions. However, contributions from other somatic cell populations surrounding the seminiferous tubules, such as peritubular myoid cells and interstitial Leydig cells, are also possible.

environmental stimuli and specific intrinsic gene expression. Recent studies suggest heterogeneity of the SSC population in mouse testes, which includes a transiently amplifying population that behaves as SSCs in specific experimental situations and a second, less mitotically active SSC population that is present during normal in vivo spermatogenesis (Nakagawa et al. 2007). Direct evidence regarding the origin of these transiently amplifying potential SSCs has not been reported; this population may originate from a subpopulation of the actual SSCs or their early proliferating progeny (Yoshida et al. 2008).

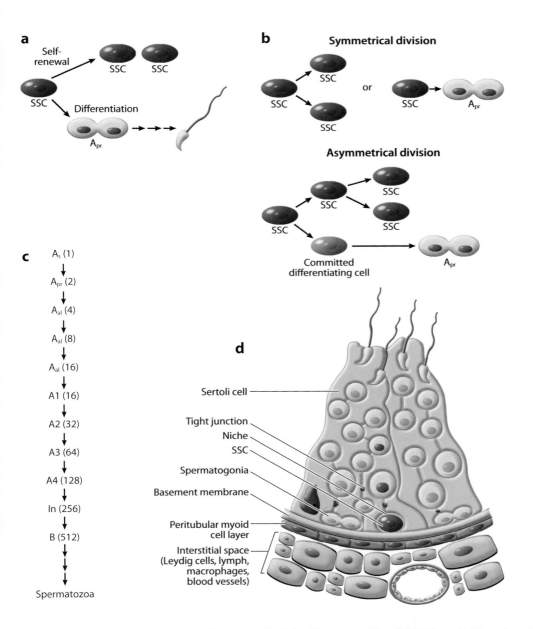

SSC Niche

The function of most, if not all, adult stem cell populations is supported within specialized microenvironments referred to as niches, which provide the extrinsic stimuli to regulate self-renewal and differentiation through both architectural support and growth factor stimulation (Spradling et al. 2001, Scadden 2006). Stem cell niches are formed by contributions of surrounding support cells. In mammalian testes, Sertoli cells are the major contributor to the SSC niche, but contributions by other testicular somatic cells, including peritubular myoid and Leydig cells, are also likely (**Figure 1d**). In recent studies, Yoshida et al. (2007) observed the accumulation of A_{pr} and A_{al} spermatogonia (differentiating daughter progeny of SSCs) in regions of seminiferous tubules adjacent to Leydig cell clusters, suggesting that these cells may contribute to the SSC niche. Additionally, preliminary experiments suggest that Leydig and possibly myoid cell production of the cytokine colony–stimulating factor-1 (CSF-1) influences the self-renewal of SSCs in mice (J.M. Oatley, M.J. Oatley, M.R. Avarbock & R.L. Brinster, unpublished data). Sertoli and Leydig cell function, and likely their niche factor output, is regulated by follicle-stimulating hormone (FSH) and luteinizing hormone (LH) stimulation, respectively. The anterior pituitary gland produces and releases both FSH and LH in response to gonadotropin-releasing hormone (GnRH) stimulation. Studies by Kanatsu-Shinohara et al. (2004b) found that inhibition of GnRH release during postnatal development in mice impairs SSC proliferation, whereas in adult males SSC proliferation is increased when GnRH is suppressed. Other preliminary studies suggest that immunoneutralization of GnRH in mice results in loss of SSC biological activity (J.M. Oatley, L.-Y. Chen, J.J. Reeves & D.J. McLean, unpublished data). These results suggest that gonadotropins play a major role in SSC niche function that may vary depending on the developmental stage of a male.

Currently, a major research focus in adult stem cell biology is the influence that impaired or failed stem cell function may play in the aging process and associated diseases. In principle, stem cells are capable of infinite self-renewal and thus are immune to the normal aging process. However, studies with hematopoietic stem cells (HSCs) suggest that stem cells undergo an aging process and contribute to tissue failure in old age (Siminovitch et al. 1964, Van Zant & Liang 2003, Geiger et al. 2005). Whether SSCs age and contribute to the age-related decline in sperm production experienced by males is currently unknown. Recent studies in mice suggest that SSCs are long-lived and that age-related decreases in fertility are due, at least in part, to impaired function of the niche microenvironment rather than reduced abilities of SSCs to undergo self-renewal and differentiation (Ryu et al. 2006, Zhang et al. 2006). This result may be due to reduced or modified concentrations of nutrients and hormones in serum of old animals. This hypothesis is supported by work from Conboy et al. (2005) demonstrating that the biological activity of aged liver and muscle progenitor cells in old mice is rejuvenated upon exposure to serum from young parabiotic donors. Clarification of the role that adult stem cells play in aging is likely to be a major research interest in the coming decade, and SSCs with their associated niche may be an effective model system to define principles of adult stem cell aging.

SSC Transplantation

The term stem cell is a biologically functional definition that describes a particular cell type capable of completely reestablishing the functionality of a tissue system from which it is derived. The most direct assay to identify stem cells and examine their biological activities is functional transplantation. In this respect, determination of stem cell identity depends on the ability of a donor cell to reestablish functionality following injection into the stem cell–depleted tissue system of a recipient and to undergo self-renewal and differentiation.

Figure 2

The spermatogonial stem cell (SSC) transplantation assay in mice. Stem cells are defined by their ability to reestablish the function of a tissue system from which they are derived. Spermatogenesis is a classic adult stem cell–dependent process in which SSCs continually produce terminally differentiated spermatozoa; thus, SSCs are defined by their functional ability to colonize a recipient testis and generate spermatogenesis. Currently, the only direct means to identify SSCs within a cell population and study their activity is the functional transplantation assay. (*a*) In this assay a testis cell population is collected fresh from a donor testis or following a culture period and microinjected into the testes of recipient males that have been depleted of germ cells with chemotoxic drugs or irradiation. Additionally, sterile mutant males that lack germ cells (e.g., W/Wv mice) can be effectively used as recipients. After a period of several months, colonies of donor-derived spermatogenesis can be detected in the recipient testes if SSCs were present in the injected cell suspension. When transgenic donors that express a marker gene (e.g., LacZ or GFP) are used, colonies of donor-derived spermatogenesis can easily be detected and quantified. Each colony is clonally derived from an individual SSC; therefore, this system provides a quantifiable measure of SSC number in an experimental cell population. In the schematic presented here, a mixed population of donor testis cells isolated from a male Rosa mouse that expresses LacZ in all germ cell types (represented as *blue* coloring) is microinjected into the seminiferous tubules of an immunologically compatible non-Rosa recipient testis that was pretreated with a chemotoxic drug (busulfan). SSCs in the injected cell suspension (distinguished from other Rosa testes cells by *dark blue* coloring) colonize the recipient seminiferous tubules and reestablish spermatogenesis. These donor SSC–derived colonies of spermatogenesis can then be visualized several months later upon incubation with X-Gal, which results in blue staining. (*b*) Use of the SSC transplantation method to assay the SSC content of different testis cell populations. (*Left*) Recipient testis injected with a donor Rosa cell suspension in which no SSC colonization occurred, indicating a lack of SSCs. (*Middle*) Recipient testis injected with a donor Rosa cell suspension containing a small number of SSCs, which is representative of a typical result from transplanting an unselected testis cell suspension. (*Right*) Recipient testis with abundant donor SSC colonization, which is indicative of results obtained following injection of an SSC-enriched cell suspension.

Stem cell transplantation assays are available for a multitude of adult stem cell populations, including HSCs (Harrison 1980), neural stem cells (Kelly et al. 2004), epidermal stem cells (Blanpain et al. 2004), and SSCs (Brinster & Avarbock 1994, Brinster & Zimmermann 1994, Nagano et al. 1999, Oatley & Brinster 2006). The SSC transplantation system involves injection of a donor testis cell suspension into the seminiferous tubules of a recipient male in which endogenous germ cells have been depleted by treatment with chemotoxic drugs (e.g., busulfan) or are naturally devoid of germ cells (e.g., W/Wv mutant males). SSCs present in the injected cell suspension are capable of colonizing the recipient seminiferous tubules and reestablishing spermatogenesis (**Figure 2**). Each colony is clonally derived from a single SSC (Dobrinski et al. 1999, Nagano et al. 1999, Kanatsu-Shinohara et al. 2006).

Spermatogonial stem cell transplantation: procedure in which a donor or experimental testis cell population is microinjected into recipient testes. Reestablishment of spermatogenesis from injected cells provides a direct measure of stem cell number and assessment of stem cell biological activity

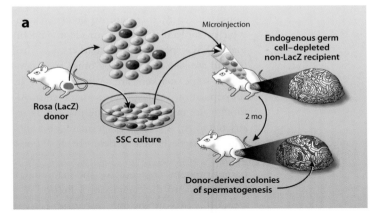

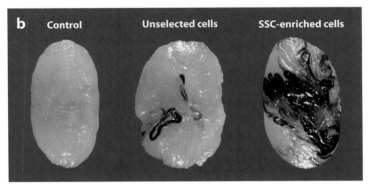

Thus, counting colonies provides a quantifiable measure of SSC number in an injected cell suspension. Currently, this transplantation system is the only unequivocal means to identify SSCs and examine their biological activity. Over the past decade, this transplantation assay system has enabled major advances in elucidating SSC identity and mechanisms that regulate their functions (Brinster 2002, 2007).

SPERMATOGONIAL STEM CELL SURFACE PHENOTYPE

Isolation and identification of SSCs from mammalian testes are essential to examine critically the mechanisms that regulate their functions. Additionally, translation of SSC transplantation techniques from rodents to humans, livestock, or endangered species as an assisted reproductive technology would be greatly benefited by the ability to isolate pure or enriched SSC fractions from total testis cell populations. Currently, there are no known phenotypic or molecular markers to identify mammalian SSCs specifically. All markers described to date are also expressed by other spermatogonia; some markers are even expressed by subpopulations of testicular somatic cells. Although the expression of some markers is restricted to A_s, A_{pr}, and A_{al} spermatogonia subtypes, none described to date can distinguish SSCs (A_s spermatogonia) from their differentiating progeny (A_{pr} and A_{al} spermatogonia). On the basis of the functional definition of a stem cell, SSCs are the only testicular cell type capable of reestablishing spermatogenesis following transplantation, making the transplantation system the only means to distinguish SSCs from their progeny spermatogonia. Investigators have described several phenotypic cell surface makers that are expressed by SSCs, as well as other spermatogonia, and isolation of testis cell populations on the basis of expression of these markers produces cell populations with varying degrees of SSC enrichment. The expression of some identified phenotypic markers has been legitimately validated by functional transplantation, whereas evidence supporting others has been based mainly on conjecture. In mouse testes, A_{pr} and A_{al} spermatogonia are 2–16 times more abundant than SSCs (de Rooij & Russell 2000). Thus, studies in which analyses are based solely on markers expressed by A_s, A_{pr}, and A_{al} spermatogonia subtypes emphasize differentiating progeny rather than SSCs. Results from those types of studies must be validated by the transplantation technique to distinguish between the different spermatogonial subtypes, or results should be interpreted lightly in regard to advancing the knowledge of SSC biology.

In recent years the expression of several molecules on the surface of SSCs has been reported (**Table 1**) and has provided an initial understanding of the surface phenotype of mammalian SSCs. There is wide variation in the specificity of these identified phenotypic markers, and no marker described to date is expressed exclusively by SSCs in the testis. Therefore, a pure population of SSCs currently cannot be isolated from any mammalian species. This review focuses on studies that have included transplantation analyses to prove SSC expression of certain markers.

Commonality of Hematopoietic Stem Cell and SSC Surface Phenotypes

Stem cells of many self-renewing tissues are thought to share several characteristics and thus may express similar cell surface molecules. On the basis of this hypothesis, Shinohara et al. (1999) identified expression of α_6- and β_1-integrins on the surface of SSCs. In those studies, cell populations expressing these molecules were isolated from testes of adult donor mice by antibody-based magnetic bead isolation and transplanted into testes of infertile adult recipient mice. Results revealed that β_1- or α_6-integrin-expressing testis cell subpopulations were enriched approximately four- and eightfold for SSCs compared with total testis cell populations, respectively. Using a multiparameter fluorescent-activated cell sorting (FACS) approach based on expressions of α_6-integrin, α_v-integrin, and low side-scatter phenotype

Table 1 Relative spermatogonial stem cell enrichment in rodent testis cell fractions isolated on the basis of expression of specific surface antigens

Surface antigen	Mammalian species examined	Donor age	Relative SSC enrichment[a]	Reference(s)
α_6-integrin	Mouse			
		Pup	?	–
		Adult	8×	Shinohara et al. 1999
β_1-integrin	Mouse			
		Pup	?	–
		Adult	4×	Shinohara et al. 1999
Thy1	Mouse			
		Pup (6 dpp)	5×	Kubota et al. 2004a
		Adult	30×	Kubota et al. 2004a
CD9	Mouse			
		Pup	?	–
		Adult	7×	Kanatsu-Shinohara et al. 2004c
	Rat			
		Pup	?	–
		Adult	5×	Kanatsu-Shinohara et al. 2004c
Ep-CAM	Rat			
		Pup (8–14 dpp)	11×	Ryu et al. 2004
		Adult	?	–
Gfrα1	Mouse			
		Pup (6–10 dpp)	1.8×,[b] 2.5×	Buageaw et al. 2005, Ebata et al. 2005
		Adult	0.13×	Ebata et al. 2005

[a]Determined by transplantation analyses. Values are approximate fold enrichment compared with unselected wild-type total testis cell populations.
[b]Compared with a Gfrα1-depleted testis cell population.

(a measure of cellular complexity), Shinohara et al. (2000) isolated, from cryptorchid testes, a testis cell population further enriched for SSCs. Results from those studies revealed that the SSC concentration in the most pure fractions is only approximately 1 in 30–40 cells.

To further increase purity of SSCs in testis cell subpopulations, Kubota et al. (2003) examined cell surface markers known to be expressed by HSCs and identified the expression of the glycosyl phosphatidylinositol (GPI)-anchored glycoprotein molecule Thy1 (CD90) on mouse SSCs. These studies determined that nearly all (~95%) of the SSCs in adult mouse testes are present in the Thy1[+] cell fraction, which has an SSC concentration of approximately 1 SSC in 15 cells, according to transplantation

analyses (Kubota et al. 2003). In adult mouse testes, the Thy1[+] cell fraction is enriched approximately 30-fold compared with unselected testis cell populations. Additionally, Thy1 expression by SSCs is constant throughout the lifetime of a male mouse (Kubota et al. 2004a). In mouse pups (4–5 dpp), the Thy1[+] testis cell population is enriched approximately fivefold compared with the total testis cell population (Kubota et al. 2004a). Together, these studies demonstrated that Thy1 is expressed on mouse SSCs and that the Thy1[+] cell fraction is highly enriched for SSCs but still does not provide an exclusive identification of SSC phenotype.

Using the same hypothesis that different adult stem cell populations express similar molecules, Kanatsu-Shinohara et al. (2004c)

Thy1: thymus cell antigen 1, theta; also termed CD90

Glial cell line–
derived neurotrophic
factor (GDNF): a
cytokine niche factor
that has an essential
role in regulating the
self-renewal of rodent
spermatogonial stem
cells

Gfrα1: GDNF family
receptor alpha 1

determined that mouse SSCs express CD9, which is also expressed by embryonic stem (ES) cells (Oka et al. 2002), neural stem cells (Klassen et al. 2001), and HSCs (Oritani et al. 1996). However, transplantation analyses revealed that the CD9$^+$ testis cell fraction is enriched only 6.9-fold for SSCs compared with the total testis cell population in adult mice (Kanatsu-Shinohara et al. 2004c). This result suggests that CD9 expression is not restricted to SSCs, which was confirmed by further characterization studies revealing CD9 expression in somatic cells and other germ cell types within mouse testes (Kanatsu-Shinohara et al. 2004c). In contrast to conserved expression of Thy1 and CD9, HSCs express high levels of c-kit (Matsui et al. 1990), but SSCs do not share this phenotype (Kubota et al. 2003, Kanatsu-Shinohara et al. 2004c), indicating that the surface phenotypes of all adult stem cells are not identical (Kubota et al. 2003). Unfortunately, the α_6/β_1-integrin$^+$, Thy1$^+$, and CD9$^+$ testis cell fractions in mice are not composed purely of SSCs. Thus, the SSC phenotype must be further characterized to identify definitive markers with the future applicability of isolating pure SSC populations from the testes of other mammalian species.

The GDNF Receptor Complex as a Specific SSC Phenotype?

The growth factor glial cell line–derived neurotrophic factor (GDNF) is an important niche factor regulating mammalian SSC function (discussed below). GDNF exerts its actions via binding a receptor complex consisting of the transmembrane tyrosine kinase molecule rearranged in transformation (c-Ret) and the GPI-anchored binding molecule GDNF family receptor alpha 1 (Gfrα1). Thus, it has been suggested that Gfrα1 expression and/or c-Ret expression are restricted to SSCs in mammalian testes. Using transplantation analyses, Ebata et al. (2005) determined that the c-Ret-expressing cell fraction in 6 dpp mice testes is not enriched for SSCs. Characterization studies revealed expression of Gfrα1 by multiple spermatogonial subtypes in mouse testes including A$_s$, A$_{pr}$, and A$_{al}$ spermatogonia (Ebata et al. 2005, Naughton et al. 2006). Hofmann et al. (2005a,b) isolated Gfrα1$^+$ cells from 6 dpp mouse testes and determined that this cell fraction expresses several germ cell and spermatogonia makers. These results led to the assumption that Gfrα1 is an SSC marker and could be used to isolate SSCs from mouse testes. Unfortunately, functional transplantation experiments did not validate this assumption, and the relative enrichment or purity of SSCs in the Gfrα1 cell suspensions isolated by Hofmann et al. (2005a,b) could not be assessed. Additionally, c-kit expression was detected on more than half of these Gfrα1$^+$ isolated cells (Hofmann et al. 2005b), indicating that Gfrα1 is expressed by most spermatogonia, because c-kit expression is first detected on type A$_1$ spermatogonia in the postnatal mouse testis (Manova et al. 1990, Yoshinaga et al. 1991, Schrans-Stassen et al. 1999). These observations suggest that the majority of Gfrα1$^+$ cells are not SSCs.

Subsequent studies by Buageaw et al. (2005) utilizing functional transplantation revealed that the Gfrα1$^+$ cell fractions of 10 dpp mouse pup testes are less than twofold enriched for SSCs compared with Gfrα1-depleted testis cell populations. Thus, the actual SSC content in Gfrα1$^+$ cell fractions may be less than that in an unselected total testis cell population. This limited SSC content in Gfrα1$^+$ testis cell fractions was also observed in studies by Ebata et al. (2005), in which SSC enrichment was approximately 2.5-fold higher in Gfrα1$^+$ cells isolated from 6 dpp mouse pup testes than in the total testis cell population, but a significant difference could not be determined because of experimental variation. Surprisingly, SSCs were reduced approximately 87% in the Gfrα1$^+$ fraction isolated from adult mouse testes (Ebata et al. 2005), indicating that the majority of Gfrα1-expressing cells are non-SSCs at this age. Collectively, these studies strongly demonstrate that the Gfrα1$^+$ cell fraction, isolated by the procedures described, is at most slightly enriched for SSCs in pup testes. These studies indicate that Gfrα1 selection does not result in isolation of SSCs and that use of Gfrα1 expression is not an adequate endpoint for analysis of SSCs but likely emphasizes other spermatogonia subtypes that are much more abundant in the testis than are SSCs.

Relation of the Mouse SSC Surface Phenotype to Other Mammalian Species

Translating results describing the SSC surface phenotype in mice to other species has been limited, but the expression of several molecules on the surface of rat SSCs has been identified, and the phenotype of primate SSCs is beginning to be defined. Ryu et al. (2004) used transplantation analyses to reveal expression of Ep-CAM (epithelial cell adhesion molecule) on the surface of rat SSCs. SSC concentration was approximately 1 in 8.5 cells in FACS-isolated Ep-CAM$^+$ cell fractions from 8–14 dpp rat pup testes (Ryu et al. 2004). Similar to mouse SSCs, the CD9$^+$ cell fraction in rat testes is also enriched for SSCs (Kanatsu-Shinohara et al. 2004c), and Ep-CAM$^+$ cell fractions express Thy1 antigen (Ryu et al. 2004). Importantly, recent evidence suggests that nonhuman primate SSCs also express Thy1 (Hermann et al. 2007), and hamster SSCs express α_6-integrin (Kanatsu-Shinohara et al. 2008). Together, these studies suggest an evolutionarily conserved phenotype of mammalian SSCs, which may be useful for isolating these cells from testes of higher-order mammals, including humans.

EXTRINSIC GROWTH FACTORS INFLUENCING SPERMATOGONIAL STEM CELL SELF-RENEWAL

GDNF Influences Spermatogonial Proliferation and Normal Spermatogenesis in Mice

Currently, knowledge of extrinsic niche factors regulating SSC functions in mammals is limited; only GDNF has been shown to have an essential function. GDNF is a related member of the TGFβ superfamily of growth factors and also plays an important role in kidney morphogenesis and the regulation of neuronal progenitor cell function (Sariola & Saarma 2003, Dressler 2006). The first insight that GDNF was an important molecule regulating SSC activity came from studies by Meng et al. (2000), who observed disrupted spermatogenesis in mutant mice carrying one GDNF null allele and accumulation of A_{pr} and A_{al} spermatogonia in testes of male mice that overexpressed GDNF. As discussed above, the GDNF receptor complex consists of c-Ret and Gfrα1 (Airaksinen & Saarma 2002). Targeted disruption of GDNF, c-Ret, or Gfrα1 results in impaired spermatogenesis in homozygous null male mice (Naughton et al. 2006). These in vivo studies implicated GDNF as a niche factor regulating SSC functions. Importantly, GDNF expression in the mouse testis was localized to Sertoli cells and regulated by the gonadotropin FSH (Tadokoro et al. 2002), which is a major regulator of Sertoli cells' ability to support quantitatively normal spermatogenesis (Griswold 1998, Krishnamurthy et al. 2000). In the course of developing culture systems that support the expansion of mouse and rat SSCs for extended periods of time, GDNF was identified as an essential molecule for self-renewal of SSCs in vitro (Kubota et al. 2004b, Kanatsu-Shinohara et al. 2005a, Ryu et al. 2005). Moreover, GDNF enhances the short-term proliferation and survival of bovine (Oatley et al. 2004, Aponte et al. 2005) SSCs and the long-term expansion of hamster (Kanatsu-Shinohara et al. 2008) SSCs in vitro. Overall, the importance of GDNF as a niche factor regulating SSC self-renewal both in vivo and in vitro has been unequivocally demonstrated over the past eight years.

Evolution of Culture Systems that Support Long-Term Self-Renewal of Rodent SSCs

The creation of culture systems that support the self-renewing expansion of SSC numbers for

Ep-CAM: epithelial cell adhesion molecule

extended periods of time has been achieved over the past five years. Nagano et al. (1998) were the first to demonstrate that SSCs could be maintained in vitro for up to four months. Nagano et al. (2003) later suggested that GDNF was important for short-term SSC maintenance in vitro, but neither of these studies observed an expansion of stem cell numbers. In 2003, Kanatsu-Shinohara et al. reported the ability for long-term culture of gonocytes, the precursors to SSCs, from 0 dpp mouse pups, which the authors termed germline stem (GS) cells. Although a portion of these cells have stem cell potential, demonstrated via a capability to reinitiate spermatogenesis following transplantation into recipient testes, they likely transform into SSCs following transplantation in a similar fashion as the transformation of gonocytes into SSCs during normal in vivo development. Thus, it is possible that in vitro, prior to transplantation, GS cells are of a gonocyte or a PGC nature rather than of a true postnatal SSC nature. This reasoning is supported by the detection of Dppa3 (also termed Stella) expression in GS cultures, which is expressed by both PGCs and gonocytes but not spermatogonial subtypes. In addition, expression of Dppa3 is not detected in cultures of self-renewing SSCs established from 6 dpp mouse pups in which gonocytes have converted into SSCs (Oatley et al. 2006). In the original report, Kanatsu-Shinohara et al. (2003) were able to support self-renewing proliferation of mouse GS cells over a five-month period, in which a more-than-10^{14}-fold increase in cell number was measured. However, the conditions used could support GS cells from only donor mice of a DBA/2 background, and expansion to other donor strains was unsuccessful.

Kubota et al. (2004b) were the first to report long-term culture of postnatal SSCs isolated from 6 dpp or adult mouse testes, ages at which gonocytes have transformed into SSCs. The germ cell clumps that formed in these cultures exponentially expanded for more than five months in serum-free conditions and contained SSCs as shown by functional transplantation. Kanatsu-Shinohara et al. (2005a) subsequently developed a serum-free culture condition for GS cells, in which proliferation of cells from donor mice on a DBA/2 background for more than six months in vitro was supported. Hofmann et al. (2005a) reported the generation of immortalized mouse spermatogonial cell lines (e.g., C18-4) and, on the basis of expression of phenotypic and molecular markers including Gfrα1 and Oct3/4, concluded that these cells were SSCs. As discussed above, SSCs are defined by their functional ability to reestablish spermatogenesis following transplantation, and there are currently no known definitive phenotypic or molecular SSC markers. Unfortunately, functional transplantations were not conducted to prove the stem cell nature of cell lines created by Hofmann et al. (2005a), and such cell populations could be other non-SSC spermatogonial subtypes. Homogenous expression of markers by cultured testis cell populations does not qualify them as SSCs. Long-term cultures of GS cells and SSCs homogenously express specific molecules (including Gfrα1 and Oct3/4) but are not all true SSCs capable of colonizing a recipient testis following transplantation (Kanatsu-Shinohara et al. 2003, 2005a,b; Kubota et al. 2004b).

Extension of mouse SSC and GS culture systems to other rodent species has been limited. However, progress has been made for rats. This represents a major technical breakthrough with the potential for creating transgenic or knockout rat lines, techniques that are currently limited owing to difficulties in establishing rat ES cell lines. By optimizing the mouse serum-free condition of Kubota et al. (2004b), Ryu et al. (2005) devised a culture system that supported self-renewing expansion of rat SSCs from several different donor strains for more than seven months. Subsequently, Hamra et al. (2005) demonstrated dramatic expansion of rat SSCs when they were cultured in a complex serum condition similar to that reported by Kanatsu-Shinohara et al. (2003). Recently, Kanatsu-Shinohara et al. (2008) reported long-term culture of hamster SSCs in similar conditions. Extension of serum-free culture conditions that support rodent SSCs to other mammalian species has been slow to evolve but will undoubtedly be a major goal of SSC researchers in the coming years.

GDNF Supplementation Is Essential for Long-Term Self-Renewal of SSCs In Vitro

The development of serum-free culture systems that support SSC expansion has provided major insights into the growth factors important for SSC self-renewal. In a serum-free environment, most cell types require the addition of specific growth factors and hormones to promote their proliferation and survival (Hayashi & Sato 1976, Barnes & Sato 1980). This principle has been especially evident for mouse ES cells, in which maintenance of pluripotency requires supplementation with leukemia inhibitory factor (LIF) (Smith et al. 1988). Over the past five years, the growth factor GDNF has been determined to be an important molecule regulating the proliferation of mouse, rat, hamster, and bull SSCs in vitro (Nagano et al. 2003; Kanatsu-Shinohara et al. 2003, 2008; Kubota et al. 2004a,b; Oatley et al. 2004; Ryu et al. 2005). Using a serum-free, chemically defined condition, Kubota et al. (2004a) demonstrated that GDNF enhances SSC self-renewal over a seven-day period. Kubota et al. (2004b) subsequently reported the definitive evidence that GDNF is essential for SSC self-renewal in vitro, showing that long-term self-renewing expansion of SSCs from several different mouse strains in serum-free conditions is dependent on supplementation of media with GDNF. Recently, Seandel et al. (2007) reported the in vitro expansion of a testis cell population from adult mice, which the authors termed spermatogonia precursor cells (SPCs), for more than one year. Proliferation of SPCs was dependent on GDNF supplementation, and some of the cells were capable of reinitiating spermatogenesis after transplantation, demonstrating the presence of SSCs in the SPC populations. Additionally, long-term culture of rat (Ryu et al. 2005, Hamra et al. 2005) and hamster (Kanatsu-Shinohara et al. 2008) SSCs relies on the inclusion of GDNF in media, confirming the conservation of GDNF influence on SSC self-renewal in rodent species.

In contrast to all other reports of long-term SSC, GS cell, or SPC cultures, Guan et al. (2006) reported long-term maintenance of SSCs from adult mouse testes in culture conditions without GDNF supplementation and indicated that LIF is the important factor for SSC self-renewal from adult testes. Guan et al. (2006) claimed that the cells could reestablish spermatogenesis following transplantation, but actual evidence was not provided. Thus, it is difficult to assess the SSC content of these GDNF-independent, in vitro–derived testis cell populations on the basis of a single report.

In long-term cultures in which GDNF is the main growth factor supplement, undifferentiated germ cell populations form morula-appearing clumps that are composed of both SSCs and non-SSCs, which are likely A_{pr} and A_{al} spermatogonia produced by differentiation (Kanatsu-Shinohara et al. 2003, 2005b; Kubota et al. 2004b; Ryu et al. 2005; Oatley & Brinster 2006). The relative SSC content of these clumps varies widely at different times during a culture period (Kubota et al. 2004b, Kanatsu-Shinohara et al. 2005b), and in some cases the percentage of true SSCs that can reestablish spermatogenesis following transplantation is low, estimated to be 0.02% in one instance (Kanatsu-Shinohara et al. 2005b). Also, SSC proliferation is extremely limited in serum-free conditions with GDNF as the sole growth factor supplement (Kubota et al. 2004b). These results strongly suggest that other factors besides GDNF are important to fully sustain SSC self-renewal in vitro.

Basic Fibroblast Growth Factor and Epidermal Growth Factor, But Not Leukemia Inhibitory Factor, Supplementation Enhances GDNF-Regulated SSC Self-Renewal In Vitro

Studies to identify additional growth factors that regulate SSC self-renewal have focused on evaluating those that influence the proliferation of other stem cell types. Expansion of PGCs, the embryonic precursors to SSCs, in vitro requires the addition of basic fibroblast growth factor (bFGF) to culture media (Resnick et al. 1992). Kubota et al. (2004b) found that supplementation of bFGF in combination with GDNF enhances long-term self-renewing expansion of SSCs, but bFGF alone is incapable of producing a similar result. Similarly, studies by Kanatsu-Shinohara et al. (2003; 2005a,b; 2006) involving long-term culture of GS cells utilized both serum-containing and serum-free media supplemented with bFGF and GDNF. In feeder-free culture conditions, GS cells proliferated as long as GDNF and either bFGF or epidermal growth factor (EGF) were also included in culture media (Kanatsu-Shinohara et al. 2005a). Similarly, expansion of hamster SSCs in vitro requires supplementation with bFGF in addition to GDNF (Kanatsu-Shinohara et al. 2008). Collectively, these studies demonstrate that bFGF and possibly EGF enhance GDNF-regulation of SSC self-renewal, although the mechanism is undefined. In a quest to identify other factors influencing SSC self-renewal in vitro, several studies have evaluated the effects of supplementing culture media with the pleiotropic cytokine LIF because of its demonstrated importance in maintaining the pluripotency of mouse ES cells (Smith et al. 1988, Williams et al. 1988). The addition of LIF to serum-containing media did not affect the proliferation of mouse SSCs in short-term cultures (Nagano et al. 2003, Kubota et al. 2004a). Moreover, the inclusion of LIF in GDNF-dependent serum-free cultures did not significantly enhance the expansion of mouse SSCs (Kubota et al. 2004b). Cellular response to LIF stimulation involves binding a receptor complex consisting of the promiscuous cytokine receptor gp130 (glycoprotein 130) molecule and a specific LIF receptor (LIFR). Even though weak expression of gp130 on the surface of cultured SSCs was detected by flow cytometry (Kubota et al. 2004b), expression of the transcript was absent in similarly cultured cells (Oatley et al. 2006). Additionally, supplementation of LIF in combination with GDNF had no effect on the proliferation of rat SSCs (Ryu et al. 2005). In contrast, LIF enhances the formation of GS cell clumps in culture but does not affect their self-renewal rate during long-term culture (Kanatsu-Shinohara et al. 2007), suggesting that GS cells may be more PGC-like rather than true postnatal SSCs. Collectively, these studies indicate that, in contrast to its essential role in ES cells, LIF is not a major factor influencing the function of rodent SSCs. Knowledge of other factors that influence SSC self-renewal in vitro is limited. Preliminary studies have revealed that supplementation of GDNF-dependent SSC cultures with CSF-1 enhances mouse SSC self-renewal in vitro (J.M. Oatley, M.J. Oatley, M.R. Avarbock & R.L. Brinster, unpublished data). Because GDNF, bFGF, and CSF-1 are all classified as cytokines, other members of the large cytokine family of factors may also have important roles in regulating SSC functions. Using culture methods to identify growth factors that regulate SSC functions in vitro greatly enhances our understanding of extrinsic niche factors in vivo and provides a bridge to identify intrinsic molecular mechanisms regulating SSC fate decisions.

INTRINSIC MOLECULAR MECHANISMS REGULATING SPERMATOGONIAL STEM CELL SELF-RENEWAL

Disruption of Plzf and Taf4b Expression Impairs Spermatogonia Activity in Mice

Loss-of-function studies provide a strong approach to examine the importance of specific molecules in the function of particular cell types. Over the past four years, studies involving the assessment of impaired spermatogenesis in mice with inactivating disruption of a specific molecule through either natural mutation or experimental targeting have been used to make several discoveries of transcription regulators potentially involved in SSC functions. Disrupted expression of the transcriptional repressor Plzf (promyelocytic leukemia zinc finger protein) in male mice results in impaired spermatogenesis and infertility, which become progressively more pronounced with advancing age (Buaas et al. 2004, Costoya et al. 2004). Testes of these males contain varying percentages of seminiferous tubules with a Sertoli cell–only phenotype, which lack developing germ cells with observable spermatogonia populations, suggesting that SSC functions are impaired. Inactivation of Taf4b [TATA box–binding protein (TBP)-associated factor 4b] expression results in a similar phenotype in which Sertoli cell–only tubules are observed and males become infertile by three months of age (Falender et al. 2005). In both types of mutant animals, multiple factors may contribute to the phenotypes, and thus transplantation analyses are the only means to determine whether SSC functions are impaired. Transplantation of germ cells from targeted Plzf−/− or homozygous luxoid mutant male mice, which contain an inactivating polymorphism in *plzf* loci, failed to restore spermatogenesis in recipient testes, indicating that SSC functions are impaired in mice lacking Plzf expression. Similar transplant experiments in which Taf4b-deficient germ cells are transplanted into recipient testes have not been reported; however, Taf4b null testes do harbor reestablishment of spermatogenesis from transplanted wild-type SSCs (Falender et al. 2005), indicating that the impaired spermatogenesis in TAF4b null mice is due to germ cell defects. These in vivo–based experiments can be difficult to interpret with regard to SSC self-renewal because disrupted spermatogenesis may be due to a variety of factors in mutant or null animals. Impaired SSC self-renewal or differentiation will result in an identical phenotype of diminishing sperm production and in fertility as a male ages. Additionally, disruption of the hypothalamic-pituitary-gonadal axis will also produce a similar phenotype. Even though transplantation experiments provide a direct assessment of the activity of SSCs lacking expression of specific molecules, it is challenging to make distinctions between effects on SSC self-renewal and

differentiation because both impairments will result in a lack of donor-derived spermatogenesis within recipient testes following transplantation. Whether disrupted spermatogenesis in mice lacking Plzf or Taf4b expression or an inability of Plzf-deficient SSCs to reform spermatogenesis following transplantation is due to SSC self-renewal or differentiation is undetermined because impairment of either function would produce an identical result in vivo.

GDNF-Regulated Transcription Factors Are Important for Mouse SSC Self-Renewal

Rarity of SSCs in the testis is a major reason for the limitations of in vivo experiments in examining self-renewal and differentiation. The use of an in vitro system that supports SSC self-renewal provides a means to examine directly the effects from loss of function of a specific molecule on SSC activities. In this experimental condition, self-renewal and differentiation can be distinguished, and secondary factors that may affect SSC functions in vivo (e.g., endocrine disruption) are removed. Combining culture systems with functional SSC transplantation provides an assay system to examine SSC self-renewal specifically. Because GDNF is essential for self-renewal of rodent SSCs, microarray-based gene expression profiling was used to identify genes regulated by GDNF stimulation in cultures proven to contain SSCs by functional transplantation (Oatley et al. 2006). These studies identified the upregulation of several transcription factor–encoding genes, including dynamic regulation of *bcl6b* (B cell CLL/lymphoma 6, member B; also termed *bazf*), *etv5* (Ets variant gene 5; also termed *erm*), and *lhx1* (Lim homeobox protein 1; also termed *lim1*). Each of these molecules has transcription factor activity and plays a role in the function of other cellular systems. Disruption of Bcl6b in mice results in impaired T lymphocyte proliferation (Manders et al. 2005), ablation of Etv5 expression affects overall growth and development (Liu et al. 2003, Yang et al. 2003, Schlesser et al. 2007), and Lhx1 inactivation

Plzf: promyelocytic leukemia zinc finger protein

Bcl6b: B cell CLL/lymphoma 6, member B; also termed Bazf

Etv5: Ets variant gene 5; also termed Erm

Lhx1: Lim homeobox protein 1; also termed Lim1

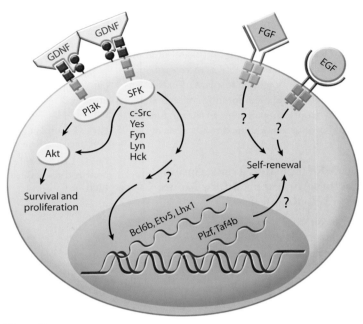

Figure 3

Current understanding of molecular mechanisms regulating spermatogonial stem cell (SSC) self-renewal in mice. Glial cell line–derived neurotrophic factor (GDNF) is the only growth factor demonstrated to have an essential role in regulating SSC self-renewal, and basic fibroblast growth factor (bFGF) or epidermal growth factor (EGF) enhances this influence. GDNF binds to a receptor complex consisting of c-Ret tyrosine kinase and the GPI (glycosyl phosphatidylinositol)-anchored binding molecule Gfrα1 (GDNF family receptor alpha 1). This interaction activates PI3K (phosphoinositide 3-kinase) and Src family kinase (SFK) intercellular signaling mechanisms, leading to downstream activation of Akt signaling, which influences general cellular functions such as survival and proliferation. SFK signaling also elicits a second pathway leading to the regulation of specific gene expression levels that are important for SSC self-renewal. The transcription factor–encoding genes *bcl6b* (B cell CLL/lymphoma 6, member B; also termed *bazf*), *etv5* (Ets variant gene 5; also termed *erm*), and *lhx1* (Lim homeobox protein 1; also termed *lim1*) are regulated through the SFK-activated pathway and are important for the maintenance of self-renewing SSC cultures. Five of the eight known mammalian SFK isoforms—c-Src (Rous sarcoma oncogene), Yes (Yamaguchi sarcoma viral oncogene), Fyn (Fyn proto-oncogene), Lyn (Lyn tyrosine kinase), and Hck (hemopoietic cell kinase)—are expressed in mouse SSCs. Additionally, observations of disrupted spermatogenesis in null mutant mice have pointed to an essential role of the transcription factors Plzf (promyelocytic leukemia zinc finger protein) and Taf4b [TATA box–binding protein (TBP)-associated factor 4b] in mouse SSC self-renewal. However, GDNF does not influence the expression of either Plzf or Taf4b in cultured SSCs, and the importance of either molecule in SSC self-renewal in vitro has not been determined. To date, mechanisms by which bFGF or EGF influences the self-renewal and survival of SSCs have not been reported.

results in craniofacial deformities in addition to inhibited gonadal morphogenesis (Kobayashi et al. 2005, Shawlot & Behringer 1995). To determine whether these GDNF-regulated transcription factors are biologically relevant to SSC functions, their expression was transiently reduced individually by RNAi in cultures of self-renewing mouse SSCs. Subsequent transplantation analyses demonstrated impairment of SSC expansion in vitro, strongly suggesting that Bcl6b, Etv5, and Lhx1 are transcription factors important for SSC self-renewal (Oatley et al. 2006, 2007).

GDNF stimulation of cultured SSCs resulted in activation of Src family kinase (SFK) signaling, and pharmacological impairment of SFK signaling completely blocked GDNF upregulation of these genes without affecting cell survival (Oatley et al. 2007). These results demonstrate a specific pathway involved in SSC self-renewal in which extrinsic GDNF stimulation activates intercellular SFK signaling to stimulate the intrinsic regulation of *bcl6b*, *etv5*, and *lhx1* gene expression levels (**Figure 3**). In contrast, GDNF stimulation also activates Akt signaling in cultured SSCs (Oatley et al. 2007) and GS cells (Lee et al. 2007), but pharmacological inhibition of Akt in SSCs results in increased apoptosis and impaired expression of both GDNF-regulated and non-GDNF-regulated genes. These results indicate a role of Akt in general cell survival rather than SSC self-renewal (Oatley et al. 2007). Studies by Hofmann et al. (2005b) measured gene expression changes in Gfrα1+ cells collected from mouse pups upon exposure to GDNF, and results revealed upregulated expression of several genes, including the transcription factor n-*myc*. Subsequent studies by Braydich-Stolle et al. (2007), using similar Gfrα1+ testis cell populations, observed an important influence of SFK signaling in proliferation, including regulation of n-*myc* expression. Unfortunately, the SSC content of Gfrα1+ cell populations used in both of those studies was not assessed with functional transplantation. Thus, interpreting whether GDNF affected SSCs as opposed to other Gfrα1-expressing germ cell types is difficult (see explanation above). Additionally, in germ cell populations proven to be enriched for SSCs by functional transplantation, the expression of n-*myc* is not affected by GDNF stimulation (Oatley et al. 2006).

In vivo, targeted disruption of Bcl6b or Etv5 expression results in impaired spermatogenesis; a Sertoli cell–only phenotype is observed in varying percentages of seminiferous tubules within adult testes (Chen et al. 2005, Oatley et al. 2006). With advancing age, Etv5 null males become infertile, whereas Bcl6b null males exhibit subfertility at puberty, but effects on their fertility at older ages have not been assessed. These phenotypic observations suggest that SSC function is disrupted in vivo when Bcl6b or Etv5 expression is ablated. Initial observations identified Etv5 expression in Sertoli cells of adult males, leading some investigators to hypothesize that Etv5 has an essential role in the maintenance of the SSC niche (Chen et al. 2005). Other studies revealed Etv5 expression in cultured SSCs, in addition to spermatogonia and Sertoli cells within pup and adult testes (Oatley et al. 2007). Collectively, those observations indicate that Etv5 may have dual roles in regulating SSC functions: intrinsically, via regulating the expression of specific gene networks, and extrinsically, via influencing niche factor output by Sertoli cells. This dynamic role of Etv5 in the testis and growth deformities observed following its inactivation may explain the pronounced infertility of male Etv5 null mice. In contrast, expression of Bcl6b and Lhx1 has been observed only in individual spermatogonia within seminiferous tubules of pup and adult male mice, suggesting a germ cell–specific function in regard to male fertility (Oatley et al. 2007). Bcl6b and Etv5 have been shown to have a role in male fertility, but assessment of Lhx1 function in spermatogenesis has been challenging because targeted disruption results in neonatal lethality (Shawlot & Behringer 1995). Even though Plzf and Taf4b have been suggested as molecules important for SSC self-renewal, their expression is not regulated by GDNF in cultured SSCs (Oatley et al. 2006, 2007), and their importance in SSC self-renewal in vitro has not been assessed. Collectively, studies over the past four years have shaped our current understanding of GDNF influence on SSC function (**Figure 3**), which involves activation of SFK signaling to regulate the expression of specific transcription factor–encoding genes, including *bcl6b*, *etv5*, and *lhx1*, which are important regulators of self-renewal.

Expression of Core Transcription Factors Regulating Self-Renewal of Pluripotent Stem Cells Is Altered in SSCs

The core transcription factors that regulate self-renewal and pluripotency of ES cells include the POU domain factor Oct3/4, Sox2, and Nanog (Boyer et al. 2005). In these cells, interaction between Oct3/4 and Sox2 controls *nanog* transcript expression (Boyer et al. 2005). Recently, several reports have described the conversion of adult somatic cells into pluripotent ES cell–like cells in vitro, referred to as induced pluripotent stem (iPS) cells (Takahashi & Yamanaka 2006, Takahashi et al. 2007, Wernig et al. 2007, Yu et al. 2007). Ectopic expression of the transcription factors Oct3/4, Sox2, Klf4, and c-Myc is adequate to induce a pluripotent ES-like state in fibroblasts of adult rodents and humans (Takahashi & Yamanaka 2006, Park et al. 2007, Takahashi et al. 2007, Wernig et al. 2007). In another report, forced expression of Oct3/4, Sox2, Nanog, and Lin28 produced similar results (Yu et al. 2007). Interestingly, Oct3/4, Sox2, Klf4, c-Myc, and Lin28 are all expressed by SSC-enriched germ cell populations in vitro (**Figure 4**), yet a pluripotent nature of these cells or tumor formation following their transplantation is not observed (Oatley et al. 2006; J.M. Oatley, M.J. Oatley, M.R. Avarbock & R.L. Brinster, unpublished data). However, expression of Nanog is not detected in these SSC cultures or similar GS cell cultures and may be the missing piece to the puzzle that would induce pluripotency in testicular stem cell populations (Kanatsu-Shinohara et al. 2005b, Oatley et al. 2006). In fact, the rare appearances

Induced pluripotent stem (iPS) cells: somatic fibroblasts induced to acquire a pluripotent state upon ectopic expression of specific transcription factors

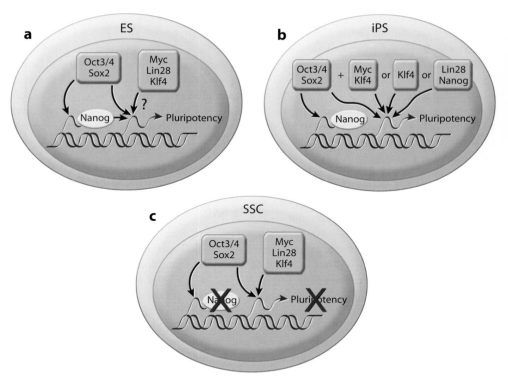

Figure 4

Expression of transcription factors in nonpluripotent spermatogonial stem cells (SSCs) that are thought to be involved in regulating the pluripotent states of embryonic stem (ES) and induced pluripotent stem (iPS) cells. (*a*) Expression of Oct3/4 and Sox2 is essential for the maintenance of pluripotency in ES cells, in which these two molecules control the expression of Nanog. (*b*) Ectopic expression of Oct3/4, Sox2, Klf4, and Myc induces pluripotency in mouse and human fibroblasts (iPS cells). Similarly, ectopic expression of Lin28 and Nanog, in addition to expression of Oct3/4 and Sox2, also induces pluripotency of human fibroblasts. Additionally, Myc expression appears to be dispensable; iPS cells can also be generated by ectopic expression of Oct3/4, Sox2, and Klf4 alone. ES cells also express high levels of Klf4, Myc, and Lin28, but the importance of these three molecules in ES cell pluripotency has not been determined. (*c*) Cultured SSCs express nearly all the transcription factors regulating ES cell pluripotency and those that induce a similar potential in fibroblasts, including Oct3/4, Sox2, Klf4, Myc, and Lin28, but do not express Nanog. The absence of Nanog expression in SSCs may signify a distinct difference in the transcription factor milieu that regulates the function of an adult stem cell population such as SSCs and that of pluripotent ES and iPS cell populations. During embryo development, the first germ cells formed, primordial germ cells (PGCs), require the expression of Nanog, and these cells can become pluripotent under appropriate conditions. However, SSCs, the postnatal descendents of PGCs, do not express Nanog, and many researchers have found their conversion to pluripotency difficult. Thus, ectopic expression of Nanog may be a missing piece to the puzzle by which SSCs can be artificially transformed into a pluripotent state because they already express the array of other molecules that induce pluripotency in somatic cells.

of apparently multipotent stem cells in GS cultures are associated with Nanog expression (Kanatsu-Shinohara et al. 2004a). Constitutive expression of Nanog promotes autonomous self-renewal of ES cells (Chambers et al. 2003) but also appears to be dispensable for this fate, likely owing to compensation from other factors (Chambers et al. 2007). However, recent evidence indicates that Nanog expression is essential for PGC maturation in the genital ridge during embryonic development (Chambers et al. 2007). SSC maturation from PGCs or gonocytes is associated with the silencing of Nanog expression, and so induction of Nanog expression may result in a pluripotent state by SSCs (**Figure 4**). The progress with iPS cells is a major forefront in potential stem cell therapy because pluripotent cells can be generated from patient-specific adult fibroblasts that are immunologically compatible. Perhaps more importantly, iPS cells will be an important model to understand pluripotency, fate commitment, and genetic diseases. SSCs may provide unique insights in this context because they represent one of the earliest fate decisions of epiblast/ES cells and biologically SSCs are of fundamental importance to species continuity.

SUMMARY POINTS

1. Spermatogenesis and thus male fertility are dependent on the functions of SSCs, which are an adult stem cell population whose self-renewal and differentiation are supported extrinsically through niche stimuli and intrinsically through the regulation of specific gene expressions. Currently, the only unequivocal means to identify SSCs and study their biological activities is functional transplantation.

2. Currently, there are no described markers that specifically identify SSCs in mammals. All phenotypic and molecular markers described to date are also expressed by other spermatogonial subtypes or subpopulations of testis somatic cells. However, SSC-enriched cell populations have been isolated on the basis of expression of α_6- or β_1-integrins, Thy1, CD9, Ep-CAM, and Gfrα1. In these populations, SSC content varies widely, with the greatest enrichment found in Thy1$^+$ and Ep-CAM$^+$ cells in mice and rats, respectively. Conversely, the lowest enrichment of SSCs is found in Gfrα1$^+$ cell populations, in which SSCs are even depleted in this cell fraction when isolated from adult testes.

3. GDNF is a niche factor essential for SSC self-renewal. Overexpression in mice results in the accumulation of undifferentiated spermatogonia, and targeted disruption causes impaired spermatogenesis, suggesting the involvement of GDNF in SSC functions in vivo. Importantly, inclusion of GDNF in culture media is essential for SSC and GS cell self-renewal in vitro, and additional supplementation with bFGF or EGF augments those effects. Currently, culture systems that support long-term SSC self-renewal are available only for mouse, rat, and hamster.

4. Expression of several transcription regulators has been associated with SSC functions. Both Plzf and Taf4b are expressed by multiple spermatogonia subtypes, including SSCs, and targeted disruption of either molecule results in impaired spermatogenesis in mice, with a progressive, age-dependent loss of all germ cells. In cultured SSCs, GDNF regulates the expression of Bcl6b, Etv5, and Lhx1, but not Plzf or Taf4b. Transiently reducing expression of these molecules by RNAi results in impaired SSC self-renewal in vitro. Additionally, inactivation of both Bcl6b and Etv5 expression in male mice results in impaired spermatogenesis, which is manifested as a Sertoli cell–only phenotype in varying percentages of seminiferous tubules.

5. GDNF regulation of the expression of self-renewal transcription factors involves activation of SFK signaling. In addition, GDNF activation of Akt signaling promotes SSC survival.

FUTURE ISSUES

1. Are there molecules solely expressed by SSCs in the mammalian testis, and can these molecules be used to isolate SSCs from a variety of species?

2. Can culture systems that support long-term proliferation of SSCs be developed for non-rodent mammals? Can rodent systems be used as a blueprint to achieve this goal?

3. Are there other niche factors besides GDNF, bFGF, and EGF that influence SSC functions? Are they needed to support in vitro expansion of SSC from nonrodent species?

4. What are the intrinsic gene regulatory networks that control SSC fate decisions, and are these networks disrupted in clinical cases of human male infertility?

DISCLOSURE STATEMENT

The University of Pennsylvania has filed two patent applications on spermatogonial stem cell culture. They are (*a*) Culture Conditions and Growth Factors Affecting Fate Determination, Self-Renewal, and Expansion of Rat Spermatogonial Stem Cells and (*b*) Culture Conditions and Growth Factors Affecting Fate Determination, Self-Renewal, and Expansion of Mouse Spermatogonial Stem Cells. R.L.B. is listed as the inventor on each. No patent has been issued.

LITERATURE CITED

Airaksinen MS, Saarma M. 2002. The GDNF family: signaling, biological functions and therapeutic value. *Nat. Rev. Neurosci.* 3:383–94

Aponte PM, Soda T, van de Kant HJ, de Rooij DG. 2005. Basic features of bovine spermatogonial culture and effects of glial cell line-derived neurotrophic factor. *Theriogenology* 65:1828–47

Barnes D, Sato G. 1980. Serum-free cell culture: a unifying approach. *Cell* 22:649–55

Bellve AR, Cavicchia JC, Millette CF, O'Brien DA, Bhatnagar YM, Dym M. 1977. Spermatogenic cells of the prepubertal mouse: isolation and morphological characterization. *J. Cell Biol.* 74:68–85

Blanpain C, Lowry WE, Geoghegan A, Polak L, Fuchs E. 2004. Self-renewal, multipotency, and the existence of two cell populations within an epithelial stem cell niche. *Cell* 118:635–48

Boyer LA, Lee TI, Cole MF, Johnstone SE, Levine SS, et al. 2005. Core transcriptional regulatory circuitry in human embryonic stem cells. *Cell* 122:947–56

Braydich-Stolle L, Kostereva N, Dym M, Hofmann MC. 2007. Role of Src family kinases and N-Myc in spermatogonial stem cell proliferation. *Dev. Biol.* 304:34–45

Brinster RL. 2002. Germline stem cell transplantation and transgenesis. *Science* 296:2174–76

Brinster RL. 2007. Male germline stem cells: from mice to men. *Science* 316:404–5

Brinster RL, Avarbock MR. 1994. Germline transmission of donor haplotype following spermatogonial transplantation. *Proc. Natl. Acad. Sci. USA* 91:11303–7

Brinster RL, Zimmermann JW. 1994. Spermatogenesis following male germ-cell transplantation. *Proc. Natl. Acad. Sci. USA* 91:11298–302

Buaas FW, Kirsh AL, Sharma M, McLean DJ, Morris JL, et al. 2004. Plzf is required in adult male germ cells for stem cell self-renewal. *Nat. Genet.* 36:647–52

Buageaw A, Sukhwani M, Ben-Yehudah A, Ehmcke J, Rawe VY, et al. 2005. GDNF family receptor α1 phenotype of spermatogonial stem cells in immature mouse testes. *Biol. Reprod.* 73:1011–16

Chambers I, Colby D, Robertson M, Nichols J, Lee S, et al. 2003. Functional expression cloning of Nanog, a pluripotency sustaining factor in embryonic stem cells. *Cell* 113:643–55

Chambers I, Silva J, Colby D, Nichols J, Nijmeijer B, et al. 2007. Nanog safeguards pluripotency and mediates germline development. *Nature* 450:1230–34

Chen C, Ouyang W, Grigura V, Zhou Q, Carnes K, et al. 2005. ERM is required for transcriptional control of the spermatogonial stem cell niche. *Nature* 436:1030–34

Clermont Y. 1962. Quantitative analysis of spermatogenesis of the rat: a revised model for the renewal of spermatogonia. *Am. J. Anat.* 111:111–29

Clermont Y. 1972. Kinetics of spermatogenesis in mammals: seminiferous epithelium cycle and spermatogonial renewal. *Physiol. Rev.* 52:198–236

Clermont Y, Oko R, Hermo L. 1993. Cell biology of mammalian spermiogenesis. In *Cell and Molecular Biology of the Testis*, ed. C Desjardins, LL Ewing, 1:332–76. New York: Oxford Univ. Press

Clermont Y, Perey B. 1957. Quantitative study of the cell population of the seminiferous tubules in immature rats. *Am. J. Anat.* 100:241–67

Conboy IM, Conboy MJ, Wagers AJ, Girma ER, Weissman IL, Rando TA. 2005. Rejuvenation of aged progenitor cells by exposure to a young systemic environment. *Nature* 433:760–64

Costoya JA, Hobbs RM, Barna M, Cattoretti G, Manova K, et al. 2004. Essential role of Plzf in maintenance of spermatogonial stem cells. *Nat. Genet.* 36:653–59

de Rooij DG. 1998. Stem cells in the testis. *Int. J. Exp. Pathol.* 79:67–80

de Rooij DG, Russell LD. 2000. All you wanted to know about spermatogonia but were afraid to ask. *J. Androl.* 21:776–98

Dobrinski I, Ogawa T, Avarbock MR, Brinster RL. 1999. Computer assisted image analysis to assess colonization of recipient seminiferous tubules by spermatogonial stem cells from transgenic donor mice. *Mol. Reprod. Dev.* 53:142–48

Dressler GR. 2006. The cellular basis of kidney development. *Annu. Rev. Cell Dev. Biol.* 22:509–29

Ebata KT, Zhang X, Nagano MC. 2005. Expression patterns of cell-surface molecules on male germ line stem cells during postnatal mouse development. *Mol. Reprod. Dev.* 72:171–81

Falender AE, Freiman RN, Geles KG, Lo KC, Hwang K, et al. 2005. Maintenance of spermatogenesis requires TAF4b, a gonad-specific subunit of TFIID. *Genes Dev.* 19:794–803

Geiger H, Rennebeck G, Van Zant G. 2005. Regulation of hematopoietic stem cell aging in vivo by a distinct genetic element. *Proc. Natl. Acad. Sci. USA* 102:5102–7

Griswold MD. 1998. The central role of Sertoli cells in spermatogenesis. *Semin. Cell Dev. Biol.* 9:411–16

Guan K, Nayernia K, Maier LS, Wagner S, Dressel R, et al. 2006. Pluripotency of spermatogonial stem cells from adult mouse testis. *Nature* 440:1199–203

Hamra FK, Chapman KM, Nguyen DM, Williams-Stephens AA, Hammer RE, Garbers DL. 2005. Self renewal, expansion, and transfection of rat spermatogonial stem cells in culture. *Proc. Natl. Acad. Sci. USA* 102:17430–35

Harrison DE. 1980. Competitive repopulation: a new assay for long-term stem cell functional capacity. *Blood* 55:77–81

Hayashi I, Sato GH. 1976. Replacement of serum by hormones permits growth of cells in a defined medium. *Nature* 259:132–34

Hermann BP, Sukhwani M, Lin CC, Sheng Y, Tomko J, et al. 2007. Characterization, cryopreservation, and ablation of spermatogonial stem cells in adult rhesus macaques. *Stem Cells* 25:2330–38

Hofmann MC, Braydich-Stolle L, Dettin L, Johnson E, Dym M. 2005a. Immortalization of mouse germ line stem cells. *Stem Cells* 23:200–10

Hofmann MC, Braydich-Stolle L, Dym M. 2005b. Isolation of male germ-line stem cells; influence of GDNF. *Dev. Biol.* 279:114–24

Huckins C. 1971. The spermatogonial stem cell population in adult rats. I. Their morphology, proliferation and maturation. *Anat. Rec.* 169:533–57

Huckins C. 1978. The morphology and kinetics of spermatogonial degeneration in normal adult rats: an analysis using a simplified classification of the germinal epithelium. *Anat. Rec.* 190:905–26

Huckins C, Clermont Y. 1968. Evolution of gonocytes in the rat testis during late embryonic and early post-natal life. *Arch. Anat. Histol. Embryol.* 51:341–54

Kanatsu-Shinohara M, Inoue K, Lee J, Yoshimoto M, Ogonuki N, et al. 2004a. Generation of pluripotent stem cells from neonatal mouse testis. *Cell* 119:1001–12

Kanatsu-Shinohara M, Inoue K, Miki H, Ogonuki N, Takehashi M, et al. 2006. Clonal origin of germ cell colonies after spermatogonial transplantation in mice. *Biol. Reprod.* 75:68–74

Kanatsu-Shinohara M, Inoue K, Ogonuki N, Miki H, Yoshida S, et al. 2007. Leukemia inhibitory factor enhances formation of germ cell colonies in neonatal mouse testis culture. *Biol. Reprod.* 76:55–62

Kanatsu-Shinohara M, Miki H, Inoue K, Ogonuki N, Toyokuni S, et al. 2005a. Long-term culture of mouse male germline stem cells under serum- or feeder-free conditions. *Biol. Reprod.* 72:985–91

Kanatsu-Shinohara M, Morimoto T, Toyokuni S, Shinohara T. 2004b. Regulation of mouse spermatogonial stem cell self-renewing division by the pituitary gland. *Biol. Reprod.* 70:1731–37

Kanatsu-Shinohara M, Muneto T, Lee J, Takenaka M, Chuma S, et al. 2008. Long-term culture of male germline stem cells from hamster testes. *Biol. Reprod.* 78:611–17

Kanatsu-Shinohara M, Ogonuki N, Inoue K, Miki H, Ogura A, et al. 2003. Long-term proliferation in culture and germline transmission of mouse male germline stem cells. *Biol. Reprod.* 69:612–16

Kanatsu-Shinohara M, Ogonuki N, Iwano T, Lee J, Kazuki Y, et al. 2005b. Genetic and epigenetic properties of mouse male germline stem cells during long-term culture. *Development* 132:4155–63

Kanatsu-Shinohara M, Toyokuni S, Shinohara T. 2004c. CD9 is a surface marker on mouse and rat male germline stem cells. *Biol. Reprod.* 70:70–75

Kelly S, Bliss TM, Shah AK, Sun GH, Ma M, et al. 2004. Transplanted human fetal neural stem cells survive, migrate, and differentiate in ischemic rat cerebral cortex. *Proc. Natl. Acad. Sci. USA* 101:11839–44

Klassen H, Schwartz MR, Bailey AH, Young MJ. 2001. Surface markers expressed by multipotent human and mouse progenitor cells include tetraspanins and nonprotein epitopes. *Neurosci. Lett.* 312:180–82

Kobayashi A, Kwan KM, Carroll TJ, McMahon AP, Mendelsohn CL, et al. 2005. Distinct and sequential tissue-specific activities of the LIM-class homeobox gene *Lim1* for tubular morphogenesis during kidney development. *Development* 132:2809–23

Krishnamurthy H, Danilovich N, Morales CR, Sairam MR. 2000. Qualitative and quantitative decline in spermatogenesis of the follicle-stimulating hormone receptor knockout (FORKO) mouse. *Biol. Reprod.* 62:1146–59

Kubota H, Avarbock MR, Brinster RL. 2003. Spermatogonial stem cells share some, but not all, phenotypic and functional characteristics with other stem cells. *Proc. Natl. Acad. Sci. USA* 100:6487–92

Kubota H, Avarbock MR, Brinster RL. 2004a. Culture conditions and single growth factors affect fate determination of mouse spermatogonial stem cells. *Biol. Reprod.* 71:722–31

Kubota H, Avarbock MR, Brinster RL. 2004b. Growth factors essential for self-renewal and expansion of mouse spermatogonial stem cells. *Proc. Natl. Acad. Sci. USA* 101:16489–94

Lee J, Kanatsu-Shinohara M, Inoue K, Ogonuki N, Miki H, et al. 2007. Akt mediates self-renewal division of mouse spermatogonial stem cells. *Development* 134:1853–59

Liu Y, Jiang H, Crawford HC, Hogan BL. 2003. Role for ETS domain transcription factors Pea3/Erm in mouse lung development. *Dev. Biol.* 261:10–24

Manders PM, Hunter PJ, Telaranta AI, Carr JM, Marshall JL, et al. 2005. BCL6b mediates the enhanced magnitude of the secondary response of memory CD8$^+$ T lymphocytes. *Proc. Natl. Acad. Sci. USA* 102:7418–25

Manova K, Nocka K, Besmer P, Bachvarova RF. 1990. Gonadal expression of c-kit encoded at the W locus of the mouse. *Development* 110:1057–69

Matsui Y, Zsebo KM, Hogan BL. 1990. Embryonic expression of a hematopoietic growth factor encoded by the Sl locus and the ligand for c-kit. *Nature* 347:667–69

Meng X, Lindahl M, Hyvönen ME, Parvinen M, de Rooij DG, et al. 2000. Regulation of cell fate decision of undifferentiated spermatogonia by GDNF. *Science* 287:1489–93

McLaren A. 2003. Primordial germ cells in the mouse. *Dev. Biol.* 262:1–15

McLean DJ, Friel PJ, Johnston DS, Griswold MD. 2003. Characterization of spermatogonial stem cell maturation and differentiation in neonatal mice. *Biol. Reprod.* 69:2085–91

Nagano M, Avarbock MR, Brinster RL. 1999. Pattern and kinetics of mouse donor spermatogonial stem cell colonization in recipient testes. *Biol. Reprod.* 60:1429–36

Nagano M, Avarbock MR, Leonida EB, Brinster CJ, Brinster RL. 1998. Culture of mouse spermatogonial stem cells. *Tissue Cell* 30:389–97

Nagano M, Ryu BY, Brinster CJ, Avarbock MR, Brinster RL. 2003. Maintenance of mouse male germ line stem cells in vitro. *Biol. Reprod.* 68:2207–14

Nakagawa T, Nabeshima Y, Yoshida S. 2007. Functional identification of the actual and potential stem cell compartments in mouse spermatogenesis. *Dev. Cell* 12:195–206

Naughton CK, Jain S, Strickland AM, Gupta A, Milbrandt J. 2006. Glial cell-line derived neurotrophic factor-mediated RET signaling regulates spermatogonial stem cell fate. *Biol. Reprod.* 74:314–21

Oakberg EF. 1971. Spermatogonial stem-cell renewal in the mouse. *Anat. Rec.* 169:515–31

Oatley JM, Avarbock MR, Brinster RL. 2007. Glial cell line-derived neurotrophic factor regulation of genes essential for self-renewal of mouse spermatogonial stem cells is dependent on Src family kinase signaling. *J. Biol. Chem.* 282:25842–51

Oatley JM, Avarbock MR, Telaranta AI, Fearon DT, Brinster RL. 2006. Identifying genes important for spermatogonial stem cell self-renewal and survival. *Proc. Natl. Acad. Sci. USA* 103:9524–29

Oatley JM, Brinster RL. 2006. Spermatogonial stem cell. *Methods Enzymol.* 419:259–82

Oatley JM, Reeves JJ, McLean DJ. 2004. Biological activity of cryopreserved bovine spermatogonial stem cells during in vitro culture. *Biol. Reprod.* 71:942–47

Oka M, Tagoku K, Russell TL, Nakano Y, Hamazaki T, et al. 2002. CD9 is associated with leukemia inhibitory factor-mediated maintenance of embryonic stem cells. *Mol. Biol. Cell* 13:1274–81

Oritani K, Wu X, Medina K, Hudson J, Miyake K, et al. 1996. Antibody ligation of CD9 modifies production of myeloid cells in long-term cultures. *Blood* 87:2252–61

Park IH, Zhao R, West JA, Yabuuchi A, Huo H, et al. 2008. Reprogramming of human somatic cells to pluripotency with defined factors. *Nature* 451:141–46

Resnick JL, Bixler LS, Cheng L, Donovan PJ. 1992. Long-term proliferation of mouse primordial germ cells in culture. *Nature* 359:550–51

Russell LD. 1993. Form, dimension, and cytology of mammalian Sertoli cells. In *The Sertoli Cell*, ed. LD Russell, MD Griswold, 1:1–37. Florida: Cache River

Russell LD, Ettlin RA, Hikim AP, Clegg ED. 1990. Mammalian spermatogenesis. In *Histological and Histopathological Evaluation of the Testis*, ed. LD Russell, R Ettlin, AP Sinha Hikim, ED Clegg, pp. 1–40. Florida: Cache River

Ryu BY, Kubota H, Avarbock MR, Brinster RL. 2005. Conservation of spermatogonial stem cell self-renewal signaling between mouse and rat. *Proc. Natl. Acad. Sci. USA* 102:14302–7

Ryu BY, Orwig KE, Kubota H, Avarbock MR, Brinster RL. 2004. Phenotypic and functional characteristics of spermatogonial stem cells in rats. *Dev. Biol.* 274:158–70

Ryu BY, Orwig KE, Oatley JM, Avarbock MR, Brinster RL. 2006. Effects of aging and niche microenvironment on spermatogonial stem cell self-renewal. *Stem Cells* 24:1505–11

Sapsford CS. 1962. Changes in the cells of the sex cords and the seminiferous tubules during development of the testis of the rat and the mouse. *Austr. J. Zool.* 101:178–92

Sariola H, Saarma M. 2003. Novel functions and signaling pathways for GDNF. *J. Cell. Sci.* 116:3855–62

Scadden DT. 2006. The stem-cell niche as an entity of action. *Nature* 441:1075–79

Schlesser HN, Simon L, Hofmann MC, Murphy KM, Murphy T, et al. 2008. Effects of ETV5 (Ets Variant Gene 5) on testis and body growth, time course of spermatogonial stem cell loss, and fertility in mice. *Biol. Reprod.* 78:483–89

Schrans-Stassen BH, van de Kant HJ, de Rooij DG, van Pelt AM. 1999. Differential expression of c-kit in mouse undifferentiated and differentiating type A spermatogonia. *Endocrinology* 140:5894–900

Seandel M, James D, Shmelkov SV, Falciatori I, Kim J, et al. 2007. Generation of functional multipotent adult stem cells from GPR125+ germline progenitors. *Nature* 449:346–50

Sharpe R. 1994. Regulation of spermatogenesis. In *The Physiology of Reproduction*, ed. E Knobil, JD Neill, 1:1363–434. New York: Raven

Shawlot W, Behringer RR. 1995. Requirement for Lim1 in head-organizer function. *Nature* 374:425–30

Shinohara T, Avarbock MR, Brinster RL. 1999. β1- and α6-integrin are surface markers on mouse spermatogonial stem cells. *Proc. Natl. Acad. Sci. USA* 96:5504–9

Shinohara T, Orwig KE, Avarbock MR, Brinster RL. 2000. Spermatogonial stem cell enrichment by multiparameter selection of mouse testis cells. *Proc. Natl. Acad. Sci. USA* 97:8346–51

Siminovitch L, Till JE, McCulloch EA. 1964. Decline in colony forming ability of marrow cells subjected to serial transplantation to irradiated mice. *J. Cell Physiol.* 64:23–31

Smith AG, Heath JK, Donaldson DD, Wong GG, Moreau J, et al. 1988. Inhibition of pluripotential embryonic stem cell differentiation by purified polypeptides. *Nature* 336:688–90

Spradling A, Drummond-Barbosa D, Kai T. 2001. Stem cells find their niche. *Nature* 414:98–104

Stern H. 1993. The process of meiosis. In *Cell and Molecular Biology of the Testis*, ed. C Desjardins, LL Ewing, 1:296–331. New York: Oxford Univ. Press

Tadokoro Y, Yomogida K, Ohta H, Tohda A, Nishimune Y. 2002. Homeostatic regulation of germinal stem cell proliferation by the GDNF/FSH pathway. *Mech. Dev.* 113:29–39

Takahashi K, Tanabe K, Ohnuki M, Narita M, Ichisaka T, et al. 2007. Induction of pluripotent stem cells from adult human fibroblasts by defined factors. *Cell* 131:861–72

Takahashi K, Yamanaka S. 2006. Induction of pluripotent stem cells from mouse embryonic and adult fibroblast cultures by defined factors. *Cell* 126:663–76

Tegelenbosch RAJ, de Rooij DG. 1993. A quantitative study of spermatogonial multiplication and stem cell renewal in the C3H/101 F1 hybrid mouse. *Mutat. Res.* 290:193–200

Van Zant G, Liang Y. 2003. The role of stem cells in aging. *Exp. Hematol.* 31:659–72

Wernig M, Meissner A, Foreman R, Brambrink T, Ku M, et al. 2007. In vitro reprogramming of fibroblasts into a pluripotent ES-cell-like state. *Nature* 448:318–24

Williams RL, Hilton DJ, Pease S, Willson TA, Stewart CL, et al. 1988. Myeloid leukaemia inhibitory factor maintains the developmental potential of embryonic stem cells. *Nature* 336:684–87

Yang HS, Alexander K, Santiago P, Hinds PW. 2003. ERM proteins and Cdk5 in cellular senescence. *Cell Cycle* 2:517–20

Yoshida S, Nabeshima YI, Nakagawa T. 2008. Stem cell heterogeneity: actual and potential stem cell compartments in the mouse spermatogenesis. *Ann. N.Y. Acad. Sci.* 1120:47–58

Yoshida S, Sukeno M, Nabeshima Y. 2007. A vasculature-associated niche for undifferentiated spermatogonia in the mouse testis. *Science* 317:1722–26

Yoshida S, Sukeno M, Nakagawa T, Ohbo K, Nagamatsu G, et al. 2006. The first round of mouse spermatogenesis is a distinctive program that lacks the self-renewing spermatogonia stage. *Development* 133:1495–505

Yoshinaga K, Nishikawa S, Ogawa M, Hayashi S, Kunisada T, et al. 1991. Role of c-kit in mouse spermatogenesis: identification of spermatogonia as a specific site of c-kit expression and function. *Development* 113:689–99

Yu J, Vodyanik MA, Smuga-Otto K, Antosiewicz-Bourget J, Frane JL, et al. 2007. Induced pluripotent stem cell lines derived from human somatic cells. *Science* 318:1917–20

Zhang X, Ebata KT, Robaire B, Nagano MC. 2006. Aging of male germ line stem cells in mice. *Biol. Reprod.* 74:119–24

ACKNOWLEDGMENTS

The authors' research programs are supported by grants from the National Institutes of Health HD052728 (R.L.B.) and HD058137 (J.M.O.) and United States Department of Agriculture NRI 2008-00546 (J.M.O.). Additionally, research is supported by the Robert J. Kleberg, Jr. and Helen C. Kleberg Foundation and start-up funds from the Pennsylvania State University.

Unconventional Mechanisms of Protein Transport to the Cell Surface of Eukaryotic Cells

Walter Nickel[1] and Matthias Seedorf[2]

[1]Heidelberg University Biochemistry Center (BZH) and [2]Zentrum für Molekulare Biologie der Universität Heidelberg (ZMBH), 69120 Heidelberg, Germany; email: walter.nickel@bzh.uni-heidelberg.de, m.seedorf@zmbh.uni-heidelberg.de

Annu. Rev. Cell Dev. Biol. 2008. 24:287–308

First published online as a Review in Advance on June 27, 2008

The *Annual Review of Cell and Developmental Biology* is online at cellbio.annualreviews.org

This article's doi:
10.1146/annurev.cellbio.24.110707.175320

1081-0706/08/1110-0287$20.00

Key Words

unconventional protein secretion, nonclassical export, protein targeting, local protein biosynthesis, Golgi-independent trafficking, fibroblast growth factor-1 and -2, galectin, thioredoxin, HMGB-1, annexin, Ist2

Abstract

The classical secretion of soluble proteins and transport of integral membrane proteins to the cell surface require transit into and through the endoplasmic reticulum and the Golgi apparatus. Signal peptides or transmembrane domains target proteins for translocation into the lumen or insertion into the membrane of the endoplasmic reticulum, respectively. Here we discuss two mechanisms of unconventional protein targeting to plasma membranes, i.e., transport processes that are active in the absence of a functional Golgi system. We first focus on integral membrane proteins that are inserted into the endoplasmic reticulum but that, however, are transported to plasma membranes in a Golgi-independent manner. We then discuss soluble secretory proteins that are secreted from cells without any involvement of the endoplasmic reticulum and the Golgi apparatus.

Contents

GOLGI-INDEPENDENT TRANSPORT OF MEMBRANE PROTEINS TO THE PLASMA MEMBRANE

Distinct Pathways Out of the ER

Transport along the classical secretory pathway is mediated by vesicular carriers, which recruit cargo, bud off a donor membrane, and fuse with a specific target membrane. Coated vesicles (COPII and COPI) transport the cargo between the endoplasmic reticulum (ER) and the Golgi apparatus (Lee et al. 2004). The sorting of proteins begins to occur as COPII vesicles exit the ER and continues in the Golgi network, allowing for the delivery of cargo to various places, including the plasma membrane (Griffiths & Simons 1986). There are a few examples of proteins that leave the ER in the absence of functioning COPII coat components. Secretion of Hsp150 in the yeast *Saccharomyces cerevisiae* occurs normally in the presence of defective COPII coat proteins Sec24 and Sec13 (Fatal et al. 2002, Karhinen et al. 2005). Reduced activity of Sar1 GTPase fails to abolish the trafficking of voltage-gated K^+ channel (Kv4) and its regulator KChlP1 in dendritic outposts of neurons (Hasdemir et al. 2005). Transport of proteins directly to the plasma membrane from the ER may also occur during phagocytosis in dendritic cells of the mouse immune system (Gagnon et al. 2002). Desjardins and collegues speculated that a SNARE-mediated direct fusion of ER-derived vesicles with the plasma membrane allows rapid forward transport without passage through the Golgi (Gagnon et al. 2002). This was based on the in vitro observation of a fusogenic SNARE pair consisting of the ER- and Golgi-localized Sec22 and the plasma membrane–localized Sec9 proteins (McNew et al. 2000). However, the existence of this pathway remains controversial (Becker et al. 2005, Touret et al. 2005, Rogers & Foster 2007).

Researchers have reported various lines of evidence for Golgi-independent transport of membrane proteins to cell surfaces. During passage through the Golgi, N-linked glycan chains are modified so that glycoproteins at the cell surface are endoglycosidase H (endo H) resistant. However, an endo H–sensitive form of the receptor protein-tyrosine phosphatase CD45 rapidly accumulates at the cell surface in T lymphoma cells (Baldwin & Ostergaard 2001, 2002). A similar phenomenon has been observed for the trafficking of the cell adhesion molecules caspr/paranodin and F3/contactin in neuroblastoma N2a cells. These proteins are recruited into lipid microdomains and reach the interface of axonal membranes and myelinating glial cells as endo H–sensitive glycoproteins as well (Bonnon et al. 2003). Moreover, the rapid transport of CD45 and cell adhesion molecules is brefeldin A (BFA) resistant (Baldwin & Ostergaard 2002, Bonnon et al. 2003). BFA is a fungal metabolite that inhibits the activation of ADP-ribosylation factor 1 (ARF1) on Golgi membranes and, therefore, blocks vesicular transport along the secretory pathway (Misumi et al. 1986, Lippincott-Schwartz et al. 1989, Orci et al. 1991). Golgi-independent trafficking occurs only in specific cell types, indicating that it is a regulated process limited to specific physiological conditions that can operate in addition to trafficking along the classical secretory pathway (Baldwin & Ostergaard 2002, Bonnon et al. 2003).

Trafficking of Ist2 Defines a Novel Pathway for Direct Transport from the ER to the Plasma Membrane

Although the molecular function of the polytopic membrane protein Ist2 remains elusive, it has been observed that ist2Δ mutants showed an increased sodium tolerance, which led to the name Ist2 (Entian et al. 1999). Ist2 belongs to a group of proteins that are translated from localized mRNAs (Long et al. 1997; Takizawa et al. 1997, 2000; Shepard et al. 2003; Aronov et al. 2007). Localized mRNAs are transported along a polarized actin cytoskeleton into the growing daughter cells (buds) of *S. cerevisiae* (summarized by Gonsalvez et al. 2005, Müller et al. 2007). The coordinated transport of She2-bound mRNAs and tubular ER leads to the translation of mRNAs for membrane proteins at the cortical ER in the bud (Schmid et al. 2006, Aronov et al. 2007). The transport of Ist2 to the periphery of mother and daughter cells occurs independently of trafficking through the ER/Golgi system, as shown by the localization of Ist2 in conditional yeast mutants defective in COPII vesicle formation (*sec23-1* and *sec12-4* mutants), intra-Golgi transport (*sec7-1* mutant), and general transport vesicle fusion (*sec18-1* mutant) (Juschke et al. 2004, 2005). *SEC18* encodes the ATPase N-ethylmaleimide-sensitive fusion (NSF) protein. All SNARE-mediated

vesicular transport ceases rapidly after a shift to the nonpermissive temperature in *sec18-1* mutants (Graham & Emr 1991). This suggests that the transport of Ist2 occurs without or at low activity of SNARE-mediated membrane fusion. The detection of newly synthesized Ist2 at peripheral patches by fluorescence microscopy, and the degradation of the majority of Ist2 (50–100%) by externally added proteases in intact *Sec* mutant cells, demonstrates that Ist2 can reach specific domains of the cell surface without ER-to-Golgi transport (Juschke et al. 2004, 2005). Some of the Ist2 may remain at specific sites of the cortical ER because the Ist2 patches colocalize with certain cortical ER proteins (Juschke et al. 2004).

Experiments with a chimera of Prm1, a pheromone-induced membrane protein, and the C-terminal domain of Ist2 show that the C terminus is sufficient for Ist2 sorting (Juschke et al. 2005). On its own, Prm1 accumulates at contact sites between cells of opposite mating types before being endocytosed (Heiman & Walter 2000). Tagging with the Ist2 C terminus efficiently relocates the chimera into stable peripheral sites, demonstrating that the Ist2 C terminus contains a dominant sorting signal (Juschke et al. 2005). Although the Prm1-Ist2 chimera receives complete N-linked glycosylation, indicating passage through the ER, only a minor fraction is modified in the *cis*-Golgi. Because this modification depends on the function of Sec18/NSF, one can assume that a small amount of Ist2 enters the classical secretory pathway. None of the Prm1-Ist2 chimera are further modified at the medial- or the *trans*-Golgi. On the basis of these results and the presence of a di-lysine ER-retrieval signal at the extreme C terminus of Ist2, it is likely that Ist2 returns from the *cis*-Golgi to the ER, instead of traveling through the entire Golgi. Also, the Ist2 sorting signal redirects a Gef1-Ist2 chimera from *trans*-Golgi network/endosomes to the cell periphery and circumvents cleavage of Gef1 by the Golgi protease Kex2 (Juschke et al. 2005).

Is the local translation of Ist2 at the cortical ER a prerequisite for unconventional transport to the neighboring plasma membrane, or does Ist2 trafficking operate independently of mRNA localization? The direct coupling of local translation and trafficking may occur at contact sites between the cortical ER and the plasma membrane. At these sites, the minimal distance between the two membranes is less than 10 nm (Pichler et al. 2001), which approximates the size of a single protein. There is evidence that such narrow cytoplasmic gaps are involved in nonvesicular exchange of lipids (Baumann et al. 2005, Raychaudhuri et al. 2006). However, experiments in mutants without mRNA transport and disruption of the IST2 mRNA localization element reveal that a coupling of local translation and trafficking is unlikely (Takizawa et al. 2000, Juschke et al. 2004, Franz et al. 2007). Instead of an essential role in targeting, IST2 mRNA localization operates upstream and separately from a post-translational sorting mechanism. The localization of mRNA ensures that buds express Ist2 locally but has no effect on the sorting of Ist2 to the cell periphery per se.

The sorting of Ist2 can be further divided in two distinct steps. First, the efficient accumulation of Ist2 at the cortical ER of mother and daughter cells depends on a protein-sorting signal at the C terminus. A C-terminal truncation of the last 18 residues trapped Ist2 in dot-like structures at the perinuclear ER and cortical ER (Franz et al. 2007). The existence of transport from the general ER to domains of the cortical ER is supported by the observation that wild-type cells, with functioning IST2 mRNA transport, synthesize small amounts of Ist2 protein at the perinuclear ER (K. Maass, M.A. Fischer, M. Seiler, K. Temmerman, W. Nickel & M. Seedorf, submitted manuscript). Ist2 has not been detected in the perinuclear ER at steady state because it is rapidly transported to the cortical ER via ER tubules (Takizawa et al. 2000; Juschke et al. 2004, 2005; Franz et al. 2007). This rapid transport to the cortical ER depends on two basic clusters at the Ist2 C terminus (K. Maass, M.A. Fischer, M. Seiler, K. Temmerman, W. Nickel & M. Seedorf, submitted manuscript). Each cluster contains four lysines. Owing to the proximity of the cortical ER and the plasma membrane, these basic clusters may bind negatively charged derivates of phosphoinositides (PIPs) at the plasma membrane (McLaughlin et al. 2002), leading to a recruitment of Ist2 at specific sites of the cortical ER. Compared with uncharged or single negatively charged lipids, phosphatidylinositol 4,5 bisphosphate [$PI(4,5)P_2$] has a valence of -4 at pH 7.0 (McLaughlin et al. 2002). Therefore, a protein with a cluster of four or more basic residues on its surface could be sequestered by a $PI(4,5)P_2$-containing membrane.

Figure 1

Three different models for the transfer of Ist2 from specific domains of the cortical endoplasmic reticulum (ER) to the plasma membrane. (*a*) The Ist2 sorting signal recruits Ist2 into vesicles that bud off the cortical ER, and these vesicles fuse SNARE-dependently (*left*) or SNARE-independently (*right*) with the plasma membrane. The penetration of the amphipathic α-helix of the Ist2 sorting signal into the cortical ER promotes vesicle budding. Instead of a SNARE-mediated fusion, the activity of the Ist2 sorting signal alone mediates the fusion of vesicles from the cortical ER with the plasma membrane. (*b*) The interaction between the Ist2 sorting signal and cortical ER destabilizes the lipid bilayer and allows the transition of lipid-embedded Ist2 from the ER into the plasma membrane. (*c*) The Ist2 sorting signal binds to phosphatidylinositol 4,5 bisphosphate [$PI(4,5)P_2$] (*red dots*) at the plasma membrane, which triggers the formation of the amphipathic α-helix. The insertion of multiple amphipathic α-helices into the cytosolic leaflet of the plasma membrane induces bending of this membrane domain toward the cortical ER, resulting in transient formation of a fusion pore. This allows diffusion of Ist2 followed by disassembly of the pore and separation of cortical ER and plasma membrane. (*Inset*) Schematic representations of a SNARE protein (in *green, left*) and Ist2 [membrane-spanning part with eight transmembrane (TM) domains in *yellow*] with two conformations of the sorting signal (in *blue*). The triangle indicates the transition of the sorting signal into an amphipathic α-helical fold.

Models for the Direct Transfer of Ist2 from the ER to the Plasma Membrane

Three models may explain the transfer of Ist2 from specific sites of the cortical ER to the plasma membrane. The first model is based on a mechanism involving the recruitment of Ist2 into vesicles that bud from domains of the cortical ER and fuse with the neighboring plasma membrane (**Figure 1a**). Efficient transport of Ist2 requires the last 69 amino acid residues. When fused to the C terminus of a membrane protein, this sequence was sufficient for transport to the cell periphery (Franz et al. 2007). A multimerization domain can replace the activity of the N-terminal part of the sorting signal (Franz et al. 2007), suggesting that the Ist2 sorting signal functions as multimer. The C-terminal part contains two basic clusters, which partially overlap with a short amphipathic α-helix, and a consensus sequence of a di-lysine ER retrieval signal, which is part of the most C-terminally located basic cluster

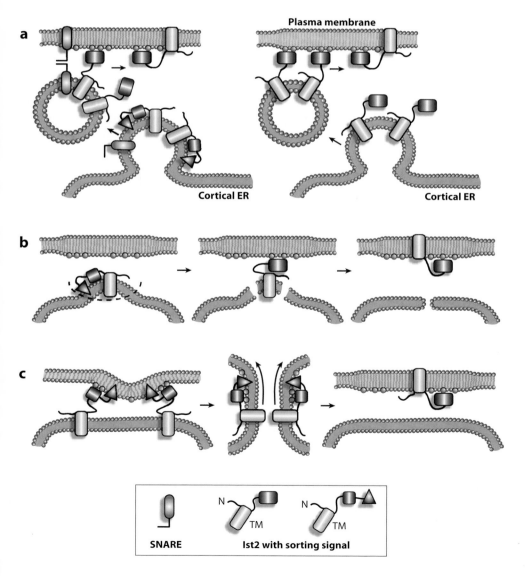

KLKKKL (K. Maass, M.A. Fischer, M. Seiler, K. Temmerman, W. Nickel & M. Seedorf, submitted manuscript). Amphipathic α-helices have the potential to penetrate into one leaflet of a membrane, and this penetration can result in local membrane curvature (McMahon & Gallop 2005, Zimmerberg & Kozlov 2006). If the Ist2 sorting signal interacts with the cortical ER, penetration of the amphipathic α-helix may promote vesicle budding, which may be assisted by the recruitment of a COPI coat via the di-lysine ER retrieval signal. In vitro experiments have shown that the COPI coat can bud vesicles directly from the ER (Bednarek et al. 1995). Following budding from the cortical ER, these vesicles may fuse with the plasma membrane, and the ER-located v-SNARE Sec22 and the plasma membrane t-SNARE Sec9 are candidates to mediate this type of membrane fusion (McNew et al. 2000). However, normal trafficking of Ist2 to the cell periphery in *sec18-1* (Juschke et al. 2005) and *sec22Δ* (C. Juschke & M. Seedorf, unpublished observation) mutants argues against SNARE-mediated fusion between the ER and the plasma membrane. Perhaps the Ist2 sorting signal itself can mediate vesicle fusion. The specific environment of the plasma membrane may induce a conformational change of the Ist2 sorting signal so that the signal can switch between states interacting with either the cortical ER or the plasma membrane. An interaction between the positive residues of the Ist2 sorting signal with specific lipids at the plasma membrane may bring Ist2-containing vesicles and the plasma membrane in close proximity (**Figure 1*a***, right). Certain lipids such as $PI(4,5)P_2$ can be highly concentrated on the cytoplasmic side of the plasma membrane and therefore are good candidates as binding sites of the Ist2 sorting signal (McLaughlin et al. 2002). Whether such interactions may lead to membrane fusion remains unclear.

In a second, nonvesicular mechanism, the Ist2 sorting signal could target Ist2 to a specific microenvironment of the interface between the cortical ER and the plasma membrane. Lipid-embedded Ist2 could be extracted from the ER by a mechanism similar to the ER disloca-tion of class I major histocompatibility complex (MHC) molecules (Ploegh 2007) followed by pore closure of the cortical ER and the reinsertion of Ist2 into the proximal plasma membrane (**Figure 1*b***). This model requires the formation of unstable nonbilayer cortical ER domains containing Ist2. Again, a candidate lipid for this membrane destabilization is $PI(4,5)P_2$, which may be synthesized by the plasma membrane–located lipid kinases Stt4 and Mss4 at cortical ER plasma membrane contact sites (Strahl & Thorner 2007).

A third nonvesicular mechanism could be based on the penetration of the amphipathic α-helix into specific domains of the plasma membrane. At a high local concentration of Ist2, penetration could lead to a bending of the plasma membrane toward the cortical ER, which could cause a fusion pore to form (**Figure 1*c***). Such a pore would allow diffusion of Ist2 from the cortical ER to the plasma membrane. To avoid a substantial release of luminal ER content, the postulated fusion pores must be tightly regulated and transient. The described increased sodium tolerance of *ist2Δ* mutants is consistent with a fusion pore model (Entian et al. 1999).

Taken together, in addition to transport along the classical secretory pathway, eukaryotic cells employ an alternative transport route for fast and regulated transport of specific membrane proteins to specific regions of the plasma membrane. The future goal will be to identify the lipid and protein factors required for the function of this pathway. For that task, trafficking of Ist2 in yeast is an excellent model, and it will be interesting to see which steps of this pathway are conserved in mammalian cells.

UNCONVENTIONAL SECRETION OF SOLUBLE PROTEINS FROM EUKARYOTIC CELLS

History of the Discovery of Unconventional Secretory Processes

Interleukin 1β (Rubartelli et al. 1990) and galectin-1 (Cooper & Barondes 1990) were first demonstrated to be secreted by unconventional means almost 20 years ago. These proteins are not unusual exceptions, but rather these findings led to the identification of additional examples of secretory proteins that escape cells by unconventional means. Initially, it was thought that cells unspecifically released unconventional secretory proteins following exposure to either stress or mechanical wounding (McNeil et al. 1989), as occurs during inflammation and angiogenesis. However, further studies clearly demonstrated that unconventional protein secretion is not paralleled by the release of unrelated cytoplasmic proteins and, in many cases, represents a temperature-sensitive and energy-consuming process (Cleves 1997, Hughes 1999, Nickel 2003). What are the criteria being used to define unconventional secretory proteins? Originally, on the basis of primary structure, factors known to act in the extracellular space, such as interleukin 1β, were recognized as leaderless secretory proteins because they lacked classical signal peptides (Muesch et al. 1990, Rubartelli et al. 1990). Furthermore, BFA, a drug that blocks the ER/Golgi-dependent secretory pathway, does not inhibit secretion of unconventional secretory proteins (Cleves 1997, Hughes 1999, Nickel 2003, Prudovsky et al. 2003). Consistent with these observations, unconventional secretory proteins do not localize to the ER/Golgi system and do not contain posttranslational modifications specific for these compartments (Hughes 1999, Nickel 2003).

An Overview of Extracellular Proteins Secreted by Unconventional Means

Many of the known unconventional secretory proteins are cytokines, growth factors, or other molecules with important signaling roles in physiological processes such as inflammation, angiogenesis, cell differentiation, or proliferation. In most cases, unconventional protein secretion is a regulated process that is induced by external triggers. Also, unconventional secretory proteins can be grouped into two subclasses. The first class can be defined by factors that function primarily in the extracellular space and are represented by interleukin 1α (Siders et al. 1993, Watanabe & Kobayashi 1994, Tarantini et al. 2001) and interleukin 1β (Rubartelli et al. 1990, Hamon et al. 1997, Zhou et al. 2002). Various cell types release interleukin 1α following heat shock treatment, whereas monocytes and macrophages export interleukin 1β in response to bacterial lipopolysaccharides (LPS) and extracellular ATP. Other examples of unconventional secretory proteins with extracellular functions are galectin-1 (Cooper & Barondes 1990, Cho & Cummings 1995, Cleves et al. 1996, Hughes 1999, Seelenmeyer et al. 2005) and galectin-3 (Sato et al. 1993; Sato & Hughes 1994; Mehul & Hughes 1997, 1999; Thery et al. 2001; Zhu & Ochieng 2001), as well as fibroblast growth factor-1 (FGF-1) (Jackson et al. 1992, 1995; Carreira et al. 1998; LaVallee et al. 1998; Landriscina et al. 2001a,b; Prudovsky et al. 2002) and fibroblast growth factor-2 (FGF-2) (Mignatti & Rifkin 1991, Mignatti et al. 1992, Florkiewicz et al. 1995, Trudel et al. 2000, Engling et al. 2002, Backhaus et al. 2004, Schäfer et al. 2004, Zehe et al. 2006). Galectin-1, a cell-fate regulator with multiple signaling functions in cell differentiation and related processes (Liu & Rabinovich 2005), as well as FGF-2, a growth factor involved in tumor-induced angiogenesis (Bikfalvi et al. 1997), are secreted from a large variety of cells, and both constitutive secretion and regulated secretion have been reported (Hughes 1999, Nickel 2003, Prudovsky et al. 2003).

The members of the second group of unconventional secretory proteins normally localize in the cytoplasm or the nucleoplasm of cells, where they mediate well-characterized intracellular functions. However, in the presence of a specific external stimulus, they are released from cells to mediate functions distinct from their intracellular roles. Examples of cytoplasmic proteins that can become extracellular signaling molecules are thioredoxin, a cytoplasmic factor involved in redox balance (Arner & Holmgren 2000), and high-mobility group box 1 (HMGB-1), a nuclear protein that binds to chromatin and regulates gene expression (Agresti & Bianchi 2003, Bianchi & Agresti 2005). Several cell types release both full-length and truncated forms of thioredoxin (Ericson et al. 1992, Rubartelli et al. 1992), and oxidative stress induces its secretion from T lymphocytes (Kondo et al. 2004). Although the molecular mechanism of export has remained elusive, extracellular functions of thioredoxin, including its role as a cytokine in inflammatory processes, have been well documented (Pekkari et al. 2000, 2001, 2003, 2005; Angelini et al. 2002; Nishinaka et al. 2002; Nakamura et al. 2006). Also, Schwertassek et al. (2007) identified a cell surface receptor whose redox state is catalytically controlled by extracellular thioredoxin. Extracellular thioredoxin also controls TRPC, a member of the TRP family of cation channels involved in a broad range of sensory processes such as pain perception and thermosensation (Flockerzi 2007, Venkatachalam & Montell 2007). Thioredoxin activates TRPC by breaking a disulfide bridge in an extracellular loop of the ion channel and, therefore, may be an endogenous chemical factor that is sensed by TRP channels (Xu et al. 2008).

Monocytes and macrophages, activated by inflammatory signals such as bacterial LPS and lysophosphatidylcholine, are the predominant sources of secreted HMGB-1 (Gardella et al. 2002). This observation is consistent with an extracellular role of HMGB-1 as a proinflammatory cytokine (Erlandsson et al. 1998; Wang et al. 1999, 2004b; Müller et al. 2001; Scaffidi et al. 2002; Degryse & de Virgilio 2003; Yang et al. 2005). Receptors, through which HMGB-1 signaling occurs, have been identified, and pharmacological manipulation of the corresponding signal transduction pathways improves survival in experimental sepsis (Wang et al. 2004a). A prerequisite for HMGB-1 secretion is its redistribution from the nucleus to the cytoplasm. HMGB-1 actively shuttles between the nucleus and the cytoplasm, with a steady-state localization in the nucleus. Upon LPS-induced activation of macrophages, HMGB-1 becomes hyperacylated, causing a shift of its steady-state localization to the cytoplasm. This process appears to be essential for the subsequent secretion of HMGB-1 (Bonaldi et al. 2003).

There are further examples of unconventional secretory proteins, such as annexins (Chapman et al. 2002, 2003; Gerke & Moss 2002; Danielsen et al. 2003; Peterson et al. 2003; Deora et al. 2004; Wein et al. 2004; Omer et al. 2006), the S100 family of Ca^{2+} binding proteins (Davey et al. 2001, Landriscina et al. 2001b, Prudovsky et al. 2002, Mandinova et al. 2003, Flatmark et al. 2004), epimorphin (Radisky et al. 2003, Flaumenhaft et al. 2007, Hirai et al. 2007), Engrailed homeoproteins (Joliot et al. 1998; Maizel et al. 1999, 2002; Dupont et al. 2007), and an acyl-CoA binding protein required for terminal differentiation of spore cells in *Dictyostelium* development (Kinseth et al. 2007). The last protein represents an example of unconventional protein secretion in lower eukaryotes. In unicellular eukaryotes such as *S. cerevisiae*, it is not clear whether unconventional secretion of larger, soluble proteins exists. So far, the only known example of ER/Golgi-independent secretion in yeast is a-factor, a prenylated mating peptide whose secretion is mediated by the ABC transporter Ste6 (McGrath & Varshavsky 1989).

Additional examples of unconventional secretory proteins have recently been summarized elsewhere (Nickel 2003, Prudovsky et al. 2007). However, at this point, their extracellular functions and/or molecular details of their export mechanisms are poorly understood.

Potential Intracellular Pathways of Unconventional Protein Secretion

Four principal mechanisms of intracellular trafficking have been proposed to mediate unconventional secretory pathways (Nickel 2005):

1. direct translocation from the cytoplasm across the plasma membrane into the extracellular space,

2. lysosomal secretion,

3. secretion by exosomes derived from multivesicular bodies (MVBs), and

4. secretion by plasma membrane blebbing and vesicle shedding.

As evident from this list, both vesicular and nonvesicular pathways of unconventional protein secretion have been proposed. Among the classical examples, FGF-1 and FGF-2 as well as interleukin 1α have been suggested to directly translocate across the plasma membrane (Tarantini et al. 2001, Prudovsky et al. 2002, Schäfer et al. 2004). By contrast, interleukin 1β was proposed to make use of secretory lysosomes (Andrei et al. 1999, 2004), a mechanism that has also been proposed for HMGB-1 (Gardella et al. 2002, Bonaldi et al. 2003). Galectin-1 and galectin-3 associate with the inner leaflet of plasma membranes and may be released in membrane-bound vesicles (Cooper & Barondes 1990, Mehul & Hughes 1997) by a process termed plasma membrane blebbing or shedding. Another secretory mechanism that releases vesicles into the medium is based on exosomes, which are internal vesicles of MVBs (a subset of endosomes). Although MVBs primarily deliver cytoplasmic proteins for degradation by fusion with lysosomes (Piper & Katzmann 2007), they also fuse with plasma membranes, releasing exosomes into the extracellular space (Murk et al. 2002, Stoorvogel et al. 2002, Fevrier & Raposo 2004).

Possible mechanisms in interleukin 1β secretion. Secretion of interleukin 1β may occur via multiple mechanisms. First, an inflammatory signal such as bacterial LPS activates monocytes, leading to the synthesis of the precursor form of interleukin 1β, which is not secreted. In a second step, another trigger such as extracellular ATP induces LPS-activated monocytes to convert the precursor form of interleukin 1β into the mature secretion-competent form. Caspase 1 mediates this processing event (Thornberry et al. 1992), and the overall signaling process that results in the secretion of interleukin 1β involves a multimeric protein complex termed

the inflammasome (Burns et al. 2003, Ogura et al. 2006). Although these initial signaling events are not debated, the following steps, i.e., the molecular mechanism of secretion of the mature form of interleukin 1β, are controversial. All unconventional secretory mechanisms involving membrane-bound compartments (see above and Nickel 2005) have been suggested to play a role in interleukin 1β release. First, Rubartelli and coworkers reported evidence that the mature form of interleukin 1β is generated within lysosomes and that extracellular ATP, concomitant with an increase in cytoplasmic $[Ca^{2+}]$, causes the fusion of secretory lysosomes with the plasma membrane (Andrei et al. 1999, 2004). This process results in the release of soluble interleukin 1β that directly affects its targets. An alternative view by Surprenant and coworkers suggests that ATP-dependent activation of P2X7 receptors mediates shedding of plasma membrane vesicles that are positive for extracellular interleukin 1β (MacKenzie et al. 2001). However, conflicting studies indicate that interleukin 1β secretion does not depend on ATP-induced plasma membrane blebbing concomitant with shedding of microvesicles (Brough et al. 2003, Verhoef et al. 2003). Another study also concludes that neither lysosomal secretion nor plasma membrane shedding represents a major pathway of interleukin 1β secretion (Qu et al. 2007). This latter conclusion was based on differential requirements for extracellular $[Ca^{2+}]$ and differential sensitivities of interleukin 1β release and of plasma membrane shedding to pharmacological manipulations of primary macrophages. Moreover, Qu et al. (2007) provided evidence that, upon stimulation of P2X7 receptors, interleukin 1β is secreted as a luminal component of exosomes.

Thus, three molecular mechanisms have been suggested as the main pathways of interleukin 1β secretion: (*a*) lysosomal secretion, (*b*) plasma membrane shedding, and (*c*) exosomes derived from MVBs. It is presently unclear whether these data are indicative of several distinct and physiologically relevant pathways or whether the complexity of the experimental systems and the functional overlap with other pathways, such as P2X7-induced cell death, prevent the identification of a single pathway with physiological relevance. An obvious problem is that only factors involved in the induction of interleukin 1β secretion have been identified. By contrast, molecular factors involved in translocation of interleukin 1β into endolysosomal compartments or sorting into membrane blebs remain elusive.

Possible molecular mechanisms in FGF-2 secretion. As for interleukin 1β (see previous subsection), investigators have suggested multiple export mechanisms for FGF-2 and galectin-1. Using an in vitro system employing plasma membrane inside-out vesicles, Schäfer et al. (2004) showed that FGF-2 and galectin-1 can directly translocate across plasma membranes. In line with these findings, heparan sulfate proteoglycans (HSPGs) directly facilitate FGF-2 secretion (Zehe et al. 2006). According to one proposed model, FGF-2 is initially recruited to the inner leaflet of plasma membranes, followed by membrane translocation in an HSPG-dependent manner (Nickel 2007). That cell surface receptors form a molecular trapping mechanism for unconventional secretory lectins has also been shown for galectin-1 (Seelenmeyer et al. 2005), and following secretion from various cell types, FGF-2 and galectin-1 are quantitatively retained on cell surfaces (Trudel et al. 2000, Seelenmeyer et al. 2005, Zehe et al. 2006). Thus, for both FGF-2 and galectin-1, researchers have described nonvesicular pathways of secretion that rely on direct protein translocation across plasma membranes (Nickel 2007).

Two additional modes of FGF-2 externalization have been proposed. Extensive plasma membrane blebbing, concomitant with shedding of vesicles into the extracellular space, may play a role in FGF-2 secretion (Taverna et al. 2003, Schiera et al. 2007, Proia et al. 2008). Vittorelli and colleagues reported that, upon serum starvation, SK-Hep1 cells release vesicles containing FGF-2 (Taverna et al. 2003). In these cells, however, FGF-2 expression does not induce plasma membrane blebbing. Rather, prolonged serum starvation followed by a serum shock was used to induce plasma membrane blebbing. Quantitative analysis of the relative amounts of FGF-2 released in shed vesicles and controls for a potential concomitant release of unrelated cytoplasmic proteins have not been performed (Taverna et al. 2003). Another molecular mechanism potentially involved in FGF-2 secretion relates to the finding that the expression of the Epstein-Barr virus protein LMP1 results in increased FGF-2 export efficiency (Wakisaka et al. 2002). Recently, Ceccarelli et al. (2007) proposed that LMP-1-dependent release of FGF-2 involves exosomes derived from MVBs. Thus, besides direct membrane translocation, investigators have suggested two additional modes to play a role in FGF-2 secretion that are based on FGF-2 export in cell-derived membrane vesicles.

These controversies have been addressed in a recent study using a cellular model system in which efficient export of both FGF-2 and galectin-1 was demonstrated (Cho & Cummings 1995, Engling et al. 2002, Backhaus et al. 2004, Seelenmeyer et al. 2005, Zehe et al. 2006). Although exposing significant amounts of FGF-2 and galectin-1 on their surfaces, these cells did not form plasma membrane blebs (Seelenmeyer et al. 2008). These cells do not release vesicles into the cell culture supernatant carrying FGF-2 or galectin-1, nor do they release soluble forms of these proteins. Finally, this study (Seelenmeyer et al. 2008) showed that the Rho kinase inhibitor Y27632, which blocks plasma membrane blebbing, has no impact on FGF-2 secretion efficiency. Similar results were obtained for galectin-1. In the light of these data, it seems likely that the findings of Vittorelli and coworkers (Taverna et al. 2003) are related to the induction of apoptosis, a process that is induced by serum deprivation (Fuhrmann et al. 2001, Schamberger et al. 2005). Although Taverna et al. (2003) claim that FGF-2 vesicles being shed into the cell culture supernatant were not derived from apoptotic cells, apoptotic programs may have been induced under the experimental conditions described. Perhaps the experimental conditions being used in this study did not result in cell death because FGF-2 inhibited certain stages in the progression of apoptotic programs (Schamberger et al. 2004). Finally, the fact that Taverna et al. (2003) were able to use annexin V–coupled beads to purify these vesicles, i.e., these vesicles present phosphatidylserine on their surfaces, also supports the conclusion that they are derived from cells in which apoptosis was induced. On the basis of these considerations, plasma membrane shedding of FGF-2-containing vesicles may not play a role in FGF-2 secretion under physiologically relevant conditions.

With regard to a potential role of exosomes in FGF-2 secretion (Ceccarelli et al. 2007), it is again not clear whether these findings are of physiological relevance. One issue is that the authors make use of model systems in which FGF-2 secretion cannot be observed at all when LMP-1 is absent. Additionally, the amounts of FGF-2 being found in exosomes were not quantified, and therefore it is difficult to compare them with the amounts of FGF-2 that associate with cell surfaces in other well-established model systems (Trudel et al. 2000, Engling et al. 2002, Backhaus et al. 2004, Zehe et al. 2006). Another issue is that, owing to the fact that flotation analyses have not been performed (Ceccarelli et al. 2007), it is not clear whether FGF-2 found in sediments derived from cell culture supernatants is associated solely with membrane vesicles or also reflects material present in protein aggregates.

In the case of galectin-1, early studies proposed plasma membrane blebbing as a potential mechanism of secretion occuring during the differentiation of myoblasts into myotubes (Cooper & Barondes 1990). As opposed to other model systems in which secreted galectin-1 is retained on cell surfaces (Seelenmeyer et al. 2003, 2005), myotubes release galectin-1 into the medium (Cooper & Barondes 1990). Even though CHO cells efficiently secrete galectin-1, resulting in their association with cell surfaces (Cho & Cummings 1995; Seelenmeyer et al. 2003, 2005), galectin-1 does not induce plasma membrane blebbing in these cells (Seelenmeyer et al. 2008). These discrepancies may be due to differences in cell processing for imaging purposes. In the studies of Cooper & Barondes (1990), cells were fixed prior to analysis, a treatment that causes both membrane blebbing and the release of vesicles into the extracellular space (Scott 1976). Therefore, in the more recent study (Seelenmeyer et al. 2008), galectin-1-expressing cells were analyzed by live-cell imaging, and plasma membrane blebbing was undetectable. Thus, it is not clear whether plasma membrane blebbing observed in fixed cells is related to physiologically relevant processes.

From the combined data discussed above, we conclude that efficient secretion of FGF-2 and galectin-1 in a well-characterized model system such as CHO cells is not mediated by either plasma membrane blebbing or the release of exosomes derived from MVBs. Rather, direct translocation across the plasma membrane, requiring cell surface counter receptors, appears to mediate unconventional secretion of these factors (Seelenmeyer et al. 2005, 2008; Zehe et al. 2006; Nickel 2007).

Molecular Mechanism of FGF-2 Membrane Translocation as a Paradigm for Unconventional Protein Secretion

Among secretory proteins exported by unconventional means, FGF-2 is currently the best-characterized example with regard to the molecular mechanisms involved. As outlined below, its subcellular site of membrane translocation, cis-elements, and interacting molecules required for FGF-2 sorting into its unusual secretory pathway as well as folding aspects and energy requirements have been addressed recently.

Known key features of FGF-2 secretion. Investigators have elucidated a number of key features of the overall process of FGF-2 secretion from cells. As revealed by an in vitro system, FGF-2 membrane translocation requires neither ATP hydrolysis nor a membrane potential (Schäfer et al. 2004). Cytoplasmic FGF-2 is not incorporated into transport vesicles but rather directly traverses the plasma membrane to access the extracellular space (Schäfer et al. 2004, Zehe et al. 2006). HSPGs provide the membrane-proximal binding sites required for FGF-2 export (Zehe et al. 2006, Nickel 2007). These data suggest that FGF-2 translocation across the plasma membrane is a diffusion-controlled process mediated by either a proteinaceous transporter or a so-far-unrecognized ability of FGF-2 to pass through the plasma membrane by a transporter-independent mechanism. These findings have led to the conclusion that HSPGs form an extracellular molecular trap that is essential for both directional transport and storage of FGF-2 in the extracellular space (Zehe et al. 2006, Nickel 2007). This aspect of the FGF-2 export mechanism appears to be similar to another unconventional secretory protein, galectin-1 (Seelenmeyer et al. 2005).

FGF-2 targeting to the inner leaflet of plasma membranes as the entry point of the FGF-2 secretory pathway. A major aspect of recent studies was to elucidate the molecular mechanism by which FGF-2 export is initiated, i.e., the factors that mediate a transient interaction with the inner leaflet of plasma membranes. In addition to having multiple functions in cellular physiology (Di Paolo & De Camilli 2006), PIPs have been identified as landmarks for cytoplasmic proteins that associate with a specific subcellular membrane (Behnia & Munro 2005). The PIP $PI(4,5)P_2$ has been specifically implicated in the recruitment of cytosolic proteins to the inner leaflet of the plasma membrane (McLaughlin et al. 2002). Various recognition motifs for PIPs, including polybasic clusters (Heo et al. 2006), have been described (Ellson et al. 2002, Stenmark et al. 2002, Lemmon 2003).

That FGF-2 contains a relatively large number of lysine and arginine residues near its C terminus led to the hypothesis that FGF-2 might be able to bind PIPs. Further evidence for this hypothesis came from the observation that a phosphate ion cocrystallized with recombinant FGF-2 coordinated by amino acid residues Asn 35, Arg 128, and Lys 133 (Kastrup et al. 1997). Starting from these observations, a recent study showed that FGF-2 efficiently binds to liposomes containing $PI(4,5)P_2$ (Temmerman et al. 2008). $PI(4,5)P_2$ is found mainly in plasma membranes, whereas other PIPs are enriched in the Golgi complex [PI(4)P], early endosomes [PI(3)P], or late endosomes [$PI(3,5)P_2$] (Di Paolo & De Camilli 2006). Therefore, the observed interaction of FGF-2 with $PI(4,5)P_2$ is also consistent with studies demonstrating that the plasma membrane is the subcellular site of FGF-2 membrane translocation (Schäfer et al. 2004, Zehe et al. 2006). Intriguingly, the interaction of FGF-2 with $PI(4,5)P_2$ depends on a lipid background resembling plasma membranes; only background levels of FGF-2 binding were observed when $PI(4,5)P_2$ was reconstituted in liposomes made of phosphatidylcholine. Omission of cholesterol and sphingomyelin also reduced binding of FGF-2 to $PI(4,5)P_2$-containing liposomes. These and other data, as well as the fact that $PI(4,5)P_2$ is strongly enriched in cholesterol-dependent lipid microdomains (McLaughlin et al. 2002), led to the proposal that $PI(4,5)P_2$ clustering within a specialized membrane domain may be required for FGF-2 recruitment to plasma membranes. This view is consistent with a failure of $PI(4,5)P_2$ to form clusters in a pure phosphatidylcholine lipid background at physiological concentrations (Fernandes et al. 2006). Two findings anchor the conclusion that the interaction of $PI(4,5)P_2$ with FGF-2 is of biological relevance. First, RNAi-mediated downregulation of type I PIP kinases reduces $PI(4,5)P_2$ levels by 90% and significantly impairs FGF-2 secretion. Second, FGF-2 variant forms that fail to bind $PI(4,5)P_2$ are also secreted inefficiently. Taken together, these data demonstrate that binding to $PI(4,5)P_2$ at the inner leaflet of plasma membranes represents the entry point of the unconventional secretory pathway of FGF-2 (Temmerman et al. 2008).

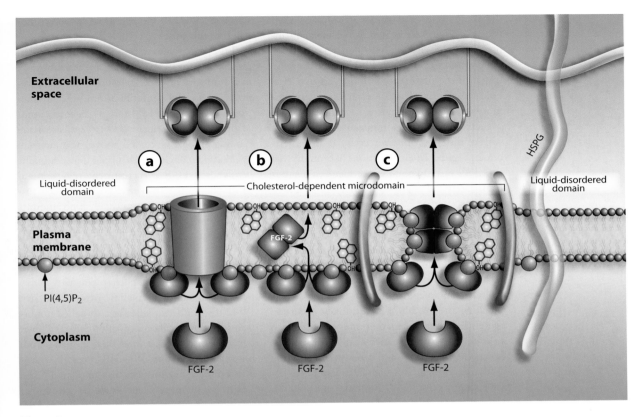

Figure 2

Potential mechanisms of fibroblast growth factor-2 (FGF-2) membrane translocation. (*a*) FGF-2 membrane translocation mediated by a protein-conducting channel. In this model, FGF-2 is recruited to the inner leaflet by binding to phosphatidylinositol 4,5 bisphosphate [PI(4,5)P$_2$]. Transport within the channel is diffusion controlled, and HSPG-mediated trapping ensures net transport into the extracellular space. (*b*) FGF-2 membrane translocation based on a PI(4,5)P$_2$-induced conformational change that allows for penetration of the lipid bilayer. (*c*) FGF-2 membrane translocation based on the generation of a hydrophilic pore whose opening is initiated by multivalent interactions of FGF-2 with PI(4,5)P$_2$ enriched within a cholesterol-dependent lipid microdomain. Both positive membrane curvature induced by high concentrations of PI(4,5)P$_2$ and an additional proteinaceous factor may facilitate this process. HSPG denotes heparan sulfate proteoglycan.

Working hypotheses on how FGF-2 physically traverses plasma membranes as a key aspect of its unconventional secretory route. Figure 2 illustrates various molecular aspects of the unconventional secretory pathway of FGF-2, such as PI(4,5)P$_2$-dependent recruitment of FGF-2 to the inner leaflet of plasma membranes and an extracellular trapping mechanism mediated by HSPGs. A key aim of future research will be to elucidate the molecular mechanism by which FGF-2 physically traverses the plasma membrane. One obvious option would be a plasma membrane–resident transporter forming a protein-conducting channel with specificity for FGF-2 (**Figure 2*a***). Such a pore might allow FGF-2 membrane translocation by passive diffusion and could work in conjunction with both PI(4,5)P$_2$ at the inner leaflet and the HSPG-mediated molecular trap at the extracellular side. So far, such a transporter has not been identified; however, genome-wide screening procedures based on RNAi-mediated gene silencing might reveal such a gene product.

Alternatively, an as-yet-unrecognized property of FGF-2 may enable its passage through the membrane by a transporter-independent process. There are two possible mechanisms, both of which are likely to depend on the interaction of FGF-2 with $PI(4,5)P_2$ at the inner leaflet of the plasma membrane (**Figure 2b,c**). One possibility would be that this interaction causes a conformational change in FGF-2 that allows for its transient solubilization within the hydrophobic core of the membrane (**Figure 2b**). Interactions of proteins with $PI(4,5)P_2$ at a membrane interface can result in conformational changes (Milburn et al. 2003). In this scenario, FGF-2 may exit the plasma membrane on the extracellular side by binding to HSPGs, a process that would be accompanied by another conformational change back to its water-soluble structure. With regard to solubilization within a hydrophobic environment, molten globule conformations may play a role (Rajalingam et al. 2007). Additionally, in certain proteins, such conformations may be induced in an acidic environment such as the interface between the cytoplasm and a plasma membrane lipid microdomain in which PIPs like $PI(4,5)P_2$ are strongly enriched (Prudovsky et al. 2007). However, in the case of FGF-2, this hypothesis is very difficult to reconcile with some of the experimental data on FGF-2 secretion. In various model systems, FGF-2 can be fused to a variety of other protein domains such as green fluorescent protein (GFP) and dihydrofolate reductase (DHFR) without an appreciable loss of export efficiency (Florkiewicz et al. 1995, Engling et al. 2002, Backhaus et al. 2004). In particular, the DHFR domain is characterized by a very stable fold in the presence of its ligands methotrexate or aminopterin, and therefore import of corresponding fusion proteins into mitochondria is inhibited under such experimental conditions (Eilers & Schatz 1986, Wienhues et al. 1991). By contrast, the addition of the DHFR domain to FGF-2 was compatible with FGF-2 secretion in the presence of aminopterin (Backhaus et al. 2004). These findings make it rather unlikely that FGF-2 secretion involves an intermediate that is transiently dissolved in the hydrophobic core of the membrane because it is difficult to reconcile how the GFP or the aminopterin-

stabilized DHFR domain could be accommodated in this process.

Figure 2c illustrates a second potential mechanism for FGF-2 membrane translocation in a transporter-independent manner. This hypothesis is again centered around the interaction of FGF-2 with $PI(4,5)P_2$ as the entry point of this secretory pathway. On the basis of the binding studies discussed above, Temmerman et al. (2008) concluded that lipid microdomains involved in FGF-2 recruitment may contain as much as 30 mol% of $PI(4,5)P_2$. Such microdomains containing unusually high amounts of $PI(4,5)P_2$ may be preexisting, or FGF-2 binding may cause an additional enrichment of $PI(4,5)P_2$ in these membrane structures. In either case, the result would be a unique membrane structure. In particular, owing to its bulky head group relative to its slim hydrophobic part, $PI(4,5)P_2$ can be classified as a so-called nonbilayer lipid (McMahon & Gallop 2005). This is because, in a regular lipid bilayer made from phosphatidylcholine, $PI(4,5)P_2$ present in just one monolayer cannot be accommodated in the absence of membrane curvature. In the context of the plasma membrane, in which $PI(4,5)P_2$ localizes exclusively to the inner leaflet, domains containing large amounts of $PI(4,5)P_2$ are characterized by positive membrane curvature, i.e., curvature directed toward the cytoplasm (McMahon & Gallop 2005).

At this point our knowledge about the ultrastructure of cholesterol-dependent and $PI(4,5)P_2$-enriched lipid microdomains is quite limited. We can only speculate on the structural consequences of FGF-2 binding to such domains. An interesting point to keep in mind is that extracellular FGF-2 has the intrinsic ability to oligomerize (Facchiano et al. 2003). Intracellular FGF-2 may oligomerize as well, maybe even as a result of its interaction with $PI(4,5)P_2$ at the inner leaflet of plasma membranes. Thus, this process would render FGF-2 multivalent with regard to $PI(4,5)P_2$ binding. An exciting hypothesis is that, on the basis of positive membrane curvature due to high concentrations of $PI(4,5)P_2$ coordinated through multivalent interactions between $PI(4,5)P_2$ and FGF-2 molecules, a transient and highly ordered structure may be established; such a structure can provide a hydrophilic environment through which FGF-2 can translocate across the plasma membrane (**Figure 2c**). Accessory proteins yet to be identified may help to stabilize such a membrane structure, which is likely to occur only transiently. In this scenario, HSPGs trap FGF-2 molecules on the extracellular side, ensuring directional transport toward the extracellular space. Because it is likely that FGF-2 binding to PI(4,5)P$_2$ and HSPGs is mutually exclusive, HSPGs may play an even more active role by extracting FGF-2 molecules bound to PI(4,5)P$_2$ at the membrane. This mechanism of transport would explain the observations that FGF-2 secretion does not depend on ATP hydrolysis (Schäfer et al. 2004) and that FGF-2 membrane translocation is compatible with tags such as GFP and DHFR domains (Engling et al. 2002, Backhaus et al. 2004, Zehe et al. 2006). This hypothesis remains highly speculative and needs to be challenged by new approaches such as in vitro reconstitution of FGF-2 membrane translocation with chemically defined components as well as by biophysical methods such as solid-state nuclear magnetic resonance to elucidate ultrastructural aspects of the interaction of FGF-2 with PI(4,5)P$_2$-enriched lipid microdomains.

CONCLUSIONS

In addition to transport along the classical secretory pathway, eukaryotic cells employ various alternative routes for cell surface delivery of both soluble and membrane proteins. Although all these pathways share the commonality of not requiring a functional Golgi apparatus, they otherwise appear to be different in many regards. On the one hand, direct transfer of membrane proteins from peripheral ER domains to the plasma membrane occurs in a Golgi-independent manner. On the other hand, researchers have described more than 20 soluble proteins that can be secreted from cells by mechanisms that involve neither the ER nor the Golgi apparatus. The molecular mechanisms of these unusual pathways are now beginning to emerge, and these long-standing problems in molecular cell biology may be solved in the years to come.

DISCLOSURE STATEMENT

The authors are not aware of any biases that might be perceived as affecting the objectivity of this review.

LITERATURE CITED

Agresti A, Bianchi ME. 2003. HMGB proteins and gene expression. *Curr. Opin. Genet. Dev.* 13:170–78

Andrei C, Dazzi C, Lotti L, Torrisi MR, Chimini G, Rubartelli A. 1999. The secretory route of the leaderless protein interleukin 1β involves exocytosis of endolysosome-related vesicles. *Mol. Biol. Cell* 10:1463–75

Andrei C, Margiocco P, Poggi A, Lotti LV, Torrisi MR, Rubartelli A. 2004. Phospholipases C and A2 control lysosome-mediated IL-1β secretion: implications for inflammatory processes. *Proc. Natl. Acad. Sci. USA* 101:9745–50

Angelini G, Gardella S, Ardy M, Ciriolo MR, Filomeni G, et al. 2002. Antigen-presenting dendritic cells provide the reducing extracellular microenvironment required for T lymphocyte activation. *Proc. Natl. Acad. Sci. USA* 99:1491–96

Arner ES, Holmgren A. 2000. Physiological functions of thioredoxin and thioredoxin reductase. *Eur. J. Biochem.* 267:6102–9

Aronov S, Gelin-Licht R, Zipor G, Haim L, Safran E, Gerst JE. 2007. mRNAs encoding polarity and exocytosis factors are cotransported with the cortical endoplasmic reticulum to the incipient bud in *Saccharomyces cerevisiae*. *Mol. Cell Biol.* 27:3441–55

Backhaus R, Zehe C, Wegehingel S, Kehlenbach A, Schwappach B, Nickel W. 2004. Unconventional protein secretion: Membrane translocation of FGF-2 does not require protein unfolding. *J. Cell Sci.* 117:1727–36

Baldwin TA, Ostergaard HL. 2001. Developmentally regulated changes in glucosidase II association with, and carbohydrate content of, the protein tyrosine phosphatase CD45. *J. Immunol.* 167:3829–35

Baldwin TA, Ostergaard HL. 2002. The protein-tyrosine phosphatase CD45 reaches the cell surface via Golgi-dependent and -independent pathways. *J. Biol. Chem.* 277:50333–40

Baumann NA, Sullivan DP, Ohvo-Rekila H, Simonot C, Pottekat A, et al. 2005. Transport of newly synthesized sterol to the sterol-enriched plasma membrane occurs via nonvesicular equilibration. *Biochemistry* 44:5816–26

Becker T, Volchuk A, Rothman JE. 2005. Differential use of endoplasmic reticulum membrane for phagocytosis in J774 macrophages. *Proc. Natl. Acad. Sci. USA* 102:4022–26

Bednarek SY, Ravazzola M, Hosobuchi M, Amherdt M, Perrelet A, et al. 1995. COPI- and COPII-coated vesicles bud directly from the endoplasmic reticulum in yeast. *Cell* 83:1183–96

Behnia R, Munro S. 2005. Organelle identity and the signposts for membrane traffic. *Nature* 438:597–604

Bianchi ME, Agresti A. 2005. HMG proteins: dynamic players in gene regulation and differentiation. *Curr. Opin. Genet. Dev.* 15:496–506

Bikfalvi A, Klein S, Pintucci G, Rifkin DB. 1997. Biological roles of fibroblast growth factor-2. *Endocr. Rev.* 18:26–45

Bonaldi T, Talamo F, Scaffidi P, Ferrera D, Porto A, et al. 2003. Monocytic cells hyperacetylate chromatin protein HMGB1 to redirect it towards secretion. *EMBO J.* 22:5551–60

Bonnon C, Goutebroze L, Denisenko-Nehrbass N, Girault JA, Faivre-Sarrailh C. 2003. The paranodal complex of F3/contactin and caspr/paranodin traffics to the cell surface via a nonconventional pathway. *J. Biol. Chem.* 278:48339–47

Brough D, Le Feuvre RA, Wheeler RD, Solovyova N, Hilfiker S, et al. 2003. Ca^{2+} stores and Ca^{2+} entry differentially contribute to the release of IL-1β and IL-1α from murine macrophages. *J. Immunol.* 170:3029–36

Burns K, Martinon F, Tschopp J. 2003. New insights into the mechanism of IL-1β maturation. *Curr. Opin. Immunol.* 15:26–30

Carreira CM, LaVallee TM, Tarantini F, Jackson A, Lathrop JT, et al. 1998. S100A13 is involved in the regulation of fibroblast growth factor-1 and p40 synaptotagmin-1 release in vitro. *J. Biol. Chem.* 273:22224–31

Ceccarelli S, Visco V, Raffa S, Wakisaka N, Pagano JS, Torrisi MR. 2007. Epstein-Barr virus latent membrane protein 1 promotes concentration in multivesicular bodies of fibroblast growth factor 2 and its release through exosomes. *Int. J. Cancer* 121:1494–506

Chapman L, Nishimura A, Buckingham JC, Morris JF, Christian HC. 2002. Externalization of annexin I from a folliculo-stellate-like cell line. *Endocrinology* 143:4330–38

Chapman LP, Epton MJ, Buckingham JC, Morris JF, Christian HC. 2003. Evidence for a role of the adenosine 5′-triphosphate-binding cassette transporter A1 in the externalization of annexin I from pituitary folliculo-stellate cells. *Endocrinology* 144:1062–73

Cho M, Cummings RD. 1995. Galectin-1, a β-galactoside-binding lectin in Chinese hamster ovary cells. II. Localization and biosynthesis. *J. Biol. Chem.* 270:5207–12

Cleves AE. 1997. Protein transports: the nonclassical ins and outs. *Curr. Biol.* 7:R318–20

Cleves AE, Cooper DN, Barondes SH, Kelly RB. 1996. A new pathway for protein export in *Saccharomyces cerevisiae*. *J. Cell Biol.* 133:1017–26

Cooper DN, Barondes SH. 1990. Evidence for export of a muscle lectin from cytosol to extracellular matrix and for a novel secretory mechanism. *J. Cell Biol.* 110:1681–91

Danielsen EM, Van Deurs B, Hansen GH. 2003. "Nonclassical" secretion of annexin A2 to the lumenal side of the enterocyte brush border membrane. *Biochemistry* 42:14670–76

Davey GE, Murmann P, Heizmann CW. 2001. Intracellular Ca^{2+} and Zn^{2+} levels regulate the alternative cell density-dependent secretion of S100B in human glioblastoma cells. *J. Biol. Chem.* 276:30819–26

Degryse B, de Virgilio M. 2003. The nuclear protein HMGB1, a new kind of chemokine? *FEBS Lett.* 553:11–17

Deora AB, Kreitzer G, Jacovina AT, Hajjar KA. 2004. An annexin 2 phosphorylation switch mediates p11-dependent translocation of annexin 2 to the cell surface. *J. Biol. Chem.* 279:43411–18

Di Paolo G, De Camilli P. 2006. Phosphoinositides in cell regulation and membrane dynamics. *Nature* 443:651–57

Dupont E, Prochiantz A, Joliot A. 2007. Identification of a signal peptide for unconventional secretion. *J. Biol. Chem.* 282:8994–9000

Eilers M, Schatz G. 1986. Binding of a specific ligand inhibits import of a purified precursor protein into mitochondria. *Nature* 322:228–32

Ellson CD, Andrews S, Stephens LR, Hawkins PT. 2002. The PX domain: a new phosphoinositide-binding module. *J. Cell Sci.* 115:1099–105

Engling A, Backhaus R, Stegmayer C, Zehe C, Seelenmeyer C, et al. 2002. Biosynthetic FGF-2 is targeted to nonlipid raft microdomains following translocation to the extracellular surface of CHO cells. *J. Cell Sci.* 115:3619–31

Entian KD, Schuster T, Hegemann JH, Becher D, Feldmann H, et al. 1999. Functional analysis of 150 deletion mutants in *Saccharomyces cerevisiae* by a systematic approach. *Mol. Gen. Genet.* 262:683–702

Ericson ML, Horling J, Wendel-Hansen V, Holmgren A, Rosen A. 1992. Secretion of thioredoxin after in vitro activation of human B cells. *Lymphokine Cytokine Res.* 11:201–7

Erlandsson L, Andersson K, Sigvardsson M, Lycke N, Leanderson T. 1998. Mice with an inactivated joining chain locus have perturbed IgM secretion. *Eur. J. Immunol.* 28:2355–65

Facchiano A, Russo K, Facchiano AM, De Marchis F, Facchiano F, et al. 2003. Identification of a novel domain of fibroblast growth factor 2 controlling its angiogenic properties. *J. Biol. Chem.* 278:8751–60

Fatal N, Suntio T, Makarow M. 2002. Selective protein exit from yeast endoplasmic reticulum in absence of functional COPII coat component Sec13p. *Mol. Biol. Cell* 13:4130–40

Fernandes F, Loura LM, Fedorov A, Prieto M. 2006. Absence of clustering of phosphatidylinositol-(4,5)-bisphosphate in fluid phosphatidylcholine. *J. Lipid Res.* 47:1521–25

Fevrier B, Raposo G. 2004. Exosomes: endosomal-derived vesicles shipping extracellular messages. *Curr. Opin. Cell Biol.* 16:415–21

Flatmark K, Maelandsmo GM, Mikalsen SO, Nustad K, Varaas T, et al. 2004. Immunofluorometric assay for the metastasis-related protein S100A4: Release of S100A4 from normal blood cells prohibits the use of S100A4 as a tumor marker in plasma and serum. *Tumour Biol.* 25:31–40

Flaumenhaft R, Rozenvayn N, Feng D, Dvorak AM. 2007. SNAP-23 and syntaxin-2 localize to the extracellular surface of the platelet plasma membrane. *Blood* 110:1492–501

Flockerzi V. 2007. An introduction on TRP channels. *Handb. Exp. Pharmacol.* 179:1–19

Florkiewicz RZ, Majack RA, Buechler RD, Florkiewicz E. 1995. Quantitative export of FGF-2 occurs through an alternative, energy-dependent, non-ER/Golgi pathway. *J. Cell Physiol.* 162:388–99

Franz A, Maass K, Seedorf M. 2007. A complex peptide-sorting signal, but no mRNA signal, is required for the Sec-independent transport of Ist2 from the yeast ER to the plasma membrane. *FEBS Lett.* 581:401–5

Fuhrmann G, Leisser C, Rosenberger G, Grusch M, Huettenbrenner S, et al. 2001. Cdc25A phosphatase suppresses apoptosis induced by serum deprivation. *Oncogene* 20:4542–53

Gagnon E, Duclos S, Rondeau C, Chevet E, Cameron PH, et al. 2002. Endoplasmic reticulum-mediated phagocytosis is a mechanism of entry into macrophages. *Cell* 110:119–31

Gardella S, Andrei C, Ferrera D, Lotti LV, Torrisi MR, et al. 2002. The nuclear protein HMGB1 is secreted by monocytes via a nonclassical, vesicle-mediated secretory pathway. *EMBO Rep.* 3:995–1001

Gerke V, Moss SE. 2002. Annexins: from structure to function. *Physiol. Rev.* 82:331–71

Gonsalvez GB, Urbinati CR, Long RM. 2005. RNA localization in yeast: moving towards a mechanism. *Biol. Cell* 97:75–86

Graham TR, Emr SD. 1991. Compartmental organization of Golgi-specific protein modification and vacuolar protein sorting events defined in a yeast *sec*18 (*NSF*) mutant. *J. Cell Biol.* 114:207–18

Griffiths G, Simons K. 1986. The trans Golgi network: sorting at the exit site of the Golgi complex. *Science* 234:438–43

Hamon Y, Luciani MF, Becq F, Verrier B, Rubartelli A, Chimini G. 1997. Interleukin-1β secretion is impaired by inhibitors of the Atp binding cassette transporter, ABC1. *Blood* 90:2911–15

Hasdemir B, Fitzgerald DJ, Prior IA, Tepikin AV, Burgoyne RD. 2005. Traffic of Kv4 K⁺ channels mediated by KChIP1 is via a novel post-ER vesicular pathway. *J. Cell Biol.* 171:459–69

Heiman MG, Walter P. 2000. Prm1p, a pheromone-regulated multispanning membrane protein, facilitates plasma membrane fusion during yeast mating. *J. Cell Biol.* 151:719–30

Heo WD, Inoue T, Park WS, Kim ML, Park BO, et al. 2006. PI(3,4,5)P$_3$ and PI(4,5)P$_2$ lipids target proteins with polybasic clusters to the plasma membrane. *Science* 314:1458–61

Hirai Y, Nelson CM, Yamazaki K, Takebe K, Przybylo J, et al. 2007. Non-classical export of epimorphin and its adhesion to α_v-integrin in regulation of epithelial morphogenesis. *J. Cell Sci.* 120:2032–43

Hughes RC. 1999. Secretion of the galectin family of mammalian carbohydrate-binding proteins. *Biochim. Biophys. Acta* 1473:172–85

Jackson A, Friedman S, Zhan X, Engleka KA, Forough R, Maciag T. 1992. Heat shock induces the release of fibroblast growth factor 1 from NIH 3T3 cells. *Proc. Natl. Acad. Sci. USA* 89:10691–95

Jackson A, Tarantini F, Gamble S, Friedman S, Maciag T. 1995. The release of fibroblast growth factor-1 from NIH 3T3 cells in response to temperature involves the function of cysteine residues. *J. Biol. Chem.* 270:33–36

Joliot A, Maizel A, Rosenberg D, Trembleau A, Dupas S, et al. 1998. Identification of a signal sequence necessary for the unconventional secretion of Engrailed homeoprotein. *Curr. Biol.* 8:856–63

Juschke C, Ferring D, Jansen RP, Seedorf M. 2004. A novel transport pathway for a yeast plasma membrane protein encoded by a localized mRNA. *Curr. Biol.* 14:406–11

Juschke C, Wachter A, Schwappach B, Seedorf M. 2005. SEC18/NSF-independent, protein-sorting pathway from the yeast cortical ER to the plasma membrane. *J. Cell Biol.* 169:613–22

Karhinen L, Bastos RN, Jokitalo E, Makarow M. 2005. Endoplasmic reticulum exit of a secretory glycoprotein in the absence of Sec24p family proteins in yeast. *Traffic* 6:562–74

Kastrup JS, Eriksson ES, Dalboge H, Flodgaard H. 1997. X-ray structure of the 154-amino-acid form of recombinant human basic fibroblast growth factor comparison with the truncated 146-amino-acid form. *Acta Crystallogr. D* 53:160–68

Kinseth MA, Anjard C, Fuller D, Guizzunti G, Loomis WF, Malhotra V. 2007. The Golgi-associated protein GRASP is required for unconventional protein secretion during development. *Cell* 130:524–34

Kondo N, Ishii Y, Kwon YW, Tanito M, Horita H, et al. 2004. Redox-sensing release of human thioredoxin from T lymphocytes with negative feedback loops. *J. Immunol.* 172:442–48

Landriscina M, Bagala C, Mandinova A, Soldi R, Micucci I, et al. 2001a. Copper induces the assembly of a multiprotein aggregate implicated in the release of fibroblast growth factor 1 in response to stress. *J. Biol. Chem.* 276:25549–57

Landriscina M, Soldi R, Bagala C, Micucci I, Bellum S, et al. 2001b. S100a13 participates in the release of fibroblast growth factor 1 in response to heat shock in vitro. *J. Biol. Chem.* 276:22544–52

LaVallee TM, Tarantini F, Gamble S, Carreira CM, Jackson A, Maciag T. 1998. Synaptotagmin-1 is required for fibroblast growth factor-1 release. *J. Biol. Chem.* 273:22217–23

Lee MC, Miller EA, Goldberg J, Orci L, Schekman R. 2004. Bi-directional protein transport between the ER and Golgi. *Annu. Rev. Cell Dev. Biol.* 20:87–123

Lemmon MA. 2003. Phosphoinositide recognition domains. *Traffic* 4:201–13

Lippincott-Schwartz J, Yuan LC, Bonifacino JS, Klausner RD. 1989. Rapid redistribution of Golgi proteins into the ER in cells treated with brefeldin A: evidence for membrane cycling from Golgi to ER. *Cell* 56:801–13

Liu FT, Rabinovich GA. 2005. Galectins as modulators of tumour progression. *Nat. Rev. Cancer* 5:29–41

Long RM, Singer RH, Meng X, Gonzalez I, Nasmyth K, Jansen RP. 1997. Mating type switching in yeast controlled by asymmetric localization of ASH1 mRNA. *Science* 277:383–87

MacKenzie A, Wilson HL, Kiss-Toth E, Dower SK, North RA, Surprenant A. 2001. Rapid secretion of interleukin-1β by microvesicle shedding. *Immunity* 15:825–35

Maizel A, Bensaude O, Prochiantz A, Joliot A. 1999. A short region of its homeodomain is necessary for engrailed nuclear export and secretion. *Development* 126:3183–90

Maizel A, Tassetto M, Filhol O, Cochet C, Prochiantz A, Joliot A. 2002. Engrailed homeoprotein secretion is a regulated process. *Development* 129:3545–53

Mandinova A, Soldi R, Graziani I, Bagala C, Bellum S, et al. 2003. S100A13 mediates the copper-dependent stress-induced release of IL-1α from both human U937 and murine NIH 3T3 cells. *J. Cell Sci.* 116:2687–96

McGrath JP, Varshavsky A. 1989. The yeast *STE6* gene encodes a homologue of the mammalian multidrug resistance P-glycoprotein. *Nature* 340:400–4

McLaughlin S, Wang J, Gambhir A, Murray D. 2002. PIP$_2$ and proteins: interactions, organization, and information flow. *Annu. Rev. Biophys. Biomol. Struct.* 31:151–75

McMahon HT, Gallop JL. 2005. Membrane curvature and mechanisms of dynamic cell membrane remodelling. *Nature* 438:590–96

McNeil PL, Muthukrishnan L, Warder E, D'Amore PA. 1989. Growth factors are released by mechanically wounded endothelial cells. *J. Cell Biol.* 109:811–22

McNew JA, Parlati F, Fukuda R, Johnston RJ, Paz K, et al. 2000. Compartmental specificity of cellular membrane fusion encoded in SNARE proteins. *Nature* 407:153–59

Mehul B, Hughes RC. 1997. Plasma membrane targeting, vesicular budding and release of galectin 3 from the cytoplasm of mammalian cells during secretion. *J. Cell Sci.* 110:1169–78

Menon RP, Hughes RC. 1999. Determinants in the N-terminal domains of galectin-3 for secretion by a novel pathway circumventing the endoplasmic reticulum-Golgi complex. *Eur. J. Biochem.* 264:569–76

Mignatti P, Morimoto T, Rifkin DB. 1992. Basic fibroblast growth factor, a protein devoid of secretory signal sequence, is released by cells via a pathway independent of the endoplasmic reticulum-Golgi complex. *J. Cell Physiol.* 151:81–93

Mignatti P, Rifkin DB. 1991. Release of basic fibroblast growth factor, an angiogenic factor devoid of secretory signal sequence: a trivial phenomenon or a novel secretion mechanism? *J. Cell. Biochem.* 47:201–7

Milburn CC, Deak M, Kelly SM, Price NC, Alessi DR, Van Aalten DM. 2003. Binding of phosphatidylinositol 3,4,5-trisphosphate to the pleckstrin homology domain of protein kinase B induces a conformational change. *Biochem. J.* 375:531–38

Misumi Y, Misumi Y, Miki K, Takatsuki A, Tamura G, Ikehara Y. 1986. Novel blockade by brefeldin A of intracellular transport of secretory proteins in cultured rat hepatocytes. *J. Biol. Chem.* 261:11398–403

Muesch A, Hartmann E, Rohde K, Rubartelli A, Sitia R, Rapoport TA. 1990. A novel pathway for secretory proteins? *Trends Biochem. Sci.* 15:86–88

Müller M, Heuck A, Niessing D. 2007. Directional mRNA transport in eukaryotes: lessons from yeast. *Cell Mol. Life Sci.* 64:171–80

Müller S, Scaffidi P, Degryse B, Bonaldi T, Ronfani L, et al. 2001. The double life of HMGB1 chromatin protein: architectural factor and extracellular signal. *EMBO J.* 20:4337–40

Murk JL, Stoorvogel W, Kleijmeer MJ, Geuze HJ. 2002. The plasticity of multivesicular bodies and the regulation of antigen presentation. *Semin. Cell Dev. Biol.* 13:303–11

Nakamura H, Masutani H, Yodoi J. 2006. Extracellular thioredoxin and thioredoxin-binding protein 2 in control of cancer. *Semin. Cancer Biol.* 16:444–51

Nickel W. 2003. The mystery of nonclassical protein secretion. *Eur. J. Biochem.* 270:2109–19

Nickel W. 2005. Unconventional secretory routes: direct protein export across the plasma membrane of mammalian cells. *Traffic* 6:607–14

Nickel W. 2007. Unconventional secretion: an extracellular trap for export of fibroblast growth factor 2. *J. Cell Sci.* 120:2295–99

Nishinaka Y, Nakamura H, Yodoi J. 2002. Thioredoxin cytokine action. *Methods Enzymol.* 347:332–38

Ogura Y, Sutterwala FS, Flavell RA. 2006. The inflammasome: first line of the immune response to cell stress. *Cell* 126:659–62

Omer S, Meredith D, Morris JF, Christian HC. 2006. Evidence for the role of adenosine 5′-triphosphate-binding cassette (ABC)-A1 in the externalization of annexin 1 from pituitary folliculostellate cells and ABCA1-transfected cell models. *Endocrinology* 147:3219–27

Orci L, Tagaya M, Amherdt M, Perrelet A, Donaldson JG, et al. 1991. Brefeldin A, a drug that blocks secretion, prevents the assembly of nonclathrin-coated buds on Golgi cisternae. *Cell* 64:1183–95

Pekkari K, Avila-Carino J, Bengtsson A, Gurunath R, Scheynius A, Holmgren A. 2001. Truncated thioredoxin (Trx80) induces production of interleukin-12 and enhances CD14 expression in human monocytes. *Blood* 97:3184–90

Pekkari K, Avila-Carino J, Gurunath R, Bengtsson A, Scheynius A, Holmgren A. 2003. Truncated thioredoxin (Trx80) exerts unique mitogenic cytokine effects via a mechanism independent of thiol oxido-reductase activity. *FEBS Lett.* 539:143–48

Pekkari K, Goodarzi MT, Scheynius A, Holmgren A, Avila-Carino J. 2005. Truncated thioredoxin (Trx80) induces differentiation of human CD14[+] monocytes into a novel cell type (TAMs) via activation of the MAP kinases p38, ERK, and JNK. *Blood* 105:1598–605

Pekkari K, Gurunath R, Arner ES, Holmgren A. 2000. Truncated thioredoxin is a mitogenic cytokine for resting human peripheral blood mononuclear cells and is present in human plasma. *J. Biol. Chem.* 275:37474–80

Peterson EA, Sutherland MR, Nesheim ME, Pryzdial EL. 2003. Thrombin induces endothelial cell-surface exposure of the plasminogen receptor annexin 2. *J. Cell Sci.* 116:2399–408

Pichler H, Gaigg B, Hrastnik C, Achleitner G, Kohlwein SD, et al. 2001. A subfraction of the yeast endoplasmic reticulum associates with the plasma membrane and has a high capacity to synthesize lipids. *Eur. J. Biochem.* 268:2351–61

Piper RC, Katzmann DJ. 2007. Biogenesis and function of multivesicular bodies. *Annu. Rev. Cell Dev. Biol.* 23:519–47

Ploegh HL. 2007. A lipid-based model for the creation of an escape hatch from the endoplasmic reticulum. *Nature* 448:435–38

Proia P, Schiera G, Mineo M, Ingrassia AM, Santoro G, et al. 2008. Astrocytes shed extracellular vesicles that contain fibroblast growth factor-2 and vascular endothelial growth factor. *Int. J. Mol. Med.* 21:63–67

Prudovsky I, Bagala C, Tarantini F, Mandinova A, Soldi R, et al. 2002. The intracellular translocation of the components of the fibroblast growth factor 1 release complex precedes their assembly prior to export. *J. Cell Biol.* 158:201–8

Prudovsky I, Mandinova A, Soldi R, Bagala C, Graziani I, et al. 2003. The nonclassical export routes: FGF1 and IL-1α point the way. *J. Cell Sci.* 116:4871–81

Prudovsky I, Tarantini F, Landriscina M, Neivandt D, Soldi R, et al. 2008. Secretion without Golgi. *J. Cell Biochem.* 103:1327–43

Qu Y, Franchi L, Nunez G, Dubyak GR. 2007. Nonclassical IL-1β secretion stimulated by P2×7 receptors is dependent on inflammasome activation and correlated with exosome release in murine macrophages. *J. Immunol.* 179:1913–25

Radisky DC, Hirai Y, Bissell MJ. 2003. Delivering the message: epimorphin and mammary epithelial morphogenesis. *Trends Cell Biol.* 13:426–34

Rajalingam D, Graziani I, Prudovsky I, Yu C, Kumar TK. 2007. Relevance of partially structured states in the nonclassical secretion of acidic fibroblast growth factor. *Biochemistry* 46:9225–38

Raychaudhuri S, Im YJ, Hurley JH, Prinz WA. 2006. Nonvesicular sterol movement from plasma membrane to ER requires oxysterol-binding protein-related proteins and phosphoinositides. *J. Cell Biol.* 173:107–19

Rogers LD, Foster LJ. 2007. The dynamic phagosomal proteome and the contribution of the endoplasmic reticulum. *Proc. Natl. Acad. Sci. USA* 104:18520–25

Rubartelli A, Bajetto A, Allavena G, Wollman E, Sitia R. 1992. Secretion of thioredoxin by normal and neoplastic cells through a leaderless secretory pathway. *J. Biol. Chem.* 267:24161–64

Rubartelli A, Cozzolino F, Talio M, Sitia R. 1990. A novel secretory pathway for interleukin-1β, a protein lacking a signal sequence. *EMBO J.* 9:1503–10

Sato S, Burdett I, Hughes RC. 1993. Secretion of the baby hamster kidney 30-kDa galactose-binding lectin from polarized and nonpolarized cells: a pathway independent of the endoplasmic reticulum-Golgi complex. *Exp. Cell Res.* 207:8–18

Sato S, Hughes RC. 1994. Regulation of secretion and surface expression of Mac-2, a galactoside-binding protein of macrophages. *J. Biol. Chem.* 269:4424–30

Scaffidi P, Misteli T, Bianchi ME. 2002. Release of chromatin protein HMGB1 by necrotic cells triggers inflammation. *Nature* 418:191–95

Schäfer T, Zentgraf H, Zehe C, Brügger B, Bernhagen J, Nickel W. 2004. Unconventional secretion of fibroblast growth factor 2 is mediated by direct translocation across the plasma membrane of mammalian cells. *J. Biol. Chem.* 279:6244–51

Schamberger CJ, Gerner C, Cerni C. 2004. bFGF rescues 423-cells from serum starvation-induced apoptosis downstream of activated caspase-3. *FEBS Lett.* 573:19–25

Schamberger CJ, Gerner C, Cerni C. 2005. Caspase-9 plays a marginal role in serum starvation-induced apoptosis. *Exp. Cell Res.* 302:115–28

Schiera G, Proia P, Alberti C, Mineo M, Savettieri G, Di Liegro I. 2007. Neurons produce FGF2 and VEGF and secrete them at least in part by shedding extracellular vesicles. *J. Cell Mol. Med.* 11:1384–94

Schmid M, Jaedicke A, Du TG, Jansen RP. 2006. Coordination of endoplasmic reticulum and mRNA localization to the yeast bud. *Curr. Biol.* 16:1538–43

Schwertassek U, Balmer Y, Gutscher M, Weingarten L, Preuss M, et al. 2007. Selective redox regulation of cytokine receptor signaling by extracellular thioredoxin-1. *EMBO J.* 26:3086–97

Scott RE. 1976. Plasma membrane vesiculation: a new technique for isolation of plasma membranes. *Science* 194:743–45

Seelenmeyer C, Stegmayer C, Nickel W. 2008. Unconventional secretion of fibroblast growth factor 2 and galectin-1 does not require shedding of plasma membrane-derived vesicles. *FEBS Lett.* 582:1362–68

Seelenmeyer C, Wegehingel S, Lechner J, Nickel W. 2003. The cancer antigen CA125 represents a novel counter receptor for galectin-1. *J. Cell Sci.* 116:1305–18

Seelenmeyer C, Wegehingel S, Tews I, Kunzler M, Aebi M, Nickel W. 2005. Cell surface counter receptors are essential components of the unconventional export machinery of galectin-1. *J. Cell Biol.* 171:373–81

Shepard KA, Gerber AP, Jambhekar A, Takizawa PA, Brown PO, et al. 2003. Widespread cytoplasmic mRNA transport in yeast: identification of 22 bud-localized transcripts using DNA microarray analysis. *Proc. Natl. Acad. Sci. USA* 100:11429–34

Siders WM, Klimovitz JC, Mizel SB. 1993. Characterization of the structural requirements and cell type specificity of IL-1α and IL-1β secretion. *J. Biol. Chem.* 268:22170–74

Stenmark H, Aasland R, Driscoll PC. 2002. The phosphatidylinositol 3-phosphate-binding FYVE finger. *FEBS Lett.* 513:77–84

Stoorvogel W, Kleijmeer MJ, Geuze HJ, Raposo G. 2002. The biogenesis and functions of exosomes. *Traffic* 3:321–30

Strahl T, Thorner J. 2007. Synthesis and function of membrane phosphoinositides in budding yeast, *Saccharomyces cerevisiae*. *Biochim. Biophys. Acta* 1771:353–404

Takizawa PA, DeRisi JL, Wilhelm JE, Vale RD. 2000. Plasma membrane compartmentalization in yeast by messenger RNA transport and a septin diffusion barrier. *Science* 290:341–34

Takizawa PA, Sil A, Swedlow JR, Herskowitz I, Vale RD. 1997. Actin-dependent localization of an RNA encoding a cell-fate determinant in yeast. *Nature* 389:90–93

Tarantini F, Micucci I, Bellum S, Landriscina M, Garfinkel S, et al. 2001. The precursor but not the mature form of IL1α blocks the release of FGF1 in response to heat shock. *J. Biol. Chem.* 276:5147–51

Taverna S, Ghersi G, Ginestra A, Rigogliuso S, Pecorella S, et al. 2003. Shedding of membrane vesicles mediates fibroblast growth factor-2 release from cells. *J. Biol. Chem.* 278:51911–19

Temmerman K, Ebert AD, Müller HM, Sinning I, Tews I, Nickel W. 2008. A direct role for phosphatidylinositol 4,5 bisphosphate in unconventional secretion of fibroblast growth factor 2. *Traffic* 9:1204–17

Thery C, Boussac M, Veron P, Ricciardi-Castagnoli P, Raposo G, et al. 2001. Proteomic analysis of dendritic cell-derived exosomes: a secreted subcellular compartment distinct from apoptotic vesicles. *J. Immunol.* 166:7309–18

Thornberry NA, Bull HG, Calaycay JR, Chapman KT, Howard AD, et al. 1992. A novel heterodimeric cysteine protease is required for interleukin-1β processing in monocytes. *Nature* 356:768–74

Touret N, Paroutis P, Terebiznik M, Harrison RE, Trombetta S, et al. 2005. Quantitative and dynamic assessment of the contribution of the ER to phagosome formation. *Cell* 123:157–70

Trudel C, Faure-Desire V, Florkiewicz RZ, Baird A. 2000. Translocation of FGF2 to the cell surface without release into conditioned media. *J. Cell Physiol.* 185:260–68

Venkatachalam K, Montell C. 2007. TRP channels. *Annu. Rev. Biochem.* 76:387–417

Verhoef PA, Estacion M, Schilling W, Dubyak GR. 2003. P2×7 receptor-dependent blebbing and the activation of Rho-effector kinases, caspases, and IL-1β release. *J. Immunol.* 170:5728–38

Wakisaka N, Murono S, Yoshizaki T, Furukawa M, Pagano JS. 2002. Epstein-Barr virus latent membrane protein 1 induces and causes release of fibroblast growth factor-2. *Cancer Res.* 62:6337–44

Wang H, Bloom O, Zhang M, Vishnubhakat JM, Ombrellino M, et al. 1999. HMG-1 as a late mediator of endotoxin lethality in mice. *Science* 285:248–51

Wang H, Liao H, Ochani M, Justiniani M, Lin X, et al. 2004a. Cholinergic agonists inhibit HMGB1 release and improve survival in experimental sepsis. *Nat. Med.* 10:1216–21

Wang H, Yang H, Tracey KJ. 2004b. Extracellular role of HMGB1 in inflammation and sepsis. *J. Intern. Med.* 255:320–31

Watanabe N, Kobayashi Y. 1994. Selective release of a processed form of interleukin 1α. *Cytokine* 6:597–601

Wein S, Fauroux M, Laffitte J, de Nadai P, Guaini C, et al. 2004. Mediation of annexin 1 secretion by a probenecid-sensitive ABC-transporter in rat inflamed mucosa. *Biochem. Pharmacol.* 67:1195–202

Wienhues U, Becker K, Schleyer M, Guiard B, Tropschug M, et al. 1991. Protein folding causes an arrest of preprotein translocation into mitochondria in vivo. *J. Cell Biol.* 115:1601–9

Xu SZ, Sukumar P, Zeng F, Li J, Jairaman A, et al. 2008. TRPC channel activation by extracellular thioredoxin. *Nature* 451:69–72

Yang H, Wang H, Czura CJ, Tracey KJ. 2005. The cytokine activity of HMGB1. *J. Leukoc. Biol.* 78:1–8

Zehe C, Engling A, Wegehingel S, Schafer T, Nickel W. 2006. Cell-surface heparan sulfate proteoglycans are essential components of the unconventional export machinery of FGF-2. *Proc. Natl. Acad. Sci. USA* 103:15479–84

Zhou X, Engel T, Goepfert C, Erren M, Assmann G, von Eckardstein A. 2002. The ATP binding cassette transporter A1 contributes to the secretion of interleukin 1β from macrophages but not from monocytes. *Biochem. Biophys. Res. Commun.* 291:598–604

Zhu WQ, Ochieng J. 2001. Rapid release of intracellular galectin-3 from breast carcinoma cells by fetuin. *Cancer Res.* 61:1869–73

Zimmerberg J, Kozlov MM. 2006. How proteins produce cellular membrane curvature. *Nat. Rev. Mol. Cell Biol.* 7:9–19

The Immunoglobulin-Like Cell Adhesion Molecule Nectin and Its Associated Protein Afadin

Yoshimi Takai, Wataru Ikeda, Hisakazu Ogita, and Yoshiyuki Rikitake

Division of Molecular and Cellular Biology, Department of Biochemistry and Molecular Biology, Kobe University Graduate School of Medicine, Kobe 650-0017, Japan; email: ytakai@med.kobe-u.ac.jp

Annu. Rev. Cell Dev. Biol. 2008. 24:309–42

First published online as a Review in Advance on July 1, 2008

The *Annual Review of Cell and Developmental Biology* is online at cellbio.annualreviews.org

This article's doi: 10.1146/annurev.cellbio.24.110707.175339

Key Words

nectin-like molecule, integrin, growth factor receptor

Abstract

Nectins are immunoglobulin-like cell adhesion molecules (CAMs) that compose a family of four members. Nectins homophilically and heterophilically interact in *trans* with each other to form cell-cell adhesions. In addition, they heterophilically interact in *trans* with other immunoglobulin-like CAMs. Nectins bind afadin, an actin filament (F-actin)-binding protein, at its cytoplasmic tail and associate with the actin cytoskeleton. Afadin additionally serves as an adaptor protein by further binding many scaffolding proteins and F-actin-binding proteins and contributes to the association of nectins with other cell-cell adhesion and intracellular signaling systems. Nectins and afadin play roles in the formation of a variety of cell-cell junctions cooperatively with, or independently of, cadherins. Cooperation between nectins and cadherins is required for the formation of cell-cell junctions; cadherins alone are not sufficient. Additionally, nectins regulate many other cellular activities (such as movement, proliferation, survival, differentiation, polarization, and the entry of viruses) in cooperation with other CAMs and cell surface membrane receptors.

Contents

INTRODUCTION

Cell-cell and cell-matrix junctions are involved in fundamental cellular activities, including not only adhesion but also movement, proliferation, survival, differentiation, and polarization. Many cell adhesion molecules (CAMs) have been identified and characterized: Cadherins and integrins are the most extensively investigated of these and play key roles in cell-cell and cell-matrix junctions, respectively. The cadherin family consists of more than 80 members, most of which are single-membrane-spanning molecules (Takeichi 1991, Yagi & Takeichi 2000). The extracellular regions of cadherins homophilically interact in *trans* with each other to form cell-cell adhesions in a Ca^{2+}-dependent manner. The cytoplasmic tails of cadherin molecules bind the actin filament

(F-actin)-binding protein α-catenin through β-catenin and many other F-actin-binding proteins through α-catenin and are associated with the actin cytoskeleton. Members of the classical cadherin family (such as E-, N-, and VE-cadherins) form adherens junctions (AJs) in cooperation with the actin cytoskeleton. The integrin family consists of heterodimers of α and β subunits (van der Flier & Sonnenberg 2001). To date, 18 α subunits and 8 β subunits have been identified, with a reported 24 combinations. The extracellular region of each member interacts with its specific extracellular matrix (ECM) proteins (such as collagen, fibronectin, laminin, and vitronectin) to form cell-matrix junctions called focal complexes and focal adhesions. The cytoplasmic tails of integrin β subunits bind many F-actin-binding

CAM: cell adhesion molecule

AJ: adherens junction

proteins, such as talin, and signaling molecules, such as FAK. Thus, integrins are associated with the actin cytoskeleton and signaling pathways, and integrins and the actin cytoskeleton form focal complexes and focal adhesions.

Nectins are Ca^{2+}-independent immunoglobulin (Ig)-like CAMs that compose a family of four members. The extracellular regions of nectins homophilically and heterophilically interact in *trans* with each other to cause cell-cell adhesion. In addition, they heterophilically interact in *trans* with other Ig-like molecules. The cytoplasmic tails of nectins bind the F-actin-binding protein afadin and associate with the actin cytoskeleton, similar to the cadherin and integrin systems. Afadin additionally serves as an adaptor protein by binding many scaffolding proteins and F-actin-binding proteins and contributes to the association of nectins with other cell-cell adhesion and intracellular signaling systems. Nectins and afadin have pleiotropic functions not only in cell-cell adhesion but also in cell movement, proliferation, survival, differentiation, polarization, and the entry of viruses, cooperatively with other CAMs and cell surface receptors. This review describes the properties, functions, and modes of action of nectins and afadin and their involvement in diseases.

HISTORY

Among the four members of the nectin family, nectin-1α and -2α were originally isolated as poliovirus receptor–related proteins PRR-1 and -2, respectively (Aoki et al. 1997, Eberlé et al. 1995, Lopez et al. 1995, Morrison & Racaniello 1992); however, neither of them was reported to actually serve as a poliovirus receptor. They were later shown to serve as receptors for α-herpes virus, facilitating its entry and cell-cell spread, and therefore were renamed HveC and HveB, respectively (Geraghty et al. 1998, Warner et al. 1998). Nectin-1α and -2α were then clarified to serve as CAMs, and PRR-1/HveC and PRR-2/HveB were renamed nectin-1α and -2α, respectively, from the Latin word *necto*, meaning "to

connect" (Takahashi et al. 1999) (**Figure 1a**). Thereafter, nectin-3 and -4 were identified as members of the nectin family (Reymond et al. 2001, Satoh-Horikawa et al. 2000). All nectin family members have two or three splice variants, so that nectin-1α, -1β, -1γ, -2α, -2δ, -3α, -3β, and -3γ isoforms exist. Nectin-4 also has two splice variants. Hereafter, we use the term nectin to refer to the α variant because the expression levels of the α variants are much higher than those of the other variants.

Afadin was originally identified as an F-actin-binding protein that localized at AJs and showed a structure similar to that of the *AF-6* gene product (Mandai et al. 1997). The human *AF-6* gene product was originally identified as an *ALL-1* fusion partner involved in acute myeloid leukemias (Prasad et al. 1993). Afadin has several alternative splicing sites in the C-terminal region, and four splicing variants have been identified in humans (Mandai et al. 1997, Saito et al. 1998) (**Figure 1b**). Hereafter, we use the term afadin to refer to the longest variant. Nectin-1α and -2α were first identified as afadin-binding proteins and found to serve as CAMs at AJs (Takahashi et al. 1999).

STRUCTURAL PROPERTIES

Nectin family members have an extracellular region with three Ig-like loops, a single transmembrane region, and a cytoplasmic tail region (**Figure 1a**), with the exception of nectin-1γ, which is a secreted protein that lacks the transmembrane region. Furthermore, with the exception of nectin-1β, -3γ, and -4, nectins have a conserved motif of four amino acid residues at their C termini (E/A-X-Y-V, with X being any amino acid), which binds the PDZ domain of afadin, contributing to the association of nectins with the actin cytoskeleton, other cell-cell adhesion systems, and signaling pathways. Although nectin-4 lacks this conserved motif, it binds the PDZ domain of afadin at its C terminus.

Afadin has multiple domains (**Figure 1b**) and binds many proteins: The RA domains bind Rap1 small G protein (Linnemann et al. 1999);

a

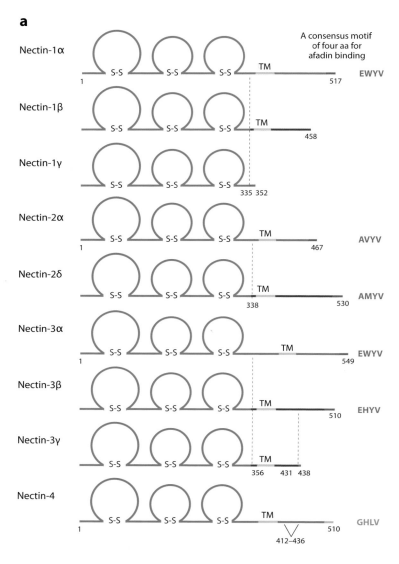

Nectin-1α
Nectin-1β
Nectin-1γ
Nectin-2α
Nectin-2δ
Nectin-3α
Nectin-3β
Nectin-3γ
Nectin-4

A consensus motif of four aa for afadin binding

EWYV
AVYV
AMYV
EWYV
EHYV
GHLV

b

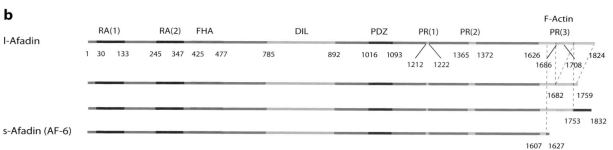

l-Afadin

RA(1) RA(2) FHA DIL PDZ PR(1) PR(2) F-Actin PR(3)

s-Afadin (AF-6)

the DIL domain binds afadin DIL-domain-interacting protein (ADIP) (Asada et al. 2003); the PDZ domain binds nectins (Takahashi et al. 1999), a subset of Eph receptor (Buchert et al. 1999, Hock et al. 1998), SPA-1 (Su et al. 2003), Bcr (Radziwill et al. 2003), and c-Src (Radziwill et al. 2007); the first and second PR domains bind ZO-1 (T. Ooshio & Y. Takai, unpublished observations), although ZO-1 interacts with the RA domains of afadin (Yamamoto et al. 1997); and the third PR domain binds ponsin (Mandai et al. 1999). The C-terminal region containing the F-actin-binding domain binds LIM domain only 7 (LMO7) (Ooshio et al. 2004). Furthermore, it directly binds the deubiquitinating enzyme Fam (Taya et al. 1998), profilin (Boettner et al. 2000), and α-catenin (Pokutta et al. 2002, Tachibana et al. 2000), although the detailed regions involved in these bindings remain unknown. Afadin is phosphorylated by c-Src at Tyr^{1237} and binds the SH2 region of the protein tyrosine phosphatase SHP-2 through this phosphorylated tyrosine (Nakata et al. 2007).

CELL ADHESION ACTIVITY OF NECTINS

The extracellular regions of nectins homophilically and heterophilically interact in *trans* with each other (Reymond et al. 2001, Satoh-Horikawa et al. 2000, Takahashi et al. 1999) (**Figure 2**). In contrast to nectins, the extracellular regions of cadherins only homophilically interact in *trans* with each other (Takeichi 1995). When this *trans*-interaction occurs between two apposing cells, the cells adhere to each other. The *trans*-interaction between cadherin molecules is Ca^{2+}-dependent, whereas that between nectin molecules is Ca^{2+}-

independent. In addition, the extracellular regions of nectins heterophilically interact in *trans* with the extracellular regions of other Ig-like molecules, including nectin-like molecules (Necls), CD226/DNAM-1, and CD96/Tactile (Bottino et al. 2003, Ikeda et al. 2003, Kakunaga et al. 2005, Seth et al. 2007, Shingai et al. 2003).

Necls have domain structures similar to those of nectin family members, but they do not bind afadin (Takai et al. 2003). They consist of five molecules: Necl-1, -2, -3, -4, and -5. CD226/DNAM-1 has two Ig-like loops at its extracellular region and is expressed mainly in cytotoxic T lymphocyte and natural killer cells (Wang et al. 1992). Of the combinations of *trans*-interactions, the one between nectin-1 and -3 is the strongest, followed by that between nectin-3 and Necl-5 and that between nectin-2 and -3. The K_d values of nectin-3 for nectin-1, Necl-5, and nectin-2 are approximately 2 nM, 17 nM, and 360 nM, respectively (Ikeda et al. 2003), far smaller than that for the *trans*-interaction between E-cadherin molecules, which is approximately 80 μM (Koch et al. 1997). Intermolecular force microscopy measurements have revealed that nectins show weak adhesion activity under the weak loading condition, whereas E-cadherin shows roughly constant adhesion activity irrespective of loading conditions (Tsukasaki et al. 2007). However, under the strong loading condition, the adhesion activity of nectins increases up to that of E-cadherin. Two nectin molecules at the surface of the same cell first form *cis*-dimers, followed by *trans*-interaction by the *cis*-dimers on apposing cells (Miyahara et al. 2000) (**Figure 2a**). The first Ig-like loop of the extracellular region of nectin-1 is necessary for the formation of *trans*-dimers, but not for *cis*-dimers, whereas the

Necl: nectin-like molecule

Figure 1

Molecular structures of nectins and afadin. (*a*) Each nectin molecule contains three immunoglobulin-like loops in the extracellular region, a single transmembrane (TM) segment, and one cytoplasmic region. Nectin-1, -2, and -3 have two or three splice variants. Nectin-4 has two splice variants, one of which lacks amino acids (aa) 412–436. A consensus motif of four amino acids in each nectin molecule, which is necessary for its binding to afadin, is shown on the right-hand side. (*b*) Afadin has four splicing variants: The longest one is named l-afadin, and the shortest one is named s-afadin (AF-6), which lacks the F-actin-binding domain. Here we use the term afadin to refer to l-afadin. RA, Ras-associated domain; FHA, forkhead-associated domain, DIL, dilute domain; PDZ, PDZ domain; PR, proline-rich domain.

second Ig-like loop contributes to the formation of *cis*-dimers (Momose et al. 2002, Yasumi et al. 2003). The function of the third Ig-like loop is currently unknown. Measurements from intermolecular force microscopy have furthermore revealed that nectins have another adhesion state in addition to the adhesion mediated through the interaction between the first Ig-like loops (Tsukasaki et al. 2007) (**Figure 2*a***). In this novel adhesion state, the first, second,

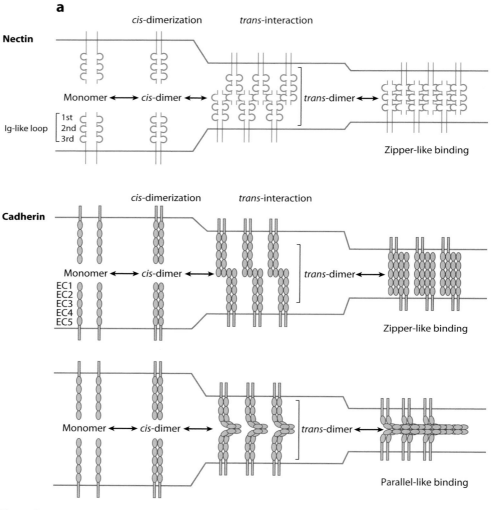

Figure 2

Models for the *trans*-interactions of nectins and cadherins and for those among nectins, nectin-like molecules (Necls), and other immunoglobulin (Ig)-like molecules. (*a*) Two nectin molecules of the same plasma membrane first form *cis*-dimers and then form a *trans*-interaction by the *cis*-dimers on apposing cells through each first Ig-like loop or in a zipper-like fashion with all three Ig-like loops (*upper panel*). Similar to nectins, two cadherin molecules of the same plasma membrane first form *cis*-dimers, followed by a *trans*-interaction by the *cis*-dimers on apposing cells through each EC1 ectodomain or in a zipper-like fashion with all five ectodomains (*middle panel*). A recent study proposed that this *trans*-interaction may be formed by a parallel-like multiply bonded system with four ectodomains (*lower panel*). (*b*) *Trans*-interactions among nectins, Necls, and other Ig-like molecules. Only known homophilic (*looped arrows*) and heterophilic (*double arrows*) interactions are indicated.

and third Ig-like loops interact in *trans* with the third, second, and first Ig-like loops of another nectin molecule, respectively, in a zipper-like fashion. However, the adhesion activity of this state is lower than that of the adhesion mediated through the interaction between the first Ig-like loops. E-Cadherin, a classical cadherin in epithelial cells, consists of one extracellular region with five tandemly repeated ectodomains (EC1–EC5), one transmembrane segment, and a cytoplasmic tail. E-Cadherin was considered to form a *trans*-interaction by the *cis*-dimers on apposing cells through each EC1 ectodomain or in a zipper-like fashion with all five ectodomains. Intermolecular force microscopy measurements have, however, revealed that four of the EC domains act cooperatively as a parallel-like multiply bonded sys-tem; namely, EC1, EC2, EC3, and EC4 interact in *trans* with the EC1, EC2, EC3, and EC4 domains of another E-cadherin molecule, respectively (Tsukasaki et al. 2007) (**Figure 2a**). The total adhesion activity of cadherin is remarkably strong compared with that of nectin.

COOPERATION WITH CADHERINS IN ADHERENS JUNCTION FORMATION

AJs are formed between two apposing cells, such as epithelial cells, endothelial cells, and fibroblasts. In epithelial and endothelial cells, tight junctions (TJs) localize at the apical side of AJs. These two types of junctions are continuously and circumferentially connected along cell-cell contact sites and are observed

TJ: tight junction

b

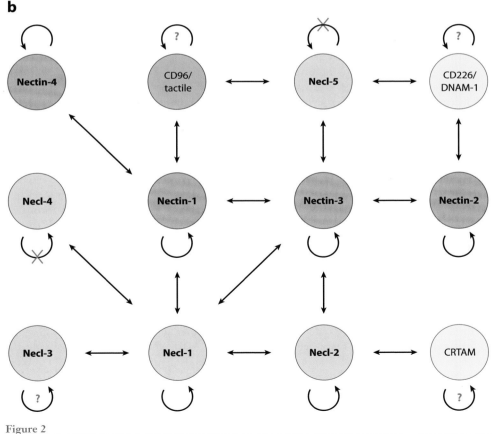

Figure 2

(*Continued*)

as belt-like structures. In fibroblasts, TJs are absent, and AJs are not continuously or circumferentially connected along cell-cell contact sites; rather, they are observed as punctuate or streak-like structures. Farquhar & Palade (1963) first observed the typical junctional complex in rat small-intestine absorptive epithelial cells, using electron microscopy. E-, VE-, and N-cadherin are the major CAMs at AJs in epithelial cells, endothelial cells, and fibroblasts, respectively (Takeichi 1988, 1995). These cadherin molecules associate with many proteins at their cytoplasmic tail: They directly bind β-catenin through the C-terminal tail and p120[ctn] through the juxtamembrane region (Anastasiadis & Reynolds 2000, Takeichi 1995). β-Catenin directly interacts with α-catenin, which binds to α-actinin and vinculin. α-Catenin, α-actinin, and vinculin are all F-actin-binding proteins. Thus, cadherin molecules are anchored to the actin cytoskeleton through these proteins. The association of cadherins with the actin cytoskeleton is necessary for the efficient clustering of cadherin molecules at cell-cell adhesion sites and for the enhancement of the adhesion activity of clustered cadherin molecules, which strengthens the adhesive tension at AJs. These molecules, with the exception of α-actinin and vinculin, are widely distributed along the lateral plasma membrane as well as AJs in epithelial cells, whereas α-actinin and vinculin localize strictly at AJs as well as focal adhesions. In contrast to the components of the cadherin-catenin system, nectins and afadin are strictly localized at AJs. In fibroblasts, the components of the cadherin and nectin systems all colocalize at AJs.

Cell biological studies of epithelial cells and fibroblasts and studies of knockout mouse models have revealed that nectins and afadin initiate AJ formation before E- or N-cadherin starts to form cell-cell adhesions. Once nectin- and afadin-based cell-cell adhesions have formed, E- or N-cadherin is recruited to these sites in epithelial cells or fibroblasts, respectively, eventually forming strong cell-cell adhesions. The nectin and cadherin systems are physically associated with one another to establish AJs. Typical lines of evidence for these roles of nectins and afadin are as follows: (*a*) The K_d value between nectin molecules is much lower than that between cadherin molecules. (*b*) Nectin-2 is more diffusible on the plasma membrane of MTD-1A cells than E-cadherin (2×10^{-9} cm^2 s^{-1} for nectin-2 and 5×10^{-10} cm^2 s^{-1} for E-cadherin), as estimated by total internal reflection fluorescence microscopic analysis (T. Katsuno, K. Takeuchi, A. Kusumi & Y. Takai, unpublished observations). (*c*) In experiments using cultured cell lines [such as Madin-Darby canine kidney (MDCK) and NIH3T3 cells], inhibitors of nectin-based cell-cell adhesions block the formation of cadherin-based AJs. The inhibitors used in these experiments were recombinant proteins of the extracellular region of nectin-3 and glycoprotein D (an envelope protein of herpes simplex virus type 1) fused to the Fc portion of IgG (Nef-3 and gD, respectively), both of which bind to nectin-1 and inhibit the formation of not only a homo-*trans*-dimer of nectin-1 but also a hetero-*trans*-dimer between nectin-1 and -3. These inhibitors interact with cellular nectins and thereby inhibit the *trans*-interactions between cellular nectin molecules and nectin-based cell-cell adhesions. (*d*) In experiments using afadin-knockdown cell lines or afadin-knockout mice, the deficiency of afadin inhibits cadherin-based AJ formation. (*e*) Finally, in experiments using α-catenin-knockdown cell lines (such as MDCK cells), a deficiency of α-catenin inhibits the formation of cadherin-based AJs, but not that of nectin-based cell-cell adhesions.

The association between nectin and cadherin molecules is physically mediated by afadin, α-catenin, and their binding proteins (Pokutta et al. 2002, Tachibana et al. 2000) (**Figure 3**). Afadin and α-catenin interact with one another directly and indirectly through ponsin, ADIP, LMO7, and vinculin. Afadin directly binds ponsin, ADIP, and LMO7 (Asada et al. 2003, Mandai et al. 1999, Ooshio et al. 2004). Ponsin binds vinculin, which binds to α-catenin (Mandai et al. 1999). Both ADIP and LMO7 directly bind α-actinin, which binds to α-catenin (Asada et al. 2003, Ooshio et al. 2004). All these molecules colocalize with afadin and α-catenin at AJs, but ponsin, vinculin, and α-actinin additionally localize at focal adhesions (Mandai et al. 1999). It still remains unknown how or at which stage of AJ formation these molecules associate with afadin and α-catenin.

COOPERATION WITH INTEGRIN IN INTRACELLULAR SIGNALING AND ADHERENS JUNCTION FORMATION

There is cross talk between cell-cell and cell-matrix junctions (Pignatelli 1998, Siu & Cheng 2004). Integrin positively or negatively regulates the formation and stability of cell-cell junctions through protein tyrosine kinases associated with integrin, such as FAK and c-Src (Geiger et al. 2001, Parsons 2003). Nectin-1 and -3, but not nectin-2 or -4, physically interact with integrin $\alpha_v\beta_3$ at nectin-based cell-cell adhesion sites through their extracellular regions (Sakamoto et al. 2006). Integrin $\alpha_v\beta_3$ has at least two forms: the low-affinity form and the high-affinity form (Takagi et al. 2002). The low-affinity form shows weak adhesion activity for ECMs (such as vitronectin and fibronectin) and is inactive, whereas the high-affinity form exhibits increased adhesion activity for ECMs and is active (Calderwood 2004). The binding of talin to the cytoplasmic tail of the β_3 subunit of integrin $\alpha_v\beta_3$ is one mechanism underlying the integrin activation through inside-out signaling (Tadokoro et al. 2003). Nectins can associate with both the low-affinity and high-affinity forms of integrin $\alpha_v\beta_3$ and always colocalize and interact with integrin $\alpha_v\beta_3$ from the initial to the final stage of AJ formation (Sakamoto et al. 2006). However, during the initial stage, nectins associate with the high-affinity form of integrin $\alpha_v\beta_3$, which is then gradually converted into the low-affinity form by AJ establishment.

The *trans*-interaction of two nectin molecules, which associate with the high-affinity form of integrin $\alpha_v\beta_3$, first induces c-Src activation (Fukuhara et al. 2004) (**Figure 4**). This requires the activation of protein kinase C (PKC) and FAK, which is induced by binding of integrin $\alpha_v\beta_3$ to ECM proteins (Ozaki et al. 2007, Sakamoto et al. 2006). c-Src activated in this way then induces the activation of Rap1 small G protein through the adaptor protein Crk and the GDP/GTP exchange factor for Rap1 (C3G) and tyrosine phosphorylates the GDP/GTP exchange factor for Cdc42 (FRG) and for Rac (Vav2) (Fukuhara et al. 2004, Fukuyama et al. 2005, Kawakatsu et al. 2005). Activated Rap1 fully activates phosphorylated FRG, resulting in the activation of Cdc42 small G protein and filopodia formation. Activated Cdc42 enhances the activation of phosphorylated Vav2 and eventually induces the activation of Rac small G protein and the formation of lamellipodia. Notably, nectins and integrin $\alpha_v\beta_3$ synergistically enhance the activation of these signaling pathways.

Protrusions, such as filopodia and lamellipodia, formed in moving cells are also formed by these signaling pathways and contribute to the formation of cell-cell junctions; filopodia increase the contact sites between apposing cells, whereas lamellipodia efficiently zip up the gaps between these contact sites (Ehrlich et al. 2002, Vasioukhin et al. 2000, Yonemura et al. 1995) (**Figure 5**). Conversely, activated Cdc42 and Rac reorganize the actin cytoskeleton and recruit the cadherin-catenin complex to nectin-based cell-cell adhesion sites through many F-actin-binding proteins, such as IQGAP1 and annexin II (Fukuhara et al. 2003; Katata et al. 2003; Yamada et al. 2004, 2005).

The E-cadherin-catenin complex recruited to nectin-based cell-cell adhesion sites shows only weak or no adhesion activity, as revealed by tests in cultured MDCK cells (Sato et al. 2006). Weakly *trans*-interacting or non-*trans*-interacting E-cadherin located at the cell surface tends to be internalized by endocytosis (Izumi et al. 2004). However, when afadin interacts with Rap1 activated by *trans*-interacting nectins, it can inhibit the endocytosis of weakly *trans*-interacting or non-*trans*-interacting E-cadherin through the association between afadin and p120^ctn (Hoshino et al. 2005). The Rap1-dependent association of afadin with p120^ctn also enhances the binding of p120^ctn to the juxtamembrane region of E-cadherin and increases the adhesion activity of E-cadherin through p120^ctn. This induces the *trans*-interaction of weakly *trans*-interacting or non-*trans*-interacting E-cadherin molecules that cluster nearby nectin-based cell-cell adhesion sites (Hoshino et al. 2005, Sato et al. 2006), consequently increasing the number of *trans*-interacting cadherin molecules there. This induces Rac activation and the consequent formation of lamellipodia, which is important for AJ formation (Fukuyama et al. 2006, Kovacs et al. 2002, Nakagawa et al. 2001). This Rac

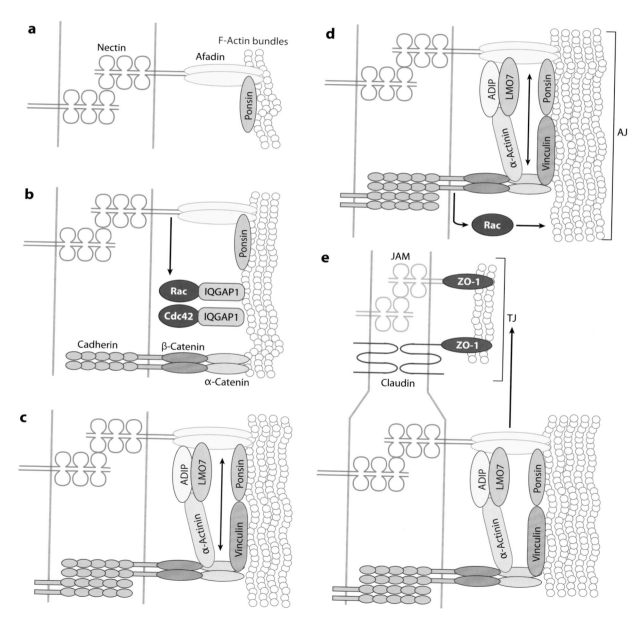

activation inhibits the endocytosis of E-cadherin through IQGAP1 and the actin cytoskeleton (Izumi et al. 2004). Similar to nectin-induced intracellular signaling, the *trans*-interaction of E-cadherin first induces c-Src activation locally at E-cadherin-based cell-cell adhesion sites (Fukuyama et al. 2006). Activated c-Src, on the one hand, induces Rap1 activation through the Crk-C3G complex and, on the other hand, tyrosine phosphorylates Vav2. The c-Src-catalyzed phosphorylation of Vav2 is not sufficient for the full activation of Vav2; the Rap1-mediated activation of phosphatidylinositol 3-kinase (PI3K) is additionally necessary. Vav2 activation then leads to Rac activation. It remains unknown whether the E-cadherin-induced activation of c-Src requires the activation of another integrin, although E-cadherin does not physically or functionally associate with integrin $\alpha_v \beta_3$.

Taken together, these findings suggest that at least four sequential steps of dynamic reorganization of the actin cytoskeleton are involved in AJ formation: (*a*) the direct or indirect association of F-actin-binding proteins with nectins (**Figure 3a**), (*b*) the nectin-induced activation of Cdc42 and Rac (**Figure 3b**), (*c*) the direct or indirect association of F-actin-binding proteins with cadherins (**Figure 3c**), and (*d*) the cadherin-induced activation of Rac (**Figure 3d**). The *trans*-interactions of the extracellular regions of nectin and cadherin molecules are essential for their respective cell-cell adhesions but are not sufficient for AJ formation. Additionally, the association of these CAMs with the actin cytoskeleton is likely necessary for CAM clustering, which eventually strengthens the adhesion activity of these clusters. Both outside-in and inside-out signaling pathways facilitate AJ formation, as described for the formation of cell-matrix junctions by the integrin system (Hood & Cheresh 2002).

PI3K: phosphatidylinositol 3-kinase

SJ: synaptic junction

PAJ: puncta adherentia junction

OTHER CELL-CELL JUNCTIONS

Puncta Adherentia Junctions

Synapses, special junctions formed between the axons and dendrites of neurons, are sites of neurotransmission. They are not formed between axons or between dendrites. Two types of junctions are known: synaptic junctions (SJs) and puncta adherentia junctions (PAJs) (Spacek & Lieberman 1974). SJs function as neurotransmission sites, whereas PAJs are regarded as mechanical adhesion sites between axon terminals and their targets. At the presynaptic side of SJs, active zones form, whereas at the postsynaptic side, the postsynaptic density forms. Neurotransmission occurs at the active zone, and

---

Figure 3

Association of the nectin-afadin system with the cadherin-catenin system during the formation of cell-cell junctions. (*a*) Initial cell-cell contact with the nectin-afadin system. At this stage, ponsin (which interacts with vinculin to recruit the cadherin-catenin system) seems to bind to afadin. (*b*) Nectin-induced reorganization of the actin cytoskeleton mediates the recruitment of the cadherin-catenin system. The *trans*-interaction of nectins induces the activation of Rac and Cdc42, followed by the reorganization of the actin cytoskeleton through several F-actin-binding proteins, such as IQGAP1. This is important for the recruitment of the cadherin-catenin system to nectin-based cell-cell adhesion sites. At this stage, cadherins do not *trans*-interact with each other. (*c*) Several connector units involved in the association of the nectin-afadin system with the cadherin-catenin system. Besides the actin cytoskeleton, three connector units are also involved in the recruitment of the cadherin-catenin system to nectin-based cell-cell adhesion sites. The first connector unit is the ponsin-vinculin unit, the second is the afadin DIL-domain-interacting protein (ADIP)-α-actinin unit, and the third is the LIM domain only 7 (LMO7)-α-actinin unit. Moreover, the direct interaction of afadin with α-catenin is assumed, but this interaction does not seem to be strong. After the recruitment of the cadherin-catenin system to nectin-based cell-cell adhesion sites, the adhesion activity of cadherins is increased, and the *trans*-interaction of cadherins occurs. (*d*) Adherens junction (AJ) formation. After the formation of the *trans*-interaction of cadherins, AJs are formed. The *trans*-interaction of cadherins induces the activation of Rac, which is involved in the inhibition of cadherin endocytosis and contributes to the stabilization of the *trans*-interaction of cadherins at AJs. (*e*) Tight junction (TJ) formation. After AJ formation, TJs are formed at the apical side of AJs in epithelial cells by recruiting junctional adhesion molecules (JAMs) and claudins. The nectin-afadin system plays an important role in this process. This figure omits the involvement of annexin II and the activated RAP1-afadin-p120^{ctn} association in the formation of cell-cell junctions.

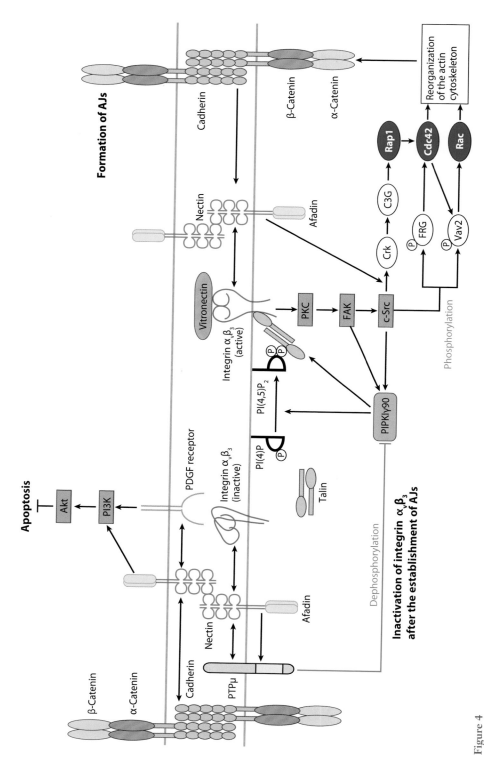

Figure 4

Diverse functions of the nectin-afadin system during and after adherens junction (AJ) formation. In the process of AJ formation, nectins associate with activated integrin $\alpha_v\beta_3$, and these cell adhesion molecules cooperatively induce the activation of many intracellular signaling molecules essential for AJ formation. After AJ formation, integrin $\alpha_v\beta_3$ is inactivated through the nectin-induced activation of protein tyrosine phosphatase μ (PTPμ) and the consequent dephosphorylation and suppression of phosphatidylinositol phosphate kinase type Iγ90 (PIPKIγ90), which is involved in the activation of integrin through talin. This is important for AJ stabilization because the prolonged activation of integrin tends to disrupt AJ formation. The nectin-afadin system also enhances cell survival by inhibiting apoptosis. This is mediated by the association of nectin with platelet-derived growth factor (PDGF) receptor, resulting in the enhancement of the PDGF-induced activation of phosphatidylinositol 3-kinase (PI3K)-Akt signaling.

released neurotransmitters bind to their receptors localized at the postsynaptic density. PAJs are particularly developed in the CA3 region of the hippocampus. The synapses between the mossy fiber terminals and dendrites of pyramidal cells in this region are postnatally formed and gradually remodeled to SJs and PAJs, resulting in their maturation (Amaral & Dent 1981). After this maturation, remodeling occurs briskly and is implicated in synaptic plasticity, a principal mechanism of memory and learning. Thus, SJs are structurally and functionally asymmetric, in contrast to AJs in epithelial cells and fibroblasts, which are structurally and functionally symmetric between two attaching cells. N-Cadherin and other cadherins, such as cadherin-8 and cadherin-11, exist at PAJs. The active zone and postsynaptic density are surrounded by N-cadherin-based cell-cell adhesions (Uchida et al. 1996). In addition, at PAJs formed between the mossy fiber terminals and the dendrites of CA3 pyramidal cells in the hippocampus of the adult brain, nectin-1 and -3 asymmetrically localize at presynaptic and postsynaptic sides, respectively, whereas afadin symmetrically localizes at both sides (Mizoguchi et al. 2002) (**Figure 6a**). In primary cultured hippocampal neurons, nectin-1 and -3 are involved in synapse formation; nectin-1 preferentially localizes in axons, whereas nectin-3 is present in both axons and dendrites (Togashi et al. 2006). The addition of an inhibitor of nectin-1 (gD) to cultured hippocampal neurons results in a decrease in synapse size and a concomitant increase in synapse number (Mizoguchi et al. 2002), indicating the important role of nectin-based cell-cell adhesion in synaptogenesis, at least in vitro. Studies involving overexpression and knockout of these nectin molecules have shown that the asymmetric distribution of nectin-1 and -3 is critical for the specific interactions between axons and dendrites to form proper synapses, consistent with the fact that the homophilic *trans*-interactions between nectin-1 molecules and nectin-3 molecules are far weaker than the heterophilic *trans*-interaction between nectin-1 and -3 (Togashi et al. 2006). It remains un-

known how these nectin molecules are asymmetrically distributed to axons and dendrites. By analogy with AJs in epithelial cells and fibroblasts, it is likely that nectin-based cell-cell adhesions form first, followed by the recruitment of N-cadherin-based cell-cell adhesions to form synapses, which are finally segregated into SJs and PAJs in vivo. Consistently, in nectin-1$^{-/-}$ and nectin-3$^{-/-}$ mice, the number of PAJs in the CA3 region of the hippocampus of the adult brain is reduced, and an abnormal mossy fiber trajectory is observed (Honda et al. 2006). Once the fiber terminals pass over nectin-based adhesion sites, N-cadherin is recruited to form stronger and more stable junctions, resulting in the segregation and maturation of SJs and PAJs in the CA3 region of the hippocampus.

Formation of Weak Cell-Cell Junctions or Contacts Independent of Cadherins

Nectins and afadin are expressed in almost all tissues in both embryos and adults and in a variety of cell types, including epithelial cells, neurons, and fibroblasts (Ikeda et al. 1999; Inagaki et al. 2005; Mandai et al. 1997; Matsushima et al. 2003; Mizoguchi et al. 2002; Okabe et al. 2004a,b; Ozaki-Kuroda et al. 2002; Takahashi et al. 1999). They participate mainly in the formation of cell-cell junctions in cooperation with cadherins. However, nectins also exist in some tissues or cells in which cadherins are absent. In such places, as described below, nectins function in a cadherin-independent manner and are involved in the formation of weak cell-cell junctions that may preferentially contribute to the dynamic regulation of cell junctional architecture and the rapid remodeling of tissues.

Contacts between elongating commissural axons and floor plate cells in the hindbrain. Weak adhesion mediated by nectins also plays an important role in contacts between elongating commissural axons and floor plate cells. Commissural axons grow toward the ventral midline, cross the floor plate, and then abruptly change their trajectory from the

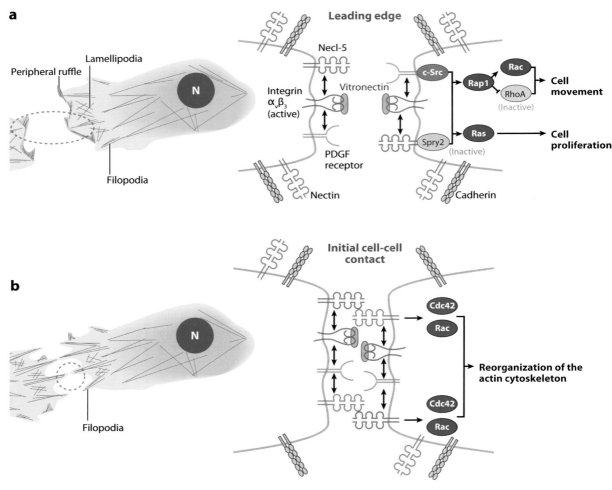

Figure 5

The formation of leading-edge structures and adherens junctions (AJs) and the contact inhibition of cell movement and proliferation by Necl-5 and nectin-3. (*a*) The leading edge of a moving cell, at which Necl-5, integrin $\alpha_v\beta_3$, and platelet-derived growth factor (PDGF) receptor interact. A complex of these three molecules enhances cell movement by inducing Rap1 activation, which leads to Rac activation together with Rho inhibition. Conversely, the ternary complex enhances cell proliferation by inducing activation of the Ras-Raf-MEK-ERK signaling pathway by inhibiting Necl-5-associated sprouty2 (Spry2). (*b*) The initial cell-cell contact. When two moving cells collide, the initial cell-cell contact is formed by the *trans*-interaction of nectin-3 with Necl-5. At this stage, integrin $\alpha_v\beta_3$ remains active. (*c*) Formation of nectin-based cell-cell adhesion. The *trans*-interaction of nectin-3 with Necl-5 is transient, and then Necl-5 is downregulated from the cell surface by clathrin-dependent endocytosis. Nectin-3 then interacts in *trans* with nectin-1. (*d*) AJ formation. Cadherins are recruited at nectin-based cell-cell adhesion sites and homophilically interact in *trans* to form AJs. At this stage, integrin $\alpha_v\beta_3$ becomes inactive. Spry2, released from Necl-5, is tyrosine phosphorylated by c-Src and becomes active to inhibit Ras-mediated cell proliferation signals. The intracellular signaling mediated by integrin $\alpha_v\beta_3$ and PDGF receptor is then suppressed, thus resulting in the inhibition of cell movement and proliferation (known as contact inhibition). This model is dependent on results obtained from experiments using mainly NIH3T3 cells.

circumferential to the longitudinal axis. The cadherin-catenin system is not found at the contact sites between commissural axons and floor plate cells, and the CAMs responsible for these contact sites remain unknown. Nectin-1 and -3 asymmetrically localize at the commissural axon side and the floor plate cell side, respectively, and are involved in the contacts between the commissural axons and the floor plate cells (Okabe et al. 2004b) (**Figure 6***b*). This *trans*-interaction between nectin-1 and -3 is critical to change the trajectory of commissural axons

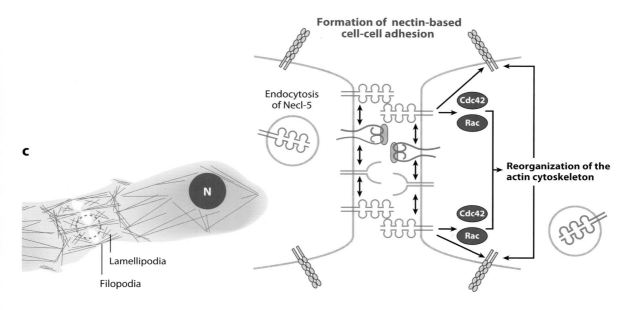

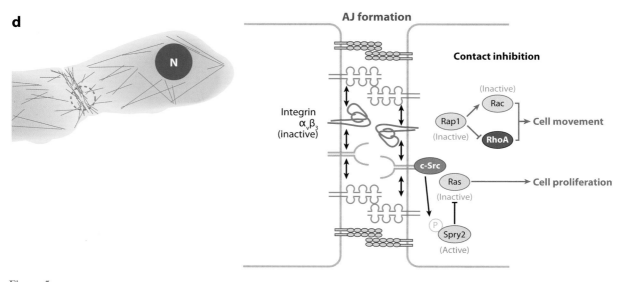

Figure 5

(*Continued*)

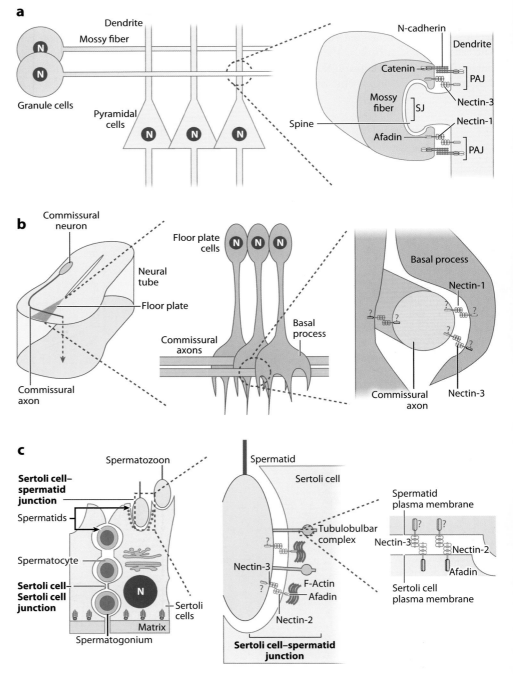

Figure 6

The involvement of nectins in the formation of various types of cell-cell junctions and cell-cell contacts. (*a*) Synapses between the mossy fiber terminals and dendrites of pyramidal cells in the CA3 region of the hippocampus. PAJ, puncta adherentia junction; SJ, synaptic junction. (*b*) Contacts between the commissural axons and the floor plate cells in the neural tube. (c) Sertoli cell–spermatid junctions in the testis.

because inhibition of the endogenous *trans*-interaction between nectin-1 and -3 (by gD and Nef-3) impairs (*a*) the contacts between commissural axons and floor plate cells and (*b*) the longitudinal turn of the commissural axons in contralateral sites of the rat hindbrain. The weak adhesion activity of nectins, rather than the strong adhesion activity of cadherins, may be more suitable for the commissural axons to continuously elongate, attaching to floor plate cells, and this weak attachment is critical for determining the trajectory of the elongating axons. In addition, the commissural axons and floor plate cells communicate or transfer signals through their contact sites (Stoeckli & Landmesser 1998). The abnormal turn and loss of proper direction of the commissural axons induced by inhibition of the *trans*-interaction of nectins may result from the failure of signal transduction in addition to mechanically weak contact between the commissural axons and the floor plate cells.

Junctions between differentiating spermatids and Sertoli cells. Nectin-mediated weak adhesion also plays a role in germ cell differentiation in the testis. Spermatogenic cells are embraced and cultivated by Sertoli cells during spermatogenesis. In the latter half of spermatogenesis, spermatids form prominent cell-cell junctions with Sertoli cells called Sertoli cell–spermatid junctions. In contrast to Sertoli-Sertoli junctions, which are equipped with AJs and TJs and serve as the blood-testis barrier (Cheng & Mruk 2002), Sertoli cell–spermatid junctions do not contain AJs or TJs. Sertoli cell–spermatid junctions play an essential role in spermatid development. Nectin-2 and -3 reside specifically in Sertoli cells and spermatids, respectively (Ozaki-Kuroda et al. 2002) (**Figure 6***c*). Because the existence of the cadherin system has been questionable at Sertoli cell–spermatid junctions (Cheng & Mruk 2002), the junctions appear to depend mainly on the *trans*-interaction between nectin-2 and -3. The existence of afadin in Sertoli cells is clearly known, but its existence in spermatids is obscure. Consistent with the importance of

nectin-2 and -3 for the formation of Sertoli cell–spermatid junctions, nectin-2$^{-/-}$ and nectin-3$^{-/-}$ mice show differentiation abnormalities in spermatogenesis, resulting in male-specific infertility (Inagaki et al. 2006, Mueller et al. 2003, Ozaki-Kuroda et al. 2002). These knockout mice also exhibit distorted nuclei and abnormal distribution of mitochondria in sperm morphogenesis. The localization signal for nectin-2 at Sertoli cell–spermatid junctions completely disappears in the nectin-3$^{-/-}$ testis, whereas the signal for nectin-3 is disorganized but still remains in the nectin-2$^{-/-}$ testis, suggesting that nectin-3 in spermatids may also *trans*-interact with CAM(s) other than nectin-2 in Sertoli cells. However, such interactions may not be as important as that between nectin-2 and -3 because loss of nectin-2 in Sertoli cells dramatically affects the organization of nectin-3 in spermatids at Sertoli cell–spermatid junctions.

In the apical regions of the seminiferous epithelium, structures termed tubulobulbar complexes are developed between Sertoli cells and spermatids (Russell & Clermont 1976). In tubulobulbar complexes, the spermatid plasma membrane protrudes, in a finger-like process, into the adjacent Sertoli cell plasma membrane, ending with a bulb-like swelling. Nectin-2 and -3 localize at tubulobulbar complexes and appear to participate in the adhesion between the plasma membranes of Sertoli cells and spermatids at these structures (Guttman et al. 2004). When spermatids are released as spermatozoa, Sertoli cell and spermatid membrane elements including nectin-2 and -3 are likely to be internalized together with tubulobulbar complexes, and Sertoli cell–spermatid junctions are disassembled.

INTERACTION WITH NECL-5 AND REGULATION OF CELL MOVEMENT AND PROLIFERATION

Formation of Leading-Edge Structures and Cell Movement

Many cell types, including fibroblasts, respond to chemoattractants [such as platelet-derived growth factor (PDGF), epidermal growth factor, and fibroblast growth factor], polarize, and move in the direction of higher concentrations of chemoattractants (Ronnstrand & Heldin 2001) (**Figures 5** and **7**). At the leading edges of moving cells, special structures necessary for cell movement are dynamically formed; such structures include protrusions such as filopodia and lamellipodia, peripheral ruffles, focal complexes, and focal adhesions (Hall 1998, Rottner et al. 1999, Zaidel-Bar et al. 2004). These structures are formed by reorganization of the actin cytoskeleton, which is regulated by the actions of the Rho family small G proteins: Lamellipodia and ruffles are formed by the action of Rac, filopodia by the action of Cdc42, and focal complexes by the action of Rac and Cdc42 (Rottner et al. 1999). The formation of these leading-edge structures is inhibited by the action of Rho. Focal complexes are transformed into focal adhesions by the inactivation of Cdc42 and Rac and the activation of Rho (Ballestrem et al. 2001, Rottner et al. 1999). However, the dynamic activation and inactivation of these small G proteins are not fully understood.

Interaction of Necl-5 with Integrin $\alpha_v\beta_3$ and PDGF Receptor

PDGF receptor physically and functionally interacts with integrin $\alpha_v\beta_3$, and activation of these two transmembrane proteins is essential for the formation of leading-edge structures and cell movement (Woodard et al. 1998). In addition, Necl-5 physically and functionally interacts in *cis* with both PDGF receptor and integrin $\alpha_v\beta_3$ and is essential not only for this activity but also for the formation of leading-edge structures in at least NIH3T3 cells (Amano et al. 2008, Minami et al. 2007a) (**Figure 5a**). Because Necl-5, PDGF receptor, and integrin $\alpha_V\beta_3$ can form any combination of binary complexes, these three molecules may form a ternary complex, although this is practically difficult to prove. The Necl-5–PDGF receptor–integrin $\alpha_v\beta_3$ complex localizes at peripheral ruffles over lamellipodia; the Necl-5–integrin $\alpha_v\beta_3$ complex, but not PDGF receptor, localizes at focal complexes; and integrin $\alpha_v\beta_3$, but not PDGF receptor or Necl-5, localizes at focal adhesions. These results indicate a key role for Necl-5 in directional cell movement by physically and functionally interacting with both integrin $\alpha_v\beta_3$ and PDGF receptor. PDGF receptor is likely to be internalized and dissociated from Necl-5 and integrin $\alpha_v\beta_3$ upon binding of PDGF, followed by the attachment of peripheral ruffles over lamellipodia to the matrix through the Necl-5–integrin $\alpha_v\beta_3$ complex and the formation of new focal complexes. Necl-5 is then dissociated from integrin $\alpha_v\beta_3$ during the transformation of focal complexes to focal adhesions. Thus, along with PDGF receptor and integrin $\alpha_v\beta_3$, Necl-5 plays a crucial role in the formation of leading-edge structures and directional cell movement.

Dynamic Formation of Leading-Edge Structures by the Necl-5–Integrin $\alpha_v\beta_3$–PDGF Receptor Complex

Leading-edge structures are dynamically formed and disassembled during cell

---

Figure 7

Dynamic formation of leading-edge structures by the Necl-5–integrin $\alpha_v\beta_3$–platelet-derived growth factor (PDGF) receptor complex. (*a*) Upon stimulation by PDGF, Rap1 is locally activated at the leading edges by the Necl-5–PDGF receptor (PDGFR)–integrin $\alpha_v\beta_3$ complex. (*b*) Activated Rap1 induces the activation of Rac by binding to Vav2. (*c*) Activated Rac induces the formation of lamellipodia peripheral ruffles and focal complexes. (*d*) Activated Rap1 induces the inactivation of RhoA by binding to Rho-GAP ARAP1. (*e*) Activated Rap1 binds to afadin, which does not bind to nectins, and recruits it to the leading edges. Afadin then prevents Rap-GAP SPA-1 from inactivating Rap1. (*f*) When PDGF receptor is downregulated from the cell surface by endocytosis, the activation of Rap1 stops. SPA-1 also inactivates Rap1. (*g*) The role of inactivated Rap1. The inactivation of Rap1 leads to the inactivation of Rac and the activation of RhoA. (*h*) Activated RhoA induces the dissociation of Necl-5 from focal complexes through its downstream Rho kinase (ROCK) and thereby enhances the transformation of focal complexes to focal adhesions.

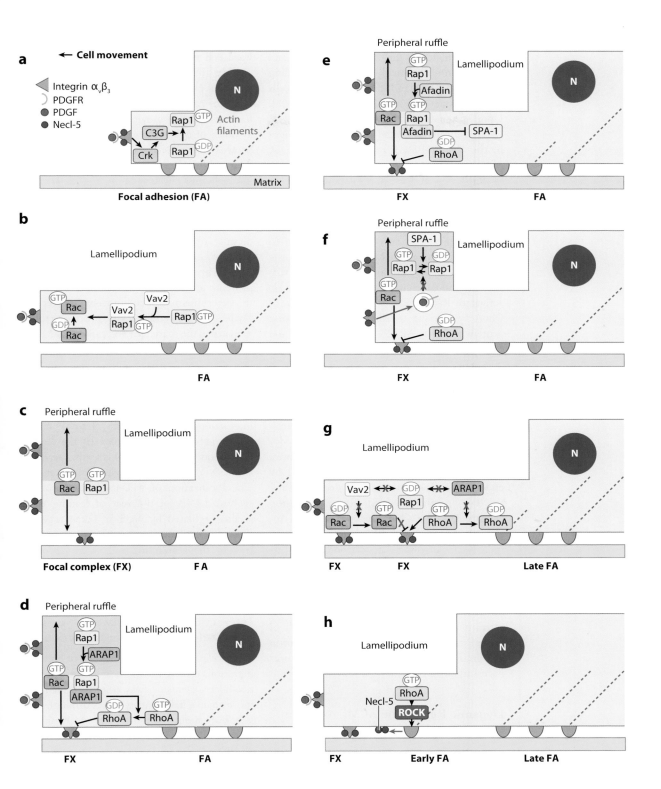

movement. These dynamic events are tightly regulated by the dynamic activation and inactivation of the small G proteins (including at least Rap1, Rac, and RhoA) in NIH3T3 cells (Nagamatsu et al. 2008, Takahashi et al. 2008). Upon stimulation of NIH3T3 cells by PDGF, Rap1 is locally activated at the leading edges by the Necl-5–PDGF receptor–integrin $\alpha_v\beta_3$ complex (**Figure 7a**). The local activation of Rap1 has at least three critical roles in the formation of leading-edge structures (Takahashi et al. 2008; Y. Rikitake & Y. Takai, unpublished observations): (*a*) Activated Rap1 induces the activation of Rac by binding to Vav2, and activated Rac then induces the formation of lamellipodia, peripheral ruffles, and focal complexes (**Figure 7b,c**); (*b*) activated Rap1 induces the inactivation of RhoA by binding to Rho-GTPase-activating protein (GAP) ARAP1 (**Figure 7d**); and (*c*) activated Rap1 binds to afadin, which does not bind to nectins, and recruits it to the leading edges (**Figure 7e**). Afadin then prevents Rap-GAP SPA-1 from inactivating Rap1. Additionally, the downregulation of PDGF receptor from the cell surface may be involved in the mechanisms of the dynamic formation of leading-edge structures: When PDGF receptor is downregulated by endocytosis, Rap1 activation stops, leading to Rac inactivation and RhoA activation (**Figure 7f,g**). SPA-1 also inactivates Rap1. Activation of RhoA and its downstream Rho kinase induces Necl-5 dissociation from focal complexes and thereby enhances the transformation of focal complexes into focal adhesions (**Figure 7b**). Collectively, the Necl-5–PDGF receptor–integrin $\alpha_v\beta_3$ complex–mediated cyclical activation and inactivation of these small G proteins are critical for the dynamic formation and disassembly of the leading-edge structures necessary for directional cell movement.

Dynamic Regulation of Microtubule Orientation by Necl-5

Reorientation of the microtubule (MT) network is necessary for directional cell movement and for the search for the membrane cue toward cell movement. Usually, MT plus ends explore the cellular space, switching rapidly between phases of growth and shrinkage, a behavior called dynamic instability. When the leading edges of moving cells form, one sees a subset of MTs that grow into leading-edge protrusions, called growing (pioneer) MTs. The plus ends of growing MTs experience markedly less shrinkage and spend more time growing than the majority of MTs. At the plus ends of growing MTs, many proteins localize as plus-end-tracking proteins, including cytoplasmic dynein/dynactin, cytoplasmic linker proteins, and EB1 (Mimori-Kiyosue & Tsukita 2003, Perez et al. 1999). Plus-end-tracking proteins are involved in this search for and the determination of cell movement direction. Dynein is a plus-end-tracking protein that participates in the search for and capture of MTs as well as the intracellular retrograde transport of molecules (Mimori-Kiyosue & Tsukita 2003). Necl-5 binds to the dynein light chain Tctex-1 in the cytoplasmic region of Necl-5 (Mueller et al. 2002, Ohka et al. 2004). The direct interaction of Necl-5 with Tctex-1 targets the dynein/dynactin complex to the leading edges and recruits MT plus ends there (W. Ikeda & Y. Takai, unpublished observations). The localization of MT-stabilizing proteins, such as LL5β, at the rear of leading edges is also regulated by Necl-5. Taken together, these findings suggest that Necl-5 plays a key role in the search for and reorientation of MT networks and directional cell movement mediated by MT-related proteins.

Interaction in *trans* Between Nectin-3 and Necl-5 and Contact Inhibition

Contact inhibition of cell movement and proliferation, crucial for the homeostasis of multicellular organisms, was originally identified more than a half century ago. Although little is known about the underlying mechanism of contact inhibition, the involvement of nectin-3 and Necl-5, especially their *trans*-interaction, in this mechanism was shown recently.

Contact inhibition of cell movement. When normal cells become confluent and do not find any cell-free areas, they cease movement and start to form cell-cell junctions. This phenomenon, referred to as contact inhibition of cell movement (Bell 1978), was originally described in fibroblasts and occurs when a cell ceases to migrate in the same direction after contact with another cell (Abercrombie & Heaysman 1953, 1954). Since its first description, the concept of contact inhibition has included the observation that cells become immobilized and are unable to continue moving once they form cell-cell adhesions, which has been demonstrated in epithelial wound healing (Abercrombie 1970, Abercrombie & Ambrose 1962). Presently, the term is used quite broadly (Huttenlocher et al. 1998, Zegers et al. 2003). The mechanism underlying contact inhibition is critically important in organogenesis and wound healing. Many mechanisms for contact inhibition have been proposed, but these are not fully understood.

Downregulation of Necl-5 by nectin-3 and adherens junction formation. Necl-5 localizes at the leading edges of moving cells and enhances cell movement (Ikeda et al. 2004), whereas nectins initiate cell-cell adhesion. In addition, Necl-5 and nectin-3 heterophilically interact in *trans*. These properties strongly suggest the involvement of Necl-5 and nectin-3 in contact inhibition of cell movement. Indeed, initial cell-cell contact is mediated by the heterophilic *trans*-interaction of Necl-5 at the leading edges, with nectin-3 on the adjacent cell surface, when individually moving cells collide (Fujito et al. 2005) (**Figure 5a,b**). This *trans*-interaction induces the activation of Cdc42 and Rac (Sato et al. 2005), both of which reorganize the actin cytoskeleton and increase the number of cell-cell adhesion sites, similar to the *trans*-interaction of nectin molecules. However, the *trans*-interaction of Necl-5 with nectin-3 is transient, and Necl-5 is downregulated from the cell surface by endocytosis in a clathrin-dependent manner (Fujito et al. 2005) (**Figure 5c**). The decrease in the level of Necl-5 leads to a reduction in cell movement because it inhibits signaling initiated by PDGF receptor and integrin $\alpha_v\beta_3$. The Necl-5 promoter has an AP-1-binding site, and expression of the *Necl-5* gene is enhanced by the activation of the Ras-Raf-MEK-ERK-AP-1 pathway associated with PDGF receptor (Hirota et al. 2005). Because Necl-5 is necessary for the activation of this signaling pathway (as described below), its downregulation from the cell surface in turn decreases the total amount of Necl-5 as a negative feedback loop. Nectin-3 dissociated from Necl-5 is retained on the cell surface and subsequently *trans*-interacts with nectin-1, which most feasibly *trans*-interacts with nectin-3 among the nectin family members (Ikeda et al. 2003). The *trans*-interaction of these two nectin molecules induces the recruitment of cadherins to nectin-based adhesion sites, eventually leading to AJ establishment (**Figure 5d**).

Inactivation of integrin $\alpha_v\beta_3$ by nectins. After the establishment of AJs, the high-affinity form of integrin $\alpha_v\beta_3$ is converted into the low-affinity form, which also continues to associate with nectins (Ozaki et al. 2007, Sakamoto et al. 2006). This inactivation seems to be beneficial for AJ maintenance because the sustained activation of integrin $\alpha_v\beta_3$ renders cells highly motile, which tends to disrupt cell-cell junctions. Integrin $\alpha_v\beta_3$ is activated by the binding of talin to the cytoplasmic tail of the β_3 subunit (Calderwood 2004). The binding of talin to integrin $\alpha_v\beta_3$ is enhanced by an increased amount of phosphatidylinositol 4,5-bisphosphate (Martel et al. 2001), which is generated by phosphatidylinositol phosphate kinases such as phosphatidylinositol phosphate kinase type Iγ90 (PIPKIγ90). The activation of PIPKIγ is correlated with its phosphorylation state. The tyrosine phosphatase protein tyrosine phosphatase μ (PTPμ) effectively dephosphorylates PIPKIγ and thus cancels the PIPKIγ-dependent activation of integrin $\alpha_v\beta_3$ by blocking the interaction of integrin $\alpha_v\beta_3$ with talin (Sakamoto et al. 2008). PTPμ is a single-membrane-spanning molecule with an extracellular region containing an MAM

(Merpin/A5/PTPµ) domain, an Ig-like domain, four fibronectin type III repeats, and a cytoplasmic region containing two phosphatase domains. All nectin family members potentially interact with PTPµ through their extracellular regions, and the *trans*-interactions of nectins enhance its phosphatase activity, leading to a decrease in the phosphorylation of PIPKIγ90 (**Figure 4**). In this way, nectins essentially function in the inactivation of integrin $\alpha_v\beta_3$ at AJs, and this is an additional mechanism of contact inhibition of cell movement.

Regulation of cell proliferation by Necl-5 through sprouty. When proliferating normal cultured cells become confluent, they cease to proliferate. This phenomenon was identified as the contact inhibition of cell proliferation (Fisher & Yeh 1967). However, there is no clear evidence that this phenomenon is dependent on cell contact; in fact, there is compelling evidence that it is not (Dunn & Ireland 1984, Martz & Steinberg 1972). Therefore, the phenomenon of confluent cells downregulating mitosis is also called the density-dependent inhibition of mitosis (Stoker & Rubin 1967). This contact inhibition is also critically important in organogenesis, similar to the contact inhibition of cell movement. The mechanism underlying this contact inhibition is not fully understood. Many growth factors transduce cell proliferation signals, such as activation of the Ras-Raf-MEK-ERK pathway. This pathway regulates cell-cycle regulators. Many cell-cycle regulators have been identified as involved in the transition from the G_0 phase to the G_1 phase and in progression from the G_1 phase to the S phase (Morgan 1995, Sherr 1996). During the G_1 phase in NIH3T3 cells, first cyclin D is upregulated, then cyclin-dependent kinase inhibitor p27^{Kip1} is downregulated, and finally cyclin E is upregulated (Uren et al. 1997). Necl-5 enhances growth factor–induced activation of the Ras-Raf-MEK-ERK pathway, causing the up- and downregulation of cell-cycle regulators, including cyclins D2 and E and p27^{kip1}, thereby shortening the period of the G_1 phase of the cell cycle (Kakunaga et al. 2004). Sprouty

is a negative regulator of growth factor–induced signaling for cell proliferation (Christofori 2003, Kim & Bar-Sagi 2004), although it was originally identified as an antagonist of the fibroblast growth factor signaling that patterns apical branching of *Drosophila* airways (Hacohen et al. 1998). When sprouty is tyrosine phosphorylated by c-Src in response to growth factors, it inhibits the growth factor–induced activation of Ras and the subsequent activation of Raf-MEK-ERK signaling at a site upstream of Ras and downstream of growth factor receptors (Kim & Bar-Sagi 2004). Binding of growth factors to their receptors induces activation of both Ras and c-Src, but during cell proliferation, Ras signaling is activated and sprouty is inactivated. The mechanism underlying this regulation remains unknown, but Necl-5 appears to be involved. Necl-5 interacts with sprouty2, which prevents sprouty2 from being tyrosine phosphorylated by c-Src (Kajita et al. 2007) (**Figure 5a,d**). When Necl-5 is downregulated from the cell surface by *trans*-interacting with nectin-3 at cell-cell adhesion sites, sprouty2 is released from Necl-5, is phosphorylated by c-Src, and inhibits the PDGF-induced activation of Ras. This inhibition further suppresses de novo synthesis of Necl-5. Thus, this system is at least one of the mechanisms underlying contact inhibition of cell proliferation.

Loss of contact inhibition by transformation. When cells are transformed, they lose contact inhibition of cell movement and proliferation, causing abnormal cell proliferation, invasion, and metastasis (Abercrombie 1979, Thiery 2002). Necl-5 is upregulated in transformed cells (Chadeneau et al. 1994, Gromeier et al. 2000, Ikeda et al. 2003, Masson et al. 2001). Necl-5 is also upregulated in NIH3T3 cells overexpressing oncogenic Ki-Ras (V12Ras) through the V12Ras-Raf-MEK-ERK-AP-1 pathway (Hirota et al. 2005). This uncontrolled excess expression of Necl-5 overwhelms the rate of Necl-5 internalization upon cell-cell adhesion, resulting in the loss of contact inhibition in V12Ras-NIH3T3 cells (Minami et al. 2007b). Consistent with this, an in vivo study showed that V12Ras-NIH3T3 cells gain metastatic ability owing to the upregulation of Necl-5 (Ikeda et al. 2004). Therefore, upregulation of Necl-5 following transformation contributes to the loss of contact inhibition in transformed cells.

CELL SURVIVAL

After cells become confluent and establish cell-cell junctions, they stop moving and proliferating but continue to survive. A number of reports demonstrate physical and functional associations between CAMs and growth factor receptors (Comoglio et al. 2003, Perez-Moreno et al. 2003, Yap & Kovacs 2003). Comoglio et al. (2003) have proposed that three types of signal transduction pathways are mediated by CAMs (such as integrins and cadherins) and growth factor receptors (such as epidermal growth factor receptor, PDGF receptor, and vascular endothelial growth factor receptor-2): (*a*) collaborative signaling pathways in which the signaling downstream of CAMs and growth factor receptors is individually or cooperatively transduced to intracellular signaling molecules, (*b*) the CAM-dependent activation of growth factor receptor signaling that first requires the formation of cell-cell or cell-matrix junctions by CAMs before growth factor receptor is activated, and (*c*) the growth factor receptor–dependent activation of CAM signaling in which the growth factor receptor is first activated by its cognate growth factor, sequentially regulating the function of CAM-related molecules.

PDGF-induced cell survival signaling is modified by nectin-3 and afadin (Kanzaki et al. 2008) (**Figure 4**). Nectin-3 (but not nectin-1, -2, or -4) associates with PDGF receptor at cell-cell adhesion sites, and both nectin-3 and PDGF receptor function in a cooperative manner in PDGF-induced activation of PI3K-Akt signaling. The PDGF-induced phosphorylation of Akt in nectin-3- or afadin-knockdown NIH3T3 cells is attenuated compared with that in wild-type NIH3T3 cells. PI3K activity enhanced by PDGF is also suppressed in nectin-3- or afadin-knockdown NIH3T3 cells, indicating that the regulation of PI3K-Akt signaling by nectin-3 and afadin is conducted with the activation of PI3K. Moreover, association of afadin with nectin-3 is necessary for the activation of PI3K-Akt signaling because the transfection of NIH3T3 cells with a nectin-3 mutant that cannot bind to afadin fails to mediate the PDGF-induced phosphorylation of Akt. Similarly, embryoid bodies derived from afadin$^{-/-}$ embryonic stem cells have an enormous number of apoptotic cells in their cavity compared with wild-type embryonic stem cells, indicating an inhibitory effect of afadin on apoptosis.

APICO-BASAL CELL POLARIZATION

Polarity is especially well developed in epithelial cells, and cell-cell and cell-matrix junctions play important roles in the formation and maintenance of apico-basal cell polarity (Nelson 2003, Tsukita et al. 2001). One characteristic feature of this polarity is that TJs are formed at the apical side of AJs. TJs mainly consist of CAMs [including claudins, occludin, and junctional adhesion molecules (JAMs)] and their undercoating molecules (including ZO proteins). Claudins and occludin are structurally similar, with two extracellular loops, four transmembrane segments, and N and C termini facing the cytoplasm. Although claudins compose a large family consisting of at least 24 members, no occludin-related genes have been identified. JAMs are a single-membrane-spanning CAM with two Ig-like loops in the extracellular region. Investigators have identified four JAMs and one JAM-like molecule: JAM-A (also referred to JAM-1), JAM-B (also known as VE-JAM/mouse JAM-3/human JAM2), JAM-C (also known as mouse JAM-2/human JAM3), JAM-4, and JAM-like. There are three ZO proteins (ZO-1, ZO-2, and ZO-3), which link these CAMs to the actin cytoskeleton. Several lines of evidence suggest that AJ establishment is a prerequisite for TJ formation (Gumbiner et al. 1988). Studies using inhibitors of nectins (Nef-3 and gD) and knockdown or knockout of afadin have shown that TJ formation is dependent on nectin- and afadin-based cell-cell adhesions (Fukuhara et al. 2002a,b; Ikeda et al. 1999; Komura et al. 2008; Sato et al. 2006). Additionally, the formation of TJs is not completely dependent on the formation of the E-cadherin-based AJs under certain conditions (Capaldo & Macara 2007, Harris & Peifer 2004, Okamoto et al. 2005, Yamada et al. 2006). Balda et al. (1993) observed the AJ-independent formation of a TJ-like structure in MDCK cells cultured in a low-Ca^{2+} medium containing a tumor-promoting phorbol ester, 12-*O*-tetradecanoyl-phorbol-13-acetate, at cell-cell adhesion sites in the absence of E-cadherin-based cell-cell adhesion. In such conditions, non-*trans*-interacting E-cadherin (which associates with β-catenin, α-catenin, and p120^{ctn}) is recruited to nectin-based cell-cell adhesion sites, and inhibition of the *trans*-interactions of nectins by Nef-3 and gD significantly blocks TJ formation (Okamoto et al. 2005). Another study demonstrated that knockdown of annexin II caused the formation of a normal TJ structure at cell-cell adhesion sites in the absence of E-cadherin-based cell-cell adhesion in MDCK cells, and inhibition of the *trans*-interactions of nectins by Nef-3 and gD significantly blocked TJ formation (Fukuhara et al. 2002a,b; Yamada et al. 2006). Although the precise molecular mechanism underlying the recruitment of the TJ constituents such as claudins, occludin, and JAMs to the apical side of AJs remains unclear, this recruitment is mediated at least by the nectin-afadin system (**Figure 3e**). Three mechanisms have been proposed for this recruitment: (*a*) the interaction of afadin with ZO-1, (*b*) nectin-induced intracellular signaling and the reorganization of the actin cytoskeleton, and (*c*) the function of annexin II, which positively and negatively regulates the formation of AJs and TJs, respectively (Yamada et al. 2006).

The Par complex (including Par-3, Par-6, and aPKC) is crucial for TJ formation as well as apico-basal polarization in epithelial cells (Ohno 2001, Roh & Margolis 2003). The formation of the Par-3/aPKC/Par-6 complex is dynamically regulated by Lgl and Cdc42, and the interaction of this complex with JAMs is important for the formation of TJs (Nelson 2003). However, it remains unknown how these cell polarity proteins regulate TJ formation following AJ formation. Par-3 directly binds to nectin-1 and -3, but not nectin-2, between the first PDZ domain of Par-3 and the C-terminal four amino acids of the cytoplasmic tail of these nectins (Takekuni et al. 2003). Par-3 is necessary for the formation of not only AJs but also TJs, although Par-3 is dispensable for the formation of nectin-based cell-cell adhesion (Ooshio et al. 2007). At the initial stage of cell-cell contacts, Par-3 contributes to the interaction of afadin with nectins, facilitating AJ formation. However, this is not sufficient for the formation of AJs and TJs because overexpression of afadin in Par-3-knockdown MDCK cells results in the assembly of afadin at nectin-based cell-cell adhesion sites but does not induce AJ or TJ formation, indicating cooperative roles for Par-3 and afadin. Taken together, these findings suggest that the nectin-afadin system is essential for the entire formation process of cell-cell junctions, including the formation of AJs and TJs and the regulation of cell polarization.

DEVELOPMENT AND CELL DIFFERENTIATION

During the early stages of mouse development, nectin-1, -2, -3, and afadin are equally concentrated at AJs of homotypic columnar epithelia, such as neuroepithelia and epithelial somites. These nectin and afadin molecules are highly expressed during epithelial remodeling in the mouse embryo (Okabe et al. 2004a). In vivo studies have clearly demonstrated the importance of nectins for the maintenance of various kinds of cell-cell adhesion and many cellular functions, including cell differentiation. All lines of nectin-null mice show drastic phenotypes at specific sites, such as Sertoli cell–spermatid junctions and the apex-apex junctions between the pigment and nonpigment cell layers of the ciliary epithelia, in which the functional redundancy of nectins is not available (Inagaki et al. 2005, 2006; Ozaki-Kuroda et al. 2002). However, all nectin-null mice are viable and show relatively moderate phenotypes, not life-threatening disorders. This may depend on the functional redundancy of nectins in nectin-null mice. In contrast to nectin-null mice, afadin-knockout mice show embryonic lethality because there is no redundancy in the function of afadin (Ikeda et al. 1999). The disruption of afadin in mice causes disorganization of the ectoderm, impaired migration of the mesoderm, and loss of somites and other structures derived from the ectoderm and the mesoderm at stages during and after gastrulation. Moreover, cell-cell junctions, including AJs and TJs, are improperly achieved, and loss of cell polarization is observed in the ectoderm of afadin$^{-/-}$ embryos and embryonic bodies (Ikeda et al. 1999, Komura et al. 2008). These impairments mainly result from the loss of the activities of afadin in the formation of cell-cell junctions, cell movement, and cell differentiation.

Human, as well as mouse, epidermis expresses nectin-1 at cell-cell junctions, at which nectin-1 colocalizes with E-cadherin (Matsushima et al. 2003, Wakamatsu et al. 2007). In humans, the expression of nectin-1 at cell-cell junctions is reduced in human epithelial cancer cells located at the advancing border of the tumor, leading to a loss of cell-cell junctions and facilitating the invasion of cancer cells into the neighboring tissue. Conversely, mutations in human nectin-1 are responsible for cleft lip/palate-ectodermal dysplasia, which includes Zlotogora-Ogur syndrome and Margarita Island ectodermal dysplasia (Sozen et al. 2001; Suzuki et al. 1998, 2000), autosomal recessive disorders that are clinically characterized by unusual faces, dental anomalies, hypotrichosis, palmoplantar hyperkeratosis and onychodysplasia, syndactyly, cleft lip/palate, and, in some cases, mental retardation. In mice, newborn nectin-1$^{-/-}$ pups show a shiny and slightly reddish skin owing to the reduced amount of loricrin, a differentiation marker and a major component of corni-

fied cell envelopes in the epidermis (Wakamatsu et al. 2007). A Ca^{2+}-induced differentiation assay using primary keratinocytes from nectin-1$^{-/-}$ mice showed the impaired phosphorylation of ERK mediated by Rap1 activation compared with keratinocytes from wild-type mice, resulting in the reduced expression of loricrin. Transcription of the *loricrin* gene is regulated by binding of protein factors to an AP-1 consensus site in the loricrin proximal promoter sequence (DiSepio et al. 1995). Because ERK is an activator of AP-1 transcription factors, the reduction in ERK phosphorylation in nectin-1-null keratinocytes seems to cause the downregulation of loricrin expression, suggesting the aberrant differentiation in the epidermis of nectin-1$^{-/-}$ mice.

COMMON REGULATORY MECHANISMS IN CELL MOVEMENT AND ADHESION

Individually moving and proliferating cells first form primordial cell-cell contacts through collision. Mature cell-cell junctions in epithelial cells then form with specialized cell-cell junction complexes, such as AJs and TJs, and with apico-basal cell polarization at cell-cell adhesion sites. After the formation of mature cell-cell junctions, cells cease movement and proliferation. This process is called mesenchymal-epithelial transition (MET). In contrast, under certain physiological and pathological conditions (such as embryonic development and cancer progression), disruption of cell-cell junctions preferentially occurs. Cells lose their connection to neighboring cells and become free, which increases migration and proliferation. This phenomenon is called epithelial-mesenchymal transition (EMT). The dynamic regulation between MET and EMT is crucial for the survival of multicellular organisms. The same components of cell adhesion and signaling systems are often utilized in this regulation. The same molecules used in the regulation of the cellular structures, such as leading edges, cell-matrix junctions,

MET: mesenchymal-epithelial transition

EMT: epithelial-mesenchymal transition

and cell-cell junctions, are often seamlessly reutilized in the formation of these cellular structures.

For instance, integrin $\alpha_v\beta_3$ and PDGF receptor play key roles in both cell movement and proliferation when cells migrate individually. These cell surface molecules are crucial during and even after the formation of cell-cell junctions. Nectin-3 physically and functionally associates with PDGF receptor at cell-cell adhesion sites, contributing to cell survival following the establishment of cell-cell junctions, as described above. Integrin $\alpha_v\beta_3$ and nectins function in a cooperative manner in AJ formation. Although the role of integrin $\alpha_v\beta_3$ after the formation of cell-cell junctions is not clear, two possible roles are conceivable. (*a*) Because cell-cell junctions are dynamically reconstructed and exhibit cyclical formation/disruption after the formation of cell-cell junctions, integrin $\alpha_v\beta_3$ activated immediately after the disruption of cell-cell junctions may support the reformation of cell-cell junctions by enhancing nectin-mediated signaling. (*b*) Integrin $\alpha_v\beta_3$ may be involved in hepatocyte growth factor–induced cell scattering cooperatively with the hepatocyte growth factor receptor c-Met, which localizes at AJs. The signaling molecules associated with nectins and involved in the formation of cell-cell junctions mostly overlap with those associated with integrin $\alpha_v\beta_3$, which are involved in movement, as described above. Afadin, which directly interacts with nectins at AJs, also localizes at the leading edge of moving cells and regulates the formation of leading-edge structures (H. Ogita & Y. Takai, unpublished observations). Afadin may help Necl-5 recruit nectin-3 for their *trans*-interaction upon cell collision. It also helps nectin-3 recruit nectin-1 for their *trans*-interaction. Thus, afadin may play crucial roles in both MET and EMT.

CONCLUSIONS AND PERSPECTIVES

Above we describe the properties, functions, and modes of action of nectins and afadin and their involvement in diseases. Nectins and afadin play critical roles in cell-cell adhesion cooperatively with, or independently of, cadherins in a variety of cell-cell junctions. They play particularly important roles in cell-cell junctions that are not stiff or strong but are dynamic and require remodeling. In addition, they regulate many other cellular activities, such as movement, proliferation, survival, differentiation, polarization, and the entry of viruses, in cooperation with other CAMs and cell surface membrane receptors. However, because our knowledge of the cellular functions of these molecules has been restricted by the use of a limited number of cell lines, further studies are necessary for generalization in and application to other cell types. Many issues concerning the functions and modes of action of nectins and afadin still remain elusive: for instance, how nectins and afadin form TJs at the apical side of AJs in epithelial cells and how they are involved in axon elongation, axon attachment to dendrites, synapse formation, and the cessation of axon elongation. If nectin and afadin are involved in the cessation of axon elongation, how are synapses actively remodeled, particularly in the CA3 region of the hippocampus? If nectins and afadin are involved in this remodeling, what is their role? Necls other than Necl-5 are currently under extensive investigation. Necl-1, -2, -3, and -4 play important roles not only in interepithelial cell adhesion but also in the adhesion between neurons and glia cells and between Sertoli cells and spermatids. In addition, investigators have focused on other Ig-like molecules with one or two Ig-like loops, such as CD96/Tactile, CD226/DNAM-1, and CRTAM, which function as receptors for the recognition of target cells in cytotoxic T lymphocyte and natural killer cells. The regulation of diverse and complicated biological functions is integrated by many CAMs, receptors, signaling molecules, and cytoskeletal molecules. The mechanism underlying such integration is one of the important issues to be elucidated in the future.

SUMMARY POINTS

1. The nectin-afadin complex that localizes at AJs plays a critical role in the formation of not only cadherin-based AJs but also claudin-based TJs in epithelial cells.

2. The activation of integrin $\alpha_v\beta_3$ and its downstream signaling molecules is necessary for the nectin-induced formation of AJs, indicating the existence of cross talk between cell-cell and cell-matrix junctions.

3. The nectin-afadin complex is involved in many cellular functions, including cell survival, differentiation, and polarization, as well as cell adhesion.

4. Necl-5 significantly promotes cell movement and proliferation in cooperation with PDGF receptor and integrin $\alpha_v\beta_3$; in turn, Necl-5 is downregulated from the cell surface after the establishment of cell-cell junctions to cease cell movement and proliferation, indicating its primary involvement in the contact inhibition of cell movement and proliferation.

5. Studies using afadin-knockout and nectin-knockout mice have revealed that the nectin-afadin system is essential for the embryonic development and maintenance of many organs.

6. Cell adhesion and signaling systems are often utilized for cell movement, suggesting the possible involvement of the nectin-afadin system in both EMT and MET.

FUTURE ISSUES

1. It remains to be elucidated how nectins and afadin participate in the positioning of TJs, which are formed at the apical side of AJs, during the formation of cell-cell junctions.

2. Studies on the roles of the nectin-afadin system in the formation and remodeling of synapses are important.

3. Extensive investigation of Necls other than Necl-5 will provide new insight into the mechanisms underlying adhesions in several tissues, such as the nervous system and the testis.

DISCLOSURE STATEMENT

The authors are not aware of any biases that might be perceived as affecting the objectivity of this review.

ACKNOWLEDGMENTS

The work presented in this review article began at ERATO (Exploratory Research for Advanced Technology of Japan, 1994–1999) and was subsequently performed at the Department of Molecular Biology and Biochemistry, Osaka University Graduate School of Medicine and Faculty of Medicine, Suita, Japan, with the support of grants-in-aid for Scientific Research and for Cancer Research from the Ministry of Education, Culture, Sports, Science and Technology, Japan (2000–2008). Many faculty members, including Drs. H. Nakanishi (Kumamoto University,

Kumamoto, Japan), J. Miyoshi (Osaka Medical Center for Cancer and Cardiovascular Diseases, Osaka, Japan), K. Mandai (Johns Hopkins University, Maryland), T. Matozaki (Gunma University, Gunma, Japan), K. Shimizu (Kobe Medical Center, Kobe, Japan), K. Irie (University of Tsukuba, Ibaraki, Japan), T. Sakisaka (Kobe University, Kobe, Japan), and N. Fujita (Kumamoto University, Kumamoto, Japan); many graduate students; postdoctoral fellows; and collaborators made great contributions to this work. We thank them for their excellent achievements.

LITERATURE CITED

Abercrombie M. 1970. Contact inhibition in tissue culture. *In Vitro* 6:128–42

Abercrombie M. 1979. Contact inhibition and malignancy. *Nature* 281:259–62

Abercrombie M, Ambrose EJ. 1962. The surface properties of cancer cells: a review. *Cancer Res.* 22:525–48

Abercrombie M, Heaysman JE. 1953. Observations on the social behaviour of cells in tissue culture. I. Speed of movement of chick heart fibroblasts in relation to their mutual contacts. *Exp. Cell Res.* 5:111–31

Abercrombie M, Heaysman JE. 1954. Observations on the social behaviour of cells in tissue culture. II. Monolayering of fibroblasts. *Exp. Cell Res.* 6:293–306

Amaral DG, Dent JA. 1981. Development of the mossy fibers of the dentate gyrus. I. A light and electron microscopic study of the mossy fibers and their expansions. *J. Comp. Neurol.* 195:51–86

Anastasiadis PZ, Reynolds AB. 2000. The p120 catenin family: complex roles in adhesion, signaling and cancer. *J. Cell Sci.* 113:1319–34

Aoki J, Koike S, Asou H, Ise I, Suwa H, et al. 1997. Mouse homolog of poliovirus receptor-related gene 2 product, mPRR2, mediates homophilic cell aggregation. *Exp. Cell Res.* 235:374–84

Asada M, Irie K, Morimoto K, Yamada A, Ikeda W, et al. 2003. ADIP, a novel afadin- and α-actinin-binding protein localized at cell-cell adherens junctions. *J. Biol. Chem.* 278:4103–11

Balda MS, Gonzalez-Mariscal L, Matter K, Cereijido M, Anderson JM. 1993. Assembly of the tight junction: the role of diacylglycerol. *J. Cell Biol.* 123:293–302

Ballestrem C, Hinz B, Imhof BA, Wehrle-Haller B. 2001. Marching at the front and dragging behind: Differential $\alpha_V\beta_3$-integrin turnover regulates focal adhesion behavior. *J. Cell Biol.* 155:1319–32

Bell PB Jr. 1978. Contact inhibition of movements in transformed and nontransformed cells. *Birth Defects Orig. Artic. Ser.* 14:177–94

Boettner B, Govek EE, Cross J, Van Aelst L. 2000. The junctional multidomain protein AF-6 is a binding partner of the Rap1A GTPase and associates with the actin cytoskeletal regulator profilin. *Proc. Natl. Acad. Sci. USA* 97:9064–69

Bottino C, Castriconi R, Pende D, Rivera P, Nanni M, et al. 2003. Identification of PVR (CD155) and Nectin-2 (CD112) as cell surface ligands for the human DNAM-1 (CD226) activating molecule. *J. Exp. Med.* 198:557–67

Buchert M, Schneider S, Meskenaite V, Adams MT, Canaani E, et al. 1999. The junction-associated protein AF-6 interacts and clusters with specific Eph receptor tyrosine kinases at specialized sites of cell-cell contact in the brain. *J. Cell Biol.* 144:361–71

Calderwood DA. 2004. Integrin activation. *J. Cell Sci.* 117:657–66

Capaldo CT, Macara IG. 2007. Depletion of E-cadherin disrupts establishment but not maintenance of cell junctions in Madin-Darby canine kidney epithelial cells. *Mol. Biol. Cell* 18:189–200

Chadeneau C, LeMoullac B, Denis MG. 1994. A novel member of the immunoglobulin gene superfamily expressed in rat carcinoma cell lines. *J. Biol. Chem.* 269:15601–5

Cheng CY, Mruk DD. 2002. Cell junction dynamics in the testis: Sertoli-germ cell interactions and male contraceptive development. *Physiol. Rev.* 82:825–74

Christofori G. 2003. Split personalities: the agonistic antagonist Sprouty. *Nat. Cell Biol.* 5:377–79

Comoglio PM, Boccaccio C, Trusolino L. 2003. Interactions between growth factor receptors and adhesion molecules: breaking the rules. *Curr. Opin. Cell Biol.* 15:565–71

DiSepio D, Jones A, Longley MA, Bundman D, Rothnagel JA, Roop DR. 1995. The proximal promoter of the mouse loricrin gene contains a functional AP-1 element and directs keratinocyte-specific but not differentiation-specific expression. *J. Biol. Chem.* 270:10792–99

Dunn GA, Ireland GW. 1984. New evidence that growth in 3T3 cell cultures is a diffusion-limited process. *Nature* 312:63–65

Eberlé F, Dubreuil P, Mattei MG, Devilard E, Lopez M. 1995. The human *PRR2* gene, related to the human poliovirus receptor gene (*PVR*), is the true homolog of the murine *MPH* gene. *Gene* 159:267–72

Ehrlich JS, Hansen MDH, Nelson WJ. 2002. Spatio-temporal regulation of Rac1 localization and lamellipodia dynamics during epithelial cell-cell adhesion. *Dev. Cell* 3:259–70

Farquhar MG, Palade GE. 1963. Junctional complexes in various epithelia. *J. Cell Biol.* 17:375–409

Fisher HW, Yeh J. 1967. Contact inhibition in colony formation. *Science* 155:581–82

Fujito T, Ikeda W, Kakunaga S, Minami Y, Kajita M, et al. 2005. Inhibition of cell movement and proliferation by cell-cell contact-induced interaction of Necl-5 with nectin-3. *J. Cell Biol.* 171:165–73

Fukuhara A, Irie K, Nakanishi H, Takekuni K, Kawakatsu T, et al. 2002a. Involvement of nectin in the localization of junctional adhesion molecule at tight junctions. *Oncogene* 21:7642–55

Fukuhara A, Irie K, Yamada A, Katata T, Honda T, et al. 2002b. Role of nectin in organization of tight junctions in epithelial cells. *Genes Cells* 7:1059–72

Fukuhara A, Shimizu K, Kawakatsu T, Fukuhara T, Takai Y. 2003. Involvement of nectin-activated Cdc42 small G protein in organization of adherens and tight junctions in Madin-Darby canine kidney cells. *J. Biol. Chem.* 278:51885–93

Fukuhara T, Shimizu K, Kawakatsu T, Fukuyama T, Minami Y, et al. 2004. Activation of Cdc42 by *trans* interactions of the cell adhesion molecules nectins through c-Src and Cdc42-GEF FRG. *J. Cell Biol.* 166:393–405

Fukuyama T, Ogita H, Kawakatsu T, Fukuhara T, Yamada T, et al. 2005. Involvement of the c-Src-Crk-C3G-Rap1 signaling in the nectin-induced activation of Cdc42 and formation of adherens junctions. *J. Biol. Chem.* 280:815–25

Fukuyama T, Ogita H, Kawakatsu T, Inagaki M, Takai Y. 2006. Activation of Rac by cadherin through the c-Src-Rap1-phosphatidylinositol 3-kinase-Vav2 pathway. *Oncogene* 25:8–19

Geiger B, Bershadsky A, Pankov R, Yamada KM. 2001. Transmembrane crosstalk between the extracellular matrix–cytoskeleton crosstalk. *Nat. Rev. Mol. Cell Biol.* 2:793–805

Geraghty RJ, Krummenacher C, Cohen GH, Eisenberg RJ, Spear PG. 1998. Entry of alphaherpesviruses mediated by poliovirus receptor-related protein 1 and poliovirus receptor. *Science* 280:1618–20

Gromeier M, Lachmann S, Rosenfeld MR, Gutin PH, Wimmer E. 2000. Intergeneric poliovirus recombinants for the treatment of malignant glioma. *Proc. Natl. Acad. Sci. USA* 97:6803–8

Gumbiner B, Stevenson B, Grimaldi A. 1988. The role of the cell adhesion molecule uvomorulin in the formation and maintenance of the epithelial junctional complex. *J. Cell Biol.* 107:1575–87

Guttman JA, Takai Y, Vogl AW. 2004. Evidence that tubulobulbar complexes in the seminiferous epithelium are involved with internalization of adhesion junctions. *Biol. Reprod.* 71:548–59

Hacohen N, Kramer S, Sutherland D, Hiromi Y, Krasnow MA. 1998. Sprouty encodes a novel antagonist of FGF signaling that patterns apical branching of the *Drosophila* airways. *Cell* 92:253–63

Hall A. 1998. Rho GTPases and the actin cytoskeleton. *Science* 279:509–14

Harris TJ, Peifer M. 2004. Adherens junction-dependent and -independent steps in the establishment of epithelial cell polarity in *Drosophila*. *J. Cell Biol.* 167:135–47

Hirota T, Irie K, Okamoto R, Ikeda W, Takai Y. 2005. Transcriptional activation of the mouse Necl-5/Tage4/PVR/CD155 gene by fibroblast growth factor or oncogenic Ras through the Raf-MEK-ERK-AP-1 pathway. *Oncogene* 24:2229–35

Hock B, Bohme B, Karn T, Yamamoto T, Kaibuchi K, et al. 1998. PDZ-domain-mediated interaction of the Eph-related receptor tyrosine kinase EphB3 and the ras-binding protein AF6 depends on the kinase activity of the receptor. *Proc. Natl. Acad. Sci. USA* 95:9779–84

Honda T, Sakisaka T, Yamada T, Kumazawa N, Hoshino T, et al. 2006. Involvement of nectins in the formation of puncta adherentia junctions and the mossy fiber trajectory in the mouse hippocampus. *Mol. Cell Neurosci.* 31:315–25

Hood JD, Cheresh DA. 2002. Role of integrins in cell invasion and migration. *Nat. Rev. Cancer* 2:91–100

Hoshino T, Sakisaka T, Baba T, Yamada T, Kimura T, Takai Y. 2005. Regulation of E-cadherin endocytosis by nectin through afadin, Rap1, and p120^{ctn}. *J. Biol. Chem.* 280:24095–103

Provides the critical implication of Necl-5 in the regulation of contact inhibition of cell movement and proliferation.

Huttenlocher A, Lakonishok M, Kinder M, Wu S, Truong T, et al. 1998. Integrin and cadherin synergy regulates contact inhibition of migration and motile activity. *J. Cell Biol.* 141:515–26

Ikeda W, Kakunaga S, Itoh S, Shingai T, Takekuni K, et al. 2003. Tage4/nectin-like molecule-5 heterophilically *trans*-interacts with cell adhesion molecule nectin-3 and enhances cell migration. *J. Biol. Chem.* 278:28167–72

Ikeda W, Kakunaga S, Takekuni K, Shingai T, Satoh K, et al. 2004. Nectin-like molecule-5/Tage4 enhances cell migration in an integrin-dependent, nectin-3-independent manner. *J. Biol. Chem.* 279:18015–25

Ikeda W, Nakanishi H, Miyoshi J, Mandai K, Ishizaki H, et al. 1999. Afadin: a key molecule essential for structural organization of cell-cell junctions of polarized epithelia during embryogenesis. *J. Cell Biol.* 146:1117–32

Inagaki M, Irie K, Ishizaki H, Tanaka-Okamoto M, Miyoshi J, Takai Y. 2006. Role of cell adhesion molecule nectin-3 in spermatid development. *Genes Cells* 11:1125–32

Inagaki M, Irie K, Ishizaki H, Tanaka-Okamoto M, Morimoto K, et al. 2005. Roles of cell-adhesion molecules nectin 1 and nectin 3 in ciliary body development. *Development* 132:1525–37

Izumi G, Sakisaka T, Baba T, Tanaka S, Morimoto K, Takai Y. 2004. Endocytosis of E-cadherin regulated by Rac and Cdc42 small G proteins through IQGAP1 and actin filaments. *J. Cell Biol.* 166:237–48

Kajita M, Ikeda W, Tamaru Y, Takai Y. 2007. Regulation of platelet-derived growth factor-induced Ras signaling by poliovirus receptor Necl-5 and negative growth regulator Sprouty2. *Genes Cells* 12:345–57

Kakunaga S, Ikeda W, Itoh S, Deguchi-Tawarada M, Ohtsuka T, et al. 2005. Nectin-like molecule-1/TSLL1/SynCAM3: a neural tissue-specific immunoglobulin-like cell-cell adhesion molecule localizing at nonjunctional contact sites of presynaptic nerve terminals, axons, and glia cell processes. *J. Cell Sci.* 118:1267–77

Kakunaga S, Ikeda W, Shingai T, Fujito T, Yamada A, et al. 2004. Enhancement of serum- and platelet-derived growth factor-induced cell proliferation by Necl-5/Tage4/poliovirus receptor/CD155 through the Ras-Raf-MEK-ERK signaling. *J. Biol. Chem.* 279:36419–25

Kanzaki N, Ogita H, Komura H, Ozaki H, Sakamoto Y, et al. 2008. Involvement of the nectin-afadin complex in platelet-derived growth factor-induced cell survival. *J. Cell Sci.* 121:2008–17

Katata T, Irie K, Fukuhara A, Kawakatsu T, Yamada A, et al. 2003. Involvement of nectin in the localization of IQGAP1 at the cell-cell adhesion sites through the actin cytoskeleton in Madin-Darby canine kidney cells. *Oncogene* 22:2097–109

Kawakatsu T, Ogita H, Fukuhara T, Fukuyama T, Minami Y, et al. 2005. Vav2 as a Rac-GEF responsible for the nectin-induced, c-Src- and Cdc42-mediated activation of Rac. *J. Biol. Chem.* 280:4940–47

Kim HJ, Bar-Sagi D. 2004. Modulation of signalling by Sprouty: a developing story. *Nat. Rev. Mol. Cell Biol.* 5:441–50

Koch AW, Pokutta S, Lustig A, Engel J. 1997. Calcium binding and homoassociation of E-cadherin domains. *Biochemistry* 36:7697–705

Komura H, Ogita H, Ikeda W, Mizoguchi A, Miyoshi J, Takai Y. 2008. Establishment of cell polarity by afadin during the formation of embryoid bodies. *Genes Cells* 13:79–90

Kovacs EM, Ali RG, McCormack AJ, Yap AS. 2002. E-cadherin homophilic ligation directly signals through Rac and phosphatidylinositol 3-kinase to regulate adhesive contacts. *J. Biol. Chem.* 277:6708–18

Linnemann T, Geyer M, Jaitner BK, Block C, Kalbitzer HR, et al. 1999. Thermodynamic and kinetic characterization of the interaction between the Ras binding domain of AF6 and members of the Ras subfamily. *J. Biol. Chem.* 274:13556–62

Lopez M, Eberlé F, Mattei MG, Gabert J, Birg F, et al. 1995. Complementary DNA characterization and chromosomal localization of a human gene related to the poliovirus receptor-encoding gene. *Gene* 155:261–65

Mandai K, Nakanishi H, Satoh A, Obaishi H, Wada M, et al. 1997. Afadin: a novel actin filament-binding protein with one PDZ domain localized at cadherin-based cell-to-cell adherens junction. *J. Cell Biol.* 139:517–28

Mandai K, Nakanishi H, Satoh A, Takahashi K, Satoh K, et al. 1999. Ponsin/SH3P12: an l-afadin- and vinculin-binding protein localized at cell-cell and cell-matrix adherens junctions. *J. Cell Biol.* 144:1001–17

Martel V, Racaud-Sultan C, Dupe S, Marie C, Paulhe F, et al. 2001. Conformation, localization, and integrin binding of talin depend on its interaction with phosphoinositides. *J. Biol. Chem.* 276:21217–27

Martz E, Steinberg MS. 1972. The role of cell-cell contact in "contact" inhibition of cell division: a review and new evidence. *J. Cell Physiol.* 79:189–210

Masson D, Jarry A, Baury B, Blanchardie P, Laboisse C, et al. 2001. Overexpression of the *CD155* gene in human colorectal carcinoma. *Gut* 49:236–40

Matsushima H, Utani A, Endo H, Matsuura H, Kakuta M, et al. 2003. The expression of nectin-1α in normal human skin and various skin tumours. *Br. J. Dermatol.* 148:755–62

Mimori-Kiyosue Y, Tsukita S. 2003. "Search-and-capture" of microtubules through plus-end-binding proteins (+TIPs). *J. Biochem.* 134:321–26

Minami Y, Ikeda W, Kajita M, Fujito T, Amano H, et al. 2007a. Necl-5/poliovirus receptor interacts in *cis* with integrin $\alpha_v\beta_3$ and regulates its clustering and focal complex formation. *J. Biol. Chem.* 282:18481–96

Minami Y, Ikeda W, Kajita M, Fujito T, Monden M, Takai Y. 2007b. Involvement of up-regulated Necl-5/Tage4/PVR/CD155 in the loss of contact inhibition in transformed NIH3T3 cells. *Biochem. Biophys. Res. Commun.* 352:856–60

Miyahara M, Nakanishi H, Takahashi K, Satoh-Horikawa K, Tachibana K, Takai Y. 2000. Interaction of nectin with afadin is necessary for its clustering at cell-cell contact sites but not for its *cis* dimerization or *trans* interaction. *J. Biol. Chem.* 275:613–18

Mizoguchi A, Nakanishi H, Kimura K, Matsubara K, Ozaki-Kuroda K, et al. 2002. Nectin: an adhesion molecule involved in formation of synapses. *J. Cell Biol.* 156:555–65

Momose Y, Honda T, Inagaki M, Shimizu K, Irie K, et al. 2002. Role of the second immunoglobulin-like loop of nectin in cell-cell adhesion. *Biochem. Biophys. Res. Commun.* 293:45–49

Morgan DO. 1995. Principles of CDK regulation. *Nature* 374:131–34

Morrison ME, Racaniello VR. 1992. Molecular cloning and expression of a murine homolog of the human poliovirus receptor gene. *J. Virol.* 66:2807–13

Mueller S, Cao X, Welker R, Wimmer E. 2002. Interaction of the poliovirus receptor CD155 with the dynein light chain Tctex-1 and its implication for poliovirus pathogenesis. *J. Biol. Chem.* 277:7897–904

Mueller S, Rosenquist TA, Takai Y, Bronson RA, Wimmer E. 2003. Loss of nectin-2 at Sertoli-spermatid junctions leads to male infertility and correlates with severe spermatozoan head and midpiece malformation, impaired binding to the zona pellucida, and oocyte penetration. *Biol. Reprod.* 69:1330–40

Nagamatsu Y, Rikitake Y, Takahashi M, Deki Y, Ikeda W, et al. 2008. Roles of Necl-5/Poliovirus receptor and ROCK in the regulation of transformation of integrin $\alpha_v\beta_3$-based focal complexes into focal adhesions. *J. Biol. Chem.* 283:14532–41

Nakagawa M, Fukata M, Yamaga M, Itoh N, Kaibuchi K. 2001. Recruitment and activation of Rac1 by the formation of E-cadherin-mediated cell-cell adhesion sites. *J. Cell Sci.* 114:1829–38

Nakata S, Fujita N, Kitagawa Y, Okamoto R, Ogita H, Takai Y. 2007. Regulation of PDGF receptor activation by afadin through SHP-2: implications for cellular morphology. *J. Biol. Chem.* 282:37815–25

Nelson WJ. 2003. Adaptation of core mechanisms to generate cell polarity. *Nature* 422:766–74

Ohka S, Matsuda N, Tohyama K, Oda T, Morikawa M, et al. 2004. Receptor (CD155)-dependent endocytosis of poliovirus and retrograde axonal transport of the endosome. *J. Virol.* 78:7186–98

Ohno S. 2001. Intercellular junctions and cellular polarity: the PAR-aPKC complex, a conserved core cassette playing fundamental roles in cell polarity. *Curr. Opin. Cell Biol.* 13:641–48

Okabe N, Ozaki-Kuroda K, Nakanishi H, Shimizu K, Takai Y. 2004a. Expression patterns of nectins and afadin during epithelial remodeling in the mouse embryo. *Dev. Dyn.* 230:174–86

Okabe N, Shimizu K, Ozaki-Kuroda K, Nakanishi H, Morimoto K, et al. 2004b. Contacts between the commissural axons and the floor plate cells are mediated by nectins. *Dev. Biol.* 273:244–56

Okamoto R, Irie K, Yamada A, Katata T, Fukuhara A, Takai Y. 2005. Recruitment of E-cadherin associated with α- and β-catenins and p120[ctn] to the nectin-based cell-cell adhesion sites by the action of 12-*O*-tetradecanoylphorbol-13-acetate in MDCK cells. *Genes Cells* 10:435–45

Ooshio T, Fujita N, Yamada A, Sato T, Kitagawa Y, et al. 2007. Cooperative roles of Par-3 and afadin in the formation of adherens and tight junctions. *J. Cell Sci.* 120:2352–65

Ooshio T, Irie K, Morimoto K, Fukuhara A, Imai T, Takai Y. 2004. Involvement of LMO7 in the association of two cell-cell adhesion molecules, nectin and E-cadherin, through afadin and α-actinin in epithelial cells. *J. Biol. Chem.* 279:31365–73

Indicates the importance of Necl-5's association with integrin $\alpha_v\beta_3$ for the formation of leading edges and cell movement.

Clearly proposes the novel role of afadin during the formation of not only AJs but also TJs.

Ozaki M, Ogita H, Takai Y. 2007. Involvement of integrin-induced activation of protein kinase C in the formation of adherens junctions. *Genes Cells* 12:651–62

Ozaki-Kuroda K, Nakanishi H, Ohta H, Tanaka H, Kurihara H, et al. 2002. Nectin couples cell-cell adhesion and the actin scaffold at heterotypic testicular junctions. *Curr. Biol.* 12:1145–50

Parsons JT. 2003. Focal adhesion kinase: the first ten years. *J. Cell Sci.* 116:1409–16

Perez F, Diamantopoulos GS, Stalder R, Kreis TE. 1999. CLIP-170 highlights growing microtubule ends in vivo. *Cell* 96:517–27

Perez-Moreno M, Jamora C, Fuchs E. 2003. Sticky business: orchestrating cellular signals at adherens junctions. *Cell* 112:535–48

Pignatelli M. 1998. Integrins, cadherins, and catenins: molecular cross-talk in cancer cells. *J. Pathol.* 186:1–2

Pokutta S, Drees F, Takai Y, Nelson WJ, Weis WI. 2002. Biochemical and structural definition of the l-afadin- and actin-binding sites of α-catenin. *J. Biol. Chem.* 277:18868–74

Prasad R, Gu Y, Alder H, Nakamura T, Canaani O, et al. 1993. Cloning of the *ALL-1* fusion partner, the *AF-6* gene, involved in acute myeloid leukemias with the t(6;11) chromosome translocation. *Cancer Res.* 53:5624–28

Radziwill G, Erdmann RA, Margelisch U, Moelling K. 2003. The Bcr kinase downregulates Ras signaling by phosphorylating AF-6 and binding to its PDZ domain. *Mol. Cell Biol.* 23:4663–72

Radziwill G, Weiss A, Heinrich J, Baumgartner M, Boisguerin P, et al. 2007. Regulation of c-Src by binding to the PDZ domain of AF-6. *EMBO J.* 26:2633–44

Reymond N, Fabre S, Lecocq E, Adelaide J, Dubreuil P, Lopez M. 2001. Nectin4/PRR4, a new afadin-associated member of the nectin family that *trans*-interacts with nectin1/PRR1 through V domain interaction. *J. Biol. Chem.* 276:43205–15

Roh MH, Margolis B. 2003. Composition and function of PDZ protein complexes during cell polarization. *Am. J. Physiol. Renal Physiol.* 285:F377–87

Ronnstrand L, Heldin CH. 2001. Mechanisms of platelet-derived growth factor-induced chemotaxis. *Int. J. Cancer* 91:757–62

Rottner K, Hall A, Small JV. 1999. Interplay between Rac and Rho in the control of substrate contact dynamics. *Curr. Biol.* 9:640–48

Russell L, Clermont Y. 1976. Anchoring device between Sertoli cells and late spermatids in rat seminiferous tubules. *Anat. Rec.* 185:259–78

Saito S, Matsushima M, Shirahama S, Minaguchi T, Kanamori Y, et al. 1998. Complete genomic structure DNA polymorphisms, and alternative splicing of the human *AF-6* gene. *DNA Res.* 5:115–20

Sakamoto Y, Ogita H, Hirota T, Kawakatsu T, Fukuyama T, et al. 2006. Interaction of integrin $\alpha_v\beta_3$ with nectin: implication in cross-talk between cell-matrix and cell-cell junctions. *J. Biol. Chem.* 281:19631–44

Sakamoto Y, Ogita H, Komura H, Takai Y. 2008. Involvement of nectin in inactivation of integrin $\alpha_v\beta_3$ after the establishment of cell-cell adhesion. *J. Biol. Chem.* 283:496–505

Sato T, Fujita N, Yamada A, Ooshio T, Okamoto R, et al. 2006. Regulation of the assembly and adhesion activity of E-cadherin by nectin and afadin for the formation of adherens junctions in Madin-Darby canine kidney cells. *J. Biol. Chem.* 281:5288–99

Sato T, Irie K, Okamoto R, Ooshio T, Fujita N, Takai Y. 2005. Common signaling pathway is used by the *trans*-interaction of Necl-5/Tage4/PVR/CD155 and nectin, and of nectin and nectin during the formation of cell-cell adhesion. *Cancer Sci.* 96:578–89

Satoh-Horikawa K, Nakanishi H, Takahashi K, Miyahara M, Nishimura M, et al. 2000. Nectin-3, a new member of immunoglobulin-like cell adhesion molecules that shows homophilic and heterophilic cell-cell adhesion activities. *J. Biol. Chem.* 275:10291–99

Seth S, Maier MK, Qiu Q, Ravens I, Kremmer E, et al. 2007. The murine pan T cell marker CD96 is an adhesion receptor for CD155 and nectin-1. *Biochem. Biophys. Res. Commun.* 364:959–65

Sherr CJ. 1996. Cancer cell cycles. *Science* 274:1672–77

Shingai T, Ikeda W, Kakunaga S, Morimoto K, Takekuni K, et al. 2003. Implications of nectin-like molecule-2/IGSF4/RA175/SgIGSF/TSLC1/SynCAM1 in cell-cell adhesion and transmembrane protein localization in epithelial cells. *J. Biol. Chem.* 278:35421–27

Proposes the significance of nectin and integrin $\alpha_v\beta_3$ in cross talk between cell-matrix and cell-cell junctions during AJ formation.

Siu MK, Cheng CY. 2004. Dynamic cross-talk between cells and the extracellular matrix in the testis. *Bioessays* 26:978–92

Sozen MA, Suzuki K, Tolarova MM, Bustos T, Fernandez Iglesias JE, Spritz RA. 2001. Mutation of PVRL1 is associated with sporadic, nonsyndromic cleft lip/palate in northern Venezuela. *Nat. Genet.* 29:141–42

Spacek J, Lieberman AR. 1974. Ultrastructure and three-dimensional organization of synaptic glomeruli in rat somatosensory thalamus. *J. Anat.* 117:487–516

Stoeckli ET, Landmesser LT. 1998. Axon guidance at choice points. *Curr. Opin. Neurobiol.* 8:73–79

Stoker MG, Rubin H. 1967. Density dependent inhibition of cell growth in culture. *Nature* 215:171–72

Su L, Hattori M, Moriyama M, Murata N, Harazaki M, et al. 2003. AF-6 controls integrin-mediated cell adhesion by regulating Rap1 activation through the specific recruitment of Rap1GTP and SPA-1. *J. Biol. Chem.* 278:15232–38

Suzuki K, Bustos T, Spritz RA. 1998. Linkage disequilibrium mapping of the gene for Margarita Island ectodermal dysplasia (ED4) to 11q23. *Am. J. Hum. Genet.* 63:1102–7

Suzuki K, Hu D, Bustos T, Zlotogora J, Richieri-Costa A, et al. 2000. Mutations of PVRL1, encoding a cell-cell adhesion molecule/herpesvirus receptor, in cleft lip/palate-ectodermal dysplasia. *Nat. Genet.* 25:427–30

Tachibana K, Nakanishi H, Mandai K, Ozaki K, Ikeda W, et al. 2000. Two cell adhesion molecules, nectin and cadherin, interact through their cytoplasmic domain-associated proteins. *J. Cell Biol.* 150:1161–76

Tadokoro S, Shattil SJ, Eto K, Tai V, Liddington RC, et al. 2003. Talin binding to integrin β tails: a final common step in integrin activation. *Science* 302:103–6

Takagi J, Petre BM, Walz T, Springer TA. 2002. Global conformational rearrangements in integrin extracellular domains in outside-in and inside-out signaling. *Cell* 110:599–611

Takahashi K, Nakanishi H, Miyahara M, Mandai K, Satoh K, et al. 1999. Nectin/PRR: an immunoglobulin-like cell adhesion molecule recruited to cadherin-based adherens junctions through interaction with afadin, a PDZ domain-containing protein. *J. Cell Biol.* 145:539–49

Takahashi M, Rikitake Y, Nagamatsu Y, Hara T, Ikeda W, et al. 2008. Sequential activation of Rap1 and Rac1 small G proteins by PDGF locally at leading edges of NIH3T3 cells. *Genes Cells* 13:549–69

Takai Y, Irie K, Shimizu K, Sakisaka T, Ikeda W. 2003. Nectins and nectin-like molecules: roles in cell adhesion, migration, and polarization. *Cancer Sci.* 94:655–67

Takeichi M. 1988. The cadherins: cell-cell adhesion molecules controlling animal morphogenesis. *Development* 102:639–55

Takeichi M. 1991. Cadherin cell adhesion receptors as a morphogenetic regulator. *Science* 251:1451–55

Takeichi M. 1995. Morphogenetic roles of classic cadherins. *Curr. Opin. Cell Biol.* 7:619–27

Takekuni K, Ikeda W, Fujito T, Morimoto K, Takeuchi M, et al. 2003. Direct binding of cell polarity protein PAR-3 to cell-cell adhesion molecule nectin at neuroepithelial cells of developing mouse. *J. Biol. Chem.* 278:5497–500

Taya S, Yamamoto T, Kano K, Kawano Y, Iwamatsu A, et al. 1998. The Ras target AF-6 is a substrate of the Fam deubiquitinating enzyme. *J. Cell Biol.* 142:1053–62

Thiery JP. 2002. Epithelial-mesenchymal transitions in tumour progression. *Nat. Rev. Cancer* 2:442–54

Togashi H, Miyoshi J, Honda T, Sakisaka T, Takai Y, Takeichi M. 2006. Interneurite affinity is regulated by heterophilic nectin interactions in concert with the cadherin machinery. *J. Cell Biol.* 174:141–51

Tsukasaki Y, Kitamura K, Shimizu K, Iwane AH, Takai Y, Yanagida T. 2007. Role of multiple bonds between the single cell adhesion molecules, nectin and cadherin, revealed by high sensitive force measurements. *J. Mol. Biol.* 367:996–1006

Tsukita S, Furuse M, Itoh M. 2001. Multifunctional strands in tight junctions. *Nat. Rev. Mol. Cell Biol.* 2:285–93

Uchida N, Honjo Y, Johnson KR, Wheelock MJ, Takeichi M. 1996. The catenin/cadherin adhesion system is localized in synaptic junctions bordering transmitter release zones. *J. Cell Biol.* 135:767–79

Uren A, Jakus J, de Mora JF, Yeudall A, Santos E, et al. 1997. Carboxyl-terminal domain of p27[Kip1] activates CDC2. *J. Biol. Chem.* 272:21669–72

van der Flier A, Sonnenberg A. 2001. Function and interactions of integrins. *Cell Tissue Res.* 305:285–98

Vasioukhin V, Bauer C, Yin M, Fuchs E. 2000. Directed actin polymerization is the driving force for epithelial cell-cell adhesion. *Cell* 100:209–19

Originally demonstrated the presence of an Ig-like CAM nectin that interacts with afadin at AJs.

Shows the direct binding of PAR-3 to nectin-1 and nectin-3 at AJs in neuroepithelial cells that lack TJs.

Wakamatsu K, Ogita H, Okabe N, Irie K, Tanaka-Okamoto M, et al. 2007. Up-regulation of loricrin expression by cell adhesion molecule nectin-1 through Rap1-ERK signaling in keratinocytes. *J. Biol. Chem.* 282:18173–81

Wang PL, O'Farrell S, Clayberger C, Krensky AM. 1992. Identification and molecular cloning of tactile: a novel human T cell activation antigen that is a member of the Ig gene superfamily. *J. Immunol.* 148:2600–8

Warner MS, Geraghty RJ, Martinez WM, Montgomery RI, Whitbeck JC, et al. 1998. A cell surface protein with herpesvirus entry activity (HveB) confers susceptibility to infection by mutants of herpes simplex virus type 1, herpes simplex virus type 2, and pseudorabies virus. *Virology* 246:179–89

Woodard AS, Garcia-Cardena G, Leong M, Madri JA, Sessa WC, Languino LR. 1998. The synergistic activity of $\alpha_v\beta_3$ integrin and PDGF receptor increases cell migration. *J. Cell Sci.* 111:469–78

Yagi T, Takeichi M. 2000. Cadherin superfamily genes: functions, genomic organization, and neurologic diversity. *Genes Dev.* 14:1169–80

Yamada A, Fujita N, Sato T, Okamoto R, Ooshio T, et al. 2006. Requirement of nectin, but not cadherin, for formation of claudin-based tight junctions in annexin II-knockdown MDCK cells. *Oncogene* 25:5085–102

Yamada A, Irie K, Fukuhara A, Ooshio T, Takai Y. 2004. Requirement of the actin cytoskeleton for the association of nectins with other cell adhesion molecules at adherens and tight junctions in MDCK cells. *Genes Cells* 9:843–55

Yamada A, Irie K, Hirota T, Ooshio T, Fukuhara A, Takai Y. 2005. Involvement of the annexin II-S100A10 complex in the formation of E-cadherin-based adherens junctions in Madin-Darby canine kidney cells. *J. Biol. Chem.* 280:6016–27

Yamamoto T, Harada N, Kano K, Taya S, Canaani E, et al. 1997. The Ras target AF-6 interacts with ZO-1 and serves as a peripheral component of tight junctions in epithelial cells. *J. Cell Biol.* 139:785–95

Yap AS, Kovacs EM. 2003. Direct cadherin-activated cell signaling: a view from the plasma membrane. *J. Cell Biol.* 160:11–16

Yasumi M, Shimizu K, Honda T, Takeuchi M, Takai Y. 2003. Role of each immunoglobulin-like loop of nectin for its cell-cell adhesion activity. *Biochem. Biophys. Res. Commun.* 302:61–66

Yonemura S, Itoh M, Nagafuchi A, Tsukita S. 1995. Cell-to-cell adherens junction formation and actin filament organization: similarities and differences between nonpolarized fibroblasts and polarized epithelial cells. *J. Cell Sci.* 108:127–42

Zaidel-Bar R, Cohen M, Addadi L, Geiger B. 2004. Hierarchical assembly of cell-matrix adhesion complexes. *Biochem. Soc. Trans.* 32:416–20

Zegers MM, Forget MA, Chernoff J, Mostov KE, ter Beest MB, Hansen SH. 2003. Pak1 and PIX regulate contact inhibition during epithelial wound healing. *EMBO J.* 22:4155–65

REFERENCE ADDED IN PROOF

Amano H, Ikeda W, Kawano S, Kajita M, Tamaru Y, et al. 2008. Interaction and localization of Necl-5 and PDGF receptor β at the leading edges of moving NIH3T3 cells: implications for directional cell movement. *Genes Cells* 13:269–84

Regulation of MHC Class I Assembly and Peptide Binding

David R. Peaper and Peter Cresswell[*]

Howard Hughes Medical Institute, Department of Immunobiology, Yale University School of Medicine, New Haven, Connecticut 06520; email: david.peaper@yale.edu, peter.cresswell@yale.edu

Annu. Rev. Cell Dev. Biol. 2008. 24:343–68

First published online as a Review in Advance on July 1, 2008

The *Annual Review of Cell and Developmental Biology* is online at cellbio.annualreviews.org

This article's doi: 10.1146/annurev.cellbio.24.110707.175347

1081-0706/08/1110-0343$20.00

*Corresponding author.

Key Words

tapasin, ERp57, glycoprotein folding, antigen processing

Abstract

Peptide binding to MHC class I molecules is a component of a folding and assembly process that occurs in the endoplasmic reticulum (ER) and uses both cellular chaperones and dedicated factors. The involvement of glycoprotein quality-control chaperones and cellular oxidoreductases in peptide binding has led to models that are gradually being refined. Some aspects of the peptide loading process (e.g., the biosynthesis and degradation of MHC class I complexes) conform to models of glycoprotein quality control, but other aspects (e.g., the formation of a stable disulfide-linked dimer between tapasin and ERp57) deviate from models of chaperone and oxidoreductase function. Here we review what is known about the intersection of glycoprotein folding, oxidative reactions, and MHC class I peptide loading, emphasizing events that occur in the ER and within the MHC class I peptide loading complex.

Contents

OVERVIEW OF THE MHC SYSTEM

Major histocompatibility complex (MHC) class I molecules are composed of MHC-encoded heavy chains (HC) [human leukocyte antigen (HLA)-A, -B, or -C] and the invariant subunit β_2-microglobulin (β_2m). At the cell surface, antigen-specific CD8$^+$ T cells recognize peptides of eight to ten amino acids long that are associated with MHC class I/β_2m complexes. Classically, the peptides presented by MHC

class I complexes are derived from proteins degraded in the cytosol by the proteasome, and CD8$^+$ T cells respond to peptides derived from intracellular pathogens.

Cell surface expression of MHC class I HC/β_2m/peptide complexes is the end result of a process that begins in the endoplasmic reticulum (ER). The generation of stable MHC class I/peptide complexes depends, in most cases, upon the TAP (transporter associated with antigen processing) heterodimer and the MHC class I–specific chaperone tapasin. TAP transports peptides from the cytosol into the ER lumen, and tapasin promotes the formation of stable MHC class I/peptide complexes. Additionally, calnexin (CNX) facilitates the early folding of MHC class I HC, whereas calreticulin (CRT) and ERp57 are involved in peptide loading. Many factors involved in the generation of stable MHC class I complexes, including TAP1, TAP2, tapasin, MHC class I HC, β_2m, ERAAP (ER aminopeptidase associated with antigen presentation), and proteasome components, are upregulated by cell exposure to interferon-γ (IFN-γ). The loading and assembly of MHC class I complexes are considered specialized cases of protein folding, and a discussion of the general aspects of protein folding and quality control is needed before MHC class I peptide loading is considered.

PROTEIN FOLDING IN THE ER

The ER facilitates the folding of proteins destined for the secretory pathway. ER resident proteins act as chaperones including BiP, GRP94, CNX, and CRT. CNX and CRT are carbohydrate-binding proteins (lectins) involved in glycoprotein folding, and BiP and GRP94 are members of the conserved heat shock protein 70 (Hsp70) and heat shock protein 90 (Hsp90) families, respectively. These proteins, in conjunction with oxidoreductases of the thioredoxin (Trx) family such as protein disulfide isomerase (PDI), ERp57, and ERp72, prevent the aggregation of newly synthesized, unfolded polypeptides, facilitate the acquisition of correct disulfide bonding patterns,

HLA: human
leukocyte antigen

MHC: major
histocompatibility
complex

TAP: transporter
associated with antigen
processing

and/or initiate protein degradation (Kleizen & Braakman 2004, Ma & Hendershot 2004).

Folding proteins utilize either the CNX/CRT/ERp57 or the BiP/PDI folding pathways, and the system used is determined by the location of the first glycan in the polypeptide chain (Molinari & Helenius 2000). Some proteins successively interact with BiP and CNX (Hammond & Helenius 1994), but complexes composed of BiP/PDI and CNX/CRT/ERp57 are not present at high levels (Meunier et al. 2002). MHC class I HC interacts with BiP during its early folding stages, but the folding and assembly of MHC class I/β_2m/peptide complexes predominantly involve the glycoprotein folding chaperones CNX, CRT, and ERp57.

Glycoprotein Folding

Approximately 45% of the total eukaryotic protein pool may undergo N-linked glycosylation in the ER (Apweiler et al. 1999). N-linked glycans are added to proteins cotranslationally by the oligosaccharide transferase (OST) complex. The OST is associated with the translocon and recognizes the consensus sequence NXS/T in unfolded polypeptides shortly after passage through the translocon. OST adds the core glycan cotranslationally to the Asn residue of the consensus sequence, and glucosidase I quickly removes the terminal glucose residue of the core glycan. Glucosidase II performs further trimming to generate a monoglucosylated glycan (Hammond et al. 1994).

CNX is a transmembrane protein of 572 amino acids, and CRT is a 400-residue soluble CNX homolog (Fliegel et al. 1989, Tjoelker et al. 1994). These evolutionarily conserved proteins consist of a lectin-like globular domain that mediates glycan binding and an extended proline-rich P-domain that recruits ERp57 (Ellgaard et al. 2002, Frickel et al. 2002, Leach et al. 2002). The crystal structure of the CNX globular domain has been solved, and the CRT P-domain structure has been interpreted by nuclear magnetic resonance (Ellgaard et al. 2001a,b; Schrag et al. 2001). The globu-

BASICS OF MHC BIOLOGY

Work performed in mice identified a genomic region responsible for mediating graft rejection, and this region was labeled the major histocompatibility complex (MHC). The human MHC is located on chromosome 6 and encodes the human leukocyte antigens (HLA), and MHC class I antigens are encoded by HLA-A, -B, and -C alleles. The comparable antigens in mice are derived from the H-2 locus located on mouse chromosome 17 (e.g., H2-K^b). HLA alleles are expressed codominantly, with a maximum of 6 MHC class I alleles expressed by an individual. T cells recognize peptide/MHC complexes with their T cell receptor (TCR). The HLA antigens are genetically diverse, but most polymorphisms are located in areas of peptide or TCR binding. The sequence of the peptide-binding groove determines the repertoire of bound peptides, but the interaction of specific anchor residues in the peptide with pockets in the MHC-binding groove has the greatest effect on the affinity and stability of peptide binding. Anchor residue preferences vary for different alleles, and the expression of different alleles and different peptides by the same allele gives rise to the diversity of the adaptive immune response.

lar domain of CNX contains the glycan-binding pocket, and the P-domain curves away from the globular domain, partially shielding the glycan-binding site (Schrag et al. 2001). On the basis of sequence similarity, CRT is assumed to adopt a similar structure, but the P-domains of these proteins differ in length. The significance of this difference is unknown, but a soluble version of CNX cannot fully compensate for the absence of CRT in the folding of some substrates, including MHC class I HC (Gao et al. 2002, Molinari et al. 2004). Some data argue for non-glycan-mediated substrate binding by CNX and CRT, but most data support the predominant role of glycans in the function of CNX and CRT (Leach & Williams 2004).

CNX and CRT prevent the aggregation of folding substrates, retain improperly folded proteins in the ER, and, at least in the case of CNX, facilitate the targeting of terminally misfolded proteins for degradation (Hebert et al. 1996, Jackson et al. 1994, Molinari et al. 2003, Oda et al. 2003). Whereas BiP and GRP94 recognize misfolded polypeptides, CNX and

Calnexin (CNX) and calreticulin (CRT): glycoprotein folding chaperones that recognized monoglucosylated N-linked glycans

ERAAP: ER aminopeptidase associated with antigen presentation

Protein disulfide isomerase (PDI): a highly conserved oxidoreductase in the ER lumen that is the primary factor controlling disulfide bonding patterns

UGGT: UDP-
Glc:glycoprotein
glucosyltransferase

CRT recognize a single glucose residue exposed on an *N*-linked glycan (Hebert et al. 1995, Ware et al. 1995). Folding substrates undergo successive rounds of CNX/CRT binding, release, glucose trimming, reglucosylation, and rebinding in what is referred to as the glycoprotein quality-control cycle (**Figure 1**) (Helenius & Aebi 2004). CNX and CRT bind nascent glycoproteins shortly after synthesis, but the temporal relationship between glucose trimming and CRT/CNX release is unclear (Daniels et al. 2003, Wang et al. 2005). The ER resident enzyme UDP-Glc:glycoprotein glucosyltransferase (UGGT) detects exposed hydrophobic patches near *N*-linked glycans, and reglucosylation by UGGT causes ER retention and further interactions with CNX and/or

CRT (Caramelo et al. 2003, Labriola et al. 1995, Sousa & Parodi 1995, Van Leeuwen & Kearse 1997). Terminally misfolded proteins marked by mannosidase-trimmed glycans are targeted for ER-associated degradation (ERAD) through the ER degradation–enhancing (α)-mannosidase-like (EDEM) protein pathway (Molinari et al. 2003, Oda et al. 2003).

Several substrates that substantiate this model have been examined; these include MHC class I, influenza hemagglutinin (HA), and the surface glycoprotein of vesicular stomatitis virus (Hammond & Helenius 1994, Hebert et al. 1995, Vassilakos et al. 1996). When glucose trimming is inhibited with castanospermine (CST) or *N*-butyldeoxynojirimycin (NB-DNJ), generation of the lectin-binding substrate is prevented, and CRT and CNX binding does not occur (Hammond & Helenius 1994, Hammond et al. 1994, Keller et al. 1998). Genetic deletion of CRT or CNX differentially affects substrate folding; some proteins absolutely require CNX, whereas others can fold efficiently with either CNX or CRT (Molinari

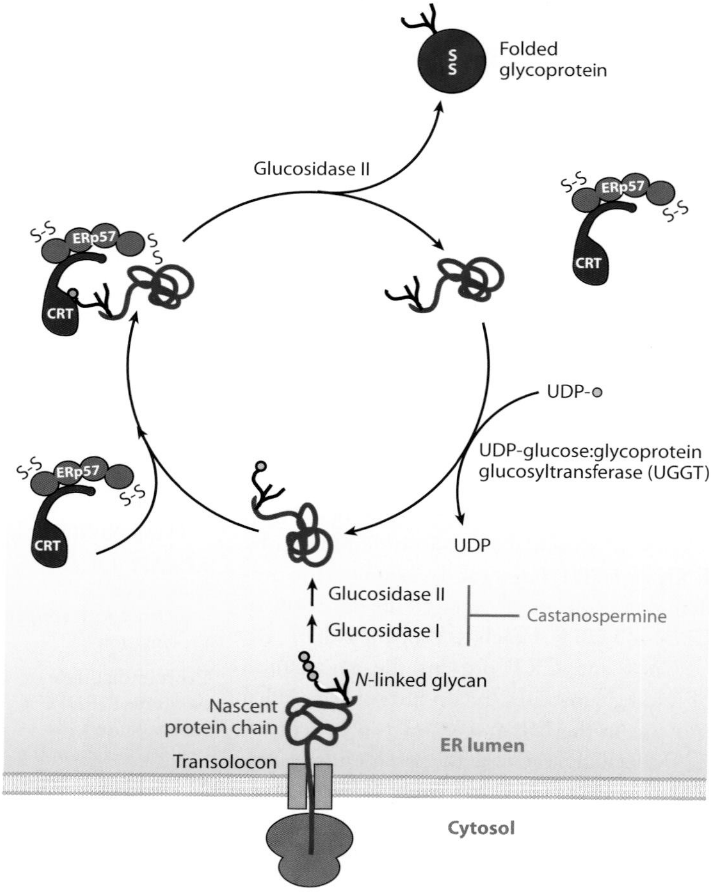

Figure 1

The glycoprotein quality-control pathway. The triple-glucosylated core *N*-linked glycan is added to nascent polypeptide chains cotranslationally. The sequential actions of glucosidases I and II generate the monoglucosylated glycan recognized by calreticulin (CRT) and calnexin (CNX) (not shown). CRT recruits the oxidoreductase ERp57 to folding glycoproteins to facilitate disulfide bond formation. Glucosidase II trimming of the *N*-linked glycan is related to substrate release from CRT, and nonglucosylated proteins cannot interact further with CRT. UDP-glucose:glycoprotein glucosyltransferase (UGGT) acts as a folding sensor by detecting exposed hydrophobic patches in close proximity to *N*-linked glycans. Upon recognizing such patches, UGGT reglucosylates the folding substrate, leading to ER retention and reengagement with CRT. The absence of UGGT-mediated reglucosylation on folded glycoproteins allows their egress from the ER. This cycle repeats itself until the proper structure is achieved and the protein is no longer reglucosylated. CST prevents CRT binding by inhibiting the action of glucosidases I and II.

et al. 2004). The disruption of CNX and CRT binding with CST or NB-DNJ reduces folding efficiency and disrupts ER quality control.

Oxidative Protein Folding: The PDI family

The sulfhydryl (-SH) side group (thiol) of cysteine is unique among amino acids. When two cysteines are within close proximity, a disulfide bond can form, and many proteins within the secretory pathway contain disulfide bonds that stabilize the folded conformation. Disulfide bond formation requires the deprotonation of one cysteine thiol and donation of two electrons to an acceptor such as oxygen; these processes are dictated by the local redox conditions (Sevier & Kaiser 2002). The environment of the ER is relatively oxidizing, and this partially enables spontaneous disulfide bond formation in folding proteins (Hwang et al. 1992). However, not all bonds are formed cotranslationally, and those that form may not be correct (Darby et al. 1995). In vivo oxidation rates are often much faster than in vitro oxidation rates because within the ER, a family of proteins that facilitate the transfer of electrons has evolved. The addition of these oxidoreductases to in vitro reactions accelerates the acquisition of native structures (Weissman & Kim 1993).

Disulfide bond formation is oxidation, breaking of a disulfide bond is reduction, and rearrangement (coupled reduction and oxidation) of a bond within a protein is isomerization (Sevier & Kaiser 2002). PDI can mediate all three reactions but acts primarily as an oxidase and isomerase in vivo (Frand & Kaiser 1999, Laboissiere et al. 1995, Pollard et al. 1998). PDI is a member of the Trx superfamily with high sequence and structural homology to Trx. Trx is a cytoplasmic reductase that acts through a conserved functional motif consisting of two cysteine residues separated by two amino acids (CXXC motif) (Sevier & Kaiser 2002). PDI is composed of four Trx-like domains, and the extreme N- and C-terminal domains contain CXXC motifs, generating an overall *abb'a'* arrangement in which the *a* and *a'* domains possess redox activity (**Figure 2a,b**). The *b'* domain of PDI mediates substrate interactions, and recognition likely involves exposed hydrophobic patches in nonnative proteins (Klappa et al. 1998, Pirneskoski et al. 2004). In both the crystal structure of yeast PDI and a small angle X-ray scattering study of its human homolog, PDI adopts a compact, horseshoe-like structure. The substrate-binding face of the *b'* domain is oriented toward the innermost surface of the structure, and this arrangement may stabilize enzyme/substrate interactions and facilitate CXXC motif access to disulfide bonds (Li et al. 2006, Tian et al. 2006).

Reduction mediated by the Trx motif is depicted in **Figure 2c**, and oxidation reactions proceed in the opposite direction. Attack of an intraprotein disulfide bond by the thiolate anion of the CXXC motif generates a free cysteine in the substrate that is able to react with another cysteine residue (isomerization) or remain reduced (Sevier & Kaiser 2002). The accumulation of mixed disulfide intermediates is limited by deprotonation of the C-terminal cysteine of the CXXC motif and attack on the mixed disulfide (Darby & Creighton 1995). This is referred to as the Trx motif escape pathway. Activation of the escape pathway within PDI is rapid and occurs in both native and denatured proteins, and the rate constant for formation of the intradomain disulfide bond within the PDI *a* domain is 10–30 s^{-1} (Darby & Creighton 1995, Walker & Gilbert 1997). Mutation of the C-terminal cysteine of the CXXC motif eliminates the escape pathway, leading to the accumulation of PDI/substrate mixed disulfides (Walker & Gilbert 1997, Walker et al. 1996). Thus, the Trx domain has evolved to release bound substrates rapidly and efficiently for subsequent rounds of oxidative folding.

Disulfide bond formation is continuously occurring in the ER, and pathways have evolved to maintain the ER redox balance. The ER oxidoreductin (Ero) proteins maintain the oxidizing capacity of the ER by transferring electrons from the cytosol to PDI, and glutathione directly reduces the active sites of PDI-like molecules (Benham et al. 2000; Cabibbo et al.

Glutathione: a tripeptide of glutamic acid, cysteine, and glycine. It can exist in reduced (GSH) or oxidized (GSSG) forms

2000; Frand & Kaiser 1998, 1999; Jessop & Bulleid 2004; Molteni et al. 2004; Pagani et al. 2000; Pollard et al. 1998). Thus, the Ero1 pathway maintains the oxidative capacity of the ER, and reducing equivalents arise from glutathione and its associated transporters and biosynthetic enzymes (Mezghrani et al. 2001).

The PDI family is large, and family members consist of different combinations of redox-active and -inactive domains (**Figure 2a**). Some are specifically expressed in highly exocytic tissues, but others, such as ERp72 and ERp57, are broadly expressed (Sevier & Kaiser 2002). ERp57 is a glycoprotein-specific oxidoreductase, and the functional differences among PDI family members have only recently begun to be addressed. There may be subtle mechanistic differences between ER Trx family members (Kulp et al. 2006). One report suggests that PDI directs proteins for retrotranslocation, whereas ERp72 retains substrates in the ER (Forster et al. 2006).

ERp57: A Glycoprotein-Specific Oxidoreductase

Different enzymatic functions have been ascribed to ERp57, but it has become clear

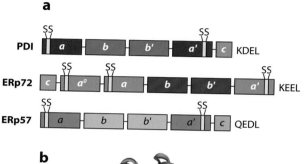

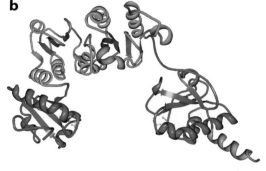

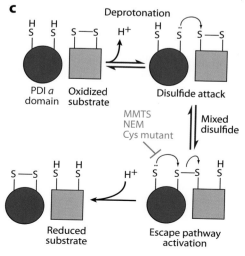

Figure 2

The mammalian PDI family is diverse. (*a*) Domain organization of ERp57, protein disulfide isomerase (PDI), and ERp72. Both ERp57 and PDI possess two redox-active *a* domains and two redox-inactive *b* domains; ERp72 possesses an additional *a* domain. The *a* domain of ERp57 forms a mixed disulfide with tapasin, and the *b* and *b′* domains mediate CNX and CRT binding. The *b′* domain of PDI binds hydrophobic residues on substrate proteins. The substrate-binding mechanism of ERp72 is unknown. All three proteins have KDEL-based ER retrieval motifs. (*b*) The crystal structure of yeast PDI. PDI is composed of four thioredoxin domains with two redox-active domains (*a* and *a′*) shown in blue and two redox-inactive domains (*b* and *b′*) shown in green. Active-site cysteines are shown in yellow. (*c*) PDI CXXC motif–mediated disulfide bond reduction. Deprotonation of the N-terminal cysteine of the CXXC motif generates a thiolate anion, and this highly reactive moiety attacks a disulfide bond, contributing an electron to a sulfhydryl group in the substrate and forming a PDI/substrate mixed disulfide. To limit the accumulation of PDI/substrate mixed disulfides, the escape pathway is activated by the deprotonation of the C-terminal cysteine of the CXXC motif and attack of the mixed disulfide bond. Inactivation of the escape pathway through mutation of the C-terminal cysteine of the CXXC motif or cellular treatment with *N*-ethyl maleimide (NEM) or methyl methanethiosulfonate (MMTS) is required to detect mixed disulfides.

that ERp57 is functionally related to PDI and mediates disulfide bond formation in folding glycoproteins (Ellgaard & Frickel 2003). Like PDI, ERp57 is composed of two CXXC-containing, redox-active Trx domains and two redox-inactive Trx domains with an arrangement of *abb'a'* (**Figure 2a**) (Frickel et al. 2004, Russell et al. 2004, Silvennoinen et al. 2004). ERp57 exhibits reductase, oxidase, and isomerase activity in vitro, but the primary activity in vivo remains unclear (Frickel et al. 2004). ERp57 can interact with Ero1, and glutathione directly reduces ERp57, regenerating its enzymatic activity (Jessop & Bulleid 2004, Jessop et al. 2007).

ERp57 is recruited to folding glycoproteins through interactions with CNX and CRT (**Figure 1**) (Oliver et al. 1997, 1999). The P-domains of CNX and CRT bind the *b'* domain of ERp57, and additional contacts between the ERp57 *b* domain and the P-domain stabilize this interaction (Frickel et al. 2002, Pollock et al. 2004, Russell et al. 2004). The crystal structure of the *bb'* fragment of ERp57 has been solved, and there are several differences from PDI in this region. Not surprisingly, these differences correlate to regions of CNX binding (Kozlov et al. 2006).

ERp57 forms mixed disulfides with newly translated glycoproteins, and disruption of CNX and CRT interactions using CST or NB-DNJ prevents substrate interactions with ERp57 (Molinari & Helenius 1999). CST treatment alters the kinetics of oxidative folding for several glycoprotein substrates (Kang & Cresswell 2002, Molinari et al. 2004). The presence of CNX or CRT enhances the in vitro activity of ERp57 toward glycosylated substrates (Zapun et al. 1998). Thus, ERp57 appears to function specifically with CNX and CRT to promote correct disulfide bond formation in folding glycoproteins. Inhibition of lectin/substrate interactions abolishes ERp57 recruitment.

When the C-terminal cysteines of the ERp57 CXXC motifs are mutated, ERp57/substrate mixed disulfides accumulate, and this approach was used to examine the substrate specificity of ERp57 (Dick & Cresswell 2002, Jessop et al. 2007). A two-dimensional nonreducing/reducing SDS-PAGE system was used to identify several ERp57 substrates in a human cell line. These substrates all had regions of poorly ordered tertiary structure, and the authors confirmed the importance of ERp57 in their oxidative folding in ERp57-deficient mouse embryonic fibroblasts (MEFs). Jessop et al. (2007) suggest that ERp57 may act primarily as an isomerase for a subset of substrates in vivo.

ERp57-deficient MEFs were used to confirm the role of ERp57 in glycoprotein oxidative folding (Solda et al. 2006). In the absence of ERp57, influenza HA folding was delayed, suggesting that HA is an obligate ERp57 substrate. In contrast, two Semliki Forest virus proteins that normally interact with ERp57 were able to fold through alternative oxidative and chaperone pathways (Solda et al. 2006). The existing data suggest that a primary function of CNX and CRT is to recruit ERp57 (Molinari et al. 2004, Solda et al. 2006). The major defects seen in the maturation of viral glycoproteins in the absence of CNX or CRT or in the presence of CST are altered oxidative folding and aggregation. In particular, HA translated in cells treated with CST or cells deficient in ERp57 matures and aggregates with remarkable similarities. Thus, glycoprotein folding and oxidative folding intersect at ERp57.

MHC CLASS I PEPTIDE LOADING: GENERAL AND SPECIFIC CELLULAR REACTIONS

The MHC Class I Peptide Loading Complex

The early folding of MHC class I molecules and association with β_2m occur within minutes after synthesis. However, rather than leaving the ER like most folding substrates, most MHC class I/β_2m complexes associate with the peptide loading complex (PLC) (**Figure 3**). In addition to MHC class I HC/β_2m dimers,

Peptide loading complex (PLC): the association of MHC class I HC, β_2m, tapasin, ERp57, and CRT with TAP1 and TAP2. Resides in the ER

NEM: *N*-ethyl maleimide

MMTS: methyl methanethiosulfonate

Peptide quality: the ability of peptides to confer stability to MHC class I complexes. Quality correlates with affinity but applies to unknown peptides

the PLC contains the TAP heterodimer, CRT, and a disulfide-linked conjugate of tapasin and ERp57. Cys-95 of tapasin forms a disulfide bond with Cys-57 in the *a* domain of ERp57. This bond becomes reduced during biochemical isolation and detection unless the ERp57 *a* domain escape pathway is inhibited through rapid cellular acidification or treatment of cells with thiol-reactive compounds (Antoniou & Powis 2003, Dick et al. 2002). Typical thiol-reactive reagents are *N*-ethyl maleimide (NEM) or methyl methanethiosulfonate (MMTS), and when cells are treated with MMTS, all tapasin is conjugated to ERp57 (Peaper et al. 2005). Unfortunately, many studies of the PLC were undertaken prior to the widespread use of NEM or MMTS, thus complicating assessments of PLC composition. Within the PLC there are also two noncovalent interactions between MHC class I HC and tapasin. All human and mouse MHC alleles contain at least one *N*-linked glycan, and CRT binds the monoglucosylated glycan of MHC class I HC with an affinity of approximately 1 μM (Wearsch et al. 2004). ERp57 almost certainly acts as a bridge between tapasin and CRT, and the P-domain of CRT binds ERp57 with a $K_d \approx 9$ μM (Frickel et al. 2002). The combination of these weak interactions seems likely to stabilize the PLC.

To exit the ER, MHC class I complexes must pass the glycoprotein quality-control checkpoints, including glucosidase II trimming and UGGT-mediated reglucosylation, and the folding state of MHC class I complexes likely correlates with the loading of high-quality peptides. The tapasin/MHC class I interaction is sensitive to the quality of bound peptide, and the sensing mechanism of tapasin is likely more stringent than the normal ER quality control. Thus, the central questions of MHC class I biology we wish to address are, How are high-quality peptides generated? How does the PLC promote the loading of high-quality peptides? How does MHC class I loading intersect with glycoprotein and oxidative folding pathways? How do allelic differences affect these points of intersection?

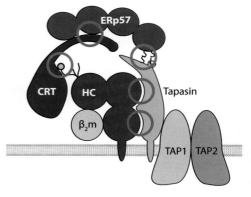

- CRT/glycan: 1 μM
- CRT/ERp57: 9 μM
- ERp57/tapasin: covalent
- Tapasin/MHC HC: unknown

Figure 3

Different interactions contribute to the stability of the MHC class I peptide loading complex (PLC). Within the PLC the transmembrane domain of tapasin interacts with TAP1 and TAP2 (transporter associated with antigen processing 1 and 2, respectively), and there is a disulfide bond between Cys-57 of the *a* domain of ERp57 and Cys-95 of tapasin. There are two sites of interaction between MHC class I and tapasin, but the binding characteristics of these proteins are not known. The interaction between the N terminus of tapasin and the α_2 domain of MHC class I appears to be the most functionally significant. CRT binds the *N*-linked glycan at Asn-86 of MHC class I heavy chain (HC) with an affinity of approximately 1 μM, and the 9 μM interaction of ERp57 with the CRT P-domain likely stabilizes the association of MHC class I and CRT within the PLC.

The Generation, Translocation, and Polishing of Peptide Ligands

MHC class I–binding peptides are traditionally derived from protein antigens in the cytosol, and the initial step in the generation of MHC class I–binding peptides is proteasomal degradation (Strehl et al. 2005, Yewdell & Nicchitta 2006). Inhibition of proteasome activity decreases the pool of MHC class I–binding peptides (Hughes et al. 1996). Proteasomal cleavage typically creates a peptide C terminus compatible with MHC class I binding, and peptides are typically extended at their N terminus (Cascio et al. 2001). Proteasome composition and function are altered by IFN-γ, leading to the generation of peptides more suitable for MHC class I binding (Strehl et al. 2005).

The TAP transporter is the PLC component that transfers peptides from the cytosol to the ER lumen. TAP is a heterodimeric member of the ATP-binding cassette (ABC) family of transporters, and peptide binding induces ATP hydrolysis and translocation. Peptides of 8 to 12 amino acids are translocated most efficiently, a near-ideal length for binding MHC class I molecules. The structure and function of TAP were recently reviewed (Abele & Tampe 2004) and are not further addressed here.

ERAAP (also known as ERAP1) trims N-extended peptides to a length appropriate for MHC class I binding (Saric et al. 2002, Serwold et al. 2002, York et al. 2002). Knockdown of ERAAP decreased the expression of MHC class I complexes at the cell surface and impaired presentation of T cell epitopes (Serwold et al. 2002, York et al. 2002). Similar presentation defects were seen in ERAAP-deficient mice, but these mice did not have severe immune defects (Hammer et al. 2006, Yan et al. 2006, York et al. 2006). Intriguingly, a recent study showed that the class I–bound repertoire of peptides in ERAAP-deficient mice is sufficiently altered such that congenic wild-type (WT) mice generate T and B cell responses to ERAAP-deficient cells (Hammer et al. 2007).

The original observation that ERAAP preferentially trims peptides to eight amino acids suggested that it acts a "molecular ruler," and this hypothesis appeared to be confirmed (Chang et al. 2005, York et al. 2002). However, another study found that, in the absence of appropriate MHC class I complexes, ERAAP is capable of destroying at least one peptide epitope, suggesting that its action is not limited to extended peptides (Kanaseki et al. 2006). It is clear that ERAAP plays an important role in the polishing of peptides prior to their presentation by MHC class I complexes, but its exact molecular mechanism remains controversial.

Biosynthesis and Folding of MHC Class I Complexes

Human MHC class I HC undergo cotranslational glycosylation at residue Asn-86 and quickly interact with BiP and then with CNX (Nossner & Parham 1995). CNX recruits ERp57 to facilitate disulfide bond formation within the membrane-proximal Ig-like α_3 domain at this time, and ERp57 knockdown leads to impaired oxidative folding of MHC class I HC (Zhang et al. 2006). However, CNX is dispensable for MHC class I HC folding and assembly (Sadasivan et al. 1995). A second disulfide bond between Cys-101 and Cys-164 within the α_2 domain subsequently forms. β_2m association greatly enhances the stability of this bond; β_2m deletion results in the degradation and low expression of misfolded MHC class I molecules (Warburton et al. 1994). After initial oxidative folding, MHC class I/β_2m complexes dissociate from CNX, but they remain monoglucosylated and associate with CRT. At this point, MHC class I HC/β_2m/CRT complexes are found associated with the PLC.

Formation and Maintenance of the MHC Class I PLC

The TAP heterodimer is the core of the PLC, but the number and arrangement of other PLC-associated proteins remain controversial. Following biochemical purification and quantitative amino acid analysis, we suggested a 4:1 ratio of tapasin to TAP (Ortmann et al. 1997). This study was conducted prior to our knowledge of the participation of ERp57 in the PLC, and no efforts were made to preserve the tapasin-ERp57 conjugate. An assumption of a homogeneous PLC subcomplex composition (four subcomplexes each of tapasin, ERp57, CRT, MHC class I HC, and β_2m) results in an estimated molecular weight of approximately 1 MDa. However, a recent study used a 2-D-native gel/SDS-PAGE system to examine the PLC, identifying two TAP-containing complexes of 350 kDa and 450 kDa with only two tapasin molecules per TAP heterodimer (Rufer et al. 2007). Detergent is required for PLC solubilization, and its effects on the apparent M_r (molecular mass) measured in this system were not considered. When the lateral diffusion in the ER membrane of PLCs incorporating GFP-tagged TAP1 was measured, the estimated size of the TAP-associated protein complex was much larger than either biochemical estimate (Marguet et al. 1999).

Both the transport molecule BAP31 (B cell receptor–associated protein 31) and PDI are reportedly associated with the PLC (Paquet et al. 2004, Park et al. 2006). BAP31 facilitates the export of MHC class I complexes from the ER and their retrieval from the Golgi, but there is only one report of its localization within the PLC (Ladasky et al. 2006, Paquet et al. 2004, Spiliotis et al. 2000). Two groups have identified PDI associated with TAP (Park et al. 2006, Santos et al. 2007), but several others have failed to detect this association (Kienast et al. 2007, Peaper et al. 2005, Rufer et al. 2007). In mice, the association of CNX with MHC class I is maintained within the PLC, but although CNX can be detected with TAP in human cells, CNX does not appear to interact directly with PLC-associated MHC class I HC (Diedrich et al. 2001, Ortmann et al. 1997, Rufer et al. 2007, Suh et al. 1996). The reasons for these discrepancies are unclear. The accurate determination of PLC composition is important for the development of a complete model of PLC action. However, the identification of the contributions of each PLC component to peptide loading and the mechanism of action of tapasin are independent of this information.

Functional Roles of MHC Class I PLC Components

Cell lines and animals lacking different components of the MHC class I loading pathway have clarified the role of each protein, and these results are summarized in **Figure 4**. β_2m association occurs very early during MHC class I folding, and β_2m is an obligate partner for MHC class I HC. The absence of β_2m precludes almost all subsequent folding, assembly, and loading steps. Cells lacking β_2m do not express MHC class I complexes on their surface, and mice lacking β_2m have severely impaired CD8 T cell immunity (D'Urso et al. 1991, Williams et al. 1989, Zijlstra et al. 1990).

The stability of MHC class I complexes assembled in TAP-deficient cells is severely impaired, as measured by decreased to absent cell surface expression and rapid MHC class I complex degradation (Salter & Cresswell 1986, Spies & DeMars 1991, Spies et al. 1992). Mice lacking TAP1 have no peripheral CD8$^+$ T cells owing to absent MHC class I expression on cells of the thymus, and their peripheral cells resemble TAP-deficient cell lines in their MHC class I phenotype (Van Kaer et al. 1992). Thus, peptide transport by TAP is essential for the generation of stable MHC class I/peptide complexes and productive CD8$^+$ T cell immunity.

In mice, CRT deficiency is embryonic lethal, but MHC class I peptide loading was examined in CRT-deficient MEFs (Gao et al. 2002). With the exception of CRT, PLC composition was qualitatively normal, but the assembly and transport of MHC class I complexes were impaired. Unstable, poorly loaded MHC class I complexes exited the ER more rapidly in CRT-deficient MEFs than in WT cells, and there were defects in the generation of some CD8 T cell–specific epitopes. It is impossible to conclude if the defects in MHC class I antigen presentation seen in CRT-deficient cells were due to effects in the ER in general or those within the PLC, but CRT plays a key role in regulating the export of properly loaded MHC class I molecules.

Many years ago the laboratory of Robert DeMars selected mutant human cell lines lacking MHC class I surface expression. In one of these lines, 721.220, most transfected class I alleles were poorly expressed at the cell surface despite normal mRNA levels (Greenwood et al. 1994). This cell line was later found to lack expression of a novel glycoprotein named tapasin (Sadasivan et al. 1996). Reexpression of tapasin restored the surface expression of the human class I allele HLA-B*0801, confirming the importance of tapasin in MHC class I loading (Ortmann et al. 1997).

Two groups independently created tapasin-deficient mice, in which CD8 T cell immunity was grossly impaired. The surface expression of the mouse class I alleles H2-K^b and H2-D^b was decreased by approximately 100-fold compared with WT cells but remained 10-fold higher than on TAP-deficient cells. Presentation of different antigenic peptides was decreased but was better than that by TAP-deficient cells. Consistent with this finding, the peripheral CD8 T cell frequency of tapasin-negative mice was intermediate between the frequencies observed in WT- and TAP-negative mice. These data strongly argue that tapasin is essential for presentation of a number of different T cell epitopes and that, in its absence, the generation of CD8 T cell responses is impaired (Garbi et al. 2000, Grandea et al. 2000).

ERp57 was originally expected to bind to MHC class I HC in the PLC, analogous to the interactions of ERp57 with other glycoprotein folding substrates (Hughes & Cresswell 1998, Lindquist et al. 1998, Morrice & Powis 1998). Thus, the discovery of the identity of the conjugate between ERp57 and tapasin was surprising (Dick et al. 2002). When conjugate formation in 720.220 cells was prevented by mutating Cys-95 of tapasin, the class I allele HLA-B*4402 exhibited decreased stability and impaired peptide loading. Additionally, the redox state of HLA-B*4402 associated with C95A mutant tapasin

was altered; the Cys-101/Cys-164 bond was reduced after PLC isolation and SDS-PAGE. However, in the same cells expressing H2-K^b, the inability of tapasin to form the conjugate did not affect the loading hierarchy onto H2-K^b

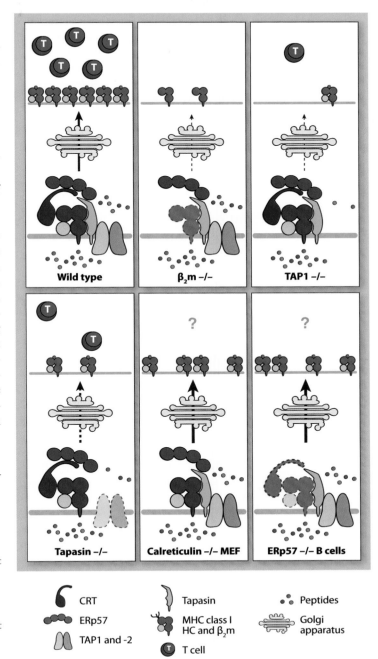

Figure 4

Roles for PLC proteins defined in deficient animals and cells. Surface expression and CD8 T cell selection are impaired in β_2m-, TAP-, and tapasin-deficient mice but could not be assessed in the absence of CRT or ERp57 because of lethality. Few MHC class I complexes exit the endoplasmic reticulum (ER) in β_2m- and TAP-deficient cells, but passage through the Golgi is accelerated in CRT- and ERp57-negative cells. Tapasin deficiency differentially affects human and mouse alleles. PLC composition is altered in the absence of different PLC components, but quantitative analyses have not been undertaken for all cell lines and alleles. MEF, mouse embryonic fibroblasts.

of a peptide systematically altered to vary its affinity (Howarth et al. 2004).

The importance of ERp57 incorporation into the PLC was emphasized by the generation of mice lacking expression of ERp57 in B cells. In these cells, surface H2-K^b expression was reduced and displayed enhanced turnover compared with WT cells. Additionally, the recruitment of H2-K^b into the PLC was altered, and trafficking of H2-K^b through the Golgi apparatus accelerated. ERp57-deficient fibroblasts had slightly decreased presentation of an epitope bound to H2-K^b, but no alterations in the redox state of PLC-associated H2-K^b were seen (Garbi et al. 2006).

Relationship between PLC Composition and Function

TAP1 and TAP2 have several different domains, but the N-terminal transmembrane regions of both TAP1 and TAP2 are responsible for recruiting tapasin (Koch et al. 2004, Leonhardt et al. 2005). Tapasin expression stabilizes TAP, leading to increased steady-state TAP levels and peptide transport (Bangia et al. 1999, Garbi et al. 2003). Mutation of residues in the tapasin transmembrane domain disrupts the TAP/tapasin interaction, and in the absence of productive TAP/tapasin interactions, MHC class I/β_2m dimers, CRT, and ERp57 form subcomplexes with tapasin (Hughes & Cresswell 1998, Petersen et al. 2005, Tan et al. 2002).

In the absence of tapasin, MHC class I HC, β_2m, CRT, and ERp57 do not appreciably associate with TAP, and in the absence of β_2m, tapasin and ERp57 associate with TAP, but CRT and MHC class I HC do not (Bangia et al. 1999, Hughes & Cresswell 1998, Sadasivan et al. 1996, Suh et al. 1999, Tan et al. 2002). Thus, tapasin functions as a bridge between MHC class I/β_2m complexes and TAP. However, this action is not essential for the function of tapasin because a soluble version of tapasin that does not interact with TAP mediates peptide loading to a great extent, although this version of tapasin does not promote full

peptide optimization (Lehner et al. 1998, Tan et al. 2002, Williams et al. 2002).

The N terminus of tapasin is essential for MHC class I association and peptide loading. Tapasin mutants truncated at the N terminus associate with TAP but poorly recruit MHC class I, and peptide loading in cells expressing these mutants is indistinguishable from cells lacking tapasin altogether (Bangia et al. 1999, Momburg & Tan 2002). The N terminus of tapasin constitutes a distinct domain, and an intraprotein disulfide bond between Cys-7 and Cys-71 is required for optimal tapasin stability and/or function (Chen et al. 2002, Dick et al. 2002).

TAP with tapasin was thought to compose the core of the PLC, but under steady-state conditions all tapasin is conjugated to ERp57 (Momburg & Tan 2002, Peaper et al. 2005, Santos et al. 2007). Thus, it is no longer appropriate to consider the function of tapasin independently of associated ERp57. Conjugate formation occurs in the absence of β_2m, MHC class I HC, TAP1 and TAP2, CRT, or CNX or in the complete absence of glucose trimming (Peaper et al. 2005). Conjugation also occurs in vitro following the mixing of tapasin and ERp57. The normal enzymatic escape pathway of the ERp57 *a* domain is not initiated when it is associated with tapasin, but the elimination of noncovalent interactions by denaturation relieves the inhibition and allows reduction to proceed normally, as it would for a typical ERp57 substrate. Denaturation-induced reduction of the conjugate can be prevented by mutation of Cys-60 of the *a* domain CXXC motif or treatment with MMTS or NEM. Thus, tapasin has evolved to specifically recruit and stabilize ERp57 within the MHC class I loading complex (Peaper et al. 2005). This may be a relatively recent adaptation because chicken tapasin lacks Cys-95 (Frangoulis et al. 1999).

Studies of ERp57 function in peptide loading have examined HLA-B*4402 or H2-K^b. In both human and mouse PLCs lacking ERp57, the recruitment to, and stabilization within, the PLCs of MHC class I HC is reduced, but the trafficking and maturation of these two alleles differ when they are assembled in the absence of ERp57 (Dick et al. 2002, Garbi et al. 2006, Turnquist et al. 2004; D. Peaper & P. Cresswell, manuscript in preparation). H2-K^b passed through the Golgi more quickly in the absence of ERp57, but the passage of HLA-B^*4402 through the Golgi in cells expressing C95A tapasin was slightly delayed. In tapasin-deficient mouse cells, H2-K^b molecules traffic rapidly through the Golgi, but they are quickly internalized from the cell surface (Grandea et al. 2000). In human cells, tapasin does not affect the surface expression of H2-K^b, but its trafficking is accelerated (Barnden et al. 2000). In fact, H2-K^b is expressed on the cell surface in human cells even in the absence of TAP (Wei & Cresswell 1992). In contrast, in the absence of tapasin HLA-B^*4402 surface levels are greatly reduced, and very few MHC class I/β_2m complexes reach the Golgi apparatus (Dick et al. 2002, Peh et al. 1998). H2-K^b assembled with or without high-quality peptides appears able to pass the quality-control checkpoints in the ER, but these unstable complexes dissociate in post-ER compartments. Under similar conditions, HLA-B^*4402 does not appear capable of exiting the ER and likely undergoes ERAD.

Studies examining the PLC in cells expressing different MHC class I HC and tapasin mutants were undertaken prior to the use of NEM or MMTS to stabilize the tapasin/ERp57 disulfide bond, and loss of conjugation may affect the apparent PLC composition. With this caveat, the data indicate that there are at least two sites of interaction between MHC class I HC and tapasin. The membrane-proximal Ig domain of tapasin interacts with the MHC class I α_3 domain, and mutants in these domains interfere with MHC class I recruitment into the PLC (Suh et al. 1999; Turnquist et al. 2001, 2004). There is also an interaction between the N-terminal domain of tapasin and the α_2 domain of MHC class I HC best defined using T134K mutant MHC class I HC, and tapasin was not able to promote peptide dissociation from T134K mutant HLA-B^*0801 in vitro (Bangia et al. 1999, Chen & Bouvier 2007, Harris et al. 2001, Lewis & Elliott 1998,

Peace-Brewer et al. 1996). However, the binding affinities for MHC class I/β_2m complexes with tapasin have not been determined. Finally, the presence of CRT in the PLC is directly correlated with the presence of MHC class I/β_2m complexes (Sadasivan et al. 1996, Solheim et al. 1997).

Tapasin Is an MHC Class I–Specific Chaperone

Numerous studies have sought to identify tapasin's mechanism of action, but in vivo studies have generated conflicting data regarding the effects of tapasin on peptide loading. The crux of the disagreement was whether MHC class I interactions with tapasin led to the preferential displacement of low-quality peptides for high-quality peptides; i.e., does tapasin act as a peptide editor? The binding affinities for the pool of HLA-B^*0801-bound peptides were approximately fivefold higher in the absence of tapasin (Zarling et al. 2003). However, similar or lower binding affinities were seen in studies of peptides bound to HLA-B^*2705 and HLA-A^*0201 expressed in tapasin-negative cells (Barber et al. 2001, Purcell et al. 2001, Williams et al. 2002). For all alleles studied, the diversity of peptides bound in the presence of tapasin was dramatically increased (Barber et al. 2001, Barnden et al. 2000, Purcell et al. 2001, Zarling et al. 2003). For H2-K^b binding of a single peptide and variant peptides based on its sequence, tapasin expression led to a defined hierarchy of binding that correlated with peptide-binding half-life (Howarth et al. 2004). In a non-peptide-specific approach, the quality of bound peptides increased with time in the presence of tapasin (Williams et al. 2002). To complicate matters further, a recent study found slight differences in the identities of peptides bound in the presence of mouse or human tapasin (Sesma et al. 2005). Tapasin also exerts a second quality-control function in the ER, preventing the export of empty or poorly loaded MHC class I complexes (Barnden et al. 2000).

Although most groups seemed to support the peptide-editor model, resolution of this debate was delayed until the development of in vitro assays to assess tapasin function directly. The low affinity of the interaction between soluble MHC class I HC and soluble, unconjugated tapasin impaired the development of such assays. Two recent papers used different approaches to overcome this difficulty. In one paper, leucine zipper peptides were attached to the C termini of non-membrane-associated versions of tapasin and MHC class I HC, stabilizing their interaction (Chen & Bouvier 2007). The ability of tapasin to promote the association or dissociation of fluorescently labeled peptides was then measured; MHC class I HC, β_2m, tapasin, and peptide were the only components examined. In the other paper, conjugation of soluble tapasin with ERp57 was used to stabilize association with MHC class I complexes in a cell-free system (Wearsch & Cresswell 2007). Digitonin lysates of tapasin-negative 721.220 cells expressing different class I alleles were supplemented with recombinant conjugate, free tapasin, free ERp57, and/or CRT. The loading of ^{125}I-labeled peptides onto MHC class I/β_2m complexes in the extracts was assessed by immunoprecipitation. Both studies focused on the loading of HLA-B*0801, but recombinant conjugate also promoted loading of HLA-B*2705 (Wearsch & Cresswell 2007). When the interaction between HLA-B*0801 and tapasin was forced through the leucine zippers, the rates of peptide association and disassociation were much more rapid than in the absence of C-terminal stabilization. Tapasin was able to promote peptide exchange, but the nature of the two peptides examined made it difficult to assess if tapasin functioned as a peptide editor (Chen & Bouvier 2007). In the cell-free system, the conjugate promoted the binding of higher-affinity peptides despite a 50-fold excess of low- or intermediate-affinity peptides, and the conjugate was able to displace preloaded lower-affinity peptides and allow binding of higher-affinity peptides, meeting the criteria for peptide editing (Wearsch & Cresswell 2007). Additionally, incubation with high-affinity, but not low-affinity, peptides led to MHC class I

release from the conjugate, a finding partially confirmed by another study (Rizvi & Raghavan 2006, Wearsch & Cresswell 2007). Multiple interactions are needed to stabilize the tapasin/MHC class I interaction for tapasin to exert its editing function, and the conjugate partially fulfills this role in vivo.

HLA-B*4405 and HLA-B*4402 differ by a single amino acid in the peptide-binding groove at position 116. Among HLA alleles examined, surface expression of HLA-B*4402 requires tapasin (i.e., it is tapasin dependent), but the absence of tapasin does not affect surface levels of HLA-B*4405 (i.e., it is tapasin independent). In the absence of tapasin, HLA-B*4405 folding and maturation are largely intact, but the stability of MHC class I complexes is slightly impaired (Kienast et al. 2007, Park et al. 2003, Williams et al. 2002). Polymorphisms at residue 114 also correlate with tapasin dependence (Park et al. 2003). The precise importance of individual binding groove residues is unresolved, but these differences can affect efficient PLC-independent peptide loading (Thammavongsa et al. 2006, Zernich et al. 2004).

Redox Reactions and MHC Class I Loading

The hallmark of oxidoreductase-substrate interactions is the transient existence of a mixed disulfide between the two proteins, and several groups have identified ERp57/MHC class I HC mixed disulfides in vitro and in vivo (Antoniou et al. 2002, 2007; Kienast et al. 2007; Lindquist et al. 2001). Despite extensive examination, there are no definitive reports of PLC-associated mixed disulfides of ERp57 and MHC class I HC (Dick et al. 2002, Kienast et al. 2007; D. Peaper, unpublished observations). Recent studies have identified a triple conjugate of MHC class I HC, tapasin, and ERp57 in the PLC, but it is not clear that the association of MHC class I HC involves luminal cysteines in tapasin (Chambers et al. 2008, Santos et al. 2007).

A difficulty in assessing the importance of redox reactions in MHC class I peptide loading is the need for oxidation of the Cys-101/Cys-164 bond. ERp57 preferentially reduces incompletely folded and peptide-deficient MHC class I complexes in vitro, suggesting that ERp57-mediated reduction may occur after failed attempts at peptide loading, perhaps as a precursor of MHC class I HC degradation (Antoniou et al. 2002). Thus, which comes first, poor peptide loading or disulfide bond reduction? A recent paper argues that ERp57-mediated reduction of the MHC class I HC impairs peptide loading and that tapasin-mediated inactivation of ERp57 restrains this reductase activity (Kienast et al. 2007). The redox state of HLA-B*4402, but not that of HLA-B*4405, was altered in cells expressing C95A tapasin, but peptide loading is also impaired under these conditions (Dick et al. 2002), whereas H2-K^b associated with the PLC was completely oxidized in cells lacking ERp57 (Garbi et al. 2006). Although the former finding is consistent with a role for ERp57 in mediating Cys-101/Cys-164 reduction, these alleles intrinsically differ in their stability and ability to bind peptide spontaneously. In our view, the existing data do not sufficiently distinguish between populations of MHC class I complexes that have undergone failed rounds of peptide binding prior to imminent degradation and those that have become reduced shortly after synthesis and are unable to bind peptide. Perhaps more controversial is the role of PDI in the redox regulation of MHC class I loading. Park et al. (2006) showed that RNAi-mediated knockdown of PDI led to the presence of partially oxidized HLA-A*0201 in HeLa cells, including in the PLC. Additionally, these researchers argued that PDI-mediated reoxidation of the Cys-101/Cys-164 bond was essential for the optimization of HLA-A*0201-bound peptides. The possibility of redox changes in MHC class I HC, tapasin, ERp57, and/or PDI as an aspect of peptide loading will certainly be further investigated in the future, but currently the situation is somewhat obscure.

PUTTING IT ALL TOGETHER: MODELS OF PLC ACTION

With the discovery of the tapasin/ERp57 conjugate, investigators proposed models wherein the conjugation state of tapasin could be related to peptide loading. One model predicted that preassembled complexes of CRT, ERp57, MHC class I HC, and β_2m were incorporated into the loading complex through associations with tapasin (Antoniou et al. 2003). A nonmutually exclusive model predicted that conjugate reduction precedes the release of peptide-loaded MHC class I molecules (Dick 2004, Wright et al. 2004). However, the tapasin/ERp57 conjugate is a uniquely stable heterodimer that does not undergo reduction associated with peptide loading, and conjugate reduction/ERp57 release do not appear to regulate MHC class I release from the PLC (**Figure 5**).

Tapasin has three distinct functional luminal domains: (*a*) a membrane-proximal, nonediting domain that interacts with MHC class I; (*b*) an N-terminal, editing domain; and (*c*) a domain responsible for recruiting, binding, and stabilizing ERp57. Loss of either the membrane-proximal interactions or ERp57 recruitment impairs peptide loading to a variable extent depending on the class I allele, and this likely explains the need for conjugation or the addition of C-terminal leucine zippers for efficient peptide loading in vitro. Thus, ERp57 conjugation itself may not be essential for peptide loading, and the defects in MHC class I stability seen in the absence of ERp57 may arise from decreased recruitment to, and/or stabilization of, MHC class I and CRT within the PLC. Whether this is due to a decreased number of MHC class I/β_2m complexes interacting with the PLC or decreased duration and/or quality of the interaction for all complexes remains to be determined. Elimination of the lectin-binding site(s) of ERp57 may recapitulate the phenotype of ERp57 −/− cells, and a quantitative analysis of PLC composition in CRT −/− fibroblasts may reveal unappreciated alterations in MHC class I recruitment/stabilization. Of course, this

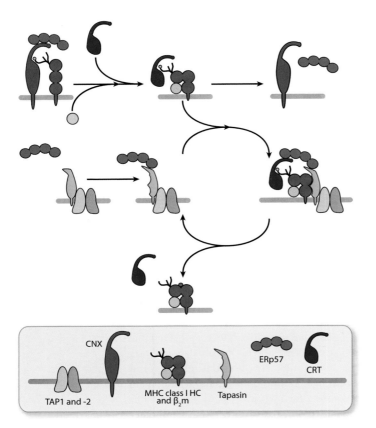

Figure 5

The folding and assembly of MHC class I loading complex components. CNX mediates the early folding stages of MHC class I HC prior to its association with β₂m. Complete HC oxidation occurs during this time, and ERp57 facilitates this process. Once associated and properly oxidized, MHC class I HC/β₂m complexes rapidly associate with CRT. In parallel, newly synthesized tapasin associates with TAP with a reduced Cys7/Cys71 disulfide bond; this bond becomes oxidized at some point during complex assembly. Conjugate formation with ERp57 proceeds rapidly after TAP association independently of lectin binding by CRT or CNX. CRT/HC/β₂m subcomplexes rapidly associate with the TAP/tapasin/ERp57 subcomplex. Through unknown mechanisms in a tapasin-dependent manner, the loading complex facilitates the generation of highly stable MHC class I/peptide complexes, leading to the release of loaded MHC class I molecules and CRT. The core subcomplex of TAP/tapasin/ERp57 is then able to recruit additional MHC class I molecules.

does not exclude the possibility of direct effects of ERp57 on tapasin and/or MHC class I recruitment.

MHC class I complexes may undergo multiple rounds of editing after associating with the PLC, or they may undergo multiple cycles of PLC binding and release with a single edit-

ing event for each interaction. The essential question of peptide loading is, Once associated with the PLC, how does tapasin edit the peptides bound by MHC class I complexes? This will likely not be answered until the structure of tapasin is solved, but tapasin has been proposed to disrupt bonds between the MHC class I binding groove and peptide, leading to an open, peptide-receptive conformation (Chen & Bouvier 2007, Wright et al. 2004). Peptides that do not have sufficient affinity to remain bound, likely owing to poor anchor residue interactions, would be released, allowing binding of higher-affinity peptides and dissociation of MHC class I complexes from the PLC. The presence of PLC-associated open MHC class I complexes is suggested by the ability of a unique monoclonal antibody specific for open MHC class I conformers to precipitate tapasin and other PLC components (Harris et al. 2001).

The points of intersection of the quality-control enzymes glucosidases I and II and UGGT with the MHC class I loading process are unresolved (**Figure 6**). If glucosidase II trimming of the MHC class I/β₂m dimer occurred prior to PLC incorporation, UGGT-mediated reglucosylation would be required to engage the PLC, and the absence of stably associated peptide could initiate this step. This could explain the differences in trafficking and PLC association seen for tapasin-dependent alleles and those that bind peptide independently of tapasin; UGGT would determine whether MHC class I complexes associate with the PLC. Alternatively, newly synthesized MHC class I complexes together with CRT could be immediately recruited to the PLC by the conjugate, and tapasin-mediated editing could proceed. A rapid handoff from CNX to CRT would protect the monoglucosylation of the MHC class I glycan, allowing ERp57 and CRT to stabilize the MHC class I/tapasin interaction. MHC class I complexes loaded with high-quality peptide may not stably associate with tapasin, and this may initiate CRT release and glucose trimming. Given the stochastic nature of glucosidase II activity, both of these pathways are likely followed to some extent, but the relative emphasis

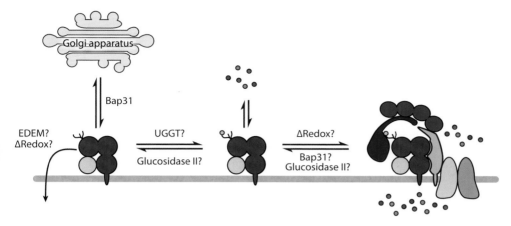

Figure 6

Intersection of the MHC class I loading and ER folding pathways. Glucosidase II and UGGT may act between CNX-mediated MHC class I HC folding and PLC incorporation, or MHC class I HC may remain monoglucosylated throughout this time. Glucosidase II trimming, needed for ER egress, may occur during or after MHC class I association with the PLC. Redox changes in the MHC class I binding groove may prevent peptide binding or signal the failure of multiple rounds of peptide editing and precede degradation. This may be mediated by EDEM (ER degradation–enhancing (α)-mannosidase-like protein). Bap31 (B cell receptor–associated protein 31) mediates MHC class I trafficking to and from the Golgi and may extract MHC class I complexes from the PLC.

will have to be experimentally determined for different MHC class I alleles.

CONCLUDING REMARKS

Much progress has been made toward a comprehensive understanding of MHC class I peptide loading. Models of glycoprotein and oxidative folding have guided studies of MHC class I assembly, and important similarities and differences have been found. Gaps remain in our knowledge of MHC class I peptide loading that can be attributed to technical factors (e.g., the unknown structure and mechanism of tapasin). However, other factors have contributed to controversies in the field, including the diversity of model systems used (e.g., species, cell lines, and alleles) and the inherent complexity of the process itself (e.g., multiple populations of MHC class I complexes coexist within the cell and ER). Future studies should carefully consider the populations of MHC class I molecules (PLC associated or not) that are examined. Designing experiments that differentiate between these populations should lead to greater clarity.

SUMMARY POINTS

1. Peptide loading onto MHC class I complexes is a dynamic event involving multiple steps within the ER. The folding of MHC class I HC with β_2m prior to PLC association is a classic case of glycoprotein folding involving glucosylation-dependent interactions of substrate (MHC class I HC) with CNX and ERp57-facilitated disulfide bond oxidation.

2. The aminopeptidase ERAAP plays an important role in "polishing" the repertoire of peptides presented via MHC class I. Its absence does not grossly affect T cell development, but subtle and significant alterations in the repertoire of presented peptides are seen in ERAAP-deficient mice.

3. The recruitment and retention of ERp57 in the PLC deviate from current models of glycoprotein folding and oxidoreductase function. All cellular tapasin is conjugated to ERp57, and tapasin and ERp57 remain in a mixed disulfide, even though tapasin has achieved a native state. Protein-protein interactions between tapasin and ERp57 are sufficient for conjugate formation, and tapasin inhibits the normally rapid Trx escape pathway in the ERp57 a domain.

4. The core of the PLC is composed of the TAP heterodimer and the associated tapasin/ERp57 conjugate.

5. Multiple, weak interactions within the PLC are necessary for optimal peptide loading. Disruption of any of the interactions affects peptide loading to some extent, and when the interaction of MHC class I with tapasin is completely prevented, peptide loading is severely impaired for most alleles. Future studies of PLC composition must incorporate methods that preserve the tapasin/ERp57 disulfide bond into their isolation protocols.

6. Tapasin can sense the quality of peptide bound by MHC class I complexes, acting as a peptide editor by displacing low-quality peptides. Tapasin allows successive rounds of peptide binding until a certain affinity threshold is met. After peptide loading, MHC class I complexes must pass conventional quality-control checkpoints prior to ER egress.

FUTURE ISSUES

1. The precise molecular composition of the intact PLC remains controversial. There is a strong discordance between PLC size and composition determined by biochemical and immunofluoresence methods. New approaches that incorporate conjugate-preserving techniques are needed.

2. The roles of glycoprotein quality-control enzymes in controlling MHC class I loading and trafficking are undefined. There are multiple points during the biosynthesis, folding, and loading of MHC class I complexes that are potential sites of UGGT and glucosidase action. Careful biochemical studies are needed to parse out these details.

3. Tapasin has been refractory to crystallization. The structure of tapasin with or without ERp57 will provide insight into the molecular mechanism of tapasin, but the structure of the conjugate with MHC class I complexes could provide a definitive answer to this question.

4. The mechanism by which tapasin recruits and sequesters ERp57 in the PLC is unknown. The structure of the tapasin/ERp57 conjugate could inform biochemical studies of ERp57 retention.

5. Most biochemical studies have taken place in a limited number of cell lines, and it is assumed that observations in transformed B cell lines and fibroblasts also apply to physiological antigen-presenting cells such as dendritic cells. Future studies should confirm the applicability of these findings to other cell systems.

6. Redox reactions involving MHC class I HC are integral for proper peptide loading, but the temporal relationship between disulfide bond reduction, peptide loading, and MHC class I HC degradation is unclear. The functional significance of mixed disulfides between PLC components other than tapasin and ERp57 remains unknown.

DISCLOSURE STATEMENT

The authors are not aware of any biases that might be perceived as affecting the objectivity of this review.

ACKNOWLEDGMENTS

We thank Dr. Pamela Wearsch for helpful discussions and Nancy Dometios for assistance in preparing this manuscript. Unpublished work was supported by the Howard Hughes Medical Institute (P.C.) and the NIH/National Institute of General Medical Sciences Medical Scientist Training Grant—GM07205 (D.P.).

LITERATURE CITED

Abele R, Tampe R. 2004. The ABCs of immunology: structure and function of TAP, the transporter associated with antigen processing. *Physiology* 19:216–24

Antoniou AN, Ford S, Alphey M, Osborne A, Elliott T, Powis SJ. 2002. The oxidoreductase ERp57 efficiently reduces partially folded in preference to fully folded MHC class I molecules. *EMBO J.* 21:2655–63

Antoniou AN, Powis SJ. 2003. Characterization of the ERp57-Tapasin complex by rapid cellular acidification and thiol modification. *Antioxid. Redox Signal.* 5:375–79

Antoniou AN, Powis SJ, Elliott T. 2003. Assembly and export of MHC class I peptide ligands. *Curr. Opin. Immunol.* 15:75–81

Antoniou AN, Santos SG, Campbell EC, Lynch S, Arosa FA, Powis SJ. 2007. ERp57 interacts with conserved cysteine residues in the MHC class I peptide-binding groove. *FEBS Lett.* 581:1988–92

Apweiler R, Hermjakob H, Sharon N. 1999. On the frequency of protein glycosylation, as deduced from analysis of the SWISS-PROT database. *Biochim. Biophys. Acta* 1473:4–8

Bangia N, Lehner PJ, Hughes EA, Surman M, Cresswell P. 1999. The N-terminal region of tapasin is required to stabilize the MHC class I loading complex. *Eur. J. Immunol.* 29:1858–70

Barber LD, Howarth M, Bowness P, Elliott T. 2001. The quantity of naturally processed peptides stably bound by HLA-A*0201 is significantly reduced in the absence of tapasin. *Tissue Antigens* 58:363–68

Barnden MJ, Purcell AW, Gorman JJ, McCluskey J. 2000. Tapasin-mediated retention and optimization of peptide ligands during the assembly of class I molecules. *J. Immunol.* 165:322–30

Benham AM, Cabibbo A, Fassio A, Bulleid N, Sitia R, Braakman I. 2000. The CXXCXXC motif determines the folding, structure and stability of human Ero1-Lα. *EMBO J.* 19:4493–502

Cabibbo A, Pagani M, Fabbri M, Rocchi M, Farmery MR, et al. 2000. ERO1-L, a human protein that favors disulfide bond formation in the endoplasmic reticulum. *J. Biol. Chem.* 275:4827–33

Caramelo JJ, Castro OA, Alonso LG, De Prat-Gay G, Parodi AJ. 2003. UDP-Glc:glycoprotein glucosyltransferase recognizes structured and solvent accessible hydrophobic patches in molten globule-like folding intermediates. *Proc. Natl. Acad. Sci. USA* 100:86–91

Cascio P, Hilton C, Kisselev AF, Rock KL, Goldberg AL. 2001. 26S proteasomes and immunoproteasomes produce mainly N-extended versions of an antigenic peptide. *EMBO J.* 20:2357–66

Chambers JE, Jessop CE, Bulleid NJ. 2008. Formation of a major histocompatibility complex class I tapasin disulfide indicates a change in spatial organization of the peptide-loading complex during assembly. *J. Biol. Chem.* 283:1862–69

Chang SC, Momburg F, Bhutani N, Goldberg AL. 2005. The ER aminopeptidase, ERAP1, trims precursors to lengths of MHC class I peptides by a "molecular ruler" mechanism. *Proc. Natl. Acad. Sci. USA* 102:17107–12

Chen M, Bouvier M. 2007. Analysis of interactions in a tapasin/class I complex provides a mechanism for peptide selection. *EMBO J.* 26:1681–90

Chen M, Stafford WF, Diedrich G, Khan A, Bouvier M. 2002. A characterization of the lumenal region of human tapasin reveals the presence of two structural domains. *Biochemistry* 41:14539–45

Daniels R, Kurowski B, Johnson AE, Hebert DN. 2003. N-linked glycans direct the cotranslational folding pathway of *influenza* hemagglutinin. *Mol. Cell* 11:79–90

Darby NJ, Creighton TE. 1995. Characterization of the active site cysteine residues of the thioredoxin-like domains of protein disulfide isomerase. *Biochemistry* 34:16770–80

Darby NJ, Morin PE, Talbo G, Creighton TE. 1995. Refolding of bovine pancreatic trypsin inhibitor via non-native disulphide intermediates. *J. Mol. Biol.* 249:463–77

Dick TB. 2004. Assembly of MHC class I peptide complexes from the perspective of disulfide bond formation. *Cell. Mol. Life Sci.* 61:547–56

Dick TP, Bangia N, Peaper DR, Cresswell P. 2002. Disulfide bond isomerization and the assembly of MHC class I-peptide complexes. *Immunity* 16:87–98

Dick TP, Cresswell P. 2002. Thiol oxidation and reduction in major histocompatibility complex class I-restricted antigen processing and presentation. *Methods Enzymol.* 348:49–54

Diedrich G, Bangia N, Pan M, Cresswell P. 2001. A role for calnexin in the assembly of the MHC class I loading complex in the endoplasmic reticulum. *J. Immunol.* 166:1703–9

D'Urso CM, Wang ZG, Cao Y, Tatake R, Zeff RA, Ferrone S. 1991. Lack of HLA class I antigen expression by cultured melanoma cells FO-1 due to a defect in B2m gene expression. *J. Clin. Investig.* 87:284–92

Ellgaard L, Bettendorff P, Braun D, Herrmann T, Fiorito F, et al. 2002. NMR structures of 36 and 73-residue fragments of the calreticulin P-domain. *J. Mol. Biol.* 322:773–84

Ellgaard L, Frickel EM. 2003. Calnexin, calreticulin, and ERp57: teammates in glycoprotein folding. *Cell. Biochem. Biophys.* 39:223–47

Ellgaard L, Riek R, Braun D, Herrmann T, Helenius A, Wuthrich K. 2001a. Three-dimensional structure topology of the calreticulin P-domain based on NMR assignment. *FEBS Lett.* 488:69–73

Ellgaard L, Riek R, Herrmann T, Guntert P, Braun D, et al. 2001b. NMR structure of the calreticulin P-domain. *Proc. Natl. Acad. Sci. USA* 98:3133–38

Fliegel L, Burns K, MacLennan DH, Reithmeier RA, Michalak M. 1989. Molecular cloning of the high affinity calcium-binding protein (calreticulin) of skeletal muscle sarcoplasmic reticulum. *J. Biol. Chem.* 264:21522–28

Forster ML, Sivick K, Park YN, Arvan P, Lencer WI, Tsai B. 2006. Protein disulfide isomerase-like proteins play opposing roles during retrotranslocation. *J. Cell. Biol.* 173:853–59

Frand AR, Kaiser CA. 1998. The *ERO1* gene of yeast is required for oxidation of protein dithiols in the endoplasmic reticulum. *Mol. Cell* 1:161–70

Frand AR, Kaiser CA. 1999. Ero1p oxidizes protein disulfide isomerase in a pathway for disulfide bond formation in the endoplasmic reticulum. *Mol. Cell* 4:469–77

Frangoulis B, Park I, Guillemot F, Séverac V, Auffray C, Zoorob R. 1999. Identification of the Tapasin gene in the chicken major histocompatibility complex. *Immunogenetics* 49:328–37

Frickel EM, Frei P, Bouvier M, Stafford WF, Helenius A, et al. 2004. ERp57 is a multifunctional thiol-disulfide oxidoreductase. *J. Biol. Chem.* 279:18277–87

Frickel EM, Riek R, Jelesarov I, Helenius A, Wuthrich K, Ellgaard L. 2002. TROSY-NMR reveals interaction between ERp57 and the tip of the calreticulin P-domain. *Proc. Natl. Acad. Sci. USA* 99:1954–59

Gao B, Adhikari R, Howarth M, Nakamura K, Gold MC, et al. 2002. Assembly and antigen-presenting function of MHC class I molecules in cells lacking the ER chaperone calreticulin. *Immunity* 16:99–109

In vitro analysis directly demonstrating tapasin-mediated peptide loading.

Identified the tapasin/ERp57 conjugate and provided a preliminary analysis of conjugate-free PLC function.

Garbi N, Tan P, Diehl AD, Chambers BJ, Ljunggren HG, et al. 2000. Impaired immune responses and altered peptide repertoire in tapasin-deficient mice. *Nat. Immunol.* 1:234–38

Garbi N, Tanaka S, Momburg F, Hammerling GJ. 2006. Impaired assembly of the major histocompatibility complex class I peptide-loading complex in mice deficient in the oxidoreductase ERp57. *Nat. Immunol.* 7:93–102

Garbi N, Tiwari N, Momburg F, Hammerling GJ. 2003. A major role for tapasin as a stabliizer of the TAP peptide transporter and consequences for MHC class I expression. *Eur. J. Immunol.* 33:264–73

Grandea AG 3rd, Golovina TN, Hamilton SE, Sriram V, Spies T, et al. 2000. Impaired assembly yet normal trafficking of MHC class I molecules in *Tapasin* mutant mice. *Immunity* 13:213–22

Greenwood R, Shimizu Y, Sekhon GS, DeMars R. 1994. Novel allele-specific, post-translational reduction in HLA class I expression in a mutant human B cell line. *J. Immunol.* 153:5525–36

Hammer GE, Gonzalez F, Champsaur M, Cado D, Shastri N. 2006. The aminopeptidase ERAAP shapes the peptide repertoire displayed by major histocompatibility complex class I molecules. *Nat. Immunol.* 7:103–12

Hammer GE, Gonzalez F, James E, Nolla H, Shastri N. 2007. In the absence of aminopeptidase ERAAP, MHC class I molecules present many unstable and highly immunogenic peptides. *Nat. Immunol.* 8:101–8

Hammond C, Braakman I, Helenius A. 1994. Role of N-linked oligosaccharide recognition, glucose trimming, and calnexin in glycoprotein folding and quality control. *Proc. Natl. Acad. Sci. USA* 91:913–17

Hammond C, Helenius A. 1994. Folding of VSV G protein: sequential interaction with BiP and calnexin. *Science* 266:456–58

Harris MR, Lybarger L, Yu YY, Myers NB, Hansen TH. 2001. Association of ERp57 with mouse MHC class I molecules is tapasin dependent and mimics that of calreticulin and not calnexin. *J. Immunol.* 166:6686–92

Hebert DN, Foellmer B, Helenius A. 1995. Glucose trimming and reglucosylation determine glycoprotein association with calnexin in the endoplasmic reticulum. *Cell* 81:425–33

Hebert DN, Foellmer B, Helenius A. 1996. Calnexin and calreticulin promote folding, delay oligomerization and suppress degradation of influenza hemagglutinin in microsomes. *EMBO J.* 15:2961–68

Helenius A, Aebi M. 2004. Roles of N-linked glycans in the endoplasmic reticulum. *Annu. Rev. Biochem.* 73:1019–49

Howarth M, Williams A, Tolstrup AB, Elliott T. 2004. Tapasin enhances MHC class I peptide presentation according to peptide half-life. *Proc. Natl. Acad. Sci. USA* 101:11737–42

Hughes EA, Cresswell P. 1998. The thiol oxidoreductase ERp57 is a component of the MHC class I peptide-loading complex. *Curr. Biol.* 8:709–12

Hughes EA, Ortmann B, Surman M, Cresswell P. 1996. The protease inhibitor, N-acetyl-L-leucyl-L-leucyl-leucyl-L-norleucinal, decreases the pool of major histocompatibility complex class I-binding peptides and inhibits peptide trimming in the endoplasmic reticulum. *J. Exp. Med.* 183:1569–78

Hwang C, Sinskey AJ, Lodish HF. 1992. Oxidized redox state of glutathione in the endoplasmic reticulum. *Science* 257:1496–502

Jackson MR, Cohen-Doyle MF, Peterson PA, Williams DB. 1994. Regulation of MHC class I transport by the molecular chaperone, calnexin (p88, IP90). *Science* 263:384–87

Jessop CE, Bulleid NJ. 2004. Glutathione directly reduces an oxidoreductase in the endoplasmic reticulum of mammalian cells. *J. Biol. Chem.* 279:55341–47

Jessop CE, Chakravarthi S, Garbi N, Hammerling GJ, Lovell S, Bulleid NJ. 2007. ERp57 is essential for efficient folding of glycoproteins sharing common structural domains. *EMBO J.* 26:28–40

Kanaseki T, Blanchard N, Hammer GE, Gonzalez F, Shastri N. 2006. ERAAP synergizes with MHC class I molecules to make the final cut in the antigenic peptide precursors in the endoplasmic reticulum. *Immunity* 25:795–806

Kang SJ, Cresswell P. 2002. Calnexin, calreticulin, and ERp57 cooperate in disulfide bond formation in human CD1d heavy chain. *J. Biol. Chem.* 277:44838–44

Keller SH, Lindstrom J, Taylor P. 1998. Inhibition of glucose trimming with castanospermine reduces calnexin association and promotes proteasome degradation of the α-subunit of the nicotinic acetylcholine receptor. *J. Biol. Chem.* 273:17064–72

Kienast A, Preuss M, Winkler M, Dick TP. 2007. Redox regulation of peptide receptivity of major histocompatibility complex class I molecules by ERp57 and tapasin. *Nat. Immunol.* 8:864–72

Identified defects in MHC class I recruitment and peptide loading in B cells lacking ERp57.

Used trapping mutants to identify ERp57 substrates with common structural motifs.

Klappa P, Ruddock LW, Darby NJ, Freedman RB. 1998. The b' domain provides the principal peptide-binding site of protein disulfide isomerase but all domains contribute to binding of misfolded proteins. *EMBO J.* 17:927–35

Kleizen B, Braakman I. 2004. Protein folding and quality control in the endoplasmic reticulum. *Curr. Opin. Cell Biol.* 16:343–49

Koch J, Guntrum R, Heintke S, Kyritsis C, Tampe R. 2004. Functional dissection of the transmembrane domains of the transporter associated with antigen processing (TAP). *J. Biol. Chem.* 279:10142–47

Kozlov G, Maattanen P, Schrag JD, Pollock S, Cygler M, et al. 2006. Crystal structure of the bb' domains of the protein disulfide isomerase ERp57. *Structure* 14:1331–39

Kulp MS, Frickel EM, Ellgaard L, Weissman JS. 2006. Domain architecture of protein-disulfide isomerase facilitates its dual role as an oxidase and an isomerase in Ero1p-mediated disulfide formation. *J. Biol. Chem.* 281:876–84

Laboissiere MC, Sturley SL, Raines RT. 1995. The essential function of protein-disulfide isomerase is to unscramble non-native disulfide bonds. *J. Biol. Chem.* 270:28006–9

Labriola C, Cazzulo JJ, Parodi AJ. 1995. Retention of glucose units added by the UDP-GLC:glycoprotein glucosyltransferase delays exit of glycoproteins from the reticulum. *J. Cell Biol.* 130:771–79

Ladasky JJ, Boyle S, Seth M, Li H, Pentcheva T, et al. 2006. Bap31 enhances the endoplasmic reticulum export and quality control of human class I MHC molecules. *J. Immunol.* 177:6172–81

Leach MR, Cohen-Doyle MF, Thomas DY, Williams DB. 2002. Localization of the lectin, ERp57 binding, and polypeptide binding sites of calnexin and calreticulin. *J. Biol. Chem.* 277:29686–97

Leach MR, Williams DB. 2004. Lectin-deficient calnexin is capable of binding class I histocompatibility molecules in vivo and preventing their degradation. *J. Biol. Chem.* 279:9072–79

Lehner PJ, Surman MJ, Cresswell P. 1998. Soluble tapasin restores MHC class I expression and function in the tapasin-negative cell line .220. *Immunity* 8:221–31

Leonhardt RM, Keusekotten K, Bekpen C, Knittler MR. 2005. Critical role for the tapasin-docking site of TAP2 in the functional integrity of the MHC class I-peptide-loading complex. *J. Immunol.* 175:5104–14

Lewis JW, Elliott T. 1998. Evidence for successive peptide binding and quality control stages during MHC class I assembly. *Curr. Biol.* 8:717–20

Li SJ, Hong XG, Shi YY, Li H, Wang CC. 2006. Annular arrangement and collaborative actions of four domains of protein-disulfide isomerase: a small angle X-ray scattering study in solution. *J. Biol. Chem.* 281:6581–88

Lindquist JA, Hammerling GJ, Trowsdale J. 2001. ER60/ERp57 forms disulfide-bonded intermediates with MHC class I heavy chain. *FASEB J.* 15:1448–50

Lindquist JA, Jensen ON, Mann M, Hammerling GJ. 1998. ER-60, a chaperone with thiol-dependent reductase activity involved in MHC class I assembly. *EMBO J.* 17:2186–95

Ma Y, Hendershot LM. 2004. ER chaperone functions during normal and stress conditions. *J. Chem. Neuroanat.* 28:51–65

Marguet D, Spiliotis ET, Pentcheva T, Lebowitz M, Schneck J, Edidin M. 1999. Lateral diffusion of GFP-tagged H2Ld molecules and of GFP-TAP1 reports on the assembly and retention of these molecules in the endoplasmic reticulum. *Immunity* 11:231–40

Meunier L, Usherwood YK, Chung KT, Hendershot LM. 2002. A subset of chaperones and folding enzymes form multiprotein complexes in endoplasmic reticulum to bind nascent proteins. *Mol. Biol. Cell* 13:4456–69

Mezghrani A, Fassio A, Benham A, Simmen T, Braakman I, Sitia R. 2001. Manipulation of oxidative protein folding and PDI redox state in mammalian cells. *EMBO J.* 20:6288–96

Molinari M, Calanca V, Galli C, Lucca P, Paganetti P. 2003. Role of EDEM in the release of misfolded glycoproteins from the calnexin cycle. *Science* 299:1397–400

Molinari M, Eriksson KK, Calanca V, Galli C, Cresswell P, et al. 2004. Contrasting functions of calreticulin and calnexin in glycoprotein folding and ER quality control. *Mol. Cell* 13:125–35

Molinari M, Helenius A. 1999. Glycoproteins form mixed disulphides with oxidoreductases during folding in living cells. *Nature* 402:90–93

Molinari M, Helenius A. 2000. Chaperone selection during glycoprotein translocation into the reticulum. *Science* 288:331–33

With Solda et al. (2006), suggests an important role for calnexin- and calreticulin-recruited ERp57 in glycoprotein folding.

Molteni SN, Fassio A, Ciriolo MR, Filomeni G, Pasqualetto E, et al. 2004. Glutathione limits Ero1-dependent oxidation in the endoplasmic reticulum. *J. Biol. Chem.* 279:32667–73

Momburg F, Tan P. 2002. Tapasin—the keystone of the loading complex optimizing peptide binding by MHC class I molecules in the endoplasmic reticulum. *Mol. Immunol.* 39:217–33

Morrice NA, Powis SJ. 1998. A role for the thiol-dependent reductase ERp57 in the assembly of MHC class I molecules. *Curr. Biol.* 8:713–16

Nossner E, Parham P. 1995. Species-specific differences in chaperone interaction of human and mouse major histocompatibility complex class I molecules. *J. Exp. Med.* 181:327–37

Oda Y, Hosokawa N, Wada I, Nagata K. 2003. EDEM as an acceptor of terminally misfolded glycoproteins released from calnexin. *Science* 299:1394–97

Oliver JD, Roderick HL, Llewellyn DH, High S. 1999. ERp57 functions as a subunit of specific complexes formed with the ER lectins calreticulin and calnexin. *Mol. Biol. Cell* 10:2573–82

Oliver JD, van der Wal FJ, Bulleid NJ, High S. 1997. Interaction of the thiol-dependent reductase ERp57 with nascent glycoproteins. *Science* 275:86–88

Ortmann B, Copeman J, Lehner PJ, Sadasivan B, Herberg JA, et al. 1997. A critical role for tapasin in the assembly and function of multimeric MHC class I-TAP complexes. *Science* 277:1306–9

Pagani M, Fabbri M, Benedetti C, Fassio A, Pilati S, et al. 2000. Endoplasmic reticulum oxidoreductin 1-Lβ (*ERO1-Lβ*), a human gene induced in the course of the unfolded protein response. *J. Biol. Chem.* 275:23685–92

Paquet ME, Cohen-Doyle M, Shore GC, Williams DB. 2004. Bap29/31 influences the intracellular traffic of MHC class I molecules. *J. Immunol.* 172:7548–55

Park B, Lee S, Kim E, Ahn K. 2003. A single polymorphic residue within the peptide-binding cleft of MHC class I molecules determines spectrum of tapasin dependence. *J. Immunol.* 170:961–68

Park B, Lee S, Kim E, Cho K, Riddell SR, et al. 2006. Redox regulation facilitates optimal peptide selection by MHC class I during antigen processing. *Cell* 127:369–82

Peace-Brewer AL, Tussey LG, Matsui M, Li G, Quinn DG, Frelinger JA. 1996. A point mutation in HLA-A*0201 results in failure to bind the TAP complex and to present virus-derived peptides to CTL. *Immunity* 4:505–14

Peaper DR, Wearsch PA, Cresswell P. 2005. Tapasin and ERp57 form a stable disulfide-linked dimer within the MHC class I peptide-loading complex. *EMBO J.* 24:3613–23

Peh CA, Burrows SR, Barnden M, Khanna R, Cresswell P, et al. 1998. HLA-B27-restricted antigen presentation in the absence of tapasin reveals polymorphism in mechanisms of HLA class I peptide loading. *Immunity* 8:531–42

Petersen JL, Hickman-Miller HD, McIlhaney MM, Vargas SE, Purcell AW, et al. 2005. A charged amino acid residue in the transmembrane/cytoplasmic region of tapasin influences MHC class I assembly and maturation. *J. Immunol.* 174:962–69

Pirneskoski A, Klappa P, Lobell M, Williamson RA, Byrne L, et al. 2004. Molecular characterization of the principal substrate binding site of the ubiquitous folding catalyst protein disulfide isomerase. *J. Biol. Chem.* 279:10374–81

Pollard MG, Travers KJ, Weissman JS. 1998. Ero1p: a novel and ubiquitous protein with an essential role in oxidative protein folding in the endoplasmic reticulum. *Mol. Cell* 1:171–82

Pollock S, Kozlov G, Pelletier MF, Trempe JF, Jansen G, et al. 2004. Specific interaction of ERp57 and calnexin determined by NMR spectroscopy and an ER two-hybrid system. *EMBO J.* 23:1020–29

Purcell AW, Gorman JJ, Garcia-Peydro M, Paradela A, Burrows SR, et al. 2001. Quantitative and qualitative influences of tapasin on the class I peptide repertoire. *J. Immunol.* 166:1016–27

Rizvi SM, Raghavan M. 2006. Direct peptide-regulatable interactions between MHC class I molecules and tapasin. *Proc. Natl. Acad. Sci. USA* 103:18220–25

Rufer E, Leonhardt RM, Knittler MR. 2007. Molecular architecture of the TAP-associated MHC class I peptide-loading complex. *J. Immunol.* 179:5717–27

Russell SJ, Ruddock LW, Salo KE, Oliver JD, Roebuck QP, et al. 2004. The primary substrate binding site in the b′ domain of ERp57 is adapted for endoplasmic reticulum lectin association. *J. Biol. Chem.* 279:18861–69

Initial description of tapasin and demonstration that tapasin is a key factor promoting PLC function.

Demonstrated that tapasin sequesters ERp57 in the PLC through inactivation of the escape pathway of ERp57.

Sadasivan B, Lehner PJ, Ortmann B, Spies T, Cresswell P. 1996. Roles for calreticulin and a novel glycoprotein, tapasin, in the interaction of MHC class I molecules with TAP. *Immunity* 5:103–14

Sadasivan BK, Cariappa A, Waneck GL, Cresswell P. 1995. Assembly, peptide loading, and transport of MHC class I molecules in a calnexin-negative cell line. *Cold Spring Harb. Symp. Quant. Biol.* 60:267–75

Salter RD, Cresswell P. 1986. Impaired assembly and transport of HLA-A and -B antigens in a mutant TxB cell hybrid. *EMBO J.* 5:943–49

Santos SG, Campbell EC, Lynch S, Wong V, Antoniou AN, Powis SJ. 2007. Major histocompatibility complex class I-ERp57-tapasin interactions within the peptide-loading complex. *J. Biol. Chem.* 282:17587–93

Saric T, Chang SC, Hattori A, York IA, Markant S, et al. 2002. An IFN-γ-induced aminopeptidase in the ER, ERAP1, trims precursors to MHC class I-presented peptides. *Nat. Immunol.* 3:1169–76

Schrag JD, Bergeron JJ, Li Y, Borisova S, Hahn M, et al. 2001. The structure of calnexin, an ER chaperone involved in quality control of protein folding. *Mol. Cell* 8:633–44

Serwold T, Gonzalez F, Kim J, Jacob R, Shastri N. 2002. ERAAP customizes peptides for MHC class I molecules in the endoplasmic reticulum. *Nature* 419:480–83

Sesma L, Galocha B, Vazquez M, Purcell AW, Marcilla M, et al. 2005. Qualitative and quantitative differences in peptides bound to HLA-B27 in the presence of mouse versus human tapasin define a role for tapasin as a size-dependent peptide editor. *J. Immunol.* 174:7833–44

Sevier CS, Kaiser CA. 2002. Formation and transfer of disulphide bonds in living cells. *Nat. Rev. Mol. Cell Biol.* 3:836–47

Silvennoinen L, Myllyharju J, Ruoppolo M, Orru S, Caterino M, et al. 2004. Identification and characterization of structural domains of human ERp57: Association with calreticulin requires several domains. *J. Biol. Chem.* 279:13607–15

Solda T, Garbi N, Hammerling GJ, Molinari M. 2006. Consequences of ERp57 deletion on oxidative folding of obligate and facultative clients of the calnexin cycle. *J. Biol. Chem.* 281:6219–26

Solheim JC, Harris MR, Kindle CS, Hansen TH. 1997. Prominence of beta 2-microglobulin, class I heavy chain conformation, and tapasin in the interactions of class I heavy chain with calreticulin and the transporter associated with antigen processing. *J. Immunol.* 158:2236–41

Sousa M, Parodi AJ. 1995. The molecular basis for the recognition of misfolded glycoproteins by the UDP-Glc:glycoprotein glucosyltransferase. *EMBO J.* 14:4196–203

Spies T, Cerundolo V, Colonna M, Cresswell P, Townsend A, DeMars R. 1992. Presentation of viral antigen by MHC class I molecules is dependent on a putative peptide transporter heterodimer. *Nature* 355:644–46

Spies T, DeMars R. 1991. Restored expression of major histocompatibility class I molecules by gene transfer of a putative peptide transporter. *Nature* 351:323–24

Spiliotis ET, Manley H, Osorio M, Zuniga MC, Edidin M. 2000. Selective export of MHC class I molecules from the ER after their dissociation from TAP. *Immunity* 13:841–51

Strehl B, Seifert U, Kruger E, Heink S, Kuckelkorn U, Kloetzel PM. 2005. Interferon-γ, the functional plasticity of the ubiquitin-proteasome system, and MHC class I antigen processing. *Immunol. Rev.* 207:19–30

Suh WK, Derby MA, Cohen-Doyle MF, Schoenhals GJ, Fruh K, et al. 1999. Interaction of murine MHC class I molecules with tapasin and TAP enhances peptide loading and involves the heavy chain α3 domain. *J. Immunol.* 162:1530–40

Suh WK, Mitchell EK, Yang Y, Peterson PA, Waneck GL, Williams DB. 1996. MHC class I molecules form ternary complexes with calnexin and TAP and undergo peptide-regulated interaction with TAP via their extracellular domains. *J. Exp. Med.* 184:337–48

Tan P, Kropshofer H, Mandelboim O, Bulbuc N, Hammerling GJ, Momburg F. 2002. Recruitment of MHC class I molecules by tapasin into the transporter associated with antigen processing-associated complex is essential for optimal peptide loading. *J. Immunol.* 168:1950–60

Thammavongsa V, Raghuraman G, Filzen TM, Collins KL, Raghavan M. 2006. HLA-B44 polymorphisms at position 116 of the heavy chain influence TAP complex binding via an effect on peptide occupancy. *J. Immunol.* 177:3150–61

Tian G, Xiang S, Noiva R, Lennarz WJ, Schindelin H. 2006. The crystal structure of yeast protein disulfide isomerase suggests cooperativity between its active sites. *Cell* 124:61–73

With Molinari et al. (2004), suggests an important role for ERp57 in glycoprotein folding in vivo.

Crystal structure of yeast PDI demonstrating a horseshoe shape and the orientation of domains.

Tjoelker LW, Seyfried CE, Eddy RL Jr, Byers MG, Shows TB, et al. 1994. Human, mouse, and rat calnexin cDNA cloning: identification of potential calcium binding motifs and gene localization to human
chromosome 5. *Biochemistry* 33:3229–36

Turnquist HR, Petersen JL, Vargas SE, McIlhaney MM, Bedows E, et al. 2004. The Ig-like domain of tapasin
influences intermolecular interactions. *J. Immunol.* 172:2976–84

Turnquist HR, Vargas SE, Reber AJ, McIlhaney MM, Li S, et al. 2001. A region of tapasin that affects L^d
binding and assembly. *J. Immunol.* 167:4443–49

Van Kaer L, Ashton-Rickardt PG, Ploegh HL, Tonegawa S. 1992. TAP1 mutant mice are deficient in antigen
presentation, surface class I molecules, and CD4$^-$8$^+$ T cells. *Cell* 71:1205–14

Van Leeuwen JE, Kearse KP. 1997. Reglucosylation of N-linked glycans is critical for calnexin assembly with
T cell receptor (TCR) α proteins but not TCRβ proteins. *J. Biol. Chem.* 272:4179–86

Vassilakos A, Cohen-Doyle MF, Peterson PA, Jackson MR, Williams DB. 1996. The molecular chaperone
calnexin facilitates folding and assembly of class I histocompatibility molecules. *EMBO J.* 15:1495–506

Walker KW, Gilbert HF. 1997. Scanning and escape during protein-disulfide isomerase-assisted folding.
J. Biol. Chem. 272:8845–48

Walker KW, Lyles MM, Gilbert HF. 1996. Catalysis of oxidative protein folding by mutants of protein
disulfide isomerase with a single active-site cysteine. *Biochemistry* 35:1972–80

Wang N, Daniels R, Hebert DN. 2005. The cotranslational maturation of the type I membrane glycoprotein
tyrosinase: The heat shock protein 70 system hands off to the lectin-based chaperone system. *Mol. Biol.
Cell* 16:3740–52

Warburton RJ, Matsui M, Rowland-Jones SL, Gammon MC, Katzenstein GE, et al. 1994. Mutation of the
α2 domain disulfide bridge of the class I molecule HLA-A*0201. Effect on maturation and peptide
presentation. *Hum. Immunol.* 39:261–71

Ware FE, Vassilakos A, Peterson PA, Jackson MR, Lehrman MA, Williams DB. 1995. The molecular chaperone
calnexin binds Glc1Man9GlcNAc2 oligosaccharide as an initial step in recognizing unfolded glycoproteins. *J. Biol. Chem.* 270:4697–704

**Wearsch PA, Cresswell P. 2007. Selective loading of high-affinity peptides onto major histocompati-
bility complex class I molecules by the tapasin-ERp57 heterodimer. *Nat. Immunol.* 8:873–81**

Wearsch PA, Jakob CA, Vallin A, Dwek RA, Rudd PM, Cresswell P. 2004. Major histocompatibility complex
class I molecules expressed with monoglucosylated N-linked glycans bind calreticulin independently of
their assembly status. *J. Biol. Chem.* 279:25112–21

Wei ML, Cresswell P. 1992. HLA-A2 molecules in an antigen-processing mutant cell contain signal sequence-
derived peptides. *Nature* 356:443–46

Weissman JS, Kim PS. 1993. Efficient catalysis of disulphide bond rearrangements by protein disulphide
isomerase. *Nature* 365:185–88

Williams AP, Peh CA, Purcell AW, McCluskey J, Elliott T. 2002. Optimization of the MHC class I peptide
cargo is dependent on tapasin. *Immunity* 16:509–20

Williams DB, Barber BH, Flavell RA, Allen H. 1989. Role of beta 2-microglobulin in the intracellular transport
and surface expression of murine class I histocompatibility molecules. *J. Immunol.* 142:2796–806

Wright CA, Kozik P, Zacharias M, Springer S. 2004. Tapasin and other chaperones: models of the MHC class
I loading complex. *Biol. Chem.* 385:763–78

Yan J, Parekh VV, Mendez-Fernandez Y, Olivares-Villagomez D, Dragovic S, et al. 2006. In vivo role of ER-
associated peptidase activity in tailoring peptides for presentation by MHC class Ia and class Ib molecules.
J. Exp. Med. 203:647–59

Yewdell JW, Nicchitta CV. 2006. The DRiP hypothesis decennial: support, controversy, refinement and
extension. *Trends Immunol.* 27:368–73

York IA, Brehm MA, Zendzian S, Towne CF, Rock KL. 2006. Endoplasmic reticulum aminopeptidase 1
(ERAP1) trims MHC class I-presented peptides in vivo and plays an important role in immunodominance.
Proc. Natl. Acad. Sci. USA 103:9202–7

York IA, Chang SC, Saric T, Keys JA, Favreau JM, et al. 2002. The ER aminopeptidase ERAP1 enhances or
limits antigen presentation by trimming epitopes to 8–9 residues. *Nat. Immunol.* 3:1177–84

Zapun A, Darby NJ, Tessier DC, Michalak M, Bergeron JJ, Thomas DY. 1998. Enhanced catalysis of ribonuclease B folding by the interaction of calnexin or calreticulin with ERp57. *J. Biol. Chem.* 273:6009–12

Provided clear evidence
that the tapasin-ERp57
conjugate functions as a
peptide editor in a
cell-free system.

Zarling AL, Luckey CJ, Marto JA, White FM, Brame CJ, et al. 2003. Tapasin is a facilitator, not an editor, of class I MHC peptide binding. *J. Immunol.* 171:5287–95

Zernich D, Purcell AW, Macdonald WA, Kjer-Nielsen L, Ely LK, et al. 2004. Natural HLA class I polymorphism controls the pathway of antigen presentation and susceptibility to viral evasion. *J. Exp. Med.* 200:13–24

Zhang Y, Baig E, Williams DB. 2006. Functions of ERp57 in the folding and assembly of major histocompatibility complex class I molecules. *J. Biol. Chem.* 281:14622–31

Zijlstra M, Bix M, Simister NE, Loring JM, Raulet DH, Jaenisch R. 1990. Beta 2-microglobulin deficient mice lack CD4$^-$8$^+$ cytolytic T cells. *Nature* 344:742–46

RELATED RESOURCES

Reviews on all aspects of MHC biology: Cresswell P. 2005. Antigen processing and presentation. *Immunol. Rev.* 207:5–7

Cross presentation: Ackerman AL, Cresswell P. 2004. Cellular mechanisms governing cross-presentation of exogenous antigens. *Nat. Immunol.* 5:678–84

MHC class II antigen processing and presentation: Watts C. 2004. The exogenous pathway for antigen presentation on major histocompatibility complex class II and CD1 molecules. *Nat. Immunol.* 5:685–92

CD1d antigen presentation: Barral DC, Brenner MB. 2007. CD1 antigen presentation: how it works. *Nat. Rev. Immunol.* 7:929–41

Structural and Functional Aspects of Lipid Binding by CD1 Molecules

Jonathan D. Silk,[1] Mariolina Salio,[1] James Brown,[2] E. Yvonne Jones,[2] and Vincenzo Cerundolo[1]

[1]Tumour Immunology Unit, Weatherall Institute of Molecular Medicine, University of Oxford, John Radcliffe Hospital, Oxford OX3 9DS, United Kingdom; email: vincenzo.cerundolo@imm.ox.ac.uk

[2]Cancer Research UK Receptor Structure Research Group, The Henry Wellcome Building for Genomic Medicine, University of Oxford, Headington, Oxford OX3 7BN, United Kingdom; email: yvonne@strubi.ox.ac.uk

Annu. Rev. Cell Dev. Biol. 2008. 24:369–95

First published online as a Review in Advance on July 1, 2008

The *Annual Review of Cell and Developmental Biology* is online at cellbio.annualreviews.org

This article's doi: 10.1146/annurev.cellbio.24.110707.175359

Key Words

iNKT cells, structure, CD1, antigen presentation, trafficking

Abstract

Over the past ten years, investigators have shown that T lymphocytes can recognize not only peptides in the context of MHC class I and class II molecules but also foreign and self-lipids in association with the non-classical MHC class I molecules the CD1 proteins. We describe the events that have led to the discovery of the role of CD1 molecules, their pattern of intracellular trafficking, and their ability to sample different intracellular compartments for self- and foreign lipids. Structural and functional aspects of lipid presentation by CD1 molecules are presented in the context of the function of CD1-restricted T cells in antimicrobial responses, antitumor immunity, and the regulation of the tolerance and autoimmunity immunoregulatory axis. Particular emphasis is on invariant NKT (iNKT) cells and their ability to modulate innate and adaptive immune responses.

Contents

CD1 GENES

The monoclonal antibody NA1/34 was identified after screening hybridomas derived from mice injected with human thymocytes (McMichael et al. 1979). NA1/34 was shown to stain a large proportion of human thymocytes and was found to recognize the 45-kDa protein HTA1, later renamed CD1 (Bernard et al. 1984). We now know that the human CD1 gene family is composed of five nonpolymorphic genes (*CD1A, -B, -C, -D,* and *-E*), located in a cluster on human chromosome 1 (Calabi & Milstein 2000). In contrast, mice express

β-2m: β-2 microglobulin

DC: dendritic cell

TLR: Toll-like receptor

only two CD1d orthologs; these are located in chromosome 3, likely the result of duplication events. CD1 genes have an intron/exon structure similar to that of MHC class I genes, encoding type I integral membrane proteins consisting of α1, α2, and α3 domains noncovalently linked to β-2 microglobulin (β-2m). On the basis of sequence identities in the α1 and α2 domains, the CD1 isoforms are separated into two groups: group 1, consisting of CD1a, -b, -c, and -e molecules, and group 2, consisting of CD1d molecules (Calabi & Milstein 2000).

CD1 CELLULAR EXPRESSION

Group 1 CD1a, -b, and -c molecules are expressed on cortical thymocytes and on myeloid cells, such as dendritic cells (DCs) and Langerhans cells (Dougan et al. 2007a). Although CD1a molecules are expressed on most double-positive (DP) and some single-positive thymocytes, they are not expressed on mature T cells in the periphery, and their downregulation is associated with T cell maturation (Res et al. 1997). CD1c molecules (but not CD1a or CD1b molecules) are also expressed by marginal zone B cells and 50% of peripheral blood B cells (Delia et al. 1988). During differentiation of monocytes with GM-CSF, expression of CD1a, CD1b, and CD1c is induced and is either upregulated (CD1b and c) or downregulated (CD1a) following DC maturation (Cao et al. 2002, Porcelli et al. 1992).

CD1d molecules are found on most cells of the hematopoietic lineage, although the highest levels of expression are generally on antigen-presenting cells (APCs), such as DCs and B cells (Exley et al. 2000). Marginal zone B cells have among the highest levels of surface expression of CD1d (Roark et al. 1998). CD1d is also expressed by hepatocytes, intestinal epithelial cells and keratinocytes (Dougan et al. 2007a), and activated T cells (Exley et al. 2000). Expression of CD1d on the surface of APCs is enhanced by cytokines, such as IFN-β, IFN-γ, and TNF-α, and by Toll-like receptor (TLR) 2 and TLR4 ligands (Skold et al. 2005). The peroxisome proliferator–activated receptor γ

(PPARγ) controls CD1d expression by triggering retinoic acid synthesis in human DCs (Szatmari et al. 2006). Furthermore, a number of pathogens modulate CD1d expression levels. Viruses such as Kaposi sarcoma–associated herpes virus (Sanchez et al. 2005) and HIV mediate their immune-evasive effects by downregulating CD1d expression (Cho et al. 2005). Elegant mechanistic studies have shown that both herpes simplex virus-1 (HSV-1) and vesicular stomatitis virus (VSV) can cause a downregulation of CD1d expression by suppressing CD1d recycling (Yuan et al. 2006).

LIPID ANTIGENS

Several CD1-restricted antigens have been characterized. These are shown in **Figure 1**.

CD1a-Presented Lipid Antigens

Very few CD1a-presented lipid antigens from either self or microbial origin have been characterized. The two main ligands that have been shown to induce an immune response are sulfatide and didehydroxymycobactin (DDM).

Sulfatide. The sphingolipid sulfatide is a sulfate ester of β-D-galactosylceramide, the main constituent of mammalian brain lipids, is also presented by CD1b and -c as well as mouse CD1d, and stimulates T cell responses (Jahng et al. 2004, Shamshiev et al. 2002).

Didehydroxymycobactin. To date the only characterized exogenous CD1a-restricted lipid antigen is DDM (Moody et al. 2004) **(Figure 1a)**. Initial experiments demonstrated that a lipid fraction derived from *Mycobacterium tuberculosis* was capable of sensitizing responses in a CD1a-restricted fashion (Rosat et al. 1999). Subsequent experiments led to the identification of the antigenic lipopeptide DDM, consisting of a complex peptide linked via acylation of a lysine moiety to a single alkyl chain of approximately 20 carbons (Moody et al. 2004). Because this group of lipopeptides, defined as mycobactins, is widely produced by mycobac-

teria, DDM-related structures may also be presented to CD1-restricted T lymphocytes.

CD1b-Presented Lipid Antigens

Mycolic acid. Porcelli and colleagues first described CD1-restricted T cells by stimulating peripheral blood lymphocytes from tuberculosis patients with extracts of *M. tuberculosis* cell walls (Porcelli et al. 1992). The cognate antigen was demonstrated to be mycolic acid, providing the first direct evidence for T cell recognition of lipids (Beckman et al. 1994). Mycolic acids are a family of α-branched and β-hydroxy fatty acids produced by several bacteria and differ in chain length and head-group derivatives. Mycobacterial mycolic acids have a much longer meromycolate branch (up to 90 carbons) and α-branch chain than do *Nocardia* mycolic acids **(Figure 1b)**, which influences their recognition (Moody et al. 2002).

Glucose monomycolate. Glucose monomycolate (GMM) is a glucose ester of mycolic acid, recognized by T cells in a manner dependent on the type of esterified carbohydrate, because naturally occurring mycolate esters of glycerol and arabinose are not recognized (Moody et al. 1997). Recognition is specific for the naturally occurring sugar linkage, but not for analogs lacking either the α-branched (glucose-6-*O*-3-hydroxypalmitate) or β-hydroxy [3-tert-butyldimethylsilylated-GMM (GMM-TBDMS), glucose-6-*O*-2-tetradecylhexadecanoate] structure (Moody et al. 1997).

CD1c-Presented Lipid Antigens

The first CD1c-restricted lipid was isolated from the cell wall of both *Mycobacterium avium* and *M. tuberculosis* (Moody et al. 2000) **(Figure 1c)**. Mycobacteria-specific T cell lines recognized two previously unknown mycobacterial hexosyl-1-phosphoisoprenoids and structurally related mannosyl-1-phosphodolichols. Responses to mannosyl-1-phosphodolichols were common among CD1c-restricted T cell

GMM: glucose monomycolate

a Didehydroxymycobactin

b Glucomonomycolate

c Mannosyl-β1 phosphomycoketide

d iNKT cell agonists

Natural

iGb3

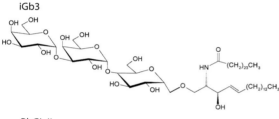

BbGL-II

PBS-30

Synthetic

α-GalCer

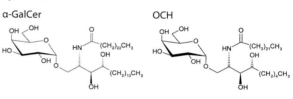

OCH

α-C-GalCer

Threitolceramide

C20:2

Figure 1

CD1-binding lipid antigens. Some representative examples of the range of ligands presented by CD1 molecules are shown. (*a*) Mycopeptides, such as didehydroxymycobactin from *Mycobacterium tuberculosis*, are presented by CD1a molecules (Moody et al. 2004). (*b*) Glucomonomycolate (GMM) from *M. tuberculosis* is presented by CD1b molecules (Moody et al. 1997). (*c*) Mannosyl-β1 phosphomycoketide from *M. tuberculosis* is presented by CD1c molecules (Moody et al. 1997). (*d*) iNKT cell agonists. Among the natural agonists are the endogenous glycosphingolipid isoglobotrihexosylceramide (iGb3), which is recognized by human and mouse iNKT cells (Speak et al. 2007, Zhou et al. 2004b). The microbial lipid antigen BbGL-II (1,2-diacyl-3-*O*-galactosyl-*sn*-glycerol) from *Borrelia burgdorferi* (Kinjo et al. 2006) and the microbial glycosphingolipid antigen PBS-30 from *Sphingomonas* (Mattner et al. 2005) are shown. Also shown is a panel of synthetic ligands (*right*): α-GalCer (α-galactosylceramide) (Kawano et al. 1997), OCH [(2S,3S,4R)-1-*O*-(α-D-galactopyranosyl)-*N*-tetracosanoyl-2-amino-1,3,4-nonanetriol] (Miyamoto et al. 2001), the C-glycoside α-C-GalCer (Schmieg et al. 2003), the nonglycosidic ligand threitolceramide (Silk et al. 2008), and C20:2 (Yu et al. 2005).

lines and peripheral blood T cells of human subjects recently infected with *M. tuberculosis* but were not seen in naive control subjects (Moody et al. 2000). These antigens contain a single fully saturated alkyl chain that is similar to isoprenoid lipids, with methyl branches at every fourth carbon, and are referred to as mannosyl phosphoisoprenoids.

Mycobacteria-specific T cells also recognized purified natural *Mycobacterium smegmatis*–derived β-D-mannopyranosyl-1-phosphoheptaprenol released by treatment of mycolated phospholipid (Moody et al. 2000). Recent work from the same laboratory analyzed the role of methyl branches within the alkyl chains of mycoketides and showed that the most potent CD1c-restricted T cell responses are generated when the stereochemistry of the branches mimics natural mannosyl-β1-phosphomycoketides (de Jong et al. 2007). The ability to detect certain methyl branching patterns, specific to defined pathogens, may be an additional means of alerting the immune system to the presence of danger.

CD1d-Presented Lipid Antigens

α-Galactosylceramide (α-GalCer) (**Figure 1d**), derived from a marine sponge (*Agelas mauritianus*), stimulates invariant natural killer T (iNKT) cells in a CD1d-dependent manner (Kawano et al. 1997). Activation of iNKT cells with α-GalCer induces secretion of IFN-γ, IL-4, IL-12, and GM-CSF, not just from the iNKT cells directly, but also from NK cells and DCs as a result of iNKT cell activation (Brigl & Brenner 2004). α-GalCer is composed of a galactose head group linked to phytosphingosine and acyl chains via an α-linkage. Natural endogenous and exogenous iNKT cell agonists are discussed elsewhere in this review.

A number of synthetic analogs of α-GalCer with different properties have also been described (Wu et al. 2005, Yu et al. 2005). $(2S,3S,4R)$-1-O-(α-D-galactopyranosyl)-N-tetracosanoyl-2-amino-1,3,4-nonanetriol (OCH) (**Figure 1d**) has a truncated sphingosine chain (Miyamoto et al. 2001) and induces

significantly reduced IFN-γ while maintaining IL-4 production from mouse iNKT cells. The OCH-induced Th2 cytokine bias is useful in ameliorating the signs of Th1 autoimmune disease (Miyamoto et al. 2001).

By modification of the length and degree of unsaturation of the acyl chain, investigators found other ligands (such as C20:2) (**Figure 1d**) that induced Th2 cytokines compared with the Th1/0 profile observed with α-GalCer (Yu et al. 2005). Interestingly, C20:2 is less dependent than α-GalCer on lysosomal trafficking for presentation by CD1d. In contrast, the α-C-glycoside analog (α-C-GalCer) (**Figure 1d**) induces enhanced production of Th1 cytokines, such as IFN-γ and IL-12, and has increased efficacy in mouse models of malaria and tumor metastasis (Fujii et al. 2006, Schmieg et al. 2003).

We recently described a family of nonglycosidic ligands (Silk et al. 2008). Threitolceramide (**Figure 1d**) efficiently activates iNKT cells, resulting in DC maturation and priming of antigen-specific T and B cells. The weaker binding affinity of the CD1d/threitolceramide complex for the iNKT T cell receptor (TCR), as compared with the binding to the α-GalCer/CD1d complex, reduces iNKT cell activation, minimizing the release of cytokines and iNKT-dependent lysis of APCs, ensuring a faster recovery of iNKT cells from activation-induced anergy. Shortening or lengthening the threitol moiety by one hydroxymethylene group modulates ligand recognition because human and murine iNKT cells recognize glycerolceramide and arabinitolceramide differentially.

CD1 MOLECULAR STRUCTURE

Unlike MHC class I and class II genes, CD1a, -b, -c, and -d genes show low levels of polymorphism, raising the question of how monomorphic lipid-binding proteins can bind and present a broad range of different lipid species to T cells. The CD1 binding groove (**Figure 2a**) has the same general architecture as MHC class I, with α1 and α2

α-GalCer: α-galactosylceramide

iNKT cells: invariant natural killer T cells

OCH: $(2S,3S,4R)$-1-O-(α-D-galactopyranosyl)-N-tetracosanoyl-2-amino-1,3,4-nonanetriol

TCR: T cell receptor

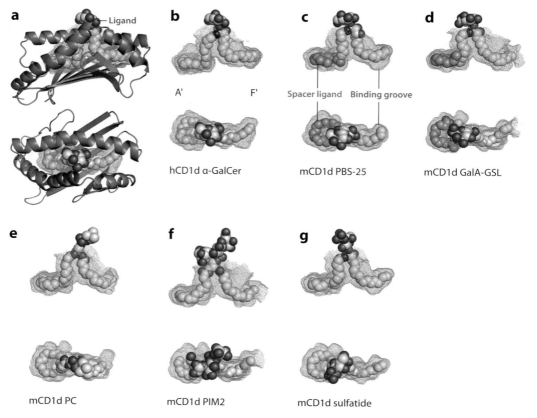

a Ligand

b A'　F'

hCD1d α-GalCer

c Spacer ligand　Binding groove

mCD1d PBS-25

d mCD1d GalA-GSL

e mCD1d PC

f mCD1d PIM2

g mCD1d sulfatide

Figure 2

Structures of CD1d/ligand complexes. (*a*) The α1 helix, α2 helix, and β sheet forming the ligand binding groove for a representative CD1 structure (human CD1d) are depicted in blue ribbon. The binding groove volume is delineated by a semitransparent surface (calculated using the VOLUMES program; R. Esnouf, unpublished), and the ligand α-galactosylceramide (α-GalCer) is shown as van der Waals spheres colored by atom type (carbon, *white*; oxygen, *red*). The binding groove is viewed from the side, through the α2 helix (*top*), and from above, which is the TCR binding surface (*bottom*). (*b*–*g*) Human and mouse CD1d/ligand complexes are shown as in panel *a* but without the blue ribbon depicting the CD1 main chain. For each panel the primary ligand is shown as van der Waals spheres colored by atom type (carbon, *white*; oxygen, *red*; nitrogen, *blue*), and any additional spacer ligand is shown in green. GalA-GSL, α-galacturonosyl ceramide; PC, phosphatidylcholine; PIM2, dipalmitoyl-phosphatidylinositol mannoside. PBS-25 is a truncated analog of α-GalCer with an 8-carbon acyl chain.

helices flanking a β-sheet floor (Zeng et al. 1997), but is somewhat narrower and deeper with a pronounced hydrophobic character. By analogy with MHC class I nomenclature, the two major pockets, or channels, common to all crystal structures of CD1 family binding grooves determined to date, are labeled A' and F' (**Figures 2–4**). These hydrophobic channels bind the lipid tails of CD1-presented antigens. Significant differences in the structure of these two pockets, as well as additional fea-

tures of the binding grooves, confer distinctive ligand binding characteristics to the different members of the CD1 family (Gadola et al. 2002b; Koch et al. 2005; Zajonc et al. 2003, 2005a).

Distinctive Binding Groove Architectures

The crystal structures of human CD1a, CD1b, and CD1d and mouse CD1d have been

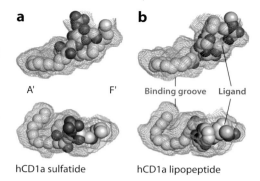

a

A' F'

hCD1a sulfatide

b

Binding groove   Ligand

hCD1a lipopeptide

Figure 3

Structures of CD1a/ligand complexes. For each CD1a/ligand structure the binding groove is viewed from the side, through the α2 helix (*top*), and from above, which is the TCR binding surface (*bottom*). The binding groove volume is delineated by a semitransparent surface (calculated using the VOLUMES program; R. Esnouf, unpublished), and the ligand is shown as van der Waals spheres colored by atom type (carbon, *white*; oxygen, *red*; nitrogen, *blue*).

determined in complex with specific antigens (**Figures 2–4**), providing a detailed mapping of the binding groove architecture for each of these CD1 family members.

CD1d. The structure of mouse CD1d was the first determined for any CD1 molecule (Zeng et al. 1997), and subsequent structural studies have underscored the prototypic character of the CD1d binding groove. The crystal structures of human and mouse CD1d in complex with α-GalCer or the variant agonist PBS-25 (Koch et al. 2005, Zajonc et al. 2005a) revealed essentially identical grooves and lipid-binding modes for the two species (**Figure 2b,c**). The groove can be described in terms of two cavities, A' and F'. A' is the more channel-like and follows a curved path circumventing a pole formed by residues Cys12 and Phe70, a feature that is common to all CD1 structures determined to date (comprising Val12 and Phe70 in CD1a and CD1b), whereas the F' cavity is more capacious. α-GalCer effectively saturates the binding capacity of the CD1d binding groove, the 26 carbon atoms of the acyl chain filling the A' channel, and the 18 carbon atoms of the sphingosine chain fitting snugly into the F' channel (Koch et al. 2005).

CD1a. The binding groove of CD1a has the smallest capacity of any of the family members

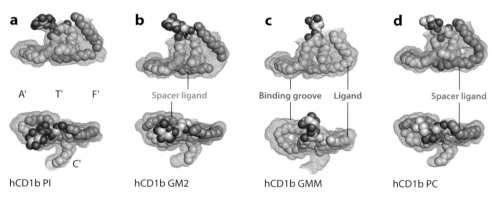

a

A'   T'   F'

C'

hCD1b PI

b

Spacer ligand

hCD1b GM2

c

Binding groove   Ligand

hCD1b GMM

d

Spacer ligand

hCD1b PC

Figure 4

Structures of CD1b/ligand complexes. For each CD1a/ligand structure the binding groove is viewed from the side, through the α2 helix (*top*), and from above. The binding groove volume is delineated by a semitransparent surface (calculated using the VOLUMES program; R. Esnouf, unpublished). The primary ligand is shown as van der Waals spheres colored by atom type (carbon, *white*; oxygen, *red*; nitrogen, *blue*), and any additional spacer ligands are shown in green and mauve. GM2, GalNAc[β]4(NeuAc[α]3)Gal[β]4Glc[β]Cer; GMM, glucose monomycolate; PC, phosphatidylcholine; PI, phosphatidylinositol.

determined to date (Zajonc et al. 2003) (**Figure 3**). The groove is composed of the two standard channels, A′ and F′, but these are either shorter or shallower than in CD1d and CD1b. The narrow A′ channel retains its characteristic curve but is truncated to a half circle (**Figure 3a**), limiting its capacity to alkyl chains of 18–23 carbon atoms, a length restriction that prompted Zajonc et al. (2003) to describe the CD1a A′ channel as a molecular ruler. In contrast, the F′ cavity is much wider and opens back up to the surface. It is shallower than in CD1d and CD1b molecules. As a result of these characteristics, binding in the CD1a F′ cavity is not restricted to antigens with acyl chains, an adaptability exemplified by the structure of CD1a in complex with a synthetic DDM-like lipopeptide for which the two peptidic branches are bound in the F′ cavity while the alkyl chain fills the A′ channel (Zajonc et al. 2005b) (**Figure 3b**). The combination of reduced capacity and enhanced accessibility (in particular of the shallow F′ cavity) also suggests that CD1a may have simpler antigen loading requirements than do other CD1 family members, permitting it to sample antigens more readily at the cell surface or within sorting endosomes (Zajonc et al. 2003).

CD1b. The first structures of CD1b in complex with specific glycolipids revealed a binding groove containing a maze of channels (Gadola et al. 2002b) that elaborates and extends the basic arrangement of A′ and F′ cavities found for the prototypic CD1d structure. The F′ cavity is subdivided into distinct C′ and F′ channels; these channels are connected to the A′ channel by the T′ tunnel, which runs along the bottom of the binding groove (**Figure 4a,b**). This buried T′ tunnel is a distinctive feature of CD1b and results from the lack of side chains at residues Gly98 and Gly116. The second novel feature of the CD1b binding groove is the C′ channel portal, a potential exit to the molecular surface located beneath the α2 helix, which can appear open (Batuwangala et al.

2004, Gadola et al. 2002b) or closed (Garcia-Alles et al. 2006). In total, this maze of channels provides the CD1b groove with the largest binding capacity among CD1 molecules but also sets the most complex challenge for lipid loading. Gadola et al. (2002b) suggested that the C′ channel could bind a relatively short C22–C26 acyl chain while the interconnected network of A′, T′, and F′ channels, uniquely, could accommodate C50–C56 long-chain meromycolates of the type found in intracellular bacteria and this was subsequently demonstrated in the crystal structure of CD1b complexed with GMM (Batuwangala et al. 2004) (**Figure 4c**).

Unfilled Capacity and Lipid Spacers

The first two crystal structures of CD1b were for the molecule in complex with glycolipids phosphatidylinositol (PI) and the ganglioside GalNAc[β]4(NeuAc[α]3)Gal[β]4Glc[β]Cer (GM2), whose acyl tails did not saturate its extensive binding capacity. Serendipitously, the spare capacity was filled by two single alkyl chain detergents, an observation that suggested that endogenous short-chain fatty acids could play an important role as chaperones, stabilizing CD1b prior to higher-affinity ligand binding (Gadola et al. 2002b). The recent observations of Garcia-Alles et al. (2006) for a natively folded CD1b (expressed in mouse cells) have borne out this hypothesis, revealing a CD1b binding groove stabilized by a C32–C36 endogenous phosphatidylcholine (PC) in combination with a C41–C44 spacer lipid. The spacer lipid occupies the T′ tunnel and F′ channel in a manner essentially identical to that originally observed for the two C16 detergent molecules in the CD1b/PI and CD1b/GM2 structures (**Figure 4a,b,d**). Garcia-Alles et al. (2006) point out that stabilization of binding capacity deep within the groove by endogenous spacers may allow direct loading and rapid presentation of short lipid antigens at the cell surface through use of the remaining capacity, whereas removal of the spacer molecule may accompany the loading of long lipid antigens in late endosomes. Spacers may play a similar role for CD1d and may indeed fill excess A′ channel capacity in three mouse CD1d structures complexed with PBS-25 (Zajonc et al. 2005a; **Figure 2c**), α-galacturonosyl ceramide (GalA-GSL) (Wu et al. 2006; **Figure 2d**), and isoglobotrihexosylceramide (iGb3) (Zajonc et al. 2008). The incorporation of a ligand appears to be crucial to the stability of the CD1 binding groove; additional electron density was noted in the A′ and F′ cavities for the original structure of mouse CD1d in the absence of a specific ligand (Zeng et al. 1997), and subsequent structural and mass spectrometric analyses of mouse CD1, produced in an insect cell expression system, identified a mixture of *Drosophila*-derived PCs in the binding groove (Giabbai et al. 2005) (**Figure 2e**). The structure determination of human CD1d/α-GalCer, using CD1d expressed in *Escherichia coli* and refolded in the presence of the specific ligand, revealed a crystal lattice comprising the CD1d/α-GalCer complex accompanied by a second empty copy of CD1d devoid of α-GalCer (Koch et al. 2005). Fragmentary electron density indicated that this non-lipid-bound CD1d may have some small-molecule species partially occupying the binding groove; however, in the absence of the crystal lattice, CD1d molecules lacking α-GalCer were inherently unstable. Comparison of the lipid-bound and non-lipid-bound CD1d grooves revealed several structural differences resulting primarily from changes in side-chain conformations to fill unoccupied capacity (Koch et al. 2005). These structural changes provide a model for how differences in non-solvent-exposed lipid length, in particular in the F′ cavity, could be propagated to the surface presented for recognition by TCRs (McCarthy et al. 2007). The balance between lipid antigen and spacer usage is clearly central to the production of functional CD1 molecules and is coordinated during trafficking.

CD1 INTRACELLULAR LOADING AND TRAFFICKING

Events Occurring in the Endoplasmic Reticulum

Within the lumen of the endoplasmic reticulum (ER), newly synthesized CD1 molecules are associated with the chaperone proteins calnexin and calreticulin (Sugita et al. 1997). Binding of calnexin is made possible by the processing of *N*-linked oligosaccharides on the newly synthesized CD1 heavy chain. CD1d molecules, unlike CD1b, can traffic to the cell surface in the absence of β-2m. This difference is thought to be a result of the association of CD1d with the thiol oxidoreductase ERp57, which is important for the formation of disulfide bonds within the CD1 heavy chain prior to assembly with β-2m (Kang & Cresswell 2002). Mutation analysis revealed that the loss of glycan-2, at the interface between CD1d and β-2m, results in faster CD1d egress from the ER and reduced stability at the cell surface (Paduraru et al. 2006). Assembly of CD1 molecules is independent of transporter associated with antigen processing (TAP), as expression of CD1 molecules is not affected by TAP deficiencies (Hanau et al. 1994). Consistent with the hypothesis that, before leaving the ER, CD1 molecules are loaded with ER-resident lipids, Joyce and colleagues showed that CD1b molecules and human and mouse CD1d molecules assemble in the ER with cellular PI (Joyce et al. 1998).

A role for the microsomal triglyceride transfer protein (MTP) in CD1d presentation of endogenous and exogenous iNKT cell ligands has been described (Brozovic et al. 2004, Dougan et al. 2005, Sagiv et al. 2007). Initial results indicated that ER-resident MTP regulates the biosynthetic pathway of CD1d molecules (Brozovic et al. 2004). In the absence of MTP, presentation of α-GalCer is dramatically impaired owing to reduced CD1d surface expression and the accumulation of CD1d molecules in the ER (Brozovic et al. 2004). Silencing MTP in professional APCs impairs their ability to present iNKT cell agonists (Dougan et al. 2005). Furthermore, purified MTP can transfer lipids to recombinant CD1d in vitro (Dougan et al. 2005). Dougan et al. (2007b) recently demonstrated that inhibition of MTP in fetal thymic organ culture results in impaired positive selection of iNKT cells, consistent with the hypothesis that MTP facilitates loading of the first endogenous lipid into the CD1d groove, allowing their traffic from the ER to the cell surface. The authors suggest that in the absence of MTP, the CD1d groove may be in a collapsed conformation or may contain a lipid refractory to editing. Thus, without MTP function, saposins and other lipid transfer proteins in the endosomal pathway are disabled in their ability to transfer lipid to CD1d.

An alternative hypothesis proposed by Bendelac and colleagues suggests that MTP deficiency may impair the recycling of CD1d from the lysosome to the plasma membrane, rather than having an impact on the transport of CD1d molecules from the ER to the lysosome (Sagiv et al. 2007). In the absence of MTP, the rate of CD1d biosynthesis and transit through the ER and Golgi is unaltered (Sagiv et al. 2007). Consistent with these findings, iNKT cell development and stimulation are partially impaired in chimeric mice, which carry a deletion of the first exon of MTP in their cortical thymocytes (Sagiv et al. 2007).

Events Occurring at the Cell Surface

From the ER, CD1 molecules traffic to the cell surface through the secretory pathway before being reinternalized into the endo-lysosomal compartment. Most CD1 isoforms contain the YXXZ motif within their cytoplasmic tail (where Y = tyrosine, X = any amino acid, and Z = bulky hydrophobic residue), allowing CD1 to bind to the specific adaptor protein (AP) complex AP-2. AP-2 is a component of clathrin-coated pits that is associated with the plasma membrane and is important for endocytosis and recruitment of cargo (Sever 2003). CD1a does not contain such a targeting motif within the cytoplasmic tail, yet is still in-ternalized, suggesting that trafficking of CD1a from the cell surface to the intracellular compartments is different from trafficking of other CD1 family members. Consistent with this possibility, Sloma et al. (2008) showed a direct association at the cell surface between CD1a and invariant chain (Ii). Surface expression of CD1a in Ii-silenced cells was increased, whereas the total cellular pool of CD1a remained constant, indicating that the internalization of CD1a is dependent on the presence of Ii. The same authors showed that CD1a/Ii complexes are located within lipid rafts at the cell surface and that disruption of the lipid rafts has a deleterious effect on the activation of CD1a-restricted T cells (Sloma et al. 2008).

After internalization, CD1a is initially found in early/sorting endosomes and is then colocalized in early/recycling endosomes with Rab11, a small GTPase that regulates the trafficking of recycling endosomes to the plasma membrane (Salamero et al. 2001). Inhibition of endocytosis leads to a flux of CD1a from the intracellular recycling endosomes and accumulation of CD1a at the cell surface. These data suggest that CD1a molecules undergo a cycle of internalization into early/sorting endosomes followed by early/recycling endosomes, where they sample distinct sets of antigens before returning to the cell surface. This recycling pathway is thought to be regulated by ADP-ribosylation factor-6 (ARF-6), a small GTPase found within the recycling vesicles in which CD1a is localized (Sugita et al. 1999).

The tyrosine-based motif within the cytoplasmic tails of CD1b, -c, and -d molecules is crucial for their targeting and subsequent antigen presentation (Jackman et al. 1998, Jayawardena-Wolf et al. 2001). The differential localization of antigen-presenting molecules is important because it allows for the sampling of antigens from distinct intracellular sites. Sugita et al. (1999) showed that CD1b was found in late-endosomal/lysosomal vesicles, including the MHC class II compartments (MIIC), and colocalized with the lysosome-associated membrane protein-1 (LAMP-1). These researchers demonstrated that, unlike for CD1a, antigen presentation in the context of CD1b depends on endosomal acidification.

To read the "address" of the sorting motif within the cytoplasmic tail and deliver CD1b to the late-endosomal/lysosomal vesicles, a molecular sorting step characterized by the binding of APs is required. The first sorting step involves binding of the CD1b cytoplasmic tail motif to AP-2 at the plasma membrane and recruitment into clathrin-coated pits (Briken et al. 2002). In the absence of AP-3, which also binds to the tyrosine tail motif, CD1b can no longer traffic to the lysosome and accumulates at the plasma membrane and in early lysosomes (Sugita et al. 2002). Antigen presentation by CD1b molecules was defective in the absence of AP-3, showing that antigen acquisition occurs within the acidic environment of the endosome. Deletion of the cytoplasmic tyrosine tail sequence led to the accumulation of CD1b at the cell surface and failure to localize to LAMP$^+$ endosomes. The ability to present both endogenously delivered lipid antigen and exogenously delivered lipid antigen was compromised (Jackman et al. 1998).

CD1c molecules also contain a tyrosine-based address sequence, which when deleted prevents their internalization (Briken et al. 2000). Because CD1c molecules do not bind AP-3 (Sugita et al. 2002), they are distributed throughout the endocytic compartment and are found within both the recycling endosomes and the late-endocytic compartments (Sugita et al. 2000). Presentation of antigens by CD1c is independent of acidification and is thought to allow a broad-spectrum sampling of lipid antigens throughout the endosomal network. This overlapping coordination of CD1 expression potentially facilitates sampling of both exogenous and endogenous antigens by CD1 molecules within different cellular compartments in different cell types.

Presentation of antigen in the context of CD1d molecules is dependent on the AP-2-binding, tyrosine-containing motif within the cytoplasmic tail. However, human CD1d and murine CD1d have different intracellular localizations. Although both are found within early endosomes as a result of binding AP-2, murine CD1d also binds to AP-3, explaining why murine CD1d molecules are found intracellularly within lysosomal/MIIC. Mutations or deletions of the cytoplasmic tail motif and modifications of CD1d trafficking to acidified lysosomes in mice with a defect in AP-3 impair antigen presentation and iNKT cell development (Chiu et al. 2002, Elewaut et al. 2003, Jayawardena-Wolf et al. 2001, Lawton et al. 2005). Although presentation of antigen to Vα14$^+$ iNKT cells is impaired when the tail motif is modified, recognition by Vα14$^-$ NKT cells is not affected (Chiu et al. 1999). This suggests that different cell populations recognize antigens loaded in different cellular compartments. Presentation of antigen by mCD1d may occur through both AP-3-dependent and -independent processes (Lawton et al. 2005), allowing for sampling of a broader spectrum of antigens in the absence of group I CD1 molecules.

In contrast, human CD1d molecules are unable to bind to AP-3 (Sugita et al. 2002). However, both mouse CD1d and human CD1d are able to complex with both Ii and MHC class II molecules (Chen et al. 2007, Jayawardena-Wolf et al. 2001, Kang & Cresswell 2002b). Chen et al. (2007) have proposed that there is an alternative mechanism allowing some trafficking of human CD1d to MIIC in the absence of AP-3 binding. Inhibition of Ii expression showed that, although responses to exogenous antigens were impaired, presentation of autoantigens was not defective (Chen et al. 2007). These researchers suggested that Ii-dependent trafficking of hCD1d is important for loading with exogenously derived antigens. In one proposed mechanism, some Ii/MHC class II–associated CD1d molecules are transported directly from the Golgi to the lysosome without necessarily trafficking via the cell surface.

Events Occurring in the Endo-Lysosomal Compartment

A number of endosomal proteins are involved in the processing and loading of glycolipids onto CD1 molecules. These proteins include glycosidases, saposins, Niemann-Pick type C2 (NPC2) protein, and CD1e and are described below.

Glycosidases, found within the endosomes and lysosomes, are involved in the catabolism of complex glycolipid precursors to simpler antigens that can be recognized. The presence of α-galactosidase in the lysosome is important for the removal of a galactose group from galactosyl $(1 \rightarrow 2)$ galactosylceramide (GalGalCer) to generate α-GalCer, which is recognized by iNKT cells (Prigozy et al. 2001).

Saposins A, B, C, and D are produced from the proteolytic cleavage of prosaposin within the endosome. Prosaposin-deficient mice have defective development of iNKT cells and reduced ability to process and present glycolipid antigens (Zhou et al. 2004a). Loading of human CD1d with α-GalCer in the absence of saposins is similarly impaired (Kang & Cresswell 2004). Saposin B is the most efficient of the saposins in transferring glycolipids onto CD1d for presentation (Yuan et al. 2007). In contrast, saposin C is involved in the loading of CD1b (Winau et al. 2004).

Mice lacking the NPC2 protein, a lysosomal lipid transfer protein, have impaired presentation of glycolipids and impaired selection of iNKT cells in the thymus (Schrantz et al. 2007). The authors show that NPC2 dimers can bind iGb3 and facilitate its loading onto CD1d molecules.

CD1e molecules are not monomorphic (Tourne et al. 2008) and are localized mainly in the lysosomes of mature DCs, where CD1e molecules are cleaved into a soluble form that is retained in the lysosome. CD1e molecules are important for the presentation of antigens, such as PIM2, to CD1b-restricted T cells (de la Salle et al. 2005), although a recently discovered CD1e isoform was unable to assist antigen loading onto CD1b molecules (Tourne et al. 2008). CD1e molecules are involved in the editing or processing of the carbohydrate portion of large complex glycolipids, such as PIM6, by lysosomal mannosidases for loading onto CD1b (de la Salle et al. 2005). Soluble CD1e molecules may extract self-lipids from the endosomal membrane and present them to lysosome-processing enzymes such as hydrolases. It is unclear whether CD1e molecules are then involved in the transfer of the processed moiety to membrane-bound CD1b molecules.

LIPID-SPECIFIC T CELLS

CD1a-, CD1b-, and CD1c-Restricted T Cells

A limited number of systematic studies have been performed to compare the frequency of T cells restricted by CD1a, -b, and -c and their role in infection. Increased frequencies of CD1-restricted, antigen-specific T cells to mycobacterial antigens derived from *Mycobacterium leprae* and *M. tuberculosis* and from previously infected, healthy donors or from people immunized with Bacillus Calmette Guérin (BCG) were reported (Gilleron et al. 2004, Kawashima et al. 2003, Moody et al. 2000, Ulrichs et al. 2003). These antigens include a diverse array of structures, including the CD1a-binding DDM (**Figure 1***a*), the CD1b-binding GMM (**Figure 1***b*), and the CD1c-binding mannosyl-phosphomycoketides (**Figure 1***c*). Tuberculoid patients infected with *M. leprae*, who were able to control the infection, had a greater frequency of CD1-restricted T cells compared with lepromatous patients, who had disseminated infection (Sieling et al. 2005). It is unclear whether CD1-restricted T cells can be protective in other nonmycobacterial diseases.

CD1d-Restricted T Cells

Invariant NKT cells. iNKT cells express a semi-invariant TCR, composed of Vα24-Jα18 segments paired with Vβ11 in humans and Vα14-Jα18 segments paired with a limited set of Vβ chains in mice (Vβ8.2, Vβ7, and Vβ2) (Brigl & Brenner 2004). Human and mouse iNKT cells are reactive to α-GalCer when presented by human and/or mouse CD1 molecules (Brossay et al. 1998). Humans have a noninvariant NKT cell subset, which can be expanded with α-GalCer in vitro and in vivo (Chang et al. 2005, Gadola et al. 2002a).

iNKT cell development. iNKT cell development occurs in the thymus from bone marrow–derived precursors. Early developmental stages of iNKT cells and MHC-restricted CD4[+] and CD8[+] T cells are similar and consistent with the TCR-instructive model of differentiation (Gapin et al. 2001). The branching between iNKT and conventional T cell development occurs at the double-positive (DP) stage, after successful rearrangement of the TCR loci. Differentiation of iNKT cells from DP thymocytes is dependent on the transcription factor RORγt (Egawa et al. 2005). In the thymus, RORγt is exclusively expressed at the DP stage. In transgenic mice in which RORγt controls the expression of green fluorescence protein (GFP), all iNKT cells in the liver and in the spleen are GFP positive, confirming their origin from DP thymocytes. By regulating expression of Bcl-xL and thus thymocyte survival, RORγt influences the window of time during which rearrangement of Vα to Jα segments occurs, therefore allowing the late Vα14-Jα18 rearrangement to take place. Consequently, inactivation of RORγt abrogates iNKT cell development, although selection of MHC-restricted CD4[+] and CD8[+] T cells is not affected, with the exception of a slightly altered T cell repertoire (Guo et al. 2002).

CD1d restricted iNKT cells can be identified by the use of α-GalCer-CD1d tetramers in mouse thymus from day 3 after birth, reaching a plateau at 4–6 weeks of age (Benlagha et al. 2005). Immature HSA[high] DP precursors differentiate into HSA[low] CD44[low] NK1.1[−] cells, which develop into CD44[high] NK1.1[−] cells and then into CD44[high] NK1.1[+] mature iNKT cells. Maturing iNKT cells acquire the capacity to transcribe the IL-4 and IFN-γ loci (Stetson et al. 2003). The terminal differentiation of iNKT cells involves the expression of other NK receptors and sensitivity to IL-15 following the upregulation of CD122 (Matsuda et al. 2002). Although acquisition of NK1.1 expression occurs mainly in the periphery, following interaction with CD1d molecules (McNab et al. 2005, Wei et al. 2005), a population of long-lived nondividing iNKT cells that acquires NK1.1 expression in the thymus also exists (Berzins et al. 2006). Moreover, a previously unrecognized population of mature and functionally distinct peripheral NK1.1[−] iNKT cells has been reported (McNab et al. 2007).

The majority (80%) of murine iNKT cells are CD4[+], whereas the remaining cells are double negative (DN) (Benlagha & Bendelac 2000, Matsuda et al. 2000). The absence of CD8[+] iNKT cells in mice and the reduction in iNKT cell numbers following overexpression of CD8 molecules in T cells (Bendelac et al. 1994) have been explained as a consequence of negative selection, although a clear demonstration of CD1d binding to CD8 molecules is lacking. Evidence for DC-mediated iNKT cell negative selection in the presence of strong agonistic signaling has been proposed on the basis of the results of fetal thymic organ culture (FTOC) systems exposed to α-GalCer and DCs from mice overexpressing CD1d (Chun et al. 2003, Schumann et al. 2005). The frequency of Vβ8.2-expressing iNKT cells, which have the highest affinity for α-GalCer/CD1d complexes (Schumann et al. 2003), was most reduced in these experimental models, consistent with the interpretation that potentially highly self-reactive iNKT cells can be deleted before they exit the thymus. Expression of inhibitory receptors of the Ly49 family also shapes the iNKT cell repertoire emerging from the thymus (Hayakawa et al. 2004, Voyle et al. 2003).

Unlike conventional peptide-specific CD4[+] and CD8[+] T cells, iNKT cells are selected by CD1d[+] DP thymocytes (Bendelac 1995; Gapin et al. 2001). CD1d expression by cortical DP thymocytes is both necessary and sufficient for iNKT cell development (Wei et al. 2005). CD1d expression on peripheral APCs is not required for the survival of terminally differentiated iNKT cells (Matsuda et al. 2002), although CD1d-expressing APCs in the periphery influence iNKT terminal differentiation and the acquisition of functional properties (Matsuda et al. 2002, McNab et al. 2005,

GSL:
glycosphingolipid

Wei et al. 2005). iNKT cells in mice expressing CD1d exclusively in the thymus, under the pLcK promoter, had enhanced TCR reactivity, which was corrected by expressing a CD1d transgene in all MHC class II–positive cells under the Eα promoter (Wei et al. 2005).

Functional iNKT cells that exclusively expressed Vβ8.2 TCRs developed in mice expressing human CD1d in cortical thymocytes under the proximal pLck promoter (Schumann et al. 2005). Because coexpression of murine CD1d restored development of Vβ7 iNKT cells but did not modify the reduced frequency of Vβ8.2 iNKT cells, these results were interpreted as evidence for iNKT cell negative selection mediated by high-avidity binding of human CD1d to the developing iNKT cells.

No preferential pairing of Vβ8.2 or Vβ7 with Vα14Jα18 chains has been shown, yet 50% of mature iNKT cells are Vβ8.2, and only 14% are Vβ7 (Schumann et al. 2006). Instead, the TCR Vβ usage of developing iNKT cells influences the avidity of iNKT TCR binding to CD1d complexed with endogenous lipids, and this has a profound effect on the positive selection of the iNKT cell repertoire (Schumann et al. 2006, Wei et al. 2006). Under competitive conditions of positive selection, such as limiting CD1d-endogenous antigen expression in CD1d$^{+/-}$ mice, an inversion of the Vβ8.2/Vβ7 ratio was demonstrated (Schumann et al. 2006). By crossing the Vα14Jα18 transgene onto a CD1d$^{-/-}$ background, Wei et al. (2006) demonstrated that the Vβ repertoire of DN cells was quite diverse and that a large proportion of these cells were able to bind CD1d/α-GalCer tetramers, although these cells were unable to recognize the endogenous glycosphingolipid (GSL) iGb3 or natural ligands expressed by DCs. Additionally, the TCR Vβ usage (and therefore avidity for CD1d/lipid complexes) influences the activation of peripheral iNKT cells by different exogenous lipids (Stanic et al. 2003b).

Endogenous iNKT cell natural selecting ligands. One important and still unanswered question is the nature of the antigen(s) presented by CD1d molecules to iNKT cells at each stage of development. Evidence from a β-glucosylceramide synthase mutant cell line unable to stimulate Vα14 iNKT cells suggested that the natural ligand(s) is a GSL (Stanic et al. 2003a). Initial studies suggested that iGb3 (**Figure 1d**) was the sole antigen selecting iNKT cells because β-hexosaminidase A/B–deficient ($hexb^{-/-}$) mice, lacking the lysosomal enzyme necessary to degrade iGb4 to iGb3, had impaired iNKT cell development (Zhou et al. 2004b). iGb3 is an agonist for human and murine iNKT cells (Schumann et al. 2006, Zhou et al. 2004b) and can activate iNKT cells in the periphery (Mattner et al. 2005). However, more recent work has shown that not only $hexb^{-/-}$ mice, but also mice with defects in other lysosomal enzymes involved in GSL catabolism and even in cholesterol transport, have severe defects in iNKT cell development (Gadola et al. 2006b, Prigozy et al. 2001, Sagiv et al. 2006, Schrantz et al. 2007, Schumann et al. 2007) A feature common to all these mutant mice is altered lipid trafficking and processing in the lysosomal compartment, which, with only one exception (Zhou et al. 2004b), result in lysosomal engulfment and the inability to process the complex glycolipid GalGalCer. In addition, analysis of iGb3 synthase–deficient mice showed normal development and function of iNKT cells (Porubsky et al. 2007). Finally, iGb3 was not detected in mouse thymus cells or DCs by a sensitive biochemical analysis (Speak et al. 2007). iGb3 was not detected in any human tissue (Speak et al. 2007), consistent with the finding that human iGb3 synthase is a pseudogene (Milland et al. 2006). However, the expression of iGb3 by human and mouse DCs and thymocytes remains an open question; a recent paper indicated the presence of iGb3 in human thymus by mass spectrometry (Li et al. 2008).

Peripheral iNKT cell activation. Activation of iNKT cells initiates a cross talk with other cell types, mainly NK cells, DCs, and B cells. The subsequent CD40L-mediated maturation of DCs and B cells results in powerful adjuvant activity, leading to enhanced CD4, CD8, and antibody responses to coinjected protein antigens, thus bridging the innate and the adaptive arms of the immune responses (Fujii et al. 2003, Galli et al. 2007, Hermans et al. 2003, Silk et al. 2004).

A number of pathogen-derived lipids recognized by iNKT cells have been characterized, further contributing to our understanding of the role of iNKT cells in infection models. Three modes of iNKT cell activation during bacterial infections can be summarized. In the first mode, iNKT cells can directly recognize exogenous bacterial lipid antigens presented on the surface of CD1d molecules of infected cells. α-Linked GSLs recognized by most human and mouse iNKT cells have been isolated from the cell wall of *Sphingomonas*, gram-negative, LPS-negative bacteria (**Figure 1d**). The importance of iNKT cell recognition of these bacterial lipids is underlined by the observation that the number of surviving bacteria was significantly increased in livers of iNKT cell–deficient CD1d$^{-/-}$ mice, and this increase affected their survival at higher bacterial numbers (Kinjo et al. 2005, Mattner et al. 2005, Sriram et al. 2005).

Not all pathogen-derived lipids are GSLs, as demonstrated by the ability of galactosyl diacylglycerol (**Figure 1d**) from *Borrelia burgdorferi* (a causative agent of Lyme disease) to activate human and mouse iNKT cells, albeit with some species-specific differences in terms of requirements for acyl chain length and saturation (Kinjo et al. 2006). Recognition of *Sphingomonas*- and *Borrelia*-derived lipids is independent of TLR-mediated activation of APCs and of IL-12 and is entirely CD1d dependent (Kinjo et al. 2005, Mattner et al. 2005).

Regarding the second mode of iNKT cell activation during bacterial infections, recognition of exogenous microbial antigens is not required for some pathogens (for example, *Salmonella typhimurium*). iNKT cells are activated indirectly, following amplification of weak reactivity to self-glycolipids by costimulatory cytokines, such as IL-12 released from DCs

upon TLR signaling (Brigl et al. 2003, Mattner et al. 2005).

In the third mode, APC-derived cytokines can also activate iNKT cells irrespective of TCR engagement (Nagarajan & Kronenberg 2007). The nature of antigens(s) responsible for iNKT cell autoreactivity is still a matter of investigation (see above). Activation of human and murine APC by synthetic agonists of TLR4, TLR7/8, and TLR9 enhances the expression of transcripts for several glycosyltransferases involved in the biosynthesis of GSLs (Paget et al. 2007, Salio et al. 2007). In this system, a charged β-linked GSL (therefore not iGb3) derived from TLR9-stimulated murine DCs elicited, together with type I IFN, iNKT cell activation (Paget et al. 2007). These findings extend previous results demonstrating an effect of LPS on lipid metabolism and presentation of self-antigens [sulfatide and monosialoganglioside GM1 (GM1)] in association with CD1a and CD1b molecules, establishing a link between microbial infections and autoimmunity (De Libero et al. 2005). These results also suggest that, in addition to directly or indirectly sensing bacteria, iNKT cells can be activated during viral infections, despite the absence of unique glycolipid antigens within viruses. In this way, TLR signaling coordinates pathogen recognition with antigen uptake and the efficient activation of class II–restricted as well as CD1-restricted T cell responses (Blander & Medzhitov 2006).

Noninvariant NKT cells. Noninvariant NKT cells, also referred to as type II NKT cells, are CD1d-restricted T cells that do not express the canonical iNKT TCR and that fail to be stained by α-GalCer/CD1d tetramers. Although the specificity of these cells remains unclear in the majority of cases, a proportion of type II NKT cells can be specifically stained by CD1d tetramers loaded with sulfatide, a self-glycolipid derived from myelin (Jahng et al. 2004, Zajonc et al. 2005c). Recent findings have indicated that activation of CD1d-restricted type II NKT cells during tumor growth results in the release of IL-13 and stimulation of myeloid-derived suppressor cells (Terabe et al. 2006).

MOLECULAR BASIS FOR RECEPTOR RECOGNITION

In all CD1/glycolipid structures determined to date, the carbohydrate head group protrudes centrally from the binding groove, providing the most exposed feature of the antigen for interaction with TCRs (**Figure 2a**). The structures of CD1d in complex with iNKT cell agonists (PBS-25, α-GalCer, GalA-GSL) (Koch et al. 2005, Wu et al. 2006, Zajonc et al. 2005a) (**Figure 2b,c,d**) and the endogenous ligand iGb3 (Zajonc et al. 2008) provide a fine-grained characterization of a series of binding surfaces, all of which can be recognized by iNKT cell semi-invariant TCRs. In addition, the structure of mouse CD1d in complex with a synthetic dipalmitoyl-phosphatidylinositol mannoside (synthetic PIM2) (Zajonc et al. 2006) (**Figure 2f**) provides insight into the mode of presentation of the mycobacterial phosphatidylinositol tetramannosides (PIM4), which can also be recognized by iNKT TCRs (Fischer et al. 2004), whereas the structure of mouse CD1d complexed with *cis*-tetracosenoyl sulfatide (Zajonc et al. 2005c) (**Figure 2g**) reveals the characteristics of an immunodominant self-antigen capable of stimulating a distinct subpopulation of CD1d-restricted NKT cells. In total these structures emphasize the role of specific hydrogen bond networks between CD1d molecule and ligand in determining head-group position, orientation, and rigidity and hence TCR binding properties.

Although the range of complex structures is less extensive, similar conclusions have been reached from comparison of CD1b/glycolipid complexes (Batuwangala et al. 2004). However, CD1/ligand structures also indicate that possible antigen-specific TCR interactions are not necessarily limited to the properties of the highly exposed head-group region of a glycolipid. The structures of complexes with sulfatide (Zajonc et al. 2003) and lipopeptide (Zajonc et al. 2005b) suggest that the contents of the shallow F′ cavity in CD1a can contribute directly to the potential TCR binding surface (**Figure 3**). Most of the substantial lipid binding capacity of CD1b is deeply buried within the binding groove; however, the maze of channels opens back out to the TCR recognition surface through F′ (Batuwangala et al. 2004, Gadola et al. 2002b, Garcia-Alles et al. 2006) (**Figure 4**) so that for some ligands [as demonstrated for GMM (Batuwangala et al. 2004)] one of the lipid tails can be presented for potentially direct interactions with TCRs. Conversely, functional studies combined with in silico modeling (on the basis of comparison of lipid-bound and non-lipid-bound CD1d grooves) indicate that, at least for CD1d, partial occupancy of the F′ channel may indirectly result in conformational changes at the recognition surface that are sufficient to modulate TCR binding (McCarthy et al. 2007).

Receptor Binding Modes

Representative crystal structures have been determined for human and mouse iNKT cell TCRs (Gadola et al. 2006a, Kjer-Nielsen et al. 2006, Zajonc et al. 2008) as well as for two human CD1d/α-GalCer-reactive Vα24⁻ TCRs (Gadola et al. 2006a). Borg et al. (2007) have provided the first template for TCR binding to CD1/glycolipid with the structure of a human iNKT cell TCR in complex with CD1d/α-GalCer. Unexpectedly, the TCR in the complex structure does not sit with complementarity-determining region 3 (CDR3) α and β loops straddling the glycolipid head group, as would be predicted from in silico modeling based on TCR/peptide/MHC class I (TCR/pMHC) complex structures. Instead, the binding footprint is shifted such that the specific interactions to the α-GalCer are made by the semi-invariant (Vα24-Jα18-encoded) CDR1α and CDR3α loops (**Figure 5a,b**). Analogous, but less extreme, offsets in the TCR footprint, to focus binding on particularly distinctive features of the recognition surface, have been observed for TCR/pMHC complexes (Stewart-Jones et al. 2003).

Detailed dissection of the energetic contributions to the human iNKT TCR interaction with CD1d/α-GalCer confirms the importance of (*a*) interactions to the α-GalCer, and particularly the CD1d, made by the Vα24-encoded CDR1α loop and the Jα18-encoded portion of the CDR3α loop and (*b*) the interactions of two CD1d-binding residues (Tyr48 and Tyr50) in the CDR2β loop (Wun et al. 2008). Collectively, these energetically dominant interactions indicate that the region directly above the F' pocket provides a binding hot spot, consistent with the hypothesis that changes in this region of the recognition surface, triggered indirectly by variation in the length of the lipid tail in the F' channel, can modulate iNKT cell TCR binding affinity (McCarthy et al. 2007).

Energetic analysis of mouse Vα14-Jα18 iNKT cell TCR binding to mouse CD1d/α-GalCer showed a similar hot-spot dependence on germline-encoded amino acids in the CDR 1α, 3α, and 2β loops and gave comparable results for CD1d complexed with a series of structurally distinct glycolipids, leading to the suggestion that this TCR functions by innate-like pattern recognition (Scott-Browne et al. 2007) and that the iNKT cell TCR binding mode in the human and mouse systems is essentially identical (Wun et al. 2008) (**Figure 5c–e**). The implications for TCR binding modes to other CD1/glycolipid complexes in general are, however, less clear-cut (**Figure 5f–j**). The available functional data for TCR recognition of CD1b/glycolipid complexes (Melian et al. 2000) (**Figure 5j**) indicate that the offset footprint of the iNKT cell TCR binding CD1d/glycolipid may be highly distinctive (**Figure 5**).

The binding mode, or not, of coreceptors such as CD8 and CD4 is even more speculative. Recent functional data suggest that CD4 may bind CD1d (Thedrez et al. 2007). In our hands, in silico modeling, based on crystal structures for CD8/pMHC class I (Gao et al. 1997, Kern et al. 1998) and CD4/pMHC class II (Wang et al. 2001) complexes, reveals that CD8 and CD4 binding to CD1 molecules is sterically possible. However, the number of amino acid differences at the putative binding interfaces precludes any confident assessment of whether such interactions would be energetically favorable.

THERAPEUTIC IMPLICATIONS

A number of groups, including our own, have shown that simultaneous administration of α-GalCer together with peptide or protein antigens enhance CD8$^+$ and CD4$^+$ T cell responses (Fujii et al. 2003, Hermans et al. 2003, Stober et al. 2003) in a manner dependent on costimulatory signals through CD40L (Fujii et al. 2004, Hermans et al. 2003).

In addition to the use of α-GalCer presented by DCs as an adjuvant, several α-GalCer analogs have been characterized (Chang et al. 2007, Fujii et al. 2006, Goff et al. 2004, McCarthy et al. 2007, Miyamoto et al. 2001, Schmieg et al. 2003, Silk et al. 2007, Tashiro et al. 2007, Yu et al. 2005). The C-glycoside variant, α-C-GalCer (**Figure 1d**), was more protective in disease models than α-GalCer either injected intravenously (Schmieg et al. 2003) or pulsed onto DCs (Fujii et al. 2006). We demonstrated that simultaneous administration of α-GalCer or analogs together with different TLR ligands could further enhance the capacity of DCs to prime antigen-specific T and B cell responses (Hermans et al. 2007, Silk et al. 2004).

Demonstrations that the adjuvant effect of α-GalCer increases specific antibody responses when coadministered with an antigen (Galli et al. 2007, Hermans et al. 2007) raise the possibility that harnessing iNKT cells can be used to stimulate antigen-specific B cell responses. The recent observation that after specific antigen B cell receptor (BCR) engagement, B cells can internalize particulate antigen and recruit T cell help through CD1d-mediated presentation of α-GalCer to iNKT cells indicates that targeting of α-GalCer to an antigen-specific BCR increases in vivo antibody responses, inducing early class-switched specific antibody production (Barral et al. 2008, Leadbetter et al. 2008).

In an attempt to enhance the capacity of DCs to activate antitumor immune responses, a number of clinical trials have been performed by injection of α-GalCer (Giaccone et al. 2002) or injection of DCs pulsed with α-GalCer (Chang et al. 2005, Ishikawa et al. 2005, Nieda et al. 2004, Uchida et al. 2008). The results of these trials have indicated activation and expansion of iNKT cells and cytokine production. One study showed an increase in serum levels

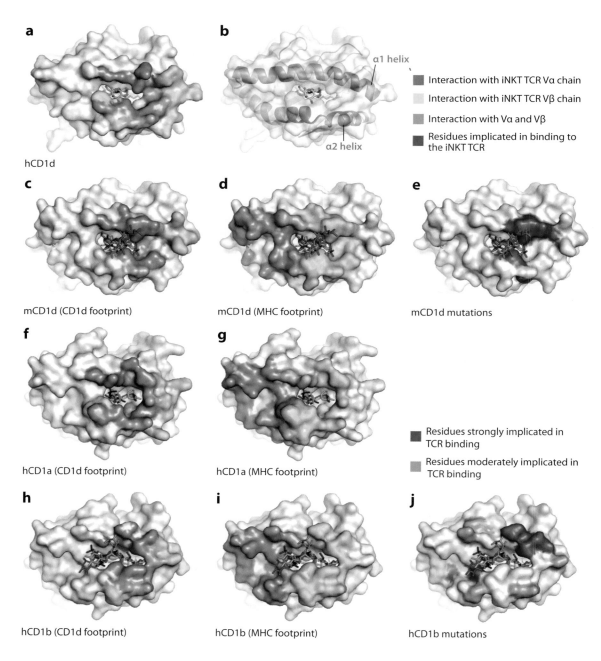

a hCD1d

b
α1 helix
α2 helix

■ Interaction with iNKT TCR Vα chain
■ Interaction with iNKT TCR Vβ chain
■ Interaction with Vα and Vβ
■ Residues implicated in binding to the iNKT TCR

c mCD1d (CD1d footprint)

d mCD1d (MHC footprint)

e mCD1d mutations

f hCD1a (CD1d footprint)

g hCD1a (MHC footprint)

■ Residues strongly implicated in TCR binding
■ Residues moderately implicated in TCR binding

h hCD1b (CD1d footprint)

i hCD1b (MHC footprint)

j hCD1b mutations

of IL-12p40 detected as a result of DC maturation and an associated increased frequency of human cytomegalovirus (CMV)-specific CD8[+] T cells (Chang et al. 2005).

Together these clinical trials have shown that the activation of iNKT cells with α-GalCer has significant potential for further development, and the future may provide interesting advances in cancer therapeutics with iNKT cell ligands. There is now potential for structure-guided design of novel iNKT cell ligands that have specific desired properties, such as differential cytokine production by iNKT cells.

FUTURE PERSPECTIVES

In recent years, many papers have provided important insights into the mechanisms controlling the uptake, trafficking, and processing of lipid antigens. Although the evidence that T lymphocytes can recognize both self-lipids and microbial lipids in the context of CD1 molecule is compelling, the molecular events controlling lipid loading onto CD1 molecules and their recognition by lipid-specific TCRs remain unclear. Combined structural, kinetic, and functional studies will significantly contribute to the understanding of the mechanisms that mediate antigenic lipid processing and presentation by CD1 molecules. It still remains to be clarified whether recognition of microbial lipids by CD1a-, CD1b-, and CD1c-restricted T cells plays a protective role during infections. Optimization of CD1 tetramer staining would allow measurement of the frequency and phenotype of lipid-specific T cells during microbial infections and clarify whether these parameters correlate with disease control.

Finally, the ability of iNKT cells to mature DCs and activate B cells has highlighted the possibility that the harnessing of iNKT cells in vivo could be used to optimize vaccination strategies and generate effective antigen-specific T and B cell responses. The challenge remains to translate these results to the clinic.

Figure 5

The TCR recognition surface. (a,b) The structure of the TCR recognition surface presented by human CD1d is shown; ligands are shown as sticks, and the default color of the CD1 surface is light gray. In panel a the surfaces of residues interacting with the human semi-invariant NKT TCR in the crystal structure of the complex with CD1d-αGalCer are colored green (interaction with Vα), yellow (interaction with Vβ), or orange (interactions with Vα and Vβ). In panel b, for orientation purposes, the surface is shown non–color coded in semitransparent form to reveal the main chain architecture of the binding groove in blue ribbon. (c) The human semi-invariant NKT TCR binding footprint from panel a is superposed onto mouse CD1d. The surface is colored as in panel a, and ligands (drawn from the individual mouse CD1d/ligand complexes of **Figure 2**) are depicted as colored sticks. (d) The TCR binding footprint for a representative MHC class I/peptide/TCR crystal structure (PDB code 2CKB) superposed onto mouse CD1d. The CD1d surface and ligands are color coded as in panel c. (e) The mouse CD1d surface and ligands are depicted as in panels c and d but with the surface colored red for residues (Ser76, Arg79, Asp80, Glu83, Asn151, Asp153, Thr156) implicated in binding to the mouse semi-invariant NKT TCR by functional studies (Burdin et al. 2000, Kamada et al. 2001, Sidobre et al. 2002). (f) The human semi-invariant NKT TCR binding footprint from panel a is superposed onto human CD1a. The surface is colored as in panel a, and ligands (drawn from the individual human CD1a/ligand complexes of **Figure 3**) are depicted as colored sticks. (g) The TCR binding footprint for a representative MHC class I/peptide/TCR crystal structure (PDB code 2CKB) superposed onto human CD1a. The CD1a surface and ligands are color coded as in panel f. (h) The human semi-invariant NKT TCR binding footprint from panel a is superposed onto human CD1b. The surface is colored as in panel a, and ligands (drawn from the individual human CD1b/ligand complexes of **Figure 4**) are depicted as colored sticks. (i) The TCR binding footprint for a representative MHC class I/peptide/TCR crystal structure (PDB code 2CKB) superposed onto human CD1b. The CD1b surface and ligands are color coded as in panel h. (j) The human CD1b surface and ligands are depicted as in panels h and i but with the surface colored red for residues (Arg79, Glu80, Asp83, Thr157, Thr165) strongly implicated and orange for residues (Glu68, Arg71, Tyr73, Asp87, Gln150, Glu156) moderately implicated in binding to TCRs by functional studies (Melian et al. 2000).

DISCLOSURE STATEMENT

The authors are not aware of any biases that might be perceived as affecting the objectivity of this review.

ACKNOWLEDGMENTS

We apologize to colleagues whose work we did not cite owing to space constraints. E.Y.J. is a Cancer Research UK Principal Research Fellow. This work was funded by Cancer Research UK (grant C399/A2291 to V.C. and grant C375/A2320 to E.Y.J.) and the Medical Research Council, UK. We wish to thank Ms. Hajar Masri for critical reading of the manuscript.

LITERATURE CITED

Barral P, Ecki-Dorma J, Harwood NE, De Santo C, Salio M, et al. 2008. B cell receptor-mediated uptake of CD1d-restricted antigen augments specific antibody responses by recruiting invariant NKT cell help in vivo. *Proc. Natl. Acad. Sci. USA* 105:8345–50

Batuwangala T, Shepherd D, Gadola SD, Gibson KJ, Zaccai NR, et al. 2004. The crystal structure of human CD1b with a bound bacterial glycolipid. *J. Immunol.* 172:2382–88

Beckman EM, Porcelli SA, Morita CT, Behar SM, Furlong ST, Brenner MB. 1994. Recognition of a lipid antigen by CD1-restricted $\alpha\beta^+$ T cells. *Nature* 372:691–94

Bendelac A. 1995. Positive selection of mouse NK1$^+$ T cells by CD1-expressing cortical thymocytes. *J. Exp. Med.* 182:2091–96

Bendelac A, Killeen N, Littman DR, Schwartz RH. 1994. A subset of CD4$^+$ thymocytes selected by MHC class I molecules. *Science* 263:1774–78

Benlagha K, Bendelac A. 2000. CD1d-restricted mouse Vα14 and human Vα24 T cells: lymphocytes of innate immunity. *Semin. Immunol.* 12:537–42

Benlagha K, Wei DG, Veiga J, Teyton L, Bendelac A. 2005. Characterization of the early stages of thymic NKT cell development. *J. Exp. Med.* 202:485–92

Bernard A, Boumsell L. 1984. The clusters of differentiation (CD) defined by the First International Workshop on Human Leucocyte Differentiation Antigens. *Hum. Immunol.* 11:1–10

Berzins SP, McNab FW, Jones CM, Smyth MJ, Godfrey DI. 2006. Long-term retention of mature NK1.1$^+$ NKT cells in the thymus. *J. Immunol.* 176:4059–65

Blander JM, Medzhitov R. 2006. Toll-dependent selection of microbial antigens for presentation by dendritic cells. *Nature* 440:808–12

Borg NA, Wun KS, Kjer-Nielsen L, Wilce MC, Pellicci DG, et al. 2007. CD1d-lipid-antigen recognition by the semi-invariant NKT T-cell receptor. *Nature* 448:44–49

Brigl M, Brenner MB. 2004. CD1: antigen presentation and T cell function. *Annu. Rev. Immunol.* 22:817–90

Brigl M, Bry L, Kent SC, Gumperz JE, Brenner MB. 2003. Mechanism of CD1d-restricted natural killer T cell activation during microbial infection. *Nat. Immunol.* 4:1230–37

Briken V, Jackman RM, Dasgupta S, Hoening S, Porcelli SA. 2002. Intracellular trafficking pathway of newly synthesized CD1b molecules. *EMBO J.* 21:825–34

Briken V, Jackman RM, Watts GF, Rogers RA, Porcelli SA. 2000. Human CD1b and CD1c isoforms survey different intracellular compartments for the presentation of microbial lipid antigens. *J. Exp. Med.* 192:281–88

Brossay L, Chioda M, Burdin N, Koezuka Y, Casorati G, et al. 1998. CD1d-mediated recognition of an α-galactosylceramide by natural killer T cells is highly conserved through mammalian evolution. *J. Exp. Med.* 188:1521–28

Brozovic S, Nagaishi T, Yoshida M, Betz S, Salas A, et al. 2004. CD1d function is regulated by microsomal triglyceride transfer protein. *Nat. Med.* 10:535–39

Burdin N, Brossay L, Degano M, Iijima H, Gui M, et al. 2000. Structural requirements for antigen presentation by mouse CD1. *Proc. Natl. Acad. Sci. USA* 97:10156–61

Calabi F, Milstein C. 2000. The molecular biology of CD1. *Semin. Immunol.* 12:503–9

Cao X, Sugita M, Van Der Wel N, Lai J, Rogers RA, et al. 2002. CD1 molecules efficiently present antigen in immature dendritic cells and traffic independently of MHC class II during dendritic cell maturation. *J. Immunol.* 169:4770–77

Chang DH, Osman K, Connolly J, Kukreja A, Krasovsky J, et al. 2005. Sustained expansion of NKT cells and antigen-specific T cells after injection of α-galactosyl-ceramide loaded mature dendritic cells in cancer patients. *J. Exp. Med.* 201:1503–17

Chang YJ, Huang JR, Tsai YC, Hung JT, Wu D, et al. 2007. Potent immune-modulating and anticancer effects of NKT cell stimulatory glycolipids. *Proc. Natl. Acad. Sci. USA* 104:10299–304

Chen X, Wang X, Keaton JM, Reddington F, Illarionov P, et al. 2007. Distinct endosomal trafficking requirements for presentation of autoantigens and exogenous lipids by human CD1d molecules. *J. Immunol.* 178:6181–90

Chiu YH, Jayawardena J, Weiss A, Lee D, Park SH, et al. 1999. Distinct subsets of CD1d-restricted T cells recognize self-antigens loaded in different cellular compartments. *J. Exp. Med.* 189:103–10

Chiu YH, Park SH, Benlagha K, Forestier C, Jayawardena-Wolf J, et al. 2002. Multiple defects in antigen presentation and T cell development by mice expressing cytoplasmic tail-truncated CD1d. *Nat. Immunol.* 3:55–60

Cho S, Knox KS, Kohli LM, He JJ, Exley MA, et al. 2005. Impaired cell surface expression of human CD1d by the formation of an HIV-1 Nef/CD1d complex. *Virology* 337:242–52

Chun T, Page MJ, Gapin L, Matsuda JL, Xu H, et al. 2003. CD1d-expressing dendritic cells but not thymic epithelial cells can mediate negative selection of NKT cells. *J. Exp. Med.* 197:907–18

de Jong A, Arce EC, Cheng TY, van Summeren RP, Feringa BL, et al. 2007. CD1c presentation of synthetic glycolipid antigens with foreign alkyl branching motifs. *Chem. Biol.* 14:1232–42

de la Salle H, Mariotti S, Angenieux C, Gilleron M, Garcia-Alles LF, et al. 2005. Assistance of microbial glycolipid antigen processing by CD1e. *Science* 310:1321–24

De Libero G, Moran AP, Gober HJ, Rossy E, Shamshiev A, et al. 2005. Bacterial infections promote T cell recognition of self-glycolipids. *Immunity* 22:763–72

Delia D, Cattoretti G, Polli N, Fontanella E, Aiello A, et al. 1988. CD1c but neither CD1a nor CD1b molecules are expressed on normal, activated, and malignant human B cells: identification of a new B-cell subset. *Blood* 72:241–47

Dougan SK, Kaser A, Blumberg RS. 2007a. CD1 expression on antigen-presenting cells. *Curr. Top. Microbiol. Immunol.* 314:113–41

Dougan SK, Rava P, Hussain MM, Blumberg RS. 2007b. MTP regulated by an alternate promoter is essential for NKT cell development. *J. Exp. Med.* 204:533–45

Dougan SK, Salas A, Rava P, Agyemang A, Kaser A, et al. 2005. Microsomal triglyceride transfer protein lipidation and control of CD1d on antigen-presenting cells. *J. Exp. Med.* 202:529–39

Egawa T, Eberl G, Taniuchi I, Benlagha K, Geissmann F, et al. 2005. Genetic evidence supporting selection of the Vα14i NKT cell lineage from double-positive thymocyte precursors. *Immunity* 22:705–16

Elewaut D, Lawton AP, Nagarajan NA, Maverakis E, Khurana A, et al. 2003. The adaptor protein AP-3 is required for CD1d-mediated antigen presentation of glycosphingolipids and development of Vα14i NKT cells. *J. Exp. Med.* 198:1133–46

Exley M, Garcia J, Wilson SB, Spada F, Gerdes D, et al. 2000. CD1d structure and regulation on human thymocytes, peripheral blood T cells, B cells and monocytes. *Immunology* 100:37–47

Fischer K, Scotet E, Niemeyer M, Koebernick H, Zerrahn J, et al. 2004. Mycobacterial phosphatidylinositol mannoside is a natural antigen for CD1d-restricted T cells. *Proc. Natl. Acad. Sci. USA* 101:10685–90

Fujii S, Liu K, Smith C, Bonito AJ, Steinman RM. 2004. The linkage of innate to adaptive immunity via maturing dendritic cells in vivo requires CD40 ligation in addition to antigen presentation and CD80/86 costimulation. *J. Exp. Med.* 199:1607–18

Fujii S, Shimizu K, Hemmi H, Fukui M, Bonito AJ, et al. 2006. Glycolipid α-C-galactosylceramide is a distinct inducer of dendritic cell function during innate and adaptive immune responses of mice. *Proc. Natl. Acad. Sci. USA* 103:11252–57

Fujii S, Shimizu K, Smith C, Bonifaz L, Steinman RM. 2003. Activation of natural killer T cells by α-galactosylceramide rapidly induces the full maturation of dendritic cells in vivo and thereby acts as an adjuvant for combined CD4 and CD8 T cell immunity to a coadministered protein. *J. Exp. Med.* 198:267–79

Gadola SD, Dulphy N, Salio M, Cerundolo V. 2002a. Vα24-JαQ-independent, CD1d-restricted recognition of α-galactosylceramide by human CD4+ and CD8αβ+ T lymphocytes. *J. Immunol.* 168:5514–20

Gadola SD, Koch M, Marles-Wright J, Lissin NM, Shepherd D, et al. 2006a. Structure and binding kinetics of three different human CD1d-α-galactosylceramide-specific T cell receptors. *J. Exp. Med.* 203:699–710

Gadola SD, Silk JD, Jeans A, Illarionov PA, Salio M, et al. 2006b. Impaired selection of invariant natural killer T cells in diverse mouse models of glycosphingolipid lysosomal storage diseases. *J. Exp. Med.* 203:2293–303

Gadola SD, Zaccai NR, Harlos K, Shepherd D, Castro-Palomino JC, et al. 2002b. Structure of human CD1b with bound ligands at 2.3 Å, a maze for alkyl chains. *Nat. Immunol.* 3:721–26

Galli G, Pittoni P, Tonti E, Malzone C, Uematsu Y, et al. 2007. Invariant NKT cells sustain specific B cell responses and memory. *Proc. Natl. Acad. Sci. USA* 104:3984–89

Gao GF, Tormo J, Gerth UC, Wyer JR, McMichael AJ, et al. 1997. Crystal structure of the complex between human CD8αα and HLA-A2. *Nature* 387:630–34

Gapin L, Matsuda JL, Surh CD, Kronenberg M. 2001. NKT cells derive from double-positive thymocytes that are positively selected by CD1d. *Nat. Immunol.* 2:971–78

Garcia-Alles LF, Versluis K, Maveyraud L, Vallina AT, Sansano S, et al. 2006. Endogenous phosphatidylcholine and a long spacer ligand stabilize the lipid-binding groove of CD1b. *EMBO J.* 25:3684–92

Giabbai B, Sidobre S, Crispin MD, Sanchez-Ruiz Y, Bachi A, et al. 2005. Crystal structure of mouse CD1d bound to the self ligand phosphatidylcholine: a molecular basis for NKT cell activation. *J. Immunol.* 175:977–84

Giaccone G, Punt CJ, Ando Y, Ruijter R, Nishi N, et al. 2002. A phase I study of the natural killer T-cell ligand α-galactosylceramide (KRN7000) in patients with solid tumors. *Clin. Cancer Res.* 8:3702–9

Gilleron M, Stenger S, Mazorra Z, Wittke F, Mariotti S, et al. 2004. Diacylated sulfoglycolipids are novel mycobacterial antigens stimulating CD1-restricted T cells during infection with *Mycobacterium tuberculosis*. *J. Exp. Med.* 199:649–59

Goff RD, Gao Y, Mattner J, Zhou D, Yin N, et al. 2004. Effects of lipid chain lengths in α-galactosylceramides on cytokine release by natural killer T cells. *J. Am. Chem. Soc.* 126:13602–3

Guo J, Hawwari A, Li H, Sun Z, Mahanta SK, et al. 2002. Regulation of the TCRα repertoire by the survival window of CD4+CD8+ thymocytes. *Nat. Immunol.* 3:469–76

Hanau D, Fricker D, Bieber T, Esposito-Farese ME, Bausinger H, et al. 1994. CD1 expression is not affected by human peptide transporter deficiency. *Hum. Immunol.* 41:61–68

Hayakawa Y, Berzins SP, Crowe NY, Godfrey DI, Smyth MJ. 2004. Antigen-induced tolerance by intrathymic modulation of self-recognizing inhibitory receptors. *Nat. Immunol.* 5:590–96

Hermans IF, Silk JD, Gileadi U, Masri SH, Shepherd D, et al. 2007. Dendritic cell function can be modulated through cooperative actions of TLR ligands and invariant NKT cells. *J. Immunol.* 178:2721–29

Hermans IF, Silk JD, Gileadi U, Salio M, Mathew B, et al. 2003. NKT cells enhance CD4+ and CD8+ T cell responses to soluble antigen in vivo through direct interaction with dendritic cells. *J. Immunol.* 171:5140–47

Ishikawa A, Motohashi S, Ishikawa E, Fuchida H, Higashino K, et al. 2005. A phase I study of α-galactosylceramide (KRN7000)-pulsed dendritic cells in patients with advanced and recurrent nonsmall cell lung cancer. *Clin. Cancer Res.* 11:1910–17

Jackman RM, Stenger S, Lee A, Moody DB, Rogers RA, et al. 1998. The tyrosine-containing cytoplasmic tail of CD1b is essential for its efficient presentation of bacterial lipid antigens. *Immunity* 8:341–51

Jahng A, Maricic I, Aguilera C, Cardell S, Halder RC, Kumar V. 2004. Prevention of autoimmunity by targeting a distinct, noninvariant CD1d-reactive T cell population reactive to sulfatide. *J. Exp. Med.* 199:947–57

Jayawardena-Wolf J, Benlagha K, Chiu YH, Mehr R, Bendelac A. 2001. CD1d endosomal trafficking is independently regulated by an intrinsic CD1d-encoded tyrosine motif and by the invariant chain. *Immunity* 15:897–908

Joyce S, Woods AS, Yewdell JW, Bennink JR, De Silva AD, et al. 1998. Natural ligand of mouse CD1d1: cellular glycosylphosphatidylinositol. *Science* 279:1541–44

Kamada N, Iijima H, Kimura K, Harada M, Shimizu E, et al. 2001. Crucial amino acid residues of mouse CD1d for glycolipid ligand presentation to $V_\alpha 14$ NKT cells. *Int. Immunol.* 13:853–61

Kang SJ, Cresswell P. 2002. Calnexin, calreticulin, and ERp57 cooperate in disulfide bond formation in human CD1d heavy chain. *J. Biol. Chem.* 277:44838–44

Kang SJ, Cresswell P. 2004. Saposins facilitate CD1d-restricted presentation of an exogenous lipid antigen to T cells. *Nat. Immunol.* 5:175–81

Kawano T, Cui J, Koezuka Y, Toura I, Kaneko Y, et al. 1997. CD1d-restricted and TCR-mediated activation of $V_\alpha 14$ NKT cells by glycosylceramides. *Science* 278:1626–29

Kawashima T, Norose Y, Watanabe Y, Enomoto Y, Narazaki H, et al. 2003. Cutting edge: major CD8 T cell response to live bacillus Calmette-Guerin is mediated by CD1 molecules. *J. Immunol.* 170:5345–48

Kern PS, Teng MK, Smolyar A, Liu JH, Liu J, et al. 1998. Structural basis of CD8 coreceptor function revealed by crystallographic analysis of a murine CD8αα ectodomain fragment in complex with H-2Kb. *Immunity* 9:519–30

Kinjo Y, Tupin E, Wu D, Fujio M, Garcia-Navarro R, et al. 2006. Natural killer T cells recognize diacylglycerol antigens from pathogenic bacteria. *Nat. Immunol.* 7:978–86

Kinjo Y, Wu D, Kim G, Xing GW, Poles MA, et al. 2005. Recognition of bacterial glycosphingolipids by natural killer T cells. *Nature* 434:520–25

Kjer-Nielsen L, Borg NA, Pellicci DG, Beddoe T, Kostenko L, et al. 2006. A structural basis for selection and cross-species reactivity of the semi-invariant NKT cell receptor in CD1d/glycolipid recognition. *J. Exp. Med.* 203:661–73

Koch M, Stronge VS, Shepherd D, Gadola SD, Mathew B, et al. 2005. The crystal structure of human CD1d with and without α-galactosylceramide. *Nat. Immunol.* 6:819–26

Lawton AP, Prigozy TI, Brossay L, Pei B, Khurana A, et al. 2005. The mouse CD1d cytoplasmic tail mediates CD1d trafficking and antigen presentation by adaptor protein 3-dependent and -independent mechanisms. *J. Immunol.* 174:3179–86

Li Y, Teneberg S, Thapa P, Bendelac A, Levery SB, Zhou D. 2008. Sensitive detection of isoglobo and globo series tetraglycosylceramides in human thymus by ion trap mass spectrometry. *Glycobiology* 18:158–65

Leadbetter EA, Brigl M, Illarionov P, Cohen N, Luteran MC, et al. 2008. NK T cells provide lipid antigen-specific cognate help for B cells. *Proc. Natl. Acad. Sci. USA* 105:8339–44

Matsuda JL, Gapin L, Sidobre S, Kieper WC, Tan JT, et al. 2002. Homeostasis of Vα14i NKT cells. *Nat. Immunol.* 3:966–74

Matsuda JL, Naidenko OV, Gapin L, Nakayama T, Taniguchi M, et al. 2000. Tracking the response of natural killer T cells to a glycolipid antigen using CD1d tetramers. *J. Exp. Med.* 192:741–54

Mattner J, Debord KL, Ismail N, Goff RD, Cantu C 3rd, et al. 2005. Exogenous and endogenous glycolipid antigens activate NKT cells during microbial infections. *Nature* 434:525–29

McCarthy C, Shepherd D, Fleire S, Stronge VS, Koch M, et al. 2007. The length of lipids bound to human CD1d molecules modulates the affinity of NKT cell TCR and the threshold of NKT cell activation. *J. Exp. Med.* 204:1131–44

McMichael AJ, Pilch JR, Galfre G, Mason DY, Fabre JW, Milstein C. 1979. A human thymocyte antigen defined by a hybrid myeloma monoclonal antibody. *Eur. J. Immunol.* 9:205–10

McNab FW, Berzins SP, Pellicci DG, Kyparissoudis K, Field K, et al. 2005. The influence of CD1d in postselection NKT cell maturation and homeostasis. *J. Immunol.* 175:3762–68

McNab FW, Pellicci DG, Field K, Besra G, Smyth MJ, et al. 2007. Peripheral NK1.1 NKT cells are mature and functionally distinct from their thymic counterparts. *J. Immunol.* 179:6630–37

Melian A, Watts GF, Shamshiev A, De Libero G, Clatworthy A, et al. 2000. Molecular recognition of human CD1b antigen complexes: evidence for a common pattern of interaction with αβ TCRs. *J. Immunol.* 165:4494–504

Milland J, Christiansen D, Lazarus BD, Taylor SG, Xing PX, Sandrin MS. 2006. The molecular basis for galα(1,3)gal expression in animals with a deletion of the α1,3galactosyltransferase gene. *J. Immunol.* 176:2448–54

Miyamoto K, Miyake S, Yamamura T. 2001. A synthetic glycolipid prevents autoimmune encephalomyelitis by inducing TH2 bias of natural killer T cells. *Nature* 413:531–34

Moody DB, Briken V, Cheng TY, Roura-Mir C, Guy MR, et al. 2002. Lipid length controls antigen entry into endosomal and nonendosomal pathways for CD1b presentation. *Nat. Immunol.* 3:435–42

Moody DB, Reinhold BB, Guy MR, Beckman EM, Frederique DE, et al. 1997. Structural requirements for glycolipid antigen recognition by CD1b-restricted T cells. *Science* 278:283–86

Moody DB, Ulrichs T, Muhlecker W, Young DC, Gurcha SS, et al. 2000. CD1c-mediated T-cell recognition of isoprenoid glycolipids in *Mycobacterium tuberculosis* infection. *Nature* 404:884–88

Moody DB, Young DC, Cheng TY, Rosat JP, Roura-Mir C, et al. 2004. T cell activation by lipopeptide antigens. *Science* 303:527–31

Nagarajan NA, Kronenberg M. 2007. Invariant NKT cells amplify the innate immune response to lipopolysaccharide. *J. Immunol.* 178:2706–13

Nieda M, Okai M, Tazbirkova A, Lin H, Yamaura A, et al. 2004. Therapeutic activation of $V\alpha24^+V\beta11^+$ NKT cells in human subjects results in highly coordinated secondary activation of acquired and innate immunity. *Blood* 103:383–89

Paduraru C, Spiridon L, Yuan W, Bricard G, Valencia X, et al. 2006. An *N*-linked glycan modulates the interaction between the CD1d heavy chain and β_2-microglobulin. *J. Biol. Chem.* 281:40369–78

Paget C, Mallevaey T, Speak AO, Torres D, Fontaine J, et al. 2007. Activation of invariant NKT cells by toll-like receptor 9-stimulated dendritic cells requires type I interferon and charged glycosphingolipids. *Immunity* 27:597–609

Porcelli S, Morita CT, Brenner MB. 1992. CD1b restricts the response of human $CD4^-8^-$ T lymphocytes to a microbial antigen. *Nature* 360:593–97

Porubsky S, Speak AO, Luckow B, Cerundolo V, Platt FM, Grone HJ. 2007. Normal development and function of invariant natural killer T cells in mice with isoglobotrihexosylceramide (iGb3) deficiency. *Proc. Natl. Acad. Sci. USA* 104:5977–82

Prigozy TI, Naidenko O, Qasba P, Elewaut D, Brossay L, et al. 2001. Glycolipid antigen processing for presentation by CD1d molecules. *Science* 291:664–67

Res P, Blom B, Hori T, Weijer K, Spits H. 1997. Downregulation of CD1 marks acquisition of functional maturation of human thymocytes and defines a control point in late stages of human T cell development. *J. Exp. Med.* 185:141–51

Roark JH, Park SH, Jayawardena J, Kavita U, Shannon M, Bendelac A. 1998. CD1.1 expression by mouse antigen-presenting cells and marginal zone B cells. *J. Immunol.* 160:3121–27

Rosat JP, Grant EP, Beckman EM, Dascher CC, Sieling PA, et al. 1999. CD1-restricted microbial lipid antigen-specific recognition found in the $CD8^+$ $\alpha\beta$ T cell pool. *J. Immunol.* 162:366–71

Sagiv Y, Bai L, Wei DG, Agami R, Savage PB, et al. 2007. A distal effect of microsomal triglyceride transfer protein deficiency on the lysosomal recycling of CD1d. *J. Exp. Med.* 204:921–28

Sagiv Y, Hudspeth K, Mattner J, Schrantz N, Stern RK, et al. 2006. Cutting edge: impaired glycosphingolipid trafficking and NKT cell development in mice lacking Niemann-Pick type C1 protein. *J. Immunol.* 177:26–30

Salamero J, Bausinger H, Mommaas AM, Lipsker D, Proamer F, et al. 2001. CD1a molecules traffic through the early recycling endosomal pathway in human Langerhans cells. *J. Investig. Dermatol.* 116:401–8

Salio M, Speak AO, Shepherd D, Polzella P, Illarionov PA, et al. 2007. Modulation of human natural killer T cell ligands on TLR-mediated antigen-presenting cell activation. *Proc. Natl. Acad. Sci. USA* 104:20490–95

Sanchez DJ, Gumperz JE, Ganem D. 2005. Regulation of CD1d expression and function by a herpesvirus infection. *J. Clin. Investig.* 115:1369–78

Schmieg J, Yang G, Franck RW, Tsuji M. 2003. Superior protection against malaria and melanoma metastases by a C-glycoside analogue of the natural killer T cell ligand α-galactosylceramide. *J. Exp. Med.* 198:1631–41

Schrantz N, Sagiv Y, Liu Y, Savage PB, Bendelac A, Teyton L. 2007. The Niemann-Pick type C2 protein loads isoglobotrihexosylceramide onto CD1d molecules and contributes to the thymic selection of NKT cells. *J. Exp. Med.* 204:841–52

Schumann J, Facciotti F, Panza L, Michieletti M, Compostella F, et al. 2007. Differential alteration of lipid antigen presentation to NKT cells due to imbalances in lipid metabolism. *Eur. J. Immunol.* 37:1431–41

Schumann J, Mycko MP, Dellabona P, Casorati G, MacDonald HR. 2006. Cutting edge: influence of the TCR Vβ domain on the selection of semi-invariant NKT cells by endogenous ligands. *J. Immunol.* 176:2064–68

Schumann J, Pittoni P, Tonti E, Macdonald HR, Dellabona P, Casorati G. 2005. Targeted expression of human CD1d in transgenic mice reveals independent roles for thymocytes and thymic APCs in positive and negative selection of Vα14i NKT cells. *J. Immunol.* 175:7303–10

Schumann J, Voyle RB, Wei BY, MacDonald HR. 2003. Cutting edge: influence of the TCR Vβ domain on the avidity of CD1d:α-galactosylceramide binding by invariant Vα14 NKT cells. *J. Immunol.* 170:5815–19

Scott-Browne JP, Matsuda JL, Mallevaey T, White J, Borg NA, et al. 2007. Germline-encoded recognition of diverse glycolipids by natural killer T cells. *Nat. Immunol.* 8:1105–13

Sever S. 2003. AP-2 makes room for rivals. *Dev. Cell* 5:530–32

Shamshiev A, Gober HJ, Donda A, Mazorra Z, Mori L, De Libero G. 2002. Presentation of the same glycolipid by different CD1 molecules. *J. Exp. Med.* 195:1013–21

Sidobre S, Naidenko OV, Sim BC, Gascoigne NR, Garcia KC, Kronenberg M. 2002. The Vα14 NKT cell TCR exhibits high-affinity binding to a glycolipid/CD1d complex. *J. Immunol.* 169:1340–48

Sieling PA, Torrelles JB, Stenger S, Chung W, Burdick AE, et al. 2005. The human CD1-restricted T cell repertoire is limited to cross-reactive antigens: implications for host responses against immunologically related pathogens. *J. Immunol.* 174:2637–44

Silk JD, Hermans IF, Gileadi U, Chong TW, Shepherd D, et al. 2004. Utilizing the adjuvant properties of CD1d-dependent NK T cells in T cell-mediated immunotherapy. *J. Clin. Investig.* 114:1800–11

Silk JD, Salio M, Reddy BG, Shepherd D, Gileadi U, et al. 2008. Cutting edge: nonglycosidic CD1d lipid ligands activate human and murine invariant NKT cells. *J. Immunol.* 180:6452–56

Skold M, Xiong X, Illarionov PA, Besra GS, Behar SM. 2005. Interplay of cytokines and microbial signals in regulation of CD1d expression and NKT cell activation. *J. Immunol.* 175:3584–93

Sloma I, Zilber MT, Vasselon T, Setterblad N, Cavallari M, et al. 2008. Regulation of CD1a surface expression and antigen presentation by invariant chain and lipid rafts. *J. Immunol.* 180:980–87

Speak AO, Salio M, Neville DC, Fontaine J, Priestman DA, et al. 2007. Implications for invariant natural killer T cell ligands due to the restricted presence of isoglobotrihexosylceramide in mammals. *Proc. Natl. Acad. Sci. USA* 104:5971–76

Sriram V, Du W, Gervay-Hague J, Brutkiewicz RR. 2005. Cell wall glycosphingolipids of *Sphingomonas paucimobilis* are CD1d-specific ligands for NKT cells. *Eur. J. Immunol.* 35:1692–701

Stanic AK, De Silva AD, Park JJ, Sriram V, Ichikawa S, et al. 2003a. Defective presentation of the CD1d1-restricted natural Vα14Jα18 NKT lymphocyte antigen caused by β-D-glucosylceramide synthase deficiency. *Proc. Natl. Acad. Sci. USA* 1849–54

Stanic AK, Shashidharamurthy R, Bezbradica JS, Matsuki N, Yoshimura Y, et al. 2003b. Another view of T cell antigen recognition: cooperative engagement of glycolipid antigens by Vα14Jα18 natural T (iNKT) cell receptor. *J. Immunol.* 171:4539–51

Stetson DB, Mohrs M, Reinhardt RL, Baron JL, Wang ZE, et al. 2003. Constitutive cytokine mRNAs mark natural killer (NK) and NK T cells poised for rapid effector function. *J. Exp. Med.* 198:1069–76

Stewart-Jones GB, McMichael AJ, Bell JI, Stuart DI, Jones EY. 2003. A structural basis for immunodominant human T cell receptor recognition. *Nat. Immunol.* 4:657–63

Stober D, Jomantaite I, Schirmbeck R, Reimann J. 2003. NKT cells provide help for dendritic cell-dependent priming of MHC class I-restricted CD8+ T cells in vivo. *J. Immunol.* 170:2540–48

Sugita M, Cao X, Watts GF, Rogers RA, Bonifacino JS, Brenner MB. 2002. Failure of trafficking and antigen presentation by CD1 in AP-3-deficient cells. *Immunity* 16:697–706

Sugita M, Grant EP, van Donselaar E, Hsu VW, Rogers RA, et al. 1999. Separate pathways for antigen presentation by CD1 molecules. *Immunity* 11:743–52

Sugita M, Porcelli SA, Brenner MB. 1997. Assembly and retention of CD1b heavy chains in the endoplasmic reticulum. *J. Immunol.* 159:2358–65

Sugita M, Van Der Wel N, Rogers RA, Peters PJ, Brenner MB. 2000. CD1c molecules broadly survey the endocytic system. *Proc. Natl. Acad. Sci. USA* 97:8445–50

Szatmari I, Pap A, Ruhl R, Ma JX, Illarionov PA, et al. 2006. PPARγ controls CD1d expression by turning on retinoic acid synthesis in developing human dendritic cells. *J. Exp. Med.* 203:2351–62

Tashiro T, Nakagawa R, Hirokawa T, Inoue S, Watarai H, et al. 2007. RCAI-56, a carbocyclic analogue of KRN7000: its synthesis and potent activity for natural killer (NK) T cells to preferentially produce interferon-γ. *Tetrahedron Lett.* 48:3343–47

Terabe M, Khanna C, Bose S, Melchionda F, Mendoza A, et al. 2006. CD1d-restricted natural killer T cells can down-regulate tumor immunosurveillance independent of interleukin-4 receptor-signal transducer and activator of transcription 6 or transforming growth factor-β. *Cancer Res.* 66:3869–75

Thedrez A, de Lalla C, Allain S, Zaccagnino L, Sidobre S, et al. 2007. CD4 engagement by CD1d potentiates activation of CD4$^+$ invariant NKT cells. *Blood* 110:251–58

Tourne S, Maitre B, Collmann A, Layre E, Mariotti S, et al. 2008. Cutting edge: a naturally occurring mutation in CD1e impairs lipid antigen presentation. *J. Immunol.* 180:3642–46

Uchida T, Horiguchi S, Tanaka Y, Yamamoto H, Kunii N, et al. 2008. Phase I study of α-galactosylceramide-pulsed antigen presenting cells administration to the nasal submucosa in unresectable or recurrent head and neck cancer. *Cancer Immunol. Immunother.* 57:337–45

Ulrichs T, Moody DB, Grant E, Kaufmann SH, Porcelli SA. 2003. T-cell responses to CD1-presented lipid antigens in humans with *Mycobacterium tuberculosis* infection. *Infect. Immun.* 71:3076–87

Voyle RB, Beermann F, Lees RK, Schumann J, Zimmer J, et al. 2003. Ligand-dependent inhibition of CD1d-restricted NKT cell development in mice transgenic for the activating receptor Ly49D. *J. Exp. Med.* 197:919–25

Wang JH, Meijers R, Xiong Y, Liu JH, Sakihama T, et al. 2001. Crystal structure of the human CD4 N-terminal two-domain fragment complexed to a class II MHC molecule. *Proc. Natl. Acad. Sci. USA* 98:10799–804

Wei DG, Curran SA, Savage PB, Teyton L, Bendelac A. 2006. Mechanisms imposing the Vβ bias of Vα14 natural killer T cells and consequences for microbial glycolipid recognition. *J. Exp. Med.* 203:1197–207

Wei DG, Lee H, Park SH, Beaudoin L, Teyton L, et al. 2005. Expansion and long-range differentiation of the NKT cell lineage in mice expressing CD1d exclusively on cortical thymocytes. *J. Exp. Med.* 202:239–48

Winau F, Schwierzeck V, Hurwitz R, Remmel N, Sieling PA, et al. 2004. Saposin C is required for lipid presentation by human CD1b. *Nat. Immunol.* 5:169–74

Wu D, Xing GW, Poles MA, Horowitz A, Kinjo Y, et al. 2005. Bacterial glycolipids and analogs as antigens for CD1d-restricted NKT cells. *Proc. Natl. Acad. Sci. USA* 102:1351–56

Wu D, Zajonc DM, Fujio M, Sullivan BA, Kinjo Y, et al. 2006. Design of natural killer T cell activators: structure and function of a microbial glycosphingolipid bound to mouse CD1d. *Proc. Natl. Acad. Sci. USA* 103:3972–77

Wun KS, Borg NA, Kjer-Nielsen L, Beddoe T, Koh R, et al. 2008. A minimal binding footprint on CD1d-glycolipid is a basis for selection of the unique human NKT TCR. *J. Exp. Med.* 205:939–49

Yu KO, Im JS, Molano A, Dutronc Y, Illarionov PA, et al. 2005. Modulation of CD1d-restricted NKT cell responses by using N-acyl variants of α-galactosylceramides. *Proc. Natl. Acad. Sci. USA* 102:3383–88

Yuan W, Dasgupta A, Cresswell P. 2006. Herpes simplex virus evades natural killer T cell recognition by suppressing CD1d recycling. *Nat. Immunol.* 7:835–42

Yuan W, Qi X, Tsang P, Kang SJ, Illarionov PA, et al. 2007. Saposin B is the dominant saposin that facilitates lipid binding to human CD1d molecules. *Proc. Natl. Acad. Sci. USA* 104:5551–56

Zajonc DM, Ainge GD, Painter GF, Severn WB, Wilson IA. 2006. Structural characterization of mycobacterial phosphatidylinositol mannoside binding to mouse CD1d. *J. Immunol.* 177:4577–83

Zajonc DM, Cantu C 3rd, Mattner J, Zhou D, Savage PB, et al. 2005a. Structure and function of a potent agonist for the semi-invariant natural killer T cell receptor. *Nat. Immunol.* 6:810–18

Zajonc DM, Crispin MD, Bowden TA, Young DC, Cheng TY, et al. 2005b. Molecular mechanism of lipopeptide presentation by CD1a. *Immunity* 22:209–19

Zajonc DM, Elsliger MA, Teyton L, Wilson IA. 2003. Crystal structure of CD1a in complex with a sulfatide self antigen at a resolution of 2.15 Å. *Nat. Immunol.* 4:808–15

Zajonc DM, Maricic I, Wu D, Halder R, Roy K, et al. 2005c. Structural basis for CD1d presentation of a sulfatide derived from myelin and its implications for autoimmunity. *J. Exp. Med.* 202:1517–26

Zajonc DM, Savage PB, Bendelac A, Wilson IA, Teyton L. 2008. Crystal structures of mouse CD1d-iGb3 complex and its cognate Vα14 T cell receptor suggest a model for dual recognition of foreign and self glycolipids. *J. Mol. Biol.* 377:1104–16

Zeng Z, Castano AR, Segelke BW, Stura EA, Peterson PA, Wilson IA. 1997. Crystal structure of mouse CD1: an MHC-like fold with a large hydrophobic binding groove. *Science* 277:339–45

Zhou D, Cantu C 3rd, Sagiv Y, Schrantz N, Kulkarni AB, et al. 2004a. Editing of CD1d-bound lipid antigens by endosomal lipid transfer proteins. *Science* 303:523–27

Zhou D, Mattner J, Cantu C 3rd, Schrantz N, Yin N, et al. 2004b. Lysosomal glycosphingolipid recognition by NKT cells. *Science* 306:1786–89

Prelude to a Division

Needhi Bhalla[1] and Abby F. Dernburg[2,3]

[1] Department of Molecular, Cell and Developmental Biology, University of California, Santa Cruz, California 95064; email: bhalla@biology.ucsc.edu

[2] Life Sciences Division, E.O. Lawrence Berkeley National Laboratory, Berkeley, California 94720; email: AFDernburg@lbl.gov

[3] Department of Molecular and Cell Biology, University of California, Berkeley, California 94720

Annu. Rev. Cell Dev. Biol. 2008. 24:397–424

First published online as a Review in Advance on July 2, 2008

The *Annual Review of Cell and Developmental Biology* is online at cellbio.annualreviews.org

This article's doi:
10.1146/annurev.cellbio.23.090506.123245

Key Words

meiosis, homologous chromosomes, pairing, synapsis, recombination, meiotic bouquet

Abstract

Accurate segregation of chromosomes during meiosis requires physical links between homologs. These links are usually established through chromosome pairing, synapsis, and recombination, which occur during meiotic prophase. How chromosomes pair with their homologous partners is one of the outstanding mysteries of meiosis. Surprisingly, experimental evidence indicates that different organisms have found more than one way to accomplish this feat. Whereas some species depend on recombination machinery to achieve homologous pairing, others are able to pair and synapse their homologs in the absence of recombination. To ensure specific pairing between homologous chromosomes, both recombination-dependent and recombination-independent mechanisms must strike the proper balance between forces that promote chromosome interactions and activities that temper the promiscuity of those interactions. The initiation of synapsis is likely to be a tightly regulated step in a process that must be mechanically coupled to homolog pairing.

Contents

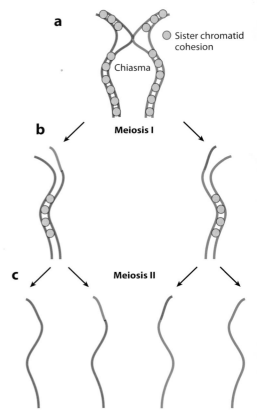

Figure 1

Meiotic chromosome segregation. (*a*) Meiotic cells of diploid organisms contain two copies of every chromosome, one inherited from each parent (*red* and *blue*). After DNA replication, sister chromatids are linked by cohesion (*purple circles*). Genetic exchange between nonsister chromatids generates chiasmata, which, in conjunction with sister chromatid cohesion, link homologous chromosomes through metaphase I. (*b*) Dissolution of cohesion distal to the chiasmata during meiosis I enables homologous chromosome segregation. (*c*) The remaining cohesion is removed during meiosis II to enable separation of sister chromatids.

INTRODUCTION

In most eukaryotes, sexual reproduction accomplishes two goals: (*a*) the production of haploid gametes from a diploid cell so that a diploid genome will be regenerated upon fertilization and (*b*) the shuffling of genetic information, which gives rise to novel combinations of alleles that underlie adaptation and natural selection. Meiosis produces haploid gametes from a diploid cell by executing two successive chromosome segregation events after a single round of replication: meiosis I, a reductional division in which homologs are partitioned, and meiosis II, an equational division when sister chromatids segregate away from each other (**Figure 1**). Meiotic chromosome missegregation can lead to aneuploidy among the resulting gametes, which is usually lethal to any zygote that results upon fertilization. In humans, approximately one-third of miscarriages occur owing to genetic imbalances in the embryo that result from chromosome segregation errors during meiosis. Some aneuploidy may be tolerated by the developing zygote but, in humans, invariably results in developmental disabilities and/or infertility (Hassold & Hunt 2001).

Sister chromatid cohesion, introduced during DNA replication, enables sisters to stay together and eventually to segregate from each other during the equational division of meiosis (**Figure 1c**), much as it does during mitotic division. However, for homologous pairs of sister chromatids to partition accurately during the reductional division, they must first establish physical linkages that enable their kinetochores to biorient, or attach to opposite poles of the meiosis I spindle (**Figure 1a**). These links are established after meiotic DNA replication, during an extended prophase period in which each chromosome becomes physically paired with its homologous partner. In most organisms, this pairing is reinforced by the assembly of the synaptonemal complex and culminates in crossover recombination between homologs.

How each chromosome finds, recognizes, synapses with, and selectively undergoes exchange of genetic material with its unique homologous partner remains one of the outstanding mysteries of meiosis. Although many of the details of this pairing process remain to be clarified, work in diverse organisms has revealed two general classes of pairing mechanisms: those that require early events in recombination and those that do not. Recent work has demonstrated that recombination-dependent and recombination-independent pairing pathways both involve a balance between mechanisms that promote pairing and opposing mechanisms that prevent inappropriate chromosome interactions. When these forces are in proper balance, pairing between homologs is selectively stabilized by synapsis. When the system breaks down, reinforcement of homologous interactions often fails, but more revealingly, interactions between nonhomologous partners can become aberrantly stabilized.

Our purpose here is to highlight recent evidence for distinct mechanisms that contribute to homologous interactions during meiosis. In particular we emphasize how these mechanisms progressively and selectively stabilize initially tenuous interactions between homologs

to culminate in synapsis and/or crossover recombination. As the molecular mechanisms and structural intermediates are defined, we can begin to consider the meiotic progression from unpaired chromosomes to fully conjoined homologs as we would any other metabolic pathway, and we can think in terms of critical transition points, thermodynamic barriers, and rate-limiting steps along the way. On the basis of this paradigm, recognition between homologous chromosomes is accomplished through the reversibility of early steps along the pathway, during which homology is assessed and inappropriate interactions are rejected.

The Progression of Chromosome Interactions

We start by defining a number of terms, because their use in the literature is inconsistent and our goal here is to be as consistent and unambiguous as possible. We describe chromosomes undergoing alignment, encounters, pairing, synapsis, and recombination (**Figure 2**).

We define alignment (**Figure 2b**) as the polarization of chromosomes within the nucleus such that chromosome arms are arrayed in parallel. In most organisms, homolog alignment during meiosis is thought to be an active process that initiates at the onset of meiotic prophase, in many cases mediated by associations between chromosomes and the nuclear envelope. As we discuss below, alignment probably plays the dual roles of promoting appropriate interhomolog contacts and restricting ectopic (or nonallelic) interactions.

Encounters (**Figure 2c**) represent an early step in establishing stable chromosome interactions. We use this term to mean transient, highly reversible contacts between chromosome loci, whether homologous or nonhomologous. These may be mediated through passive means, including diffusion, and may also be facilitated through active rearrangement of chromosomes within the nucleus. Real-time imaging can reveal the frequency and duration of encounters between homologous sequences (e.g., Ding et al. 2004), but interactions between

Pairing: also referred to as close, stable homolog juxtaposition (CSHJ); the local stabilization of homolog interactions that can be observed in the absence of synapsis

Synaptonemal complex: a morphologically conserved structure composed of axial (or lateral) elements and transverse elements; normally forms between pairs of homologous chromosomes during meiosis and structurally enforces homolog pairing

Crossover recombination: also known as genetic exchange, a reciprocal recombination event between two chromatids on homologous chromosomes that results in local gene conversion and exchange of the arms flanking the site of initiation. Crossover events result in chiasmata (singular: chiasma), which link homologs during the first meiotic division

Synapsis: assembly of the synaptonemal complex

Alignment: the polarization of chromosomes in the nucleus such that homologous interactions are favored and nonhomologous contacts are inhibited

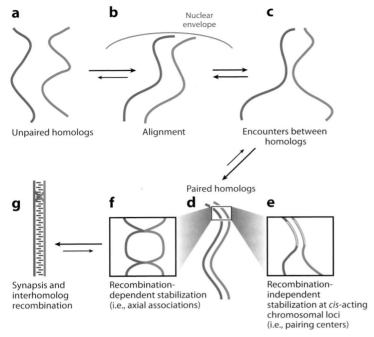

a Unpaired homologs

b Alignment — Nuclear envelope

c Encounters between homologs

Paired homologs

g Synapsis and interhomolog recombination

f Recombination-dependent stabilization (i.e., axial associations)

d

e Recombination-independent stabilization at *cis*-acting chromosomal loci (i.e., pairing centers)

Figure 2

A pairing pathway. Intermediates in the pairing pathway are depicted: (*a*) unpaired homologs (one *red* and one *blue*), (*b*) alignment, (*c*) encounters between homologous chromosomes, and (*d*) stabilized pairing. The pathway concludes with synapsis and/or homolog recombination (*g*). Alignment is often facilitated by formation of the bouquet, more specifically the attachment of chromosome ends to the nuclear envelope (*b*). Paired homologs can be stabilized by recombination-independent mechanisms (e.g., pairing at *cis*-acting loci such as pairing centers) (*e*) or recombination-dependent mechanisms (i.e., axial associations) (*f*).

Meiotic recombination: includes both noncrossover (also known as gene conversion) and crossover events

recombination events, which can be generated either by the endogenous meiotic recombination apparatus or by engineered recombinases, such as the Cre/*loxP* system (e.g., Peoples et al. 2002). The stability and reversibility of pairing interactions can be measured more directly by real-time imaging (Ding et al. 2004), but only a few studies to date have used this approach. When pairing interactions are established at multiple points between two chromosomes, this results in intimate association along their entire lengths; we do not use the term pairing here to describe this more global phenomenon.

Synapsis (**Figure 2*g***) specifically refers here to the assembly of the synaptonemal complex, a conserved protein matrix that normally forms between paired homologs, reinforcing their interaction. The term synapsis is frequently used outside the meiosis field to describe DNA recombination intermediates involving strand exchange, but we avoid this ambiguity here. The formation of the synaptonemal complex between homologs is unique to meiosis and occurs in most organisms that undergo sexual reproduction. Axial elements assemble between the sisters of replicated chromosomes prior to, or concomitant with, pairing; once the synaptonemal complex has fully assembled, these protein cores are often referred to as lateral elements. Synapsis is completed when transverse filament proteins and additional components load to form the central element of the synaptonemal complex by bridging the axial elements of homologous chromosomes (**Figure 3*b***). The resulting zipper- or ladder-like structure can be visualized in spread preparations or thin sections by transmission electron microscopy, which reveals axial elements separated by ~100 nm (reviewed in Zickler & Kleckner 1999) (**Figure 3*a***). Components of the transverse filaments have been identified in several species, and although they lack obvious sequence conservation, they are all proteins with high coiled-coil formation potential (reviewed in Colaiacovo 2006). The transverse filaments may be composed of only a single protein, as in budding yeast (Zip1) (Sym et al. 1993) and *Drosophila* [c(3)G] (Page & Hawley 2001).

nonhomologous sequences are more difficult to measure.

Pairing (**Figure 2*d***) is the most difficult term to define rigorously because it is used in the literature to encompass diverse mechanisms operating on an enormous range of size scales. We restrict our use of this term to describe the local stabilization of homologous encounters, sometimes referred to as close, stable homolog juxtaposition (CSHJ) (Peoples et al. 2002). By this definition, pairing interactions are sufficiently stable that they can be observed cytologically in fixed samples even in the absence of synapsis (e.g., MacQueen et al. 2002, 2005; Rockmill et al. 1995). Pairing can also be detected experimentally after the fact through

Elegant experiments with Zip1 have revealed that the distance between synapsed chromosomes is determined by the length of its coiled-coil portion (Sym & Roeder 1995). Multiple proteins may compose the transverse filaments in other species; for example, multiple predicted coiled-coil components of the synaptonemal complex central element have been identified so far in *Caenorhabditis elegans* (Colaiacovo et al. 2003, MacQueen et al. 2002, Smolikov et al. 2007) and in mammals (reviewed in Costa & Cooke 2007).

Meiotic recombination is initiated by a conserved topoisomerase-like enzyme, Spo11, which introduces programmed double-strand breaks (DSBs) into the genome (reviewed in Neale & Keeney 2006) (**Figure 5b**, below). DSBs usually pose a hazard to genome integrity. However, the enzymes that repair breaks through conservative homologous recombination are highly upregulated during meiosis. This machinery is also modulated during meiosis so that use of the sister chromatid as a template is inhibited and the homologous chromosome becomes the preferred donor for recombinational repair. DSBs initiate two different pathways of meiotic recombination, leading to either crossovers, which involve the reciprocal exchange of sequences flanking the repair sites, or noncrossovers (also referred to as simple gene conversions), which transfer local information, typically spanning a few hundred base pairs, from one homolog to the other (reviewed in Neale & Keeney 2006). Mounting evidence indicates that the choice between crossover and noncrossover outcomes is determined very early in the process, possibly at or soon after the time of break formation (Borner et al. 2004, Martini et al. 2006), and that the intermediates in the two pathways are also distinct (Allers & Lichten 2001, Hunter & Kleckner 2001). This view has been supplanting an older paradigm in which a common recombination intermediate could be resolved to give either a gene conversion or a crossover (Szostak et al. 1983). Whereas crossovers create persistent physical links (chiasmata) between homologs, simple gene conversions do not.

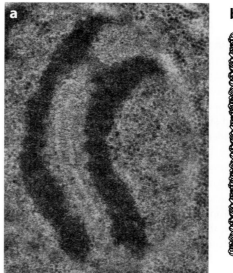
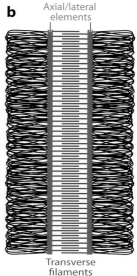

Figure 3

The synaptonemal complex. (*a*) Transmission electron micrograph of a synaptonemal complex from *Caenorhabditis elegans*, which appears as a zipper-like track flanked by electron-dense patches of chromatin. (*b*) Schematic of the synaptonemal complex. The axial/lateral elements (*red*) assemble between sister chromatids prior to or concomitant with pairing. The transverse filaments (*purple*) polymerize between paired homologs to complete synapsis.

We define these terms above on the basis of collective evidence that these processes are distinct but coordinated. A challenge in integrating results from different studies is that many of the assays that are routinely used to analyze meiosis actually measure events that occur downstream of these processes, such as crossover frequency, progeny survival, or chromosome nondisjunction. The quantitative effects of pairing or synapsis defects on each of these outputs may not be linear or obvious. In part, this is because the consequences of defects in meiotic chromosome transactions can be nondisjunction, cell cycle arrest, or cell death, depending on the activities of meiotic checkpoints. As a clearer view of the pathway leading to homolog synapsis emerges, the effects of mutations on the assembly and stability of specific intermediates in this pathway will likely be more systematically examined.

Double-strand break (DSB): essential initiating event in all meiotic recombination; catalyzed by Spo11, a conserved topoisomerase-like enzyme that acts as a dimer to simultaneously cut both strands of a DNA helix (chromatid)

Gene conversion: a recombination event involving local, unidirectional transfer of information from one nonsister chromatid to another; describes meiotic recombination events that are not accompanied by crossovers

Coordination between Pairing and Synapsis

In most organisms, local sites of homolog pairing are eventually reinforced by assembly of the synaptonemal complex, which results in global apposition of homologous chromosomes. The initiation of synapsis is likely to be a committed step in homolog association. Cytogenetic evidence from *Neurospora* and mice indicates that chromosomes can undergo synaptic adjustment to eliminate inversion loops. Synaptic adjustment presumably involves depolymerization and repolymerization of the synaptonemal complex (Bojko 1990, Davisson et al. 1981), but this occurs during mid- to late pachytene (Moses et al. 1982), perhaps after the search for a homologous partner has been completed. There is also evidence for preliminary synaptonemal complex formation near centromeres in budding yeast that is clearly reversible (Tsubouchi & Roeder 2005). However, once initiated, synaptonemal complex formation usually appears to be highly processive and potentially insensitive to homology, which probably reflects the tendency of synaptonemal complex components to self-assemble into polymers (Baier et al. 2007, Ollinger et al. 2005). This implies that synapsis initiation is likely to be a tightly regulated event, with large kinetic and/or thermodynamic barriers that must be overcome.

Mutation of transverse filament components in both *C. elegans* and budding yeast abrogates synapsis but does not eliminate intimate, local associations between homologs (MacQueen et al. 2002, 2005; Rockmill et al. 1995). Conversely, mutation of certain genes, including *HOP2* (Leu et al. 1998) or *MND1* (Tsubouchi & Roeder 2002) in budding yeast and *htp-1* (Martinez-Perez & Villeneuve 2005) or *sun-1* (Penkner et al. 2007) in *C. elegans*, results in promiscuous synapsis between nonhomologs. The effects of these mutations further indicate that synaptonemal complex assembly does not depend on homology per se and that pairing and synapsis are discrete processes that can be genetically uncoupled. Ongoing analyses of these mutant situations are providing important insight into the mechanisms that restrict synaptonemal complex assembly to paired homologous chromosomes.

Taken together, this evidence indicates that the initiation of synapsis is coupled to the establishment of stable homolog pairing. Although homolog pairing may not be sufficient for synapsis initiation, it is normally a prerequisite to overcome the kinetic and/or thermodynamic barriers to synapsis. The goal of the cell is thus to calibrate pairing and synapsis initiation mechanisms such that appropriate, homologous pairing interactions reliably trigger the synaptonemal complex to polymerize, whereas nonhomologous interactions are transient or unstable enough that this rarely occurs.

RECOMBINATION-INDEPENDENT PAIRING MECHANISMS

Abundant evidence exists that all organisms employ mechanisms that promote meiotic homolog interactions in the absence of DSBs or other recombination intermediates. At least two recombination-independent phenomena may contribute to proper chromosome segregation during meiosis: (*a*) interactions between chromosomes and the nuclear envelope and (*b*) interchromosomal interactions between heterochromatic regions of the genome.

Interactions between Chromosomes and the Nuclear Envelope

Cytologically observed interactions between chromosomes and the nuclear envelope are a widely conserved feature of meiotic prophase. Such interactions have been recognized for more than 100 years, but their contributions to homolog pairing and synapsis remain a subject of speculation and debate (reviewed in Scherthan 2001). Current experimental efforts to understand how chromosomes are actively rearranged in this phase of meiosis are revealing mechanisms that promote some interactions between chromosomes while limiting others.

Formation of the meiotic bouquet. In many organisms, the onset of meiotic prophase is accompanied by a chromosome configuration in which chromosome ends associate with the nuclear envelope, resulting in a roughly parallel alignment of the chromosome arms, particularly in regions of the genome near the telomeres (**Figure 4**). In some species, these chromosome attachment sites form a tight cluster, leading to the description of this stage as the meiotic bouquet because the chromosomes resemble a bouquet of flowers with gathered stems (reviewed in Zickler & Kleckner 1998). Although clustering of telomeres is frequently cited as a defining attribute of the meiotic bouquet, the degree of clustering varies from highly pronounced (**Figure 4a,b**) to more subtly polarized (**Figure 4c–e**) within the nucleus, suggesting that attachment to the nuclear envelope may play a more conserved, and therefore more critical, role. In most organisms with discrete microtubule-organizing centers, clustered telomeres are observed adjacent to these structures (reviewed in Zickler & Kleckner 1998).

This reconfiguration of chromosome organization coincides with the onset of alignment, pairing, and synapsis, and its contribution to these events is currently an area of vigorous investigation. Genetic and cytological analysis indicates that the bouquet stage involves three discrete but interdependent processes: nuclear

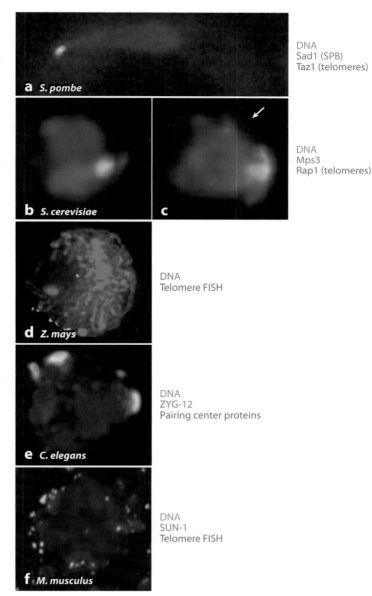

Figure 4

Examples of the meiotic bouquet. Images of the bouquet in (*a*) *Schizosaccharomyces pombe*, (*b,c*) *Saccharomyces cerevisiae*, (*d*) *Zea mays*, (*e*) *Caenorhabditis elegans*, and (*f*) *Mus musculus*. In some organisms, such as *S. pombe* (*a*), tight clustering of the telomeres is obvious. However, in other organisms, such as *Z. mays* (*d*), *C. elegans* (*e*), and *M. musculus* (*f*), clustering of chromosome ends is less pronounced. *S. cerevisiae* exhibit a mixture of "tight" (*b*) and "loose" (*c*) bouquet arrangements during prophase. The arrow in panel *c* indicates the spindle pole body. DNA is shown in blue, telomeres or chromosome ends are shown in green, and SUN (Sad1, Mps3, and SUN-1) or KASH (ZYG-12) domain proteins are indicated in red, except for in the *Z. mays* image, in which only the telomeres are shown. Images are reprinted and/or adapted from Chikashige et al. 2006 (*a*), Conrad et al. 2007 (*b,c*), Bass et al. 1997 (*d*), and Ding et al. 2007 (*f*), respectively, with permission from The Rockefeller University Press (*d*) and Elsevier (*a* and *f*).

envelope attachment, clustering of chromosome ends, and cytoskeleton-mediated chromosome movement. Each of these steps appears to contribute to proper homolog pairing.

Many of the insights into the molecular basis and purpose of bouquet formation have come from studies in fission yeast. This organism has an unusual meiosis in that it lacks synaptonemal complex formation, and the entire nucleus oscillates dramatically along the long axis of the cell for the duration of meiotic prophase in what is called horsetail movement (Chikashige et al. 1994). This phenomenon is probably a manifestation of mechanisms that underlie bouquet formation in other species, although such dramatic motion of the entire nucleus is unusual. More recently, experiments in synaptic organisms including *C. elegans* (Penkner et al. 2007; A. Sato, C.M. Phillips & A.F. Dernburg, unpublished), *Saccharomyces cerevisiae* (Chua & Roeder 1997; Conrad et al. 1997, 2007), plants (Corredor et al. 2007, Cowan & Cande 2002, Golubovskaya et al. 2002), and mammals (Ding et al. 2007, Liu et al. 2004, Schmitt et al. 2007) have shed light on both the conservation and the diversity of bouquet organization and function.

In most organisms, formation of the meiotic bouquet is thought to be mediated by association between telomeric repeats and nuclear envelope components. Molecular evidence for telomere involvement comes from *Schizosaccharomyces pombe*, in which mutations in the genes encoding constitutive telomere-associated proteins, including Taz1p, Rap1p, and Rik1p, disrupt bouquet formation and impair meiotic segregation (Cooper et al. 1998, Nimmo et al. 1998, Tuzon et al. 2004). Telomere shortening in telomerase-deficient mice has also been linked to meiotic defects (Liu et al. 2004). In a variety of other organisms, telomere repeats have been implicated in the bouquet primarily by their localization to the nuclear envelope cluster (Bass et al. 1997; reviewed in Scherthan 2001, Ding et al. 2007, Schmitt et al. 2007).

In addition to normal telomere structure, formation of the bouquet in fungi requires the expression of meiosis-specific proteins that form a bridge between telomeres and the nuclear envelope. These proteins include Ndj1 in budding yeast (Chua & Roeder 1997, Conrad et al. 1997) and Bqt1p and Bqt2p in fission yeast (Chikashige et al. 2006). Interestingly, none of the meiosis-specific components identified to date show conservation between budding and fission yeast or have obvious homologs in other species.

In the nematode *C. elegans*, a bouquet-like configuration also appears to play a major role in homolog pairing. Surprisingly, in this species the bouquet is mediated not by the telomeres, but instead by a distinct region on each chromosome known as the homolog recognition region or pairing center. Recent work has shown that pairing centers comprise a region of each chromosome enriched in short, repetitive sequences that are recognized by specific members of a zinc-finger protein family (Phillips & Dernburg 2006, Phillips et al. 2005; C.M. Phillips & A.F. Dernburg, unpublished). Further evidence indicates that these pairing centers mediate nuclear envelope attachment to fulfill their roles in stabilizing homolog pairing and facilitating synapsis (Phillips & Dernburg 2006, Phillips et al. 2005).

Some of the nuclear envelope components involved in bouquet formation are clearly conserved across evolution. The first of these to be identified were Sad1 (Niwa et al. 2000) and Kms1 (Shimanuki et al. 1997) in *S. pombe*. These transmembrane proteins were initially identified as components of the spindle pole body, the fungal microtubule-organizing center, which is embedded in the nuclear envelope. These proteins contain a SUN domain and a KASH domain, respectively. SUN domain proteins (named for founding members Sad1 and UNC-84) have recently been implicated in meiotic telomere attachment and/or homolog synapsis in mice (Ding et al. 2007) and *C. elegans* (Penkner et al. 2007; A. Sato, C.M. Phillips & A.F. Dernburg, unpublished).

SUN and KASH domains (the latter named for Klarsicht/ANC-1/Syne homology) are thought to interact physically within the lumen of the nuclear envelope, between the inner and outer nuclear membranes. The SUN domain protein usually extends into the nucleoplasm, whereas the KASH domain is connected to a protein that spans the outer nuclear envelope to the cytoplasm. Pairs of SUN/KASH proteins link nuclear components to either the microtubule cytoskeleton or actin structures in the cytoplasm in a variety of cell types (Starr & Fischer 2005). Kms1 interacts with dynein, a cytoplasmic, minus-end-directed microtubule motor. These proteins are required for the telomere clustering and horsetail movement of *S. pombe* nuclei during meiosis, respectively (Shimanuki et al. 1997, Miki et al. 2002, Yamamoto et al. 1999). In *C. elegans*, SUN-1 interacts with the KASH domain protein ZYG-12 to link chromosomes, via their pairing centers, to microtubules and cytoplasmic dynein (A. Sato, C.M. Phillips & A.F. Dernburg, unpublished). Surprisingly, dynein is dispensable for meiotic prophase in *S. cerevisiae* (Lui et al. 2006), and the meiotic bouquet is insensitive to microtubule drugs but is disrupted by latrunculin, which results in actin depolymerization (Trelles-Sticken et al. 2005). Latrunculin also reversibly disrupts telomere-led chromosome movement during meiotic prophase (Scherthan et al. 2007). This leads to the provocative conclusion that different cytoskeletal elements may govern telomere-led meiotic chromosome movements in different organisms, despite the widespread conservation of the bouquet.

Pro- and antipairing functions of the meiotic bouquet. The most detailed analyses of the functional contributions of the bouquet come from fission yeast. This is due to the early identification of bouquet components in this organism, the dramatic horsetail movements associated with bouquet formation, and the amenability of these yeast cells to real-time fluorescence imaging. Meiotic chromosome pairing dynamics have been directly analyzed by the use of locus-specific fluorescent probes, both in wild-type cells and in a variety of meiotic mutants. Homologous loci repeatedly associate and dissociate in wild-type cells, eventually becoming more stably associated (Ding

et al. 2004). Cells that lack *Rec12* (the *S. pombe* ortholog of *SPO11*) show initial kinetics and frequencies of homologous association similar to those of wild-type cells. However, in contrast to wild-type cells, the number of cells showing associations between homologous loci does not increase with progression through prophase but remains constant over time. This analysis of the dynamics of homolog pairing confirms that transient encounters between homologous chromosomes are governed by recombination-independent mechanisms but are ultimately stabilized by recombination-dependent mechanisms (Ding et al. 2004).

Mutations in *S. pombe* that disrupt telomere attachment during meiotic prophase severely reduce the frequency of encounters between homologs. The primary defect is a failure to align chromosomes. Loci on chromosome arms exhibit the most severe defect, whereas centromeres, which may have an independent pairing mechanism, still pair efficiently (Ding et al. 2004). The attachment of telomeres to the nuclear envelope seems to bring chromosomes into register with their homologs at interstitial loci. This both promotes homologous interactions and limits interactions with other chromosomes, as revealed by the fact that mutations that reduce the interaction between homologous chromosomes also result in an increase in ectopic recombination (Davis & Smith 2006, Niwa et al. 2000). These relatively simple sorting and stabilization mechanisms may be particularly effective in *S. pombe*, owing to its small number of chromosomes ($2n = 6$), the pronounced length differences among them, and the high levels of meiotic recombination in this organism.

Mutations that disrupt telomere clustering, but not nuclear envelope attachment, in either *S. pombe* or maize impair synapsis and/or recombination (Golubovskaya et al. 2002, Niwa et al. 2000, Shimanuki et al. 1997). This may reflect a direct role for clustering in mediating homolog interactions. Alternatively, clustering may be an indication that the chromosome attachments are interacting productively with other components, such as the cytoskeleton.

For example, most clustering-defective mutations in fission yeast also perturb the integrity of the spindle pole body (Jin et al. 2002, Niwa et al. 2000, Shimanuki et al. 1997). Surprisingly, disrupting nuclear movement in *S. pombe* by mutation of the microtubule motor dynein has even more severe consequences for homolog pairing than loss of telomere attachment, even at centromeres (Ding et al. 2004). This indicates that nuclear movement alone can promote homolog encounters independently of telomere-mediated alignment. Unlike telomere-clustering mutants, dynein mutants do not show an increase in ectopic recombination. One interpretation is that in the absence of nuclear oscillation, chromosomes align owing to telomere attachment but fail to pair properly (Davis & Smith 2006). Alternatively, microtubule-dependent nuclear movement may promote encounters among all chromosomes so that both allelic recombination and ectopic recombination are reduced in its absence. This would predict that the elevated ectopic recombination levels in mutants that disrupt telomere attachment should depend on nuclear oscillation.

The meiotic bouquet appears to play a less critical role in aligning homologs in *S. cerevisiae*. Although a telomere-mediated bouquet is detected during early meiotic prophase (Dresser & Giroux 1988, Trelles-Sticken et al. 1999), this bouquet can be disrupted experimentally with only subtle consequences for the cell. Deletion of the *NDJ1* gene, which encodes a meiosis-specific telomere component, results in a prophase delay and reduces telomere localization at the nuclear periphery (Trelles-Sticken et al. 2000) but has only modest effects on pairing, synapsis, and recombination (Chua & Roeder 1997, Conrad et al. 1997). An increase in ectopic recombination is also detected in *ndj1*Δ mutant cells, suggesting that homolog discrimination may be perturbed (Goldman & Lichten 2000). However, only an approximately 2-fold increase in ectopic recombination is observed, compared with the 18-fold increase in bouquet mutants of fission yeast (Davis & Smith 2006, Goldman & Lichten 2000). As in wild-type cells, an inverse relationship between the distance of loci from the telomere and the frequency of ectopic recombination is seen in this mutant (Goldman & Lichten 2000, Schlecht et al. 2004). This relationship suggests that some aspects of telomere-mediated homolog alignment or constraint are retained in the absence of Ndj1.

A general model for bouquet formation and function that is consistent with available data is as follows: Meiosis-specific proteins establish links between chromosomes and components of the inner nuclear envelope, which either contain SUN domains or interact with SUN domain proteins. A bridge across the double bilayer of the envelope is formed by interactions between the SUN domain protein and a KASH domain protein. These bridging proteins tend to aggregate within the nuclear envelope via association with each other or with components of the microtubule-organizing center. This results in telomere clustering, which contributes to homolog alignment and thereby to pairing. However, the key purpose of this bridge may be to connect chromosomes to cytoskeletal components that drive nuclear and/or chromosome movement, which is important for cells to reap the full benefit of the bouquet. The bouquet therefore contributes to chromosome alignment and increases the overall frequency of chromosome encounters, which promote proper pairing, particularly at regions proximal to the attachment sites.

Interactions between Centromeric Regions

Beyond mediating associations with the nuclear envelope, specific chromosome regions have been speculated to play additional roles in homolog segregation during meiosis. Centromeric chromosome regions are known to be "sticky," in that they tend to aggregate or form pairwise associations in a variety of cell types (Ding et al. 2004, Martinez-Perez et al. 2001, Scherthan et al. 1994), including nonmeiotic cells (reviewed in McKee 2004). This behavior may stem from the enrichment of particular chromatin components, such as co-hesins, or possibly from the enrichment of specific sequence-binding or epigenetically targeted proteins in the regions flanking the centromeres. The evidence that centromeric associations play a role in mediating partner choice or segregation during meiosis is limited and somewhat enigmatic.

In budding yeast, centromeres have been implicated in a distributive disjunction mechanism that segregates pairs of heterologous chromosomes, which are unable to recombine and synapse (Dawson et al. 1986, Kemp et al. 2004). Physical association between the centromeres of nonhomologous partner chromosomes precedes their segregation (Kemp et al. 2004), and this physical contact may contribute to the biorientation of these chromosomes in the absence of chiasmata. Even during wild-type meiosis, centromeres establish pairwise associations that are initially nonspecific but eventually resolve to homologous associations, presumably by partner switching. This progression from random to homologous pairing of centromeres requires *SPO11* activity (Tsubouchi & Roeder 2005), as does homologous synapsis in this organism (Giroux et al. 1989), indicating that such a progression is dependent on the same recombination-based mechanism that regulates homolog pairing. This may imply that the recombination machinery operates in centromeric regions or that recombination-based homology assessment elsewhere along the chromosomes eventually directs proper centromere pairing.

Nonhomologous centromere pairing requires the activity of the synaptonemal complex component Zip1 (Tsubouchi & Roeder 2005), which may indicate that Zip1 plays a functional role in homolog sorting. Alternatively, the centromeric associations may persist long enough to allow reversible loading of the synaptonemal complex, which further stabilizes pairwise associations, at least long enough to enable their detection. In other words, these nonhomologous associations may reflect the promiscuity of synaptonemal complex formation at stabilized contact sites between nonhomologous

chromosome pairs, rather than representing a productive step along the pathway to homologous synapsis. This transient synaptonemal complex formation may need to be repressed to prevent extensive synapsis between nonhomologous chromosomes.

Martinez-Perez et al. (2001) have described a similar phenomenon in allohexaploid wheat. In these plant species, each of the 7 ancestral chromosomes has become triplicated, resulting in a diploid number of 42. The chromosomes within the triploid sets do not exchange information during meiosis and have consequently diverged enough to become distinct homeologs. During meiotic prophase, each chromosome faces the problem of identifying its unique homolog not only from unrelated chromosomes but also from its four homeologs. The centromeres initially cluster in sets of six, which then resolve to homologous pairwise interactions (Martinez-Perez et al. 2001). This centromere sorting was proposed to be an active process underlying homologous synapsis in this organism. However, recent work indicates that this resolution does not depend on homology at the centromere, but rather at subtelomeric regions (Corredor et al. 2007), and also is sensitive to disruption of the telomeric bouquet by colchicine treatment (Corredor & Naranjo 2007). These findings indicate that the homologous pairing of centromeres does not drive the process of pairing and synapsis but instead is a consequence of these mechanisms. Because centromeres usually contain abundant repeats that are not unique to individual chromosomes, and thus are not optimal sites at which to assess pairwise homology, this makes teleological sense.

In fission yeast, evidence that centromeric regions are sticky during meiosis comes from observations of homolog pairing in both fixed and living cells (Ding et al. 2004, Scherthan et al. 1994). In the absence of recombination, homologous centromeres are more stably associated than interstitial regions of the chromosomes. Although homologous pairwise associations between centromeric regions in *S. pombe* are facilitated by telomere clustering and by telomere-led horsetail movement, such associations do not depend as strongly on these forces as do associations at other loci and are also more stable in the absence of DSBs (Ding et al. 2004). The pairwise association of homologous centromeres is likely facilitated by the disparate lengths of each of the three chromosome pairs. Whether centromere-specific chromatin structure or kinetochore formation contributes to their propensity to pair has not yet been tested. When recombination fails, these pairwise associations may contribute to faithful disjunction of homologs, which is slightly more robust than would be expected if the chromosomes segregated at random (Molnar et al. 2001). However, this has also not been formally tested, for example, by moving one of two homologous centromeres to a different chromosomal position to inhibit centromeric pairing.

A role for pericentric regions in mediating homolog interactions is more clearly established in *Drosophila* oocytes. Chromosomes pair along their lengths during early meiotic prophase, as in other species. Following the pachytene stage, the chromosomes condense to form a compact structure called a karyosome. The euchromatic arms separate from each other, but interactions between homologous heterochromatic regions persist until the end of meiotic prophase (Dernburg et al. 1996). In the absence of chiasmata, these persistent associations can mediate highly accurate biorientation and disjunction of homologs (reviewed in McKee 2004). Nevertheless, successful exchange between at least one or two of the chromosome pairs is critical for establishment of a bipolar spindle capable of partitioning the achiasmate chromosomes (reviewed in Hawley et al. 1993). There is no indication that heterochromatin contributes to the initial association or synapsis of homologs in *Drosophila* oocytes, and so heterochromatin is not considered to play a role in pairing by our definition.

We draw the following conclusions from these studies: (*a*) Centromeric and pericentric regions have a propensity to form both heterologous and homologous interactions during meiotic prophase. (*b*) Although it is known

that persistent centromere pairing contributes to achiasmate chromosome segregation in female flies and potentially in budding yeast, it is not yet known whether it plays a role in homologous synapsis in any organism. (*c*) Their sticky nature may contribute to pairing and synapsis by promoting global alignment of chromosomes from centromere to telomere, which may facilitate evaluation of homology at interstitial regions.

Recombination-Independent Mechanisms Are Sufficient to Promote Homologous Synapsis in Some Organisms

In many organisms, the recombination-independent activities that promote homolog associations (described above) are probably necessary but not sufficient for homologous chromosome synapsis. In budding yeast, plants, and mammals, DSBs (Baudat et al. 2000, Giroux et al. 1989, Grelon et al. 2001, Romanienko & Camerini-Otero 2000) and subsequent strand invasion (Bishop et al. 1992; Li et al. 2004, 2007; Pittman et al. 1998; Yoshida et al. 1998) are required for efficient homologous synapsis, as discussed in more detail below. However, in *C. elegans* (Dernburg et al. 1998) and the fruit fly *Drosophila melanogaster* (McKim et al. 1998), timely and apparently normal homologous synapsis occurs even when DSB formation is blocked by mutation. If recombination machinery is necessary in other organisms to promote interactions that are sufficiently stable to overcome the barriers to synapsis, then it follows that *Drosophila* and *C. elegans* must have other ways to selectively stabilize pairing.

In *C. elegans* meiocytes, stable homologous pairing interactions are detected at the pairing center regions of chromosomes in the absence of both synaptonemal complex formation and DSBs (MacQueen et al. 2002). This pairing depends on interactions between homologous pairing centers and also on a family of zinc-finger proteins that bind to these chromosome regions (MacQueen et al. 2005, Phillips & Dernburg 2006, Phillips et al. 2005).

Indirect evidence suggests that these stabilized interactions act as sites of synapsis initiation because chromosomes that are homologous in their pairing center regions but otherwise dissimilar will undergo complete synapsis (MacQueen et al. 2005). Although the pairwise interactions between pairing centers do not require DSBs or transverse filament components, they do require nuclear envelope attachment and interaction with the microtubule cytoskeleton, hallmarks of the influence of the meiotic bouquet (Penkner et al. 2007; A. Sato, C.M. Phillips & A.F. Dernburg, unpublished). Recognition between homologs may be facilitated by the organization of pairing centers, which are composed of short repeats interspersed with unique single-copy DNA sequences (C.M. Phillips & A.F. Dernburg, unpublished). However, the mechanism that mediates selective homologous recognition between these sites is unknown.

Evidence that synapsis is normally inhibited until homologs are properly associated in *C. elegans* comes from analysis of mutations in two different genes, *htp-1* and *sun-1*. HTP-1 is a component of the axial/lateral elements of the synaptonemal complex. Loss of HTP-1 function results in promiscuous loading of transverse filament components between heterologous autosomes (Couteau & Zetka 2005, Martinez-Perez & Villeneuve 2005). Interestingly, the X chromosomes still pair and synapse appropriately (Martinez-Perez & Villeneuve 2005), which is possibly related to the observed loading of the X chromosome pairing center protein HIM-8 earlier in prophase than the autosomal pairing center ZIM proteins (Phillips & Dernburg 2006; R. Kasad & A.F. Dernburg, unpublished). SUN-1 is a component of the inner nuclear envelope that is likely to interact directly or indirectly with the meiotic pairing centers. A point mutation in, or RNAi depletion of, *sun-1* during meiosis results in a phenotype very similar to that of *htp-1* deletions, except that all chromosomes, including the X chromosomes, undergo nonhomologous synapsis. Further analysis indicates that SUN-1 is necessary for normal levels of pairing (Penkner et al. 2007;

A. Sato, C.M. Phillips & A.F. Dernburg, unpublished); this may reflect a direct involvement of SUN-1 in pairing or, alternatively, that SUN-1 is necessary to sustain the phase of meiosis during which pairing is actively promoted. A parsimonious explanation for the phenotypes associated with *sun-1* and *htp-1* mutations is that these proteins are both components of a checkpoint that coordinates pairing and synapsis by testing for paired homologs before synapsis initiation is permitted (Martinez-Perez & Villeneuve 2005, Penkner et al. 2007; A. Sato, C.M. Phillips & A.F. Dernburg, unpublished).

In *Drosophila*, intimate associations between homologs are detected in somatic interphase cells, i.e., in the absence of either DSBs or synapsis (Dernburg et al. 1996, Fung et al. 1998, Hiraoka et al. 1993), but it remains unclear whether the mechanisms that promote somatic pairing (which remain poorly understood) also lead to stable homolog pairing in meiosis. It is possible that synaptonemal complex formation in *Drosophila* oocytes is promoted by activities at particular regions along the chromosome arms, although this remains uncertain (Gong et al. 2005, Hawley 1980, Sherizen et al. 2005). There is no evidence to date of a bouquet stage in *Drosophila* oocytes or that the nuclear envelope plays any role in pairing, but a recent report indicates that chromosomes do interact with the nuclear envelope during early meiosis (Lancaster et al. 2007), so this remains an open question.

RECOMBINATION-DEPENDENT MECHANISMS

In organisms that rely on recombination to generate local sites of homolog pairing, the early events of meiotic recombination promote close, stable homolog juxtaposition (CSHJ). The formation of DSBs by Spo11, the resection of DNA to reveal single-stranded DNA, and the invasion of this single-stranded DNA into the intact DNA duplex of a homologous chromosome, as catalyzed by conserved recombinases, generate intermediates that intimately link homologs. At least two enzymatic mechanisms appear to negatively regulate pairing in budding yeast: the helicase Sgs1 and the meiosis-specific protein dimer composed of Hop2 and Mnd1. Strong evidence suggests that both of these mechanisms disassemble or destabilize inappropriate recombination intermediates to ensure proper homolog pairing.

Interhomolog Recombination Promotes Pairing

Early FISH experiments in budding yeast suggested that initial pairwise interactions between homologous chromosomes can occur in the absence of recombination (Loidl et al. 1994, Nag et al. 1995, Weiner & Kleckner 1994). These tenuous interactions likely reflect the alignment of chromosomes resulting from bouquet formation. This idea is consistent with results from fission yeast, in which the bouquet promotes tenuous contacts between homologs but not stable associations (Ding et al. 2004). However, this has not yet been formally tested—for example, by FISH analysis in a double mutant in which bouquet formation and recombination have been disrupted.

The development of cytological and recombination-based assays to directly observe CSHJ has revealed the primacy of recombination in mediating homolog pairing in budding yeast. In mutants that fail to assemble the synaptonemal complex, the axes of homologous chromosomes, which can be visualized by immunofluorescence, are closely associated at several sites along their length. The appearance of these axial associations depends on regions of homology, DSB formation, and the activity of the strand-exchange proteins Dmc1 and Rad51, all of which are required for the early steps in meiotic recombination (Rockmill et al. 1995).

A site-specific recombination assay has corroborated the essential role of meiotic recombination in promoting CSHJ. This assay measures recombination events generated by the Cre recombinase at engineered *loxP* sites at homologous or heterologous chromosome sites, and can therefore be used in cells deficient in normal meiotic recombi-

nation. Because Cre-mediated recombination does not involve strand-exchange intermediates that might themselves promote pairing, this assay is thought to report on pairing without influencing it (S. Burgess, personal communication). As detected by this assay, CSHJ requires DSBs, *DMC1* (Peoples et al. 2002), *RAD51* (Lui et al. 2006), and axial element proteins (Peoples et al. 2002). Consistent with cytological analysis of axial associations, CSHJ can be detected in the absence of synapsis and crossovers (Peoples et al. 2002), indicating that the stabilization of homolog pairing depends on the initiation of crossovers, but not on their completion.

This site-specific recombination assay has also been used to evaluate the contribution of recombination-independent mechanisms of homolog interactions, such as bouquet formation. Deletion of *NDJ1*, the meiosis-specific telomere component that mediates bouquet formation in budding yeast, results in slightly reduced CSHJ, indicating some influence of telomere organization on homolog pairing. However, this influence is not detected in the absence of DSBs, suggesting that the telomere-led reorganization of chromosomes may facilitate pairing but that recombination-dependent mechanisms are essential to achieve stable homolog pairing in budding yeast (Peoples-Holst & Burgess 2005).

Recombination between homologous chromosomes requires heteroduplex formation, and it is easy to imagine that these transient intermediates may be employed to assess homology to contribute to homolog pairing. Following DSB formation (**Figure 5a**) and resection (**Figure 5b**), strand-exchange proteins, along with accessory proteins, coat the resulting single-stranded 3' DNA end to create a nucleoprotein filament (**Figure 5c**). This filament invades an intact DNA duplex. If homologous, this invaded DNA segment provides the template for DSB repair; if nonhomologous, invasion is nonproductive and transient. Productive strand invasion leads to either crossover (**Figure 5d–f**) or noncrossover (**Figure 5g–i**) recombination (reviewed in Neale & Keeney 2006). Although recombination intermediates in the noncrossover pathway have not been detected, random spore analysis confirms a popular hypothesis that a majority of noncrossovers result from DNA synthesis following strand invasion (McMahill et al. 2007) (**Figure 5g–i**). The formation of a crossover further stabilizes the linkage between homologs through the formation of a double Holliday junction (DHJ), whose resolution is eventually catalyzed by an unknown enzyme (**Figure 5e,f**).

As mentioned above, strand exchange is central to CSHJ. This activity is carried out by Rad51 and Dmc1, eukaryotic homologs of the bacterial RecA protein. Rad51 is the dominant player in mitotic recombination, when the preferred substrate for repair is the sister chromatid (Aboussekhra et al. 1992, Shinohara et al. 1992). In organisms that utilize DSB-dependent mechanisms to stabilize homolog pairing and initiate synapsis, DMC1 is required for meiotic recombination, and its activity is coordinated with that of Rad51, probably to direct it toward interhomolog repair (Bishop 1994, Bishop et al. 1992). In organisms in which DSB-independent mechanisms are sufficient to accomplish homologous synapsis, Rad51 appears to act as the only strand-exchange protein during meiosis (Stahl et al. 2004).

Editing of Homolog Pairing

The pairing promoted by recombination intermediates is likely edited by mechanisms that minimize the occurrence of these intermediates between inappropriate partners. Evidence for this comes from analysis of Sgs1 during meiosis in budding yeast. Sgs1 is a homolog of the human Bloom Syndrome helicase (BLM), a member of the RecQ family (Ellis et al. 1995, Watt et al. 1996). Mutations in *SGS1* produce the unusual phenotype of elevated numbers of axial associations in the absence of synapsis (Rockmill et al. 2003) and increased ectopic recombination in the Cre recombinase–based CSHJ assay (Lui et al. 2006). Mutation of *SGS1* also results in a mitotic hyper-recombination phenotype (Gangloff et al. 1994, Ira et al. 2003) similar to defects observed in the cancer-prone cells

from Bloom Syndrome patients (Chaganti et al. 1974). These findings indicate that Sgs1 antagonizes recombination, most likely by destabilizing recombination intermediates. Consistent with this idea, mammalian BLM can catalyze dissolution of crossover intermediates into noncrossovers in vitro, in concert with topoisomerase IIIα (Plank et al. 2006, Wu et al. 2005). The activity of Sgs1 during meiosis appears to be important for disassembly of inappropriate recombination intermediates, particularly those between sister chromatids (Jessop et al. 2006, Oh et al. 2007, Rockmill et al. 2003). One noteworthy finding is that Sgs1 antagonizes recombination intermediates that form between homologous sequences (e.g., between sister chromatids and closely spaced interhomolog recombination events) as well as potentially nonhomologous sequences, suggesting that Sgs1 modulates pairing by raising the energetic requirements for all recombination, appropriate and otherwise.

An additional player in the editing of homolog pairing is the Hop2/Mnd1 complex. Hop2 and Mnd1 were initially implicated as negative regulators of homolog pairing and synapsis by the extensive nonhomologous synapsis observed when either of the *HOP2* or *MND1* genes is mutated in budding yeast (Leu et al. 1998, Tsubouchi & Roeder 2002). Further characterization in both budding yeast and mice showed that these mutants fail to repair DSBs (Leu et al. 1998, Petukhova et al. 2003). In principle, a defect in repair could be a consequence of failed pairing. However, the defect in recombination can be observed in the absence of synapsis (Tsubouchi & Roeder 2003), indicating a direct role for the Hop2/Mnd1 complex in recombination. When the *HOP2* and *MND1* genes are disrupted in mice or plants, asynapsis results (Kerzendorfer et al. 2006, Panoli et al. 2006, Petukhova et al. 2003), suggesting that the Hop2/Mnd1 complex is responsible for promoting homolog interactions in these organisms. Moreover, this complex can both stabilize and stimulate the strand-exchange activity of either Dmc1 or Rad51 nucleoprotein filaments (Chi et al. 2007, Pezza et al. 2007),

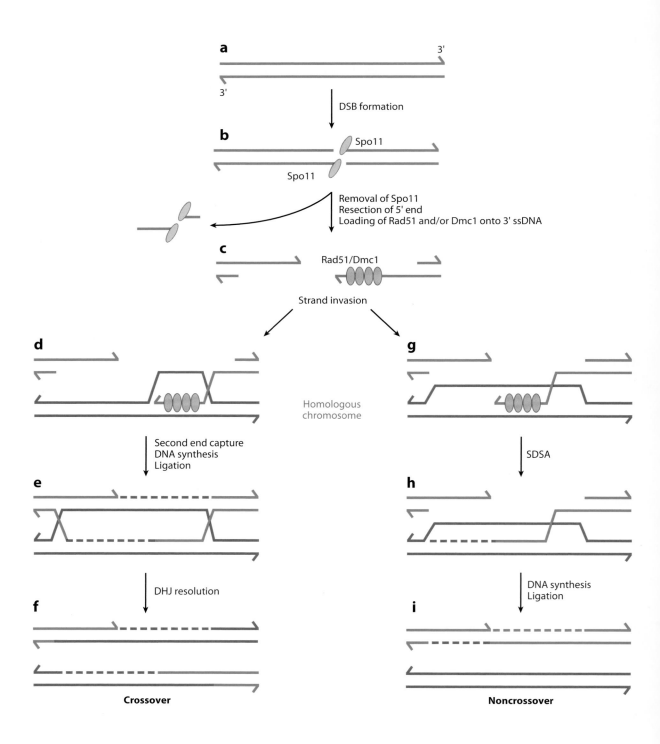

a

3'

3'

DSB formation

b

Spo11

Spo11

Removal of Spo11
Resection of 5' end
Loading of Rad51 and/or Dmc1 onto 3' ssDNA

c

Rad51/Dmc1

Strand invasion

Homologous
chromosome

d

Second end capture
DNA synthesis
Ligation

e

DHJ resolution

f

Crossover

g

SDSA

h

DNA synthesis
Ligation

i

Noncrossover

although it stimulates a Dmc1-dependent reaction more robustly than a Rad51-dependent reaction (Petukhova et al. 2005). The absence of axial associations in *hop2 zip1* mutant cells would also support a role for Hop2 in promoting strand-exchange reactions (Leu et al. 1998).

However, analysis of the Hop2/Mnd1 complex in budding yeast suggests a more complex contribution of Hop2/Mnd1 to recombination. In the absence of *HOP2*, Dmc1 and Rad51 accumulate on chromosomes (Leu et al. 1998, Tsubouchi & Roeder 2002). Disruption of *RAD51*, *DMC1*, or both of these genes in a *hop2* mutant results in significant suppression of the *hop2* mutant phenotype. However, only mutation of *DMC1* restores spore viability to the *hop2* mutant (Tsubouchi & Roeder 2003). These experiments indicate that in *hop2* mutants, Dmc1, and to a lesser degree Rad51, promotes both appropriate and inappropriate strand-exchange reactions. The increase in ectopic recombination in *hop2 rad51* and *mnd1 rad51* mutants (Henry et al. 2006) supports a role of the Hop2/Mnd1 complex in rejecting nonhomologous Dmc1-containing recombination intermediates to contribute to proper homolog pairing.

Ectopic recombination is not observed in *mnd1 dmc1* double mutants (Henry et al. 2006), suggesting that when recombination intermediates include only Dmc1, they exhibit greater promiscuity. These data offer a potential explanation for the presence of *HOP2* and *MND1* in organisms that also include *DMC1*: If Dmc1 acts as a less selective recombinase than Rad51, it may require additional regulators, such as Hop2/Mnd1, to modulate its activity. Moreover, these data may provide an explanation for why organisms that rely on DSBs to accomplish homolog pairing, such as budding yeast, mammals, and plants, require both Dmc1 and Rad51 to complete meiotic recombination.

Homologous chromosomes must search for and identify their unique partner within the limited time frame of meiotic prophase. For organisms that rely on the recombination machinery to carry out this task, the presence of a more promiscuous recombinase, whose activity can be checked in situations in which homology is not satisfied, may facilitate homology assessment. Surprisingly, however, Rad51 can substitute for Dmc1 if overexpressed (Tsubouchi & Roeder 2003), albeit with some delays in meiotic progression (Niu et al. 2005). Nevertheless, there are mechanisms in place to ensure that Dmc1 is the dominant recombinase in budding yeast meiosis: The protein Hed1 colocalizes with Rad51 to inhibit Rad51 activity in meiosis (Tsubouchi & Roeder 2006). Aside from its promiscuity, does Dmc1 confer an additional advantage to the process of interhomolog pairing and recombination in these organisms?

The homology search occurs concomitantly with other events in meiotic chromosome behavior, such as the establishment of a block to sister chromatid exchange (BSCE). This block is imposed by the formation of the axial core between sister chromatids and potentially by the development of higher-order chromosome structure that limits access to sister chromatids (Schwacha & Kleckner 1997, Thompson & Stahl 1999, Zierhut et al. 2004). Dmc1 may be

---

Figure 5

Meiotic recombination. (*a–c*) Double-strand break (DSB) formation and resection. DSB formation is catalyzed by the Spo11 enzyme (*orange ovals*) (*b*). Endonuclease activity releases Spo11 covalently bound to an oligonucleotide, and 5'-to-3' exonuclease activity exposes single-stranded (ss) 3' ends. Recombinases such as Rad51 and/or Dmc1 coat the ssDNA tail and catalyze strand invasion into the intact DNA duplex of a homologous chromosome (*c*). (*d–f*) Crossover pathway. Invasion of the Rad51/Dmc1-containing nucleoprotein filament results in an asymmetric strand-exchange intermediate (*d*). DNA synthesis (*dashed line*) is primed from the invading 3' end. The second end is captured and primes DNA synthesis. Ligation produces a double Holliday junction (DHJ) (*e*). The DHJ is resolved by an unknown enzyme to produce a mature crossover with the exchange of flanking DNA (*f*). (*g–i*) Noncrossover pathway by synthesis-dependent strand annealing (SDSA). Strand invasion (*g*) and DNA synthesis (*h*) are inferred but have not been experimentally detected. The newly synthesized DNA strand is displaced and anneals with the other DSB end; break repair is accomplished by DNA synthesis and ligation.

preferred to promote interhomolog recombination while this block is still being established. Such a model is consistent with the minor role Dmc1 plays in meiotic DSB repair in *S. pombe* (Young et al. 2004), an organism in which there is no apparent interhomolog bias and intersister repair intermediates predominate (Cromie et al. 2006). Moreover, this model may also explain why Rad51 can suffice in organisms in which synapsis occurs independently of recombination. For example, in *C. elegans* and *Drosophila*, most DSB formation occurs on already synapsed or synapsing chromosomes (Colaiacovo et al. 2003, Jang et al. 2003), when BSCE is likely to be fully established by axial elements capable of sustaining synaptonemal complex assembly.

The ability of overexpressed Rad51 to substitute for Dmc1 indicates that Rad51 can also catalyze interhomolog recombination. Schwacha & Kleckner (1997) suggested the existence of two mechanisms to introduce interhomolog recombination: one that directs recombination only between homologs and an alternate pathway that introduces intersister interactions with some interhomolog byproducts. Additional work by Tsubouchi & Roeder (2003) suggests that this first mechanism involves Dmc1, Rad51, Hop2, and Mnd1 whereas the primarily intersister pathway is dependent solely on Rad51.

Other than overexpression, other experimental manipulations also appear to upregulate the function of Rad51. Deletion of *HED1*, a negative regulator of Rad51 (Tsubouchi & Roeder 2006), or overexpression of Rad54, which probably promotes turnover and availability of Rad51 (Bishop et al. 1999), also suppresses recombination and sporulation defects in *dmc1* mutants. Elevated activity of Rad51 may mediate enough interhomolog recombination, along with many more intersister events, to suppress the defects of the *hop2* and *dmc1* mutants. Alternatively, Rad51 may repair DSBs preferentially by interhomolog mechanisms at a later stage of meiosis, once the block to sister chromatid exchange is fully established. Three lines of evidence support this possibility:

(*a*) The ability of Rad51 overexpression to suppress a *dmc1* mutant depends on functional BSCE (Niu et al. 2005), (*b*) the repair of DSBs in *dmc1* mutants overexpressing Rad51 occurs later than in wild-type cells and is accompanied by a delay in meiosis I progression (Niu et al. 2005), and (*c*) the formation of crossovers is also delayed in a *hed1 dmc1* double mutant (Tsubouchi & Roeder 2006).

The role of the Hop2/Mnd1 complex remains somewhat unclear. Its biochemical characterization clearly shows a positive function in stimulating Dmc1 and Rad51 recombinase activity and stabilizing the resulting recombination intermediates. Conversely, mutational analysis in budding yeast indicates that Hop2/Mnd1 functions as an editor during pairing and recombination, destabilizing inappropriate recombination intermediates. These results could be reconciled if Hop2/Mnd1 facilitates Dmc1 function in both directions so that it promotes strand exchange but also helps to liberate Dmc1 and Rad51 from recombination intermediates. The complex may be aided in this capacity by additional modulators of Dmc1, such as Tid1, that affect the dissociation of these recombinases from sites of double-stranded DNA (Holzen et al. 2006). However, localization of the Hop2/Mnd1 dimer to chromatin independent of DSBs (Tsubouchi & Roeder 2002, Zierhut et al. 2004) suggests that the complex may modulate Dmc1/Rad51 activity indirectly, perhaps by affecting chromatin structure. In support of this idea, the fission yeast *HOP2* homolog *meu13+* affects homolog pairing dynamics independently of recombination (Nabeshima et al. 2001).

In summary, homolog pairing in budding yeast is a consequence of the stabilization of recombination intermediates between regions of homology. Early recombination intermediates, rather than crossovers per se, are necessary and sufficient to intimately pair homologs even in the absence of synapsis. The formation of DSBs and the strand-exchange reaction catalyzed by Rad51 and Dmc1 serve to link homologs, whereas enzymatic activities, including Sgs1 and Hop2/Mnd1, ensure that these linkages occur between appropriate partners. Many of these conclusions are likely to extend to mammals and plants, although no assay for CSHJ currently exists in these organisms.

Synapsis Initiation

Homolog pairing, as accomplished by DSB formation and strand exchange, is by itself not sufficient to satisfy the barrier to synapsis. Additional experiments in budding yeast have suggested that it is the subset of DSBs that will become crossovers that act as sites of synapsis initiation (Fung et al. 2004). This link between crossover formation and synapsis initiation is supported in a variety of organisms by observations of synapsis defects resulting from mutation of genes that can initiate recombination but fail to make crossovers (de Vries et al. 1999, Edelmann et al. 1999, Higgins et al. 2004, Kneitz et al. 2000, Novak et al. 2001).

In principle, the formation of a crossover intermediate could stabilize interhomolog interactions to overcome a kinetic barrier to synapsis. Alternatively, there may be an enzymatic mechanism that couples crossover commitment to synapsis initiation. Analysis of the *ZIP3* and *UBC9* genes in budding yeast suggests that SUMOylation may be involved in this coupling. *ZIP3* is a member of a synapsis initiation complex (SIC) (Agarwal & Roeder 2000, Fung et al. 2004) that includes the additional proteins Zip2 and Zip4 (Chua & Roeder 1998, Tsubouchi et al. 2006) and is required for both chromosome synapsis and crossover formation (Agarwal & Roeder 2000). These SIC proteins colocalize at chromosomal foci prior to synapsis. In synapsis-defective mutants such as *zip1*, SIC proteins colocalize at some sites of axial associations (Agarwal & Roeder 2000, Chua & Roeder 1998, Tsubouchi et al. 2006), reinforcing the idea that not all sites of stable homolog pairing have the capacity to initiate synapsis. Zip3 contains a ring-finger domain, suggesting that it has ubiquitin or SUMO ligase activity (Perry et al. 2005). Cheng and colleagues verified that Zip3 acts as a SUMO ligase in vitro and showed that the transverse element protein

Zip1 can bind to SUMO moieties (Cheng et al. 2006). Crippling the SUMOylation pathway by mutating an additional component of the SUMO conjugation pathway, *UBC9*, results in defective synapsis without reducing crossovers (Hooker & Roeder 2006), suggesting that the SUMO ligase activity of Zip3 may be required only for its role in synapsis. Caveats of this interpretation are that *UBC9* is essential and these conclusions are based on a non-null allele.

The direct targets of Zip3 are unknown, but cytological experiments and two-hybrid assays (Cheng et al. 2006, Hooker & Roeder 2006) suggest a mechanism for synapsis initiation. Zip3, in concert with other proteins, stabilizes those strand-exchange intermediates designated to become crossovers [termed single-end invasions (SEIs)]. Simultaneously, Zip3-regulated SUMOylation of proteins along these paired chromosomes (for instance, axial element proteins) restricts Zip1 polymerization to properly paired homologs that have initiated crossover formation. This is consistent with the timing of the appearance of SEIs in wild-type meiosis, which is concomitant with synaptonemal complex formation (Hunter & Kleckner 2001). SUMOylation of some target(s) by Zip3, in response to the formation of crossovers, may thereby provide a means to overcome the thermodynamic barriers to synapsis initiation in budding yeast (de Carvalho & Colaiacovo 2006).

Situations that give rise to nonhomologous synapsis, e.g., mutations in *HOP2* or *MND1*, may result in either inappropriate SUMOylation or SUMO-independent polymerization of Zip1. Inappropriate stabilization of Dmc1-containing strand-exchange intermediates may mimic SEIs and lead to synaptonemal complex assembly. The absence of cytologically detectable axial associations in *hop2 zip1* double mutants indicates that these putative intermediates would have to be relatively short-lived (Leu et al. 1998). Alternatively, synapsis initiation mechanisms typically inhibited during wild-type meiosis (i.e., synaptonemal complex formation at centromeres) may be responsible for the synapsis observed in these mutant backgrounds. Localization of synapsis initiation components, such as Zip2, -3, and -4, in *hop2* or *mnd1* mutants will likely provide insight into this aberrant synapsis initiation.

In contrast to budding yeast, deletion of *HOP2* in mice (Petukhova et al. 2003) or of *MND1* in plants (Kerzendorfer et al. 2006, Panoli et al. 2006) results in asynapsis with very low levels of nonhomologous synapsis, suggesting that the kinetic requirements to initiate synapsis may be more stringent in these organisms. In plants and mammals, there may be additional conditions that need to be met to initiate synapsis, aside from the transient stabilization of strand-exchange intermediates. This additional level of regulation in these organisms may reflect the greater complexity of their genomes; the existence of considerable homologous sequence on nonhomologous chromosomes would provide more possibilities for incorrect Dmc1-containing strand-exchange intermediates and potential synapsis initiation sites.

WHY SYNAPSE AT ALL?

Given that stable homolog pairing and crossover recombination can occur in the absence of synapsis, and normally do so in *S. pombe* and other fungi, why do chromosomes synapse in most known organisms? As with all teleological questions, we cannot answer this one conclusively. A long-standing and still potentially valid idea is that the synaptonemal complex mediates control of crossover placement, also known as crossover interference, which is important for proper segregation. Evidence for this is somewhat correlative: Organisms that lack synapsis, including *S. pombe* and *Aspergillus nidulans*, also lack crossover interference. Moreover, recent results have shown that the relationship between synaptonemal complex and crossover regulation is not as straightforward as previously believed. For example, at least some interference can be imposed in the absence of normal synaptonemal complex polymerization in yeast, mice, and other organisms (Borner et al. 2004, de

Boer et al. 2007, Fung et al. 2004, Osman et al. 2006). Despite these interesting cases, it remains possible that synaptonemal complex formation plays important roles in controlling the number and position of crossover events.

The primary function of the synaptonemal complex may be to enable the cell to globally monitor interhomolog associations, which, as described throughout this review, are initially mediated through local interactions. By refraining from completing crossovers between homologous sequences until this assurance is obtained, the cell may be able to minimize the ectopic crossover events that would lead to chromosome translocations. According to this view, it is in the interest of the cell to make synapsis a prerequisite for the completion of crossing over. This is consistent with the observation that late nodules, cytological manifestations of crossover resolution, are rarely seen in the absence of the synaptonemal complex (reviewed in Zickler & Kleckner 1999). In *Drosophila*, separation-of-function alleles of the transverse filament protein c(3)G have demonstrated that the domains of the protein necessary for crossovers can be uncoupled from domains essential for synapsis (R.S. Hawley, personal communication). Such evidence reinforces the idea that crossover resolution and synapsis are not inherently codependent but that the proteins of the synaptonemal complex have evolved to couple these events. In some organisms, crossovers can form in the absence of the synaptonemal complex, but these events involve different intermediates (Cromie et al. 2006) and are resolved by a different enzymatic mechanism than those that occur in the context of the synaptonemal complex (Berchowitz et al. 2007, de los Santos et al. 2003, Higgins et al. 2008, Osman et al. 2003, Smith et al. 2003).

SYNTHESIS

We discuss above the interaction of homologous chromosomes during the meiotic process as a dynamic process in which unstable but appropriate associations between homologs are progressively reinforced and incorrect partner choices are rejected such that assembly of the synaptonemal complex and crossover recombination occur only between homologous chromosomes. Studies of the dramatic horsetail movement in fission yeast initially illuminated how the polarized arrangement of chromosomes into the bouquet facilitates interactions between homologous loci and limited associations between nonhomologous regions. It is highly likely that tenuous interactions between homologs in other species are also promoted by telomere attachment to the nuclear envelope and associated chromosome dynamics. These interactions are stabilized by recombination-dependent or -independent mechanisms, which usually lead to homolog synapsis.

Budding yeast, in which recombination-independent mechanisms play only a subtle role in pairing and synapsis, may represent an extreme case. Mutations that perturb formation of the bouquet have modest effects on homolog pairing, synapsis, and recombination in this species (Chua & Roeder 1997, Conrad et al. 1997, Goldman & Lichten 2000, Schlecht et al. 2004). Alternatively, the nonhomologous centromeric associations that have been observed early in meiosis in this organism (Tsubouchi & Roeder 2005) may also contribute to the alignment of chromosomes; in the absence of both telomere attachment to the nuclear envelope and centromere coupling (i.e., a *ndj1 zip1* double mutant), a more severe defect in homolog

alignment, as assayed by levels of ectopic recombination above those in either single mutant, might be apparent.

The ecdysozoans *C. elegans* and *D. melanogaster* present an interesting counterpoint to budding yeast, in that recombination-independent mechanisms are sufficient to achieve homolog pairing and synapsis. Investigations of meiosis in these organisms raise a fundamental issue: How is homology assessed in the (presumed) absence of strand invasion? Furthermore, if homologs can recognize each other without recombination, to what extent do these mechanisms operate in organisms that couple homolog synapsis to recombination?

It is likely that the smattering of model organisms that have been analyzed in depth does not represent the full range of pairing mechanisms used during meiosis. There are numerous known exceptions, such as *Drosophila* males, in which homologs pair and synapse in the absence of both crossovers and the synaptonemal complex. Given that the goal of pairing homologous chromosomes is intrinsic to meiosis, it is curious how the details of these mechanisms have diverged in fundamental ways even among those few species that have been investigated. As we learn more about how pairing is achieved and coupled to synapsis, it will also be interesting to see what emerges from studies of more deeply rooted eukaryotes, which do not share a common ancestor with these familiar species.

SUMMARY POINTS

1. Pairing and synapsis are distinct processes that must be coordinated to ensure that synapsis selectively enforces interactions between homologous chromosomes.

2. The initiation of synapsis is probably a tightly regulated event during meiosis and is therefore subject to large thermodynamic or kinetic barriers. Mutations that uncouple pairing and synapsis can illuminate both the physical nature of the barriers and the intermediates that allow them to be overcome.

3. Homology is likely "recognized" through both the stabilization of appropriate interactions and the rejection of nonhomologous contacts. Defects in either the stabilization or the rejection machinery may result in failed or inappropriate pairing and synapsis.

4. Recombination-independent and -dependent mechanisms contribute to the assessment of homology during meiotic prophase. Most organisms probably employ a combination of both mechanisms to accomplish homolog pairing.

FUTURE ISSUES

1. What are the relative contributions of recombination-independent mechanisms to homolog pairing and synapsis in organisms that ultimately use recombination-dependent mechanisms to stabilize pairing and initiate synapsis? Does the recombination machinery play a role in organisms that can accomplish pairing and synapsis in the absence of Spo11-induced DSBs?

2. How is homology assessed in organisms that rely solely on recombination-independent mechanisms to accomplish pairing and synapsis?

3. What are the molecular mechanisms responsible for overcoming the barrier to synapsis?

4. To what extent are common mechanisms to stabilize pairing and initiate synapsis present in all organisms? Do organisms repress some of these mechanisms so that others appear to dominate?

DISCLOSURE STATEMENT

The authors are not aware of any biases that might be perceived as affecting the objectivity of this review.

ACKNOWLEDGMENTS

The authors would like to thank Scott Hawley, Doug Kellogg, and members of the Dernburg Lab for careful reading of the manuscript. This work was written while N.B. was a postdoctoral fellow in the lab of A.F.D. and affiliated with Lawrence Berkeley National Labs and University of California, Berkeley. Both authors are supported by the NIH (N.B.: K99RR0241110; A.F.D.: R01 GM065591).

Along with Borner et al. (2004), Hunter & Kleckner (2001), and Martini et al. (2006), presented evidence that crossovers and noncrossovers are the products of different recombination pathways with distinct intermediates and that the crossover/ noncrossover decision is made quite early in meiotic prophase, potentially when double-strand-break formation occurs.

LITERATURE CITED

Aboussekhra A, Chanet R, Adjiri A, Fabre F. 1992. Semidominant suppressors of Srs2 helicase mutations of *Saccharomyces cerevisiae* map in the *RAD51* gene, whose sequence predicts a protein with similarities to procaryotic RecA proteins. *Mol. Cell Biol.* 12:3224–34

Agarwal S, Roeder GS. 2000. Zip3 provides a link between recombination enzymes and synaptonemal complex proteins. *Cell* 102:245–55

Allers T, Lichten M. 2001. Differential timing and control of noncrossover and crossover recombination during meiosis. *Cell* 106:47–57

Baier A, Alsheimer M, Benavente R. 2007. Synaptonemal complex protein SYCP3: conserved polymerization properties among vertebrates. *Biochim. Biophys. Acta* 1774:595–602

Baudat F, Manova K, Yuen JP, Jasin M, Keeney S. 2000. Chromosome synapsis defects and sexually dimorphic meiotic progression in mice lacking Spo11. *Mol. Cell* 6:989–98

Bass HW, Marshall WF, Sedat JW, Agard DA, Cande WZ. 1997. Telomeres cluster de novo before the initiation of synapsis: a three-dimensional spatial analysis of telomere positions before and during meiotic prophase. *J. Cell Biol.* 137:5–18

Berchowitz LE, Francis KE, Bey AL, Copenhaver GP. 2007. The role of AtMUS81 in interference-insensitive crossovers in *A. thaliana*. *PLoS Genet.* 3:e132

Bishop DK. 1994. RecA homologs Dmc1 and Rad51 interact to form multiple nuclear complexes prior to meiotic chromosome synapsis. *Cell* 79:1081–92

Bishop DK, Nikolski Y, Oshiro J, Chon J, Shinohara M, Chen X. 1999. High copy number suppression of the meiotic arrest caused by a dmc1 mutation: REC114 imposes an early recombination block and RAD54 promotes a DMC1-independent DSB repair pathway. *Genes Cells* 4:425–44

Bishop DK, Park D, Xu L, Kleckner N. 1992. *DMC1*: a meiosis-specific yeast homolog of *E. coli recA* required for recombination, synaptonemal complex formation, and cell cycle progression. *Cell* 69:439–56

Bojko M. 1990. Synaptic adjustment of inversion loops in *Neurospora crassa*. *Genetics* 124:593–98

Borner GV, Kleckner N, Hunter N. 2004. Crossover/noncrossover differentiation, synaptonemal complex formation, and regulatory surveillance at the leptotene/zygotene transition of meiosis. *Cell* 117:29–45

Chaganti RS, Schonberg S, German J. 1974. A manyfold increase in sister chromatid exchanges in Bloom's syndrome lymphocytes. *Proc. Natl. Acad. Sci. USA* 71:4508–12

Cheng CH, Lo YH, Liang SS, Ti SC, Lin FM, et al. 2006. SUMO modifications control assembly of synaptonemal complex and polycomplex in meiosis of *Saccharomyces cerevisiae*. *Genes Dev.* 20:2067–81

Chi P, San Filippo J, Sehorn MG, Petukhova GV, Sung P. 2007. Bipartite stimulatory action of the Hop2-Mnd1 complex on the Rad51 recombinase. *Genes Dev.* 21:1747–57

Chikashige Y, Ding DQ, Funabiki H, Haraguchi T, Mashiko S, et al. 1994. Telomere-led premeiotic chromosome movement in fission yeast. *Science* 264:270–73

Chikashige Y, Tsutsumi C, Yamane M, Okamasa K, Haraguchi T, Hiraoka Y. 2006. Meiotic proteins bqt1 and bqt2 tether telomeres to form the bouquet arrangement of chromosomes. *Cell* 125:59–69

Chua PR, Roeder GS. 1997. Tam1, a telomere-associated meiotic protein, functions in chromosome synapsis and crossover interference. *Genes Dev.* 11:1786–800

Chua PR, Roeder GS. 1998. Zip2, a meiosis-specific protein required for the initiation of chromosome synapsis. *Cell* 93:349–59

Colaiacovo MP. 2006. The many facets of SC function during *C. elegans* meiosis. *Chromosoma* 115:195–211

Colaiacovo MP, MacQueen AJ, Martinez-Perez E, McDonald K, Adamo A, et al. 2003. Synaptonemal complex assembly in *C. elegans* is dispensable for loading strand-exchange proteins but critical for proper completion of recombination. *Dev. Cell* 5:463–7

Conrad MN, Dominguez AM, Dresser ME. 1997. Ndj1p, a meiotic telomere protein required for normal chromosome synapsis and segregation in yeast. *Science* 276:1252–55

Conrad MN, Lee CY, Wilkerson JL, Dresser ME. 2007. MPS3 mediates meiotic bouquet formation in *Saccharomyces cerevisiae*. *Proc. Natl. Acad. Sci. USA* 104:8863–68

Cooper JP, Watanabe Y, Nurse P. 1998. Fission yeast Taz1 protein is required for meiotic telomere clustering and recombination. *Nature* 392:828–31

Corredor E, Lukaszewski AJ, Pachon P, Allen DC, Naranjo T. 2007. Terminal regions of wheat chromosomes select their pairing partners in meiosis. *Genetics* 177:699–706

Corredor E, Naranjo T. 2007. Effect of colchicine and telocentric chromosome conformation on centromere and telomere dynamics at meiotic prophase I in wheat-rye additions. *Chromosome Res.* 15:231–45

Costa Y, Cooke HJ. 2007. Dissecting the mammalian synaptonemal complex using targeted mutations. *Chromosome Res.* 15:579–89

Couteau F, Zetka M. 2005. HTP-1 coordinates synaptonemal complex assembly with homolog alignment during meiosis in *C. elegans*. *Genes Dev.* 19:2744–56

Cowan CR, Cande WZ. 2002. Meiotic telomere clustering is inhibited by colchicine but does not require cytoplasmic microtubules. *J. Cell Sci.* 115:3747–56

Cromie GA, Hyppa RW, Taylor AF, Zakharyevich K, Hunter N, Smith GR. 2006. Single Holliday junctions are intermediates of meiotic recombination. *Cell* 127:1167–78

Davis L, Smith GR. 2006. The meiotic bouquet promotes homolog interactions and restricts ectopic recombination in *Schizosaccharomyces pombe*. *Genetics* 174:167–77

Provided an initial description of meiotic bouquet formation and described the role of telomeres and microtubules in meiotic bouquet formation in fission yeast.

Along with Nimmo et al. (1998). showed that telomere function is required for proper bouquet formation and meiotic progression in *S. pombe*.

Davisson MT, Poorman PA, Roderick TH, Moses MJ. 1981. A pericentric inversion in the mouse. *Cytogenet. Cell Genet.* 30:70–76

Dawson DS, Murray AW, Szostak JW. 1986. An alternative pathway for meiotic chromosome segregation in yeast. *Science* 234:713–17

de Boer E, Dietrich AJ, Hoog C, Stam P, Heyting C. 2007. Meiotic interference among MLH1 foci requires neither an intact axial element structure nor full synapsis. *J. Cell Sci.* 120:731–36

de Carvalho CE, Colaiacovo MP. 2006. SUMO-mediated regulation of synaptonemal complex formation during meiosis. *Genes Dev.* 20:1986–92

de los Santos T, Hunter N, Lee C, Larkin B, Loidl J, Hollingsworth NM. 2003. The Mus81/Mms4 endonuclease acts independently of double-Holliday junction resolution to promote a distinct subset of crossovers during meiosis in budding yeast. *Genetics* 164:81–94

de Vries SS, Baart EB, Dekker M, Siezen A, de Rooij DG, et al. 1999. Mouse MutS-like protein Msh5 is required for proper chromosome synapsis in male and female meiosis. *Genes Dev.* 13:523–31

Dernburg AF, McDonald K, Moulder G, Barstead R, Dresser M, Villeneuve AM. 1998. Meiotic recombination in *C. elegans* initiates by a conserved mechanism and is dispensable for homologous chromosome synapsis. *Cell* 94:387–98

Dernburg AF, Sedat JW, Hawley RS. 1996. Direct evidence of a role for heterochromatin in meiotic chromosome segregation. *Cell* 86:135–46

Ding DQ, Yamamoto A, Haraguchi T, Hiraoka Y. 2004. Dynamics of homologous chromosome pairing during meiotic prophase in fission yeast. *Dev. Cell* 6:329–41

Ding X, Xu R, Yu J, Xu T, Zhuang Y, Han M. 2007. SUN1 is required for telomere attachment to nuclear envelope and gametogenesis in mice. *Dev. Cell* 12:863–72

Dresser ME, Giroux CN. 1988. Meiotic chromosome behavior in spread preparations of yeast. *J. Cell Biol.* 106:567–73

Edelmann W, Cohen PE, Kneitz B, Winand N, Lia M, et al. 1999. Mammalian MutS homologue 5 is required for chromosome pairing in meiosis. *Nat. Genet.* 21:123–27

Ellis NA, Groden J, Ye TZ, Straughen J, Lennon DJ, et al. 1995. The Bloom's syndrome gene product is homologous to RecQ helicases. *Cell* 83:655–66

Fung JC, Marshall WF, Dernburg A, Agard DA, Sedat JW. 1998. Homologous chromosome pairing in *Drosophila melanogaster* proceeds through multiple independent initiations. *J. Cell Biol.* 141:5–20

Fung JC, Rockmill B, Odell M, Roeder GS. 2004. Imposition of crossover interference through the nonrandom distribution of synapsis initiation complexes. *Cell* 116:795–802

Gangloff S, McDonald JP, Bendixen C, Arthur L, Rothstein R. 1994. The yeast type I topoisomerase Top3 interacts with Sgs1, a DNA helicase homolog: a potential eukaryotic reverse gyrase. *Mol. Cell Biol.* 14:8391–98

Giroux CN, Dresser ME, Tiano HF. 1989. Genetic control of chromosome synapsis in yeast meiosis. *Genome* 31:88–94

Goldman AS, Lichten M. 2000. Restriction of ectopic recombination by interhomolog interactions during *Saccharomyces cerevisiae* meiosis. *Proc. Natl. Acad. Sci. USA* 97:9537–42

Golubovskaya IN, Harper LC, Pawlowski WP, Schichnes D, Cande WZ. 2002. The *pam1* gene is required for meiotic bouquet formation and efficient homologous synapsis in maize (*Zea mays* L.). *Genetics* 162:1979–93

Gong WJ, McKim KS, Hawley RS. 2005. All paired up with no place to go: pairing, synapsis, and DSB formation in a balancer heterozygote. *PLoS Genet.* 1:e67

Grelon M, Vezon D, Gendrot G, Pelletier G. 2001. AtSPO11-1 is necessary for efficient meiotic recombination in plants. *EMBO J.* 20:589–600

Hassold T, Hunt P. 2001. To err (meiotically) is human: the genesis of human aneuploidy. *Nat. Rev. Genet.* 2:280–91

Hawley RS. 1980. Chromosomal sites necessary for normal levels of meiotic recombination in *Drosophila melanogaster*. I. Evidence for and mapping of the sites. *Genetics* 94:625–46

Hawley RS, McKim KS, Arbel T. 1993. Meiotic segregation in *Drosophila melanogaster* females: molecules, mechanisms, and myths. *Annu. Rev. Genet.* 27:281–317

Henry JM, Camahort R, Rice DA, Florens L, Swanson SK, et al. 2006. Mnd1/Hop2 facilitates Dmc1-dependent interhomolog crossover formation in meiosis of budding yeast. *Mol. Cell Biol.* 26:2913–23

Along with McKim et al. (1998), revealed that meiotic recombination in *C. elegans* and *D. melanogaster* was catalyzed by the conserved enzyme Spo11 but that such recombination was not required for synapsis.

Revealed the frequency and duration of homolog interactions during meiotic prophase and evaluated the relative contributions of recombination and bouquet formation to the persistence of such interactions.

Characterized *spo11* mutants as defective in meiotic recombination and synapsis and suggested that recombination is necessary for synapsis in budding yeast.

Tested and validated the hypothesis that defects in homolog alignment may be accompanied by an increase in ectopic recombination, suggesting that discrimination is an important aspect of the homology search.

Higgins JD, Armstrong SJ, Franklin FC, Jones GH. 2004. The *Arabidopsis* MutS homolog AtMSH4 functions at an early step in recombination: evidence for two classes of recombination in *Arabidopsis*. *Genes Dev.* 18:2557–70

Higgins JD, Buckling EF, Franklin FC, Jones GH. 2008. Expression and functional analysis of AtMUS81 in *Arabidopsis* meiosis reveals a role in the second pathway of crossing-over. *Plant J.* 54:152–62

Hiraoka Y, Dernburg AF, Parmelee SJ, Rykowski MC, Agard DA, Sedat JW. 1993. The onset of homologous chromosome pairing during *Drosophila melanogaster* embryogenesis. *J. Cell Biol.* 120:591–600

Holzen TM, Shah PP, Olivares HA, Bishop DK. 2006. Tid1/Rdh54 promotes dissociation of Dmc1 from nonrecombinogenic sites on meiotic chromatin. *Genes Dev.* 20:2593–604

Hooker GW, Roeder GS. 2006. A role for SUMO in meiotic chromosome synapsis. *Curr. Biol.* 16:1238–43

Hunter N, Kleckner N. 2001. The single-end invasion: an asymmetric intermediate at the double-strand break to double-Holliday junction transition of meiotic recombination. *Cell* 106:59–70

Ira G, Malkova A, Liberi G, Foiani M, Haber JE. 2003. Srs2 and Sgs1-Top3 suppress crossovers during double-strand break repair in yeast. *Cell* 115:401–11

Jang JK, Sherizen DE, Bhagat R, Manheim EA, McKim KS. 2003. Relationship of DNA double-strand breaks to synapsis in *Drosophila*. *J. Cell Sci.* 116:3069–77

Jessop L, Rockmill B, Roeder GS, Lichten M. 2006. Meiotic chromosome synapsis-promoting proteins antagonize the anti-crossover activity of Sgs1. *PLoS Genet.* 2:e155

Jin Y, Uzawa S, Cande WZ. 2002. Fission yeast mutants affecting telomere clustering and meiosis-specific spindle pole body integrity. *Genetics* 160:861–76

Kemp B, Boumil RM, Stewart MN, Dawson DS. 2004. A role for centromere pairing in meiotic chromosome segregation. *Genes Dev.* 18:1946–51

Kerzendorfer C, Vignard J, Pedrosa-Harand A, Siwiec T, Akimcheva S, et al. 2006. The *Arabidopsis thaliana* MND1 homologue plays a key role in meiotic homologous pairing, synapsis and recombination. *J. Cell Sci.* 119:2486–96

Kneitz B, Cohen PE, Avdievich E, Zhu L, Kane MF, et al. 2000. MutS homolog 4 localization to meiotic chromosomes is required for chromosome pairing during meiosis in male and female mice. *Genes Dev.* 14:1085–97

Lancaster OM, Cullen CF, Ohkura H. 2007. NHK-1 phosphorylates BAF to allow karyosome formation in the *Drosophila* oocyte nucleus. *J. Cell Biol.* 179:817–24

Leu JY, Chua PR, Roeder GS. 1998. The meiosis-specific Hop2 protein of *S. cerevisiae* ensures synapsis between homologous chromosomes. *Cell* 94:375–86

Li J, Harper LC, Golubovskaya I, Wang CR, Weber D, et al. 2007. Functional analysis of maize RAD51 in meiosis and double-strand break repair. *Genetics* 176:1469–82

Li W, Chen C, Markmann-Mulisch U, Timofejeva L, Schmelzer E, et al. 2004. The *Arabidopsis AtRAD51* gene is dispensable for vegetative development but required for meiosis. *Proc. Natl. Acad. Sci. USA* 101:10596–601

Liu L, Franco S, Spyropoulos B, Moens PB, Blasco MA, Keefe DL. 2004. Irregular telomeres impair meiotic synapsis and recombination in mice. *Proc. Natl. Acad. Sci. USA* 101:6496–501

Loidl J, Klein F, Scherthan H. 1994. Homologous pairing is reduced but not abolished in asynaptic mutants of yeast. *J. Cell Biol.* 125:1191–200

Lui DY, Peoples-Holst TL, Mell JC, Wu HY, Dean EW, Burgess SM. 2006. Analysis of close stable homolog juxtaposition during meiosis in mutants of *Saccharomyces cerevisiae*. *Genetics* 173:1207–22

MacQueen AJ, Colaiacovo MP, McDonald K, Villeneuve AM. 2002. Synapsis-dependent and -independent mechanisms stabilize homolog pairing during meiotic prophase in *C. elegans*. *Genes Dev.* 16:2428–42

MacQueen AJ, Phillips CM, Bhalla N, Weiser P, Villeneuve AM, Dernburg AF. 2005. Chromosome sites play dual roles to establish homologous synapsis during meiosis in *C. elegans*. *Cell* 123:1037–50

Martinez-Perez E, Shaw P, Moore G. 2001. The *Ph1* locus is needed to ensure specific somatic and meiotic centromere association. *Nature* 411:204–7

Martinez-Perez E, Villeneuve AM. 2005. HTP-1-dependent constraints coordinate homolog pairing and synapsis and promote chiasma formation during *C. elegans* meiosis. *Genes Dev.* 19:2727–43

Attributed stabilization of homolog pairing and synapsis initiation to *cis*-acting sites in an organism (*C. elegans*) that does not require recombination to initiate synapsis.

Martini E, Diaz RL, Hunter N, Keeney S. 2006. Crossover homeostasis in yeast meiosis. *Cell* 126:285–95

McKee BD. 2004. Homologous pairing and chromosome dynamics in meiosis and mitosis. *Biochim. Biophys. Acta* 1677:165–80

McKim KS, Green-Marroquin BL, Sekelsky JJ, Chin G, Steinberg C, et al. 1998. Meiotic synapsis in the absence of recombination. *Science* 279:876–78

McMahill MS, Sham CW, Bishop DK. 2007. Synthesis-dependent strand annealing in meiosis. *PLoS Biol.* 5:e299

Miki F, Okazaki K, Shimanuki M, Yamamoto A, Hiraoka Y, Niwa O. 2002. The 14-kDa dynein light chain-family protein Dlc1 is required for regular oscillatory nuclear movement and efficient recombination during meiotic prophase in fission yeast. *Mol. Biol. Cell* 13:930–46

Molnar M, Bahler J, Kohli J, Hiraoka Y. 2001. Live observation of fission yeast meiosis in recombination-deficient mutants: a study on achiasmate chromosome segregation. *J. Cell Sci.* 114:2843–53

Moses MJ, Poorman PA, Roderick TH, Davisson MT. 1982. Synaptonemal complex analysis of mouse chromosomal rearrangements. IV. Synapsis and synaptic adjustment in two paracentric inversions. *Chromosoma* 84:457–74

Nabeshima K, Kakihara Y, Hiraoka Y, Nojima H. 2001. A novel meiosis-specific protein of fission yeast, Meu13p, promotes homologous pairing independently of homologous recombination. *EMBO J.* 20:3871–81

Nag DK, Scherthan H, Rockmill B, Bhargava J, Roeder GS. 1995. Heteroduplex DNA formation and homolog pairing in yeast meiotic mutants. *Genetics* 141:75–86

Neale MJ, Keeney S. 2006. Clarifying the mechanics of DNA strand exchange in meiotic recombination. *Nature* 442:153–58

Nimmo ER, Pidoux AL, Perry PE, Allshire RC. 1998. Defective meiosis in telomere-silencing mutants of *Schizosaccharomyces pombe*. *Nature* 392:825–28

Niu H, Wan L, Baumgartner B, Schaefer D, Loidl J, Hollingsworth NM. 2005. Partner choice during meiosis is regulated by Hop1-promoted dimerization of Mek1. *Mol. Biol. Cell* 16:5804–18

Niwa O, Shimanuki M, Miki F. 2000. Telomere-led bouquet formation facilitates homologous chromosome pairing and restricts ectopic interaction in fission yeast meiosis. *EMBO J.* 19:3831–40

Novak JE, Ross-Macdonald PB, Roeder GS. 2001. The budding yeast Msh4 protein functions in chromosome synapsis and the regulation of crossover distribution. *Genetics* 158:1013–25

Oh SD, Lao JP, Hwang PY, Taylor AF, Smith GR, Hunter N. 2007. BLM ortholog, Sgs1, prevents aberrant crossing-over by suppressing formation of multichromatid joint molecules. *Cell* 130:259–72

Ollinger R, Alsheimer M, Benavente R. 2005. Mammalian protein SCP1 forms synaptonemal complex-like structures in the absence of meiotic chromosomes. *Mol. Biol. Cell* 16:212–17

Osman F, Dixon J, Doe CL, Whitby MC. 2003. Generating crossovers by resolution of nicked Holliday junctions: a role for Mus81-Eme1 in meiosis. *Mol. Cell* 12:761–74

Osman K, Sanchez-Moran E, Higgins JD, Jones GH, Franklin FC. 2006. Chromosome synapsis in *Arabidopsis*: Analysis of the transverse filament protein ZYP1 reveals novel functions for the synaptonemal complex. *Chromosoma* 115:212–19

Page SL, Hawley RS. 2001. *c(3)G* encodes a *Drosophila* synaptonemal complex protein. *Genes Dev.* 15:3130–43

Panoli AP, Ravi M, Sebastian J, Nishal B, Reddy TV, et al. 2006. AtMND1 is required for homologous pairing during meiosis in *Arabidopsis*. *BMC Mol. Biol.* 7:24

Penkner A, Tang L, Novatchkova M, Ladurner M, Fridkin A, et al. 2007. The nuclear envelope protein Matefin/SUN-1 is required for homologous pairing in *C. elegans* meiosis. *Dev. Cell* 12:873–85

Peoples TL, Dean E, Gonzalez O, Lambourne L, Burgess SM. 2002. Close, stable homolog juxtaposition during meiosis in budding yeast is dependent on meiotic recombination, occurs independently of synapsis, and is distinct from DSB-independent pairing contacts. *Genes Dev.* 16:1682–95

Peoples-Holst TL, Burgess SM. 2005. Multiple branches of the meiotic recombination pathway contribute independently to homolog pairing and stable juxtaposition during meiosis in budding yeast. *Genes Dev.* 19:863–74

Perry J, Kleckner N, Borner GV. 2005. Bioinformatic analyses implicate the collaborating meiotic crossover/chiasma proteins Zip2, Zip3, and Spo22/Zip4 in ubiquitin labeling. *Proc. Natl. Acad. Sci. USA* 102:17594–99

Petukhova GV, Pezza RJ, Vanevski F, Ploquin M, Masson JY, Camerini-Otero RD. 2005. The Hop2 and Mnd1 proteins act in concert with Rad51 and Dmc1 in meiotic recombination. *Nat. Struct. Mol. Biol.* 12:449–53

Petukhova GV, Romanienko PJ, Camerini-Otero RD. 2003. The Hop2 protein has a direct role in promoting interhomolog interactions during mouse meiosis. *Dev. Cell* 5:927–36

Pezza RJ, Voloshin ON, Vanevski F, Camerini-Otero RD. 2007. Hop2/Mnd1 acts on two critical steps in Dmc1-promoted homologous pairing. *Genes Dev.* 21:1758–66

Phillips CM, Dernburg AF. 2006. A family of zinc-finger proteins is required for chromosome-specific pairing and synapsis during meiosis in *C. elegans*. *Dev. Cell* 11:817–29

Phillips CM, Wong C, Bhalla N, Carlton PM, Weiser P, et al. 2005. HIM-8 binds to the X chromosome pairing center and mediates chromosome-specific meiotic synapsis. *Cell* 123:1051–63

Pittman DL, Cobb J, Schimenti KJ, Wilson LA, Cooper DM, et al. 1998. Meiotic prophase arrest with failure of chromosome synapsis in mice deficient for *Dmc1*, a germline-specific RecA homolog. *Mol. Cell* 1:697–705

Plank JL, Wu J, Hsieh TS. 2006. Topoisomerase IIIα and Bloom's helicase can resolve a mobile double Holliday junction substrate through convergent branch migration. *Proc. Natl. Acad. Sci. USA* 103:11118–23

Rockmill B, Fung JC, Branda SS, Roeder GS. 2003. The Sgs1 helicase regulates chromosome synapsis and meiotic crossing over. *Curr. Biol.* 13:1954–62

Rockmill B, Sym M, Scherthan H, Roeder GS. 1995. Roles for two RecA homologs in promoting meiotic chromosome synapsis. *Genes Dev.* 9:2684–95

Romanienko PJ, Camerini-Otero RD. 2000. The mouse *Spo11* gene is required for meiotic chromosome synapsis. *Mol. Cell* 6:975–87

Scherthan H, Bahler J, Kohli J. 1994. Dynamics of chromosome organization and pairing during meiotic prophase in fission yeast. *J. Cell Biol.* 127:273–85

Scherthan H. 2001. A bouquet makes ends meet. *Nat. Rev. Mol. Cell Biol.* 2:621–27

Scherthan H, Wang H, Adelfalk C, White EJ, Cowan C, et al. 2007. Chromosome mobility during meiotic prophase in *Saccharomyces cerevisiae*. *Proc. Natl. Acad. Sci. USA* 104:16934–39

Schlecht HB, Lichten M, Goldman AS. 2004. Compartmentalization of the yeast meiotic nucleus revealed by analysis of ectopic recombination. *Genetics* 168:1189–203

Schmitt J, Benavente R, Hodzic D, Hoog C, Stewart CL, Alsheimer M. 2007. Transmembrane protein Sun2 is involved in tethering mammalian meiotic telomeres to the nuclear envelope. *Proc. Natl. Acad. Sci. USA* 104:7426–31

Schwacha A, Kleckner N. 1997. Interhomolog bias during meiotic recombination: Meiotic functions promote a highly differentiated interhomolog-only pathway. *Cell* 90:1123–35

Sherizen D, Jang JK, Bhagat R, Kato N, McKim KS. 2005. Meiotic recombination in *Drosophila* females depends on chromosome continuity between genetically defined boundaries. *Genetics* 169:767–81

Shimanuki M, Miki F, Ding DQ, Chikashige Y, Hiraoka Y, et al. 1997. A novel fission yeast gene, *kms1+*, is required for the formation of meiotic prophase-specific nuclear architecture. *Mol. Gen. Genet.* 254:238–49

Shinohara A, Ogawa H, Ogawa T. 1992. Rad51 protein involved in repair and recombination in *S. cerevisiae* is a RecA-like protein. *Cell* 69:457–70

Smith GR, Boddy MN, Shanahan P, Russell P. 2003. Fission yeast Mus81·Eme1 Holliday junction resolvase is required for meiotic crossing over but not for gene conversion. *Genetics* 165:2289–93

Smolikov S, Eizinger A, Schild-Prufert K, Hurlburt A, McDonald K, et al. 2007. SYP-3 restricts synaptonemal complex assembly to bridge paired chromosome axes during meiosis in *Caenorhabditis elegans*. *Genetics* 176:2015–25

Stahl FW, Foss HM, Young LS, Borts RH, Abdullah MF, Copenhaver GP. 2004. Does crossover interference count in *Saccharomyces cerevisiae*? *Genetics* 168:35–48

Starr DA, Fischer JA. 2005. KASH 'n Karry: the KASH domain family of cargo-specific cytoskeletal adaptor proteins. *Bioessays* 27:1136–46

Sym M, Engebrecht JA, Roeder GS. 1993. ZIP1 is a synaptonemal complex protein required for meiotic chromosome synapsis. *Cell* 72:365–78

Sym M, Roeder GS. 1995. Zip1-induced changes in synaptonemal complex structure and polycomplex assembly. *J. Cell Biol.* 128:455–66

Szostak JW, Orr-Weaver TL, Rothstein RJ, Stahl FW. 1983. The double-strand-break repair model for recombination. *Cell* 33:25–35

Thompson DA, Stahl FW. 1999. Genetic control of recombination partner preference in yeast meiosis. Isolation and characterization of mutants elevated for meiotic unequal sister-chromatid recombination. *Genetics* 153:621–41

Trelles-Sticken E, Adelfalk C, Loidl J, Scherthan H. 2005. Meiotic telomere clustering requires actin for its formation and cohesin for its resolution. *J. Cell Biol.* 170:213–23

Trelles-Sticken E, Dresser ME, Scherthan H. 2000. Meiotic telomere protein Ndj1p is required for meiosis-specific telomere distribution, bouquet formation and efficient homologue pairing. *J. Cell Biol.* 151:95–106

Trelles-Sticken E, Loidl J, Scherthan H. 1999. Bouquet formation in budding yeast: Initiation of recombination is not required for meiotic telomere clustering. *J. Cell Sci.* 112(Pt. 5):651–58

Tsubouchi H, Roeder GS. 2002. The Mnd1 protein forms a complex with hop2 to promote homologous chromosome pairing and meiotic double-strand break repair. *Mol. Cell. Biol.* 22:3078–88

Tsubouchi H, Roeder GS. 2003. The importance of genetic recombination for fidelity of chromosome pairing in meiosis. *Dev. Cell* 5:915–25

Tsubouchi H, Roeder GS. 2006. Budding yeast Hed1 down-regulates the mitotic recombination machinery when meiotic recombination is impaired. *Genes Dev.* 20:1766–75

Tsubouchi T, Roeder GS. 2005. A synaptonemal complex protein promotes homology-independent centromere coupling. *Science* 308:870–73

Tsubouchi T, Zhao H, Roeder GS. 2006. The meiosis-specific Zip4 protein regulates crossover distribution by promoting synaptonemal complex formation together with Zip2. *Dev. Cell* 10:809–19

Tuzon CT, Borgstrom B, Weilguny D, Egel R, Cooper JP, Nielsen O. 2004. The fission yeast heterochromatin protein Rik1 is required for telomere clustering during meiosis. *J. Cell Biol.* 165:759–65

Watt PM, Hickson ID, Borts RH, Louis EJ. 1996. *SGS1*, a homologue of the Bloom's and Werner's syndrome genes, is required for maintenance of genome stability in *Saccharomyces cerevisiae*. *Genetics* 144:935–45

Weiner BM, Kleckner N. 1994. Chromosome pairing via multiple interstitial interactions before and during meiosis in yeast. *Cell* 77:977–91

Wu L, Chan KL, Ralf C, Bernstein DA, Garcia PL, et al. 2005. The HRDC domain of BLM is required for the dissolution of double Holliday junctions. *EMBO J.* 24:2679–87

Yamamoto A, West RR, McIntosh JR, Hiraoka Y. 1999. A cytoplasmic dynein heavy chain is required for oscillatory nuclear movement of meiotic prophase and efficient meiotic recombination in fission yeast. *J. Cell Biol.* 145:1233–49

Yoshida K, Kondoh G, Matsuda Y, Habu T, Nishimune Y, Morita T. 1998. The mouse *RecA*-like gene *Dmc1* is required for homologous chromosome synapsis during meiosis. *Mol. Cell* 1:707–18

Young JA, Hyppa RW, Smith GR. 2004. Conserved and nonconserved proteins for meiotic DNA breakage and repair in yeasts. *Genetics* 167:593–605

Zickler D, Kleckner N. 1998. The leptotene-zygotene transition of meiosis. *Annu. Rev. Genet.* 32:619–97

Zickler D, Kleckner N. 1999. Meiotic chromosomes: integrating structure and function. *Annu. Rev. Genet.* 33:603–754

Zierhut C, Berlinger M, Rupp C, Shinohara A, Klein F. 2004. Mnd1 is required for meiotic interhomolog repair. *Curr. Biol.* 14:752–62

Provided compelling evidence that the uncoupling of pairing and synapsis observed in the *hop2* and *mnd1* mutants is the result of misregulation of meiotic recombination.

Evolution of Coloration Patterns

Meredith E. Protas[1] and Nipam H. Patel[2,3]

[1]Department of Integrative Biology, [2]Department of Molecular and Cell Biology, and [3]Howard Hughes Medical Institute, University of California, Berkeley, California 94720-3140; email: nipam@uclink.berkeley.edu

Annu. Rev. Cell Dev. Biol. 2008. 24:425–46

First published online as a Review in Advance on July 1, 2008

The *Annual Review of Cell and Developmental Biology* is online at cellbio.annualreviews.org

This article's doi: 10.1146/annurev.cellbio.24.110707.175302

Key Words

pigmentation, morphological change, genetic mapping, mimicry

Abstract

There is an amazing amount of diversity in coloration patterns in nature. The ease of observing this diversity and the recent application of genetic and molecular techniques to model and nonmodel animals are allowing us to investigate the genetic basis and evolution of coloration in an ever-increasing variety of animals. It is now possible to ask questions about how many genes are responsible for any given pattern, what types of genetic changes have occurred to generate the diversity, and if the same underlying genetic changes occur repeatedly when coloration phenotypes arise through convergent evolution or parallel evolution.

Contents

BACKGROUND

The remarkable diversity of coloration patterns seen in animals is one of the most striking features in the natural world. Examples include *Melanitis* butterflies that resemble dried vegetation, flounder and flatfish that are pigmented on only one-half of their body and alter their appearance to match their surroundings, the bold black and white stripes of zebras, brilliantly colored tropical fish and birds, and cavefish that lack pigment altogether (**Figure 1**). Countless examples exist of unique colors and patterns for all types of animals. This varia-

tion, and the ease of observing it, has made the study of coloration patterns a popular and tractable subject for scientific inquiry. In the past few decades, genetic, molecular, biochemical, and cellular approaches in both model and nonmodel species have allowed us to understand many details of the basis for color patterns during development. In addition, it is possible to surmise, and sometimes experimentally validate, the selective pressures behind animal coloration, allowing one to approach the question of how these patterns evolved.

FUNCTIONS OF COLORATION

When one is studying coloration from an evolutionary perspective, the first question that comes to mind is, What is the function of a particular pattern? In cases such as the dead-leaf butterfly, functional significance is fairly obvious: Appearing leaf-like may cause predators to misidentify potential prey (**Figure 2**). The functional and evolutionary significance of other examples, such as a zebra's stripes, is not as obvious. Many functions of coloration have been proposed: concealment, thermoregulation, warning of toxicity, mimicry, sexual selection, and linkage to beneficial characteristics such as immunity and salinity tolerance (reviewed in Roulin 2004). Finally, it is always possible that a certain coloration pattern evolved by chance through processes such as genetic drift.

Concealment is a very common function of coloration. Many animals, for example, sea dragons, when viewed in their natural habitat, blend in almost perfectly with their surroundings (**Figure 3a**). This is all the more striking when multiple populations of a single species living in different habitats have distinct coloration forms that match each environment (**Figure 4**). This phenomenon has been observed in many species; rock pocket mice, beach mice, deer mice, and fence lizards are just some examples within the vertebrates (Hoekstra 2006, Hoekstra et al. 2006, Mundy 2005). Rock pocket mice of the southwestern United States and Mexico provide a particularly clear example. Most live predominantly on

Figure 1

Some samples of the diversity of animal coloration patterns. (*a*) *Melanitis* butterfly, whose underside resembles the dried vegetation on which it sits. (*b*) Flatfish that can change coloration on the upper side of its body to blend into the background. (*c*) A group of zebras with their striking black and white stripes. (*d*) Blueface angelfish. (*e*) Rainbow lorikeet. (*f*) The unpigmented blind cave loach *Nemacheilus troglocataractus*, from Thailand (image courtesy of R. Borowsky).

lightly colored rocks, and these mice have light-colored fur. However, there are also some populations of rock pocket mice that colonized dark lava flows (some of which are just a few thousand years old), and these individuals have dark fur (Hoekstra & Nachman 2003). It is thought that the melanic form provides better camouflage in the lava flow environment, lessening the chance of predation.

Coloration is often a constant feature of an animal throughout its life. However, there are cases when the animal's coloration changes at different times and in different environments. This ability to change coloration is often advantageous for animals that move around on different-colored substrates. One classic example is that of the cuttlefish (**Figure 3***b*). Cuttlefish skin changes in both color and texture as the animal moves. It is thought that this change of color and pattern is advantageous for camouflage as well as for signaling to other individuals (Barbato et al. 2007).

Another mechanism by which coloration patterns disguise an animal is by disruptive coloration, a phenomenon in which a color pattern breaks up the animal's form so that it is difficult to identify the real outline of the animal. A common way of disguising the boundaries of an animal is to hide the eyes by an eye mask pattern and thus distort one of the most identifiable features of a prey item. Also potentially disruptive are black and white lines intersecting the outline of the animal, e.g., tapirs and pandas (Caro 2005).

Whereas many forms of coloration camouflage an animal, there are many examples of conspicuous coloration used as a warning to potential predators. Black, red, orange, and yellow often indicate that the species is distasteful. The yellow and black ant, *Cremato-gaster inflata*, produces chemicals, including 5-*n*-alkyl resorcinols, that make them unpalatable to some predators, and the predators learn to avoid these ants (Ito et al. 2004). Often, multiple

Figure 2

The within-population morphological diversity of dead-leaf butterflies of the species *Kallima inachus*. The butterflies were all collected within a small geographic region. Although all the butterflies resemble dead leaves on their undersides, the variation on the basic leaf pattern is quite remarkable. This variation may help ensure that predators cannot cue on a specific pattern element to distinguish the butterflies from the general leaf litter.

Müllerian mimicry: phenomenon in which an unpalatable organism mimics the appearance of another unpalatable one

Batesian mimicry: phenomenon in which a palatable organism mimics the appearance of an unpalatable one

unpalatable species not only will use the same bright colors but will closely mimic other species in pattern as well. This phenomenon, in which multiple species share the same warning coloration pattern, is called Müllerian mimicry and is particularly well studied in butterflies and moths (**Figures 5** and **6**) (reviewed in Parchem et al. 2007). Batesian mimicry, in contrast, refers to instances in which a palatable species mimics the coloration pattern of an unpalatable one and thereby evades predation (**Figure 5**). Ants of the genus *Camponotus* may utilize Batesian mimicry; *Camponotus* individuals overlap in territory with the previously mentioned unpalatable *C. inflata* and have a very similar coloration. Chick-feeding experiments determined that *Camponotus* individuals were palatable whereas *C. inflata* individuals were not. Chicks that had previously eaten *C. inflata*, however, rarely attempted to eat *Camponotus* (Ito et al. 2004).

Some animals also employ coloration to startle predators. For example, some moths, when resting, rely primarily on cryptic coloration but, when startled, raise their forewings to expose a brightly colored area on their hindwings (**Figure 3c,d**). A variation of the startle response is to have a striking coloration pattern (false heads, eye spots, or vivid coloration of tails) in a noncritical part of the animal to draw the predators' attention away from the most vulnerable area of the body.

Coloration also seems to play an important role in sexual selection (**Figure 3e**). Studies in birds and other animals with color polymorphisms show that pigmentation can influence mate choice. In feral pigeons, irrespective of the female phenotype, the most desired male phenotype is that of blue checker males (reviewed in

Figure 3

Examples of the many functions of coloration. (*a*) Both the coloration and shape of the leafy sea dragon help it to blend in perfectly with its surroundings. (*b*) A cuttlefish can quickly change its colors either to blend in or to communicate. (*c*) While at rest, the moth *Automeris io* is well camouflaged. (*d*) Shown is the same moth as in panel *c*, but after being disturbed. By raising its forewings, it displays the brightly colored eyespots of the hindwings, which are thought to startle a would-be predator. (*e*) A male peacock, whose brilliant coloration is thought to be due to sexual selection. (*f*) The cavefish *Astyanax mexicanus*, which lacks the pigmentation found on its surface relatives (image courtesy of R. Borowsky).

Roulin 2004). Additionally, in guppies, females prefer males with the most orange color, and this preference is strongest in populations that contain males with a large amount of orange color (Houde & Endler 1990). There is a balance, however, between the advantage of being conspicuous to females and the disadvantage of being conspicuous to predators.

Figure 4

Intraspecific pigmentation differences in oldfield mice, *Peromyscus polionotus*. (*a*) A beach-dwelling mouse whose coloration matches its light-colored sandy habitat (image courtesy of C. Steiner). (*b*) A mainland-dwelling mouse whose brown color matches its habitat (image courtesy of S. Cary).

Figure 5

Examples of Batesian and Müllerian mimicry. In the left-most column are heliconid and ithomid butterflies that are thought to be unpalatable. In the middle column are pericopid moths that are also thought to be unpalatable. In the right-most column are pierid butterflies of the genus *Dismorphia* that are thought to be palatable. Thus, within each row, the left and middle Lepidoptera are examples of Müllerian mimics, whereas the right-most specimen is a Batesian mimic.

Figure 6

Heliconius mimicry. Each quadrant shows two *Heliconius* butterflies that look strikingly similar, but within each quadrant, the left specimen is *Heliconius erato*, whereas the right specimen is *Heliconius melpomene*. Thus, the two species show incredible variation, but where their geographic ranges overlap, the two species have evolved to be comimics (Müllerian mimics). For example, the *erato/melpomene* specimens shown in the upper left quadrant are found in the Chanchamayo region of Peru, whereas the ones in the lower left quadrant are found in Ecuador.

A particular pattern may not have an adaptive function. One potential example is the loss of pigmentation in cave animals (**Figure 3*f***). Because of the dark habitat of these animals, pigmentation cannot provide typical functions, e.g., protection from ultraviolet radiation, concealment from predators and prey, and mate choice. Indeed, one of the theories for pigmentation loss in cavefish is that the cave environment predicts no selective advantage for this trait and therefore the trait is lost (Culver 1982). There are many other examples for which there appears to be no obvious adaptive function of a particular coloration pattern, but it is difficult to know what additional characteristics are affected by, or linked to, coloration.

All these possible functions give us some idea of the evolutionary forces that underlie the remarkable diversity of coloration patterns in animals. In recent years, it has been possible to move beyond observation and begin exploring the evolution of this amazing diversity at the genetic and molecular levels. By the use of both model and nonmodel species, it is now possible to begin addressing the following kinds of questions: What is the molecular basis of coloration patterns? How many genes are involved in orchestrating differences in coloration between species or between individuals within a population? What types of mutations cause phenotypic changes? If the same coloration pattern occurs repeatedly across taxa, will the same genes be responsible?

EARLY GENETIC STUDIES OF COLORATION AND STUDIES OF COLORATION IN MODEL SYSTEMS

Genetic methods have been used for many years to study coloration differences. More than a thousand years ago in China, selective breeding was used to create various colors of goldfish. Mice breeding for coat color variation started in China and Japan as early as the eighteenth century. Later, in the nineteenth century, Mendel's laws of inheritance were formulated by the use of traits in peas that included flower, seed, and pod color. Mendel's rules were then applied in the early 1900s to examine the genetic basis of coat coloration in rodents (reviewed in Russell 1985).

Since these early days of genetic studies of coloration, extensive work has been performed to study coloration in various model species, including the fly *Drosophila melanogaster*, the mouse *Mus musculus*, and the zebrafish *Danio rerio*. Traditionally, large-scale mutagenesis screens for color mutants were carried out, the mutations were mapped, and the causative (i.e., mutated) genes were identified and cloned. We briefly discuss some of the major players in the pigmentation pathways of these three model systems (focusing on those that have been further studied in nonmodel systems) and then discuss nonmodel systems.

In *D. melanogaster*, epidermal cells produce and secrete cuticular pigments that give the body its characteristic brownish color with black bristles and dark abdominal stripes. Several structural genes that function in pigment synthesis include *yellow*, *pale*, *Ddc* (*dopa decarboxylase*), *ebony*, *black*, *tan*, and *aaNAT* (*N-acetyl transferase*), whereas regulatory genes, such as *optomotor-blind* and *bric-a-brac*, function in establishing the pigment pattern in *D. melanogaster* (reviewed in Wittkopp et al. 2003a).

Pigmentation in mice is also a vast field of research. There are more than 127 loci in mice affecting coloration (Bennett & Lamoreux 2003). Mammalian melanocytes, or pigment cells, are derived from the neural crest and migrate to various areas of the body (Bennett & Lamoreux 2003). Just as in *D. melanogaster*, there are several classes of genes that affect pigmentation in mice. For example, there are the spotting loci that affect melanocyte development. Examples of these genes are *Kit* and *Mitf*. Other genes such as *Tyrp1* (*Tyrosinase-related protein 1*), *Tyrosinase*, *Oca2* (*Ocular and cutaneous albinism 2*), and *Matp* (*Membrane-associated transporter protein*) affect the synthesis of melanin. Yet another group of genes affecting pigment includes those that control the switch between eumelanin and phaeomelanin production.

Melanophores, melanocytes: brown pigment– or black pigment–containing cells

Chromatophore: a cell in amphibians, reptiles, and fish that contains pigment or reflects light

Xanthopore: a yellow pigment–containing cell

Iridophore: an iridescent pigment cell

Complementation test: mating two individuals that have similar phenotypes to each other to ascertain if they have mutations in the same or different genes

Linkage map: the arrangement of genetic markers into groups that correspond to either entire chromosomes or pieces of chromosomes

Eumelanin produces a dark (brown to black) color, and phaeomelanin produces a light (red to yellow) color. Major genes involved in this switch are *Melanocortin-1 receptor* (*Mc1r*), *Melanocyte-stimulating hormone* (*MSH*), and *Agouti signaling protein* (*ASP*).

Pigment cells in *D. rerio* also derive from the neural crest. There are three different types of pigment cells or chromatophores: black melanophores; yellow or orange xanthophores; and blue, silver, or gold iridophores (Kelsh 2004, Kelsh et al. 1996, Parichy 2006). Mutagenesis screens have generated many different phenotypes that fall into various classes: no chromatophores, fewer melanophores, fewer xanthophores, fewer iridophores, patterning defects, and ectopic chromatophores (Kelsh et al. 1996). Several of the genes responsible for these mutations have been cloned, and many of the genes involved in pigmentation in mice and humans are conserved in zebrafish (Camp & Lardelli 2001, Quigley & Parichy 2002).

When one is studying natural color variation, however, it is important to keep in mind the ways in which natural variants differ from the mutants uncovered by mutagenesis screens. First, coloration mutants created by mutagenesis may be viable in the controlled environment of a laboratory but may not be capable of surviving in the natural environment. As a caveat, however, it is important to remember that the phenotype of null alleles may be most obvious in a screen, but natural variation may still utilize weaker alleles of the same gene. Second, the timescale, population size, and genetic background in a genetic screen are very different from those that exist during the evolutionary processes that generate natural variation. One potential consequence of this is that phenotypes that can result from the mutation of a single gene in the lab may be created by the sum of several mutations in the natural world. Thus, to truly understand the evolution of coloration, it is necessary to examine color variation within naturally occurring species.

In some ways, studying coloration patterns in domestic animals provides an intermediate between genetic model systems and natural populations (Andersson & Georges 2004, Schmutz & Berryere 2007). The insights from these studies are highly informative for questions of the evolution of coloration and coloration pattern, but owing to space constraints, this review discusses only examples of naturally occurring populations.

NATURAL COLOR VARIATION IN NONMODEL SPECIES

Certain species are better suited than others for investigating questions of natural variation. For example, there is an enormous difference in the color and pattern of a giraffe versus those of a zebra. However, it is difficult to compare these two animals because they differ in so many other ways. But it is useful, at least initially, to examine coloration on a microevolutionary scale—within single species that are polymorphic in coloration or between related species that have diverged in coloration but are still close enough to interbreed. This kind of intraspecific variation in coloration is fairly common; for example, such variation exists in 3.5% of all bird species (Roulin 2004). Data from such microevolutionary studies can then be applied to understand coloration changes on a macroevolutionary scale.

The types of methods used to study coloration on a microevolutionary scale include genetic crosses, gene expression analyses (through in situ hybridization and microarray analysis), complementation studies, and linkage mapping. First, we describe each of these methods along with examples in which color patterns have been investigated. Then, we return to the question of how pigment patterns evolve, and we discuss the insights that recent studies have provided.

Among the first methods used to study coloration in nonmodel species were genetic crosses between individuals from populations with distinct coloration differences. One classic example comes from the snail *Cepea nemoralis*. The lip of the shell can be black, dark brown, pink, or white, whereas the rest of the shell is light tan, pink, orange, or red with one to five dark bands (Cain & Sheppard 1954). Crosses between individuals with different coloration patterns indicated that a single locus is responsible for shell and lip color, the presence or absence of bands, and band pigmentation (reviewed in Jones et al. 1977). The number of bands, however, appears to be unlinked to this gene.

Crossing individuals with different phenotypes allows investigators to ask how many genes are responsible for a certain phenotype, which alleles are recessive and which are dominant, and what phenotypes are linked to each other. The next step is to delve into the pathways, and ultimately the mutations, that are modified to create variation in coloration. To accomplish this, one can use information known about pigmentation and coloration in model species and apply that information to nonmodel species.

CANDIDATE GENE APPROACH: GENETIC ASSOCIATIONS IN WILD POPULATIONS

The most common method employed in recent years to study the genetic basis of evolutionary variation in color is a candidate gene approach. As discussed above, pigmentation pathways in model organisms are generally well studied, and some of the major genes are conserved. These genes then become candidates for study in nonmodel systems. The disadvantages of using the candidate gene approach include selection bias and potentially long (and, ultimately, unsuccessful) lists of numerous candidate genes. A candidate gene approach, however, is sometimes the only option if one is working with a nonmodel species with few genetic resources.

The most studied coloration gene in nonmodel vertebrates is *Mc1r*, a transmembrane receptor expressed in melanocytes that, when modified, generally produces changes in coloration of the entire body. *Mc1r* is thought to be responsible for intraspecies coloration differences in at least four different bird species (Doucet et al. 2004, Mundy et al. 2004, Theron et al. 2001). For example, Caribbean

bananaquits have melanic morphs, which generally live in forests, and paler morphs, which usually live in drier lowland areas. *Mc1r* was sequenced from pale and melanic individuals, and the melanic form of the bird has an amino acid substitution also found in melanic forms of chicken and mice (Theron et al. 2001). In Arctic skuas, another polymorphism in *Mc1r* correlates with the coloration phenotype (Mundy et al. 2004). The lesser snow goose has six different classes of pigmentation, and the degree of melanism is associated with a different amino acid substitution in *Mc1r* (Mundy et al. 2004). One final example, in birds, is that of the fairy wren. Male mainland fairy wrens have bright blue nuptial coloring, whereas island populations have black nuptial coloring, a phenotypic difference also associated with polymorphisms in *Mc1r* (Doucet et al. 2004).

Pocket mice are another example in which the candidate gene approach was used to test if there was an association between coloration and *Mc1r*. As mentioned above, the sandy-colored mice live in an area that has pale rocks, whereas the melanic form lives on dark lava flows. An association was found between four linked amino acid polymorphisms in *Mc1r* and coloration in one lava-dwelling population of melanic rock pocket mice (Hoekstra & Nachman 2003). Furthermore, *Mc1r* is associated with variation in coloration in jaguars, jaguarundis, and reptiles (Eizirik et al. 2003, Rosenblum et al. 2004).

Most of these studies used the approach of sequencing the coding region of *Mc1r* from wild individuals and comparing genotypes with coloration. This allows for the discovery of associations while avoiding laborious and time-consuming interspecific and intraspecific breeding programs. The primary disadvantage of this approach is that it is often difficult to determine experimentally that the changes in the *Mc1r* sequence actually cause the coloration differences. Even when the results from this approach are combined with genetic mapping data (see below), the observed association between an *Mc1r* genotype in the coding sequence and a melanic phenotype may instead be due to a regulatory mutation in *Mc1r* or a mutation in a different gene very closely linked to *Mc1r*.

CANDIDATE GENE APPROACH: COMPARATIVE EXPRESSION ANALYSIS

Above, we discuss the candidate gene approach in the context of testing whether genetic polymorphisms are associated with a certain phenotype. Another method used to investigate a particular candidate gene is to see if the gene's expression pattern is correlated with a coloration phenotype. Such an association does not necessarily mean that a particular gene is the locus modified to produce the genetic change; e.g., changes in a gene's expression pattern may also be the result of regulatory changes in upstream regulators of that gene. An example of the utility of the expression analysis method is a wing spot study done in *Drosophila biarmipes* (Gompel et al. 2005). *D. biarmipes* has a dark pigmented spot on its wing that is absent from the closely related *D. melanogaster*. The gene, *yellow*, is expressed at very low levels throughout the wing of *D. melanogaster* but highly expressed in the area that forms the pigmented spot in *D. biarmipes* (Gompel et al. 2005). The advantage to working with species closely related to a model system (such as *D. melanogaster*) is the myriad of ways to functionally test hypotheses about coloration patterns. Indeed, Gompel et al. (2005) were able to provide evidence that changes in the *yellow* gene itself, as opposed to changes in a different gene that acts as a regulator of *yellow* expression, are responsible for the expression differences. These authors made transgenic *D. melanogaster* that contained the upstream regulatory region of *yellow* from *D. biarmipes* driving expression of the fluorescent protein GFP. These investigators found that this reporter construct was expressed in *D. melanogaster* in a similar manner to that seen for *yellow* in *D. biarmipes*. This provides good evidence that the expression pattern differences seen for *yellow* between the two species are due to evolutionary changes in the regulatory regions of the *yellow* gene. However, when Gompel et al. (2005) rescued *D. melanogaster yellow* mutants with a construct of the *D. biarmipes yellow* gene that presumably drives expression in the wing, no pigmented wing spot was observed. Because of this, the authors argue that other genetic changes, in addition to a regulatory change in *yellow*, are responsible for the observed coloration difference.

Another example of the candidate gene expression analysis approach was taken with the gene *bric-a-brac* in *Drosophila willistoni* and *D. melanogaster*. *D. melanogaster* has sexually dimorphic pigmentation patterns, whereas *D. willistoni* does not; expression of *bric-a-brac* is correlated with these coloration differences, and the gene maps to a locus accounting for the coloration differences (Kopp et al. 2000). Finally, within cichlid fish, a correlation was seen between the expression of *fms*, a type III receptor tyrosine kinase thought to be a duplicated form of *kit*, and the presence of egg dummies (pigmentation spots that look like eggs) on the anal fins of male cichlids (Mellgren & Johnson 2002, Salzburger et al. 2007).

This sort of expression analysis is a powerful tool, but it is sometimes difficult to perform on nonmodel organisms. Also, coloration occurs relatively late during embryonic development, and it is not always possible to conduct these analyses on late-stage embryos or juvenile animals for technical reasons. As an alternative, other methods, including microarray analysis and quantitative polymerase chain reaction (PCR), can also be used to look at expression levels in different parts of the animal during development (Reed et al. 2008).

COMPLEMENTATION CROSSES WITH MUTANTS IN A MODEL SPECIES

Another clever way to figure out the genetic basis of a coloration pattern is by a complementation test, a method that can be used only to detect recessive genetic determinants. Complementation tests allow one to ask if the same gene is affected in two species (that have similar phenotypes) by crossing them. If the variation is in the same gene, the offspring will have the same pattern as both parents. If, however, the affected genes are not the same, complementation will occur, and the offspring will look different from either parent.

A modified version of this method has been used to investigate the genetic makeup of coloration in species of the *Danio* genus. By crossing different *Danio* species to *D. rerio* mutants, investigators could assay whether certain genes were responsible for the difference in coloration between different *Danio* species. *D. rerio* has four to five horizontal stripes on its body. The closely related *Danio albolineatus* has no stripes and a more dispersed pattern of pigment cells (Parichy & Johnson 2001). Numerous screens have been performed in *D. rerio* to isolate coloration mutants. Seventeen *D. rerio* mutants in genes of the coloration pathway or neural crest development were crossed to *D. albolineatus* (Quigley et al. 2005). All the mutants complemented except for *fms* mutants (zebrafish *fms* and *kit* are thought to have resulted from an ancient duplication of *kit*). This indicates that the *fms* gene or *fms* pathway underlies the difference in appearance in the two species.

Further experiments addressed whether characteristics of pigment cell development in the *D. rerio fms* mutant were similar to those of *D. albolineatus*. *D. albolineatus* had fewer melanophores, increased melanophore death, and aberrant melanophore migration, all similar characteristics of the *D. rerio fms* mutant (Quigley et al. 2005). However, *D. rerio fms* mutants also have fewer xanthopores than does *D. albolineatus*. Because of this discrepancy, Quigley et al. (2005) suggest that genetic changes in the *fms* gene are not responsible for the difference in coloration between *D. rerio* and *D. albolineatus*. Instead, changes in the *fms* pathway are responsible for the observed phenotypic differences. This would imply that the reduced functions of two different genes in the *fms* pathway combined cause the cross between *D. albolineatus* and the *D. rerio fms* mutant not to complement.

MAPPING APPROACH

The candidate gene approach is very powerful for systems in which many of the genes involved are known and well conserved in nonmodel organisms. Although the candidate gene approach often works well, novel gene(s) may be responsible for the observed coloration differences. For example, candidate genes for coloration differences may include members of the biosynthetic pathway of a pigment. However, previously uncharacterized genes that are upstream of this pathway or that regulate the pathway may also affect the coloration of an animal. A mapping approach is a less biased method that can also uncover novel genes. Such an approach involves examining a cross of individuals with a number of genetic markers, phenotyping the members of the cross, and from this determining regions of the genome where loci responsible for these phenotypes occur. The initial results of such an approach generally narrow down the search significantly, but hundreds of genes can be within the mapped region. Often a candidate gene approach may then further narrow the analysis to a small handful of genes. It is starting to become possible, however, to use a completely unbiased approach (positional cloning) on nonmodel organisms in which sequence information from BAC or whole-genome sequencing is available (e.g., Colosimo et al. 2005, Miller et al. 2007).

Mapping approaches have been used to examine morphological changes in the extremely diverse group of East African cichlid fishes (**Figure 7**) (Albertson et al. 2003). One coloration phenotype examined is the orange blotch phenotype (**Figure 7a**), which is found mainly in females and is of unknown function (Streelman et al. 2003). Another coloration phenotype found in the same species is blue with black bars (**Figure 7b**). A blue-with-black-bar male was crossed to an orange blotch female to generate F1 hybrids that were then crossed to generate F2s (Streelman et al. 2003). Multiple genetic markers were used to genotype the F2s, and then these genetic data were compared with phenotypes to define a region containing a gene or genes responsible for

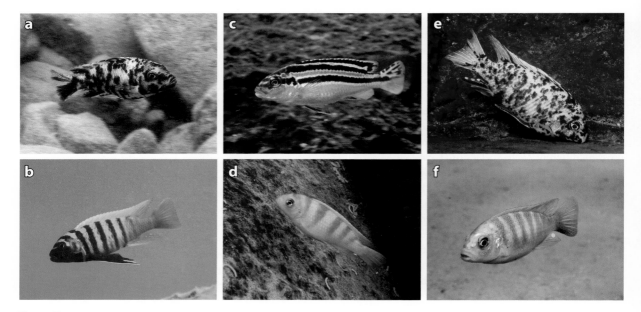

Figure 7

Coloration differences in cichlids. In the Great Lakes of East Africa, there are almost 2000 species of cichlids that have evolved relatively recently with a wide variety of color patterns. (*a*) Orange blotch phenotype in a female *Metriaclima zebra*. (*b*) Blue-with-black-bar phenotype in a male *M. zebra*. (*c*) *Metriaclima aurora*. (*d*) *Metriaclima lombardoi*. (*e*) *Labeotropheus fuelleborni*. (*f*) *Metriaclima auratus*. (All cichlid images are courtesy of R. Roberts.)

Monogenic: a trait that is encoded by one gene

Polygenic: a trait that is encoded by more than one gene

Quantitative trait locus (QTL): an area on a genetic linkage map that is responsible for a certain amount of variance in a measured trait

the orange blotch phenotype. Then, the researchers genotyped approximately 65 wild-caught individuals for the markers flanking this region to see whether this region was associated with the coloration phenotype in the wild. The same genetic marker that showed the highest association to coloration phenotype in the lab-raised cross also showed the highest association to coloration in the wild-caught individuals. Because there was little genomic information available for this species, the markers flanking the orange blotch locus were compared with sequence information from the pufferfish *Takifugu rubripes*. From this, the researchers identified a syntenic region that contained several genes, some of which are promising candidate genes. Ideally, one would now attempt to test these candidate genes within the cichlids by transgenesis, knockdown, or overexpression. Indeed, in other nonmodel fish species, some of these techniques have already been described (Colosimo et al. 2005, Hosemann et al. 2004, Yamamoto et al. 2004).

Figuring out the genetic basis of phenotypic variation is easiest for monogenic traits. However, some coloration variation appears to be polygenic. One recent example is the oldfield mouse, *Peromyscus polionotus*, which has darkly colored populations and lightly colored populations (**Figure 4**) (Hoekstra et al. 2006, Steiner et al. 2007). The lightly colored beach mouse lives in dunes and islands, and it is thought that the light color protects the animals from predators by providing camouflage. A large F2 cross between the beach and mainland populations was used to generate a linkage map, which identified three quantitative trait loci (QTLs) (regions where genes responsible for a certain trait reside). The coloration pathway of both mice and humans has been well studied. Ten coloration candidate genes were placed on the map, and of these, *Agouti*, *Mc1r*, and *Kit* mapped to the three QTLs. Mapping to a QTL does not prove that the gene is responsible for a particular QTL because there are many other unidentified genes in that region. However, a previous paper examined the sequence of *Mc1r* in beach and mainland mice and found that there was an amino acid change in a critical part of the protein (Hoekstra et al. 2006). Comparing the beach and mainland MC1R in an in vitro assay to test MC1R function showed that the beach MC1R had a significantly lower activity level than did the mainland MC1R. The coding sequence of *Agouti* in the beach and mainland mice was also compared, but no differences were observed (Steiner et al. 2007). The expression level of *Agouti* was examined, comparing beach and mainland mice by RT-PCR, and it was found that the level of *Agouti* was higher in the beach versus the mainland mice—consistent with the observation in laboratory mouse strains that higher levels of *Agouti* lead to light pigmentation (Steiner et al. 2007). The authors hypothesize that a regulatory mutation in *Agouti*, rather than a coding mutation, is responsible for the phenotypic difference between the two populations.

As outlined above, mapping combined with the candidate gene approach has potential for successfully investigating the genetic basis of coloration pattern. However, it is always possible that no matter how many candidate genes are added to the map, few, if any, will ever coincide with the loci responsible for coloration differences. For example, extensive genetic crosses and mapping have been done between different species and populations of *Heliconius* to map loci responsible for the position, size, and shape of patterns on the wings (**Figure 6**) (Jiggins et al. 2005, Kapan et al. 2006, Tobler et al. 2005). Many different genes known to be involved in *Drosophila* wing patterning or pigment biosynthesis, such as *apterous*, *distal-less*, *hedgehog*, *patched*, *cubitus interruptus*, *vermillion*, and *cinnabar*, have been placed on the map, and none of them map to the pattern loci being studied (Jiggins et al. 2005, Kapan et al. 2006, Tobler et al. 2005). Therefore, it remains to be determined whether novel wing-patterning genes or candidate genes other than those studied are responsible for the varied coloration phenotypes in *Heliconius* butterflies.

Similar to the difficulties experienced in predicting the genes responsible for coloration differences in *Heliconius* butterflies, the majority of studies in drosophilid species have not observed associations between candidate genes and coloration phenotypes (Wittkopp et al. 2003a). However, an association was seen between variation in coloration and the gene *ebony* in the offspring of crosses between *Drosophila americana* and *Drosophila novamexicana* (Wittkopp et al. 2003b), and as mentioned above, sexually dimorphic pigmentation in *D. melanogaster* is associated with the gene *bric-a-brac* (Kopp et al. 2003). In cases in which the candidate gene method is not able to predict the genes responsible for a coloration trait, the ideal method to use is a positional cloning approach. The difficulty is that to use this approach one must have either the genome sequence of the species of interest or a large amount of sequence information from BAC sequencing. Within this sequence, it is possible to identify a large number of polymorphic sites that can then be used for high-resolution mapping.

Recently, a coloration difference in sticklebacks was investigated by high-resolution mapping and a candidate gene approach (Miller et al. 2007). Some freshwater populations have lightly melanized gills and ventral surfaces, whereas marine populations have heavily melanized gills and ventral surfaces. A major QTL was found for this phenotype and narrowed down by genotyping a total of 1182 F2 fish. The recombination data from these individuals and a draft of the stickleback genome allowed the area to be narrowed down to a 4.5-mb region. Additional genetic markers were designed within this region. By typing the recombinants with the new markers, Miller et al. (2007) narrowed the gene responsible for this QTL to an interval of 315 kb. Fifteen genes resided within this region, and only one had been previously implied to function in pigmentation, *Kit ligand*. If there had been no promising candidate genes within the 15 genes, the authors would have had to take a functional approach to test each gene and see if each gene affected gill pigmentation. As this example shows, it is possible to use high-resolution mapping to narrow down a mapped region to a small number of genes that contain the loci responsible for genetic variation in a naturally occurring vertebrate population.

THE GENETIC BASIS OF ENVIRONMENTAL EFFECTS ON COLORATION

The environment can play a large part in determining an individual's coloration. Arctic foxes have a brownish coat during the summer and a white coat during the winter (Vage et al. 2005). The different seasonal forms of the butterfly *Precis octavia* are so different from each other that one might easily assume that they were actually different species (**Figure 8**). Another example is *Manduca quinquemaculata*, a species closely related to *Manduca sexta*, the tobacco hornworm moth (Suzuki & Nijhout 2006). *M. quinquemaculata* larvae are black when raised at 20°C and green when raised at 28°C. In *M. sexta*, a species that has only green larvae, a mutation causing a reduction of juvenile hormone secretion results in only black larva. Heat shocking these black larvae often resulted in a color change to green. The individuals that showed the most marked color change upon heat shock were selected and bred to one another. After 13 generations of such selection, the larvae mimicked *M. quinquemaculata* in that they were green when raised at 28°C without heat shock. The researchers were able to generate environmentally plastic coloration through reduction of juvenile hormone production and subsequent selection of the uncovered phenotypic variation (Suzuki & Nijhout 2006). Further studies determined that one major gene and several modifier genes were responsible for the artificially selected phenotype (Suzuki & Nijhout 2008). It is unclear how the coloration system evolved in *M. quinquemaculata*, but this system may have taken a path similar to the artificial selection in *M. sexta*. This example demonstrates a more complicated example of coloration differences and shows how the field is adapting

Figure 8

Example of environmentally influenced coloration. These two butterflies are both males of the species *Precis octavia* collected in South Africa. The only difference is that they were collected at different times of the year and represent the two very different seasonal forms of this species. It appears that both temperature and day/night length during the larval period determine the coloration pattern of the adult.

methods to address even these more complex phenomena.

Having examined the many different approaches for studying the genetic basis of pigmentation patterns, and having sampled some of the results, we can now return to the evolutionary questions we hope to address by studying coloration systems.

MANY GENES OR FEW GENES?

How many genes are responsible for the evolution of new forms of coloration? One factor to consider is that there is a bias in examining species with a simple genetic basis of coloration because it is easier to study such systems. With that in mind, there are many examples of single genes responsible for coloration differences (Brown et al. 2001, Curtis 2002, Nachman et al. 2003, Trapezov 1997, Wittkopp et al. 2003a). It is easy to see how an overall change in body pigmentation could be affected by modification of one gene in a pigment synthesis pathway. However, differences in the coloration pattern may be easier to explain via a polygenic mode of inheritance. Polygenic modes of inheritance have been identified for wing spots, abdomen, and overall pigmentation in various *Drosophila* species as well as pigmentation in the oldfield mouse (Carbone et al. 2005, Steiner et al. 2007, Wittkopp et al. 2003a, Yeh et al. 2006). In some cases, observed so far mainly in *Lepidoptera*, it is unclear whether a mode of inheritance is monogenic or polygenic with a tightly linked cluster of genes (Clarke & Sheppard 1959, 1960a,b; Joron et al. 2006b). Many recent studies looking at noncoloration variability have also documented that a few genes of large effect account for a large amount of phenotypic difference (Albertson et al. 2003; Colosimo et al. 2004, 2005; Peichel et al. 2001; Shapiro et al. 2004).

REGULATORY VERSUS CODING CHANGES?

What kinds of mutations are responsible for phenotypic changes—regulatory or coding changes? Again, there is bias in the studies that address this question because it is very difficult to find regulatory changes in nonmodel species when there is a lack of knowledge of structure of the gene regulatory elements or when detailed gene expression studies are not possible. Most often, regulatory changes are not identified but are hypothesized when no coding changes are found. An example of a gene that appears prone to coding changes in pigment evolution is *Mc1r*. Potential coding changes have been found in the rock pocket mouse, bananaquit, lesser snow goose, arctic skua, beach mouse, jaguars, jaguarundis, and Neanderthals (Baião et al. 2007, Eizirik et al.

2003, Hoekstra et al. 2006, Lalueza-Fox et al. 2007, Mundy et al. 2004, Nachman et al. 2003, Rosenblum et al. 2004, Theron et al. 2001). Most of these studies show an association between *Mc1r* changes and coloration phenotype. Often the changes are in conserved amino acids, implying that the function of the receptor is affected, and recently an in vitro test was devised to test the function of variants of beach mouse *Mc1r* (Hoekstra et al. 2006). Examples of predicted coding changes in other genes causing pigmentation differences include *Agouti* in domestic cats, *Tyrp1* in Soay sheep, and *Oca2* in the Mexican cave tetra (Eizirik et al. 2003, Gratten et al. 2007, Protas et al. 2006).

Examples of regulatory changes causing pigmentation differences are much fewer in number. However, likely examples are *yellow* and the wing pigmentation spot and male-specific pigmentation in drosophilids (Gompel et al. 2005, Jeong et al. 2006, Prud'homme et al. 2006). Another predicted regulatory change is in *Agouti* in beach mice (Steiner et al. 2007), and a regulatory mutation in *Kit ligand* is probably responsible for the gill pigmentation differences between marine and freshwater sticklebacks (Miller et al. 2007). Coding changes involved in the evolution of coloration may be prevalent because genes involved in pigment biosynthesis are relatively free to alter biochemical function without causing lethality. Genes involved in other processes during development often have pleiotropic effects, and coding changes would likely result in lethality. Whether coding or regulatory sequences are more common agents of evolutionary change is still hotly debated (Hoekstra & Coyne 2007).

SAME GENES OR DIFFERENT GENES?

The third question that can be addressed by genetic studies of coloration is, If the same phenotype comes up multiple times, is it the same or different genes that are responsible? Above we see that *Mc1r* appears to be involved in pigmentation differences in multiple cases. However, we must keep in mind that *Mc1r* is a highly conserved gene with only one exon and is therefore relatively easy to amplify from a nonmodel organism. Regardless of the bias, *Mc1r* seems to be involved in pigmentation differences between closely related species or populations in many different types of vertebrates. However, *Mc1r* polymorphisms are not always associated with pigmentation differences. For example, pocket gophers with coat colors corresponding to the color of the substrate that they live on do not show an association of coloration phenotype with *Mc1r* genotype (Wlasiuk & Nachman 2007). Also, leaf warblers with small, unmelanized patches and multiple nonhuman primates do not show an association of coloration with *Mc1r* (MacDougall-Shackleton et al. 2003, Mundy & Kelly 2003). Other examples can be found in populations of rock pocket mice, as well as in beach mice, in which one population does show an association between *Mc1r* variants and the melanic phenotype, whereas another population does not (Hoekstra & Nachman 2003, Hoekstra et al. 2006). This implies that the melanic phenotype evolved by a different mechanism in the separate populations. So, if there is a bias for mutation in *Mc1r*, it is not a complete bias.

In the Mexican cave tetra (**Figure 3f**), the genetic basis of albinism was studied in three different cave populations: Molino, Japonés, and Pachón (Protas et al. 2006). The gene *Oca2* was linked to the phenotype of albinism in crosses from the Molino and Pachón populations. These two cave populations both had deletions, but in different parts of the *Oca2* coding region. To test whether the cave forms of *Oca2* were functional, constructs of the surface *Oca2* and *Oca2* with the two deletions were transfected into a mouse melanocyte cell line deficient in *Oca2*. The surface form was able to rescue pigmentation in the cell line, but the two cave forms were unable to rescue pigmentation. Therefore, it appears that these two deletions cause the protein to be nonfunctional. As for the Japonés population, complementation tests were performed with the Molino and Pachón cave populations, and the offspring did not complement, indicating that the Japonés

population was likely also deficient in *Oca2*. A construct containing the coding sequence of *Oca2* in the Japonés population was able to rescue pigmentation in the *Oca2*-deficient melanocyte cell line, suggesting a possible regulatory change. Therefore, it is likely that albinism arose three times separately, in an example of parallel evolution, and that, in each case, the same gene was targeted. This is different from the previously discussed role of *Mc1r* in the evolution of pigmentation phenotypes in beach mice and rock pocket mice. In this latter case, some mouse populations utilized *Mc1r*, whereas others used something else. It is unclear why this bias is seen with *Oca2*, perhaps because the gene is very large and therefore more vulnerable to mutation. It is also important to keep in mind that the different types of coloration changes, such as loss of coloration, gain of coloration, and change in coloration pattern, are quite different from one another and may come about by the alteration of very different genetic programs.

Another example of parallel evolution is coloration patterns from *Heliconius* butterflies (**Figure 6**). As discussed above, *Heliconius* butterflies are a classic example of Müllerian mimicry. Each species has many different geographical races with varied pigmentation patterns, but where races of different species coexist they have matching pigmentation patterns. This provides a unique scenario in which several species have evolved virtually the same pigmentation pattern, allowing investigators to ask whether the same genetic path or different genetic paths were taken to achieve this result. This scenario is different from that of *Mc1r* in rock pocket mice and *Oca2* in cavefish because here we have multiple species—rather than multiple populations of species—evolving the same phenotypes.

Heliconius erato and *Heliconius melpomene* are two of the better-studied *Heliconius* species—they are distantly related but have very similar coloration patterns for 23 geographical races (**Figure 6**) (Joron et al. 2006a). Initial genetic experiments suggest that approximately a dozen loci are responsible for the variation seen within each species. Genetic linkage maps have been generated, and the positions of a number of coloration loci, including four to five alleles of major effect (Joron et al. 2006a), have now been mapped for both *H. erato* and *H. melpomene* (Jiggins et al. 2005, Kapan et al. 2006). In another species, *Heliconius numata*, most of the variation in wing patterning appears to be controlled by a single genomic locus (possibly one or more tightly linked genes). By investigating the placement of flanking genetic markers relative to the position of each of the color pattern loci in *H. erato*, *H. melpomene*, and *H. numata*, Joron et al. (2006b) determined that the loci responsible for specific color patterns were located in homologous chromosomal regions. Similarly, three color patterning loci were compared between the *Heliconius himera*/*H. erato* group and the *Heliconius cydno*/*Heliconius pachinus* group and were also found to be located in homologous chromosomal regions (Kronforst et al. 2006). Given the current resolution of the mapping data, these results do not yet prove that the same genes are affected but do support the idea of parallel evolution.

Although it is striking to see similar phenotypes mapping to similar genomic regions in *H. erato* and *H. melpomene* (something we see in examples above), the mapping of very different phenotypes to the same location (e.g., when comparing *H. erato*/*H. melpomene* with *H. numata*) is remarkable. Future work will hopefully show how the same region can encode such different phenotypes and uncover the specifics of the genetic architecture controlling these color patterns.

A very detailed example of convergence and parallel evolution is that of wing spot evolution in drosophilids. We discuss above one instance of wing spot difference between *D. melanogaster* and *D. biarmipes* (Gompel et al. 2005). Another example of wing spot gain is *Drosophila tristis* (Prud'homme et al. 2006). A *D. tristis* sequence homologous to that responsible for wing spot gain in *D. biarmipes* did not cause a wing spot pattern when inserted into *D. melanogaster*. Only when a *D. tristis yellow* intronic sequence was included in the reporter construct did the

sequence drive wing spot–specific expression. Therefore, the same gene seems to be involved in wing spot gain in two species of *Drosophila*, but different regulatory elements are involved (Prud'homme et al. 2006). Prud'homme et al. (2006) suggest that the evolution of these novel patterns came about by co-option of regulatory elements with preexisting functions.

STANDING VERSUS NOVEL VARIATION?

Our last question regarding the evolution of morphological change is whether change comes about by standing variation in the ancestral population or novel variation. Answering this type of question requires a system for which one knows the direction of morphological change. For example, in the Mexican cave tetra, we know that the albino cave form evolved from the pigmented surface form. The example of *Oca2* in cavefish showed that albinism was likely caused by novel variation in the cave populations because, although the same gene was affected, there were at least two different mutations (Protas et al. 2006). Another system in which the question of standing versus novel variation is being examined is with oldfield mice. Again, we know the direction of change—the lightly pigmented beach mice are derived from the more highly pigmented mainland mice. As stated above, three QTLs were found for pigmentation in this species, and two of them mapped to the genes *Agouti* and *Mc1r* (Steiner et al. 2007). *Agouti* is epistatic to *Mc1r*. Epistasis may allow the beach *Mc1r* allele to remain hidden in the mainland population as standing variation (Barrett & Schluter 2007). To examine this idea further, *Mc1r* needs to be sequenced from many individuals of the mainland population to see if the beach *Mc1r* alleles are preexisting in that population. Another likely evolution via standing variation is gill pigmentation in sticklebacks (Miller et al. 2007). Three freshwater populations of sticklebacks have *Kit ligand* alleles associated with light pigmentation. Even though the populations are geographically separate, they share the same

Standing variation: variation that exists in the population

alleles at *Kit ligand*. One possible explanation for this is that standing variation in the ancestral (marine) population was fixed in each of the freshwater populations. To investigate this hypothesis, *Kit ligand* was sequenced in 107 marine individuals; the light allele was present at a frequency of 12%, supporting the idea that the evolution of lightly colored gills occurred by the repeated fixation of standing variation.

CONCLUSION

There has been much progress in understanding the genetic basis of morphological change in the evolution of pigmentation and coloration patterns. The advantages to studying the genetic basis of coloration include the extreme ease of observing this phenotype, the vast knowledge of pigment synthesis pathways in model organisms, and the great diversity of coloration and patterns within and between species. Pigmentation is hence a relatively simple system in which we can explore the possible processes by which phenotypes evolve. Although broad trends in the evolution of pigmentation patterns emerge from the discussion above, there are clearly multiple ways in which evolution of coloration occurs. Also, most of the examples we discuss above are relatively simple pigmentation differences that are more easily examined with existing tools. However, there is a huge diversity of more complicated pigmentation systems being studied that will yield a more complete picture as to how coloration differences evolve.

SUMMARY POINTS

1. There are many advantages to studying coloration and coloration patterns in nature, including ease of observation and great morphological diversity within and between species.

2. Molecular and genetic techniques can now be applied to nonmodel organisms to ask questions about evolution.

3. Variation in coloration can evolve by single gene changes or by multiple gene changes.

4. Differences in coloration can evolve by regulatory or coding changes.

5. The evolution of similar phenotypic changes can be accomplished by the same genes or by different genes.

6. Changes in coloration can evolve by selection on standing variation or on novel mutations.

FUTURE ISSUES

1. There is a need to identify genes responsible for more quantitative trait loci encoding a small-percent variance of a coloration trait as well as those responsible for a large-percent variance of a trait.

2. Systems that have a more complicated coloration phenotype, for example, those with partially environmentally determined coloration, should be examined.

3. More cases of parallel and convergent evolution of coloration variation require examination.

4. Regulatory changes responsible for coloration variation should be determined.

5. Investigators need to determine other characteristics that evolve in tandem with color variation and how the genetic architecture of these traits interacts with the genetic architecture of coloration traits.

6. The genetics behind examples in which alleles of a single locus can create many different coloration phenotypes merits investigation.

DISCLOSURE STATEMENT

The authors are not aware of any biases that might be perceived as affecting the objectivity of this review.

ACKNOWLEDGMENTS

We thank C. Chaw, C. Grande, J. Gross, H. Hoekstra, M. Modrell, R. Parchem, E.J. Rehm, and A. VanHook for helpful comments. We also thank H. Hoekstra, S. Cary, and C. Steiner for providing the oldfield/beach mice images, R. Borowsky for supplying the cavefish images, and R. Roberts for providing the cichlid images. Thanks to K. Koenig for mounting and photographing some of the *Heliconius* butterflies used in this review and to Américo Bonkewitzz for providing the specimens of *Precis octavia*.

LITERATURE CITED

Albertson RC, Streelman JT, Kocher TD. 2003. Directional selection has shaped the oral jaws of Lake Malawi cichlid fishes. *Proc. Natl. Acad. Sci. USA* 100:5252–57

Andersson L, Georges M. 2004. Domestic-animal genomics: deciphering the genetics of complex traits. *Nat. Rev. Genet.* 5:202–12

Baião PC, Schreiber E, Parker PG. 2007. The genetic basis of the plumage polymorphism in red-footed boobies (*Sula sula*): a *melanocortin-1 receptor* (*MC1R*) analysis. *J. Hered.* 98:287–92

Barbato M, Bernard M, Borrelli L, Fiorito G. 2007. Body patterns in cephalopods: "Polyphenism" as a way of information exchange. *Pattern Recognit. Lett.* 28:1854–64

Barrett RD, Schluter D. 2007. Adaptation from standing genetic variation. *Trends Ecol. Evol.* 23:38-44

Bennett DC, Lamoreux ML. 2003. The color loci of mice—a genetic century. *Pigment Cell Res.* 16:333–44

Brown TM, Cho SY, Evans CL, Park S, Pimprale SS, Bryson PK. 2001. A single gene (*yes*) controls pigmentation of eyes and scales in *Heliothis virescens*. *J. Insect Sci.* 1:1

Cain AJ, Sheppard PM. 1954. Natural selection in Cepaea. *Genetics* 39:89–116

Camp E, Lardelli M. 2001. Tyrosinase gene expression in zebrafish embryos. *Dev. Genes Evol.* 211:150–53

Carbone MA, Llopart A, de Angelis M, Coyne JA, Mackay TF. 2005. Quantitative trait loci affecting the difference in pigmentation between *Drosophila yakuba* and *D. santomea*. *Genetics* 171:211–25

Caro T. 2005. The adaptive significance of coloration in mammals. *BioScience* 55:125–36

Clarke CA, Sheppard PM. 1959. The genetics of *Papilio dardanus*, Brown. I. Race *cenea* from South Africa. *Genetics* 44:1347–58

Clarke CA, Sheppard PM. 1960a. The genetics of *Papilio dardanus*, Brown. II. Races *dardanus*, *polytrophus*, *meseres*, and *tibullus*. *Genetics* 45:439–57

Clarke CA, Sheppard PM. 1960b. The genetics of *Papilio dardanus*, Brown. III. Race *antinorii* from Abyssinia and race *meriones* from Madagascar. *Genetics* 45:683–98

Colosimo PF, Hosemann KE, Balabhadra S, Villarreal G Jr, Dickson M, et al. 2005. Widespread parallel evolution in sticklebacks by repeated fixation of Ectodysplasin alleles. *Science* 307:1928–33

Colosimo PF, Peichel CL, Nereng K, Blackman BK, Shapiro MD, et al. 2004. The genetic architecture of parallel armor plate reduction in threespine sticklebacks. *PLoS Biol.* 2:E109

Culver DC. 1982. *Cave Life*. Cambridge, MA: Harvard Univ. Press

Curtis JT. 2002. A blond coat color variation in meadow vole (*Microtus pennsylvanicus*). *J. Hered.* 93:209–10

Doucet SM, Shawkey MD, Rathburn MK, Mays HL Jr, Montgomerie R. 2004. Concordant evolution of plumage colour, feather microstructure and a melanocortin receptor gene between mainland and island populations of a fairy-wren. *Proc. Biol. Sci.* 271:1663–70

Eizirik E, Yuhki N, Johnson WE, Menotti-Raymond M, Hannah SS, O'Brien SJ. 2003. Molecular genetics and evolution of melanism in the cat family. *Curr. Biol.* 13:448–53

Gompel N, Prud'homme B, Wittkopp PJ, Kassner VA, Carroll SB. 2005. Chance caught on the wing: *cis*-regulatory evolution and the origin of pigment patterns in *Drosophila*. *Nature* 433:481–87

Gratten J, Beraldi D, Lowder BV, McRae AF, Visscher PM, et al. 2007. Compelling evidence that a single nucleotide substitution in TYRP1 is responsible for coat-colour polymorphism in a free-living population of Soay sheep. *Proc. Biol. Sci.* 274:619–26

Hoekstra HE. 2006. Genetics, development and evolution of adaptive pigmentation in vertebrates. *Heredity* 97:222–34

Hoekstra HE, Coyne JA. 2007. The locus of evolution: evo devo and the genetics of adaptation. *Evol. Int. J. Org. Evol.* 61:995–1016

Hoekstra HE, Hirschmann RJ, Bundey RA, Insel PA, Crossland JP. 2006. A single amino acid mutation contributes to adaptive beach mouse color pattern. *Science* 313:101–4

Hoekstra HE, Nachman MW. 2003. Different genes underlie adaptive melanism in different populations of rock pocket mice. *Mol. Ecol.* 12:1185–94

Hosemann KE, Colosimo PF, Summers BR, Kingsley DM. 2004. A simple and efficient microinjection protocol for making transgenic sticklebacks. *Behaviour* 141:1345–55

Houde AE, Endler JA. 1990. Correlated evolution of female mating preferences and male color patterns in the guppy *Poecilia reticulata*. *Science* 248:1405–8

Ito F, Hashim R, Huei YS, Kaufmann E, Akino T, Billen J. 2004. Spectacular Batesian mimicry in ants. *Naturwissenschaften* 91:481–84

Jeong S, Rokas A, Carroll SB. 2006. Regulation of body pigmentation by the Abdominal-B Hox protein and its gain and loss in *Drosophila* evolution. *Cell* 125:1387–99

Jiggins CD, Mavarez J, Beltran M, McMillan WO, Johnston JS, Bermingham E. 2005. A genetic linkage map of the mimetic butterfly *Heliconius melpomene*. *Genetics* 171:557–70

Jones JS, Leith BH, Rawlings P. 1977. Polymorphism in Cepaea: a problem with too many solutions? *Annu. Rev. Ecol. Syst.* 8:109–43

Joron M, Jiggins CD, Papanicolaou A, McMillan WO. 2006a. Heliconius wing patterns: an evo-devo model for understanding phenotypic diversity. *Heredity* 97:157–67

Joron M, Papa R, Beltran M, Chamberlain N, Mavarez J, et al. 2006b. A conserved supergene locus controls colour pattern diversity in *Heliconius* butterflies. *PLoS Biol.* 4:e303

Kapan DD, Flanagan NS, Tobler A, Papa R, Reed RD, et al. 2006. Localization of Müllerian mimicry genes on a dense linkage map of *Heliconius erato*. *Genetics* 173:735–57

Kelsh RN. 2004. Genetics and evolution of pigment patterns in fish. *Pigment Cell Res.* 17:326–36

Kelsh RN, Brand M, Jiang YJ, Heisenberg CP, Lin S, et al. 1996. Zebrafish pigmentation mutations and the processes of neural crest development. *Development* 123:369–89

Kopp A, Duncan I, Godt D, Carroll SB. 2000. Genetic control and evolution of sexually dimorphic characters in *Drosophila*. *Nature* 408:553–59

Kopp A, Graze RM, Xu S, Carroll SB, Nuzhdin SV. 2003. Quantitative trait loci responsible for variation in sexually dimorphic traits in *Drosophila melanogaster*. *Genetics* 163:771–87

Kronforst MR, Kapan DD, Gilbert LE. 2006. Parallel genetic architecture of parallel adaptive radiations in mimetic *Heliconius* butterflies. *Genetics* 174:535–39

Lalueza-Fox C, Römpler H, Caramelli D, Stäubert C, Catalano G, et al. 2007. A melanocortin 1 receptor allele suggests varying pigmentation among Neanderthals. *Science* 318:1453–55

Investigated the regulation of *yellow* in *D. melanogaster* and *D. biarmipes* and the involvement of *yellow* in a pigmented wingspot.

MacDougall-Shackleton EA, Blanchard L, Igdoura SA, Gibbs HL. 2003. Unmelanized plumage patterns in Old World leaf warblers do not correspond to sequence variation at the melanocortin-1 receptor locus (MC1R). *Mol. Biol. Evol.* 20:1675–81

Mellgren EM, Johnson SL. 2002. The evolution of morphological complexity in zebrafish stripes. *Trends Genet.* 18:128–34

Miller CT, Beleza S, Pollen AA, Schluter D, Kittles RA, et al. 2007. *cis*-regulatory changes in Kit ligand expression and parallel evolution of pigmentation in sticklebacks and humans. *Cell* 131:1179–89

Mundy NI. 2005. A window on the genetics of evolution: MC1R and plumage colouration in birds. *Proc. Biol. Sci.* 272:1633–40

Mundy NI, Badcock NS, Hart T, Scribner K, Janssen K, Nadeau NJ. 2004. Conserved genetic basis of a quantitative plumage trait involved in mate choice. *Science* 303:1870–73

Mundy NI, Kelly J. 2003. Evolution of a pigmentation gene, the melanocortin-1 receptor, in primates. *Am. J. Phys. Anthropol.* 121:67–80

Nachman MW, Hoekstra HE, D'Agostino SL. 2003. The genetic basis of adaptive melanism in pocket mice. *Proc. Natl. Acad. Sci. USA* 100:5268–73

Parchem RJ, Perry MW, Patel NH. 2007. Patterns on the insect wing. *Curr. Opin. Genet. Dev.* 17:300–8

Parichy DM. 2006. Evolution of danio pigment pattern development. *Heredity* 97:200–10

Parichy DM, Johnson SL. 2001. Zebrafish hybrids suggest genetic mechanisms for pigment pattern diversification in Danio. *Dev. Genes Evol.* 211:319–28

Peichel CL, Nereng KS, Ohgi KA, Cole BL, Colosimo PF, et al. 2001. The genetic architecture of divergence between threespine stickleback species. *Nature* 414:901–5

Protas ME, Hersey C, Kochanek D, Zhou Y, Wilkens H, et al. 2006. Genetic analysis of cavefish reveals molecular convergence in the evolution of albinism. *Nat. Genet.* 38:107–11

Prud'homme B, Gompel N, Rokas A, Kassner VA, Williams TM, et al. 2006. Repeated morphological evolution through *cis*-regulatory changes in a pleiotropic gene. *Nature* 440:1050–53

Quigley IK, Manuel JL, Roberts RA, Nuckels RJ, Herrington ER, et al. 2005. Evolutionary diversification of pigment pattern in *Danio* fishes: differential *fms* dependence and stripe loss in *D. albolineatus*. *Development* 132:89–104

Quigley IK, Parichy DM. 2002. Pigment pattern formation in zebrafish: a model for developmental genetics and the evolution of form. *Microsc. Res. Tech.* 58:442–55

Reed RD, McMillan WO, Nagy LM. 2008. Gene expression underlying adaptive variation in *Heliconius* wing patterns: nonmodular regulation of overlapping cinnabar and vermilion prepatterns. *Proc. Biol. Sci.* 275:37–45

Rosenblum EB, Hoekstra HE, Nachman MW. 2004. Adaptive reptile color variation and the evolution of the *Mc1r* gene. *Evol. Int. J. Org. Evol.* 58:1794–808

Roulin A. 2004. The evolution, maintenance and adaptive function of genetic colour polymorphism in birds. *Biol. Rev. Camb. Philos. Soc.* 79:815–48

Russell ES. 1985. A history of mouse genetics. *Annu. Rev. Genet.* 19:1–28

Salzburger W, Braasch I, Meyer A. 2007. Adaptive sequence evolution in a color gene involved in the formation of the characteristic egg-dummies of male haplochromine cichlid fishes. *BMC Biol.* 5:51

Schmutz SM, Berryere TG. 2007. Genes affecting coat colour and pattern in domestic dogs: a review. *Anim. Genet.* 38:539–49

Shapiro MD, Marks ME, Peichel CL, Blackman BK, Nereng KS, et al. 2004. Genetic and developmental basis of evolutionary pelvic reduction in threespine sticklebacks. *Nature* 428:717–23

Steiner CC, Weber JN, Hoekstra HE. 2007. Adaptive variation in beach mice produced by two interacting pigmentation genes. *PLoS Biol.* 5:e219

Streelman JT, Albertson RC, Kocher TD. 2003. Genome mapping of the orange blotch colour pattern in cichlid fishes. *Mol. Ecol.* 12:2465–71

Suzuki Y, Nijhout HF. 2006. Evolution of a polyphenism by genetic accommodation. *Science* 311:650–52

Suzuki Y, Nijhout HF. 2008. Genetic basis of adaptive evolution of a polyphenism by genetic accommodation. *J. Evol. Biol.* 21:57–66

Used high-resolution mapping to identify a gene involved in gill pigmentation variation in different populations of sticklebacks.

The authors performed a quantitative trait and candidate gene analysis of a polygenic pigmentation trait in the oldfield mice.

Investigated a pigmentation trait that changes with the environment by carrying out artificial-selection experiments in a related species.

Theron E, Hawkins K, Bermingham E, Ricklefs RE, Mundy NI. 2001. The molecular basis of an avian plumage polymorphism in the wild: A melanocortin-1-receptor point mutation is perfectly associated with the melanic plumage morph of the bananaquit, *Coereba flaveola*. *Curr. Biol.* 11:550–57

Tobler A, Kapan D, Flanagan NS, Gonzalez C, Peterson E, et al. 2005. First-generation linkage map of the warningly colored butterfly *Heliconius erato*. *Heredity* 94:408–17

Trapezov OV. 1997. Black crystal: a novel color mutant in the American mink (*Mustela vision Schreber*). *J. Hered.* 88:164–66

Vage DI, Fuglei E, Snipstad K, Beheim J, Landsem VM, Klungland H. 2005. Two cysteine substitutions in the MC1R generate the blue variant of the arctic fox (*Alopex lagopus*) and prevent expression of the white winter coat. *Peptides* 26:1814–17

Wittkopp PJ, Carroll SB, Kopp A. 2003a. Evolution in black and white: genetic control of pigment patterns in *Drosophila*. *Trends Genet.* 19:495–504

Wittkopp PJ, Williams BL, Selegue JE, Carroll SB. 2003b. *Drosophila* pigmentation evolution: divergent genotypes underlying convergent phenotypes. *Proc. Natl. Acad. Sci. USA* 100:1808–13

Wlasiuk G, Nachman MW. 2007. The genetics of adaptive coat color in gophers: Coding variation at Mc1r is not responsible for dorsal color differences. *J. Hered.* 98:567–74

Yamamoto Y, Stock DW, Jeffery WR. 2004. Hedgehog signalling controls eye degeneration in blind cavefish. *Nature* 431:844–47

Yeh SD, Liou SR, True JR. 2006. Genetics of divergence in male wing pigmentation and courtship behavior between *Drosophila elegans* and *D. gunungcola*. *Heredity* 96:383–95

Polar Targeting and Endocytic Recycling in Auxin-Dependent Plant Development

Jürgen Kleine-Vehn and Jiří Friml

Department of Plant Systems Biology, VIB, and Department of Molecular Genetics, Ghent University, 9052 Ghent, Belgium; email: jiri.friml@psb.ugent.be

Annu. Rev. Cell Dev. Biol. 2008. 24:447–73

The *Annual Review of Cell and Developmental Biology* is online at cellbio.annualreviews.org

This article's doi:
10.1146/annurev.cellbio.24.110707.175254

Key Words

trafficking, endocytosis, polar auxin transport, PIN proteins

Abstract

Plant development is characterized by a profound phenotypic plasticity that often involves redefining of the developmental fate and polarity of cells within differentiated tissues. The plant hormone auxin and its directional intercellular transport play a major role in these processes because they provide positional information and link cell polarity with tissue patterning. This plant-specific mechanism of transport-dependent auxin gradients depends on subcellular dynamics of auxin transport components, in particular on endocytic recycling and polar targeting. Recent insights into these cellular processes in plants have revealed important parallels to yeast and animal systems, including clathrin-dependent endocytosis, retromer function, and transcytosis, but have also emphasized unique features of plant cells such as diversity of polar targeting pathways; integration of environmental signals into subcellular trafficking; and the link between endocytosis, cell polarity, and cell fate specification. We review these advances and focus on the translation of the subcellular dynamics to the regulation of whole-plant development.

Contents

Polar auxin transport: the directional transport of the plant hormone auxin from cell to cell

DEVELOPMENTAL INTRODUCTION

Animals and plants evolved basic biological differences that characterize their survival strategies. Animals developed elaborate sensory and locomotory capacities that enable complex behavioral responses, such as the fight-or-flight response, to overcome environmental stress. In contrast, during their evolution plants emphasized increased physiological tolerance and phenotypic plasticity. These different life strategies are also adequately reflected in the various ways in which animals and plants establish their body architecture. Whereas during embryogenesis animals are already defining their adult shape to a large extent, in plants this early developmental phase just sketches a basic body plan, and the final shape of a plant will be largely defined by an elaborate postembryonic development (Weigel & Jürgens 2002). To achieve this developmental plasticity, plants maintain permanent populations of stem cells (meristems) at the growing root and shoot apices and are able to redefine the developmental programs as well as the polarity of already specified tissues. Thus, plants can sustain and regulate their growth rate, can postembryonically form new organs, and possess a high capacity for tissue regeneration (Steeves & Sussex 1989, Weigel & Jürgens 2002). Different animal species also retain these capabilities to some extent; however, plants are far superior in utilizing these mechanisms for individually shaping their body according to the demands of the environment. The plant signaling molecule auxin determines many aspects of this flexible plant development. Auxin acts as a prominent signal, providing, by its local accumulation in selected cells, a spatial and temporal reference for changes in the developmental program (Reinhardt et al. 2000, Friml 2003, Leyser 2006, Esmon et al. 2006, Tanaka et al. 2006, Dubrovsky et al. 2008). Auxin is distributed through tissues by a directional cell-to-cell transport system, termed polar auxin transport, that depends on specific auxin carrier proteins (**Figure 1**) (Benjamins et al. 2005, Blakeslee et al. 2005, Kramer & Bennett 2006, Vieten et al. 2007). Auxin efflux carriers of the PIN-FORMED (PIN) family (Gälweiler et al. 1998, Luschnig et al. 1998, Chen et al. 1998, Utsono et al. 1998, Petrášek et al. 2006) show a polar subcellular localization that correlates with and determines the

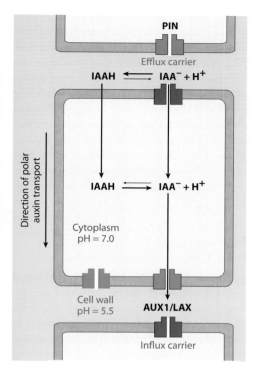

PIN
Efflux carrier

IAAH $\rightleftharpoons$ IAA$^-$ + H$^+$

IAAH $\rightleftharpoons$ IAA$^-$ + H$^+$

Direction of polar auxin transport

Cytoplasm
pH = 7.0

Cell wall
pH = 5.5

AUX1/LAX
Influx carrier

Figure 1

The chemiosmotic hypothesis: far ahead of its time! Rubery & Sheldrake postulated in the mid-1970s the so-called chemiosmotic hypothesis for directional intercellular auxin movement (Rubery & Sheldrake 1974 and, independently, Raven 1975). Accordingly, the auxin indole acetic acid (IAAH) is largely protonated at the lower pH of the cell wall and can pass through the plasma membrane into the cell. In the higher-pH cytosol, part of the IAAH is deprotonated, and the resulting charged IAA$^-$ is largely membrane impermeable and requires transporter activity to exit the cell. The localization of the PIN-FORMED (PIN) auxin efflux carrier at the plasma membrane determines the auxin exit site from an individual cell. Coordinated polar localization of PINs in a given tissue hence determines the direction of cell-to-cell auxin transport. AUX1/LAX1 denotes auxin influx carriers AUXIN RESISTANT1/LIKE AUX1.

direction of auxin flow through tissues (Friml et al. 2004, Wiśniewska et al. 2006). In plants, polarities of tissue and of individual cells are closely connected by the flow of auxin (Sauer et al. 2006), and the cell biological processes depending on vesicle trafficking and polar targeting have an immediate developmental

output related to auxin-mediated signaling. At the level of polar auxin transport, many developmental and environmental signals are integrated. By rearranging the subcellular localization of PIN auxin efflux carriers, such signals influence auxin-dependent patterning and contribute substantially to the adaptive and flexible nature of plant development.

Our aim is to review recent advances on subcellular trafficking and polar targeting in plants and to highlight links with physiology and development. A special focus is given to auxin-dependent regulation of development because this area is intimately linked to endocytic recycling and polar targeting. Most of these concepts were formulated on the basis of studies in the model plant *Arabidopsis thaliana*; nonetheless, they seem to apply to a large extent to higher plants in general.

POLAR TARGETING

The establishment and maintenance of cell polarity are central themes of developmental and cell biology because individual cell polarities, transmitted by cell divisions, are translated into tissue and organ polarity and, ultimately, shape. In addition, cell polarity plays a key role in directional signaling and intercellular communication.

At the level of individual cells, polarity is typically reflected by the asymmetric distribution of intracellular components that can form functionally and/or morphologically distinct domains (Bonifacino & Lippincott-Schwartz 2003). Mechanisms for generating or maintaining cell polarity have been extensively studied in different model organisms, such as worms, flies, mammals, and yeasts (e.g., Knoblich 2000, Irazoqui & Lew 2004, Margolis & Borg 2005, Nance 2005). Animal epithelial cells are a favorite model system because their plasma membrane harbors two distinct domains that are separated by tight junctions: an apical domain facing the lumen and a basolateral domain (Mostov et al. 2003, Janssens & Chavrier 2004). These protein-based barriers in the membrane prevent lateral diffusion of proteins and lipids

Recycling: membranes and other molecules recycle from intracellular endocytic compartments back to the plasma membrane

Tight junctions: anchored protein complexes forming a physical barrier between polar domains; limit lateral diffusion and are involved in polarity establishment and maintenance in animal epithelial cells

trans-Golgi network (TGN): the main sorting compartment of the secretory pathway in eukaryotic cells; may act as an early-endosomal compartment in plants

between the two distinct polar domains, maintaining the distribution of various polar-competent proteins. Researchers have identified numerous polar cargos that reside in a cell-line-specific manner preferentially at the apical and/or basolateral plasma membranes in polarized epithelial cells. Apical and basolateral components are recruited differentially by the targeted delivery of membrane and secretory proteins to these domains as a result of three processes. (*a*) Newly synthesized proteins are sorted in the trans-Golgi network (TGN) into carrier vesicles that specifically deliver them to the apical surface or the basolateral surface. (*b*) Some proteins are selectively retained at the plasma membrane. (*c*) Proteins that are not retained are rapidly endocytosed and either recycled back through recycling endosomes or, alternatively, delivered to a different, polar plasma membrane domain by a process called transcytosis (Rodriguez-Boulan et al. 2005).

Passengers and Destinations: Polar Cargos and Polar Domains

Even though in no other kingdom is the relation between individual cell polarity and macroscopic patterning as prominent as in plants, knowledge on cell polarity and mechanisms of targeted cargo delivery is still lacking in plants. Most of our understanding on polar targeting has been gained by study of the polar delivery of auxin efflux carriers from the PIN family (**Figure 2**). PIN proteins have emerged in recent years from genetic studies in *A. thaliana* as key regulators of a plethora of auxin-mediated developmental processes, including axis formation in embryogenesis (Friml et al. 2003b), postembryonic organogenesis (Okada et al. 1991, Benková et al. 2003, Reinhardt et al. 2003, Heisler et al. 2005), root meristem maintenance (Friml et al. 2002a, Blilou et al. 2005), vascular tissue differentiation and regeneration (Gälweiler et al. 1998, Sauer et al. 2006, Scarpella et al. 2006), and tropic growth (Luschnig et al. 1998, Friml et al. 2002b).

PIN proteins act as mediators of the auxin efflux from cells (Petrášek et al. 2006) and have different subcellular distributions—including apolar, basal, apical, and lateral plasma membrane localizations—depending on the PIN protein as well as the cell type (Wiśniewska et al. 2006). The most typical are basal (root tip–facing) localization of the PIN1 protein in the inner cells of both shoots and roots, apical (shoot apex–facing) localization of PIN2 in the

Polar distribution of PINs

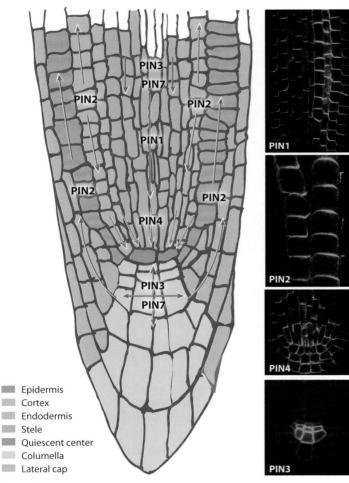

Epidermis
Cortex
Endodermis
Stele
Quiescent center
Columella
Lateral cap

Figure 2

Patterns of PIN protein localization in the *Arabidopsis* root tip. Schematic and immunolocalizations of PIN proteins in the *Arabidopsis* root tip. Arrows indicate polar PIN localization at the plasma membrane, illustrating cell type–dependent decisions in the PIN polar localization. Note the differential PIN2 targeting in the epidermis (apical) and young cortex (basal) cells.

root epidermis and lateral root cap cells, and lateral localization of PIN3 at the inner side of shoot endodermis cells (Gälweiler et al. 1998; Müller et al. 1998; Friml et al. 2002b, 2003a).

Other components of auxin transport, such as the auxin influx carrier AUXIN RESISTANT1/LIKE AUX1 (AUX1/LAX) (Bennett et al. 1996, Yang et al. 2006, Swarup et al. 2008) and multiple drug resistance/P-glycoprotein (MDR/PGP) transporters (Geisler et al. 2005, Terasaka et al. 2005), are also localized in a polar manner in some cells while being symmetrically localized in most cells (Mravec et al. 2008). For example, AUX1 localizes to the apical side of protophloem cells opposite to PIN1 or to the same side as PIN1 in the shoot apical meristem (Swarup et al. 2001, Reinhardt et al. 2003). In contrast, PGP4 has a basal or an apical localization in root epidermal cells (Terasaka et al. 2005).

In addition to components of the auxin transport, other polar cargos in plants, including transporters for boron (BOR1 and BOR4) and for silicon in rice (LSI1 and LSI2), have been identified. Such cargos are localized at either the inner or the outer lateral sides of cells, as well as the regulator of anisotropic expansion, COBRA, which is similarly polarly targeted to both longitudinal cell sides (Roudier et al. 2005; Takano et al. 2005; Ma et al. 2006, 2007; Miwa et al. 2007). The PLEIOTROPIC DRUG RESISTENCE (PDR)-type transporter for the auxin-like compounds PIS1/PDR9 resides at the outer lateral side of root epidermis cells. The lateral cargo POLAR AUXIN TRANSPORT INHIBITOR-SENSITIVE1 (PIS1), the basal cargo PIN1, and the apical cargo PIN2 have been simultaneously visualized in the same cells, highlighting that plant cells are able to maintain at least three polar domains within a single cell (Růžička et al. 2008). Future studies will address whether epidermal root cells are potent to maintain, besides the apical, basal, and outer lateral domains, an additional inner lateral polar domain. Nonetheless, although apical-basal targeting in plants and apical-basolateral delivery in animals can

reflect a comparable polar competence among the divergent kingdoms, the simultaneous delivery of lateral cargos hints at a more complex situation for cell polarity in plant cells that may once again stress the flexibility and enormous importance of cell polarity regulation in plants (**Figure 3**).

Endocytosis: the uptake of material into a cell by the formation of a membrane-bound vesicle

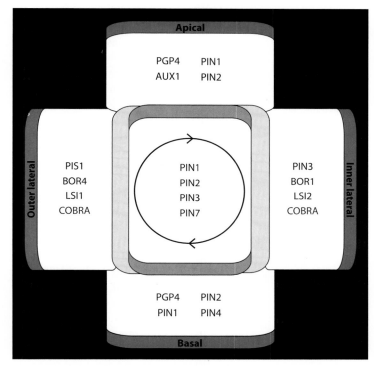

Figure 3

The black box of plant polarity. A schematic representation of various polar cargos in plant cells. Plants are competent to deliver cargos to apical, basal, inner, and outer polar domains. Apical cargos include PGP4 (root epidermis cells), AUX1 (root protophloem cells), PIN1 (epidermal cells of shoot apex and embryonal protoderm cells), and PIN2 (root epidermis and older cortex cells). Basal cargos encompass PGP4 (root epidermis cells), PIN1 (e.g., root stele), PIN2 (young cortex cells), and PIN4 (in the proximal part of the root meristem). Outer lateral cargos are represented by, e.g., PIS1 (root epidermis), BOR4 (root epidermis), LSI1 (root exodermis and endodermis cells), and COBRA (root epidermis). Inner lateral polarity can be defined by PIN3 (shoot endodermis and root pericycle), BOR1 (root pericycle cells), LSI2 (root exodermis and endodermis cells), and COBRA (root epidermis). Moreover, several PIN cargos undergo rapid polarity alterations (depicted in the *middle*), including the establishment of basal localization of PIN1 during embryogenesis or lateral root development, an apical-to-basal polarity shift of PIN7 during embryogenesis in suspensor cells, a basal-to-apical shift in upper cortex cells of PIN2, and dynamic relocation of PIN3 to the bottom sides of root cap cells after gravity stimulation.

Tickets to Go or to Stay: Polar Targeting Signals

Transcytosis: the dynamic translocation of the same molecules from one distinct plasma membrane domain to another via recycling endosomes

Basal polarity: polarity of the lower cell side, the polar plasma membrane domain that faces the root apex

Apical polarity: polarity of the upper cell side, the polar plasma membrane domain that faces the shoot apex

Inner lateral polarity: polarity of the inner periclinal cell side, which points away from the body surface

Outer lateral polarity: polarity of the outer periclinal cell side, which points to the body surface

In animal systems, polar cargo proteins carry signals that determine their residence at different polar domains. These signals may be a combination of plasma membrane retention, internalization, and polar sorting signals (Dugani & Klip 2005, Rodriguez-Boulan et al. 2005). In plants, different polar cargos such as PIN1, PIN2, and PIS1 localize to different polar destinations in the same cell type, suggesting polarity determinants in the protein sequence itself. Moreover, an insertion of green fluorescent protein (GFP) at a specific position within the middle hydrophilic loop causes PIN1 localization to shift to the opposite side of the cell compared with wild-type PIN1 (Wiśniewska et al. 2006). These results demonstrate the presence of polarity signals in the sequence of polar cargos, but detailed insight is still lacking. Polarity signals probably decide to recruit PINs to the distinct apical and basal targeting machineries that are related to phosphorylation sides, because the Ser/Thr protein kinase PINOID (PID) (Friml et al. 2004) as well as the protein phosphatase 2A (PP2A) (Michniewicz et al. 2007) act on PIN phosphorylation and play a decisive role in the apical-versus-basal targeting of PIN proteins. Loss of the PID function causes an apical-to-basal shift in the PIN polarity corresponding with defects in embryo and shoot organogenesis (Christensen et al. 2000, Benjamins et al. 2001, Friml et al. 2004). Accordingly, PID gain of function results in an opposite basal-to-apical PIN polarity shift, leading to auxin depletion from the root meristem and collapse of the root growth (Friml et al. 2004). Similar phenotypes, including the basal-to-apical shift of PIN polarity, can be observed in the loss-of-function mutants of the A regulatory subunits of PP2A (Michniewicz et al. 2007). Importantly, PID directly phosphorylates the hydrophilic loop of PIN proteins, and PP2A antagonizes this action (Michniewicz et al. 2007).

A possible scenario may be that phosphorylated PIN proteins are preferentially recruited into the apical pathway, whereas dephosphorylated PINs become a substrate of the basal targeting pathway (**Figure 4**). This model incorporates important features of mammalian epithelial cells, in which cargos are phosphorylated to influence their polar delivery (Casanova et al. 1990). Importantly, phosphorylation-dependent PIN targeting provides a means for any signaling pathway upstream of PID and PP2A activities to modulate PIN polar targeting and thus directional auxin fluxes. Different relative expression levels of PID and PP2A in various cell types in combination with divergent

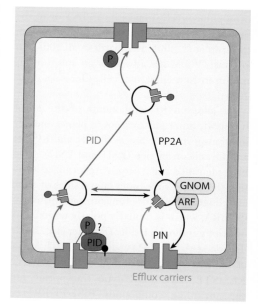

Figure 4

Contribution of PIN-FORMED (PIN) phosphorylation to the decision on the PIN polar distribution. PINOID (PID)-dependent phosphorylation of PIN proteins may affect affinity to distinct apical and basal targeting pathways. An increase in PID kinase or a decrease in protein phosphatase 2A (PP2A) activities leads to a basal-to-apical PIN polarity shift. On the contrary, increased PP2A activity counteracts the PID effect and leads to preferential GNOM-dependent basal PIN targeting. The place of PID and PP2A action is not entirely clear, but PID and PP2A are also partially associated with the plasma membrane. ARF denotes adenosyl ribosylation factor.

phosphorylation sites (some of which would be phosphorylated more or less efficiently) would explain how both PIN-specific and cell type–specific signals are integrated to determine the polar localization of the given PIN protein into a given cell type. The regulation of PID kinase may also be connected with phospholipid signaling. The plant 3-phosphoinositide-dependent kinase 1 (PDK1) binds PID in vitro and increases PID kinase activity (Zegzouti et al. 2006). The involvement of phosphorylation events for the polar delivery of other cargos besides PINs has not been thoroughly addressed. Outer lateral delivery of PIS1 seems to occur independently of the PID activity, but comparable information for other polar cargos is missing.

Extensive work in the coming years is expected to focus on the identification and thorough characterization of polar targeting signals for different polar cargos in plants. The other crucial issues that are completely unknown in plants concern where and how the polar targeting signals are recognized as well as where and how the polar cargos are sorted.

Staying at the Station: Retention at the Polar Domains

Despite the pronounced importance of polar localization of proteins in plant cells for plant development, mechanisms for this phenomenon are still ill defined. So far no indications exist for anything analogical to tight junctions, and we lack even fundamental knowledge of how polar-competent cargos are kept in their polar domains.

Cytoskeleton- and membrane sterol–dependent constitutive endocytosis and targeted recycling may be involved in maintaining the localization of proteins localized in their polar domains. All these cellular components and processes are required for localization of different cargos. Both basal PIN1 localization and even more apical AUX1 localization are sensitive to the disruption of the actin cytoskeleton, leading to internalization and loss of polar localization (Kleine-Vehn

et al. 2006). In contrast, disruption of microtubules affects only indirectly the localization of AUX1 and PIN proteins that is observed only when the overall cell morphology is altered (Kleine-Vehn et al. 2006). In contrast, intact microtubules are required to maintain the outer lateral localization of PIS1; following its disruption, PIS1 is found predominantly at apical and basal positions (Růžička et al. 2008).

Polar localization of PIN and AUX1 proteins as well as auxin signaling depend on the sterol composition of plasma membranes (Souter et al. 2002, Grebe et al. 2003, Willemsen et al. 2003, Kleine-Vehn et al. 2006). *Arabidopsis* plantlets defective in the *STEROL METHYLTRANSFERASE1* (*SMT1*) gene, which is involved in sterol biosynthesis and affects membrane sterol composition, have cell polarity defects, including impaired polar localization of PIN proteins and AUX1 (Willemsen et al. 2003, Kleine-Vehn et al. 2006). Furthermore, sterols and PIN proteins have overlapping subcellular trafficking pathways (Grebe et al. 2003). Detergent-resistant, sterol-enriched plasma membrane microdomains, sometimes called lipid rafts, are important for various types of plasma membrane–based signaling processes and are present in higher plants as well (reviewed in Bhat & Panstruga 2005). There are indications that PIN and PGP proteins are directly associated with these structures (Titapiwatanakun et al. 2008), but what the functional relevance could be of such associations remains to be established.

In conclusion, despite the obvious requirements of cytoskeleton and sterol composition for polar localization of various cargos, it is still unclear whether or eventually in which cases they are involved in keeping cargos at their polar positions or whether they play a role in the polar delivery of these proteins to the plasma membrane.

How to Get There: Polar Targeting Pathways

The existence of diverse polar cargos with various polar targeting signals implies a diversified

Sterol: plant sterols are amphiphilic molecules and vital constituents of all membranes, including the plasma membrane

Adenosyl
ribosylation factor
(ARF): a class of small
GTPases; a regulator
of clathrin- and
COPI-dependent
vesicle budding

Guanine nucleotide
exchange factor
(GEF): induces
GDP-to-GTP
exchange and hence
the activation of small
GTPases

Brefeldin A (BFA): a
specific inhibitor of
some ARF GEFs

network of distinct polar targeting pathways. Indeed, for example, AUX1 and PIN1 polar delivery occurs by two distinct targeting machineries with different molecular requirements and different sensitivities to inhibitors of cellular processes (Dharmasiri et al. 2006, Kleine-Vehn et al. 2006).

An important factor for the delivery of PIN proteins to the plasma membrane is an endosomal regulator of the vesicle budding, GNOM, which encodes a guanine nucleotide exchange factor for adenosyl ribosylation factors (ARF GEF) (Shevell et al. 1994; Geldner et al. 2001, 2003). In *gnom* (also designated *emb30*) mutant embryos, the coordinated polar localization of PIN1 is impaired (Steinmann et al. 1999), seemingly the result of a failure to establish the initial basal localization of PIN1 at the globular stage (Kleine-Vehn et al. 2008a). Also, in the postembryonic roots, GNOM function seems to be crucial for basal targeting, whereas apical localization of PINs or AUX1 is unaffected in *gnom* mutants (Kleine-Vehn et al. 2006, 2008a). Collectively, these studies demonstrate that apical cargos utilize a targeting pathway that is molecularly distinct from that used by basally localized PIN proteins (Kleine-Vehn et al. 2006, 2008a). In addition, outer lateral PIS1 targeting appears to differ fundamentally from apical and basal pathways because PIS1 polar localization does not involve any known molecular components of apical/basal targeting, such as GNOM or PINOID (Růžička et al. 2008). Although apical and basal PIN targeting appears to be interconnected and, thus, to be used alternatively by PIN proteins, the relation between apical/basal and outer lateral polar targeting needs to be unraveled.

In summary, genetic and pharmacological interference with different cellular processes as well as the simultaneous localization of cargos to the apical, basal, and outer lateral domains in single cells strongly suggest that there are at least three distinct polar targeting mechanisms in plants. However, molecular insight into these pathways remains very limited.

ENDOCYTIC RECYCLING IN PLANT CELLS

The Back and Forth: Constitutive Endocytic Recycling of Plasma Membrane Proteins

The internalization of proteins from the plasma membrane is a critical event for all eukaryotic cells. Whereas many internalized molecules are degraded in the lysosomal/vacuolar pathway, other cell surface proteins and molecules undergo sequential rounds of recycling back to the plasma membrane. Eukaryotic cells possess the remarkable ability to turn over the entire plasma membrane on an hourly basis (Tuvim et al. 2001). As such, endocytic recycling is a key for the regulation of the cell surface identity and contributes to rapid cellular responses to intrinsic and extrinsic cues. Regarding the fundamental importance of endocytic recycling, various integral plasma membrane proteins, such as signaling components and transporters, appear to display recycling events to the plasma membrane in plants.

Pharmacological inhibitors have been valuable tools for unraveling the internalization of plant proteins to endosomal compartments and subsequent recycling back to the plasma membrane (Carter et al. 2004). The fungal toxin brefeldin A (BFA) interferes with various vesicle trafficking processes in cells and specifically targets ARF GEFs. Cytosolic GDP-bound ARF proteins are inactive and become recruited to the target membrane by ARF GEF–dependent GDP-to-GTP exchange. ARF proteins play an important role in the formation of vesicle coats required for their budding and cargo selection in different subcellular compartments. BFA is a noncompetitive inhibitor that stabilizes ARF/ARF GEF intermediates and freezes both proteins inactively at the place of action (reviewed by Donaldson & Jackson 2000). In cultured cells of tobacco, BFA interferes with ARF GEF–dependent endoplasmic reticulum (ER)-to-Golgi trafficking, leading to ER-Golgi hybrids (Ritzenthaler et al. 2002). In contrast, in *Arabidopsis*, this process is catalyzed by the

BFA-resistant ARF GEF GNOM-LIKE1 (GNL1) (Richter et al. 2007). The prominent BFA target in *Arabidopsis* is the endosomal ARF GEF GNOM, which mediates mainly the endosomal recycling to the plasma membrane, whereas endocytosis from the plasma membrane seems to remain operational (Geldner et al. 2003). By this differential effect of BFA on exocytosis and endocytosis in *Arabidopsis*, plasma membrane proteins are internally accumulated into so-called BFA compartments (Geldner et al. 2001, 2003).

In *Arabidopsis* seedlings, following BFA treatments PIN1 rapidly disappears from the plasma membrane and simultaneously aggregates in BFA compartments (Steinmann et al. 1999). This process is fully reversible because BFA removal causes PIN proteins to relocalize to their original position at the plasma membrane (Geldner et al. 2001). Both the internalization and the recovery after washout also occur in the presence of protein synthesis inhibitors, indicating that they are not de novo–synthesized proteins but involve continuous endocytosis and recycling of the same PIN molecules (Geldner et al. 2001). The utilization of a green-to-red photoconvertible fluorescent reporter (EosFP) directly visualizes the internalization of PIN proteins and their subsequent recycling to the plasma membrane (Dhonukshe et al. 2007a). These findings indicate an operational constitutive cycling mechanism in plant cells.

BFA-sensitive subcellular dynamics have been demonstrated for a number of plasma membrane proteins, including, for instance, the aquaporin PIP2, the brassinosteroid receptor BRI1, the plasma membrane H^+-ATPase, the stress-responsive plasma membrane protein Lti6a, and the auxin influx carrier AUX1 (Geldner et al. 2001; Grebe et al. 2002, 2003; Russinova et al. 2004; Paciorek et al. 2005). This BFA sensitivity may reflect a PIN-like mechanism of constitutive endocytosis and recycling, as is seemingly the case for many intrinsic plasma membrane proteins, and has been demonstrated for BRI1, whose endocytic recycling rate may be regulated by het-

erodimerization with the associated kinase BAK1 (Russinova et al. 2004). However, endocytic recycling is not necessarily accompanied with BFA-sensitive trafficking, as exemplified by both polar and nonpolar delivery of AUX1 to the plasma membrane that is largely insensitive to BFA (Kleine-Vehn et al. 2006). Another example for a recycling plasma membrane protein is the inwardly directed K^+ channel KAT1. The hormone abscisic acid, which controls ion transport and transpiration in plants under water stress, may trigger the selective endocytosis of the KAT1 in epidermal and guard cells, leading to changes in K^+ channel activities at the plasma membrane. Abscisic acid treatment sequesters the K^+ channel within an endosomal membrane pool that recycles back to the plasma membrane within hours (Sutter et al. 2007).

Despite the mostly indirect evidence (based mainly on BFA-sensitive targeting), the number of plant proteins that constitutively recycle at different rates from and to the plasma membrane is constantly growing. In fact, it seems rather difficult to find an intrinsic plant plasma membrane protein that would not undergo BFA-sensitive or BFA-insensitive constitutive recycling. However, besides the fact that almost all plant plasma membrane proteins appear to recycle between the plasma membrane and some intracellular compartments, the mechanisms underlying their differential endocytosis and recycling are still not well characterized.

Getting Away: Endocytosis in Plant Cells

Endocytosis occurs at the cell surface and is characterized by membrane invagination and pinching off at the plasma membrane, ultimately leading to closed membrane vesicles in the cytoplasm. These mechanisms facilitate the absorption of material from the outside of the plasma membrane and have been studied mainly in animal cells. Several distinct pathways for endocytosis have been unraveled; among these are the relatively well-defined processes of macropinocytosis, clathrin-mediated endocytosis, and caveolae-mediated endocytosis

Exocytosis: the process by which materials in the vesicles are secreted from a cell when the vesicle membrane fuses with the plasma membrane

BFA compartment: BFA treatment–induced mixture of aggregated vesicles in *Arabidopsis* that consists of endosomal and TGN-derived structures in the core and that becomes surrounded by aggregating Golgi stacks

(Pelkmans & Helenius 2003, Cheng et al. 2006, Benmerah & Lamaze 2007). Macropinocytosis is a less specific invagination of the cell membrane, resulting in the pinching off of vesicles (Pelkmans & Helenius 2003). In contrast, clathrin-dependent endocytosis and caveolae-dependent endocytosis regulate receptor-mediated internalization of specific cargos (Benmerah & Lamaze 2007).

In plants, the existence of endocytosis has been regarded with skepticism, and there have been decades of controversial debates as to whether the high turgor of plant cells renders the plant plasma membrane unsuitable for invagination and subsequent internalization (Saxton & Breidenbach 1988, Gradmann & Robinson 1989). Experimental results have often settled the theoretical discussions: Electrondense as well as lipophilic tracers have been taken up into plant cells (Robinson & Hillmer 1990, Bolte et al. 2004), endocytic (clathrin-coated) vesicles have been detected at the ultrastructure level (reviewed in Holstein 2002, Paul & Frigerio 2007), and numerous proteins have been found to be internalized from the plasma membrane (Geldner et al. 2001; Paciorek et al. 2005; Takano et al. 2005; Dhonukshe et al. 2006, 2007a; Robatzek et al. 2006), even in high-turgor guard cells (Meckel et al. 2004). However, the underlying mechanism of endocytosis in plants has remained unclear until recently (Pérez-Gómez & Moore 2007). There were growing lines of evidence that the endocytosis mechanism involving the coat protein clathrin is operational in plant cells. The deciphering of several plant genomes revealed that homologs to mammalian proteins of the clathrin coat (e.g., clathrin heavy chain, clathrin light chain, adaptor protein (AP)2 subunits, and AP180) and downstream effectors (e.g., epsin, dynamin, auxilin, heat shock cognate 70, and synaptojanin) are encoded in plant genomes (Hirst & Robinson 1998, Holstein 2002, Paul & Frigerio 2007). Additionally, electron microscopy has detected different stages of clathrin-coated vesicle formation at plasma membranes of different plant species (reviewed in Holstein 2002, Paul & Frigerio

2007). Finally, genetic and pharmacological interference with clathrin-dependent processes in plants blocks internalization of PINs and other plasma membrane proteins (Dhonukshe et al. 2007a). Altogether, these studies have demonstrated operational clathrin-dependent endocytosis in plants and have identified the endogenous cargos of this process. Clathrin-dependent endocytosis seems to be remarkably evolutionarily conserved because mammalian cargos of this pathway, such as the transferrin receptor, are internalized by this mechanism in plant cells (Ortiz-Zapater et al. 2006). Moreover, because the internalization of all tested cargos, including general endocytic tracers, requires clathrin, clathrin-dependent endocytosis seems to constitute the predominant pathway for the internalization of numerous plasma membrane–resident proteins in plant cells.

It remains to be seen whether clathrin-independent pathways are operational in plant cells. Pathways for sterol-dependent, caveolae-mediated endocytosis are unlikely to exist because caveolae-like components have not been identified in plants. However, there are indications suggesting the involvement of sterols in endocytosis or endocytic recycling in plants. Polar PIN protein localization is affected in sterol biosynthesis mutants, and sterols notably share a common early-endocytic trafficking pathway with the PIN2 protein (Grebe et al. 2003, Willemsen et al. 2003). Moreover, the depletion of sterols from plant membranes leads to reduced endocytosis in plants (Kleine-Vehn et al. 2006).

During cytokinesis, plants construct cell plates for the separation of a binucleated cell. PIN proteins are inserted into both sides of the plate, resulting in apical-basal localization following plate fusion with the plasma membrane. Sterols also seem to play a crucial role in the endocytosis-dependent reestablishment of apical PIN2 polarity after the division of epidermis cells (Men et al. 2008). Collectively, these results suggest that endocytic sterol trafficking and endocytosis or polar sorting events in plant cells are linked. It remains to be seen how sterols contribute to endocytosis in plants, but sterols may define microdomains in plant membranes that regulate recruitment or retrieval from clathrin-coated pits.

Besides sterols, other lipids, such as phosphatidylinositol-related signals, are well established to affect vesicle trafficking in animal cells (McMaster 2001, Davletov et al. 2007). In contrast, only little is known on the role of these compounds in plant cells. One of the few reports shows that phospholipase D and its product, phosphatidic acid, appear to regulate the endocytosis rate and vesicle trafficking in general and the PIN2 protein in particular (Li & Xue 2007). In plant cells, as in animals, phosphatidylinositol-dependent signals may regulate endocytosis and vesicle trafficking.

Recent research has demonstrated the importance of endocytosis in a multitude of developmental and physiological processes in plants. Consequently, this field is finally receiving deserved attention and will rapidly progress in coming years.

Getting Back: Recycling in Plant Cells

Following the internalization of material from the plasma membrane, the regulation of the transfer of internalized receptors, transporters, or other molecules back to the plasma membrane is of tremendous importance for cell membrane integrity. In animal cells, various proteins are competent for recycling from distinct endosomal compartments to the plasma membrane. Furthermore, their endocytic routes are relatively well described by distinct molecular markers (Saraste & Goud 2007). In contrast, mechanisms and pathways that guide recycling in plants are still poorly characterized. Endocytic compartments in plants are often defined solely by their ability to incorporate lipophilic endocytic tracers (Bolte et al. 2004), making unambiguous designation of various early- and late-endocytic compartments difficult owing to differences in experimental conditions and possible compartment maturations.

The best-characterized cargo that exhibits constitutive recycling in plants is PIN1. The

Arabidopsis BFA-sensitive endosomal ARF GEF GNOM, a vesicle transport regulator, is required for the polar localization and recycling of PIN1 (Steinmann et al. 1999, Geldner et al. 2001). Moreover, the utilization of an engineered BFA-resistant version of GNOM proved that the inhibitory effect of BFA on PIN1 cycling is due to the specific inhibition of GNOM (Geldner et al. 2003), indicating that GNOM defines the recycling rate of PIN1 to the plasma membrane. GNOM localizes to intracellular structures that are labeled by the endocytic tracer FM4-64 within 10 min and may define a recycling, but not an early, endosome (Geldner et al. 2003, Chow et al. 2008). GNOM does not exclusively mediate endosomal recycling of PIN proteins. Also, other, nonpolar plasma membrane cargos and cell wall components show BFA-sensitive, GNOM-dependent recycling and are affected in *gnom* loss-of-function mutants (Shevell et al. 2000, Geldner et al. 2003). Notably, the involvement of GNOM in basal-versus-apical targeting differs substantially. GNOM preferentially regulates recycling of PIN proteins to the basal plasma membrane, whereas apical localization of proteins at the apical plasma membrane is largely BFA insensitive and may be controlled by one or more BFA-resistant ARF GEFs (Kleine-Vehn et al. 2008a). Hence, apical and basal PIN targeting pathways are molecularly distinct by means of the ARF GEF vesicle trafficking regulators (Kleine-Vehn et al. 2008a), enabling simultaneous apical and basal polar PIN delivery in a single plant cell (**Figure 5**).

Basal cargos, such as PIN1, rapidly internalize in response to ARF GEF inhibition by BFA, implying that only recycling, but not internalization, of basal cargos is sensitive to BFA treatment (Geldner et al. 2001). This finding illustrates a possible employment of a BFA-resistant ARF GEF in cargo internalization from the basal plasma membrane. The GNL1, which is a BFA-resistant ARF GEF, may be involved in selective endocytosis of PIN proteins (Teh & Moore 2007). However, GNL1 is very important in ER-Golgi trafficking (Richter et al. 2007), and it remains to be seen whether GNL1

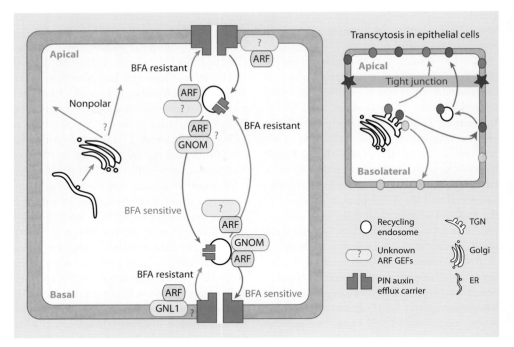

Figure 5

Transcytosis and apical and basal targeting of PIN-FORMED (PIN) proteins. Distinct ARF GEF–dependent apical and basal targeting pathways regulate polar PIN distribution. Alternative utilization of both pathways by the same PIN molecules enables dynamic translocation of PIN cargos between different cell sides. Inhibition of the GNOM component of the basal targeting pathway genetically or by BFA leads to the preferential recruitment of cargos by the apical pathway and to a reversible basal-to-apical PIN polarity shift. The top right panel illustrates that a similar process occurs in animal epithelial cells, in which several polar-competent proteins (depicted in *red*) are initially targeted to the basolateral cell side and subsequently transcytosed to their final destination (the apical cell side). However, other polar cargos (depicted in *yellow* and *blue*) do not require transcytosis for polar localization. Moreover, transcytosis in epithelial cells is also sensitive to BFA. Abbreviations used: ARF GEF, GDP/GTP exchange factor for adenosyl ribosylation factors; BFA, brefeldin A; ER, endoplasmic reticulum; GNL1, GNOM-LIKE1; TGN, trans-Golgi network.

directly or indirectly regulates the PIN endocytosis at the plasma membrane.

Besides the ARF GEF contribution in PIN recycling, SORTING NEXIN1 (SNX1) may define an endosome specific for PIN2, but not PIN1, trafficking (Jaillais et al. 2006) because PIN2 accumulates in SNX1 compartments that are distinct from the GNOM endosomes, after treatment with the phosphatidylinositol-3-kinase (PI3K) inhibitor wortmannin (Jaillais et al. 2006). However, pharmacological or genetic interference with the SNX1 compartment does not affect apical-basal polarity of PIN proteins but preferentially affects vacuolar sorting of plasma membrane proteins, including PIN2 (**Figure 6**) (Kleine-Vehn et al. 2008b). Enhanced PIN2 localization in the SNX1 compartment following gravity stimulation (Jaillais et al. 2006) coincides with enhanced vacuolar targeting and degradation of PIN2 (Abas et al. 2006, Kleine-Vehn et al. 2008b). Interestingly, SNX1 orthologs in yeast and animals are components of the retromer complex that assures the retrieval of vacuolar receptors back from the prevacuolar compartment (PVC) to the TGN (Seaman 2005). In plants, putative retromer components localize to the PVC and may interact with vacuolar sorting receptors (Oliviusson

Retromer: is important in recycling transmembrane receptors from PVCs/multivesicular bodies to the TGN

et al. 2006), which may also be a preferential role for SNX proteins in plants because SNX1 colocalizes with the putative plant retromer component VPS29 at the PVC (Oliviusson et al. 2006, Jaillais et al. 2008). VPS29 is required for storage vacuole formation during embryogenesis (Shimada et al. 2006), indicating that the putative plant retromer complex may be involved in general processes for the formation of multiple vacuole types (Bassham & Raikhel 2000). Furthermore, VPS29 is needed for endosome homeostasis, PIN protein cycling, and dynamic PIN1 repolarization during development (Jaillais et al. 2007). In one possible model, PIN1 first internalizes into GNOM-based endosomes and subsequently is recycled back via VPS29/SNX1-positive endosomes (Jaillais et al. 2007). However, inactivation of retromer-dependent receptor retrieval at the PVC may inhibit anterograde traffic from the PVC to the TGN. Because the TGN may act in plants as an early endosome (Dettmer et al. 2006), recycling of endocytosed cargo would be impaired indirectly (Jürgens & Geldner 2007). Alternatively, the retromer complex may have a gating function for endocytic vacuolar targeting of plasma membrane-localized proteins. Hence, the observed defects in *snx1* and *vps29* mutants (Jaillais et al. 2007, Kleine-Vehn et al. 2008b) may be explained by enhanced vacuolar targeting of PIN proteins (Kleine-Vehn et al. 2008b).

Going to the Other Side: Transcytosis Linking Endocytic Recycling and Polar Targeting

In animal epithelial cells, endocytic recycling is important for the establishment and maintenance of cell polarity (Rodriguez-Boulan et al. 2005, Leibfried & Bellaïche 2007). The endocytosis and subsequent retargeting to the other cell side by the process of transcytosis illustrate the tight linkage of endocytic recycling and polar targeting in animal cells (**Figure 5**).

In plants, apical and basal PIN targeting is realized by an alternative use of distinct polar targeting pathways by the same cargos (Kleine-

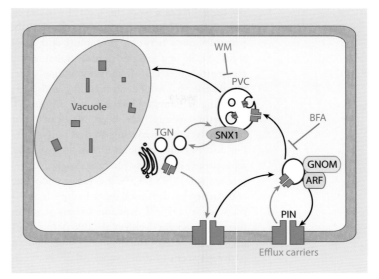

Figure 6

Vacuolar targeting of PIN-FORMED (PIN) proteins. Developmentally important posttranslational downregulation of PIN2 is realized by regulated targeting to the vacuole. PIN2 degradation is controlled by multiple sorting events at the plasma membrane, endosomes, and prevacuolar compartments (PVCs). The putative retromer complex component SORTING NEXIN1 (SNX1) is required for PVC identity. SNX1/VPS29-labeled PVCs appear to have a gating function for endocytic targeting to the vacuole. Other abbreviations used: ARF, adenosyl ribosylation factor; BFA, brefeldin A; TGN, trans-Golgi network; WM, wortmannin.

Vehn et al. 2008a). Analysis of the GNOM contribution to apical-basal PIN targeting has yielded important mechanistic insights into dynamic polar PIN targeting. When GNOM-dependent, basal targeting is manipulated, for example, by pharmalogical or genetic inhibition of the GNOM function, basal PIN cargos internalize from the basal domain, first accumulate in the BFA compartments, and gradually appear at the apical cell side. This process is independent of de novo protein synthesis and, therefore, hints at a dynamic PIN translocation between distinct polar plasma membrane domains. Live-cell imaging with photoconvertible PIN2 versions visualizes the directional BFA-induced translocation from the basal plasma membrane, through endosomes, to the apical plasma membrane. After BFA removal, the basal localization of PINs is restored by a translocation in an

Prevacuolar compartment (PVC): a multivesicular body/membrane-bound organelle that sorts proteins from the Golgi apparatus to vacuoles, sending missorted proteins back to the Golgi and receiving endocytosed proteins from the plasma membrane

opposite direction from the apical-to-basal cell side (Kleine-Vehn et al. 2008a). Thus, PIN proteins move between the apical and basal sides of cells in a manner similar to that of the transcytosis mechanism known in animal cells, illustrating that endocytic recycling and polar targeting in plants are linked as well (**Figure 5**).

Sorting nexins have been implicated not only in receptor recycling at the TGN/PVC but also in transcytotic events in animal cells. In contrast, genetic or pharmacological interference with SNX1/VPS29-positive endocytic compartments does not seem to interfere directly with GNOM-dependent transcytosis in plant cells (Kleine-Vehn et al. 2008a). In agreement with these findings, SNX-dependent pathways seem to differ substantially between plants and animals. For instance, the human genome encodes for 47 PHOX domain proteins, of which approximately 30 are tentatively referred to as sorting nexins (Seet & Hong 2006). In contrast, *Arabidopsis* encodes only 11 PHOX domain–containing proteins (SMART search at **http://smart.embl-heidelberg.de**), of which 3 (AtSNX1, AtSNX2a, and AtSNX2b) show similarities to the human SNX1/SNX2 and 2 (AtSNX13a and AtSNX13b) show weak similarities to human SNX13. The small number of SNX-like proteins found in plants suggests low evolutionary divergence and, hence, a rather conserved SNX function in the putative plant retromer complex at the PVC/TGN interface.

In animal cells, a prominent example for transcytotic cargo is the transferrin receptor, which resides preferentially at the apical and/or basolateral plasma membranes in polarized epithelial cells. This receptor is able to transcytose from one plasma membrane domain to the other (Cerneus et al. 1993). Madin–Darby canine kidney cells predominantly display a basolateral plasma membrane localization of the transferrin receptor, which is subject to a basolateral-to-apical shift after BFA treatment (Wan et al. 1992, Shitara et al. 1998). The action of BFA on transferrin receptor transcytosis reflects the inhibitory effects of the drug on basolateral recycling, whereas transcytosis to the

apical plasma membrane is unaffected (Wang et al. 2001). In an astonishing analogy, apical-to-basal transcytosis of PIN proteins displays a very similar involvement of BFA-sensitive ARF GEFs. Thus, basal targeting in polarized plant cells and basolateral localization in animal cells are remarkably analogous and may follow an evolutionarily conserved principle. However, in plants, the transcytosis mechanism may have acquired unique developmental roles because it may also regulate the dynamic changes in the PIN polarity that accompanies and mediates developmentally important processes such as tropisms and embryonic and postembryonic organ formation (Friml et al. 2002b, 2003b; Benková et al. 2003; Kleine-Vehn et al. 2008a).

Despite obvious analogies between polar targeting mechanisms in plant and animal cells, the overall organization of the polar targeting machinery differs fundamentally. In animal epithelial cells, tight junctions function as barriers to the diffusion of some membrane proteins and lipids between apical and basolateral domains of the plasma membrane (Leibfried & Bellaïche 2007, Niessen 2007). In contrast, such a tight junction–like complex has not been observed in plant cells. Therefore, how plants facilitate the maintenance of distinct membrane compositions remains unclear. PIN proteins display only slow lateral diffusion within the plasma membrane (Dhonukshe et al. 2007a, Men et al. 2008). Thus, a constitutive transcytosis mechanism for polar PIN distribution may be rapid enough to counteract the lateral diffusion of PIN proteins within the plasma membrane and to constantly reestablish the apical-basal localization of cargos. Additionally, this mechanism can mediate the establishment of the polar localization of de novo–synthesized proteins. Polar targeting of de novo–synthesized PIN proteins seems to rely on a three-step mechanism that encompasses nonpolar PIN secretion, clathrin-dependent endocytosis, and subsequent polar endocytic recycling (Dhonukshe et al. 2008b). Therefore, it is tempting to speculate that a transcytosis mechanism regulates dynamic PIN polarity alterations during plant development as well as establishes and maintains PIN polar localization in polarized cells.

Separating the Daughters: Endocytic Recycling in Cytokinetic Cells

Following mitosis, both animal and plant cells usually split a binucleated cell into two daughter cells. However, animal and plant cells evolved fundamentally different mechanisms of cytokinesis (Barr & Gruneberg 2007). By virtue of the rigid cell wall, plant cells, in contrast to the outside-in constriction of animal cells, construct a cell plate that is formed by intensive delivery and fusion of vesicles containing the components of the future plasma membrane and cell walls. Eventually, the growing cell plate fuses with the lateral sides of the cell, thus completing cytokinesis and separating the two daughter cells.

There is an ongoing debate concerning the origin of the cell plate–forming material. It remains unclear whether cell plate formation depends solely on the secretory pathway or whether endocytosis and, hence, endocytic recycling also contribute. Various endocytic tracers get rapidly incorporated from the extracellular space into the forming cell plate along with multiple plasma membrane proteins and cell wall material (Dhonukshe et al. 2006). Furthermore, endocytosis seems to be upregulated during cytokinesis, and the interference with endocytosis affects cell plate formation and cytokinesis (Dhonukshe et al. 2006). In contrast, the inhibition of secretion dramatically interferes with cytokinesis in plants, illustrating the importance of the secretion of the cytokinesis-specific syntaxin KNOLLE as well as other secreted molecules (Reichardt et al. 2007). In addition, pharmacological reduction of PI3K-dependent endocytosis does not lead to any obvious defects in cell plate formation (Reichardt et al. 2007).

Whether or to what degree endocytic recycling contributes to cell division in plants still remains to be seen. Established molecular tools to satisfactorily tackle this controversial issue in plants are lacking. Unraveling of the contribution of endocytic recycling or secretion is difficult because endocytosed and secreted materials are already merged in early-endosomal/TGN compartments (Dettmer et al. 2006; Lam et al. 2007a,b; Chow et al. 2008). Therefore, targeting of endocytosed material to the cell plate may constitute a default pathway because the endocytosed material may simply follow the bulked secretory flow from the TGN to the cell plate. In the most plausible scenario, which would be consistent with all the data, both the secretory and the endocytic components would contribute to cell plate formation. This model would allow simultaneous arrival of the secretory and endocytosed materials to the forming cell plate, not only to build it with de novo–synthesized material but also to identify it as a future cell surface by incorporating components specific to the mother cell's plasma membrane and cell wall (Dhonukshe et al. 2007b).

The scenario in which the cell plate also incorporates components of the cell surface presents a problem of polarity reestablishment of the polar cargos after completion of cell division. PIN proteins are also targeted to the forming cell plate (Geldner et al. 2001, Kleine-Vehn et al. 2008a); after the plasma membrane is formed, the PIN proteins would be present at both the apical and the basal sides of one of the daughter cells. To maintain the polarity of the mother cell in both daughter cells, there must be a mechanism whereby the polar cargos are stabilized on one side and retrieved from the opposite side of the newly formed cell wall. Very little is known as to which cellular and molecular mechanisms are involved. Sterols seem to play a crucial role in the reestablishment of apical PIN2 polarity (Men et al. 2008). The *cpi1* mutants are defective in endocytosis and deposit PIN2 at both the apical and the basal plasma membranes in postcytokinetic cells (Men et al. 2008), suggesting a model in which sterol-dependent endocytosis retrieves PIN2 from the "wrong" side of the cell to reestablish uniform polarity in both daughter cells (**Figure 7**). It is possible that the internalized PIN2 is therefore resorted to the opposite,

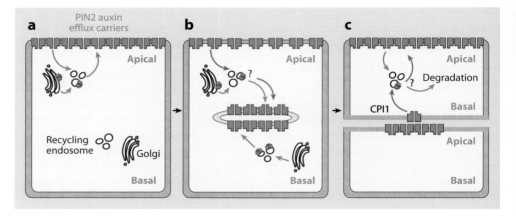

Figure 7

Sterol-dependent endocytosis of PIN2 in postcytokinetic cells. PIN2 displays preferential apical localization in interphase cells (*a*) but is deposited on both sides of the cell plate by transcytosis from the plasma membrane and/or by secretion (*b*). (*c*) PIN2 is retrieved from the newly formed basal plasma membrane by a sterol (CPI1)-dependent mechanism. Following internalization, the PIN2 proteins may translocate to the vacuole for degradation and/or may transcytose to the apical cell side.

"correct" side of the cell, which would be another demonstration of the role of transcytosis in plant cells. However, this scenario and whether similar mechanisms operate for other polar cargos need to be verified experimentally.

EXEMPLIFIED CASES: POLAR TARGETING AND ENDOCYTIC RECYCLING IN PLANT DEVELOPMENT

Induced Endocytosis in Plants

Eukaryotic cells have acquired an enormous adaptive capacity, enabling flexible responses to developmental or environmental cues. In animal cells, ligand- or substrate-induced endocytosis of plasma membrane–resident receptors or transporters has been studied extensively, suggesting a general mechanism for regulated endocytosis in response to external signals (Dugani & Klip 2005). In contrast, in plants, developmental and environmental cues that trigger differential endocytosis are poorly understood.

The first, and so far only, demonstration of ligand-induced receptor endocytosis was in the plant defense response against bacterial

pathogens and concerned the bacterial peptide–based signal called flagellin. The *Arabidopsis* flagellin receptor FLS2 localizes to the plasma membrane in various cell types and, upon binding of the flagellin epitope, undergoes internalization in intracellular vesicles, likely leading to subsequent degradation of the receptor/ligand complex (Robatzek et al. 2006).

Interestingly, after binding of the ligand, FLS2 forms a complex with the brassinosteroid receptor–associated kinase BAK1, which seems to be crucial for its internalization (Chinchilla et al. 2007, Heese et al. 2007). Hence, the leucine-rich repeat receptor–like kinase BAK1 not only is instrumental for the brassinosteroid receptor BRI1 (Li et al. 2002, Russinova et al. 2004) but also plays a role in plant immunity by regulating ligand-induced endocytosis. However, although BAK1 may contribute to flagellin-induced FLS2 internalization, BRI1 internalization, recycling, and turnover are seemingly independent of brassinosteroid availability (Geldner et al. 2007). There are indications that brassinosteroids signal through BRI1 at the endosomal level, suggesting that the use of endosomes as signaling compartments is an unexpectedly broad phenomenon in eukaryotes (Geldner et al. 2007). In contrast, treatment with another inhibitor of vesicle trafficking, Endosidin1, leads to intracellular BRI1 accumulation and downregulates BRI1-dependent signaling, suggesting complex regulation of endosomal competence for potential brassinosteroid signaling (Robert et al. 2008). The utilization of a mutual coreceptor for two distinct receptors may influence the availability and/or kinetics of BAK1 binding and, hence, may be involved not only in brassinosteroid signaling or pathogen defense but also in cross talk of these two pathways.

Selective endocytosis has been demonstrated not only for plant receptors but also for some plasma membrane–resident transporters (Takano et al. 2005, Abas et al. 2006, Sutter et al. 2007). Prominent among such transporters is boron exporter BOR1 for xylem loading. Boron availability is crucial for plant development but toxic in high abundance. In the presence of high levels of boron, BOR1 is internalized into ARA7-positive endosomal compartments and is further targeted to the vacuole for degradation, suggesting a control mechanism for boron transporter presence at the cell surface by boron availability (Takano et al. 2005).

The potassium channel KAT1 accumulates in intracellular structures after abscisic acid concentrations are elevated (Sutter et al. 2007). Although the underlying mechanism is unknown, there may be an endocytosis-dependent mechanism for hormone-directed communication between the internal and external environments by the regulation of stomata opening and closure.

During some developmental processes, several PIN auxin efflux carriers also undergo substantial turnover and degradation in addition to constitutive endocytic recycling (Sieberer et al. 2000, Vieten et al. 2005, Abas et al. 2006, Kleine-Vehn et al. 2008b, Laxmi et al. 2008). As shown for PIN2 in **Figure 6**, following endocytosis, ARF GEF– and PI3K/SNX1-dependent sorting events at the endosomal and prevacuolar compartments contribute to the decision of whether to recycle or to translocate to the vacuole (Kleine-Vehn et al. 2008b). Auxin itself regulates PIN abundance at the

plasma membrane by inhibiting PIN internalization from the plasma membrane (Paciorek et al. 2005). In addition, prolonged high auxin levels appear to induce PIN2 ubiquitination, internalization, and degradation (Vieten et al. 2005, Abas et al. 2006). Moreover, gravitropic stimulation triggers internalization (Abas et al. 2006) and vacuole-dependent degradation of PIN2 in epidermal cells at the upper side of the root (Kleine-Vehn et al. 2008b). This gravity-induced degradation of PIN2 occurs in cells with low, not high, auxin levels and may indicate posttranslational PIN2 downregulation in response to auxin depletion. It still needs to be seen whether boron, auxin, and possibly substrates for other plasma membrane–based transporters differentially downregulate their transporters by a conserved mechanism. Transient, transport-dependent conformational changes in carrier composition may enable conditional recruitment of machineries mediating, for instance, ubiquitination and subsequent internalization of their substrates.

Although the underlying pathways are largely unknown, the examples of ligand-induced receptor endocytosis, constitutive receptor cycling, and endosome-based signaling as well as the downregulation of receptors and transporters in response to substrate availability show that plant cells use all these endocytosis mechanisms to regulate their physiology. Undoubtedly, other examples of similar regulations will be identified in the coming years.

Integrating Developmental and Environmental Signals through Polarity Modulations

Intercellular auxin transport is the process in plants that makes most apparent the developmental output of subcellular dynamics and cell polarity (Berleth et al. 2007). Polar auxin transport is distinguished by its strictly controlled directionality, which is a crucial feature in auxin-mediated plant development (reviewed by Friml 2003, Zažímalová et al. 2007). The classical chemiosmotic hypothesis proposes that auxin flow polarity is determined by the polar, subcellular localization of auxin efflux carriers (Rubery & Sheldrake 1974, Raven 1975; **Figure 1**). PIN proteins have been identified as one of the export carriers, and their polar subcellular localization indeed correlates with the direction of the auxin flow. The manipulation of PIN polarity has a clear impact on the ability of auxin to flow in a given direction, thus confirming that cellular PIN positioning is a determining factor in the directionality of polar auxin transport (Friml et al. 2004, Wiśniewska et al. 2006, Boutté et al. 2007).

The finding that PIN proteins undergo permanent subcellular movements (Geldner et al. 2001, Dhonukshe et al. 2007a) was hard to reconcile with the original models of auxin transport. Hence, the important upcoming question concerns the functional role of this constitutive cycling. Besides exotic scenarios, such as neurotransmitter-like release of auxin from cells (Baluška et al. 2003), a plausible assumption is that constitutive trafficking provides the required flexibility for the rapid transcytosis-based PIN polarity changes, allowing rapid redirection of auxin flow in response to various signals, including environmental or developmental cues (Friml 2003). Indeed, rapid PIN relocations have been observed during embryonic development (**Figure 8**) (Friml et al.

2003b), aerial and underground organogenesis (**Figure 9**) (Benková et al. 2003, Reinhardt et al. 2003, Geldner et al. 2004, Heisler et al. 2005), vascular tissue formation (Scarpella et al. 2006), and root gravity responses (**Figure 10**) (Friml et al. 2002b). In all these instances, changes in PIN polarity are followed by the redirection of auxin fluxes and the rearrangement of local patterns of auxin accumulation (auxin gradients) that triggered the changes in the developmental programs (Kramer & Bennett 2006, Leyser 2006, Parry & Estelle 2006). An early PIN polarity switch signals root initiation during embryogenesis. At early stages of *Arabidopsis* embryo development, PIN7 is localized apically (toward the apical cell) in the suspensor, and PIN1 is mostly nonpolar in the proembryo, whereas at a later-defined stage, PIN1 polarizes to the basal side of cells adjacent to the future root meristem, and PIN7 changes its polarity from apical to basal (Friml et al. 2003b). These PIN polarity alterations lead to the rearrangement of auxin gradients and the accumulation of auxin at the presumptive embryo root pole and are among the necessary factors for root specification (Friml et al. 2003b, Weijers et al. 2005).

Another example of PIN polarity reorganization relates to the perception and response to environmental stimuli. Studies on *Arabidopsis* roots demonstrated that the PIN3 protein relocates in gravity-sensing cells of the root tip in response to gravistimulation (Friml et al. 2002b, Harrison & Masson 2008). When the root is reoriented into a horizontal position, gravity-sensing statoliths in the columella cells sediment, and PIN3 rapidly relocalizes from its originally uniform distribution to the new bottom side of these cells. The asymmetric repositioning of PIN3 is followed by redirection of the auxin flow downward, leading to auxin accumulation at the lower side of the root and, consequently, to downward root bending (**Figure 10**). It is possible that a similar mechanism involving PIN relocations underlies phototropic responses, but the connection between unidirectional light stimulus and PIN relocation has not been demonstrated. The

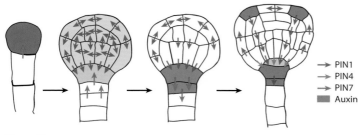

Figure 8

PIN-FORMED (PIN) polarity alterations during embryogenesis. Schematic representation of PIN distribution and polar orientation during *Arabidopsis* embryo development. PIN1 and PIN7 undergo a polarity switch at the globular stage. The GNOM-dependent focus of PIN1 to the basal sides of provascular cells coincides with an apical-to-basal shift of PIN7. These rearrangements of PIN polarity are accompanied by a dramatic change in the apical-basal auxin gradient. A new auxin maximum is established at the position of the future root, contributing to the initiation of the root specification. The analogy to GNOM-dependent transcytosis in polarized root cells may indicate polar transcytosis of PIN proteins during embryogenesis.

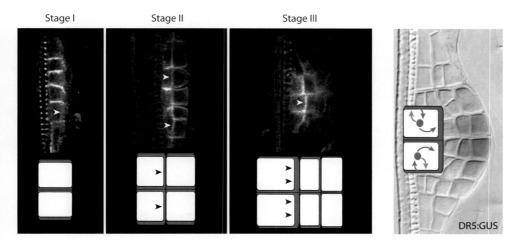

Stage I   Stage II   Stage III

DR5:GUS

Figure 9

PIN-FORMED (PIN) polarity alterations during postembryonic organ formation. Immunolocalization and model of PIN1 localization during stage I to stage III (*first three panels*) of lateral root primordia development illustrate dynamic PIN1 polarity changes from the anticlinal toward the periclinal cell sides, pointing to the presumptive primordia tip. These changes coincide with the establishment of auxin maxima (visualized here by the DR5 auxin-responsive promoter activity; *fourth panel*) at the primordium tip. GNOM dependency of this event may reveal the involvement of dynamic PIN1 transcytosis between the anticlinal and the periclinal cell sides.

constitutive PIN subcellular dynamics may play a more direct role in the mechanism of auxin efflux because several potent and well-established inhibitors of auxin efflux act as stabilizers of the actin cytoskeleton and also inhibit PIN dynamics (Dhonukshe et al. 2008a). The precise connection between actin stabilization and mechanism of auxin efflux is, however, still unclear. Nonetheless, signal-induced rearrangements of PIN polarity in response to different inputs represent a plant-specific mechanism that integrates various internal and external signals and translates them into different developmental responses.

Canalization Hypothesis and the Effect of Auxin on Its Own Efflux

An important aspect linked to cell polarity and auxin transport relates to a rather fundamental issue in developmental biology: How does the individual cell in polarizing tissues know the polarity of its neighbors and the whole macroscopic context? In plant development, this issue has a pronounced importance because

plants possess the remarkable ability to redefine cell and tissue polarities. Outstanding examples of auxin-dependent reorganization of plant tissues are the differentiation of vasculature during leaf venation, the connection of de novo–initiated organs with the preexisting vascular network, and vasculature regeneration after wounding. During these events, plant cells perceive their position within the tissue and can recognize their orientation relative to the rest of the plant body. Insights into underlying mechanisms are widely elusive, but efforts to tackle these processes have led to the formulation of the canalization hypothesis (Sachs 1981), whereby auxin can induce, by a positive-feedback mechanism, the capacity and polarity of its own transport, resulting in the gradual rearrangement of cell polarity and the repolarization of neighboring cells. Ultimately, new auxin conductive channels can be established, determining the position of new vascular strands. This intriguing hypothesis and other auxin-dependent self-organizing models (de Reuille et al. 2006, Jönsson et al. 2006, Smith et al. 2006, Kuhlemeier 2007, Merks et al. 2007)

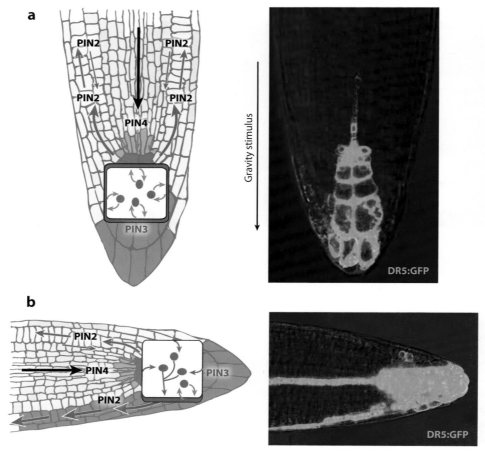

Figure 10

(*a*) PIN-FORMED (PIN)3 translocation during the root gravitropic response. Following gravity stimulation, PIN3 translocates rapidly to the bottom side of root cap cells and thus redirects auxin flow toward the lower side of the root. (*b*) PIN3- and PIN2-dependent asymmetric auxin distribution (visualized by the DR5:GFP-reliant auxin response) leads to differential growth and subsequent downward root bending. The dynamic nature of PIN3 targeting after gravity perception indicates a transcytosis-like mechanism for this polarity switch.

require the existence of positive-feedback regulation between auxin signaling and the capacity and polarity of auxin transport.

In fact, auxin feedback mechanisms regulating PIN activity, involving auxin-dependent regulation of transcription, degradation, and/or subcellular localization of auxin transport components, have been illustrated at multiple levels (Paciorek et al. 2005, Vieten et al. 2005, Sauer et al. 2006, Scarpella et al. 2006, Xu et al. 2006). On the transcriptional level, auxin-dependent cross-regulation of PIN expression may account for the extensive functional redundancy of PIN proteins, in which lack of function of one PIN protein leads to a transient increase in cellular auxin levels and transcriptional upregulation of a functional ortholog (Vieten et al. 2005). Other auxin-dependent feedbacks have been identified at the level of PIN subcellular trafficking: Auxin interferes with endocytosis, including the internalization of PIN proteins, possibly by a mechanism independent of auxin-induced transcription. This auxin effect leads to elevated PIN levels at the plasma membrane and increased auxin efflux (Paciorek et al. 2005). The underlying mechanism of the auxin effect is unclear but requires BIG, a callosin-like protein with an unclear function (Gil et al. 2001). By this mechanism, auxin regulates the PIN abundance and activity at the cell surface, accomplishing direct feedback regulation of auxin transport (Paciorek & Friml 2006).

Moreover, auxin indeed delegates the polarity of PIN proteins, hence influencing not only its own efflux rate but also its directional output (Sauer et al. 2006). This auxin effect is independent of PIN transcriptional regulation but involves the identified auxin/indole acetic acid (AUX/IAA) and auxin response factor–dependent signaling pathway (Parry & Estelle 2006, Kepinski 2007). Furthermore, auxin-dependent polarization cues are perceived in a cell type–dependent manner, eventually leading to averted polarity between neighboring cells (Sauer et al. 2006). These feedback regulations provide a conceptual framework for polarization during multiple regenerative and patterning processes in plants and are the unavoidable legacy of most models dealing with auxin-dependent patterning (Kramer 2008).

DISCLOSURE STATEMENT

The authors are not aware of any biases that might be perceived as affecting the objectivity of this review.

ACKNOWLEDGMENTS

We are grateful to M. De Cock for help in preparing the manuscript. This work was supported by grants from the Research Foundation-Flanders (Odysseus) and the EMBO Young Investigator Program.

LITERATURE CITED

Abas L, Benjamins R, Malenica N, Paciorek T, Wiśniewska J, et al. 2006. Intracellular trafficking and proteolysis of the *Arabidopsis* auxin-efflux facilitator PIN2 are involved in root gravitropism. *Nat. Cell Biol.* 8:249–56

Baluška F, Samaj J, Menzel D. 2003. Polar transport of auxin: carrier-mediated flux across the plasma membrane or neurotransmitter-like secretion? *Trends Cell Biol.* 13:282–85

Barr FA, Gruneberg U. 2007. Cytokinesis: placing and making the final cut. *Cell* 131(5):847–60

Bassham DC, Raikhel NV. 2000. Unique features of the plant vacuolar sorting machinery. *Curr. Opin. Cell Biol.* 12(4):491–95

Benjamins R, Malenica N, Luschnig C. 2005. Regulating the regulator: the control of auxin transport. *Bioessays* 27:1246–55

Benjamins R, Quint A, Weijers D, Hooykaas P, Offringa R. 2001. The PINOID protein kinase regulates organ development in *Arabidopsis* by enhancing polar auxin transport. *Development* 128:4057–67

Benková E, Michniewicz M, Sauer M, Teichmann T, Seifertová D, et al. 2003. Local, efflux-dependent auxin gradients as a common module for plant organ formation. *Cell* 115:591–602

Benmerah A, Lamaze C. 2007. Clathrin-coated pits: vive la différence? *Traffic* 8(8):970–82

Bennett MJ, Marchant A, Green HG, May ST, Ward SP, et al. 1996. *Arabidopsis AUX1* gene: a permease-like regulator of root gravitropism. *Science* 273:948–50

Berleth T, Scarpella E, Prusinkiewicz P. 2007. Towards the systems biology of auxin-transport-mediated patterning. *Trends Plant Sci.* 12(4):151–59

Bhat RA, Panstruga R. 2005. Lipid rafts in plants. *Planta* 223(1):5–19

Blakeslee JJ, Peer WA, Murphy AS. 2005. Auxin transport. *Curr. Opin. Plant Biol.* 8:494–500

Blilou I, Xu J, Wildwater M, Willemsen V, Paponov I, et al. 2005. The PIN auxin efflux facilitator network controls growth and patterning in *Arabidopsis* roots. *Nature* 433:39–44

Bolte S, Talbot C, Boutte Y, Catrice O, Read ND, Satiat-Jeunemaitre B. 2004. FM-dyes as experimental probes for dissecting vesicle trafficking in living plant cells. *J. Microsc.* 214(Pt. 2):159–73

Bonifacino JS, Lippincott-Schwartz J. 2003. Coat proteins: shaping membrane transport. *Nat. Rev. Mol. Cell Biol.* 4(5):409–14

Boutté Y, Ikeda Y, Grebe M. 2007. Mechanisms of auxin-dependent cell and tissue polarity. *Curr. Opin. Plant Biol.* 10(6):616–23

Carter CJ, Bednarek SY, Raikhel NV. 2004. Membrane trafficking in plants: new discoveries and approaches. *Curr. Opin. Plant Biol.* 7(6):701–7

Casanova JE, Breitfeld PP, Ross SA, Mostov KE. 1990. Phosphorylation of the polymeric immunoglobulin receptor required for its efficient transcytosis. *Science* 248(4956):742–45

Cerneus DP, Strous GJ, Van Der Ende A. 1993. Bidirectional transcytosis determines the steady state distribution of the transferrin receptor at opposite plasma membrane domains of BeWo cells. *J. Cell Biol.* 122(6):1223–30

Chen R, Hilson P, Sedbrook J, Rosen E, Caspar T, Masson PH. 1998. The *Arabidopsis thaliana AGRAVITROPIC 1* gene encodes a component of the polar-auxin-transport efflux carrier. *Proc. Natl. Acad. Sci. USA* 95(25):15112–17

Cheng ZJ, Singh RD, Marks DL, Pagano RE. 2006. Membrane microdomains, caveolae, and caveolar endocytosis of sphingolipids. *Mol. Membr. Biol.* 23(1):101–10

Chinchilla D, Zipfel C, Robatzek S, Kemmerling B, Nürnberger T, et al. 2007. A flagellin-induced complex of the receptor FLS2 and BAK1 initiates plant defence. *Nature* 448(7152):497–500

Chow CM, Neto H, Foucart C, Moore I. 2008. Rab-A2 and Rab-A3 GTPases define a trans-Golgi endosomal membrane domain in *Arabidopsis* that contributes substantially to the cell plate. *Plant Cell* 20(1):101–23

Christensen SK, Dagenais N, Chory J, Weigel D. 2000. Regulation of auxin response by the protein kinase PINOID. *Cell* 100:469–78

Davletov B, Connell E, Darios F. 2007. Regulation of SNARE fusion machinery by fatty acids. *Cell Mol. Life Sci.* 64(13):1597–608

de Reuille PB, Bohn-Courseau I, Ljung K, Morin H, Carraro N, et al. 2006. Computer simulations reveal properties of the cell-cell signaling network at the shoot apex in *Arabidopsis*. *Proc. Natl. Acad. Sci. USA* 103:1627–32

Dettmer J, Hong-Hermesdorf A, Stierhof YD, Schumacher K. 2006. Vacuolar H^+-ATPase activity is required for endocytic and secretory trafficking in *Arabidopsis*. *Plant Cell* 18(3):715–30

Dharmasiri S, Swarup R, Mockaitis K, Dharmasiri N, Singh SK, et al. 2006. AXR4 is required for localization of the auxin influx facilitator AUX1. *Science* 312:1218–20

Dhonukshe P, Aniento F, Hwang I, Robinson D, Mravec J, et al. 2007a. Clathrin-mediated constitutive endocytosis of PIN auxin efflux carriers in *Arabidopsis*. *Curr. Biol.* 17(6):520–27

Dhonukshe P, Baluška F, Schlicht M, Hlavacka A, Samaj J, et al. 2006. Endocytosis of cell surface material mediates cell plate formation during plant cytokinesis. *Dev. Cell* 10(1):137–50

Dhonukshe P, Samaj J, Baluška F, Friml J. 2007b. A unifying new model of cytokinesis for the dividing plant and animal cells. *Bioessays* 29:371–81

Dhonukshe P, Grigoriev I, Fischer R, Tominaga M, Robinson D, et al. 2008a. Auxin transport inhibitors block vesicle motility and actin cytoskeleton dynamics in diverse eukaryotes. *Proc. Natl. Acad. Sci. USA* 105(11):4489–94

Dhonukshe P, Tanaka H, Goh T, Ebine K, Prasad K, et al. 2008b. A cell polarity generation mechanism links endocytosis, auxin gradient and cell-fate determining transcription factors in plants. Submitted

Donaldson JG, Jackson CL. 2000. Regulators and effectors of the ARF GTPases. *Curr. Opin. Cell Biol.* 12:475–82

Dubrovsky J, Sauer M, Napsucialy-Mendivil S, Ivanchenko M, Friml J, et al. 2008. Auxin acts as a local morphogenetic trigger to specify lateral root founder cells. *Proc. Natl. Acad. Sci. USA*. Invited for revision

Dugani CB, Klip A. 2005. Glucose transporter 4: cycling, compartments and controversies. *EMBO Rep.* 6(12):1137–42

Confocal study that illustrates the involvement of Rab-A2 and Rab-A3 GTPases in cytokinesis and sheds light on the intracellular compartmentalization in plant cells.

Provides important insights into pH requirements for compartment integrity and suggests that the TGN constitutes early endosomes in plants.

Shows that clathrin-dependent endocytosis is operational in plants and used to internalize PINs from the plasma membrane.

Esmon CA, Tinsley AG, Ljung K, Sandberg G, Hearne LB, Liscum E. 2006. A gradient of auxin and auxin-dependent transcription precedes tropic growth responses. *Proc. Natl. Acad. Sci. USA* 103(1):236–41

Friml J. 2003. Auxin transport: shaping the plant. *Curr. Opin. Plant Biol.* 6:7–12

Friml J, Benková E, Blilou I, Wiśniewska J, Hamann T, et al. 2002a. AtPIN4 mediates sink-driven auxin gradients and root patterning in *Arabidopsis*. *Cell* 108:661–73

Friml J, Benková E, Mayer U, Palme K, Muster G. 2003a. Automated whole mount localization techniques for plant seedlings. *Plant J.* 34(1):115–24

Friml J, Vieten A, Sauer M, Weijers D, Schwarz H, et al. 2003b. Efflux-dependent auxin gradients establish the apical-basal axis of *Arabidopsis*. *Nature* 426:147–53

Friml J, Wiśniewska J, Benková E, Mendgen K, Palme K. 2002b. Lateral relocation of auxin efflux regulator PIN3 mediates tropism in *Arabidopsis*. *Nature* 415:806–9

Friml J, Yang X, Michniewicz M, Weijers D, Quint A, et al. 2004. A PINOID-dependent binary switch in apical basal PIN polar targeting directs auxin efflux. *Science* 306:862–65

Gälweiler L, Guan C, Müller A, Wisman E, Mendgen K, et al. 1998. Regulation of polar auxin transport by AtPIN1 in *Arabidopsis* vascular tissue. *Science* 282:2226–30

Geisler M, Blakeslee JJ, Bouchard R, Lee OR, Vincenzetti V, et al. 2005. Cellular efflux of auxin catalyzed by the *Arabidopsis* MDR/PGP transporter AtPGP1. *Plant J.* 44(2):179–94

Geldner N, Anders N, Wolters H, Keicher J, Kornberger W, et al. 2003. The *Arabidopsis* GNOM ARF-GEF mediates endosomal recycling, auxin transport, and auxin-dependent plant growth. *Cell* 112:219–30

Geldner N, Friml J, Stierhof YD, Jürgens G, Palme K. 2001. Auxin transport inhibitors block PIN1 cycling and vesicle trafficking. *Nature* 413:425–28

Geldner N, Hyman DL, Wang X, Schumacher K, Chory J. 2007. Endosomal signaling of plant steroid receptor kinase BRI1. *Genes Dev.* 21(13):1598–602

Geldner N, Richter S, Vieten A, Marquardt S, Torres-Ruiz RA, et al. 2004. Partial loss-of-function alleles reveal a role for GNOM in auxin transport-related, postembryonic development of *Arabidopsis*. *Development* 131:389–400

Gil P, Dewey E, Friml J, Zhao Y, Snowden KC, et al. 2001. BIG: a calossin-like protein required for polar auxin transport in *Arabidopsis*. *Genes Dev.* 15:1985–97

Gradmann D, Robinson DG. 1989. Does turgor prevent endocytosis in plant cells? *Plant Cell Environ.* 12:151–54

Grebe M, Friml J, Swarup R, Ljung K, Sandberg G, et al. 2002. Cell polarity signaling in *Arabidopsis* involves a BFA-sensitive auxin influx pathway. *Curr. Biol.* 12:329–34

Grebe M, Xu J, Mobius W, Ueda T, Nakano A, et al. 2003. *Arabidopsis* sterol endocytosis involves actin-mediated trafficking via ARA6-positive early endosomes. *Curr. Biol.* 13:1378–87

Harrison BR, Masson PH. 2008. ARL2, ARG1 and PIN3 define a gravity signal transduction pathway in root statocytes. *Plant J.* 53(2):380–92

Heese A, Hann DR, Gimenez-Ibanez S, Jones AM, He K, et al. 2007. The receptor-like kinase SERK3/BAK1 is a central regulator of innate immunity in plants. *Proc. Natl. Acad. Sci. USA* 104(29):12217–22

Heisler MG, Ohno C, Das P, Sieber P, Reddy GV, et al. 2005. Patterns of auxin transport and gene expression during primordium development revealed by live imaging of the *Arabidopsis* inflorescence meristem. *Curr. Biol.* 15:1899–911

Hirst J, Robinson MS. 1998. Clathrin and adaptors. *Biochim. Biophys. Acta* 1404(1–2):173–93

Holstein SE. 2002. Clathrin and plant endocytosis. *Traffic* 3(9):614–20

Irazoqui JE, Lew DJ. 2004. Polarity establishment in yeast. *J. Cell Sci.* 117(Pt. 11):2169–71

Jaillais Y, Fobis-Loisy I, Miège C, Gaude T. 2008. Evidence for a sorting endosome in *Arabidopsis* root cells. *Plant J.* 53(2):237–47

Jaillais Y, Fobis-Loisy I, Miège C, Rollin C, Gaude T. 2006. AtSNX1 defines an endosome for auxin-carrier trafficking in *Arabidopsis*. *Nature* 443(7107):106–9

Jaillais Y, Santambrogio M, Rozier F, Fobis-Loisy I, Miège C, Gaude T. 2007. The retromer protein VPS29 links cell polarity and organ initiation in plants. *Cell* 130(6):1057–70

Janssens B, Chavrier P. 2004. Mediterranean views on epithelial polarity. *Nat. Cell Biol.* 6(6):493–96

Jönsson H, Heisler MG, Shapiro BE, Meyerowitz EM, Mjolsness E. 2006. An auxin-driven polarized transport model for phyllotaxis. *Proc. Natl. Acad. Sci. USA* 103:1633–38

Demonstrates the constitutive endocytic recycling of PIN1.

Demonstrates SNX1 localization at the prevacuolar compartment, suggesting conserved function of the putative plant retromer complex.

Jürgens G, Geldner N. 2007. The high road and the low road: trafficking choices in plants. *Cell* 130(6):977–79

Kepinski S. 2007. The anatomy of auxin perception. *Bioessays* 29(10):953–56

Kleine-Vehn J, Dhonukshe P, Sauer M, Brewer P, Wiśniewska J, et al. 2008a. ARF GEF-dependent transcytosis and polar delivery of PIN auxin carriers in *Arabidopsis*. *Curr. Biol.* 18:526–31

Kleine-Vehn J, Dhonukshe P, Swarup R, Bennett M, Friml J. 2006. A novel pathway for subcellular trafficking of AUX1 auxin influx carrier. *Plant Cell* 18:3171–81

Kleine-Vehn J, Leitner J, Zwiewka M, Sauer M, Abas L, Luschnig C, Friml J. 2008b. Differential degradation of PIN auxin efflux carrier by SNX1-dependent vacuolar targeting. Submitted

Knoblich JA. 2000. Epithelial polarity: the ins and outs of the fly epidermis. *Curr. Biol.* 10(21):R791–94

Kramer EM. 2008. Computer models of auxin transport: a review and commentary. *J. Exp. Bot.* 59(1):45–53

Kramer EM, Bennett MJ. 2006. Auxin transport: a field in flux. *Trends Plant Sci.* 11(8):382–86

Kuhlemeier C. 2007. Phyllotaxis. *Trends Plant Sci.* 12(4):143–50

Lam SK, Siu CL, Hillmer S, Jang S, An G, et al. 2007a. Rice SCAMP1 defines clathrin-coated, trans-Golgi-located tubular-vesicular structures as an early endosome in tobacco BY-2 cells. *Plant Cell* 19(1):296–319

Lam SK, Tse YC, Robinson DG, Jiang L. 2007b. Tracking down the elusive early endosome. *Trends Plant Sci.* 12(11):497–505

Laxmi A, Pan J, Morsy M, Chen R. 2008. Light plays an essential role in intracellular distribution of auxin efflux carrier PIN2 in *Arabidopsis thaliana*. *PLoS ONE* 3(1):e1510

Leibfried A, Bellaïche Y. 2007. Functions of endosomal trafficking in *Drosophila* epithelial cells. *Curr. Opin. Cell Biol.* 19(4):446–52

Leyser O. 2006. Dynamic integration of auxin transport and signaling. *Curr. Biol.* 16(11):R424–33

Li G, Xue HW. 2007. *Arabidopsis* PLDζ2 regulates vesicle trafficking and is required for auxin response. *Plant Cell* 19(1):281–95

Li J, Wen J, Lease KA, Doke JT, Tax FE, Walker JC. 2002. BAK1, an *Arabidopsis* LRR receptor-like protein kinase, interacts with BRI1 and modulates brassinosteroid signaling. *Cell* 110(2):213–22

Luschnig C, Gaxiola RA, Grisafi P, Fink GR. 1998. EIR1, a root-specific protein involved in auxin transport, is required for gravitropism in *Arabidopsis thaliana*. *Genes Dev.* 12:2175–87

Ma JF, Tamai K, Yamaji N, Mitani N, Konishi S, et al. 2006. A silicon transporter in rice. *Nature* 440(7084):688–91

Ma JF, Yamaji N, Mitani N, Tamai K, Konishi S, et al. 2007. An efflux transporter of silicon in rice. *Nature* 448(7150):209–12

Margolis B, Borg JP. 2005. Apicobasal polarity complexes. *J. Cell Sci.* 118(Pt. 22):5157–59

McMaster CR. 2001. Lipid metabolism and vesicle trafficking: more than just greasing the transport machinery. *Biochem. Cell Biol.* 79(6):681–92

Meckel T, Hurst AC, Thiel G, Homann U. 2004. Endocytosis against high turgor: Intact guard cells of *Vicia faba* constitutively endocytose fluorescently labelled plasma membrane and GFP-tagged K-channel KAT1. *Plant J.* 39(2):182–93

Men S, Boutté Y, Ikeda Y, Li X, Palme K, et al. 2008. Sterol-dependent endocytosis mediates postcytokinetic acquisition of PIN2 auxin efflux carrier polarity. *Nat. Cell Biol.* 10(2):237–44

Merks RM, Van de Peer Y, Inzé D, Beemster GT. 2007. Canalization without flux sensors: a traveling-wave hypothesis. *Trends Plant Sci.* 12(9):384–90

Michniewicz M, Zago MK, Abas L, Weijers D, Schweighofer A, et al. 2007. Antagonistic regulation of PIN phosphorylation by PP2A and PINOID directs auxin flux. *Cell* 130(6):1044–56

Miwa K, Takano J, Omori H, Seki M, Shinozaki K, Fujiwara T. 2007. Plants tolerant of high boron levels. *Science* 318(5855):1417

Mostov K, Su T, ter Beest M. 2003. Polarized epithelial membrane traffic: conservation and plasticity. *Nat. Cell Biol.* 5(4):287–93

Mravec J, Kubeš M, Gaykova V, Bielach A, Petrášek J, et al. 2008. Interaction of PIN and PGP transport mechanisms in auxin distribution-dependent development. *Development*. Submitted

Müller A, Guan C, Gälweiler L, Tänzler P, Huijser P, et al. 1998. AtPIN2 defines a locus of *Arabidopsis* for root gravitropism control. *EMBO J.* 17(23):6903–11

Nance J. 2005. PAR proteins and the establishment of cell polarity during *C. elegans* development. *Bioessays* 27(2):126–35

Demonstrates ARF GEF-dependent transcytosis in plant cells and its possible involvement in embryogenesis and organogenesis.

Careful investigation of sterol involvement in endocytosis that highlights the necessity of sterol-dependent postcytokinetic establishment of PIN polarity.

Niessen CM. 2007. Tight junctions/adherens junctions: basic structure and function. *J. Investig. Dermatol.* 127(11):2525–32

Okada K, Ueda J, Komaki MK, Bell CJ, Shimura Y. 1991. Requirement of the auxin polar transport system in early stages of *Arabidopsis* floral bud formation. *Plant Cell* 3:677–84

Oliviusson P, Heinzerling O, Hillmer S, Hinz G, Tse YC, et al. 2006. Plant retromer, localized to the prevacuolar compartment and microvesicles in *Arabidopsis*, may interact with vacuolar sorting receptors. *Plant Cell* 18(5):1239–52

Ortiz-Zapater E, Soriano-Ortega E, Marcote MJ, Ortiz-Masiá D, Aniento F. 2006. Trafficking of the human transferrin receptor in plant cells: effects of tyrphostin A23 and brefeldin A. *Plant J.* 48(5):757–70

Paciorek T, Friml J. 2006. Auxin signalling. *J. Cell Sci.* 119:1199–202

Paciorek T, Zažímalová E, Ruthardt N, Petrášek J, Stierhof YD, et al. 2005. Auxin inhibits endocytosis and promotes its own efflux from cells. *Nature* 435:1251–56

Parry G, Estelle M. 2006. Auxin receptors: a new role for F-box proteins. *Curr. Opin. Cell Biol.* 18(2):152–56

Paul MJ, Frigerio L. 2007. Coated vesicles in plant cells. *Semin. Cell Dev. Biol.* 18(4):471–78

Pelkmans L, Helenius A. 2003. Insider information: what viruses tell us about endocytosis. *Curr. Opin. Cell Biol.* 15(4):414–22

Pérez-Gómez J, Moore I. 2007. Plant endocytosis: It is clathrin after all. *Curr. Biol.* 17(6):R217–19

Petrášek J, Mravec J, Bouchard R, Blakeslee JJ, Abas M, et al. 2006. PIN proteins perform a rate-limiting function in cellular auxin efflux. *Science* 3 12:914–18

Raven JA. 1975. Transport of indoleacetic acid in plant cells in relation to pH and electrical potential gradients and its significance for polar IAA transport. *New Phytol.* 74:163–72

Reinhardt D, Mandel T, Kuhlemeier C. 2000. Auxin regulates the initiation and radial position of plant lateral organs. *Plant Cell* 12(4):507–18

Reinhardt D, Pesce ER, Stieger P, Mandel T, Baltensperger K, et al. 2003. Regulation of phyllotaxis by polar auxin transport. *Nature* 426:255–60

Reichardt I, Stierhof YD, Mayer U, Richter S, Schwarz H, et al. 2007. Plant cytokinesis requires de novo secretory trafficking but not endocytosis. *Curr. Biol.* 17(23):2047–53

Richter S, Geldner N, Schrader J, Wolters H, Stierhof YD, et al. 2007. Functional diversification of closely related ARF-GEFs in protein secretion and recycling. *Nature* 448(7152):488–92

Ritzenthaler C, Nebenfuhr A, Movafeghi A, Stussi-Garaud C, Behnia L, et al. 2002. Reevaluation of the effects of brefeldin A on plant cells using tobacco Bright Yellow 2 cells expressing Golgi-targeted green fluorescent protein and COPI antisera. *Plant Cell* 14:237–61

Robatzek S, Chinchilla D, Boller T. 2006. Ligand-induced endocytosis of the pattern recognition receptor FLS2 in *Arabidopsis*. *Genes Dev.* 20(5):537–42

Robert S, Chary SN, Drakakaki G, Li S, Yang Z, et al. 2008. Endosidin1 defines a compartment involved in endocytosis of the brassinosteroid receptor BRI1 and the auxin transporters PIN2 and AUX1. *Proc. Natl. Acad. Sci. USA* 105:8464–69

Robinson H. 1990. Coated pits. In *The Plant Plasma Membrane*, ed C Larsson, IM Moller, pp. 233–55. Berlin/Heidelberg: Springer-Verlag

Rodriguez-Boulan E, Kreitzer G, Müsch A. 2005. Organization of vesicular trafficking in epithelia. *Nat. Rev. Mol. Cell Biol.* 6(3):233–47

Roudier F, Fernandez AG, Fujita M, Himmelspach R, Borner GH, et al. 2005. COBRA, an *Arabidopsis* extracellular glycosyl-phosphatidyl inositol-anchored protein, specifically controls highly anisotropic expansion through its involvement in cellulose microfibril orientation. *Plant Cell* 17(6):1749–63

Rubery PH, Sheldrake AR. 1974. Carrier-mediated auxin transport. *Planta* 188:101–21

Russinova E, Borst JW, Kwaaitaal M, Caño-Delgado A, Yin Y, et al. 2004. Heterodimerization and endocytosis of *Arabidopsis* brassinosteroid receptors BRI1 and AtSERK3 (BAK1). *Plant Cell* 16(12):3216–29

Růžička K, Nejedlá E, Murphy A, Kleine-Vehn J, Bailly A, et al. 2008. PIS1 exporter for auxinic compounds defines outer polar domain in plants. Submitted

Sachs T. 1981. The control of patterned differentiation of vascular tissues. *Adv. Bot. Res.* 9:151–262

Saraste J, Goud B. 2007. Functional symmetry of endomembranes. *Mol. Biol. Cell* 18(4):1430–36

Demonstrates the ligand-induced receptor endocytosis in plants and its role in the plant immune response.

Presents the cellular bases for the canalization hypothesis and shows that auxin modulates the polarity of PINs during organogenesis and tissue regeneration.

Sauer M, Balla J, Luschnig C, Wiśniewska J, Reinohl V, et al. 2006. Canalization of auxin flow by Aux/IAA-ARF-dependent feedback regulation of PIN polarity. *Genes Dev.* **20:2902–11**

Saxton MJ, Breidenbach RW. 1988. Receptor-mediated endocytosis in plants is energetically possible. *Plant Physiol.* 86(4):993–95

Scarpella E, Marcos D, Friml J, Berleth T. 2006. Control of leaf vascular patterning by polar auxin transport. *Genes Dev.* 20:1015–27

Seaman MN. 2005. Recycle your receptors with retromer. *Trends Cell Biol.* 15(2):68–75

Seet LF, Hong W. 2006. The Phox (PX) domain proteins and membrane traffic. *Biochim. Biophys. Acta* 1761(8):878–96

Shevell DE, Kunkel T, Chua NH. 2000. Cell wall alterations in the *Arabidopsis emb30* mutant. *Plant Cell* 12(11):2047–60

Shevell DE, Leu WM, Gillmor CS, Xia G, Feldmann KA. 1994. *EMB30* is essential for normal cell division, cell expansion, and cell adhesion in *Arabidopsis* and encodes a protein that has similarity to Sec7. *Cell* 77:1051–62

Shimada T, Koumoto Y, Li L, Yamazaki M, Kondo M, et al. 2006. AtVPS29, a putative component of a retromer complex, is required for the efficient sorting of seed storage proteins. *Plant Cell Physiol.* 47(9):1187–94

Shitara Y, Kato Y, Sugiyama Y. 1998. Effect of brefeldin A and lysosomotropic reagents on intracellular trafficking of epidermal growth factor and transferrin in Madin-Darby canine kidney epithelial cells. *J. Control Release* 55(1):35–43

Sieberer T, Seifert GJ, Hauser MT, Grisafi P, Fink GR, Luschnig C. 2000. Post-transcriptional control of the *Arabidopsis* auxin efflux carrier EIR1 requires AXR1. *Curr. Biol.* 10(24):1595–98

Smith RS, Guyomarch S, Mandel T, Reinhardt D, Kuhlemeier C, Prusinkiewicz P. 2006. A plausible model of phyllotaxis. *Proc. Natl. Acad. Sci. USA* 103:1301–6

Souter M, Topping J, Pullen M, Friml J, Palme K, et al. 2002. *hydra* mutants of *Arabidopsis* are defective in sterol profiles and auxin and ethylene signaling. *Plant Cell* 14(5):1017–31

Steeves TA, Sussex IM. 1989. Determination of leaves and branches. In *Patterns in Plant Development*, ed. TA Steeves, IM Sussex, pp. 139–44. Cambridge, UK: Cambridge Univ. Press

Steinmann T, Geldner N, Grebe M, Mangold S, Jackson CL, et al. 1999. Coordinated polar localization of auxin efflux carrier PIN1 by GNOM ARF GEF. *Science* 286:316–18

Sutter JU, Sieben C, Hartel A, Eisenach C, Thiel G, Blatt MR. 2007. Abscisic acid triggers the endocytosis of the *Arabidopsis* KAT1 K$^+$ channel and its recycling to the plasma membrane. *Curr. Biol.* 17(16):1396–402

Swarup K, Benková E, Swarup R, Casimiro I, Péret B, et al. 2008. The auxin influx carrier LAX3 promotes lateral root emergence. *Nat. Cell Biol.* 10:946–54

Swarup R, Friml J, Marchant A, Ljung K, Sandberg G, et al. 2001. Localization of the auxin permease AUX1 suggests two functionally distinct hormone transport pathways operate in the *Arabidopsis* root apex. *Genes Dev.* 15:2648–53

Takano J, Miwa K, Yuan L, von Wirén N, Fujiwara T. 2005. Endocytosis and degradation of BOR1, a boron transporter of *Arabidopsis thaliana*, regulated by boron availability. *Proc. Natl. Acad. Sci. USA* 102(34):12276–81

Tanaka H, Dhonukshe P, Brewer PB, Friml J. 2006. Spatiotemporal asymmetric auxin distribution: a means to coordinate plant development. *Cell Mol. Life Sci.* 63:2738–54

Teh OK, Moore I. 2007. An ARF-GEF acting at the Golgi and in selective endocytosis in polarized plant cells. *Nature* 448(7152):493–96

Terasaka K, Blakeslee JJ, Titapiwatanakun B, Peer WA, Bandyopadhyay A, et al. 2005. PGP4, an ATP binding cassette P-glycoprotein, catalyzes auxin transport in *Arabidopsis thaliana* roots. *Plant Cell* 17:2922–39

Titapiwatanakun B, Blakeslee J, Bandyopadhyay A, Yang H, Mravec J, et al. 2008. ABCB19/PGP19 characterizes endocytosis-resistant membrane microdomains in *Arabidopsis*. *Plant J.* Submitted

Tuvim MJ, Adachi R, Hoffenberg S, Dickey BF. 2001. Traffic control: Rab GTPases and the regulation of interorganellar transport. *News Physiol. Sci.* 16:56–61

Utsuno K, Shikanai T, Yamada Y, Hashimoto T. 1998. *AGR*, an *Agravitropic* locus of *Arabidopsis thaliana*, encodes a novel membrane-protein family member. *Plant Cell Physiol.* 39(10):1111–18

Vieten A, Sauer M, Brewer PB, Friml J. 2007. Molecular and cellular aspects of auxin-transport-mediated development. *Trends Plant Sci.* 12(4):160–68

Vieten A, Vanneste S, Wiśniewska J, Benková E, Benjamins R, et al. 2005. Functional redundancy of PIN proteins is accompanied by auxin-dependent cross-regulation of PIN expression. *Development* 132:4521–31

Wan J, Taub ME, Shah D, Shen WC. 1992. Brefeldin A enhances receptor-mediated transcytosis of transferrin in filter-grown Madin-Darby canine kidney cells. *J. Biol. Chem.* 267(19):13446–50

Wang E, Pennington JG, Goldenring JR, Hunziker W, Dunn KW. 2001. Brefeldin A rapidly disrupts plasma membrane polarity by blocking polar sorting in common endosomes of MDCK cells. *J. Cell Sci.* 114(Pt. 18):3309–21

Weigel D, Jürgens G. 2002. Stem cells that make stems. *Nature* 415(6873):751–54

Weijers D, Sauer M, Meurette O, Friml J, Ljung K, et al. 2005. Maintenance of embryonic auxin distribution for apical-basal patterning by PIN-FORMED-dependent auxin transport in *Arabidopsis*. *Plant Cell* 17:2517–26

Willemsen V, Friml J, Grebe M, Van Den Toorn A, Palme K, Scheres B. 2003. Cell polarity and PIN protein positioning in *Arabidopsis* require STEROL METHYLTRANSFERASE1 function. *Plant Cell* 15:612–25

Wiśniewska J, Xu J, Seifertová D, Brewer PB, Růžička K, et al. 2006. Polar PIN localization directs auxin flow in plants. *Science* 312:883

Xu J, Hofhuis H, Heidstra R, Sauer M, Friml J, Scheres B. 2006. A molecular framework for plant regeneration. *Science* 311(5759):385–88

Yang Y, Hammes UZ, Taylor CG, Schachtman DP, Nielsen E. 2006. High-affinity auxin transport by the AUX1 influx carrier protein. *Curr. Biol.* 16:1123–27

Zažímalová E, Krecek P, Skůpa P, Hoyerová K, Petrásek J. 2007. Polar transport of the plant hormone auxin—the role of PIN-FORMED (PIN) proteins. *Cell Mol. Life Sci.* 64(13):1621–37

Zegzouti H, Anthony RG, Jahchan N, Bögre L, Christensen SK. 2006. Phosphorylation and activation of PINOID by the phospholipid signaling kinase 3-phosphoinositide-dependent protein kinase 1 (PDK1) in *Arabidopsis*. *Proc. Natl. Acad. Sci. USA* 103(16):6404–9

Shows that subcellular polarity of the PIN localization is determined by the directionality of auxin flow during gravitropism.

Regulation of APC/C Activators in Mitosis and Meiosis

Jillian A. Pesin and Terry L. Orr-Weaver*

Whitehead Institute and Department of Biology, Massachusetts Institute of Technology, Cambridge, Massachusetts 02142; email: weaver@wi.mit.edu

Annu. Rev. Cell Dev. Biol. 2008. 24:475–99

First published online as a Review in Advance on July 3, 2008

The *Annual Review of Cell and Developmental Biology* is online at cellbio.annualreviews.org

This article's doi:
10.1146/annurev.cellbio.041408.115949

1081-0706/08/1110-0475$20.00

*Corresponding author.

Key Words

Cdc20, Cdh1, Emi1, spindle assembly checkpoint, meiosis-specific activators, Emi2

Abstract

The anaphase-promoting complex/cyclosome (APC/C) is a multisubunit E3 ubiquitin ligase that triggers the degradation of multiple substrates during mitosis. Cdc20/Fizzy and Cdh1/Fizzy-related activate the APC/C and confer substrate specificity through complex interactions with both the core APC/C and substrate proteins. The regulation of Cdc20 and Cdh1 is critical for proper APC/C activity and occurs in multiple ways: targeted protein degradation, phosphorylation, and direct binding of inhibitory proteins. During the specialized divisions of meiosis, the activity of the APC/C must be modified to achieve proper chromosome segregation. Recent studies show that one way in which APC/C activity is modified is through the use of meiosis-specific APC/C activators. Furthermore, regulation of the APC/C during meiosis is carried out by both mitotic regulators of the APC/C as well as meiosis-specific regulators. Here, we review the regulation of APC/C activators during mitosis and the role and regulation of the APC/C during female meiosis.

Contents

APC/C: anaphase-promoting complex/cyclosome

E3 ubiquitin ligase: a protein or protein complex that covalently attaches ubiquitin to a lysine residue on a target protein

Fzy: Fizzy

Fzr: Fizzy-related

INTRODUCTION

Proteolysis is a key mechanism that drives the events of mitosis. The rapid degradation of mitotic proteins provides an irreversible and directional switch to restart the cell cycle after division. The anaphase-promoting complex/cyclosome (APC/C) is a large multisubunit E3 ubiquitin ligase that targets substrates for degradation through the addition of a polyubiquitin chain onto target proteins, which are then recognized and degraded by the 26S proteasome (reviewed in Peters 2006).

Cdc20/Fzy (Fizzy) and Cdh1/Fzr (Fizzy-related) compose the noncore subunits of the APC/C and activate and confer substrate speci-

ficity to the complex (**Table 1**) (Dawson et al. 1995, Schwab et al. 1997, Sigrist & Lehner 1997, Visintin et al. 1997). Cdc20 directs the ubiquitination of Securin, mitotic cyclins, and other substrates for anaphase onset. Cdc20 is responsible for the separation of sister chromatids because the degradation of Securin leads to the activation of the Separase protease, which cleaves the cohesin complex ring responsible for physically attaching the sister chromatids. Cdh1 targets mitotic cyclins and additional substrates for degradation in mitotic exit and G1. The form of the APC/C with a specific activator is designated by a superscript, for example, APC/C^{Cdc20}. Cdc20 and Cdh1 are members of the Cdc20 protein family, whose members contain seven WD-40 repeats in their C terminus (for a review, see Smith et al. 1999). These repeats form a seven-bladed propeller structure that mediates protein-protein interactions. The mechanism of APC/C activation and substrate specification by these activators has been the subject of much research in the past several years (reviewed in Thornton & Toczyski 2006).

One important way in which APC/C activity is governed is through the regulation of these activators that act as substrate adaptors. Because the activators are essential for APC/C activity and substrate specificity, their regulation plays a crucial role in determining which target proteins are degraded as well as the timing of their degradation. In this review we focus on the control of Cdc20/Fzy and Cdh1/Fzr in mitosis and on the regulation of these activators as well as meiosis-specific activators in meiosis. (Although the nomenclature differs between experimental organisms, for consistency in this review we refer to proteins by capitalizing the first letter of the name, and genes are in lowercase italic font.)

REGULATION OF Cdc20/Fzy IN THE MITOTIC CELL CYCLE

One mechanism of regulation of APC/C^{Cdc20} is via the control of protein levels of Cdc20. In this section we discuss this control first and then

Table 1 Orthologs of APC/C activators, inhibitors, and other APC/C pathway components[a]

	Saccharomyces cerevisiae	*Schizosaccharomyces pombe*	*Drosophila melanogaster*	*Xenopus laevis*	Mouse
APC/C activators	Cdc20	Slp1	Fzy	Fizzy	Cdc20
	Cdh1/Hct1	Ste9	Fzr	Fizzy-related	Cdh1
Meiosis-specific APC/C activators	Ama1	?[b]	?	n/i[c]	n/i
	?	?	Cort	n/i	n/i
	?	Mfr1/Fzr1	?	n/i	n/i
	?	?	Fzr2	n/i	n/i
APC/C inhibitors	n/i	n/i	Rca1	Emi1	Emi1
	n/i	n/i	n/i	Erp1	Emi2
	Mnd2	n/i	n/i	n/i	n/i
	n/i	Mes1	n/i	n/i	n/i
	Acm1	n/i	n/i	n/i	n/i
Additional regulators of the metaphase-anaphase transition	Esp1	Cut1	Sse + Thr	Separase	Separase
	Pds1	Cut2	Pim	Securin	Securin
	Cdc5	Plo1	Polo	Plx1	Plk

[a]Orthologous genes from each species are contained in one row.

[b]It is unknown what the exact homologous relationship is between the meiosis-specific activators that have been identified in yeast and *Drosophila*.

[c]n/i, not identified.

review additional inhibitory mechanisms affecting APC/C^{Cdc20} in mitosis (**Figure 1**). Cdc20 protein accumulates in S phase, peaks in mitosis, and drops in G1. A combination of transcriptional upregulation in mitosis and protein degradation in G1 contributes to this profile (Fang et al. 1998, Prinz et al. 1998). Control of Cdc20 transcription is best understood in *Saccharomyces cerevisiae*, in which its cell cycle regulation is dependent on Cks1, a small Cdk-associated protein that binds to the Cdc20 promoter. It appears that Cks1 can displace Cdc28 (Cdk1) and promote association of the proteasome, which enhances Cdc20 transcription (Morris et al. 2003). It is not known whether this mechanism controls Cdc20 transcription in higher eukaryotes, but Cdc20 transcription is negatively regulated by p53 and p21 in mammalian cells (Kidokoro et al. 2008).

Cdc20 protein is subjected to APC/C-triggered degradation because it is one of several targets of APC/C^{Cdh1} when APC/C^{Cdh1} becomes active late in mitosis (**Figure 1**) (Prinz et al. 1998). Degradation of *S. cerevisiae* Cdc20 is dependent on the presence of its D-box, a recognition motif found in most APC/C substrates, in Cdc20's N terminus (Prinz et al. 1998). Vertebrate Cdc20 sequences do not contain a D-box, and analysis of human Cdc20 led to the identification of the KEN box, another recognition motif found mainly in APC/C^{Cdh1} substrates (Pfleger & Kirschner 2000). In mammalian oocytes and embryos, the degradation of Cdc20 is mediated through an additional motif called the CRY box (Reis et al. 2006b).

Another major player contributing to the presence of functional Cdc20 in cells is the CCT (chaperonin-containing TCP1) chaperonin. In *S. cerevisiae* CCT is required for proper folding of Cdc20 in an ATP-dependent manner. CCT-dependent folding of Cdc20 is required for its associations and activity with the APC/C and for its regulation by the spindle checkpoint (Camasses et al. 2003).

In addition to control of the activity of APC/C^{Cdc20} by regulation of levels of Cdc20 protein in the cell, APC/C^{Cdc20} can be inhibited by the Emi1 (Early mitotic inhibitor 1) protein, by the spindle assembly checkpoint, and by PKA signaling, as detailed below.

Securin: a protein that inhibits the catalytic activity of Separase. It is also called Pds1 in budding yeast, Cut2 in fission yeast, and Pim in *Drosophila* (**Table 1**)

Separase: a cysteine protease that triggers anaphase by cleaving a cohesin complex subunit to release sister chromatid cohesion

Sister chromatids: replicated copies of a single chromosome

Sister chromatid cohesion: the physical attachment of sister chromatids mediated by the cohesin complex

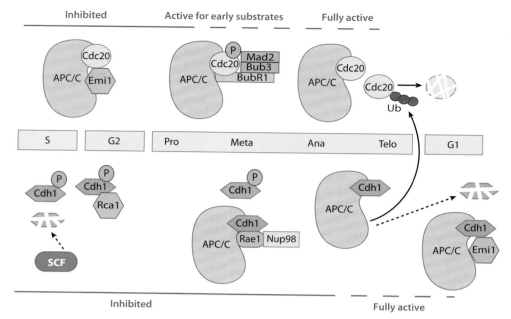

Figure 1

Regulation of Cdc20 and Cdh1 during the cell cycle. (*Top*) During S and G2 phases, Emi1 is thought to bind and inhibit APC/C^{Cdc20}. Emi1 is degraded in prometaphase, and APC/C^{Cdc20} becomes active against early mitotic APC/C substrates like Cyclin A and Nek2A. In prometaphase, APC/C^{Cdc20} remains inhibited from targeting Cyclin B, Securin, and other substrates by the spindle assembly checkpoint through direct binding of Mad2, Bub3, and BubR1. Upon release of the spindle assembly checkpoint, APC/C^{Cdc20} becomes fully active. In late anaphase and G1, Cdc20 is targeted by APC/C^{Cdh1} for degradation by the proteasome. Cdc20 will not be expressed again until S phase. (*Bottom*) Phosphorylation by cyclin-dependent kinases inhibits Cdh1 from associating with the core APC/C in S, G2, and M phases. In *Drosophila*, Rca1 is thought to inhibit Cdh1 in G2, and in vertebrates Emi1 is thought to inhibit APC/C^{Cdh1} at the G1-S transition. Recent findings suggest that APC/C^{Cdh1} must be inhibited from targeting Securin from degradation by Rae1-Nup98 in metaphase. In budding yeast, the inhibitor Acm1 binds to Cdh1 (not shown) until it is degraded by APC/C^{Cdc20}, providing an additional mechanism to restrict the timing of APC/C^{Cdh1} activation. Dephosphorylation of Cdh1 by Cdc14 phosphatase as well as a decrease in mitotic Cdk-Cyclin activity lead to loss of inhibitory phosphorylation on Cdh1 in late mitosis and allow for full activation of APC/C^{Cdh1} in late mitosis and G1. In addition, Cdh1 may be subject to ubiquitin (Ub)-mediated degradation in late G1 by APC/C^{Cdh1} (indicated by *dashed arrow*) and in S phase by SCF ubiquitin ligase (SCF). See text for references. Pro, prophase; Meta, metaphase; Ana, anaphase; Telo, telophase.

Emi1

The Emi1 protein inhibits APC/C^{Cdc20} activity by its ability to bind to Cdc20 and the core APC/C complex. As discussed in the next section, Emi1 also inhibits APC/C^{Cdh1}. Emi1 contains three motifs important for its function: an F-box protein-protein interaction domain, a C-terminal Zn^{2+}-binding region (ZBR), and a D-box (**Figure 2**). Emi1 was initially identified in *Xenopus*. In cycling embryos, levels of Emi1 increase in S phase and decrease in mi-

tosis, and the addition of recombinant Emi1 to cycling egg extracts stabilizes APC/C substrates and prevents their ubiquitination. One critical cell cycle function of Emi1 is to permit the accumulation of mitotic cyclin proteins during G2 to promote entry into mitosis and to block re-replication of DNA (Di Fiore & Pines 2007).

Emi1 inhibits APC/C activity in part by binding directly to Cdc20, but it also binds the APC/C core (Reimann et al. 2001a,b; Miller et al. 2006). Assays using an Emi1-affinity

Meiosis: two sequential cell divisions that generate four haploid cells from one diploid cell

column showed that Emi1 efficiently captures APC/C in the presence or absence of Cdc20 or Cdh1, suggesting that Emi1 binds to the APC/C core independently of an interaction with an activator protein (Miller et al. 2006). This direct interaction is dependent on the D-box in the C terminus of Emi1, but not on the ZBR domain. Both the D-box and the ZBR domain, however, contribute to Emi1's ability to compete with APC/C substrates for binding to the APC/C and to inhibit APC/C's ubiquitination activity. Finally, wild-type Emi1 is a poor substrate of the APC/C, but mutation of the ZBR domain converts Emi1 into an efficient D-box-dependent APC/C substrate. Thus, Emi1 acts as a pseudosubstrate inhibitor of the APC/C. The D-box is the domain through which Emi1 binds the D-box receptor on the core APC/C, whereas the ZBR domain seems to inhibit access of substrates to the complex.

Several mechanisms regulate levels of Emi1 in a cell cycle–dependent manner. Transcription of the Emi1 gene is activated at the G1-S transition by the E2F transcription factor. Emi1 itself is targeted for degradation by another E3 ubiquitin ligase, the $SCF^{\beta-TrCP}$ complex (**Figure 2**). Emi1 is protected from SCF-mediated degradation outside of mitosis in at least two ways. Recognition of Emi1 by the SCF requires phosphorylation by the Plk1 kinase (**Figure 2a**). In S/G2 phases, the Evi5 oncogene binds directly to Emi1 and blocks phosphorylation of Emi1 by Plk1, thus preventing recognition of Emi1 by $SCF^{\beta-TrCP}$ (Eldridge et al. 2006). Pin1, a peptidyl-prolyl *cis/trans* isomerase, seems to inhibit the degradation of Emi1 during G2. Emi1 associates with Pin1 in vivo during G2 and is stabilized by Pin1 in an isomerization-dependent pathway that prevents an association between Emi1 and $SCF^{\beta-TrCP}$ (Bernis et al. 2007).

Emi1 degradation in late prophase immediately precedes Cyclin A degradation by the APC/C, and overexpression of nondegradable Emi1 in mammalian cells causes a prometaphase block (Margottin-Goguet et al. 2003). It is not clear, however, that Emi1 degradation causes or even is essential for activation of APC/C^{Cdc20} (Di Fiore & Pines 2007).

Emi1 additionally functions as a member of a novel regulatory network END (Emi1/NuMA/dynein-dynactin), which restricts the activity of APC/C in early mitosis (Ban et al. 2007). A population of Emi1, along with the APC/C, localizes to spindle poles in early mitosis after the bulk of Emi1 has been degraded via $SCF^{\beta-TrCP}$ (Hansen et al. 2004, Ban et al. 2007). This localization is dependent on the binding of Emi1 and APC/C to microtubules through the action of dynein-dynactin, a minus-end-directed microtubule motor. APC/C, Emi1, and NuMA, a nuclear matrix and spindle assembly protein, form a complex in mitosis that spatially restricts APC/C activity. Emi1 promotes NuMA-dependent formation of microtubule asters through its inhibition of Cyclin B degradation by the APC/C at spindle poles (Ban et al. 2007).

Spindle Assembly Checkpoint

The spindle assembly checkpoint (SAC) is a surveillance mechanism that prevents premature separation of sister chromatids in mitosis by monitoring the attachment of spindles to microtubules in prometaphase. SAC inhibits the ability of APC/C^{Cdc20} to target substrates for degradation, particularly Cyclin B and Securin, to prevent anaphase onset until each kinetochore is stably bioriented on the spindle. Inhibition of Cdc20 by SAC involves many proteins and several different mechanisms, which are not discussed here but are well-reviewed by Musacchio & Salmon (2007). Exciting recent developments in the spindle checkpoint field have revealed a role for auto-ubiquitination of Cdc20 in inactivation of the checkpoint (Reddy et al. 2007, Stegmeier et al. 2007). Important structural data for Mad2, a key spindle checkpoint protein, have provided insights into conformational changes in the protein associated with binding to Cdc20 and inhibition

SCF complex: Skp-, Cullin-, F-box-containing complex

of APC/C^{Cdc20}. These changes, mediated through dimerization, may serve to propagate a signal from improperly attached kinetochores (Mapelli et al. 2007; Yang et al. 2007, 2008).

DNA Damage and PKA Pathway

One output of the DNA damage checkpoint is arrest of the cell cycle in the G2-M transition and the metaphase-to-anaphase transition. In *S. cerevisiae* the PKA pathway inhibits the

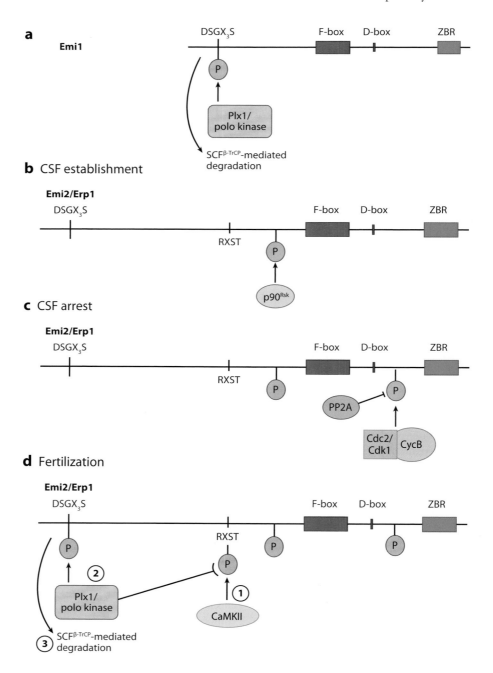

metaphase-to-anaphase transition in response to DNA damage (Searle et al. 2004). An accumulation of single-stranded DNA at telomeres causes a PKA-dependent stabilization of Clb2 and Pds1 and phosphorylation of Cdc20. Cdc20 contains two consensus sites for PKA phosphorylation that are required for this DNA damage–induced modification. In the presence of DNA damage, Cdc20 does not interact with Clb2, causing a metaphase arrest. When the phosphorylation sites of Cdc20 are mutated, Cdc20 does interact with Clb2 upon DNA damage, and Pds1 and Clb2 are degraded with faster kinetics. These results suggest that DNA damage induces PKA phosphorylation of Cdc20 to inhibit the targeting of APC/C substrates in mitosis. It is not known whether Cdc20 is inhibited by DNA damage in other organisms.

REGULATION OF Cdh1/Fzr IN THE MITOTIC CELL CYCLE

APC/C^{Cdh1} activity is regulated by protein levels as well as phosphorylation of the Cdh1 activator. In addition, APC/C^{Cdh1} activity is controlled by Emi1 and by several other proteins detailed below. Cdh1 RNA levels are constant throughout the cell cycle, and Cdh1 protein levels are high in mitosis but lowered in late-G1 and S phases (Prinz et al. 1998, Kramer et al. 2000, Hsu et al. 2002). The decrease in Cdh1 levels in late G1 and S phases is thought to be due to E3 ubiquitin ligase–mediated protein degradation, both via auto-activity of APC/C^{Cdh1} and the SCF (**Figure 1**). Cdh1 contains two putative D-boxes that are required for its degradation in G1, consistent with Cdh1 targeting its own degradation. Furthermore, Cdh1 is ubiquitinated in vitro and degraded in an APC/C^{Cdh1}-dependent manner (Listovsky et al. 2004). In S phase, Cdh1 levels remain low, but APC/C^{Cdh1} cannot be responsible for maintaining low levels of Cdh1 at this stage because it is inactivated by inhibitory phosphorylation. Benmaamar & Pagano (2005) investigated a possible role for SCF in the degradation of Cdh1 at this cell cycle stage. They found that inactivation of SCF by expression of a dominant-negative Cul1, a subunit of SCF, or by RNA interference against Cul1 results in an accumulation of Cdh1, suggesting that SCF activity is required either directly or indirectly for the degradation of Cdh1.

Phosphorylation inhibits the association of Cdh1 with APC/C. Cdh1 is phosphorylated by cyclin-dependent kinases during S, G2, and M phases, and only upon dephosphorylation in late mitosis and G1 can it bind and activate APC/C (**Figure 1**) (Zachariae et al. 1998, Jaspersen et al. 1999, Lukas et al. 1999, Blanco

Spindle assembly checkpoint (SAC): ensures that chromosomes do not segregate until they are properly attached to the spindle

---

Figure 2

Structure and regulation of Emi1 and Emi2/Erp1 (Early mitotic inhibitor 1 and 2 and Emi-related protein 1, respectively). (*a*) The Emi1 protein contains an F-box domain, a C-terminal Zn^{2+}-binding region (ZBR), and a D-box. The role of the F-box is unclear, but the D-box is the domain through which Emi1 binds the D-box receptor on the core APC/C, whereas the ZBR domain seems to inhibit access of substrates to the complex. See text for further details and references. Emi1 is a substrate of the E3 ubiquitin ligase SCF$^{\beta-TrCP}$ (Guardavaccaro et al. 2003, Margottin-Goguet et al. 2003). Phosphorylation by both Cdk and Plk1 contributes to recognition and ubiquitination of Emi1 by SCF$^{\beta-TrCP}$ in late prophase (Margottin-Goguet et al. 2003, Hansen et al. 2004, Moshe et al. 2004). (*b*) The Emi2/Erp1 protein also contains an F-box domain, a C-terminal ZBR, and a D-box. Phosphorylation of Emi2/Erp1 by p90^{Rsk}, part of the pathway that establishes cytostatic factor (CSF) arrest, is required for Emi2/Erp1 stability during oocyte maturation. (*c*) Phosphorylation of Emi2/Erp1 by Cdc2 (Cdk1)/CycB (Cyclin B) may disrupt the interaction between Emi2/Erp1 and APC/C. The action of the PP2A phosphatase counteracts this phosphorylation so that Emi2/Erp1 inhibits the APC/C during CSF arrest. Additional sites of Cdc2 (Cdk1)/CycB phosphorylation counteracted by PP2A have been recently mapped N-terminal to the p90^{Rsk} phosphorylation site (J.Q. Wu et al. 2007). (*d*) Upon fertilization, activated calmodulin kinase II (CaMKII) (*1*) acts as a priming kinase for Plx1 on Emi2/Erp1. Phosphorylation by Plx1 (*2*) targets Emi2/Erp1 for degradation targeted by SCF$^{\beta-TrCP}$ (*3*). See text for further details and references.

et al. 2000, Kramer et al. 2000, Yamaguchi et al. 2000, Huang et al. 2001, Sørensen et al. 2001, Keck et al. 2007).

Like Cdc20, Cdh1 is also subject to regulation by several inhibitors. However, unlike Cdc20, it seems to be crucial for the cell to modulate APC/C^{Cdh1} activity throughout the cell cycle, even at times when Cdh1 is already subject to inhibitory phosphorylation.

Emi1/Rca1

Emi1 is important for inhibiting APC/C^{Cdh1} at the G1-to-S-phase transition (**Figure 1**). Emi1 binds to Cdh1 and inhibits APC/C^{Cdh1} in vitro (Reimann et al. 2001b, Miller et al. 2006). Similar to Cyclin A, Emi1 transcription is activated by E2F at the G1-to-S-phase transition. HeLa cells depleted of Emi1 by RNA interference fail to accumulate Cyclin A and do not enter S phase. Overexpression of Cdh1 causes a G1 arrest. This arrest can be overcome by overexpression of Emi1, suggesting that Emi1 regulates S phase entry via inhibition of APC/C^{Cdh1} (Hsu et al. 2002).

The *Drosophila* ortholog of Emi1, *regulator of cyclin A1* (*rca1*), when mutated, causes an embryonic cell cycle arrest identical to *cyclin A* mutants. Ectopic expression of *rca1* drives cells into S phase and causes an increase in Cyclin A protein levels (Dong et al. 1997). A subsequent study demonstrated that Rca1 acts to inhibit APC/C$^{Fzr/Cdh1}$ in G2 (Grosskortenhaus & Sprenger 2002). Although vertebrate Emi1 is thought to inhibit both Cdc20 and Cdh1, Rca1 seems to affect only Cdh1. Grosskortenhaus & Sprenger (2002) failed to detect an association between Fzy/Cdc20 and Rca1 and confirmed through genetic studies that the effect of Rca1 on cyclin levels is specific to Fzr. It is not clear whether, in addition to its role in G2, Rca1 also regulates S phase entry in *Drosophila* embryos or whether Emi1 acts to inhibit Cdh1 in G2 in vertebrate cells.

RASSF1A

RASSF1A is a tumor suppressor gene that is silenced by promoter methylation in lung cancer patients. Overexpression of RASSF1A induces mitotic arrest and the accumulation of Cyclins A and B in HeLa cells, whereas depletion of RASSF1A by RNA interference accelerates cyclin degradation and mitotic progression (Song et al. 2004). RASSF1A was once thought to inhibit APC/C^{Cdc20}, but a recent report suggests that it restricts APC/C^{Cdh1} activity at the G1-S transition by inhibiting SCF$^{\beta-TrCP}$ and thereby permitting accumulation of Emi1 (Whitehurst et al. 2008).

Acm1

The APC/C^{Cdh1} modulator 1 (Acm1) protein was identified in *S. cerevisiae* by its ability to bind to Cdh1 together with a 14-3-3 protein (Martinez et al. 2006, Dial et al. 2007). Acm1 inhibits Cdh1 activity as a pseudosubstrate, and it provides an additional mechanism to restrict Cdh1 activity to the proper cell cycle phase. The inhibitory effect of Acm1 is released by its ubiquitination by APC/C^{Cdc20} after the metaphase-to-anaphase transition, when it also becomes subject to ubiquitination by activated APC/C^{Cdh1} (Enquist-Newman et al. 2008). Although the protein is conserved among budding yeast species, orthologs have not been identified in other organisms (Martinez et al. 2006).

Rae1-Nup98

In mammalian cells, as in yeast, inhibitory phosphorylation of Cdh1 was concluded to fully inactivate APC/C^{Cdh1} during mitosis. An investigation of the roles of Rae1 and Nup98, however, revealed an additional layer of regulation of APC/C^{Cdh1} in mammalian mitosis as well. This work suggests that, at least in mammalian cells, Cdh1 is bound to APC/C early in mitosis and can participate in controlling the metaphase-to-anaphase transition. Rae1 is an mRNA export factor that acts by anchoring Nup98, a nucleoporin, to the nuclear pore complex (Pritchard et al. 1999). Splenocytes from Rae1$^{+/-}$Nup98$^{+/-}$ mice exhibit premature separation of sister chromatids, and Rae1$^{+/-}$Nup98$^{+/-}$ murine embryonic fibroblasts contain decreased levels of Securin (Jeganathan et al. 2005). In mitotic HeLa cell extracts, Cdc27, Cdc16, and Cdh1 coimmunoprecipitate with Rae1 and Nup98, but Cdh1 rather than Cdc20 is associated. Rae1-Nup98 inhibits ubiquitination of Securin but not that of Cyclin B by APC/C^{Cdh1}. Interestingly, Rae1-Nup98 dissociates from APC/C^{Cdh1} at the same time that BubR1 dissociates from APC/C^{Cdc0} upon release of the spindle checkpoint–mediated metaphase arrest (Jeganathan et al. 2005). These results suggest that, contrary to the previous model, APC/C^{Cdh1} may play a role in targeting Securin for degradation upon anaphase onset. How Rae1-Nup98 mediates inhibition of APC/C^{Cdh1}, as well as how Rae1-Nup98 is targeted to the APC/C and triggered to dissociate from the APC/C, remain to be elucidated.

Finally, in addition to the Cdc20 and Cdh1 inhibitors discussed above, two transcription factors, CBP and p300, are thought to be positive regulators of the APC/C in mitosis (Turnell et al. 2005). In mammalian cells, CBP and p300 are associated with an active APC/C complex in vivo, and they coimmunoprecipitate with core APC/C subunits as well as with both Cdc20 and Cdh1. Knockdown of CBP by RNA interference leads to increases in Cyclin B and Plk1 levels and an accumulation of cells in mitosis. APC/C precipitated from these CBP-depleted cells has reduced ubiquitination activity (Turnell et al. 2005). The mechanism by which CBP-p300 positively regulates mitotic APC/C is not yet understood.

It is becoming increasingly clear that regulation of APC/C activators in mitosis as well as in G1, S, and G2 occurs in a complex network and at multiple levels: transcriptional control, protein stability, phosphorylation, and direct binding of inhibitors.

ROLE OF THE APC/C IN FEMALE MEIOSIS

Meiosis is a modified cell division in which one parent cell generates four haploid cells, in contrast to the two identical diploid cells generated in a canonical mitotic cell division. Understanding the function and regulation of the APC/C in meiosis presents an interesting and complex problem given the differences of both chromosome segregation dynamics and the developmental context in meiosis compared with mitosis.

In meiosis, two rounds of chromosome segregation without an intervening S phase generate haploid gametes. Both general cell cycle regulators as well as meiosis-specific proteins coordinate control of the meiotic divisions (reviewed in Marston & Amon 2004). Meiosis I is unique because homologous chromosome pairs, as opposed to sister chromatids, must be segregated from each other. Homologous chromosomes are held together by chiasmata and arm cohesion between the sister chromatids. Segregation is achieved by loss of cohesion along chromosome arms but not in the centromeric regions. Subsequently, in meiosis II, sister chromatids are segregated through loss of cohesion at the centromeres in a process very similar to that in mitosis. Regulation of APC/C activity is likely to be important in this process because Separase must be activated twice, in both meiosis I and meiosis II, through APC/C-mediated degradation of Securin.

Furthermore, the absence of an S phase in between meiosis I and meiosis II also likely requires specialized regulation of the APC/C. In *Xenopus* oocytes, Cdk activity is not abolished, but rather maintained at a low level in between the two meiotic divisions (**Figure 3**) (Furuno et al. 1994, Iwabuchi et al. 2000). Cdk1/Cyclin B activity must be kept at an intermediate level to satisfy the unique requirements of meiosis: Cdk activity must be low enough to allow for disassembly of the meiosis I spindle but high enough to repress the initiation of DNA replication. Presumably, APC/C-mediated degradation of cyclins must be regulated to contribute to this modulation of Cdk activity.

Regulation of APC/C activity in meiosis is particularly crucial during oogenesis of multicellular organisms. In most animals meiosis is arrested twice to coordinate development of the oocyte with the events of meiosis (**Figure 3**)

Homologous chromosomes: chromosomes from different parent cells containing the same genetic loci that pair and then segregate during meiosis I

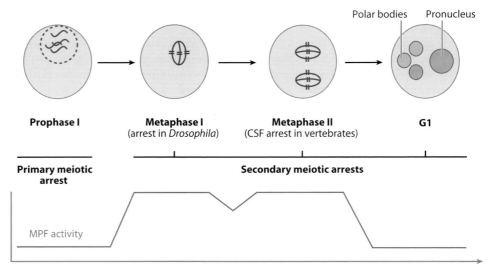

Figure 3

Meiotic progression in females. Oocytes are arrested in prophase I to allow for oocyte growth and differentiation before initiation of the meiotic divisions. Then, oocytes arrest again at different times to await egg activation or fertilization. This secondary arrest ensures that the completion of meiosis is properly coordinated with fertilization of the oocyte. In *Drosophila*, the secondary meiotic arrest takes place in metaphase I. Egg activation releases this arrest. In most vertebrates the secondary meiotic arrest takes place in metaphase II and is called cytostatic factor (CSF) arrest. Fertilization releases the CSF arrest to permit the completion of meiosis II. MPF [CycB/Cdc2 (Cdk1)] activity levels rise upon entry into the meiotic divisions. They must drop in between meiosis I and meiosis II for exit from meiosis I, but some activity must be maintained to suppress DNA replication in between the two divisions. MPF levels drop again at exit from meiosis II. See text for further details and references.

(reviewed in Kishimoto 2003, Tunquist & Maller 2003). During both meiotic arrests, APC/C activity must be suppressed. In prophase I, unscheduled activity of the APC/C may prevent proper maintenance of chromosome cohesion. In the secondary metaphase arrests, inhibition of the APC/C is crucial for preventing premature anaphase onset. Thus, understanding the function and regulation of the APC/C during meiosis is critical for understanding the control of chromosome segregation and cell cycle progression and the coordination of this control with developmental signals during meiosis.

Requirement for APC/C in Meiosis

A requirement for APC/C activity during the meiotic divisions has been shown in all or-

ganisms tested, with the exception of *Xenopus* oocytes. In yeast, Cdc20 is required for the degradation of Pds1/Securin and the resulting activation of Separase in both meiotic divisions (Salah & Nasmyth 2000). Separase activity is required for the degradation of Rec8, the meiosis-specific cohesin subunit, along chromosome arms to allow for homolog disjunction in meiosis I (Buonomo et al. 2000, Kitajima et al. 2003).

The requirement for APC/C in meiosis is conserved in multicellular organisms. In *Caenorhabditis elegans*, mutations in or RNA interference against several subunits of the APC/C cause a meiotic metaphase I arrest, as would be expected if Separase cleavage of cohesin were needed for release of arm cohesion and separation of homologs (Furuta et al. 2000, Golden et al. 2000, Davis et al. 2002).

Female-sterile mutations in *fzy* cause both meiosis I and meiosis II arrests in *Drosophila* eggs (Swan & Schupbach 2007). Finally, several studies in mouse oocytes have demonstrated a requirement for APC/C-mediated degradation of Securin and activation of Separase for Rec8 removal from chromosome arms and homolog disjunction in meiosis I (Herbert et al. 2003, Terret et al. 2003, Kudo et al. 2006). Although microinjection of *Xenopus* oocytes with antibodies against Fzy or Cdc27 or antisense oligonucleotides against Fzy does not disrupt progression through meiosis I but only causes an arrest in meiosis II (Peter et al. 2001, Taieb et al. 2001), it is possible that these experiments failed to eliminate APC/C activity. Securin and Cyclin B are degraded at anaphase I, reaccumulate before metaphase II, and are degraded again at anaphase II (Fan et al. 2006). Additionally, misexpression of Emi2/Erp1, an APC/C inhibitor that is active later in meiosis, induces a metaphase I arrest in *Xenopus* oocytes, again suggesting that APC/C is required for the transition from metaphase I to anaphase I (Ohe et al. 2007, Tung et al. 2007).

Meiosis-Specific APC/C Activators

An intriguing development in our knowledge of meiotic cell cycle control has been the identification of meiosis-specific APC/C activators in yeast and flies (**Table 1**). The existence of these activators suggests a unique role and set of substrates for the APC/C in meiosis that are outside of the functions of Cdc20 or Cdh1.

In yeast, meiosis-specific activators are expressed exclusively during meiosis and are required for proper spore formation (Cooper et al. 2000, Asakawa et al. 2001, Blanco et al. 2001). Ama1 in *S. cerevisiae* associates with the core APC/C throughout meiosis, although it does not become fully active until after meiosis I, when it is required for Clb1 and Pds1 degradation. Furthermore, it can drive the ubiquitination of Pds1 in vitro (Cooper et al. 2000, Oelschlaegel et al. 2005, Penkner et al. 2005). In *Schizosaccharomyces pombe* Mfr1/Fzr1 also associates with the core APC/C during meio-

sis and is required for the degradation of the M phase cyclin Cdc13. Degradation of Cdc13 in meiosis II is required for proper spore formation at the end of meiosis (Blanco et al. 2001).

In *Drosophila*, *cortex* (*cort*) encodes a distant member of the Cdc20/Fzy protein family that is transcribed only during oogenesis, and null mutants are viable but female sterile, indicative of a role solely in meiosis (Chu et al. 2001). *cort* mutant females lay eggs that never complete meiosis and arrest terminally in metaphase II (Lieberfarb et al. 1996, Page & Orr-Weaver 1996). *cort* seems to be required as soon as the transition from metaphase I to anaphase I occurs; meiosis II spindles often exhibit unequal numbers of chromosomes, indicating aberrant chromosome segregation in meiosis I (Page & Orr-Weaver 1996). Consistent with *cort* functioning as an APC/C activator, Cyclin A, B, and B3 levels are elevated in *cort* eggs, and misexpression of *cort* triggers degradation of these cyclins in wing imaginal discs (Pesin & Orr-Weaver 2007, Swan & Schupbach 2007).

The *Drosophila* genome also contains a fourth Cdc20-related gene, *fizzy-related 2* (*fzr2*), that is expressed exclusively in male meiosis. When misexpressed, *fzr2* can rescue *fzr* function by triggering degradation of Cyclin B, which suggests a true function for *fzr2* as an APC/C activator (Jacobs et al. 2002). The use of female meiosis–specific and male meiosis–specific APC/C activators in *Drosophila* provides an interesting system in which to delineate the meiosis-specific roles of APC/C in the two different developmental contexts of oogenesis and spermatogenesis.

Meiosis-specific activators are not the only APC/C activators present during meiosis. In *S. cerevisiae* both Cdc20 and Ama1 are thought to contribute to APC/C function in meiosis. The Ama1 protein is present beginning in premeiotic S phase, although it does not become essential for spore formation until late in meiosis (Cooper et al. 2000, Oelschlaegel et al. 2005, Penkner et al. 2005). This disparity in the timing of Ama1 presence and function is explained by the action of an APC/C^{Ama1} inhibitor that is

Germinal vesicle breakdown (GVBD): disintegration of the large meiotic nuclear envelope at the end of meiotic prophase I

discussed below. Cdc20, in contrast, is required in meiosis I; Cdc20 meiotic mutants arrest in metaphase I with high levels of Pds1 (Salah & Nasmyth 2000). However, both Ama1 and Cdc20 are likely to be involved in both meiotic divisions. Ama1 mutants do not arrest in meiosis I but do display a delay in spindle elongation and increases in Pds1 and Clb5 protein levels (Oelschlaegel et al. 2005). Cdc20 levels peak in both meiosis I and meiosis II, suggesting that it too is important for both divisions (Salah & Nasmyth 2000).

Similarly, in *Drosophila*, both *fzy* and *cort* are required for female meiotic divisions. Swan & Schupbach (2007) used double-mutant genetic analysis to demonstrate that *fzy* and *cort* have redundant roles in meiosis I but nonredundant roles in meiosis II. In *fzy* single mutants, a small percentage of eggs arrest with one spindle indicative of meiosis I, but the majority of eggs arrest in anaphase II. In *cort* single mutants, a similar percentage of eggs arrest in meiosis I, but the rest arrest in metaphase II. Double mutants display an increased number of eggs arresting in meiosis I, consistent with a redundant role for these two genes in the first division. However, the remaining double-mutant eggs exhibit the *cort* mutant phenotype of arrest in metaphase II, suggesting that *cort* is epistatic to *fzy* in meiosis II. The effects of these mutations on localized Cyclin B degradation also support the idea that *cort* and *fzy* have nonredundant and different temporal roles in meiosis II: *cort* is required for the degradation of Cyclin B specifically at the spindle midzone, whereas *fzy* seems to target Cyclin B after *cort* and along the entire spindle.

In addition to Cort and Fzy playing some nonredundant roles in meiosis, their protein expression patterns during meiosis are quite different. Fzy is expressed at a constant level throughout oogenesis and embryogenesis, whereas Cort is specifically expressed in a narrow window during the female meiotic divisions (Pesin & Orr-Weaver 2007). Both posttranscriptional control and posttranslational control contribute to the unique expression pattern of Cort. Polyadenylation of *cort* mRNA

at oocyte maturation is controlled by the Gld2 poly(A) polymerase and is required for the appearance of the Cort protein as the oocyte enters the meiotic divisions (Pesin & Orr-Weaver 2007, Benoit et al. 2008). At the completion of meiosis, APC/C-dependent degradation of Cort ensures that the protein is no longer present in the subsequent rapid embryonic mitotic divisions. In this situation, the organism is utilizing existing developmental control mechanisms to restrict activity of a meiosis-specific form of the APC/C.

The role of Cdh1 in meiosis is not entirely clear. It appears to be important for prophase I and prometaphase I. In *S. cerevisiae*, *cdh1* mutant cells show incomplete synapsis of bivalents in prophase I (Penkner et al. 2005). This result may be due to a role for Cdh1 in meiosis, or Cdh1 may be required in the previous mitotic cell cycle, and its failure may affect the subsequent meiotic prophase. In mouse oocytes, APC/C^{Cdh1}-mediated degradation of substrates appears to be required for maintaining prophase I arrest and preventing entry into meiotic divisions (Reis et al. 2006a, Marangos et al. 2007). In contrast, injection of Cdh1 antisense oligonucelotides into *Xenopus* oocytes inhibits oocyte maturation and release of the prophase I arrest (Papin et al. 2004).

Reis et al. (2007) showed a role for Cdh1 after germinal vesicle breakdown (GVBD) in mouse oocytes. Injection of oocytes with *cdh1* antisense morpholinos accelerates progression through meiosis I, resulting in premature anaphase and nondisjunction of homologs. These defects are specific to inhibition of *cdh1* after GVBD. Furthermore, Cdc20 is degraded in these oocytes shortly after GVBD in a Cdh1-dependent manner. Cdc20 must be resynthesized for proper degradation of Cyclin B1 and Securin in metaphase I and polar body extrusion. These results suggest a new paradigm for the use of APC/C activators during meiosis. In this model, APC/C^{Cdh1} prolongs prometaphase I by causing degradation of Cdc20. This delay may serve to allow more time for homologs to congress properly at the metaphase I plate.

REGULATION OF THE APC/C IN MEIOSIS

Proper regulation of the APC/C in meiosis is crucial to prevent unscheduled APC/C activity and premature activation of Separase through Securin degradation. At both metaphase I and metaphase II, premature chromosome or sister chromatid segregation may lead to aneuploid gametes and offspring, which is a leading cause of spontaneous abortion and mental retardation (Hassold & Hunt 2001). Additionally, a unique feature of female meiosis is a prolonged prophase I arrest, up to several decades in length in humans, in which sister chromatid cohesion must be maintained for proper chromosome segregation in meiosis I.

Mnd2

As mentioned above, Ama1, the meiosis-specific APC/C activator in *S. cerevisiae*, is present beginning in premeiotic S phase yet is not required until late meiosis, suggesting that Ama1 may be inhibited in early meiosis. Two studies in *S. cerevisiae* revealed a crucial inhibitor of APC/C^{Ama1} in prophase I (**Figure 4**). Mnd2 was originally identified as being associated with the APC/C core (Hall et al. 2003, Passmore et al. 2003). Subsequently, genetic suppression and in vitro ubiquitination assays revealed that Mnd2 inhibits APC/C^{Ama1} (Oelschlaegel et al. 2005, Penkner et al. 2005). The association of Mnd2 with APC/C from meiotic cells can inhibit the ubiquitination activity of APC/C^{Ama1} but not that of APC/C^{Cdc20} or APC/C^{Cdh1} (Oelschlaegel et al. 2005). The mechanism of Mnd2 inhibition of APC/C^{Ama1} is unclear. In vivo, the absence of Mnd2 causes an increased association of Ama1 with the APC/C core, but upon addition in vitro, Ama1 equally coimmunoprecipitates with APC/C that is associated with Mnd2 or not (Oelschlaegel et al. 2005). The inhibitory actions of Mnd2 may occur after both Mnd2 and Ama1 are bound to APC/C.

The mutant phenotype of *mnd2Δ* reveals the disastrous consequences of unrestrained APC/C^{Ama1} activity in meiotic prophase I. *mnd2Δ* cells fail to accumulate Pds1 in S phase and prophase I and arrest in a prophase-like state (Oelschlaegel et al. 2005, Penkner et al. 2005). Furthermore, these cells show premature sister chromatid separation as well as a failure to fully synapse homologs. Both Oelschlaegel et al. (2005) and Penkner et al. (2005) demonstrated that these defects are the result of premature activation of Separase and cleavage of Rec8 in prophase I and are dependent on APC/C^{Ama1}-mediated degradation of Pds1.

Mnd2 inhibition of APC/C^{Ama1} must be relieved in late meiosis, when Ama1 becomes required for spore formation. Mnd2 protein disappears from meiotic cells during anaphase II, and this phenomenon is thought to be one way in which APC/C^{Ama1} becomes active at this time (Oelschlaegel et al. 2005, Penkner et al. 2005). Additionally, the activity of Cdk1 kinases may inhibit Ama1. Inhibition of Cdk1 in *cdc20* mutant metaphase I–arrested cells triggers spindle disassembly and Ama1-dependent degradation of Pds1 (Oelschlaegel et al. 2005). This result suggests that APC/C^{Cdc20}-mediated degradation of cyclins in meiosis I is required for the activation of APC/C^{Ama1} in meiosis II.

Emi1

In vertebrates Emi1 may function to limit APC/C activity during the prophase I arrest (**Figure 4**). Emi1 protein is present in mouse oocytes but is degraded at GVBD in a SCF$^{β-TrCP}$-dependent manner, mirroring the timing of Emi1 destruction in mitotic cells in late prophase (Marangos et al. 2007). Reduction of mouse Emi1 function by injection of morpholinos in prophase I delays entry into the first meiotic division by preventing the accumulation of Cyclin B necessary for maturation-promoting factor (MPF) activation and progression through meiosis I. APC/C^{Cdh1} activity mediates these effects of inhibiting Emi1 function in mouse oocytes (Marangos et al. 2007).

MPF: maturation-promoting factor

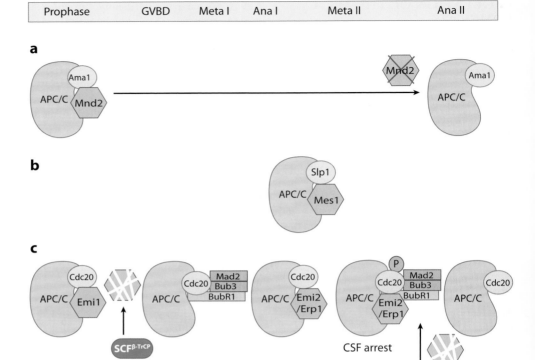

| Prophase | GVBD | Meta I | Ana I | Meta II | Ana II |

Figure 4

Meiotic APC/C regulators. (*a*) In *Saccharomyces cerevisiae* Mnd2 inhibits APC/C^{Ama1}, a meiosis-specific form of the APC/C, beginning in prophase I. Inhibition is not released until late meiosis, when the Mnd2 protein disappears from meiotic cells. Full activation of APC/C^{Ama1} may also require APC/C^{Cdc20}-mediated degradation of cyclins in meiosis I. (*b*) In *Schizosaccharomyces pombe* Mes1 is an inhibitor of APC/C$^{Slp1/Cdc20}$ in between the meiotic divisions. Mes1 is an APC/C substrate but is able to compete for binding to the APC/C more efficiently than can other substrates. (*c*) In vertebrate prophase I, prior to germinal vesicle breakdown (GVBD), inhibition of APC/C^{Cdh1} by Emi1 allows for an accumulation of MPF, which is required for entry into the first meiotic division. Emi1 is targeted for degradation by SCF$^{β-TrCP}$ at GVBD. The spindle assembly checkpoint is thought to regulate APC/C^{Cdc20} activity in meiosis I for proper homolog alignment and disjunction. Similar to the role of Mes1, Emi2/Erp1 (Emi-related protein 1) helps maintain low APC/C^{Cdc20} activity levels in between the two meiotic divisions. Emi2/Erp1 is also a main component of cytostatic factor (CSF) arrest and prevents APC/C^{Cdc20} from being active until fertilization. The spindle assembly checkpoint may play a role in establishing but not in maintaining CSF arrest. At fertilization, a transient increase in free cytosolic Ca^{2+} activates calmodulin kinase II and the phosphatase calcineurin. Calmodulin kinase II phosphorylates Emi2/Erp1, which ultimately leads to the degradation of Emi2/Erp1 by SCF$^{β-TrCP}$ (see **Figure 2**). Calcineurin dephosphorylates Apc3, a core APC/C subunit, and Cdc20/Fzy, both of which may contribute to activation of APC/C^{Cdc20} upon fertilization. See text for further references and details. Meta I and II denote metaphase I and II, respectively; Ana I and II denote anaphase I and II, respectively.

Exogenous Emi1 is rapidly degraded during oocyte maturation in *Xenopus* oocytes (Ohsumi et al. 2004). Emi1 may contribute to prophase I arrest in *Xenopus* as well as mouse, but problems with antibodies that cross react with both Emi1 and Emi2/Erp1 (see below) has led to confusion about its function in *Xenopus* meiosis (Tung & Jackson 2005).

Mes1

The transition between meiosis I and meiosis II requires a balance between lowering Cyclin B–Cdk activity sufficiently to exit meiosis I but maintaining levels high enough to suppress DNA replication and promote entry into meiosis II. In *S. pombe*, Mes1 may be the solution to this problem (**Figure 4**). *mes1* is transcribed in a narrow window between late meiosis I and late meiosis II (Mata et al. 2002). *mes1* mutants arrest before meiosis II and completely degrade M phase cyclin Cdc13 prematurely in anaphase I, instead of in anaphase II (Shimoda et al. 1985, Izawa et al. 2005). The *mes1* mutant phenotype is suppressed by mutation of *slp1*, the Cdc20 homolog in *S. pombe*, and the addition of Mes1 to a *Xenopus* egg extract inhibits APC/C activity; both of these observations are consistent with a role for Mes1 as an APC/C inhibitor (Izawa et al. 2005). Mes1 may inhibit APC/C^{Mfr1} in addition to APC/C^{Slp1} (**Table 1**), but this remains to be shown conclusively.

Mes1 appears to be a true substrate of the APC/C. It contains a KEN box and a D-box, and these motifs are required for its degradation by APC/C in an in vitro destruction assay performed in *Xenopus* egg extracts (Kimata et al. 2008). Furthermore, Mes1 is ubiquitinated, unlike other APC/C inhibitors, and this ubiquitination is required for partial degradation of Cyclin B in meiosis I and onset of anaphase I (Kimata et al. 2008). Nonubiquitulatable Mes1 cannot dissociate from a ternary APC/C-Cdc20-Mes1 complex, and this binding probably prevents APC/C from targeting other substrates. This study leads to several interesting questions about the mechanism of Mes1 inhibition of the APC/C. Mes1 behaves as a normal APC/C substrate, yet how is it able to compete for binding to the APC/C much more efficiently than do other substrates, and how does it stay bound to the complex? Further investigation should provide more insight into the regulation of Mes1 ubiquitination by the APC/C.

Emi2/Erp1

Just as Mes1 is required in *S. pombe* to inhibit APC/C activity in between meiosis I and meiosis II, Emi2/Erp1, a homolog of Emi1, is required in this role in *Xenopus* and mouse oocytes (**Figure 4**). Emi2/Erp1 is not expressed until after GVBD, and its expression is coincident with polyadenylation of *Emi2/Erp1* mRNA (Ohe et al. 2007, Tung et al. 2007). Inhibition of Emi2/Erp1 by injection of morpholinos or antisense oligonucleotides reduces Cyclin B2 reaccumulation after meiosis I, prevents entry into meiosis II, and, in the case of morpholino injection, induces DNA replication (Ohe et al. 2007, Tung et al. 2007). Injection of Emi2/Erp1 morpholinos into mouse oocytes generates a very similar phenotype, suggesting that Emi2/Erp1 inhibits APC/C-mediated degradation of Cyclin B after meiosis I to prevent DNA replication and to allow entry into meiosis II (Madgwick et al. 2006).

A second critical role for Emi2/Erp1 in meiosis is the inhibition of APC/C during cytostatic factor (CSF) arrest (**Figure 4**). Vertebrate eggs are arrested in metaphase II while they await fertilization. This arrest functions to prevent premature egg activation or the completion of meiosis before fertilization occurs. Many years of research determined that the establishment of CSF arrest involves the Mos/MAPK/p90^{Rsk} signaling pathway and Cyclin E/Cdk2 activity through the inhibition of APC/C^{Cdc20} (for a review, see Tunquist & Maller 2003). Release of CSF arrest is triggered by a transient increase in free cytosolic Ca^{2+} levels induced by fertilization.

Emi2/Erp1 is present in extracts prepared from CSF-arrested *Xenopus* eggs and degraded upon the addition of Ca^{2+}, a treatment known to release CSF arrest in these extracts (Schmidt et al. 2005). Furthermore, depletion of Emi2/Erp1 causes premature release from CSF arrest, independent of Ca^{2+} addition (Schmidt et al. 2005). Conversely, the addition of exogenous or nondegradable Emi2/Erp1 prevents Ca^{2+}-induced CSF release. Complementary

CSF: cytostatic factor

results were observed in intact *Xenopus* eggs (Tung et al. 2005). In mouse oocytes, Emi2/Erp1 appears to play the same role in CSF arrest. These effects are likely to occur through Emi2/Erp1 inhibition of APC/C^{Cdc20} because Emi2/Erp1 can inhibit ubiquitination of substrates by APC/C^{Cdc20} in vitro (Schmidt et al. 2005, Tung et al. 2005). In addition, mouse Emi2/Erp1 binds to Cdc20 in vitro (Shoji et al. 2006).

Recent studies in *Xenopus* have found additional sites of phosphorylation on Emi2/Erp1, some of which directly link Emi2/Erp1 to the Mos/MAPK/p90^{Rsk} pathway in CSF arrest (**Figure 2**). The ability of Emi2/Erp1 to inhibit APC/C after meiosis I and in CSF arrest is dependent on the MAPK pathway (Inoue et al. 2007). p90^{Rsk} phosphorylates Emi2/Erp1 in vitro, and these sites of phosphorylation are required in vivo for Emi2/Erp1 stability during oocyte maturation and for the CSF activity of Emi2/Erp1 (Inoue et al. 2007, Nishiyama et al. 2007a). This work strongly suggests that, at least in amphibian oocytes, Emi2/Erp1 is the effector protein of Mos/MAPK/p90^{Rsk} signaling in CSF arrest.

Nishiyama et al. (2007a) shed light on the mechanism of Emi2/Erp1 inhibition of APC/C. Phosphorylation of Emi2/Erp1 by p90^{Rsk} enhances the association of Emi2/Erp1 with the APC/C, consistent with the role of p90^{Rsk} in activating Emi2/Erp1 inhibitory activity. Like Emi1, Emi2/Erp1 contains a D-box that also enhances the association of Emi2/Erp1 with APC/C. This association is inhibited in vitro by D-box peptides, suggesting that Emi2/Erp1 blocks substrate access to the APC/C. In addition, phosphorylation of Emi2/Erp1 by Cyclin B/Cdc2 (Cdk1) at sites distinct from those targeted by CaMKII and p90^{Rsk} may disrupt the interaction between Emi2/Erp1 and APC/C (**Figure 2**) (Hansen et al. 2007, J.Q. Wu et al. 2007, Q. Wu et al. 2007). This phosphorylation is antagonized by protein phosphatase 2A (PP2A). PP2A is recruited to Emi2/Erp1 by p90^{Rsk} phosphorylation and may provide a feedback loop that serves to maintain proper levels of Cyclin B and Cdc2/Cdk1 kinase

activity during CSF arrest (J.Q. Wu et al. 2007).

Degradation of Emi2/Erp1 upon Ca^{2+}-induced CSF release appears to be the critical event that relieves the inhibition of APC/C^{Cdc20} and allows passage from metaphase II to anaphase II. Ca^{2+} plays a crucial role in controlling Emi2/Erp1 degradation by indirectly affecting phosphorylation of Emi2/Erp1 by Plx1 through its effect on calmodulin kinase II (CaMKII) (Lorca et al. 1993, Schmidt et al. 2005, Tung et al. 2005, Hansen et al. 2006). Plx1 kinase phosphorylation of Emi2/Erp1 promotes Emi2/Erp1 degradation by SCF$^{\beta-TrCP}$ (**Figure 2**). A relationship between CaMKII and Plx1 was shown by the observations that CSF release triggered by a constitutively active CaMKII (CamCat) requires Plx1 and Plx1-induced CSF release requires active CaMKII (Liu & Maller 2005). The polo-box domain (PBD) of Plx1 is thought to bind a phosphopeptide motif in target proteins generated by phosphorylation of the target by a priming kinase. Once Plx1 docks onto the target through its PBD, its phosphorylation of the target protein is enhanced. Phosphorylation of Emi2/Erp1 by CaMKII enhances Plx1 binding to and phosphorylation of Emi2/Erp1 in vitro, and degradation of Emi2/Erp1 in anaphase extracts is dependent on phosphorylation by CaMKII, strongly suggesting that CaMKII is the priming kinase for Plx1 upon CSF release (Liu & Maller 2005, Rauh et al. 2005, Hansen et al. 2006).

An additional Ca^{2+}-induced pathway is involved in the exit from CSF arrest in *Xenopus* egg extracts. Upon its activation at fertilization, calcineurin, a Ca^{2+}-dependent phosphatase, triggers several downstream events, including the dephosphorylation of Apc3, a core subunit of the APC/C, and that of Cdc20/Fzy (Mochida & Hunt 2007). The addition of a calcineurin inhibitor prevents this dephosphorylation, delays degradation of CyclinB2, and prevents exit from meiosis II after the addition of Ca^{2+} (Mochida & Hunt 2007, Nishiyama et al. 2007b). Mochida & Hunt (2007) report that coimmunoprecipitation experiments provide some evidence of a physical association between

Fzy/Cdc20 and calcineurin, and incubation of purified APC/C from CSF egg extracts with calcineurin causes apparent dephosphorylation of Apc3 and Fzy/Cdc20 protein. When phosphorylated, Cdc20/Fzy is inhibited from activating APC/C during spindle checkpoint arrest (Yudkovsky et al. 2000, Chung & Chen 2003, Tang et al. 2004). Thus, dephosphorylation of Cdc20/Fzy by calcineurin upon fertilization may play an important role in calcineurin's contribution to the release of the metaphase II arrest in CSF eggs (**Figure 4**). Consistent with the *Xenopus* results, calcineurin signaling is also involved in meiosis in *Drosophila* because mutations in *sarah*, a gene encoding an inhibitor of calcineurin, disrupt the meiotic divisions in females (Horner et al. 2006).

In summary, Emi2/Erp1 plays a critical role in CSF arrest by inhibition of APC/C^{Cdc20}. Mos, through p90^{Rsk}, contributes to this inhibition because p90^{Rsk} phosphorylation of Emi2/Erp1 recruits PP2A. PP2A dephosphorylates several sites of phosphorylation by Cdc2/Cyclin B on Emi2/Erp1 that would disrupt its interaction with and inhibition of APC/C^{Cdc20}. The Ca^{2+} increase at fertilization causes degradation of Emi2/Erp1 by CaMKII activation of Plx1, whose phosphorylation of Emi2/Erp1 targets it for destruction by SCF$^{\beta-TrCP}$. The Ca^{2+} increase additionally inactivates APC/C^{Cdc20} by dephosphorylation of Apc3 and Cdc20 by the calcineurin phosphatase.

Spindle Assembly Checkpoint

In mitosis the SAC inhibits APC/C^{Cdc20} in the presence of improper kinetochore microtubule attachments. Some components of the SAC are dispensable, whereas others, particularly those in metazoans, are essential. This is likely because they carry out essential mitotic functions in addition to surveillance mechanisms (Hoyt et al. 1991, Li & Murray 1991, Kitagawa & Rose 1999, Dobles et al. 2000, Kalitsis et al. 2000, Buffin et al. 2007).

In meiosis, SAC proteins appear to be required not only upon spindle damage but also for the normal mechanism of meiosis I. It remains to be determined whether this role of the SAC is mediated by inhibition of the APC/C. In *S. cerevisiae*, mutations in *mad1* or *mad2* cause increased nondisjunction of homologous chromosomes in meiosis I (Shonn et al. 2000). Levels of nondisjunction are restored if anaphase is artificially delayed, suggesting that Mad1 and Mad2 are important for inducing a metaphase I delay in a normal meiosis. Loss of recombination in a *spo11* mutant, which causes a lack of tension on kinetochores, induces a Mad2-dependent suppression of APC/C activity, suggesting that the checkpoint also responds to spindle defects in meiosis I. Furthermore, Mad2 may have an additional role in promoting the biorientation of homologs, perhaps through a mechanism other than the inhibition of APC/C (Shonn et al. 2003). The requirement for spindle checkpoint function in a normal meiosis I division may be the consequence of the increased complexity of biorienting homologous chromosome pairs on the spindle compared with biorienting sister chromatid kinetochores in mitosis.

Higher organisms also display a requirement for spindle checkpoint genes in an undisturbed meiosis I. In mouse oocytes from females heterozygous for Mad2, meiosis I is shortened and anaphase I onset accelerated (Niault et al. 2007). These oocytes display a large increase in aneuploidy in metaphase II, which is likely the result of the premature anaphase I onset. Similar to in *S. cerevisiae*, meiosis I in mouse oocytes must be of a sufficient length to allow enough time for homologous chromosomes to orient properly on the spindle and to form stable connections with microtubules. A spindle checkpoint in mouse oocytes also responds to spindle damage (Wassman et al. 2003, Niault et al. 2007). A wild-type oocyte responds to nocodazole by arresting in metaphase I and is subsequently able to properly segregate chromosomes in anaphase I. In the oocytes from Mad2 heterozygotes, however, oocytes missegregate chromosomes at a high rate after a nocodazole-induced arrest (Niault et al. 2007). Furthermore, *bubR1* mutant female mice contain oocytes with chromosome segregation defects (Baker et al. 2004). Finally, microinjection of Bub1 antibodies into mouse oocytes causes chromosome misalignment on the meiosis I spindle that is not corrected by delaying anaphase onset, suggesting that, like Mad2 in yeast, Bub1 has a specific role in chromosome alignment during metaphase I (Yin et al. 2006).

Control of chromosome segregation in meiosis I in *Drosophila* females is an interesting problem because in *Drosophila* the secondary meiotic arrest occurs in metaphase I, not metaphase II, as occurs in CSF arrest in vertebrates. Oocytes mutant for *mps1* enter anaphase I prematurely, suggesting a role for the spindle checkpoint in mediating this arrest (Gilliland et al. 2007). Reduction of *mps1* function in these oocytes causes nondisjunction of both exchange and nonexchange chromosomes, which is likely due, in part, to defects in biorientation of homologous chromosomes in meiosis I (Gilliland et al. 2005, 2007). Additionally, in female meiosis of *bubR1* mutants in *Drosophila*, nondisjunction of sister chromatids is elevated (Malmanche et al. 2007).

There is little evidence to date as to whether the SAC functions in meiosis by inhibition of the APC/C. In the *Drosophila bubR1* mutants cohesin is lost from chromosomes in prophase I of the oocytes, but it has not been determined whether this effect occurs through loss of an inhibitory effect on APC/C activity in the *bubR1* mutant. In *S. cerevisiae* Mad3 (BubR1) mediates a prophase I delay that becomes essential for chromosome segregation when chromosomes do not recombine (Cheslock et al. 2005). It is also unclear whether this defect is due to an uninhibited APC/C. The sole example of a link between the SAC in meiosis and the APC/C comes from studies in *C. elegans*, in which mutations in spindle checkpoint genes suppress a metaphase I arrest caused by leaky alleles of the *cdc23* gene, which encodes the APC8 subunit (Stein et al. 2007).

A role for the spindle checkpoint in CSF arrest in meiosis II has not been shown conclusively. The spindle checkpoint was hypothe-

sized to be a component of CSF arrest because Bub1 is phosphorylated by p90^{Rsk} during oocyte maturation in *Xenopus* oocytes, placing the SAC proteins downstream of the Mos/MAPK pathway that is required for the establishment of CSF arrest (Schwab et al. 2001). Immunodepletion of Bub1, Mad1, or Mad2 prevents the establishment of CSF arrest in *Xenopus* oocytes, and this effect is thought to occur downstream of Mos (Tunquist et al. 2002, Tunquist & Maller 2003). In contrast, inhibition of Mps1, another kinase required for spindle checkpoint–mediated arrest in mitosis, has no effect on CSF arrest (Grimison et al. 2006). Furthermore, although Bub1 and Mad2 are required for the establishment of CSF arrest, they are not required for maintenance of the arrest in CSF extracts (Tunquist et al. 2002, Tunquist & Maller 2003). In mouse oocytes, expression of dominant-negative forms of Bub1, Mad2, or BubR1 that compete with their endogenous counterparts do not affect CSF arrest, further bringing into question a role for the spindle checkpoint in inhibiting APC/C during CSF arrest (Tsurumi et al. 2004). CSF arrest is quite different from a mitotic spindle checkpoint–mediated arrest because kinetochores are already under tension and attached correctly to the spindle. If there is a role for spindle checkpoint proteins in the establishment of CSF arrest, they may act while kinetochores achieve bipolar attachments, but not after, or they may have a different role or target during CSF establishment.

CONCLUSIONS

Regulation of Cdc20/Fzy and Cdh1/Fzr is crucial for proper activity of the APC/C during the mitotic cell cycle and during meiosis. The balance of APC/C^{Cdc20} and APC/C^{Cdh1} activity is achieved with multiple mechanisms: transcriptional control, targeted degradation, phosphorylation, and the direct binding of inhibitors. During meiosis in some organisms, there are special forms of the APC/C that are activated by meiosis-specific activators. An attractive hypothesis that remains to be tested is that these activators target the degradation of a unique, meiosis-specific set of APC/C substrates. Regulation of the APC/C during meiosis utilizes both mitotic APC/C regulators in addition to meiosis-specific regulators, demonstrating a need for increased control of APC/C activity during the more complex meiotic cell cycle.

SUMMARY POINTS

1. Cdc20/Fzy is transcribed in S phase, and the protein is rapidly degraded in late mitosis and G1 through targeting by APC/C^{Cdh1}.

2. APC/C^{Cdc20} activity is inhibited by Emi1 in prophase and by spindle assembly checkpoint proteins in prometaphase and metaphase.

3. Cdh1/Fzr is uniformly transcribed during the mitotic cell cycle but inhibited by phosphorylation in S, G2, and M phases and E3 ubiquitin ligase–mediated degradation in late G1 and S.

4. APC/C^{Cdh1} activity is inhibited by Emi1 at the G1-S transition, in yeast by Acm1, and in mammals by Rae1-Nup98 in prometaphase.

5. In addition to Cdc20 and Cdh1, yeast and *Drosophila* use meiosis-specific APC/C activators: Ama1 in *S. cerevisiae*, Mfr1/Fzr1 in *S. pombe*, and Cort in *Drosophila*.

6. During metaphase I and metaphase II, APC/C activity must be suppressed. In addition, ACP/C needs to remain inactive in female meiosis (*a*) during the long prophase arrest to prevent premature loss of cohesion and (*b*) in between the two meiotic divisions to prevent DNA replication.

7. In vertebrates, Emi2/Erp1, a homolog of Emi1, is an important regulator of APC/C^{Cdc20} activity between meiosis I and meiosis II and during cytostatic factor arrest.

FUTURE ISSUES

1. What is the mechanism of Rae1-Nup98-mediated inhibition of APC/C^{Cdh1}?

2. Do meiosis-specific APC/C activators target a unique set of substrates, and how is this specificity achieved?

3. What are the substrates of APC/C^{Cdh1} in prometaphase of mouse meiosis I?

4. What is the mechanism of Mes1-mediated inhibition of the APC/C?

5. What are the relative contributions of inactivation/degradation of Emi2/Erp1 versus dephosphorylation of Apc3 and Cdc20/Fzy by calcineurin in the release of CSF arrest?

6. Are there meiosis-specific APC/C activators in vertebrates?

DISCLOSURE STATEMENT

The authors are not aware of any biases that might be perceived as affecting the objectivity of this review.

ACKNOWLEDGMENTS

We thank Jacqueline Lees for helpful comments on the manuscript. This work was funded by NIH grant GM39341.

LITERATURE CITED

Asakawa H, Kitamura K, Shimoda C. 2001. A novel Cdc20-related WD-repeat protein, Fzr1, is required for spore formation in *Schizosaccharomyces pombe*. *Mol. Genet. Genomics* 265:424–35

Baker DJ, Jeganathan KB, Cameron JD, Thompson M, Juneja S, et al. 2004. BubR1 insufficiency causes early onset of aging-associated phenotypes and infertility in mice. *Nat. Genet.* 36:744–49

Ban KH, Torres JZ, Miller JJ, Mikhailov A, Nachury MV, et al. 2007. The END network couples spindle pole assembly to inhibition of the anaphase-promoting complex/cyclosome in early mitosis. *Dev. Cell* 13:29–42

Benmaamar R, Pagano M. 2005. Involvement of the SCF complex in the control of Cdh1 degradation in S-phase. *Cell Cycle* 4:1230–32

Benoit P, Papin C, Kwak JE, Wickens M, Simonelig M. 2008. PAP- and GLD-2-type poly(A) polymerases are required sequentially in cytoplasmic polyadenylation and oogenesis in *Drosophila*. *Development* 135:1969–79

Bernis C, Vigneron S, Burgess A, Labbe JC, Fesquet D, et al. 2007. Pin1 stabilizes Emi1 during G2 phase by preventing its association with $SCF^{\beta trcp}$. *EMBO Rep.* 8:91–98

Blanco MA, Pelloquin L, Moreno S. 2001. Fission yeast mfr1 activates APC and coordinates meiotic nuclear division with sporulation. *J. Cell Sci.* 114:2135–43

Blanco MA, Sanchez-Diaz A, de Prada JM, Moreno S. 2000. $APC^{ste9/srw1}$ promotes degradation of mitotic cyclins in G_1 and is inhibited by cdc2 phosphorylation. *EMBO J.* 19:3945–55

Buffin E, Emre D, Karess RE. 2007. Flies without a spindle checkpoint. *Nat. Cell Biol.* 9:565–72

Buonomo SB, Clyne RK, Fuchs J, Loidl J, Uhlmann F, Nasmyth K. 2000. Disjunction of homologous chromosomes in meiosis I depends on proteolytic cleavage of the meiotic cohesin Rec8 by separin. *Cell* 103:387–98

Camasses A, Bogdanova A, Shevchenko A, Zachariae W. 2003. The CCT chaperonin promotes activation of the anaphase-promoting complex through the generation of functional Cdc20. *Mol. Cell* 12:87–100

Cheslock PS, Kemp BJ, Boumil RM, Dawson DS. 2005. The roles of MAD1, MAD2 and MAD3 in meiotic progression and the segregation of nonexchange chromosomes. *Nat. Genet.* 37:756–60

Chu T, Henrion G, Haegeli V, Strickland S. 2001. *Cortex*, a *Drosophila* gene required to complete oocyte meiosis, is a member of the Cdc20/fizzy protein family. *Genesis* 29:141–52

Chung E, Chen RH. 2003. Phosphorylation of Cdc20 is required for its inhibition by the spindle checkpoint. *Nat. Cell Biol.* 5:748–53

Cooper KF, Mallory MJ, Egeland DB, Jarnik M, Strich R. 2000. Ama1p is a meiosis-specific regulator of the anaphase promoting complex/cyclosome in yeast. *Proc. Natl. Acad. Sci. USA* 97:14548–53

Davis ES, Wille L, Chestnut BA, Sadler PL, Shakes DC, Golden A. 2002. Multiple subunits of the *Caenorhabditis elegans* anaphase-promoting complex are required for chromosome segregation during meiosis I. *Genetics* 160:805–13

Dawson IA, Roth S, Artavanis-Tsakonas S. 1995. The *Drosophila* cell cycle gene *fizzy* is required for normal degradation of cyclins A and B during mitosis and has homology to the CDC20 gene of *Saccharomyces cerevisiae*. *J. Cell Biol.* 129:725–37

Di Fiore B, Pines J. 2007. Emi1 is needed to couple DNA replication with mitosis but does not regulate activation of the mitotic APC/C. *J. Cell Biol.* 177:425–37

Dial JM, Petrotchenko EV, Borchers CH. 2007. Inhibition of APC^{Cdh1} activity by Cdh1/Acm1/Bmh1 ternary complex formation. *J. Biol. Chem.* 282:5237–48

Dobles M, Liberal V, Scott ML, Benezra R, Sorger PK. 2000. Chromosome missegregation and apoptosis in mice lacking the mitotic checkpoint protein Mad2. *Cell* 101:635–45

Dong X, Zavitz KH, Thomas BJ, Lin M, Campbell S, Zipursky SL. 1997. Control of G1 in the developing Drosophila eye: *rca1* regulates Cyclin A. *Genes. Dev.* 11:94–105

Eldridge AG, Loktev AV, Hansen DV, Verschuren EW, Reimann JD, Jackson PK. 2006. The *evi5* oncogene regulates cyclin accumulation by stabilizing the anaphase-promoting complex inhibitor emi1. *Cell* 124:367–80

Enquist-Newman M, Sullivan M, Morgan DO. 2008. Modulation of the mitotic regulatory network by APC-dependent destruction of the Cdh1 inhibitor Acm1. *Mol. Cell* 30:437–46

Fan HY, Sun QY, Zou H. 2006. Regulation of Separase in meiosis: Separase is activated at the metaphase I-II transition in *Xenopus* oocytes during meiosis. *Cell Cycle* 5:198–204

Fang G, Yu H, Kirschner MW. 1998. Direct binding of CDC20 protein family members activates the anaphase-promoting complex in mitosis and G1. *Mol. Cell* 2:163–71

Furuno N, Nishizawa M, Okazaki K, Tanaka H, Iwashita J, et al. 1994. Suppression of DNA replication via Mos function during meiotic divisions in *Xenopus* oocytes. *EMBO J.* 13:2399–410

Furuta T, Tuck S, Kirchner J, Koch B, Auty R, et al. 2000. EMB-30: an APC4 homologue required for metaphase-to-anaphase transitions during meiosis and mitosis in *Caenorhabditis elegans*. *Mol. Biol. Cell* 11:1401–19

Gilliland WD, Hughes SE, Cotitta JL, Takeo S, Xiang Y, Hawley RS. 2007. The multiple roles of Mps1 in *Drosophila* female meiosis. *PLoS Genet.* 3:e113

Gilliland WD, Wayson SM, Hawley RS. 2005. The meiotic defects of mutants in the *Drosophila mps1* gene reveal a critical role of Mps1 in the segregation of achiasmate homologs. *Curr. Biol.* 15:672–77

Golden A, Sadler PL, Wallenfang MR, Schumacher JM, Hamill DR, et al. 2000. Metaphase to anaphase (mat) transition-defective mutants in *Caenorhabditis elegans*. *J. Cell Biol.* 151:1469–82

Grimison B, Liu J, Lewellyn AL, Maller JL. 2006. Metaphase arrest by cyclin E-Cdk2 requires the spindle-checkpoint kinase Mps1. *Curr. Biol.* 16:1968–73

Grosskortenhaus R, Sprenger F. 2002. Rca1 inhibits APC-Cdh1^{Fzr} and is required to prevent cyclin degradation in G2. *Dev. Cell* 2:29–40

Guardavaccaro D, Kudo Y, Boulaire J, Barchi M, Busino L, et al. 2003. Control of meiotic and mitotic progression by the F box protein β-Trcp1 in vivo. *Dev. Cell* 4:799–812

Hall MC, Torres MP, Schroeder GK, Borchers CH. 2003. Mnd2 and Swm1 are core subunits of the *Saccharomyces cerevisiae* anaphase-promoting complex. *J. Biol. Chem.* 278:16698–705

Hansen DV, Loktev AV, Ban KH, Jackson PK. 2004. Plk1 regulates activation of the anaphase promoting complex by phosphorylating and triggering SCF^{βTrCP}-dependent destruction of the APC inhibitor Emi1. *Mol. Biol. Cell* 15:5623–34

Hansen DV, Pomerening JR, Summers MK, Miller JJ, Ferrell JE Jr, Jackson PK. 2007. Emi2 at the crossroads: Where CSF meets MPF. *Cell Cycle* 6:732–38

Hansen DV, Tung JJ, Jackson PK. 2006. CaMKII and Polo-like kinase 1 sequentially phosphorylate the cytostatic factor Emi2/XErp1 to trigger its destruction and meiotic exit. *Proc. Natl. Acad. Sci. USA* 103:608–13

Hassold T, Hunt P. 2001. To err (meiotically) is human: the genesis of human aneuploidy. *Nat. Rev. Genet.* 2:280–91

Herbert M, Levasseur M, Homer H, Yallop K, Murdoch A, McDougall A. 2003. Homologue disjunction in mouse oocytes requires proteolysis of securin and cyclin B1. *Nat. Cell Biol.* 5:1023–25

Horner VL, Czank A, Jang JK, Singh N, Williams BC, et al. 2006. The *Drosophila* calcipressin *sarah* is required for several aspects of egg activation. *Curr. Biol.* 16:1441–46

Hoyt MA, Totis L, Roberts BT. 1991. *S. cerevisiae* genes required for cell cycle arrest in response to loss of microtubule function. *Cell* 66:507–17

Hsu JY, Reimann JD, Sørensen CS, Lukas J, Jackson PK. 2002. E2F-dependent accumulation of hEmi1 regulates S phase entry by inhibiting APC^{Cdh1}. *Nat. Cell Biol.* 4:358–66

Huang JN, Park I, Ellingson E, Littlepage LE, Pellman D. 2001. Activity of the APC^{Cdh1} form of the anaphase-promoting complex persists until S phase and prevents the premature expression of Cdc20p. *J. Cell Biol.* 154:85–94

Inoue D, Ohe M, Kanemori Y, Nobui T, Sagata N. 2007. A direct link of the Mos-MAPK pathway to Erp1/Emi2 in meiotic arrest of *Xenopus laevis* eggs. *Nature* 446:1100–4

Iwabuchi M, Ohsumi K, Yamamoto TM, Sawada W, Kishimoto T. 2000. Residual Cdc2 activity remaining at meiosis I exit is essential for meiotic M-M transition in *Xenopus* oocyte extracts. *EMBO J.* 19:4513–23

Izawa D, Goto M, Yamashita A, Yamano H, Yamamoto M. 2005. Fission yeast Mes1p ensures the onset of meiosis II by blocking degradation of cyclin Cdc13p. *Nature* 434:529–33

Jacobs H, Richter D, Venkatesh T, Lehner C. 2002. Completion of mitosis requires neither *fzr/rap* nor *fzr2*, a male germline-specific *Drosophila* Cdh1 homolog. *Curr. Biol.* 12:1435–41

Jaspersen SL, Charles JF, Morgan DO. 1999. Inhibitory phosphorylation of the APC regulator Hct1 is controlled by the kinase Cdc28 and the phosphatase Cdc14. *Curr. Biol.* 9:227–36

Jeganathan KB, Malureanu L, van Deursen JM. 2005. The Rae1-Nup98 complex prevents aneuploidy by inhibiting securin degradation. *Nature* 438:1036–39

Kalitsis P, Earle E, Fowler KJ, Choo KH. 2000. *Bub3* gene disruption in mice reveals essential mitotic spindle checkpoint function during early embryogenesis. *Genes Dev.* 14:2277–82

Keck JM, Summers MK, Tedesco D, Ekholm-Reed S, Chuang LC, et al. 2007. Cyclin E overexpression impairs progression through mitosis by inhibiting APC^{Cdh1}. *J. Cell Biol.* 178:371–85

Kidokoro T, Tanikawa C, Furukawa Y, Katagiri T, Nakamura Y, Matsuda K. 2008. CDC20, a potential cancer therapeutic target, is negatively regulated by p53. *Oncogene* 27:1562–71

Kimata Y, Trickey M, Izawa D, Gannon J, Yamamoto M, Yamano H. 2008. A mutual inhibition between APC/C and its substrate Mes1 required for meiotic progression in fission yeast. *Dev. Cell* 14:446–54

Kishimoto T. 2003. Cell-cycle control during meiotic maturation. *Curr. Opin. Cell Biol.* 15:654–63

Kitagawa R, Rose AM. 1999. Components of the spindle-assembly checkpoint are essential in *Caenorhabditis elegans*. *Nat. Cell Biol.* 1:514–21

Kitajima TS, Miyazaki Y, Yamamoto M, Watanabe Y. 2003. Rec8 cleavage by separase is required for meiotic nuclear divisions in fission yeast. *EMBO J.* 22:5643–53

Kramer ER, Scheuringer N, Podtelejnikov AV, Mann M, Peters JM. 2000. Mitotic regulation of the APC activator proteins CDC20 and CDH1. *Mol. Biol. Cell* 11:1555–69

Kudo NR, Wassmann K, Anger M, Schuh M, Wirth KG, et al. 2006. Resolution of chiasmata in oocytes requires separase-mediated proteolysis. *Cell* 126:135–46

Li R, Murray AW. 1991. Feedback control of mitosis in budding yeast. *Cell* 66:519–31

Lieberfarb ME, Chu T, Wreden C, Theurkauf W, Gergen JP, Strickland S. 1996. Mutations that perturb poly(A)-dependent maternal mRNA activation block the initiation of development. *Development* 122:579–88

Listovsky T, Oren YS, Yudkovsky Y, Mahbubani HM, Weiss AM, et al. 2004. Mammalian Cdh1/Fzr mediates its own degradation. *EMBO J.* 23:1619–26

Liu J, Maller JL. 2005. Calcium elevation at fertilization coordinates phosphorylation of XErp1/Emi2 by Plx1 and CaMK II to release metaphase arrest by cytostatic factor. *Curr. Biol.* 15:1458–68

Lorca T, Cruzalegui FH, Fesquet D, Cavadore JC, Mery J, et al. 1993. Calmodulin-dependent protein kinase II mediates inactivation of MPF and CSF upon fertilization of *Xenopus* eggs. *Nature* 366:270–73

Lukas C, Sørensen CS, Kramer E, Santoni-Rugiu E, Lindeneg C, et al. 1999. Accumulation of cyclin B1 requires E2F and cyclin-A-dependent rearrangement of the anaphase-promoting complex. *Nature* 401:815–18

Madgwick S, Hansen DV, Levasseur M, Jackson PK, Jones KT. 2006. Mouse Emi2 is required to enter meiosis II by reestablishing cyclin B1 during interkinesis. *J. Cell Biol.* 174:791–801

Malmanche N, Owen S, Gegick S, Steffensen S, Tomkiel JE, Sunkel CE. 2007. *Drosophila* BubR1 is essential for meiotic sister-chromatid cohesion and maintenance of synaptonemal complex. *Curr. Biol.* 17:1489–97

Mapelli M, Massimiliano L, Santaguida S, Musacchio A. 2007. The Mad2 conformational dimer: structure and implications for the spindle assembly checkpoint. *Cell* 131:730–43

Marangos P, Verschuren EW, Chen R, Jackson PK, Carroll J. 2007. Prophase I arrest and progression to metaphase I in mouse oocytes are controlled by Emi1-dependent regulation of APC^{Cdh1}. *J. Cell Biol.* 176:65–75

Margottin-Goguet F, Hsu JY, Loktev A, Hsieh HM, Reimann JD, Jackson PK. 2003. Prophase destruction of Emi1 by the SCF$^{\beta TrCP/Slimb}$ ubiquitin ligase activates the anaphase promoting complex to allow progression beyond prometaphase. *Dev. Cell* 4:813–26

Marston AL, Amon A. 2004. Meiosis: Cell-cycle controls shuffle and deal. *Nat. Rev. Mol. Cell Biol.* 5:983–97

Martinez JS, Jeong D-E, Choi E, Billings BM, Hall MC. 2006. Acm1 is a negative regulator of the Cdh1-dependent anaphase-promoting complex/cyclosome in budding yeast. *Mol. Cell. Biol.* 26:9162–76

Mata J, Lyne R, Burns G, Bahler J. 2002. The transcriptional program of meiosis and sporulation in fission yeast. *Nat. Genet.* 32:143–47

Miller JJ, Summers MK, Hansen DV, Nachury MV, Lehman NL, et al. 2006. Emi1 stably binds and inhibits the anaphase-promoting complex/cyclosome as a pseudosubstrate inhibitor. *Genes Dev.* 20:2410–20

Mochida S, Hunt T. 2007. Calcineurin is required to release *Xenopus* egg extracts from meiotic M phase. *Nature* 449:336–40

Morris MC, Kaiser P, Rudyak S, Baskerville C, Watson MH, Reed SI. 2003. Cks1-dependent proteasome recruitment and activation of CDC20 transcription in budding yeast. *Nature* 423:1009–13

Moshe Y, Boulaire J, Pagano M, Hershko A. 2004. Role of Polo-like kinase in the degradation of early mitotic inhibitor 1, a regulator of the anaphase promoting complex/cyclosome. *Proc. Natl. Acad. Sci. USA* 101:7937–42

Musacchio A, Salmon ED. 2007. The spindle-assembly checkpoint in space and time. *Nat. Rev. Mol. Cell Biol.* 8:379–93

Niault T, Hached K, Sotillo R, Sorger PK, Maro B, et al. 2007. Changing mad2 levels affects chromosome segregation and spindle assembly checkpoint control in female mouse meiosis I. *PLoS ONE* 2:e1165

Nishiyama T, Ohsumi K, Kishimoto T. 2007a. Phosphorylation of Erp1 by p90rsk is required for cytostatic factor arrest in *Xenopus laevis* eggs. *Nature* 446:1096–99

Nishiyama T, Yoshizaki N, Kishimoto T, Ohsumi K. 2007b. Transient activation of calcineurin is essential to initiate embryonic development in *Xenopus laevis*. *Nature* 449:341–45

Oelschlaegel T, Schwickart M, Matos J, Bogdanova A, Camasses A, et al. 2005. The yeast APC/C subunit Mnd2 prevents premature sister chromatid separation triggered by the meiosis-specific APC/C-Ama1. *Cell* 120:773–88

Ohe M, Inoue D, Kanemori Y, Sagata N. 2007. Erp1/Emi2 is essential for the meiosis I to meiosis II transition in *Xenopus* oocytes. *Dev. Biol.* 303:157–64

Ohsumi K, Koyanagi A, Yamamoto TM, Gotoh T, Kishimoto T. 2004. Emi1-mediated M-phase arrest in *Xenopus* eggs is distinct from cytostatic factor arrest. *Proc. Natl. Acad. Sci. USA* 101:12531–36

Page AW, Orr-Weaver TL. 1996. The *Drosophila* genes *grauzone* and *cortex* are necessary for proper female meiosis. *J. Cell Sci.* 109: 1707–15

Papin C, Rouget C, Lorca T, Castro A, Mandart E. 2004. XCdh1 is involved in progesterone-induced oocyte maturation. *Dev. Biol.* 272:66–75

Passmore LA, McCormack EA, Au SW, Paul A, Willison KR, et al. 2003. Doc1 mediates the activity of the anaphase-promoting complex by contributing to substrate recognition. *EMBO J.* 22:786–96

Penkner AM, Prinz S, Ferscha S, Klein F. 2005. Mnd2, an essential antagonist of the anaphase-promoting complex during meiotic prophase. *Cell* 120:789–801

Pesin JA, Orr-Weaver TL. 2007. Developmental role and regulation of *cortex*, a meiosis-specific anaphase-promoting complex/cyclosome activator. *PLoS Genet.* 3:e202

Peter M, Castro A, Lorca T, Le Peuch C, Magnaghi-Jaulin L, et al. 2001. The APC is dispensable for first meiotic anaphase in *Xenopus* oocytes. *Nat. Cell Biol.* 3:83–87

Peters JM. 2006. The anaphase promoting complex/cyclosome: a machine designed to destroy. *Nat. Rev. Mol. Cell Biol.* 7:644–56

Pfleger CM, Kirschner MW. 2000. The KEN box: an APC recognition signal distinct from the D box targeted by Cdh1. *Genes Dev.* 14:655–65

Prinz S, Hwang ES, Visintin R, Amon A. 1998. The regulation of Cdc20 proteolysis reveals a role for APC components Cdc23 and Cdc27 during S phase and early mitosis. *Curr. Biol.* 8:750–60

Pritchard CE, Fornerod M, Kasper LH, van Deursen JM. 1999. RAE1 is a shuttling mRNA export factor that binds to a GLEBS-like NUP98 motif at the nuclear pore complex through multiple domains. *J. Cell Biol.* 145:237–54

Rauh NR, Schmidt A, Bormann J, Nigg EA, Mayer TU. 2005. Calcium triggers exit from meiosis II by targeting the APC/C inhibitor XErp1 for degradation. *Nature* 437:1048–52

Reddy SK, Rape M, Margansky WA, Kirschner MW. 2007. Ubiquitination by the anaphase-promoting complex drives spindle checkpoint inactivation. *Nature* 446:921–25

Reimann JD, Freed E, Hsu JY, Kramer ER, Peters JM, Jackson PK. 2001a. Emi1 is a mitotic regulator that interacts with Cdc20 and inhibits the anaphase promoting complex. *Cell* 105:645–55

Reimann JD, Gardner BE, Margottin-Goguet F, Jackson PK. 2001b. Emi1 regulates the anaphase-promoting complex by a different mechanism than Mad2 proteins. *Genes Dev.* 15:3278–85

Reis A, Chang HY, Levasseur M, Jones KT. 2006a. APC^{cdh1} activity in mouse oocytes prevents entry into the first meiotic division. *Nat. Cell Biol.* 8:539–40

Reis A, Levasseur M, Chang HY, Elliott DJ, Jones KT. 2006b. The CRY box: a second APC^{cdh1}-dependent degron in mammalian cdc20. *EMBO Rep.* 7:1040–45

Reis A, Madgwick S, Chang HY, Nabti I, Levasseur M, Jones KT. 2007. Prometaphase APC^{cdh1} activity prevents nondisjunction in mammalian oocytes. *Nat. Cell Biol.* 9:1192–98

Salah SM, Nasmyth K. 2000. Destruction of the securin Pds1p occurs at the onset of anaphase during both meiotic divisions in yeast. *Chromosoma* 109:27–34

Schmidt A, Duncan PI, Rauh NR, Sauer G, Fry AM, et al. 2005. *Xenopus* polo-like kinase Plx1 regulates XErp1, a novel inhibitor of APC/C activity. *Genes Dev.* 19:502–13

Schwab M, Lutum AS, Seufert W. 1997. Yeast Hct1 is a regulator of Clb2 cyclin proteolysis. *Cell* 90:683–93

Schwab MS, Roberts BT, Gross SD, Tunquist BJ, Taieb FE, et al. 2001. Bub1 is activated by the protein kinase p90^{Rsk} during *Xenopus* oocyte maturation. *Curr. Biol.* 11:141–50

Searle JS, Schollaert KL, Wilkins BJ, Sanchez Y. 2004. The DNA damage checkpoint and PKA pathways converge on APC substrates and Cdc20 to regulate mitotic progression. *Nat. Cell Biol.* 6:138–45

Shimoda C, Hirata A, Kishida M, Hashida T, Tanaka K. 1985. Characterization of meiosis-deficient mutants by electron microscopy and mapping of four essential genes in the fission yeast *Schizosaccharomyces pombe*. *Mol. Gen. Genet.* 200:252–57

Shoji S, Yoshida N, Amanai M, Ohgishi M, Fukui T, et al. 2006. Mammalian Emi2 mediates cytostatic arrest and transduces the signal for meiotic exit via Cdc20. *EMBO J.* 25:834–45

Shonn MA, McCarroll R, Murray AW. 2000. Requirement of the spindle checkpoint for proper chromosome segregation in budding yeast meiosis. *Science* 289:300–3

Shonn MA, Murray AL, Murray AW. 2003. Spindle checkpoint component Mad2 contributes to biorientation of homologous chromosomes. *Curr. Biol.* 13:1979–84

Sigrist SJ, Lehner CF. 1997. Drosophila *fizzy-related* down-regulates mitotic cyclins and is required for cell proliferation arrest and entry into endocycles. *Cell* 90:671–81

Smith TF, Gaitatzes C, Saxena K, Neer EJ. 1999. The WD repeat: a common architecture for diverse functions. *Trends Biochem. Sci.* 24:181–85

Song MS, Song SJ, Ayad NG, Chang JS, Lee JH, et al. 2004. The tumour suppressor RASSF1A regulates mitosis by inhibiting the APC-Cdc20 complex. *Nat. Cell Biol.* 6:129–37

Sørensen CS, Lukas C, Kramer ER, Peters JM, Bartek J, Lukas J. 2001. A conserved cyclin-binding domain determines functional interplay between anaphase-promoting complex-Cdh1 and cyclin A-Cdk2 during cell cycle progression. *Mol. Cell. Biol.* 21:3692–703

Stegmeier F, Rape M, Draviam VM, Nalepa G, Sowa ME, et al. 2007. Anaphase initiation is regulated by antagonistic ubiquitination and deubiquitination activities. *Nature* 446:876–81

Stein KK, Davis ES, Hays T, Golden A. 2007. Components of the spindle assembly checkpoint regulate the anaphase-promoting complex during meiosis in *Caenorhabditis elegans*. *Genetics* 175:107–23

Swan A, Schupbach T. 2007. The Cdc20 (Fzy)/Cdh1-related protein, Cort, cooperates with Fzy in cyclin destruction and anaphase progression in meiosis I and II in Drosophila. *Development* 134:891–99

Taieb FE, Gross SD, Lewellyn AL, Maller JL. 2001. Activation of the anaphase-promoting complex and degradation of cyclin B is not required for progression from meiosis I to II in *Xenopus* oocytes. *Curr. Biol.* 11:508–13

Tang Z, Shu H, Oncel D, Chen S, Yu H. 2004. Phosphorylation of Cdc20 by Bub1 provides a catalytic mechanism for APC/C inhibition by the spindle checkpoint. *Mol. Cell* 16:387–97

Terret ME, Wassmann K, Waizenegger I, Maro B, Peters JM, Verlhac MH. 2003. The meiosis I-to-meiosis II transition in mouse oocytes requires separase activity. *Curr. Biol.* 13:1797–802

Thornton BR, Toczyski DP. 2006. Precise destruction: an emerging picture of the APC. *Genes Dev.* 20:3069–78

Tsurumi C, Hoffmann S, Geley S, Graeser R, Polanski Z. 2004. The spindle assembly checkpoint is not essential for CSF arrest of mouse oocytes. *J. Cell Biol.* 167:1037–50

Tung JJ, Hansen DV, Ban KH, Loktev AV, Summers MK, et al. 2005. A role for the anaphase-promoting complex inhibitor Emi2/Erp1, a homolog of early mitotic inhibitor 1, in cytostatic factor arrest of *Xenopus* eggs. *Proc. Natl. Acad. Sci. USA* 102:4318–23

Tung JJ, Jackson PK. 2005. Emi1 class of proteins regulate entry into meiosis and the meiosis I to meiosis II transition in *Xenopus* oocytes. *Cell Cycle* 4:478–82

Tung JJ, Padmanabhan K, Hansen DV, Richter JD, Jackson PK. 2007. Translational unmasking of Emi2 directs cytostatic factor arrest in meiosis II. *Cell Cycle* 6:725–31

Tunquist BJ, Maller JL. 2003. Under arrest: cytostatic factor (CSF)-mediated metaphase arrest in vertebrate eggs. *Genes Dev.* 17:683–710

Tunquist BJ, Schwab MS, Chen LG, Maller JL. 2002. The spindle checkpoint kinase bub1 and cyclin e/cdk2 both contribute to the establishment of meiotic metaphase arrest by cytostatic factor. *Curr. Biol.* 12:1027–33

Turnell AS, Stewart GS, Grand RJ, Rookes SM, Martin A, et al. 2005. The APC/C and CBP/p300 cooperate to regulate transcription and cell-cycle progression. *Nature* 438:690–95

Visintin R, Prinz S, Amon A. 1997. CDC20 and CDH1: a family of substrate-specific activators of APC-dependent proteolysis. *Science* 278:460–63

Wassmann K, Niault T, Maro B. 2003. Metaphase I arrest upon activation of the Mad2-dependent spindle checkpoint in mouse oocytes. *Curr. Biol.* 13:1596–608

Whitehurst AW, Ram R, Shivakumar L, Gao B, Minna JD, White MA. 2008. The RASSF1A tumor suppressor restrains APC/C activity during the G1/S phase transition to promote cell cycle progression in human epithelial cells. *Mol. Cell. Biol.* 28:3190–97

Wu JQ, Hansen DV, Guo Y, Wang MZ, Tang W, Freel CD, Tung JJ, Jackson PK, Kornbluth S. 2007. Control of Emi2 activity and stability through Mos-mediated recruitment of PP2A. *Proc. Natl. Acad. Sci. USA* 104:16564–69

Wu Q, Guo Y, Yamada A, Perry JA, Wang MZ, et al. 2007. A role for Cdc2- and PP2A-mediated regulation of Emi2 in the maintenance of CSF arrest. *Curr. Biol.* 17:213–24

Yamaguchi S, Okayama H, Nurse P. 2000. Fission yeast Fizzy-related protein srw1p is a G_1-specific promoter of mitotic cyclin B degradation. *EMBO J.* 19:3968–77

Yang M, Li B, Liu CJ, Tomchick DR, Machius M, et al. 2008. Insights into Mad2 regulation in the spindle checkpoint revealed by the crystal structure of the symmetric Mad2 dimer. *PLoS Biol.* 6:e50

Yang M, Li B, Tomchick DR, Machius M, Rizo J, et al. 2007. p31[comet] blocks Mad2 activation through structural mimicry. *Cell* 131:744–55

Yin S, Wang Q, Liu JH, Ai JS, Liang CG, et al. 2006. Bub1 prevents chromosome misalignment and precocious anaphase during mouse oocyte meiosis. *Cell Cycle* 5:2130–37

Yudkovsky Y, Shteinberg M, Listovsky T, Brandeis M, Hershko A. 2000. Phosphorylation of Cdc20/fizzy negatively regulates the mammalian cyclosome/APC in the mitotic checkpoint. *Biochem. Biophys. Res. Commun.* 271:299–304

Zachariae W, Schwab M, Nasmyth K, Seufert W. 1998. Control of cyclin ubiquitination by CDK-regulated binding of Hct1 to the anaphase promoting complex. *Science* 282:1721–24

Protein Kinases: Starting a Molecular Systems View of Endocytosis

Prisca Liberali, Pauli Rämö, and Lucas Pelkmans

Institute of Molecular Systems Biology, ETH Zurich, CH-8093 Zurich, Switzerland;
email: pelkmans@imsb.biol.ethz.ch

Annu. Rev. Cell Dev. Biol. 2008. 24:501–23

First published online as a Review in Advance on
July 3, 2008

The *Annual Review of Cell and Developmental
Biology* is online at cellbio.annualreviews.org

This article's doi:
10.1146/annurev.cellbio.041008.145637

Key Words

membrane trafficking, phosphorylation, signal transduction,
complexity, nonlinear systems, genetical physics

Abstract

The field of endocytosis is in strong need of formal biophysical modeling and mathematical analysis. At the same time, endocytosis must be
much better integrated into cellular physiology to understand the former's complex behavior in such a wide range of phenotypic variations.
Furthermore, the concept that endocytosis provides the space-time for
signal transduction can now be experimentally addressed. In this review,
we discuss these principles and argue for a systematic and top-down approach to study the endocytic membrane system. We provide a summary
of published observations on protein kinases regulating endocytic machinery components and discuss global unbiased approaches to further
map out kinase regulatory networks. In particular, protein phosphorylation is at the heart of controlling the physical properties of endocytosis
and of integrating these physical properties into the signal transduction
networks of the cell to allow a fine-tuned response to the continuously
varying physiological conditions of a cell.

Contents

COMPLEXITY IN THE ENDOCYTIC MEMBRANE SYSTEM

The endocytic membrane system in mammalian cells is complex. The basic steps of membrane trafficking—cargo recruitment, vesicle formation, vesicle transport, vesicle docking, and vesicle fusion—are a concerted series of events that involves many different proteins and lipids (Gruenberg 2001, McNiven & Thompson 2006, Miaczynska & Zerial 2002, Soldati & Schliwa 2006). Although the general principle of endocytosis is always the same, there is not one particular series of molecular events that always applies. Recent progress in the field of endocytosis is rapidly dismissing our textbook view. Not only is the contribution of clathrin-dependent processes compared with alternative endocytic routes debated in numerous instances, but also the definition of clathrin-mediated endocytosis finds itself on loose ground. The canonical clathrin-mediated route now appears to have different variants, which can make use of different adaptors, different GTPases, and different trafficking itineraries and can bypass the canonical early endosome (Lakadamyali et al. 2006, Schmid & McMahon 2007). Also, recent work on *Listeria monocytogenes* entry has shown that clathrin can assemble into very large lattices that appear to support a form of phagocytosis (Veiga & Cossart 2005). The more these differences are studied, the more it becomes clear that only clathrin is the common factor. Thus, although the term clathrin-dependent endocytosis incorporates all these variants, it is hard to maintain the view that from a functional perspective, these are all just one route. Similar controversies are programmed to arise (if they have not already arisen) for terms such as caveolae-mediated, fluid phase, or macropinocytosis (Lajoie & Nabi 2007, Mayor & Pagano 2007).

The above-discussed impasse in the field of endocytosis is probably exemplary for several impasses in molecular cell biology and should be blamed on our highly reductionist, molecular, and deterministic approach to these problems in a time when global and unbiased comparisons were not possible. All pathways in cell biology will likely have to be redefined with unbiased global and quantitative methods, revealing a standardized set of rules and definitions (Kirschner 2005, Mogilner et al. 2006). In one sense, we can compare this transition in biology with that in chemistry approximately 150 years ago. At that time, alchemy (reluctantly) gave way to modern-day chemistry, founded on a standardized set of rules and definitions discovered by Antoine Lavoisier, who started to meticulously weigh metals, gases, liquids, and all kinds of materials and chemicals without any a priori hypothesis of a periodic table (Lavoisier 1789). He might have believed in finding something fundamental in the data, but there was no scientific foundation for that belief. This probably seems boring to many modern-day scientists, but from the accurate study of a comprehensive set of measurements, a systematic pattern was discovered.

We will thus have to go through a phase of painstakingly measuring, in an unbiased manner, as many relevant properties of cellular systems as possible. Essential for this phase will be methods to quantify large populations of single molecules and single particles; to quantify large populations of individual cells (eventually within tissues); and to quantify functional roles of whole genomes (of which the protein-encoding part is just a fraction), of whole proteomes (including the enormous complexity of posttranslational modifications), and of the interactions between them. One can predict that when genome-wide functional analysis of endocytosis in mammalian cells becomes more accurate and quantitative and can incorporate quantitative properties of all vesicles in a cell and all cells in a cell population, we might be astonished by the number of differences between the internalization of two ligands that both use clathrin-dependent endocytosis. Nevertheless, when this is done for a dozen of such ligands, the data might reveal certain patterns, some of which we have no notion of today. We will find functional modules of cellular components, which can be linked to functional groups of physical properties that constitute certain design principles of a vesicle pattern (Milo et al. 2002). Moreover, we might find that ligands will fall into groups of pathways assembled from similar functional modules of molecular components and similar physical design principles. Such information, when quantitative, will allow us to create a set of formal and standardized rules with which to define the properties of the endocytic membrane system

DEFINITION OF COMPLEXITY

A complex system is a system composed of interconnected parts that as a whole displays properties not obvious from the individual parts (Adami 2002, Ricard 2003). This makes every biological system with some nonlinear properties (like a simple feedback loop) complex. The field of complex systems theory adds that a system is complex when there are difficulties with its bottom-up formal modeling and simulation. For systems biology, this means that the system cannot be accurately modeled by a set of deterministic equations (for instance, differential equations) (Huang & Wikswo 2006). It is often argued that this is because the system's components, their concentrations, and their ways of interaction are not (yet) known. But there are fundamental nondeterministic properties (such as stochastic behavior) that, when amplified or dampened in nonlinear ways, make nonstatistical models inappropriate. One may regard this basic property as the uncertainty principle in biology. The biological uncertainty principle seems particularly relevant for dynamic systems that consist of many different components and interactions that span several orders of magnitude on the space-time scale. It is likely that a crucial system such as endocytosis has many built-in mechanisms to deal with this uncertainty, but this remains to be experimentally addressed.

in human cells. This phase may be expensive, take a long time, and require a large and complex infrastructure. However, this concept can be applied to smaller sets of genes, proteins, and physical properties (Pelkmans et al. 2005). The iterative process of thinking about the principal components of the endocytic membrane system on which to focus first to reveal the data and to use those data to think about how to expand the initial focus will reveal sets of rules and definitions better and quicker and will optimize them along the way.

WHY IS THE ENDOCYTIC MEMBRANE SYSTEM IN HUMAN CELLS SO COMPLEX?

The complexity of endocytosis is a specific trait of cells from multicellular organisms. There is a large increase in complexity from *Saccharomyces cerevisiae* to *Caenorhabditis elegans* and *Drosophila melanogaster* to *Homo sapiens* (Jekely 2007, Toret

STRUCTURAL VERSUS SYSTEMS BIOLOGY IN ENDOCYTOSIS

For certain aspects of endocytosis, structural biologists have visualized functional modules with a remarkable degree of resolution. Often, structural biology is seen as the ultimate foundation on which to attempt bottom-up modeling of biological systems. The molecular structure itself is a model, either an average of many possible conformations or a specific, trapped conformation that allows the growth of a crystal. The biological uncertainty principle will point out that one averaged or one specific structure will not be able to account for the complexity of the system. Thus, systematic structural biology using nuclear magnetic resonance (NMR) or X-ray crystallography on isolated components will allow us to reveal basic structural rules that are generally applied in endocytosis (e.g., the clathrin cage or matricity) (Fotin et al. 2004, Schmid & McMahon 2007), whereas single-particle or single-molecule methods, such as cryoelectron and optical microscopy with nanometer resolution, will be necessary to reveal structural variation principles that underlie systems behavior.

& Drubin 2006). Whereas the complexity of one or two core endocytic routes, and their core machinery, appeared earlier in evolution and is conserved through evolution, the particular properties of endocytosis in human cells appeared late.

In a multicellular organism, the endocytic membrane system needs to demonstrate extreme plasticity (Kennedy & Ehlers 2006, Mostov et al. 2003). It needs to transcytose massive amounts of liquid in epithelial cells of the renal duct, to transport vesicles over very long distances in neurons (Rodman et al. 1990, Südhof 2004), to relocalize specific membrane components for cell polarization and migration, and to shift from a sampling state to an antigen-presenting state during the maturation of dendritic cells (Le Roy & Wrana 2005). In these different functions, the endocytic membrane system displays very different properties. Sometimes the vesicles are of a very narrow size range and always contain the same amount of cargo (neurons) (Voglmaier & Edwards 2007), sometimes the endocytic organelles reshape into long tubular structures that fuse with the cell

surface (maturing dendritic cells) (Kleijmeer et al. 2001), and sometimes the endosomes are located at the leading or ruffling edge of a cell (migrating cells) (Rappoport & Simon 2003). Also, within an individual cell, the endocytic membrane system can display very different behavior, depending on extrinsically and intrinsically varying conditions. Recycling of membrane components is blocked during mitosis when the cells round up and overshoots the normal activity when mitosis is completed and cells spread out again (Boucrot & Kirchhausen 2007). Fluid-phase endocytosis is regulated as a function of the metabolic state and size of a cell (Hennig et al. 2006), and the activity of raft-mediated endocytosis seems to depend on the adhesive state of cells (Echarri & Del Pozo 2006, Pelkmans 2005). Molecular biology tends to explain differences in organelle behavior by the existence of cell-type- or cell-state-specific proteins. Indeed, there is tissue-, cell-type-, and cell-state-specific expression of proteins that are part of the endocytic machinery. It is, however, unclear if the behavior of the endocytic system in one cell can be changed into that of another cell by just expressing these specific proteins.

There is also a fundamental need for complexity in systems like endocytosis. Complexity makes dynamic systems robust, permits them to evolve, allows them to oscillate or be noisy (by applying negative-feedback loops) or stable (by applying positive-feedback loops), and can contain built-in adaptation principles (e.g. bistability, criticality) that result in different behavior of the system when a few key parameters are changed (Kholodenko 2006, Shinar et al. 2007). The emergent properties that arise from such changes may appear to the molecular biologist as a completely different system with different molecular requirements. But it is the complexity itself that allows one system consisting of one set of components to behave differently under different conditions (Balazsi & Oltvai 2005, Mayo et al. 2006).

This complexity brings us to an alternative principle of how plasticity of the endocytic membrane system might be achieved. Perhaps it is the particular topology of certain regulatory circuits within the endocytic membrane system that leads to a certain behavior (Kashtan et al. 2004). If so, the endocytic membrane system must have all properties intrinsically built-in. We can then imagine why the endocytic membrane system in any cell from a multicellular organism is so complex: It must have the intrinsic ability to demonstrate a wide range of different states and behaviors. This possibility remains to be empirically addressed, but we must be prepared for the prospect that in large-scale perturbation screens, all these different behaviors can emerge, even in a population of simple, nonpolarizing, nondifferentiating tissue culture cells.

ENDOCYTOSIS: SPACE-TIME FOR SIGNAL TRANSDUCTION

Another reason why the endocytic membrane system is so complex is its essential role in cell signaling. Here we discuss how the endocytic membrane system might regulate the space-time in which an input signal (extracellular and intracellular) is transduced, processed, and translated in the cell.

A variety of sensors continuously monitor the physiological status of the cell and the extracellular environment. Well-known examples are sensors that measure energy status, nutrient status, ion concentrations, levels of oxysterols, or the amount of cell stretching (Cota et al. 2006, Janowski et al. 1996). Many sensors consist of components that are associated with or span cellular membranes, such as integrins, ion channels, growth hormone and cytokine receptors, Toll-like receptors, lipid sensors on endosomes, pH sensors (e.g., the vacuolar ATPase), or redox-potential sensors (Chang et al. 2006, Morgan et al. 2007). By movement of these sensors between cellular compartments, membrane trafficking, and endocytosis in particular, will have a major impact on the sensing capability of a cell.

Endocytosis also plays important roles in signal transduction and processing (Miaczynska et al. 2004, von Zastrow & Sorkin 2007). Receptor kinases and other membrane-associated

DEFINITIONS IN SIGNAL TRANSDUCTION

The field of signal processing defines the following components of a signaling system: the primary signal, the sensor, the signal transducer, the acceptor, and the effector. This applies equally well to signal transduction in human cells. Signals are diverse and can be a sterol, a growth hormone, protons, calcium, ADP:ATP ratio, or a stretched integrin. Sensors can be (a) a cytosolic kinase that becomes activated when the concentration of cAMP changes or (b) a hormone receptor on the cell surface. Transducers often are also kinases but can be GTPases or ubiquitin ligases. These are activated by the sensors and transfer information to a downstream acceptor. Various transducers normally pass on a signal in complex ways. An acceptor receives the signal and activates a response to the signal via an effector. The specific topology of the network by which such information is received, transduced, and accepted can achieve complex signal integration and translation. Many separate signals can be integrated to create one output that is short- or long-lasting, that oscillates, or that is binary, and a simple signal can be translated into a complex output that may have everlasting consequences for the cell (such as irreversible cell differentiation).

kinases, but also signaling adaptors and signaling GTPases, can be localized to specific membrane vesicles and compartments in the cell. Such molecules can be brought into close proximity to each other by vesicle transport and membrane fusion, can be separated from each other by sorting and membrane fission, or can be inactivated or degraded by the endocytic membrane system. Not only can receptor kinases be targeted for degradation by transport to the lysosome, but the actual process of invaginating vesicles into the lumen of late endosomes (multivesicular bodies), and their regulated backfusion or degradation, provides the cell with a mechanism to target cytosolic proteins for temporary inactivation (they are shielded from the cytosol) or degradation independent of the proteasome (Hurley & Emr 2006, van der Goot & Gruenberg 2006).

Endocytosis is also essentially involved in signal translation. The eventual outcome of many signal-processing events involves the relocalization of membrane components. For example, the response might be to internalize integrins or stably assemble them in adhesion complexes on the surface, or to internalize neurotransmitter receptors or glucose channels or to accumulate them on the surface. Other cellular responses might be to migrate in one particular direction, to grow in size, or to round up during the mitotic cycle, which all need massive relocation of the surface membrane.

Thus, the endocytic membrane system lies at the very heart of signal transduction, processing, and translation. It is then likely that part of the complexity of the endocytic membrane system has evolved to incorporate specific properties that allow the system to play this central role. This picture would predict that the endocytic machinery provides many points of interaction with protein kinases (and other molecules) that sense and transduce cellular signals.

The above discussion raises another point. If the endocytic membrane system defines to a significant extent the actual space-time in which the regulation of signaling networks takes place, standard reaction-diffusion diagrams will not be appropriate for modeling signal processing. The interaction between signaling molecules will not be dictated by diffusion but by membrane dynamics, will not be able to rely on a homogeneous concentration in the cell, and will concern only a few active molecules. The collective behavior of vesicles, tubules, and organelles does not display a random walk, nor does it display consistent active motion (Holcman & Triller 2006, Taflia & Holcman 2007). Time-lapse images of cells containing fluorescent vesicles and organelles reveal the notion that vesicles display a form of mixed behavior (Holcman & Triller 2006, Taflia & Holcman 2007). It is not clear which formal models can describe this type of behavior, but perhaps certain agent-based models, such as Brownian agents, may prove useful in the future.

Furthermore, at small scales, membranes provide a quasi-two-dimensional surface (Kholodenko et al. 2000). From surface chemistry, we know that chemical reactions on

surfaces proceed according to different principles. But at larger scales, the three-dimensional structure of a vesicle or an organelle must be taken into account. Approximate simulations of complex shapes indicate that particle geometry can strongly influence reaction-diffusion kinetics (Sbalzarini et al. 2005), but formal rules still need to be discovered. It thus seems appropriate to assume that signaling that depends on the endocytic membrane system will behave according to physical rules that we do not yet know but that will be fundamentally different from standard reaction-diffusion kinetics. In **Figure 1**, we summarize these concepts.

If the endocytic membrane system constitutes the space-time for signal transduction reactions (at least to a certain extent), and signal transduction is able to change the properties of the endocytic membrane system, we deal with the situation that the actors (sensors, signal transducers, and acceptors) influence their own space-time (dynamic shapes, patterns and interactions of membranes, vesicles, and organelles), which in turn will influence the actors. In other words, the physical rules determining the diffusion-reaction kinetics of signaling components are influenced by the components themselves (**Figure 1**). This introduces an aspect of complexity that is usually not considered in systems biology. It is a type of feedforward or feedback loop, but the effect is on the space-time dimension in which the signaling reactions take place, which is fundamentally different from the kind of loops we usually consider in standard signal processing diagrams (**Figure 1**). Given the importance of dynamics of complex shapes in biology, this may be a fundamental principle of processes in living systems.

PROTEIN KINASES REGULATING ENDOCYTIC MACHINERY

The previous three sections laid out our ignorance of the integrated activities of membrane trafficking and signal transduction and the need to readjust our mindset for studying them. To a certain extent, however, there is a molecular

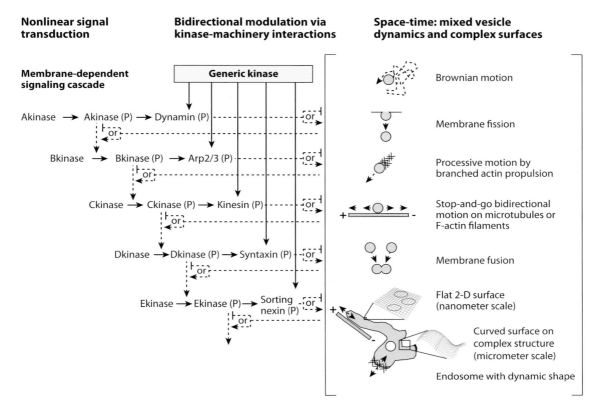

Nonlinear signal transduction

Bidirectional modulation via kinase-machinery interactions

Space-time: mixed vesicle dynamics and complex surfaces

Membrane-dependent signaling cascade

Generic kinase

Akinase → Akinase (P) → Dynamin (P) ----- or ⌐
   ⌐ or ⌐

Bkinase → Bkinase (P) → Arp2/3 (P) ----- or ⌐
   ⌐ or ⌐

Ckinase → Ckinase (P) → Kinesin (P) ----- or ⌐
   ⌐ or ⌐

Dkinase → Dkinase (P) → Syntaxin (P) ⌐ or ⌐

Ekinase → Ekinase (P) → Sorting nexin (P) ⌐ or ⌐
   ⌐ or ⌐

Brownian motion

Membrane fission

Processive motion by branched actin propulsion

Stop-and-go bidirectional motion on microtubules or F-actin filaments

Membrane fusion

Flat 2-D surface (nanometer scale)

Curved surface on complex structure (micrometer scale)

Endosome with dynamic shape

Figure 1

Endocytosis defines a flexible space-time for signal transduction. This conceptual overview shows a hypothetical membrane-dependent kinase phosphorylation cascade (*left*) in which each kinase of the cascade is localized somewhere in the endocytic membrane system. By phosphorylation of endocytic machinery components (a dynamin, Arp2/3, a kinesin, a syntaxin, a sorting nexin) along the way, the cascade will change (either increase or decrease) the dynamics of endocytic vesicles, fission and fusion reactions, and the shapes of endocytic organelles. This defines the space-time for the reaction-diffusion kinetics of signal transduction, creating a mechanism by which the cascade can regulate its own transduction kinetics (either negatively or positively). We can also imagine the existence of generic kinases that broadly influence the space-time of membrane-dependent signal transduction by regulating many endocytic machinery components. In this scenario, signal transduction reactions occur at steady state and do not require any specific input but will change their rate and direction when the dynamics of the endocytic membrane system are changed, resulting in specific signaling cascades.

foundation on which to build systems models of endocytosis, and protein phosphorylation takes a central role in this process. Phosphorylation allows the actors of signaling cascades (protein kinases) to control their space-time by regulating membrane deformation, fission, trafficking, docking, and fusion (the endocytic machinery). Phosphorylation is also a tangible observation that has been documented for many proteins and protein kinases for several decades. Therefore, we expect that a systematic inventory of these reactions will provide a first molecular

foundation on which to further develop graphical models of signaling-endocytosis networks (Pelkmans et al. 2005). Although such models do not explain systems behavior, they do provide a useful way to navigate through the system's components and to think about how systems properties might emerge.

We collected all known direct phosphorylation reactions of endocytic machinery components assigned to specific protein kinases from the literature (**Supplemental Table 1**; follow the **Supplemental Material**

NETWORK TERMINOLOGY

In general, a network consists of nodes and edges. Nodes are discrete entities, genes, proteins, or metabolites. Edges are interactions between the nodes and can be of any type. Many biologists understand an interaction as something physical, such as a (non)covalent binding between the two nodes, a biochemical modification of one node by another (such as phosphorylation), or a biochemical transition (metabolic networks). Increasingly, one finds networks in which statistical correlations between two nodes are displayed as an interaction. Such networks can be derived from transcriptome profiling, in which the profile of mRNA abundance in a series of particular conditions or in particular tissues is used to correlate genes. Above a certain correlation threshold, a connection is drawn. In functional RNAi screens, when the phenotype is described by a quantitative multivariate expression or phenotype feature vector (statistically similar to a transcription profile), clusters of phenotypes (phenoclusters) can be made. These distances can be used as connections in a network, in which a link between two nodes indicates that they have similar loss-of-function phenotypes.

link from the Annual Reviews home page at **http://www.annualreviews.org**) and annotated those kinases onto the protein kinome tree (**Figure 2**). There is not one specific class of protein kinases that phosphorylates endocytic machinery. Rather, the kinases are distributed throughout the kinome tree. This suggests that the diversity of the protein kinome and the diversity of the endocytic membrane system have coevolved. The yeast protein kinome consists of 130 kinases, compared with 518 kinases in humans (Manning et al. 2002). We can imagine that as the demands increased for both endocytosis and signal transduction to measure, process, integrate, and react to more diverse

signals, both systems grew in complexity and became intertwined, whereby the number and extent of interactions between protein kinases and endocytic machinery components increased. In addition, evolution may have favored the endocytic membrane system to become a flexible space-time scaffold for signal transduction, providing advantages for complex signal processing tasks in cells of multicellular organisms that are yet to be discovered.

We created in **Figure 3** a network of these protein kinases and the endocytic machinery components they phosphorylate. We included 40 kinases and 70 endocytic machinery components with a total of 140 interactions between them. Our definition of endocytic machinery is arbitrary. For instance, the border between endocytic machinery and machinery regulating actin dynamics is not clearly definable. The network illustrates that protein phosphorylation regulates endocytic membrane trafficking at all levels. Protein phosphorylation occurs during adaptor recruitment to the membrane, coat formation, uncoating and membrane shaping (induction or stabilization of the correct curvature for endocytic carriers), the fission of membrane carriers, actin polymerization, transport along microtubules, vesicle docking at target membranes, and vesicle fusion.

Before describing each node and each edge in more detail, we must start with a word of caution. In particular, our understanding of the human kinome is tremendously biased toward a handful of protein kinases that are being actively studied in laboratories worldwide in primarily cancer-derived tissue culture cell lines (e.g., HeLa, A431). One argument is that these are also the important kinases of each human cell, but that statement has no empirical

---

Figure 2

The human kinome tree is annotated with all protein kinases found to directly phosphorylate endocytic machinery components (*yellow circles*) and all protein kinases identified in an RNAi phenotypic screen (*blue circles*) to give a phenotype in any or more of the image-based assays scoring for infectious virus entry of simian virus 40 (SV40) or vesicular stomatitis virus (VSV); internalization of transferrin, cholera toxin B, or low-density lipoprotein (LDL); and staining patterns of early endosome antigen 1 (EEA1), lysosomal-associated membrane protein 1 (LAMP1), or caveolin-1-GFP. Kinases described in the literature and also found in the screen are annotated with yellow-blue circles. The human kinome is provided courtesy of Cell Signaling Technology (**http://www.cellsignal.com**).

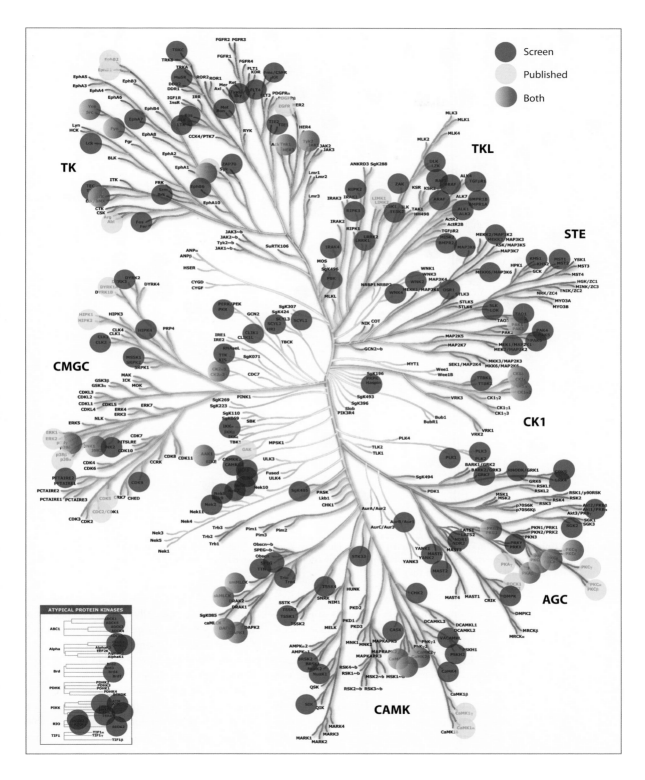

Figure 3

Network of 111 phosphorylation reactions between 32 protein kinases (isoforms have been fused to one kinase) (*black nodes*) and 61 endocytic machinery components (isoforms have been fused to one component) (*colored nodes*). Endocytic machinery is color-coded according to the functional module to which they belong.

foundation. Most of these heavily studied kinases were identified in forward genetic screens and behave well in biochemical assays. Only when human short interfering RNA (siRNA) libraries became available (in 2003) could we perform genome-wide unbiased analyses of protein kinases in human cells and empirically address the question as to which kinases, globally compared, are important regulators of the phenotypic properties of cellular processes.

Furthermore, especially in cancer cells, the set of kinases regulating cellular processes might be very different from the set of kinases regulating these same processes in primary cells from a particular tissue.

With the above considerations in mind, we can analyze the network. Seven kinases act as major hubs in the network, having at least seven endocytic machinery components as direct substrates. These kinases are cell division cycle

2 (CDC2), c-Src (SRC), casein kinase 1 and 2 (CSNK1 and -2, respectively) [here treated as one kinase, protein kinase C (PRKC)], protein kinase A (PRKA), p21-activated kinase 1 (PAK1), and calcium/calmodulin-regulated kinase 2B (CAMK2). CDC2 primarily phosphorylates RabGTPases, which is believed to occur during the mitotic cycle. SRC is a heavily studied signaling kinase that is membrane anchored and associated with the plasma membrane and perhaps also with intracellular organelles. It phosphorylates components involved in early events of the endocytic membrane trafficking cycle, namely vesicle formation, fission, and actin-mediated propulsion. It thus appears that SRC can act as a general on switch for endocytic membrane trafficking, downstream from growth factor receptors and integrins, which activate SRC. Casein kinase has a very broad range of substrates and is usually considered to be a nonspecific switch that modulates structural properties of many different types of proteins. It is activated by many receptor signals (e.g., growth factor receptors, cadherins) during mitosis. PRKC has been studied extensively in membrane trafficking and endocytosis; it has 10 isoforms, which we here, for sake of simplicity, collectively treat as one kinase. PRKC regulates fission, fusion, and the RabGTPase cycle. Many signals can activate PRKC, but most prominently among these are activated G protein–coupled receptors (GPCRs) and growth-factor receptors. PRKA regulates membrane fission, microtubule transport, actin propulsion, and membrane fusion. It is activated by cAMP downstream of GPCRs and has an important role in nutrient signaling. PAK1 receives signals from growth factor receptors, GPCRs, and integrins on the cell surface and is a well-known hub in the regulation of the actin cytoskeleton and microtubule-dependent transport. It is essential for ruffle formation, cup closure, and internalization of the membrane carriers during macropinocytosis. In our network, it regulates actin-binding and -branching proteins, molecular motors, membrane fission, and RhoGTPases. The last hub is CAMK2, which is activated by calmodulin as soon as intracellular Ca^{2+} concentrations rise. CAMK2 regulates primarily membrane fusion. The effect of intracellular Ca^{2+} on membrane fusion has been extensively studied for synaptic vesicles, where the arrival of an electrical impulse at the synapse leads to immediate opening of Ca^{2+} channels and immediate fusion of numerous synaptic vesicles already docked on the synapse membrane. Ca^{2+}-regulated fusion is not a specific characteristic of membrane trafficking in synapses but is seen in any cell type. This is an example of an element of the endocytic membrane system that is generally built-in but used more predominantly in a specific cell type (e.g., neurons). In **Figure 4**, we created a simplified hierarchical network to illustrate that, by mere consideration of these seven kinase hubs, cellular physiology is already linked in complex networks to the endocytic machinery modules.

MODULES OF ENDOCYTIC MACHINERY COMPONENTS REGULATED BY PHOSPHORYLATION

We next separated the phosphorylation networks surrounding and interconnecting each functional module of endocytic machinery components for more detailed discussion (**Figure 5**). We do not embark here on detailed descriptions of the mechanics by which these modules operate. For that, we refer to a series of excellent reviews (Cai et al. 2007, D'Souza-Schorey & Chavrier 2006, Farsad & De Camilli 2003, Jahn & Scheller 2006, McNiven & Thompson 2006, Miaczynska & Zerial 2002, Robinson 2004, Roth 2007, Soldati & Schliwa 2006). The purpose here is to create an informational network of all known phosphorylation reactions. In most cases, it is not yet understood how reversible phosphorylation can change the mechanics of the endocytic machinery. For the few cases in which more detailed insights have been obtained, we refer to the original work and their reviews (Henderson & Conner 2007, Mace et al. 2005, Yarar et al. 2007).

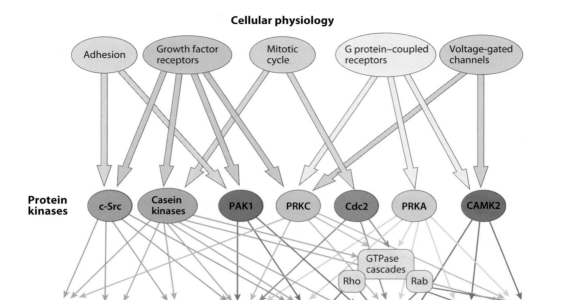

Figure 4

Hierarchical representation of a simplified view on how cell physiology, primarily via G protein–coupled receptors (GPCRs), calcium channels, growth factor receptors, adhesion sensors, and sensors of the mitotic cycle control the endocytic machinery via seven major protein kinase hubs. c-Src controls vesicle formation. Casein kinases and protein kinase C (PRKC) control all steps of the endocytic membrane trafficking cycle. p21-activated kinase 1 (PAK1) and cell division cycle 2 (CDC2) control membrane fission, cytoskeleton-dependent transport, and GTPase cascades. Protein kinase A (PRKA) and calcium/calmodulin-regulated kinase 2 (CAMK2) control fission, cytoskeleton-dependent transport, and fusion of membrane vesicles.

Adaptor Module

Components of the adaptor complexes AP1 and AP2, as well as the adaptor proteins AP180 and the β arrestins, are phosphorylated. Cyclin G–associated kinase (GAK)/auxillin phosphorylates AP1 and AP2, whereas the adaptor-associated kinase 1 (AAK1) phosphorylates just AP2 (Conner & Schmid 2002, Korolchuk & Banting 2002, Smythe 2002). The major hub SRC phosphorylates β arrestins (Fessart et al. 2007). Phosphorylation of adaptors regulates adaptor recruitment to cargo (β arrestins are usually recruited to GPCRs, thereby bridging them with clathrin) and the (dis)assembly of coat components on the adaptors (Langer et al. 2007). How phosphoryla-

tion is timed with the cycle of coat assembly and disassembly is less well understood. SRC becomes activated downstream of GPCRs, but how GAK/auxillin and AAK1 become activated or if they are constitutively active needs to be investigated.

Coat Module

We here include clathrin, caveolin, and flotillin coats, even though these coats function by very different principles (Bauer & Pelkmans 2006, Frick et al. 2007, Kirchhausen 2000, Parton & Simons 2007). It can just as well be argued that caveolin and flotillin belong to the membrane-shaping module discussed next. Coat proteins are directly phosphorylated by the two major hubs CSNK2 and SRC. SRC, which phosphorylates tyrosine 14 of caveolin, may play a role in the internalization of caveolae (Li et al. 1996). However, this reaction may also be linked to regulating cell adhesion, a prominent role of SRC in the cell. SRC-caveolin phosphorylation has roles in signal transduction (Williams & Lisanti 2004) and may regulate the caveolin-mediated scaffolding or transport of certain molecules and lipids important for cell adhesion (Echarri & Del Pozo 2006). Why SRC phosphorylates flotillin is completely unclear, but such phosphorylation may have a similar purpose as phosphorylation of caveolin, given that both proteins have similar topologies and may share a similar structural organization in scaffolding lipid raft components (Neumann-Giesen et al. 2007). The purpose of phosphorylating clathrin by SRC (Wilde et al. 1999) or by CSNK2 (Bar-Zvi & Branton 1986) is also not clear. SRC may transduce signals from growth factor receptors or integrins to clathrin, which may contribute to the initiation of clathrin coat formation around the receptor. CSNK2 is the major kinase activity associated with clathrin-coated vesicles and can phosphorylate many proteins on these vesicles. It is inactive when the clathrin coat is polymerized and becomes active as soon as uncoating starts (Korolchuk & Banting 2002). Additionally, COPI-coat components are known to be phosphorylated (Sheff et al. 1996), but to date no specific kinases have been identified.

Membrane-Shaping Module

We included in this module those BAR domain–containing proteins that are known to be phosphorylated, namely amphiphysin (AMPH) and endophilin A1 and A2 (SH3GL1 and SH3GL2). Sorting nexin 9 (SNX9) is a BAR domain–containing sorting nexin that links vesicle shaping to the actin cytoskeleton (Yarar et al. 2007). Synaptojanin 1 (SYNJ1) is a phosphoinositide lipid phosphatase involved in the uncoating of clathrin-coated vesicles (Slepnev et al. 1998). Besides the major hubs

SRC and casein kinase, we find here dual-specificity tyrosine phosphorylation–regulated kinase 1 (DYRK1), CDK5, tyrosine kinase nonreceptor 2 (TNK2), and Rho kinase 1 (ROCK1). DYRK1 and CDK5 both phosphorylate AMPH and SYNJ1. DYRK1-dependent phosphorylation of AMPH is probably involved in the formation of synaptic vesicles, and DYRK1 deletion mutants of *D. melanogaster* have brain developmental defects (minibrain mutant) (Dierssen & de Lagran 2006). CDK5-mediated phosphorylation of AMPH regulates its binding to the membrane (Liang et al. 2007). CDK5 and ephrin receptor B phosphorylation of SYNJ1 inhibits the binding to endophilin and its inositol 5-phosphatase activity (Irie et al. 2005, Lee et al. 2004). Phosphorylation of endophilin by ROCK1 regulates binding to CIN85 (Cbl-interacting protein of 85 kDa) and blocks epidermal growth factor receptor (EGFR) endocytosis (Kaneko et al. 2005).

Membrane Fission Module

In this module we list dynamin 1 and 2 as well as C-terminal binding protein1/BFA-induced ADP-ribosylated substrate (CtBP1/BARS) (Corda et al. 2006, Praefcke & McMahon 2004). The latter is not characterized to the extent as dynamins but has a role late in the formation of macropinosomes and, most likely, in the actual closure of the macropinocytic cup (Liberali et al. 2008). For the dynamins, we again find the major hubs SRC and casein kinase as well as DYRK1 and CDK5. Four additional kinases phosphorylate dynamins, the major hubs PRKC and CDC2, nonmetastatic protein 1 (NME1), and mitogen-activated protein kinase (MAPK)1. If and how these diverse phosphorylation reactions change the activity of dynamins or their recruitment to membranes remain to be investigated. CtBP1/BARS is phosphorylated by the major hubs PAK1 and PRKA and by MAPK9 and homeodomain-interacting protein kinase 2 (HIPK2). PAK1 regulates closure of the macropinocytic cup via CtBP1/BARS (Liberali et al. 2008). Given that PAK1 has an important

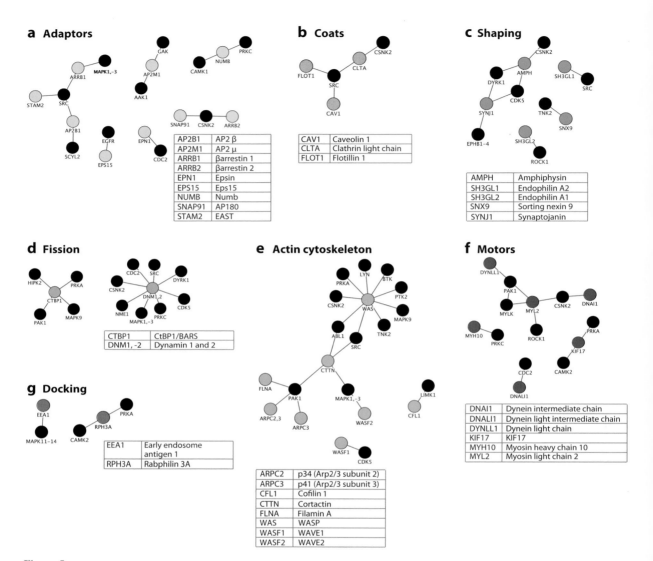

Figure 5

Modules of endocytic machinery components and protein kinases. Specific phosphorylation networks of each module are depicted. Endocytic machinery components are denoted by colored nodes, whereas protein kinases are denoted by black nodes.

role in regulating both F-actin assembly and anchoring to the membrane as well as microtubule motor activity, it emerges as a central regulator of macropinocytosis. MAPK9 and HIPK2 phosphorylation targets CtBP1/BARS for degradation (Wang et al. 2006, Zhang et al. 2005), and PRKA changes the interactions of CtBP1/BARS with other proteins (Dammer & Sewer 2008). It is interesting to note that the kinases regulating dynamin activity are all different from the kinases regulating CtBP1/BARS activity, indicating that these two types of membrane fission are downstream of different signal transduction cascades and therefore likely have nonoverlapping roles in membrane trafficking.

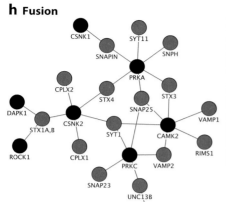

h Fusion

i GTPase cascades

CPLX1	Synaphin2
CPLX2	Synaphin1
RIMS1	Rim; Rab3-interacting protein
SNAP23	SNAP23
SNAP25	SNAP25
SNAPIN	Snapin
SNPH	Syntaphilin
STX1A, -B	Syntaxin 1A and B
STX3	Syntaxin3
STX4	Syntaxin4
SYT11	Synaptotagmin 12
UNC13B	Munc-18
VAMP1	VAMP1
VAMP2	VAMP2

ALPL	HOPS
ARHGAP4	p115 ARHGAP4
ARHGDIA	RhoGDI
ARHGEF1	p115RhoGEF
CDC42	Cdc42
DDEF1	ASAP1
RabGDI	GDI 1 and 2
RAB1	All Rab1 isoforms
RAB4	All Rab4 isoforms
RAB5	All Rab5 isoforms
RAB8	All Rab8 isoforms
RHOA	RhoA

Protein kinases	
AAK1	AAK1
ABL1	c-ABL
BTK	Btk
CAMK1	Ca^{2+}/calmodulin-dependent protein kinase 1
CAMK2	Ca^{2+}/calmodulin-dependent protein kinase 2
CDC2	cdc2
CDK5	cdk5
CSNK1	casein kinase 1 (yeast yck3)
CSNK2	All casein kinase 2 isoforms
DAPK1	DAP kinase
DYRK1	Dyrk1a and Dyrk1b
EGFR	EGFR
EPHB1–4	EphrinB-EphB1, -B2, -B3, and -B4
GAK	Cyclin G associated kinase/auxilin 2
HIPK2	HIPK2
LIMK1	LIM kinase
LYN	Lyn
MAPK1, -3	ERK1 and -2
MAPK11–14	Stress-activated MAPK p38 α, β, and Δ
MAPK9	Jnk
PAK1	Pak1
PRKA	All protein kinase A isoforms
PRKC	All protein kinase C isoforms
PRKG1	PKG
PTK2	Fak
PTK2B	Fyk2
ROCK1	Rho kinase
SCYL2	CVAK104
SRC	c-Src
TNK2	Activated Cdc42-associated kinase-2 (ACK2)

Figure 5

(*Continued*)

Actin Cytoskeleton Module

In this module, we include only those actin-binding, -nucleating, or -modulating proteins that have been functionally implicated in endocytosis and are phosphorylated by specific kinases. A protein with many known phosphorylations is N-WASP (WAS), which activates the Arp2/3 complex to initiate the formation of branched actin networks (Takenawa & Suetsugu 2007). WAVE1 (WASF1) and WAVE2 (WASF2), which have similar roles as N-WASP (Takenawa & Suetsugu 2007), are also included. The module also contains three actin-binding proteins: cortactin (CTTN), filamin A, and cofilin1. Besides the major kinase hubs SRC, which phosphorylates N-WASP and CTTN, and CSNK2, which phosphorylates N-WASP, we find here several other kinases that also phosphorylate other modules. These kinases are the hub PAK1—which phosphorylates the Arp2/3 complex, filamin A, and CTTN—and MAPK1 and -3, (Erk1/2), which phosphorylate CTTN and WAVE1.

We also find here the major hub PRKA as well as CDK5, both known to phosphorylate N-WASP. The module furthermore consists of Abelson cytoplasmic tyrosine kinase 1 (ABL1), which regulates CTTN and N-WASP, as well as MAPK9, the SRC family tyrosine kinase LYN, TNK2 (activated Cdc42-associated kinase), PTK2 (focal adhesion kinase), and Bruton's tyrosine kinase (BTK), all known to phosphorylate WASP. Finally, we include LIM kinase 1, which phosphorylates cofilin1.

Molecular-Motors Module

The following molecular motors with roles in endocytosis are known to be phosphorylated by specific kinases: (*a*) three subunits of the dynein motor complex, the dynein light chain 1 (DYNLL1), the dynein light intermediate chain 1 (DNALI1), and the dynein intermediate chain 1 (DNAI1); (*b*) myosin motor 2 heavy chain 10 (MYH10) and myosin light chain 2 (MYL2); and (*c*) the kinesin KIF17. The kinases responsible for this are the hubs CDC2, CSNK2, PAK1, PRKA, PRKC, and CAMK2 as well as the nonhubs myosin light chain kinase (MYLK) and ROCK1. A set of five kinases coordinates the activity of MYL2 and the dynein complex. PAK1 and CSNK2 are interesting because they regulate both a component of the dynein complex and myosin 2. For many endocytic events, myosin and dynein motors need to act sequentially to switch from movement on F-actin to movement on microtubules. Sequential phosphorylation of the responsible motor may establish this switch.

Membrane Docking Module

Not much is known about phosphorylation in membrane vesicle docking. Only two known docking (or tethering) proteins, namely early endosome antigen 1 (EEA1) and rabphilin 3A (RPH3A), are phosphorylated by specific kinases. EEA1 is phosphorylated by the stress response kinase p38 (MAPK11, -13, -14), and RPH3A by PRKA and CAMK2. EEA1 is phosphorylated in its FYVE domain, and this may

be important for the recruitment of EEA1 to PI(3)P-enriched membranes, such as the early endosome (Mace et al. 2005).

Membrane Fusion Module

The molecular mechanisms of membrane fusion are well characterized, and the role of phosphorylation has been studied extensively. Several kinases regulate multiple proteins involved in membrane fusion. In this module we find the hubs CAMK2, casein kinase, PRKC, and PRKA. CAMK2 phosphorylates syntaxin 3 (STX3), two vesicle-associated membrane proteins (VAMP1, -2), soluble NSF attachment protein 25 (SNAP25), synaptotagmin 1, and RIM (RIMS1) or Rab3-interacting protein. CSNK1 and CSNK2 phosphorylate a SNAP-interacting protein (SNAPIN), two syntaxins (STX1A and -4), synaphin 1 and 2 (CPLX1 and -2), and synaptotagmin. PRKC phosphorylates synaptotagmin, SNAP23 and -25, and UNC13B (also known as MUNC18). PRKA phosphorylates two syntaxins (STX3 and -4), SNAP25, SNAPIN, synaptotagmin 12, and syntaphilin. Kinases with few substrates in this module are death-associated protein kinase 1 (DAPK1) and ROCK1, which both phosphorylate syntaxin 1a.

GTPase Cascade Module

This module is not assigned to a specific step in the formation, transport, or fusion steps of a membrane vesicle. RabGTPases regulate several aspects of this cycle and have various components of these modules as their effectors. The GTPase cycle does however receive input from other sources, which can change its cycle time and, as a consequence, the activity of membrane traffic. Many of the above-mentioned kinases modulate the GTPase cascade. The general hubs casein kinase and SRC are found, but not as prominently as CDC2. CDC2 phosphorylates several RabGTPases (Rab1, Rab4, Rab5) during mitosis. Other hubs found here are PRKA and PRKC. PRKA is linked specifically to the RhoGTPases RhoA and Cdc42, which play (distant) roles in endocytosis by regulating the cytoskeleton. PRKC has been specifically linked to Rab8 and a Rho GDP/GTP exchange factor (ARHGEF1). Interestingly, we also find two major MAPKs: p38 (MAPK11, -13, -14) and Erk1/2 (MAPK1, -3). p38 is the major transducer of stress response signaling in the cell and regulates Rab GDP dissociation inhibitor (GDI). Erk1/2, the major bottleneck in transducing growth factor signals to cell proliferation, phosphorylates Rab5.

UNBIASED GLOBAL APPROACHES TO LINK ENDOCYTOSIS TO KINASE REGULATORY NETWORKS OF THE CELL

The previous section demonstrates that all modules of the endocytic machinery are highly interconnected by protein kinases and that certain modules are enriched in phosphorylation reactions. These are membrane fission, the GTPase cascade, membrane fusion, and actin-mediated propulsion (in particular N-WASP).

However, if an unbiased analysis of protein phosphorylation of all these modules were available, the picture would probably look quite different. The first step toward such a global view was taken several years ago by systematically silencing each kinase of the human kinome using siRNA and studying how this affects a variety of properties of the endocytic membrane system (Pelkmans et al. 2005). This study included the infectious entry of simian virus 40 through caveolae/raft-mediated endocytosis; the infectious entry of vesicular stomatitis virus through clathrin-mediated endocytosis; and 23 parameters of the endocytic membrane system describing internalization patterns of fluorescent transferrin, of cholera toxin subunit B, and of low-density lipoprotein and the intracellular distributions of early endosomes, of late endosomes, and of caveolin-1. Because it was the first study of its kind, and inherent to any high-throughput study, some experimental noise as well as false-positive and false-negative observations must be expected. The rapid technological development in this field, including better siRNA libraries and advanced computational methods for quantifying and classifying loss-of-function phenotypes (Kittler et al. 2007, Lamprecht et al. 2007, Pepperkok & Ellenberg 2006, Reimers & Carey 2006, Root et al. 2006), will allow much improved global and unbiased analysis of the endocytic membrane system in the future. The importance of this approach for creating a set of formal and standardized rules with which to define the properties of the endocytic membrane system justifies a large investment by the cell biology community to make these methods more mature, well adapted to the problems of membrane trafficking, and more mainstream.

The results of this first study showed that protein kinase silencing has widespread effects on the endocytic membrane system. The 140 protein kinases found to have a loss-of-function phenotype in any of the parameters studied are also annotated on the kinome tree in **Figure 2**. Of the 32 published kinases regulating endocytic machinery components, 26 had a loss-of-function phenotype in the screen. Importantly, several of these were actually found to regulate endocytic machinery components after the RNAi screen was completed (see **Supplemental Table 1**), thus independently validating several observations. It can be expected that a number of the protein kinases found in a phenotypic screen do not directly phosphorylate endocytic machinery components but have a role more upstream in signal transduction to the endocytic machinery. This hypothesis can be tested in a network in which one adds a layer of protein kinases that are upstream of the protein kinases directly phosphorylating the endocytic machinery (**Figure 6**). The information to construct such a network was derived from STRING (**http://string.embl.de**), a protein association network that quantitatively integrates predicted and known physical and functional interaction data from various sources. In this complex graph, we can now link more than half of the protein kinases identified in the screen to endocytic machinery components. There is no doubt that more extensive bioinformatics

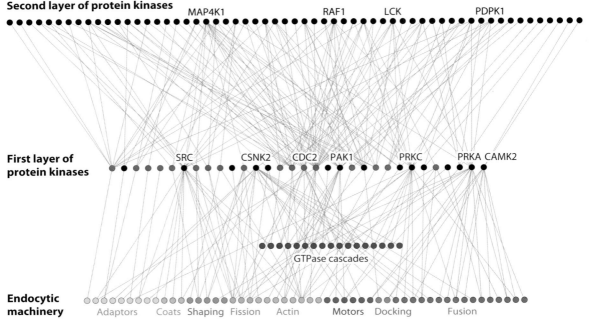

Figure 6

Integration of endocytic machinery components and the protein kinases that directly phosphorylate these components into larger kinase signaling networks of the cell. The hierarchical network consists of 69 endocytic machinery components from **Figure 3**, the first layer consists of 32 protein kinases from **Figure 3**, and the peripheral layer consists of 59 protein kinases that interact with the first layer. The major hubs of the first layer, SRC, CSNK2, CDC2, PAK1, PRKC, PRKA, and CAMK2, as well as four examples of upstream kinases in the peripheral layer (MAP4K1, RAF1, LCK, and PDPK1) are indicated. With this bioinformatics approach, we can link 74 out of 131 kinases (56%) found in a comprehensive image-based RNAi screen to interact either directly (15), or via one intermediate kinase node (59), with the endocytic machinery.

analysis, combined with advanced statistics and network modeling, will give a much better analysis of these results. It is therefore imperative that the field of endocytosis also embrace this discipline (Alon 2007, Sharan & Ideker 2006, Zaidel-Bar et al. 2007). It will be essential to validate these networks, to improve them, and to further expand them using quantitative proteomics. In particular, phosphoproteomics (Bodenmiller et al. 2007) combined with RNAi of protein kinases will be ideally suited to map out globally the cellular substrates of protein kinases and to delineate which endocytic machinery components are phosphorylated by which kinases. Combined with protein-protein interaction networks derived from quantitative proteomics and systematic pull-down experiments (Aebersold & Mann 2003), we can ob-

tain the biochemical architecture of kinase-endocytosis networks. We will then be able to understand how cell adhesion signaling controls caveolae/raft-mediated endocytosis; how nutrient sensing controls clathrin-mediated endocytosis (Galvez et al. 2007); and how mitogenic signaling, calcium signaling, and the actin cytoskeleton coordinate the activities of the two endoytic routes (Pelkmans et al. 2005).

CONCLUSIONS AND OUTLOOK

We must stress that we ignore the importance of lipids in this review. There is no doubt that the heterogeneity of lipid organization in membranes, the particular use of phosphoinositides, and their reversible phosphorylation to create membrane domains and recruit specific endocytic machinery to membranes as well as lipid second messengers are crucial elements of the endocytic membrane system (Di Paolo & De Camilli 2006). Cellular signaling regulates many lipid kinases and phosphatases, hydrolases, carbohydrate transferases, flippases, pumps, and nonvesicular transferases between compartments, which strongly influences the behavior of membranes (Di Paolo & De Camilli 2006). This topic deserves a review of its own.

If we have the ambition to create a physical explanation of the behavior of the endocytic membrane system, we need to fill in an enormous conceptual and informational gap, requiring both top-down and bottom-up approaches. In the top-down approach, we must attempt to model and predict the activity of endocytic pathways and their phenotypic diversity by identifying patterns in large sets of measurements from individual cells and vesicles. Image-based screens of individual cells in whole cell populations combined with novel image analysis methods and advanced statistical and mathematical analysis tools will be essential. Eventually, this may lead to the discovery of formal rules that describe basic principles of the endocytic membrane system, which is required to separate nondeterministic aspects from deterministic aspects of the system. Only for the latter will bottom-up approaches be useful. Meanwhile, we must identify the principal proteins, enzymes, lipids, and metabolites responsible for this deterministic behavior and delineate the tightly controlled interaction schemes between them. We have already come a long way to identifying these molecules, and the various-omics disciplines will make this list more complete. Systematic analysis of the effect of silencing, inactivating, or overexpressing these molecules will allow us to link these molecules to the physical principles underlying phenotypic complexity of endocytosis. We here coin the term genetical physics for this approach. Genetical physics links genetic perturbations (e.g., by RNAi) to specific parameters and degrees of freedom of the physical principles underlying the cellular system under scrutiny.

For accurate deterministic bottom-up models, we will have to determine the abundances and turnover of all these molecules, measure all the association and dissociation constants between these molecules, and ascertain how these variables are regulated over time. However, the biological uncertainty principle (due to small and noisy numbers of interacting components and unpredictable interaction kinetics) will prevent fully deterministic descriptions at this level. This last aim therefore lies in the very far future for a complex system such as endocytic membrane trafficking, and we may have to ask ourselves to what extent we should pursue the bottom-up approach. If we can identify predictive physical principles and link them to sets of individual molecules without having a complete biochemical model of how these molecules interact, they may be remarkably sufficient in explaining the roles of the endocytic membrane system in cellular physiology.

Genetical physics: a new discipline that quantitatively links genetic perturbations to degrees of freedom in a formal, physical model of the biological system of interest

SUMMARY POINTS

1. Protein kinases play an essential role in regulating the endocytic membrane system.

2. Protein kinases are the interface between the endocytic machinery and the physiological status of the cell.

3. Protein kinases allow the endocytic machinery to respond to changing demands from the cell and thereby ensure that the appropriate cellular phenotype is established or maintained.

4. The endocytic membrane system in turn plays an essential role in signal transduction and provides a flexible and changeable space-time for signal transduction reactions.

5. Signal transduction and the endocytic membrane system have most likely coevolved into the complex and integrated system that we observe in mammalian cells today.

DISCLOSURE STATEMENT

The authors are not aware of any biases that might be perceived as affecting the objectivity of this review.

ACKNOWLEDGMENTS

We thank all members of the laboratory for stimulating discussions. L.P. is supported by the Swiss National Science Foundation, SystemsX.ch, the European Union, and the ETH Zurich. P.L. is a long-term fellow of the Federation of European Biochemical Societies (FEBS), and P.R. is a long-term fellow of the European Molecular Biology Organization (EMBO).

LITERATURE CITED

Excellent overview of the power of modern-day quantitative proteomics.

Adami C. 2002. What is complexity? *BioEssays* 24:1085–94

Aebersold R, Mann M. 2003. Mass spectrometry-based proteomics. *Nature* 422:198–207

Alon U. 2007. Network motifs: theory and experimental approaches. *Nat. Rev. Genet.* 8:450–61

Balazsi G, Oltvai ZN. 2005. Sensing your surroundings: how transcription-regulatory networks of the cell discern environmental signals. *Sci. STKE* 2005:pe20

Early paper identifying one of the kinase activities in clathrin-coated vesicles.

Bar-Zvi D, Branton D. 1986. Clathrin-coated vesicles contain two protein kinase activities. Phosphorylation of clathrin β-light chain by casein kinase II. *J. Biol. Chem.* 261:9614–21

Bauer M, Pelkmans L. 2006. A new paradigm for membrane-organizing and -shaping scaffolds. *FEBS Lett.* 580:5559–64

Bodenmiller B, Mueller LN, Mueller M, Domon B, Aebersold R. 2007. Reproducible isolation of distinct, overlapping segments of the phosphoproteome. *Nat. Methods* 4:231–37

Boucrot E, Kirchhausen T. 2007. Endosomal recycling controls plasma membrane area during mitosis. *Proc. Natl. Acad. Sci. USA* 104:7939–44

Cai H, Reinisch K, Ferro-Novick S. 2007. Coats, tethers, Rabs, and SNAREs work together to mediate the intracellular destination of a transport vesicle. *Dev. Cell* 12:671–82

Chang TY, Chang CC, Ohgami N, Yamauchi Y. 2006. Cholesterol sensing, trafficking, and esterification. *Annu. Rev. Cell Dev. Biol.* 22:129–57

Identification of the kinase responsible for adaptor complex 2 phosphorylation.

Conner SD, Schmid SL. 2002. Identification of an adaptor-associated kinase, AAK1, as a regulator of clathrin-mediated endocytosis. *J. Cell Biol.* 156:921–29

Corda D, Colanzi A, Luini A. 2006. The multiple activities of CtBP/BARS proteins: the Golgi view. *Trends Cell Biol.* 16:167–73

Cota D, Proulx K, Smith KA, Kozma SC, Thomas G, et al. 2006. Hypothalamic mTOR signaling regulates food intake. *Science* 312:927–30

D'Souza-Schorey C, Chavrier P. 2006. ARF proteins: roles in membrane traffic and beyond. *Nat. Rev. Mol. Cell Biol.* 7:347–58

Excellent discussion of the role of phosphoinositides in membrane traffic.

Di Paolo G, De Camilli P. 2006. Phosphoinositides in cell regulation and membrane dynamics. *Nature* 443:651–57

Dierssen M, de Lagran MM. 2006. DYRK1A (dual-specificity tyrosine-phosphorylated and -regulated kinase 1A): a gene with dosage effect during development and neurogenesis. *Sci. World J.* 6:1911–22

Echarri A, Del Pozo MA. 2006. Caveolae internalization regulates integrin-dependent signaling pathways. *Cell Cycle* 5:2179–82

Farsad K, De Camilli P. 2003. Mechanisms of membrane deformation. *Curr. Opin. Cell Biol.* 15:372–81

Fessart D, Simaan M, Zimmerman B, Comeau J, Hamdan FF, et al. 2007. Src-dependent phosphorylation of β2-adaptin dissociates the β-arrestin-AP-2 complex. *J. Cell Sci.* 120:1723–32

Fotin A, Cheng Y, Sliz P, Grigorieff N, Harrison SC, et al. 2004. Molecular model for a complete clathrin lattice from electron cryomicroscopy. *Nature* 432:573–79

Frick M, Bright NA, Riento K, Bray A, Merrified C, Nichols BJ. 2007. Coassembly of flotillins induces formation of membrane microdomains, membrane curvature, and vesicle budding. *Curr. Biol.* 17:1151–56

Galvez T, Teruel MN, Heo WD, Jones JT, Kim ML, et al. 2007. siRNA screen of the human signaling proteome identifies the PtdIns(3,4,5)P$_3$-mTOR signaling pathway as a primary regulator of transferrin uptake. *Genome Biol.* 8:R142

Gruenberg J. 2001. The endocytic pathway: a mosaic of domains. *Nat. Rev. Mol. Cell Biol.* 2:721–30

Henderson DM, Conner SD. 2007. A novel AAK1 splice variant functions at multiple steps of the endocytic pathway. *Mol. Biol. Cell* 18:2698–706

Hennig KM, Colombani J, Neufeld TP. 2006. TOR coordinates bulk and targeted endocytosis in the *Drosophila melanogaster* fat body to regulate cell growth. *J. Cell Biol.* 173:963–74

Holcman D, Triller A. 2006. Modeling synaptic dynamics driven by receptor lateral diffusion. *Biophys. J.* 91:2405–15

Huang S, Wikswo J. 2006. Dimensions of systems biology. *Rev. Physiol. Biochem. Pharmacol.* 157:81–104

Hurley JH, Emr SD. 2006. The ESCRT complexes: structure and mechanism of a membrane-trafficking network. *Annu. Rev. Biophys. Biomol. Struct.* 35:277–98

Irie F, Okuno M, Pasquale EB, Yamaguchi Y. 2005. EphrinB-EphB signalling regulates clathrin-mediated endocytosis through tyrosine phosphorylation of synaptojanin 1. *Nat. Cell Biol.* 7:501–9

Jahn R, Scheller RH. 2006. SNAREs—engines for membrane fusion. *Nat. Rev. Mol. Cell Biol.* 7:631–43

Janowski BA, Willy PJ, Devi TR, Falck JR, Mangelsdorf DJ. 1996. An oxysterol signalling pathway mediated by the nuclear receptor LXRα. *Nature* 383:728–31

Jekely G. 2007. Origin of eukaryotic endomembranes: a critical evaluation of different model scenarios. *Adv. Exp. Med. Biol.* 607:38–51

Kaneko T, Maeda A, Takefuji M, Aoyama H, Nakayama M, et al. 2005. Rho mediates endocytosis of epidermal growth factor receptor through phosphorylation of endophilin A1 by Rho-kinase. *Genes Cells* 10:973–87

Kashtan N, Itzkovitz S, Milo R, Alon U. 2004. Topological generalizations of network motifs. *Phys. Rev. E* 70:031909

Kennedy MJ, Ehlers MD. 2006. Organelles and trafficking machinery for postsynaptic plasticity. *Annu. Rev. Neurosci.* 29:325–62

Kholodenko BN. 2006. Cell-signalling dynamics in time and space. *Nat. Rev. Mol. Cell Biol.* 7:165–76

Kholodenko BN, Hoek JB, Westerhoff HV. 2000. Why cytoplasmic signalling proteins should be recruited to cell membranes. *Trends Cell Biol.* 10:173–78

Kirchhausen T. 2000. Three ways to make a vesicle. *Nat. Rev. Mol. Cell Biol.* 1:187–98

Kirschner MW. 2005. The meaning of systems biology. *Cell* 121:503–4

Kittler R, Pelletier L, Heninger AK, Slabicki M, Theis M, et al. 2007. Genome-scale RNAi profiling of cell division in human tissue culture cells. *Nat. Cell Biol.* 9:1401–12

Kleijmeer M, Ramm G, Schuurhuis D, Griffith J, Rescigno M, et al. 2001. Reorganization of multivesicular bodies regulates MHC class II antigen presentation by dendritic cells. *J. Cell Biol.* 155:53–63

Korolchuk VI, Banting G. 2002. CK2 and GAK/auxilin2 are major protein kinases in clathrin-coated vesicles. *Traffic* 3:428–39

Lajoie P, Nabi IR. 2007. Regulation of raft-dependent endocytosis. *J. Cell Mol. Med.* 11:644–53

Lakadamyali M, Rust MJ, Zhuang X. 2006. Ligands for clathrin-mediated endocytosis are differentially sorted into distinct populations of early endosomes. *Cell* 124:997–1009

Summarizes several observations from the Del Pozo lab that caveolae-mediated endocytosis regulates cell adhesion signaling.

Image-based RNAi screen on transferrin uptake, in which automated image-processing algorithms were used. The authors demonstrate that the mTOR signaling pathway regulates the number of transferrin receptor molecules per endocytic vesicle.

These two discussions by Kholodenko and colleagues nicely lay out the concept that membranes define a space-time for signal transduction that is different from standard reaction-diffusion kinetics.

Indicates that the canonical endocytic pathway must be considered as a population of vesicles that display specific heterogeneity in the kinetics of internalization and transport of cargo.

Lamprecht MR, Sabatini DM, Carpenter AE. 2007. CellProfiler: free, versatile software for automated biological image analysis. *Biotechniques* 42:71–75

Langer JD, Stoops EH, Bethune J, Wieland FT. 2007. Conformational changes of coat proteins during vesicle formation. *FEBS Lett.* 581:2083–88

Lavoisier A. 1789. *Traité Élémentaire de Chimie*. Paris: Cuchet

Le Roy C, Wrana JL. 2005. Signaling and endocytosis: a team effort for cell migration. *Dev. Cell* 9:167–68

Lee SY, Wenk MR, Kim Y, Nairn AC, De Camilli P. 2004. Regulation of synaptojanin 1 by cyclin-dependent kinase 5 at synapses. *Proc. Natl. Acad. Sci. USA* 101:546–51

Li S, Seitz R, Lisanti MP. 1996. Phosphorylation of caveolin by Src tyrosine kinases. The α-isoform of caveolin is selectively phosphorylated by v-Src in vivo. *J. Biol. Chem.* 271:3863–68

Liang S, Wei FY, Wu YM, Tanabe K, Abe T, et al. 2007. Major Cdk5-dependent phosphorylation sites of amphiphysin 1 are implicated in the regulation of the membrane binding and endocytosis. *J. Neurochem.* 102:1466–76

Liberali P, Kakkonen E, Turacchio G, Valente C, Spaar A, et al. 2008. The closure of Pak1-dependent macropinosomes requires the phosphorylation of CtBP1/BARS. *EMBO J.* 27:970–81

Mace G, Miaczynska M, Zerial M, Nebreda AR. 2005. Phosphorylation of EEA1 by p38 MAP kinase regulates μ opioid receptor endocytosis. *EMBO J.* 24:3235–46

Manning G, Whyte DB, Martinez R, Hunter T, Sudarsanam S. 2002. The protein kinase complement of the human genome. *Science* 298:1912–34

Mayo AE, Setty Y, Shavit S, Zaslaver A, Alon U. 2006. Plasticity of the *cis*-regulatory input function of a gene. *PLoS Biol.* 4:e45

Mayor S, Pagano RE. 2007. Pathways of clathrin-independent endocytosis. *Nat. Rev. Mol. Cell Biol.* 8:603–12

McNiven MA, Thompson HM. 2006. Vesicle formation at the plasma membrane and trans-Golgi network: the same but different. *Science* 313:1591–94

Miaczynska M, Pelkmans L, Zerial M. 2004. Not just a sink: endosomes in control of signal transduction. *Curr. Opin. Cell Biol.* 16:400–6

Miaczynska M, Zerial M. 2002. Mosaic organization of the endocytic pathway. *Exp. Cell Res.* 272:8–14

Milo R, Shen-Orr S, Itzkovitz S, Kashtan N, Chklovskii D, Alon U. 2002. Network motifs: simple building blocks of complex networks. *Science* 298:824–27

Mogilner A, Wollman R, Marshall WF. 2006. Quantitative modeling in cell biology: What is it good for? *Dev. Cell* 11:279–87

Morgan MR, Humphries MJ, Bass MD. 2007. Synergistic control of cell adhesion by integrins and syndecans. *Nat. Rev. Mol. Cell Biol.* 8:957–69

Mostov K, Su T, ter Beest M. 2003. Polarized epithelial membrane traffic: conservation and plasticity. *Nat. Cell Biol.* 5:287–93

Neumann-Giesen C, Fernow I, Amaddii M, Tikkanen R. 2007. Role of EGF-induced tyrosine phosphorylation of reggie-1/flotillin-2 in cell spreading and signaling to the actin cytoskeleton. *J. Cell Sci.* 120:395–406

Parton RG, Simons K. 2007. The multiple faces of caveolae. *Nat. Rev. Mol. Cell Biol.* 8:185–94

Pelkmans L. 2005. Secrets of caveolae- and lipid raft-mediated endocytosis revealed by mammalian viruses. *Biochim. Biophys. Acta* 1746:295–304

Pelkmans L, Fava E, Grabner H, Hannus M, Habermann B, et al. 2005. Genome-wide analysis of human kinases in clathrin- and caveolae/raft-mediated endocytosis. *Nature* 436:78–86

Pepperkok R, Ellenberg J. 2006. High-throughput fluorescence microscopy for systems biology. *Nat. Rev. Mol. Cell Biol.* 7:690–96

Praefcke GJ, McMahon HT. 2004. The dynamin superfamily: universal membrane tubulation and fission molecules? *Nat. Rev. Mol. Cell Biol.* 5:133–47

Rappoport JZ, Simon SM. 2003. Real-time analysis of clathrin-mediated endocytosis during cell migration. *J. Cell Sci.* 116:847–55

Reimers M, Carey VJ. 2006. Bioconductor: an open source framework for bioinformatics and computational biology. *Methods Enzymol.* 411:119–34

Ricard J. 2003. What do we mean by biological complexity? *C. R. Biol.* 326:133–40

Robinson MS. 2004. Adaptable adaptors for coated vesicles. *Trends Cell Biol.* 14:167–74

Rodman JS, Mercer RW, Stahl PD. 1990. Endocytosis and transcytosis. *Curr. Opin. Cell Biol.* 2:664–72

Root DE, Hacohen N, Hahn WC, Lander ES, Sabatini DM. 2006. Genome-scale loss-of-function screening with a lentiviral RNAi library. *Nat. Methods* 3:715–19

Roth MG. 2007. Integrating actin assembly and endocytosis. *Dev. Cell* 13:3–4

Sbalzarini IF, Mezzacasa A, Helenius A, Koumoutsakos P. 2005. Effects of organelle shape on fluorescence recovery after photobleaching. *Biophys. J.* 89:1482–92

Schmid EM, McMahon HT. 2007. Integrating molecular and network biology to decode endocytosis. *Nature* 448:883–88

Sharan R, Ideker T. 2006. Modeling cellular machinery through biological network comparison. *Nat. Biotechnol.* 24:427–33

Sheff D, Lowe M, Kreis TE, Mellman I. 1996. Biochemical heterogeneity and phosphorylation of coatomer subunits. *J. Biol. Chem.* 271:7230–36

Shinar G, Milo R, Martinez MR, Alon U. 2007. Input output robustness in simple bacterial signaling systems. *Proc. Natl. Acad. Sci. USA* 104:19931–35

Slepnev VI, Ochoa GC, Butler MH, Grabs D, De Camilli P. 1998. Role of phosphorylation in regulation of the assembly of endocytic coat complexes. *Science* 281:821–24

Smythe E. 2002. Regulating the clathrin-coated vesicle cycle by AP2 subunit phosphorylation. *Trends Cell Biol.* 12:352–54

Soldati T, Schliwa M. 2006. Powering membrane traffic in endocytosis and recycling. *Nat. Rev. Mol. Cell Biol.* 7:897–908

Südhof TC. 2004. The synaptic vesicle cycle. *Annu. Rev. Neurosci.* 27:509–47

Taflia A, Holcman D. 2007. Dwell time of a Brownian molecule in a microdomain with traps and a small hole on the boundary. *J. Chem. Phys.* 126:234107

Takenawa T, Suetsugu S. 2007. The WASP-WAVE protein network: connecting the membrane to the cytoskeleton. *Nat. Rev. Mol. Cell Biol.* 8:37–48

Toret CP, Drubin DG. 2006. The budding yeast endocytic pathway. *J. Cell Sci.* 119:4585–87

Van Der Goot FG, Gruenberg J. 2006. Intra-endosomal membrane traffic. *Trends Cell Biol.* 16:514–21

Veiga E, Cossart P. 2005. Listeria hijacks the clathrin-dependent endocytic machinery to invade mammalian cells. *Nat. Cell Biol.* 7:894–900

Voglmaier SM, Edwards RH. 2007. Do different endocytic pathways make different synaptic vesicles? *Curr. Opin. Neurobiol.* 17:374–80

von Zastrow M, Sorkin A. 2007. Signaling on the endocytic pathway. *Curr. Opin. Cell Biol.* 19:436–45

Wang SY, Iordanov M, Zhang Q. 2006. c-Jun NH2-terminal kinase promotes apoptosis by down-regulating the transcriptional corepressor CtBP. *J. Biol. Chem.* 281:34810–15

Wilde A, Beattie EC, Lem L, Riethof DA, Liu SH, et al. 1999. EGF receptor signaling stimulates SRC kinase phosphorylation of clathrin, influencing clathrin redistribution and EGF uptake. *Cell* 96:677–87

Williams TM, Lisanti MP. 2004. The Caveolin genes: from cell biology to medicine. *Ann. Med.* 36:584–95

Yarar D, Waterman-Storer CM, Schmid SL. 2007. SNX9 couples actin assembly to phosphoinositide signals and is required for membrane remodeling during endocytosis. *Dev. Cell* 13:43–56

Zaidel-Bar R, Itzkovitz S, Ma'ayan A, Iyengar R, Geiger B. 2007. Functional atlas of the integrin adhesome. *Nat. Cell Biol.* 9:858–67

Zhang Q, Nottke A, Goodman RH. 2005. Homeodomain-interacting protein kinase-2 mediates CtBP phosphorylation and degradation in UV-triggered apoptosis. *Proc. Natl. Acad. Sci. USA* 102:2802–7

By applying computer simulation of diffusion in complex-shaped membranes (the endoplasmic reticulum), the authors showed that organelle shape has strong influences on diffusion at the macroscopic scale.

Discusses protein-protein interaction network approaches to dissect mechanisms of clathrin-coated pit assembly and internalization. Introduced the concept of matricity.

Important theoretical considerations of how cellular compartmentalization will affect Brownian motion.

Comparative Aspects
of Animal Regeneration

Jeremy P. Brockes and Anoop Kumar

Institute of Structural and Molecular Biology, University College London, London WC1E 6BT, England; email: j.brockes@ucl.ac.uk

Annu. Rev. Cell Dev. Biol. 2008. 24:525–49

First published online as a Review in Advance on July 3, 2008

The *Annual Review of Cell and Developmental Biology* is online at cellbio.annualreviews.org

This article's doi:
10.1146/annurev.cellbio.24.110707.175336

Key Words

salamander, zebra fish, planaria, stem cells, transdifferentiation, evolution

Abstract

Most but not all phyla include examples of species that are able to regenerate large sections of the body plan. The mechanisms underlying regeneration on this scale are currently being studied in a variety of contexts in both vertebrates and invertebrates. Regeneration generally involves the formation of a wound epithelium after transection or injury, followed by the generation of regenerative progenitor cells and morphogenesis to give the regenerate. Common mechanisms may exist in relation to each of these aspects. For example, the initial proliferation of progenitor cells often depends on the nerve supply, whereas morphogenesis reflects the generation of positional disparity between adjacent cells—the principle of intercalation. These mechanisms are reviewed here across a range of contexts. We also consider the evolutionary origins of regeneration and how regeneration may relate to both agametic reproduction and to ontogeny.

Contents

INTRODUCTION

Regeneration in an adult animal is a striking example of postembryonic morphogenesis. It involves the recognition of tissue loss or injury, followed by mechanisms that reconstruct or restore the relevant structure. This latter aspect of regeneration is redolent of development, yet although development is a universal feature of metazoans, this is not the case with regeneration. We do not understand regeneration as an evolutionary variable, in particular why some animals regenerate and others apparently do not (Brockes et al. 2001; Goss 1969, 1992; Reichman 1984; Sánchez Alvarado 2000). In this survey of current research on a variety of examples of regeneration, the emphasis is to con-

sider these comparative aspects rather than to promote any particular context, for example, in relation to regenerative medicine (Stoick-Cooper et al. 2007a).

The ability of adult animals to regenerate large sections of the primary or secondary body axes is not found in all phyla. Six phyla, including rotifers and nematodes, are considered to exhibit cell constancy after embryological development (Hughes 1989, Sánchez Alvarado 2000). A fixed number of cells become differentiated, and growth thereafter involves enlargement but not multiplication of cells. The occurrence of regenerative phenomena in all other phyla might be considered widespread from an overall perspective, yet regeneration is diminished or absent in many members of such phyla, including species closely related to those that regenerate. Regeneration is unlikely to have arisen independently in all phyla in which it can be observed. An alternative view is that regeneration is a primordial attribute of metazoans, at least for those phyla not exhibiting cell constancy, and it is lost secondarily for a variety of reasons in closely related species or more distant groups. It has often been remarked that the primordial aspects can be best appreciated in those phyla in which regeneration occurs alongside various methods of propagation by agametic (asexual) reproduction (Hughes 1989, Sánchez Alvarado 2000). Although it is not presently under intensive investigation, this relationship merits some consideration.

A quite different and radical view of regeneration is as a by-product, or epiphenomenon, of the mechanisms underlying the development and maintenance of a particular structure, rather than a primary mechanism selected in its own right. This would allow regenerative ability to be lost after a variety of secondary events. This view of regeneration has been repeatedly proposed since the monograph of T.H. Morgan (Morgan 1901), yet it has always appeared to be arbitrary or contrived in the absence of specific proposals for the linkage between primary and secondary mechanisms. This is an appropriate subject for modeling approaches, and there has recently been some interesting progress in this direction that at least outlines the possibilities as more detailed information becomes available about regeneration.

We consider current information about the early events of regeneration in the Response to Injury section (below) and then a selection of issues about the mechanisms underlying regeneration. This review is deliberately light on terminology. In some ways, regenerative phenomena present a continuum in relation to mechanisms, and exact definitions can be difficult to justify. For example, the terms epimorphic and morphallaxis have been discussed elsewhere but are not used here (Carlson 2007, Stoick-Cooper et al. 2007a). The term blastema is used in the most general sense of a regenerative cell group without reference to its origin or other properties. Regeneration of the nervous system will only be considered in relation to the nerve dependence of nonneural regeneration.

EVOLUTIONARY ORIGINS OF REGENERATION

Relation to Agametic Reproduction

(Regeneration) is fundamentally a conservative asexual process. In fact, thanks to its evident close relation with fission phenomena and cloning processes, regeneration can be regarded as the necessary and specific developmental complement to asexual reproduction, in analogy, and in parallel to what happens for embryogenesis which is the established developmental strategy complementary to sexual gametic reproduction.

-M. Candia-Carnevali (2006)

It is intriguing to consider regeneration in relation to fragmentation, fission, and budding—various forms of propagation in invertebrates. Fragmentation is the simplest form of agametic reproduction and is essentially identical to regeneration after surgical transection. Fragmentation can occur in animals that are readily broken by external forces and that regenerate from the pieces. Certain sea anemones propagate by fragmentation events that do not involve external forces, but employ a kind of laceration by tearing off pieces (Pianka 1974) (**Figure 1a**). Only a few metazoans propagate by laceration, but these include some turbellarians in which part of the body adheres to the substratum and tears away as the animal progresses (Child 1913).

Fission, in contrast to fragmentation, is usually an endogenous process (Hughes 1989) (**Figure 1b**). In echinoderms, autotomy of the arm is a striking form of fission, most familiar in some starfish in which it is a regular feature of the life cycle as a means of clonal propagation (**Figure 1c**). Interestingly, in the crinoid *Oxycomanthus japonicus* autotomy occurs as part of normal development (Shibata & Oji 2003). To maintain a relatively uniform density as the arms grow out, they autotomize proximally and regenerate new pairs of bifurcating arms from the autotomy plane. In flatworms and annelids, fission may involve the development of a distinct plane of division and new sets of organs before separation, usually referred to as paratomy (or as architomy, if differentiation occurs after separation). Both processes may occur in the same taxon, for example, triclads and naidine oligochaetes, which are small aquatic annelids. Annelids are a particularly interesting group for which to consider the evolution of regeneration (Bely & Wray 2001) (**Figure 2a,b**). Species that can reproduce by fission typically have extensive anterior and posterior regenerative abilities, but the distribution of regenerative ability among taxa is broader than that of fission, and there are many groups capable of anterior and posterior regeneration that do not reproduce by fission (Bely 1999). The ancestor in which fission evolved may have been capable of both anterior and posterior regeneration because both capabilities would have been required. According to this view, regeneration is not some mechanistic offshoot of agametic reproduction but rather the basis for the developmental processes of fission, as outlined in the quotation by Candia-Carnevali (2006) above.

A survey of segment regenerative ability in annelids exemplifies many of the problems and

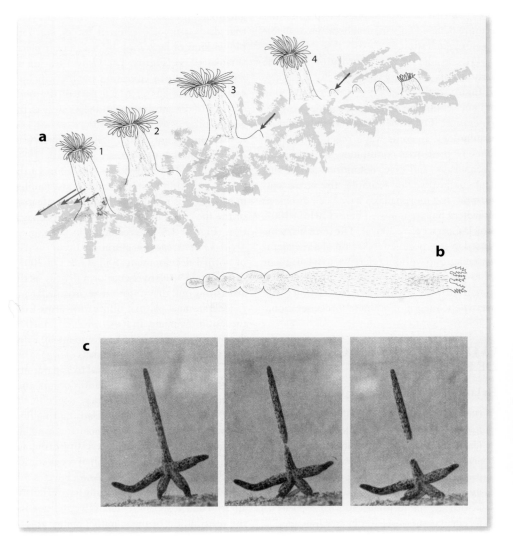

Figure 1

Examples of reproduction by fragmentation and fission. (*a*) Detachment of pieces from the basal part of the body of the actinian *Aiptasia lacerata* by translational force of body movement (*blue arrows*), followed by their conversion into daughter organisms (*purple arrows*) is illustrated in the sequence from 1 to 4. After a drawing in Vorontsova & Liosner (1960). (*b*) Fission in the holothurian *Leptosynapta inhaerens* occurs by constriction into several pieces. (*c*) Autotomy in the starfish *Linckia multifora*. Reproduced from Hughes (1989) with permission.

paradoxes found in other phyla (Bely 2006, Goss 1969, Reichman 1984). The ability to regenerate posterior segments is very common and is absent in only five groups, which include the leeches. This suggests that the ability to regenerate posteriorly may be an ancestral feature of annelids possibly related to the mechanism of continual adult growth by posterior segment addition. All taxa incapable of posterior regeneration are incapable of anterior segment regeneration, but in addition several taxa with posterior regeneration cannot do so anteriorly.

In some of these cases, closely related species do regenerate anteriorly, which suggests the loss of regeneration. If it is correct to regard these absences as losses, then anterior segment regeneration may have been lost at least a dozen times within annelids. A variety of factors have been invoked to account for the lability of regeneration, and these illustrate the complexity of the problem. First, certain species have a fixed number of segments as adults, and a disproportionate number of nonregenerating species have this property. Second, if amputation removes a structure that is acutely critical for survival, then regenerative ability may be lost because it is of no selective advantage, as frequently noted (Goss 1969, Reichman 1984). Third, if species have low amputation rates, this property may lead to a loss of regenerative ability. Fourth, if fission is present in a species, this alternative may decrease the selective advantages for regeneration. In the future it will be critical to understand the molecular basis for as many examples of loss of regeneration as possible.

Modeling Regeneration as an Emergent Property of Development

Cellular automata (CA) have been widely used to model a variety of biological processes. In a recent study the development of digital organisms was followed with an evolvable rule set of 100 genes that is inherited by all cells (Basanta et al. 2008). The organisms that exhibit a growth phase followed by homeostasis were selected according to a genetic algorithm and then subjected to rounds of mutation to further select a "zoo" of evolved CA. These were challenged with "gunshot wounds" in which ~5% of the cell population was removed. Several organisms were remarkably effective at repairing such lesions, even though wound healing did not form part of the selection criteria used in the genetic algorithm (**Figure 3**). It was possible to subject the wound-healing response to mutational analysis of the gene set. One gene (number 67 in the study) was particularly informative. Its function was critical for wound healing, even though it played no role in the normal

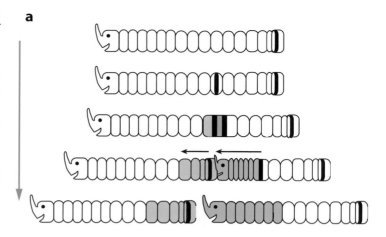

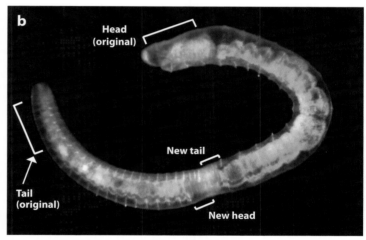

Figure 2

Reproduction by paratomic fission in naidines, by which one anterior-posterior (AP) axis becomes divided into two or more tandemly arrayed axes. (*a*) A new head and tail are intercalated in the middle of the parental worm's body. Fission is initiated when a midbody segment develops a zone of cell proliferation (*black bar in middle of body*). This zone, called a fission zone, splits into two proliferating zones, each forming new tissue anteriorly. The anterior zone forms a new tail (*blue*) for the anterior part of the worm, and the posterior zone forms a new head (*green*) for the posterior part of the worm. The black arrows indicate the common polarity of the final organisms. (*b*) A naidine oligochaete, *Paranais litoralis*, reproducing by paratomic fission. Reproduced by permission of Dr. A. Bely (Bely & Wray 2001).

development of the particular digital organism. It had been selected by the genetic algorithm during the evolution of the organism for conferring a small role in the development of an ancestor. In a mutational analysis of adult tissue

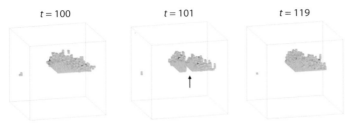

$t = 100$ $t = 101$ $t = 119$

Figure 3

Regeneration in a digital organism. The panels show an artificial organism that has been evolved to reach a state of morphological homeostasis. Following a growth phase (from $t = 0$ to $t = 50$), the organism does this by achieving a state of dynamic equilibrium in which local rates of active cell birth (*green*) and cell death (*red*) are finely balanced (from $t = 50$ to $t = 150$). Although there is no active selection for robustness to environmental perturbation during the evolution of this organism, following wounding (*arrow* at $t = 101$), the organism is able to mount a rapid regenerative repair response. Reproduced by permission of Dr. B. Baum (Basanta et al. 2008).

regeneration, it would be designated a wound-healing gene without the conventional selective justification for such a role. This study (Basanta et al. 2008) illustrates that regeneration in any context may reflect in whole or in part such a contribution, and this may help to account for the evolutionary lability referred to above.

Future attempts to model regeneration may use conditions that are closer to biological realities, but this proof of principle is already stimulating in its challenge to identify aspects of regeneration that apparently cannot be accounted for in such terms. One critical category of events is the response to injury, which in the model depends simply on the creation of vacant positions by cell removal but which in reality reflects a complex set of signals that engage the regenerative response (Martin & Parkhurst 2004).

Figure 4

Regeneration in different animals. The regenerative cells are shown with a green cytoplasm, the nerve elements in purple, and the epithelial elements in red. Examples *a–d* can be regarded as regeneration from a continuously growing adult, probably an important precondition of their regenerative ability, whereas examples *e–g* are not. (*a*) Regeneration of hydra after bisection through the body stalk (Bosch 2007, Galliot et al. 2006, Holstein et al. 2003). Hydra polyps are in a steady state of constant growth and tissue turnover. Both layers of the body wall, the ectoderm and endoderm, have multipotent stem cells whose progeny are continually displaced upward toward the tentacles. After transection, wound closure takes approximately 1–3 h, and the tentacles of the new head differentiate in approximately 36 h. (*b*) Planarian regeneration after bisection (Agata 2003, Newmark & Sánchez Alvarado 2002, Reddien & Sánchez Alvarado 2004, Rossi et al. 2008, Salo & Baguna 2002). Throughout adult life, planarians maintain a population of stem cells, called neoblasts, that are responsible for tissue maintenance in the face of cell turnover. After formation of a wound epithelium, neoblasts migrate to form a blastema. (*c*) Fin regeneration in the zebra fish (Akimenko et al. 2003, Marí-Beffa et al. 2007, Nakatani et al. 2007, Poss et al. 2003). The fin is composed of multiple bony rays separated by interray tissue. Each ray (lepidotrichium) is composed of two segmental hemirays (*darker beige*) that surround blood vessels and sensory nerve fibers. The transected surface is healed by a wound epithelium, followed by formation of a blastema. The fin grows continuously throughout the life of the fish by the distal addition of segments to each ray. Recombination experiments between rays and interrays suggest that the interray blastema is important in modulating aspects of ray morphogenesis, including the bifurcation of the rays (Murciano et al. 2002, 2007). (*d*) Tail regrowth in the *Xenopus* tadpole following transaction (Slack et al. 2008). The spinal cord (*purple*), muscle (*red*), and notochord (*beige*) give rise to distinct populations of progenitors that divide in the bud and add to the template tissues of the stump. (*e*) Limb regeneration in the salamander following amputation (Carlson 2007). The wound epithelium forms by migration, and the mesenchymal blastema accumulates underneath it. Cell division during the early stages of regeneration is dependent on the nerve supply and then on the wound epithelium. The cartilage of the stump is shown in beige. (*f*) Lens regeneration in the newt (Eguchi 1988, Okada 1991, Tsonis et al. 2004). Removal of the lens is followed by cell cycle reentry of a patch of pigment epithelial cells (PEC) at the dorsal pupillary margin. These cells transdifferentiate to lens (*yellow*), which forms as a vesicle growing from the dorsal margin. (*g*) Heart regeneration in the zebra fish (Poss et al. 2002). Resection of the ventricular apex is followed by rapid formation of a clot (*brown*) and a widespread activation of the epicardial layer (*dotted red*), which supplies cells that invade and vascularize the regenerating myocardium. The regenerative cells are presently proposed to be derived from undifferentiated progenitor cells (Lepilina et al. 2006). The bulbous arteriosus is shown in green.

Regeneration apparently involves some mechanisms that are not employed in development—one example considered below is the dependence on the nerve supply. These issues provide a basis for informing our current understanding of regeneration in different contexts.

CONTEXTS OF REGENERATION

To illustrate both common and distinctive aspects of regenerative mechanisms in different contexts, we show in **Figure 4** schematic diagrams of seven animals or organs in the process of regeneration.

RESPONSES TO INJURY

A regenerative response is initiated by the recognition of tissue loss or local injury. This critical aspect of regeneration is poorly understood, in part because there are many potential signals. One long-standing and intriguing possibility, currently receiving renewed attention, is bioelectrical signaling. The injury currents that flow after limb amputation are a reflection of altered tissue geometry and hence electrical resistance. Thrombin activation is a pivotal regulator of the vertebrate injury response, in particular hemostasis, and it has become a candidate for initiating the regenerative response in salamanders. There is currently considerable interest in the influence of the immune response on regeneration, and evidence in different contexts for positive, negative, and neutral effects. Finally, an important early response in many cases of regeneration is the formation of a wound epithelium, which is critical for subsequent events, and this aspect is considered here.

Bioelectrical Signals

The amputation of a salamander limb produces a low-resistance shunt at the end of the stump, through which ionic current flows over the next few days (Borgens 1985) (**Figure 5**). Wounds are generally electrically positive with respect to more proximal, uninjured areas, and the battery driving currents out of the limb stump resides in

the skin. The skin battery produces a transcutaneous voltage with the internal tissues positively charged relative to the exterior of the body, owing to pumping of cations. Regeneration can be inhibited by reducing the transepithelial potential with pharmacological approaches, but the basis for such inhibition can be questioned. In a critical experiment, the normal injury current was reduced or nulled by implantation of a cathode between the skin of the tail or shoulder and passing current from a regulated source connected to an external anode placed in the water of the tank (Jenkins et al. 1996). Approximately half of the experimental group showed some degree of inhibition or abnormal morphogenesis relative to controls. Atkinson et al. (2006)

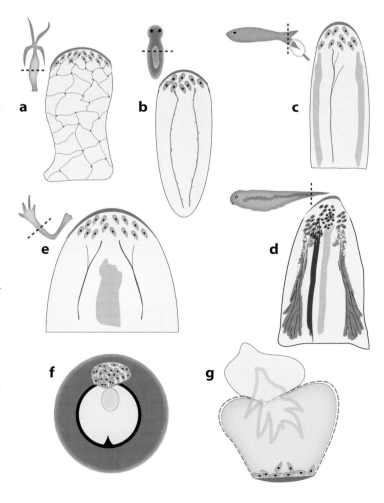

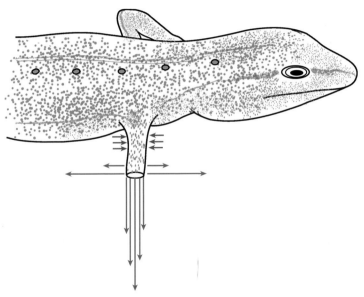

Figure 5

The flow of electrical currents in and out of the end of an amputated forelimb of a newt (after Borgens 1985). The intact skin of the stump drives charge through the amputation surface. The magnitude of the current leaving the end of the stump (proportional to the length of the *red arrows*) can be measured with a vibrating microprobe: The magnitude is maximal soon after amputation and declines to baseline over 10–14 days as the epidermis thickens and the blastema forms. The current flow returning to the limb (and also through the flank) is shown as the smaller purple arrows.

found that the larger current flows associated with electroporation promote dedifferentiation in the newt limb.

Recent experiments on the regenerating larval tail of *Xenopus* have implicated the activity of the V-ATPase proton pump in regeneration but not wound healing (Adams et al. 2007, Levin 2007). Inhibition of the pump with concanamycin inhibited regeneration, whereas expression of a concancamycin-insensitive yeast proton pump could rescue regeneration from this pharmacological blockade. Adams et al. (2007) and Levin (2007) both favor a pivotal role for the pump in setting the membrane voltage of the bud cells and posit a variety of downstream targets for voltage gradients.

If this subject is to move into the mainstream of regeneration research, it will be in part due to an enhanced understanding of mechanism, specifically of how current loops or voltage gradients are sensed and transduced in regeneration. In a recent study of a culture model of corneal wound healing, the migratory response of cells depended on the opposing activity of the enzymes phosphoinositide-3 kinase γ (PI3Kγ) and the lipid phosphatase PTEN (Zhao et al. 2006). The first enzyme was essential for the ability of cells to respond to electric fields, whereas loss of the second enzyme enhanced responsiveness. This study may be seminal if it leads to delineation of a signal transduction pathway for this cue. Epithelial migration may be a critical event that is dependent on the injury currents in limb regeneration. This is an interesting possibility, although a failure of migration is not a readily apparent feature of animals whose regeneration was inhibited by reversal of the injury currents (Jenkins et al. 1996). Stewart et al. (2007) proposed that the effective regeneration of the nerve supply, considered below as a critical regulator of limb regeneration, is the aspect influenced by the internal current loops (Jenkins et al. 1996). Adams et al. (2007) proposed that this mechanism contributes to the activity of the V-ATPase in *Xenopus* tail bud, although they proposed other possibilities.

One other relevant context of interest is planarian regeneration, in which the polarity of regeneration was reported to be manipulated by an applied electric field, such that heads always formed toward the cathode (Carlson 2007). Researchers have recently found, as discussed below, that downregulation of *β-catenin* or the *Wnt* agonist *dishevelled* causes the inappropriate regeneration of a head (Gurley et al. 2008, Petersen & Reddien 2008), and this discovery may offer an interesting opportunity to relate electrical and signal transduction aspects.

Thrombin Activation

That early events in vertebrate regeneration often occur in proximity to fibrin clots is not surprising and has been noted for intestinal (O'Steen 1958), limb (Donaldson et al. 1985), and cardiac (Oberpriller & Oberpriller 1974) regeneration in salamanders. Clots are formed from the action of the protease thrombin on plasma fibrinogen, and thrombin activation from its zymogen prothrombin is exquisitely regulated both in space and in time. The possibility that local thrombin activation is a signal for regeneration came from studies in which cultured newt myotubes returned to the cell cycle by the activity of a thrombin-generated ligand (Tanaka et al. 1999). Thrombin is sufficiently central to hemostasis and other aspects of the injury response that its activity in limb and heart regeneration cannot be blocked in a meaningful way. Lens regeneration after lens removal is a context in which the injury-related aspects are more circumscribed, because the lens is suspended in the anterior chamber and is not contiguous with the iris, the tissue from which the new lens is derived (**Figure 4f**). After lens removal in the newt, thrombin activity appears transiently on the dorsal pupillary margin of the iris and can be blocked by the introduction of inhibitors into the chamber (Imokawa & Brockes 2003). This intervention effectively curtails reentry to the cell cycle by pigment epithelial cells (PECs) on the dorsal margin and inhibits lens regeneration (Imokawa et al. 2004). Although thrombin activation at this location appears to be necessary for lens regeneration, it is not clear that it is sufficient. In a somewhat different view of the process, cell proliferation is considered to occur at the pupillary margin around the entire circumference and is dependent on upregulation of fibroblast growth factor 2 (FGF2) activity, whereas the dorsal-specific activation of the Wnt signaling system determines the location of lens regeneration (Hayashi et al. 2006).

Recent evidence for mammalian liver regeneration suggests that the release of serotonin by activated platelets after hepatectomy is a critical signal for the initiation of hepatocyte proliferation (Lesurtel et al. 2006). Platelet activation is another thrombin-dependent aspect of the response to injury, which suggests that different examples of vertebrate regeneration may share this important linkage.

Immunomodulation and Regeneration

Differences in immune mechanisms and immunomodulation following injury may be a factor regulating the occurrence of regeneration (Mescher & Neff 2005). There is a correlation in phylogeny between the development of adaptive immunity and the progressive loss of regenerative ability. This view of immune interference in regeneration is not relevant to a discussion of how injury may be linked to regeneration, other than as a possible negative influence in disrupting this linkage. In a recent study of fin regeneration in the zebra fish with a small molecule screen, Mathew et al. (2007) observed that glucocorticoid agonists were able to block regeneration in the early wound-healing phase. Amputation of the caudal fin induces neutrophil inflammation, and one possibility was that this inflammation plays a necessary role that is inhibited by the familiar anti-inflammatory action of glucocorticoids. This was tested by the use of antisense morpholinos to target *Pu.1*, a transcription factor required for myeloid cell development. After amputation of the caudal fin, neutrophils and macrophages were completely absent from *Pu.1* mutants, yet fin regeneration proceeded indistinguishably from controls. Thus, in this context there is apparently no functional link.

Recent work on salamander lens regeneration has uncovered an intriguing positive role for innate immunity. The vertebrate eye produces a restricted systemic immune response that is different from other compartments and has been termed anterior chamber–associated immune deviation (ACAID) (Streilein 2003). This specialized response may have evolved because inflammation in the eye would be a grave threat to vision. An obligatory step of ACAID involves trafficking of stimulated dendritic cells from the anterior chamber to the marginal zone of the spleen and the return of immune effector cells to the eye. If the salamander lens is damaged by local pricking, it is engulfed and destroyed by an innate immune response, followed by the concerted regeneration of a new lens from the dorsal iris (**Figure 6**). In a striking,

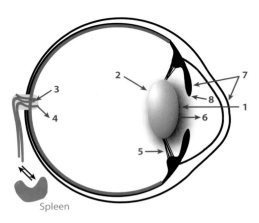

Spleen

Figure 6

Sequence of the events following pricking of the newt lens that are discussed in the text. (*1*) Lens puncture. (*2*) Autophagy of the lens. (*3*) Dendritic cells leave the eye and arrive at the spleen via the blood. (*4*) Immune effector cells return to the eye. (*5*) Zonular ligaments are ruptured by lens displacement. (*6*) Lens is removed. (*7*) New blood vessel formation occurs in central cornea and dorsal iris. (*8*) Regeneration is initiated from the dorsal iris. Reproduced with permission from Godwin & Brockes (2006).

purely immune-mediated model of regeneration, dendritic cells from a pricked eye were transferred into normal animals and evoked lens removal and regeneration (Kanao & Miyachi 2006). This process was abrogated by removal of the spleen from the recipient animals, in line with the involvement of the ACAID pathway. The relevant stimulus for lens regeneration in the natural habitat may not be lens removal but parasitic infection of the lens (Okada 2004), and hence it may be appropriate that ACAID, a modified innate immune response, is involved in replacing the lens. The only adult vertebrates able to regenerate the lens from the dorsal iris after lens removal are the newts (acquatic salamanders) and Cobitid fish. The circumstances surrounding lens regeneration should make it a very interesting case in the future to try to understand both its evolutionary and mechanistic aspects (Godwin & Brockes 2006).

Formation of a Wound Epithelium

A critical early response in most contexts is the migration of epithelial cells across the plane of amputation or tissue injury (Carlson 2007) (**Figure 4a–e**). The wound epithelium takes on a specialized and transient identity and plays a significant role in the ensuing events of regeneration. In some cases, formation of a wound epithelium does not occur (**Figure 4f,g**). Lens regeneration, as discussed above, is a process of localized epithelial transdifferentiation that does not involve the formation of a wound epithelium. Heart regeneration, as recently analyzed in zebra fish, involves a widespread early activation of the epicardium, and the epicardium may perform a role analogous to that of the wound epithelium (Lepilina et al. 2006). Another example is intestinal regeneration in salamanders, in which the transected ends are not sealed and the formation of an open blastema permits rejoining between the ends of transected intestines or even the formation of lateral T junctions by adhesion to the intact intestine (O'Steen 1958).

The roles of the wound epithelium are still not understood at a detailed level, but certain points can be made. One can prevent the formation of the salamander wound epithelium by suturing a flap of skin over the end of an amputated limb or tail. This procedure permits wound healing but prevents regeneration. In a critical experiment, the effect of a skin flap after amputation was compared with contralateral limbs that were amputated at the same time and had a wound epithelium (Mescher 1976). The experimental and control limbs were comparable in terms of the formation of the initial cohort of blastemal cells and their entry into S phase and mitosis. A study with a blastemal cell marker confirmed the generation of blastemal cells under a skin flap (Gordon & Brockes 1988). There was a marked difference, however, in the proliferation observed at two weeks after amputation, when the wound epithelium is clearly playing a key role (Mescher 1976). This may correspond to the appearance of newt anterior gradient (nAG) protein–positive gland cells, as discussed below in relation to nerve dependence (Kumar et al. 2007b). The wound epithelium may provide a distal boundary for patterning mechanisms during regeneration, although positional identity is usually considered to be encoded only in mesenchymal cells (Stocum 1984). A recent interesting proposal is that epidermal cells of different circumferential identities must migrate and meet to form a functional wound epithelium (Campbell & Crews 2008).

The formation of this epithelium is apparently a target for a variety of regulatory events. In no case do we understand the critical stimulus for migration. We consider above the possibility that currents play a role, as well as the minimal hypothesis that loss of neighboring cells is sufficient, as is apparently the case in culture. Fin regeneration has provided new information about early changes in gene expression that affect the wound epithelium. The *devoid of blastema* (*dob*) mutation was found in a screen for temperature-sensitive effects on regeneration and identified as a mutation of *fgf20a* (Whitehead et al. 2005). Its expression was detected as early as 1 h postamputation (pa) and later in mesenchymal cells at the epithelial-mesenchymal boundary. Although the wound epithelium forms in the mutant, it is notably thickened even at 6 h pa, and marker gene expression for this structure is delayed or absent. The mutant largely fails to form a mesenchymal blastema. It is interesting that the *dob* mutant has only a marginal effect on fin development at the nonpermissive temperature. Is it like gene 67 in the in silico analysis (Basanta et al. 2008), a bit player in development with a major emergent role in regeneration, or is it part of a critical regeneration-specific response linked to injury specific signals that play no role in development?

Another study found that the *Wnt* family members *wnt 10a* and *wnt 5b* were upregulated at the tip of the fin as early as 3 h pa (Stoick-Cooper et al. 2007b). The authors showed that inhibition of Wnt/β-catenin signaling also leads to a loss of expression of a wound ep-

ithelium marker and marked downregulation of *fgf20a*. They suggest that the injury signal(s), currently unknown in this system, may directly or indirectly activate *wnt 10a* expression, which then activates *fgf20a*. A separate study has also emphasized the importance of the *wnt* pathway for the formation of a normal wound epithelium in both the zebra fish and amphibian contexts (Kawakami et al. 2006).

A small-molecule screen on fin regeneration has underlined the importance of the wound epithelium as an early target for regulatory events. The glucorticoid receptor agonist beclomethasone can block regeneration after a 4 h exposure immediately following amputation, but not in subsequent time windows (Mathew et al. 2007). The wound epithelium that forms in the presence of beclamethasone fails to express a basal marker and is the presumed target of this effect identified by chemical genetics. It should be possible to use conventional genetics in the zebra fish to achieve wound epithelium–specific regulation of gene expression in a defined time window, which should permit a significantly higher level of resolution than has been possible to date in other contexts. We certainly need to understand much more about the regulation of gene expression at the beginning of regeneration, as well as the signals that are instructive for it. For example, there is no information at present about the injury signals that initiate regeneration in hydra and planaria.

ORIGIN AND MOBILIZATION OF REGENERATIVE CELLS

The origin of regenerative cells remains a central issue in regeneration research and one for which there has been much activity. It is not possible to cover every example here, and we choose to consider a subset of examples that illustrate the familiar dichotomy between reserve progenitor cells as opposed to local plasticity of differentiated cells. According to recent research, heart regeneration in salamander and zebra fish provides an interesting contrast in mechanisms (**Figure 4g**). Previous studies have supported the hypothesis that regeneration of the zebra fish myocardium proceeds by reentry into the cell cycle of adult cardiomyocytes (Poss et al. 2002). A recent study has provided evidence that the new myocardium arises from undifferentiated progenitor cells (Lepilina et al. 2006). This study employed an elegant approach with transgenic lines expressing GFP or RFP from a cardiac myosin light-chain promoter. GFP folds and fluoresces more rapidly than RFP and is also less stable than RFP. After injury to the ventricle, the authors identified, at the resection plane at days 5–7 pa, myocardial tissue that was GFP+/RFP− and not GFP−/RFP+; the latter would be predicted to arise from differentiated cardiomyocytes. The upregulation of early cardiomyocyte markers in this location further supported the interpretation that cardiomyocytes are derived from undifferentiated precursor cells. This study provides a stimulating new perspective, although it is an indirect approach and needs to be supported by the identification of unique markers and genetic lineage labeling techniques (Borchardt & Braun 2007).

Injury to the newt ventricle is followed by widespread reentry to the cell cycle by cardiomyocytes in the region of the fibrin clot (Laube et al. 2006, Oberpriller & Oberpriller 1974). This is accompanied by downregulation of sarcomeric proteins (Laube et al. 2006). Newt ventricular cardiomyocytes can be readily isolated in culture, in which, in contrast to some examples with mammalian cells, many cells retain differentiated properties. A significant proportion are able to reenter S phase and enter mitosis, in contrast to adult mammalian cardiomyocytes (Bettencourt-Dias et al. 2003). In a recent study by Laube et al. (2006), cardiomyocytes were labeled and implanted into the newt limb blastema, where the cardiomyocyte troponin T marker was lost, and the blastemal cell marker 22/18 was induced. Many labeled cells later expressed skeletal muscle markers, and the authors interpret their findings in terms of transdifferentiation of cardiomyocytes (Laube et al. 2006). This context may offer an opportunity to study the signals mediating plastic-

ity of the differentiated state. Previous claims of an activity in blastemal extracts that induces dedifferentiation of newt and mouse myotubes have not been repeated, but the cardiomyocytes could present an interesting assay system (Borchardt & Braun 2007).

Newt skeletal myotubes are able to reenter and traverse S phase in response to a thrombin-derived ligand present in vertebrate sera (Tanaka et al. 1997, 1999). Mammalian and other vertebrate myotubes do not respond to serum stimulation in this way, thus identifying a distinctive property of differentiated cells in salamanders. The activity has been purified extensively from a bovine source and is a glycoprotein (Straube et al. 2004). Its identification promises to be a step forward in understanding phylogenetic differences in regenerative ability at a molecular level. Mouse myotubes respond to partially purified preparations of the thrombin-derived factor by upregulation of some immediate early genes such as *jun* and *fos* (Loof et al. 2007). Analysis of individually purified myotubes showed that a distinct set of genes was regulated in comparison to myotubes stimulated with familiar serum growth factors. This study by Loof et al. (2007) suggests that mammalian myotubes have retained responsiveness to the thrombin-activated factor but have lost downstream elements that activate DNA synthesis.

A second aspect of plasticity in salamander skeletal muscle is the occurrence of cellularization, the conversion of multinucleate myotubes and myofibers to viable mononucleate cells. The earlier evidence that this can occur in relation to implanted myotubes, and myofibers in the regenerating tail after dissociation and culture, is not reviewed here (Brockes & Kumar 2002). The recent derivation of transgenic lines in the axolotl offers the possibility to use genetic labeling methods to follow cellularization (Sobkow et al. 2006). There is renewed interest in satellite cells in newt muscle, which have been identified with the *Pax*-7 marker and studied after a long period of neglect (Morrison et al. 2006). These cells are clearly activated during limb regeneration, and a key issue to be determined is the balance between satellite cells and cellularization as sources of myogenic cells. A recent study of jaw regeneration in newts has suggested that both sources are important (Kurosaka et al. 2008). Interestingly, in regeneration of the *Xenopus* tadpole tail there is convincing evidence for an exclusive derivation from satellite cells (Gargioli & Slack 2004). In this context the regenerating tissues appear to be templated on their adjacent counterparts in the stump, rather than by formation of an autonomous blastema, as found in salamander regeneration (Slack et al. 2008) (**Figure 4***d*).

Fin regeneration in zebra fish is emerging as an important context for vertebrate regeneration in a powerful genetic system (Curado et al. 2007), yet studies of the origin of blastemal cells have been indirect or inferential to date, and the availability of genetic labeling methods should allow more decisive evidence to be obtained.

Lens regeneration is an example in which the regenerative cells arise by transdifferentiation of iris PECs (Tsonis et al. 2004). The signaling events underlying this pathway are under investigation, as discussed above. It is possible to aggregate newt PECs of the dorsal iris, implant these cells into a lentectomized eye, and obtain an extra lens from the aggregate. Ventral PECs do not normally give a lens, but expression of the gene *Six-3* by transfection in the presence of retinoic acid leads to efficient induction of lens transdifferentiation from ventral cells. *Six-3* is normally expressed after lens removal in the dorsal iris, and these experiments identify it as a major regulator of the transdifferentiation pathway (Grogg et al. 2005). Treatment of ventral cells so as to inhibit the bone morphogenetic protein (BMP) pathway led to a low but significant induction of lens formation. Grogg et al. (2005) interpret this result to indicate that BMP signaling maintains ventral identity and that cells take on a dorsal identity after inhibition. The familiar master regulator of eye development, the *Pax-6* gene, does not substitute for *Six-3* in these assays but is apparently involved in a loop regulating proliferation

and lens fiber differentiation (Madhavan et al. 2006). The analysis of gene expression in the iris has revealed that the ventral iris appears to be activated by lentectomy but cannot normally complete the pathway followed by the dorsal cells (Makarev et al. 2007). As an example of transdifferentiation that is subject to strict spatial localization, lens regeneration remains a key subject for future studies.

Planarian regeneration is currently discussed almost exclusively in terms of the contribution from neoblasts (Salo & Baguna 2002, Sánchez Alvarado & Kang 2005), although the present evidence does not necessarily rule out a contribution from differentiated cells (Reddien & Sánchez Alvarado 2004). In hydra regeneration, the activity of epithelial stem cells underlies budding and regeneration (Bosch 2007, Galliot et al. 2006, Holstein et al. 2003). Although most cnidarian polyps grow constantly, the medusae stage of the life cycle has limited capacity for growth. Studies of the medusae of the jellyfish *Podocoryne* provide a striking example of transdifferentiation and its regulation by signaling (Schmid 1992). When patches of striated muscle were explanted, they could be activated by enzymes that degraded the extracellular matrix, and they later differentiated into smooth muscle and other cell types. The impression left by these studies on the medusa is that the control of the differentiated state is poised to allow considerable plasticity, which may be related to the important role of agametic reproduction and regeneration in these animals.

NERVE DEPENDENCE OF REGENERATION

After amputation or tissue injury, the nerve supply to the damaged region regenerates (**Figure 4***a–e*). In most contexts this regeneration involves axonal extension so as to reestablish functional contacts with the regenerate. In the case of tail regeneration in salamanders, or head regeneration in hydra, the generation of new nerve cells may also be involved. It has been widely observed that regeneration is dependent

Figure 7

The Barbel fish (*Barbus barbus*) with its two pairs of protruding taste barbels. Barbels consist of a central rod of cartilage, a nerve trunk, and a tip that is covered with taste buds. After amputation a blastema forms under the wound epithelium. The nerve is required both for regeneration to occur and for maintenance of the intact barbell (Goss 1956). Photographed at the London Aquarium.

ther motor or sensory axons is sufficient to support regeneration (Sidman & Singer 1951), and impulse traffic or release of the motor neurotransmitter acetylcholine is not required (Drachman & Singer 1971). As for the case of the wound epithelium mentioned above, the regenerating nerve is not required for formation of the initial cohort of blastemal cells, but rather for their proliferation. If a major peripheral nerve is transected and inserted into a skin wound, it can evoke formation of a supernumerary limb, as discussed below in relation to pattern formation (Egar 1988, Endo et al. 2004). Other examples of nerve dependence, in particular in annelids, show comparable effects of nerve deflection (Kiortsis & Moraitou 1965). The nerve is not instructive in a morphogenetic sense, because the nature of the appendage is determined by the location of insertion (Guyenot et al. 1948), but constitutes an essential element of the stem cell niche. It is of great interest that this property of regeneration is actually imposed on the limb when the nerves grow in during development. The outgrowth of the limb bud is not dependent on its innervation, and if the innervation is prevented, the resulting aneurogenic limb can regenerate in the absence of the nerve (Tassava & Olsen-Winner 2003, Thornton & Thornton 1970, Yntema 1959). Thus, nerve dependence is established over a nerve-independent alternative. It is important to understand these mechanisms in relation to the above issues concerning the relationship of regeneration to development.

Previous investigations (Brockes & Kintner 1986, Globus et al. 1991, Mescher et al. 1997, Mullen et al. 1996) have considered several known growth factors as candidates for mediating nerve-dependent proliferation in the blastema. A recent study has identified a new growth factor termed nAG whose expression is regulated by the nerve (Kumar et al. 2007b). nAG was identified as a secreted protein that interacted with Prod 1, a cell surface determinant of positional identity in blastemal cells (Morais da Silva et al. 2002). The anterior gradient proteins were originally discovered in

on concomitant regeneration of the nerve supply (Carlson 2007). This dependence is of great interest and importance for our understanding of regeneration for at least two reasons. First, it is widely conserved in phylogeny, being observed not only in various contexts in vertebrates (**Figure 7**) but also in examples of echinoderm (Candia-Carnevali 2006) and annelid regeneration (Boilly-Marer 1971). The nerve involvement in hydra and planaria is less obvious, and the evidence is discussed below. Second, this dependence presents perhaps the clearest example of a difference between development and regeneration. In some examples, development of the structure does not depend on its innervation. It is possible that nerve dependence of regeneration evolved as a mechanism to ensure that a regenerate is functionally innervated, and this requirement provides a plausible rationale.

The earliest example of nerve dependence to be recognized, and the most intensively studied, is the regeneration of the salamander limb (Singer 1952). An adequate complement of ei-

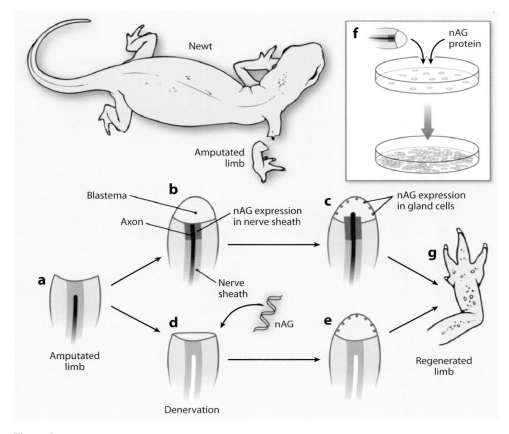

Figure 8

Role of the newt anterior gradient (nAG) protein in the nerve dependence of limb regeneration in a newt. The expression of the nAG protein during regeneration of the newt limb is shown in *a–c*. The secreted protein is mitogenic for cultured blastemal cells (*f*). The effect of denervation (*d*) can be rescued by nAG expression after electroporation of plasmid DNA (*e,g*). Reproduced from Kumar et al. (2007b) by permission of *Science*.

relation to studies of cement gland development in the *Xenopus* tadpole (Sive et al. 1989). After amputation, the severed axons retract (**Figure 8a**) and then regenerate back along the nerve sheath. The Schwann cells of the distal sheath express nAG, followed by gland cells in the wound epithelium (**Figure 8b,c**). Expression in both locations is abrogated by cutting the nerve at the base of the limb (**Figure 8d**). The recombinant nAG protein acts as a growth factor for cells dissociated from the blastema (**Figure 8f**), and this activity is blocked by antibodies to the Prod 1 protein. nAG can be expressed during regeneration by

electroporation of a construct expressing the secreted protein. One activity of the protein is to induce the appearance of nAG-positive glands in the wound epithelium after denervation (**Figure 8e**), which suggests that the release of the protein from the Schwann cells induces the appearance in the glands during normal regeneration. The proliferation of the early blastema depends on the nerve, but the wound epithelium then becomes the predominant influence, as mentioned above (Mescher 1976). This may correspond to the shift in nAG expression from Schwann cell to wound epithelium. The second activity of the protein expressed after electroporation is to rescue 50% of the denervated blastemas so that they regenerate through to the digit stage (Kumar et al. 2007b). The protein is not a direct product of the nerve but is induced in the key niche tissues through the direct (Schwann cell) or indirect (wound epithelium) activity of regenerating axons. Interestingly, Tassava & Olsen-Winner (2003) showed that denervated Schwann cells release an inhibitor of blastemal cell proliferation, thus making the switch after axonal regeneration more marked in both turning off an inhibitor and turning on the nAG activator. This study may also suggest a new direction for research on the problem of the aneurogenic limb.

In hydra the nerve net has long been regarded as a fascinating example of an early nervous system that extends throughout the animal (Westfall 1996). It is possible to derive nerve-free hydra, which clearly regenerate and bud (Marcum & Campbell 1978, Sugiyama & Fujisawa 1978), but following the example of the aneurogenic limb, it is not possible to conclude that regeneration in normal hydra is necessarily nerve independent (Galliot et al. 2006). In a recent study of head regeneration, de novo neurogenesis was disrupted by downregulation of *cnox-2*, a *hox* gene that is a specific marker for bipotent neuronal progenitors. This downregulation resulted in a marked delay in regeneration, leading to the conclusion that in wild-type hydra, head regeneration requires *cnox-2* neurogenic function, and when this function is missing, a slower program is activated (Miljkovic-Licina et al. 2007).

In planaria a large-scale RNAi screen (Reddien & Sánchez Alvarado 2004, Reddien et al. 2005) has identified five genes to date that both are expressed in the central nervous system and inhibit regeneration after silencing. One gene in particular, *NB43.2h*, codes for a zinc-finger protein, and silencing this gene results in a marked decrease in proliferation in the blastema (A. Sánchez Alvarado, personal communication). It will be interesting to follow the problem of nerve dependence as approached from this perspective.

PATTERN FORMATION

Intercalation

In this section we focus on the principle of intercalation, an aspect of pattern formation in regeneration that is found in many contexts. It is possible to consider only a subset of current work in this area. The principle of intercalation is that experimental juxtaposition of cells whose positional identities along an axis are noncontiguous leads to local stimulation of growth. The proliferating cells often show preponderance for one identity, for example, proximal rather than distal. This often regenerates the intervening identities so as to reestablish continuity. What is the mechanism by which disparity is sensed and converted into proliferation and other variables of cell behavior such as movement or adhesion? How does this mechanism operate in normal regeneration? A related but distinctive topic is that of polarity in regeneration of the primary axis in invertebrates, and recent progress in this area is also considered.

Limb regeneration in hemimetabolous insects such as the cockroach has been a classical system for studying intercalation (Anderson & French 1985). Limb regeneration in the cricket is a new context that allows gene knockdown by RNAi (Nakamura et al. 2007). When distal and proximal levels of the tibia are confronted, the intermediate levels are restored largely by proliferation from the distal partner, in confirmation of earlier work on the cockroach (Bohn 1976). These confrontations of insect epidermal cells induce the expression of signaling molecules wingless and hedgehog in the proximal partner, and Nakamura et al. (2007) suggest that these molecules act on the regenerating cells. Knockdown of the cricket *β-catenin* blocks intercalary regeneration, supporting an involvement of the canonical wnt signaling pathway (Nakamura et al. 2007). Although much remains to be understood, for example, the nature of the difference between proximal and distal cells, it is encouraging to see progress with these methods on a critical classical problem.

A recently developed accessory limb model in the axolotl has explored the necessity for positional disparity in a stepwise model of ectopic limb regeneration (Endo et al. 2004, Satoh et al. 2007). The deflection of a brachial nerve into a skin wound provides a growth stimulus to form a bump, but such bumps progress to form limbs only if a piece of skin is grafted from the opposite side of the limb. The nerve-induced ectopic blastemas have a marker profile comparable to that of normal blastemas. The skin provides dermal fibroblasts of different positional identities, and this mixing of cells from opposite sides occurs during normal limb regeneration (Gardiner et al. 1986). The dermal cells have long been recognized to be critical for tissue patterning in the limb (Carlson 1974, Lheureux 1975), and recent microarray analysis shows that human skin fibroblasts from a variety of locations have distinctive gene expression programs (Rinn et al. 2006).

In the regeneration of the axolotl limb, both the analysis of homeobox gene expression (Gardiner et al. 1995) and fate mapping after focal electroporation of distal cells (Echeverri & Tanaka 2005) indicate that the most distal elements are specified early in the process and that the intermediate elements are subsequently generated by intercalation. This principle of distalization may be a more general feature of regeneration in systems such as hydra and planaria (Agata et al. 2007). The early events that organize or rearrange the distribution of positional identities for the regenerate are clearly of great interest.

During planarian regeneration dorsal and ventral tissues adhere to each other as a result of wound closure after amputation. In experimental confrontations leading to ectopic dorsoventral (DV) interaction, this adherence leads to the formation of a blastema-like region and the generation of a structure from the grafted position to the distal tip (Kato et al. 1999, Saito et al. 2003). The authors suggest that the DV interaction after wound healing plays a key role in the normal onset of regeneration (**Figure 9**). Further studies combining X irradiation with

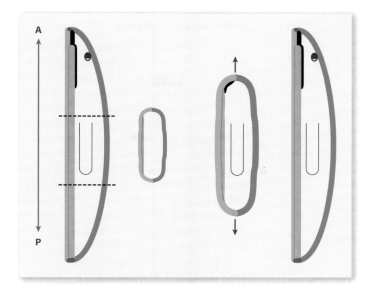

Figure 9

Model for the role of dorsoventral (DV) interaction in planarian regeneration. Dorsal (*green*) and ventral (*orange*) tissues adhere to each other as a result of wound closure. The DV boundaries are marked with red dots. Subsequently, DV interaction induces blastema formation, outgrowth, and establishment of a DV axis. The anterior (A) stump forms anterior structures, and the posterior (P) stump forms posterior structures. Reproduced with permission from Kato et al. (1999).

grafting show that the DV cues reside in differentiated cells and not in the neoblasts (Kato et al. 2001). The instructive contribution of adult tissues to patterning in regeneration is important, as exemplified by the examples of the dermal fibroblasts and planarian regeneration considered above. Another example is the regeneration of the axolotl tail. The DV orientation of the spinal cord determines the DV patterning of both the regenerating cord and nonneural elements such as cartilage (Holtzer 1956). The mature cord maintains expression of a set of DV markers, as well as Sonic hedgehog on the ventral floorplate, which is a critical signal for several aspects of tail regeneration (Schnapp et al. 2005). Schnapp et al. (2005) remark that the maintenance of patterning information in adult tissue may well be central to regenerative ability and that avian and mammalian cords do not maintain expression of some of these markers.

Positional Identity and Disparity Sensing

Positional confrontations may trigger the formation of local signaling centers and may activate transduction pathways, but what is the basis of positional identity, and how is the disparity between neighbors detected? Studies of interactions between proximal and distal limb blastemas in salamanders have suggested that cell adhesion and movement, as well as division, can be activated by disparity, leading to the plausible hypothesis that a critical aspect of positional identity is expressed at the cell surface (Stocum 1984, 2004a). The observation that proximo-distal identity in the salamander can be respecified by retinoic acid (Maden 1982) resulted in the identification of Prod 1, a member of the Ly6 family of proteins that is linked to the cell surface with a glycosylphosphatidylinositol (GPI) glycolipid anchor (Morais da Silva et al. 2002). The structure of Prod 1, as determined by nuclear magnetic resonance (NMR) (A.A. Garza-Garcia, personal communication) is the consensus three-finger motif of the Ly6 proteins. The presence of a helical segment led to the suggestion that Prod 1 is the newt ortholog of CD59, but we know now that this is not correct because salamander CD59 sequences have been identified. Prod 1 is expressed in a gradient (proximal > distal) in a normal limb as well as in proximal and distal limb blastemas (Kumar et al. 2007a). It is expressed in the dermal fibroblasts discussed above and is readily upregulated in these cells by retinoic acid (Kumar et al. 2007a).

Prod 1 is implicated in several ways as a determinant of positional identity. Distal cells of the larval axolotl blastema are converted to proximal cells by electroporation of a plasmid expressing Prod 1 (Echeverri & Tanaka 2005), and this respecification does not occur with mutations that prevent its expression on the cell surface (J.W. Godwin, unpublished data). The engulfment assays with cultured proximal and distal blastemas are blocked with antibodies to Prod 1 or by the enzyme phosphatidylinositol-specific phospholipase C (PIPLC), which re- leases GPI-anchored proteins from the cell surface (Morais da Silva et al. 2002). The nAG protein, discussed above in relation to nerve dependence, was identified as a secreted protein ligand to Prod 1. nAG acts as a mitogenic growth factor for cultured limb blastemal cells, and this action is also blocked by antibodies to Prod 1 (Kumar et al. 2007b). Finally, the expression of Prod 1 after transfection in cultured newt cells activates a pathway leading to the transcriptional activation of the gene for matrix metalloprotease (MMP) 9, a marker for several contexts of regeneration (R.A. Blassberg, unpublished data). In a proposed minimal model for disparity sensing, cell surface molecules on neighboring cells interact by homophilic adhesion, leaving spare molecules on one cell if there is a difference in expression level (Morais da Silva et al. 2002). Only spare molecules can be activated by a diffusible molecule such as nAG. The same model, but formulated with succeeding steps, has been proposed as a critical step in the regulation of cell proliferation by a morphogen gradient in the *Drosophila* wing disc (Rogulja & Irvine 2005). The problem of disparity sensing needs attention in other contexts because it is a central aspect of regenerative and developmental phenomena.

Polarity in Regeneration

Polarity is also a problem of positional identity but is sufficiently distinctive in certain contexts of invertebrate regeneration to merit separate consideration. The process of head formation that takes place during regeneration in hydra involves apoptosis, proliferation, and respecification of the cells at the amputation plane (Chera et al. 2007). These processes lead to the formation of a transient head organizer, which apparently involves wnt genes and β-catenin-dependent signaling. In the sea anemone *Nematostella* patterning along the oral aboral axis may be mediated by a Wnt code based on the staggered expression domains of members of this family (Guder et al. 2006, Kusserow et al. 2005). Recent studies on planaria have also implicated β-catenin, as mentioned above.

Signaling through β-catenin occurs at posterior amputations and is necessary and sufficient to specify cell fate, whereas signaling is blocked at anterior amputations, resulting in specification of head fate (Gurley et al. 2008, Petersen & Reddien 2008). In a striking demonstration, planarians knocked down for β-catenin and subjected to sagittal amputation to remove their lateral half can regenerate multiple side-facing head protrusions. There is also evidence for a Wnt code in planaria that is comparable to that in Cnidaria from sequential expression of five different Wnt family members along the anteroposterior axis of the planaria.

CONCLUSIONS

At present we do not have enough understanding of regeneration in different contexts to know if it is a unitary mechanism. It is possible to point to molecules such as MMPs or muscle segment homeobox proteins (Msx) that are widely expressed and play important roles in tissue remodeling or modulating the differentiated state and the cell cycle, but this is not strong evidence for a unitary mechanism. Somewhat stronger evidence is provided by common signal transduction pathways (Sánchez Alvarado & Tsonis 2006, Stoick-Cooper et al. 2007a), for example, the role of the Wnt pathway in planarian and cnidarian regeneration. An analysis of upstream activation and downstream targets is needed to be really compelling. The injury signal and the nerve dependence are two examples in which common mechanisms might be sought. For example, it would be interesting if most instances of vertebrate regeneration were initiated by the same injury signal.

It is often stated that regeneration involves a reactivation of development, but the relationship to development may be closer to that described above as an epiphenomenon. Such a relationship obviates the necessity to evolve this aspect of the mechanism quite independently in different contexts while it provides one rationale for the lability of regeneration in related species. Modules that are specific to regeneration versus development, such as the response

to injury or the nerve dependence, could have been added on to the aspect that is derived from development and broadly devoted to morphogenesis. One important goal for the future is to identify the mutations that are proposed to occur naturally and that prevent regeneration. One context in which this might be possible is a comparison between regenerating and non-regenerating species of planaria. There are also cases in which one member of a pair has lost the ability to regenerate a particular structure—for example, the axolotl has lost lens regeneration relative to the newt (Grogg et al. 2005, Imokawa & Brockes 2003). There are no cases in which partial regeneration occurs, and it is apparently the early events in relation to the response to injury and the generation of regenerative cells that are the main targets for loss. It is interesting to compare regeneration with another, and better understood, example in which differences occur between closely related species: the gain and loss of introns (Kiontke et al. 2004, Roy & Gilbert 2006). In nematode species the pattern of conservation of a particular intron leads to models of multiple independent losses or gains in the same position (Kiontke et al. 2004). Although the mechanisms of intron loss and gain are well understood, at least in principle, these phylogenetic differences remain a matter of intense debate between explanations based on molecular cell biology on the one hand and population genetics on the other hand (Lynch 2007).

The implications for regenerative medicine have been discussed elsewhere (Brockes & Kumar 2005; Stocum 2004b, 2006; Stoick-Cooper et al. 2007a), and the remarks here are more by way of summary. In general, there are probably a number of differences that prevent mammalian regeneration occurring on the scale of a salamander. It is most unlikely, on this view, that any realistic corrective intervention could unlock the potential for such events. However, some phenomena, such as the restoration of hole injuries in the pinna of the ear that occurs in some mouse strains, are redolent of a blastema and are of great interest (Heber-Katz et al. 2004). More generally, regenerative biology can inform regenerative medicine in a variety of ways with respect to overall strategy. We have argued, for example, that the morphogenetic autonomy of the limb blastema in a salamander would be a desirable property to implement in a mammalian context (Brockes & Kumar 2005). It would be very surprising if regenerative medicine did not have a lot to learn from the various species discussed here that regenerate so successfully.

SUMMARY POINTS

1. It is difficult to understand regeneration as an evolutionary variable, for example, its distribution among closely related species as well as within vertebrates or between phyla.

2. Regeneration in some invertebrates is closely related to methods of agametic reproduction, particularly fission and fragmentation, but the precise relationships are not clear.

3. Modeling approaches may now test the hypothesis that the mechanism of regeneration, or certain aspects of the mechanism, may be secondary or derived.

4. There is currently renewed interest in the role of bioelectrical signals early in regeneration, as well as the possible influence of the immune system. Establishment of a functional wound epithelium is a critical early event in many contexts of regeneration and a target of various regulatory mechanisms.

5. The origin of the progenitor cells for regeneration continues to be debated in the contexts of amphibian and fish regeneration, whereas hydra and planaria depend on resident stem cells.

6. Most contexts of regeneration are dependent on the concomitant regeneration of the nerve supply, and in the salamander limb this dependence reflects the ability of regenerating axons to induce expression of a growth factor in the nerve sheath and the wound epithelium.

7. Intercalation is a central principle of patterning during regeneration in many contexts, including planaria and hemimetabolous insects. There has been some progress in understanding the mechanisms whereby local disparities are sensed and transduced. The phenomenon of polarity in hydra and planarian regeneration apparently depends on Wnt signaling.

DISCLOSURE STATEMENT

The authors are not aware of any biases that might be perceived as affecting the objectivity of this review.

ACKNOWLEDGMENTS

We thank Drs. A. Bely and B. Baum for their help with figures. We apologize to those whose work could not be cited owing to space limitations. Supported by an MRC Research Professorship and Program Grant to J.P.B.

LITERATURE CITED

Adams DS, Masi A, Levin M. 2007. H^+ pump-dependent changes in membrane voltage are an early mechanism necessary and sufficient to induce *Xenopus* tail regeneration. *Development* 134:1323–35

Agata K. 2003. Regeneration and gene regulation in planarians. *Curr. Opin. Genet. Dev.* 13:492–96

Agata K, Saito Y, Nakajima E. 2007. Unifying principles of regeneration I: epimorphosis versus morphallaxis. *Dev. Growth Differ.* 49:73–78

Akimenko MA, Marí-Beffa M, Becerra J, Geraudie J. 2003. Old questions, new tools, and some answers to the mystery of fin regeneration. *Dev. Dyn.* 226:190–201

Anderson H, French V. 1985. Cell division during intercalary regeneration in the cockroach leg. *J. Embryol. Exp. Morphol.* 90:57–78

Atkinson DL, Stevenson TJ, Park EJ, Riedy MD, Milash B, Odelberg SJ. 2006. Cellular electroporation induces dedifferentiation in intact newt limbs. *Dev. Biol.* 299:257–71

Basanta D, Miodownik M, Baum B. 2008. The evolution of robust development and homeostasis in artificial organisms. *PLoS Comput. Biol.* 4:e1000030

Bely AE. 1999. Decoupling of fission and regenerative capabilities in an asexual oligochaete. *Hydrobiologia* 406:243–51

Bely AE. 2006. Distribution of segment regeneration ability in the Annelida. *Int. Comp. Biol.* 46:508–18

Bely AE, Wray GA. 2001. Evolution of regeneration and fission in annelids: insights from *engrailed*- and *orthodenticle*-class gene expression. *Development* 128:2781–91

Bettencourt-Dias M, Mittnacht S, Brockes JP. 2003. Heterogeneous proliferative potential in regenerative adult newt cardiomyocytes. *J. Cell Sci.* 116:4001–9

Bohn H. 1976. Regeneration of proximal tissues from a more distal amputation level in the insect leg (*Blaberus craniifer*, Blattaria). *Dev. Biol.* 53:285–93

Boilly-Marer Y. 1971. Role du système nerveux parapodial dans l'induction de parapodes supernumeraries par greffes hétérologues chez *Nereis pelagica*. *Comptes Rendus Acad. Sci.* 272:261–64

Borchardt T, Braun T. 2007. Cardiovascular regeneration in nonmammalian model systems: What are the differences between newts and man? *Throm. Haemost.* 98:311–18

Borgens RB. 1985. Natural voltage gradients and the generation and regeneration of limbs. In *Regulation of Veretebrate Limb Regeneration*, ed. RE Sicard, pp. 6–31. New York/Oxford: Oxford Univ. Press

Bosch TC. 2007. Why polyps regenerate and we don't: towards a cellular and molecular framework for hydra regeneration. *Dev. Biol.* 303:421–33

Brockes JP, Kintner CR. 1986. Glial growth factor and nerve-dependent proliferation in the regeneration blastema of urodele amphibians. *Cell* 45:301–6

Brockes JP, Kumar A. 2002. Plasticity and reprogramming of differentiated cells in amphibian regeneration. *Nat. Rev. Mol. Cell Biol.* 3:566–74

Brockes JP, Kumar A. 2005. Appendage regeneration in adult vertebrates and implications for regenerative medicine. *Science* 310:1919–23

Brockes JP, Kumar A, Velloso CP. 2001. Regeneration as an evolutionary variable. *J. Anat.* 199:3–11

Campbell LJ, Crews CM. 2008. Molecular and cellular basis of regeneration and tissue repair: wound epidermis formation and function in urodele amphibian limb regeneration. *Cell. Mol. Life Sci.* 65:73–79

Candia-Carnevali M. 2006. Regeneration in echinoderms: repair, regrowth, cloning. *Invertebr. Surviv. J.* 3:64–76

Carlson BM. 1974. Morphogenetic interactions between rotated skin cuffs and underlying stump tissues in regenerating axolotl forelimbs. *Dev. Biol.* 39:263–85

Carlson BM. 2007. *Principles of Regenerative Biology*. London: Elsevier. 379 pp.

Chera S, Kaloulis K, Galliot B. 2007. The cAMP response element binding protein (CREB) as an integrative HUB selector in metazoans: clues from the hydra model system. *Biosystems* 87:191–203

Child CM. 1913. The asexual cycle of *Planaria velata* in relation to senescence and rejuvenescence. *Biol. Bull.* 1:181–203

Curado S, Anderson RM, Jungblut B, Mumm J, Schroeter E, Stainier DY. 2007. Conditional targeted cell ablation in zebrafish: a new tool for regeneration studies. *Dev. Dyn.* 236:1025–35

Donaldson DJ, Mahan JT, Hasty DL, McCarthy JB, Furcht LT. 1985. Location of a fibronectin domain involved in newt epidermal cell migration. *J. Cell Biol.* 101:73–78

Drachman DB, Singer M. 1971. Regeneration in botulinum-poisoned forelimbs of the newt, *Triturus*. *Exp. Neurol.* 32:1–11

Echeverri K, Tanaka EM. 2005. Proximodistal patterning during limb regeneration. *Dev. Biol.* 279:391–401

Egar MW. 1988. Accessory limb production by nerve-induced cell proliferation. *Anat. Rec.* 221:550–64

Eguchi G. 1988. Cellular and molecular background of Wolffian lens regeneration. *Cell Differ. Dev.* 25(Suppl.):147–58

Endo T, Bryant SV, Gardiner DM. 2004. A stepwise model system for limb regeneration. *Dev. Biol.* 270:135–45

Galliot B, Miljkovic-Licina M, de Rosa R, Chera S. 2006. Hydra, a niche for cell and developmental plasticity. *Semin. Cell Dev. Biol.* 17:492–502

Gardiner DM, Blumberg B, Komine Y, Bryant SV. 1995. Regulation of *HoxA* expression in developing and regenerating axolotl limbs. *Development* 121:1731–41

Gardiner DM, Muneoka K, Bryant SV. 1986. The migration of dermal cells during blastema formation in axolotls. *Dev. Biol.* 118:488–93

Gargioli C, Slack JM. 2004. Cell lineage tracing during *Xenopus* tail regeneration. *Development* 131:2669–79

Globus M, Smith MJ, Vethamany-Globus S. 1991. Evidence supporting a mitogenic role for substance P in amphibian limb regeneration. Involvement of the inositol phospholipid signaling pathway. *Ann. N.Y. Acad. Sci.* 632:396–99

Godwin JW, Brockes JP. 2006. Regeneration, tissue injury and the immune response. *J. Anat.* 209:423–32

Gordon H, Brockes JP. 1988. Appearance and regulation of an antigen associated with limb regeneration in *Notophthalmus viridescens*. *J. Exp. Zool.* 247:232–43

Goss RJ. 1956. An experimental analysis of taste barbel regeneration in the catfish. *J. Exp. Zool.* 131:27–49

Goss RJ. 1969. *Principles of Regeneration*. New York: Academic. 287 pp.

Goss RJ. 1992. The evolution of regeneration: adaptive or inherent? *J. Theor. Biol.* 159:241–60

Grogg MW, Call MK, Okamoto M, Vergara MN, Del Rio-Tsonis K, Tsonis PA. 2005. BMP inhibition-driven regulation of *six-3* underlies induction of newt lens regeneration. *Nature* 438:858–62

Guder C, Philipp I, Lengfeld T, Watanabe H, Hobmayer B, Holstein TW. 2006. The Wnt code: Cnidarians signal the way. *Oncogene* 25:7450–60

Gurley KA, Rink JC, Sánchez Alvarado A. 2008. β-Catenin defines head versus tail identity during planarian regeneration and homeostasis. *Science* 319:323–27

Guyenot EJ, Dinichert-Favarger J, Galland M. 1948. L'exploration du territoire de la patte antérieure du *Triton*. *Rev. Suisse Zool.* 55(Suppl. 2):1–120

Hayashi T, Mizuno N, Takada R, Takada S, Kondoh H. 2006. Determinative role of Wnt signals in dorsal iris-derived lens regeneration in newt eye. *Mech. Dev.* 123:793–800

Heber-Katz E, Leferovich JM, Bedelbaeva K, Gourevitch D. 2004. Spallanzani's mouse: a model of restoration and regeneration. *Curr. Top. Microbiol. Immunol.* 280:165–89

Holstein TW, Hobmayer E, Technau U. 2003. Cnidarians: an evolutionarily conserved model system for regeneration? *Dev. Dyn.* 226:257–67

Holtzer SW. 1956. The inductive activity of the spinal cord in urodele tail regeneration. *J. Morphol.* 99:1–15

Hughes RN. 1989. *A Functional Biology of Clonal Animals*. London: Chapman and Hall. 331 pp.

Imokawa Y, Brockes JP. 2003. Selective activation of thrombin is a critical determinant for vertebrate lens regeneration. *Curr. Biol.* 13:877–81

Imokawa Y, Simon A, Brockes JP. 2004. A critical role for thrombin in vertebrate lens regeneration. *Philos. Trans. R. Soc. London Ser. B* 359:765–76

Jenkins LS, Duerstock BS, Borgens RB. 1996. Reduction of the current of injury leaving the amputation inhibits limb regeneration in the red spotted newt. *Dev. Biol.* 178:251–62

Kanao T, Miyachi Y. 2006. Lymphangiogenesis promotes lens destruction and subsequent lens regeneration in the newt eyeball, and both processes can be accelerated by transplantation of dendritic cells. *Dev. Biol.* 290:118–24

Kato K, Orii H, Watanabe K, Agata K. 1999. The role of dorsoventral interaction in the onset of planarian regeneration. *Development* 126:1031–40

Kato K, Orii H, Watanabe K, Agata K. 2001. Dorsal and ventral positional cues required for the onset of planarian regeneration may reside in differentiated cells. *Dev. Biol.* 233:109–21

Kawakami Y, Rodriguez Esteban C, Raya M, Kawakami H, Marti M, et al. 2006. Wnt/β-catenin signaling regulates vertebrate limb regeneration. *Genes Dev.* 20:3232–37

Kiontke K, Gavin NP, Raynes Y, Roehrig C, Piano F, Fitch DH. 2004. *Caenorhabditis* phylogeny predicts convergence of hermaphroditism and extensive intron loss. *Proc. Natl. Acad. Sci. USA* 101:9003–8

Kiortsis V, Moraitou M. 1965. Factors of regeneration in *Spirographis spallanzani*. In *Regeneration in Animals and Related Problems*, ed. V Kiortsis, HAL Trampusch, pp. 250–61. Amsterdam: North-Holland

Kumar A, Gates PB, Brockes JP. 2007a. Positional identity of adult stem cells in salamander limb regeneration. *Comptes Rendus Biol.* 330:485–90

Kumar A, Godwin JW, Gates PB, Garza-Garcia AA, Brockes JP. 2007b. Molecular basis for the nerve dependence of limb regeneration in an adult vertebrate. *Science* 318:772–77

Kurosaka H, Takano-Yamamoto T, Yamashiro T, Agata K. 2008. Comparison of molecular and cellular events during lower jaw regeneration of newt (*Cynops pyrrhogaster*) and West African clawed frog (*Xenopus tropicalis*). *Dev. Dyn.* 237:354–65

Kusserow A, Pang K, Sturm C, Hrouda M, Lentfer J, et al. 2005. Unexpected complexity of the *Wnt* gene family in a sea anemone. *Nature* 433:156–60

Laube F, Heister M, Scholz C, Borchardt T, Braun T. 2006. Re-programming of newt cardiomyocytes is induced by tissue regeneration. *J. Cell Sci.* 119:4719–29

Lepilina A, Coon AN, Kikuchi K, Holdway JE, Roberts RW, et al. 2006. A dynamic epicardial injury response supports progenitor cell activity during zebrafish heart regeneration. *Cell* 127:607–19

Lesurtel M, Graf R, Aleil B, Walther DJ, Tian Y, et al. 2006. Platelet-derived serotonin mediates liver regeneration. *Science* 312:104–7

Levin M. 2007. Large-scale biophysics: ion flows and regeneration. *Trends Cell Biol.* 17:261–70

Lheureux E. 1975 . Nouvelles données sur le rôle de la peau et des tissus internes dans la régénération du membre du triton *Pleurodeles waltii* Michah. (Urodéle). *Wilhelm Roux Archiv.* 176:285–301

Loof S, Straube WL, Drechsel D, Tanaka EM, Simon A. 2007. Plasticity of mammalian myotubes upon stimulation with a thrombin-activated serum factor. *Cell Cycle* 6:1096–101

Lynch M. 2007. *The Origins of Genome Architecture*. Sunderland, MA: Sinauer Assoc. 389 pp.

Maden M. 1982. Vitamin A and pattern formation in the regenerating limb. *Nature* 295:672–75

Madhavan M, Haynes TL, Frisch NC, Call MK, Minich CM, et al. 2006. The role of *Pax-6* in lens regeneration. *Proc. Natl. Acad. Sci. USA* 103:14848–53

Makarev E, Call MK, Grogg MW, Atkinson DL, Milash B, et al. 2007. Gene expression signatures in the newt irises during lens regeneration. *FEBS Lett.* 581:1865–70

Marcum BA, Campbell RD. 1978. Development of hydra lacking nerve and interstitial cells. *J. Cell Sci.* 29:17–33

Marí-Beffa M, Santamaría JA, Murciano C, Santos-Ruiz L, Andrades JA, et al. 2007. Zebrafish fins as a model system for skeletal human studies. *Sci. World J.* 7:1114–27

Martin P, Parkhurst SM. 2004. Parallels between tissue repair and embryo morphogenesis. *Development* 131:3021–34

Mathew LK, Sengupta S, Kawakami A, Andreasen EA, Lohr CV, et al. 2007. Unraveling tissue regeneration pathways using chemical genetics. *J. Biol. Chem.* 282:35202–10

Mescher AL. 1976. Effects on adult newt limb regeneration of partial and complete skin flaps over the amputation surface. *J. Exp. Zool.* 195:117–28

Mescher AL, Connell E, Hsu C, Patel C, Overton B. 1997. Transferrin is necessary and sufficient for the neural effect on growth in amphibian limb regeneration blastemas. *Dev. Growth Differ.* 39:677–84

Mescher AL, Neff AW. 2005. Regenerative capacity and the developing immune system. *Adv. Biochem. Eng. Biotechnol.* 93:39–66

Miljkovic-Licina M, Chera S, Ghila L, Galliot B. 2007. Head regeneration in wild-type hydra requires de novo neurogenesis. *Development* 134:1191–201

Morais da Silva S, Gates PB, Brockes JP. 2002. The newt ortholog of CD59 is implicated in proximodistal identity during amphibian limb regeneration. *Dev. Cell* 3:547–55

Morgan TH. 1901. *Regeneration*. New York/London: Macmillan. 316 pp.

Morrison JI, Loof S, He P, Simon A. 2006. Salamander limb regeneration involves the activation of a multipotent skeletal muscle satellite cell population. *J. Cell Biol.* 172:433–40

Mullen LM, Bryant SV, Torok MA, Blumberg B, Gardiner DM. 1996. Nerve dependency of regeneration: the role of Distal-less and FGF signaling in amphibian limb regeneration. *Development* 122:3487–97

Murciano C, Fernández TD, Durán I, Maseda D, Ruiz-Sánchez J, et al. 2002. Ray-interray interactions during fin regeneration of *Danio rerio*. *Dev. Biol.* 252:214–24

Murciano C, Pérez-Claros J, Smith A, Avaron F, Fernández TD, et al. 2007. Position dependence of hemiray morphogenesis during tail fin regeneration in *Danio rerio*. *Dev. Biol.* 312:272–83

Nakamura T, Mito T, Tanaka Y, Bando T, Ohuchi H, Noji S. 2007. Involvement of canonical Wnt/Wingless signaling in the determination of the positional values within the leg segment of the cricket *Gryllus bimaculatus*. *Dev. Growth Differ.* 49:79–88

Nakatani Y, Kawakami A, Kudo A. 2007. Cellular and molecular processes of regeneration, with special emphasis on fish fins. *Dev. Growth Differ.* 49:145–54

Newmark PA, Sánchez Alvarado A. 2002. Not your father's planarian: A classic model enters the era of functional genomics. *Nat. Rev. Genet.* 3:210–19

O'Steen WK. 1958. Regeneration of the intestine in adult urodeles. *J. Morphol.* 103:435–78

Oberpriller JO, Oberpriller JC. 1974. Response of the adult newt ventricle to injury. *J. Exp. Zool.* 187:249–53

Okada TS. 1991. *Transdifferentiation*. Oxford, UK: Clarendon Press. 238 pp.

Okada TS. 2004. From embryonic induction to cell lineages: revisiting old problems for modern study. *Int. J. Dev. Biol.* 48:739–42

Petersen CP, Reddien PW. 2008. Smed-βcatenin-1 is required for anteroposterior blastema polarity in planarian regeneration. *Science* 319:327–30

Pianka HD. 1974. Ctenophora. In *Reproduction of Marine Invertebrates. Volume 1. Acoelomate and Pseudocoelomate Metazoans*, ed. AC Giese, JS Pearse, pp. 201–65. New York: Academic

Poss KD, Keating MT, Nechiporuk A. 2003. Tales of regeneration in zebrafish. *Dev. Dyn.* 226:202–10

Poss KD, Wilson LG, Keating MT. 2002. Heart regeneration in zebrafish. *Science* 298:2188–90

Reddien PW, Oviedo NJ, Jennings JR, Jenkin JC, Sánchez Alvarado A. 2005. SMEDWI-2 is a PIWI-like protein that regulates planarian stem cells. *Science* 310:1327–30

Reddien PW, Sánchez Alvarado A. 2004. Fundamentals of planarian regeneration. *Annu. Rev. Cell Dev. Biol.* 20:725–57

Reichman OJ. 1984. Evolution of regeneration capabilities. *Am. Nat.* 123:752–63

Rinn JL, Bondre C, Gladstone HB, Brown PO, Chang HY. 2006. Anatomic demarcation by positional variation in fibroblast gene expression programs. *PLoS Genet.* 2:e119

Rogulja D, Irvine KD. 2005. Regulation of cell proliferation by a morphogen gradient. *Cell* 123:449–61

Rossi L, Salvetti A, Batistoni R, Deri P, Gremigni V. 2008. Planarians, a tale of stem cells. *Cell. Mol. Life Sci.* 65:16–23

Roy SW, Gilbert W. 2006. The evolution of spliceosomal introns: patterns, puzzles and progress. *Nat. Rev. Genet.* 7:211–21

Saito Y, Koinuma S, Watanabe K, Agata K. 2003. Mediolateral intercalation in planarians revealed by grafting experiments. *Dev. Dyn.* 226:334–40

Salo E, Baguna J. 2002. Regeneration in planarians and other worms: new findings, new tools, and new perspectives. *J. Exp. Zool.* 292:528–39

Sánchez Alvarado A. 2000. Regeneration in the metazoans: Why does it happen? *BioEssays* 22:578–90

Sánchez Alvarado A, Kang H. 2005. Multicellularity, stem cells, and the neoblasts of the planarian *Schmidtea mediterranea*. *Exp. Cell Res.* 306:299–308

Sánchez Alvarado A, Tsonis PA. 2006. Bridging the regeneration gap: genetic insights from diverse animal models. *Nat. Rev. Genet.* 7:873–84

Satoh A, Gardiner DM, Bryant SV, Endo T. 2007. Nerve-induced ectopic limb blastemas in the axolotl are equivalent to amputation-induced blastemas. *Dev. Biol.* 312:231–44

Schmid V. 1992. Transdifferentiation in medusae. *Int. Rev. Cytol.* 142:213–61

Schnapp E, Kragl M, Rubin L, Tanaka EM. 2005. Hedgehog signaling controls dorsoventral patterning, blastema cell proliferation and cartilage induction during axolotl tail regeneration. *Development* 132:3243–53

Shibata TF, Oji T. 2003. Autotomy and arm number increase in *Oxycomanthus japonicus* (Echinodermata, Crinoidea). *Invert. Biol.* 122:375–79

Sidman RL, Singer M. 1951. Stimulation of forelimb regeneration in the newt, *Triturus viridescens*, by a sensory nerve supply isolated from the central nervous system. *Am. J. Physiol.* 165:257–60

Singer M. 1952. The influence of the nerve in regeneration of the amphibian extremity. *Q. Rev. Biol.* 27:169–200

Sive HL, Hattori K, Weintraub H. 1989. Progressive determination during formation of the anteroposterior axis in *Xenopus laevis*. *Cell* 58:171–80

Slack JM, Lin G, Chen Y. 2008. Molecular and cellular basis of regeneration and tissue repair: the *Xenopus* tadpole: a new model for regeneration research. *Cell. Mol. Life Sci.* 65:54–63

Sobkow L, Epperlein HH, Herklotz S, Straube WL, Tanaka EM. 2006. A germline GFP transgenic axolotl and its use to track cell fate: dual origin of the fin mesenchyme during development and the fate of blood cells during regeneration. *Dev. Biol.* 290:386–97

Stewart S, Rojas-Muñoz A, Belmonte JC. 2007. Bioelectricity and epimorphic regeneration. *BioEssays* 29:1133–37

Stocum DL. 1984. The urodele limb regeneration blastema. Determination and organization of the morphogenetic field. *Differentiation* 27:13–28

Stocum DL. 2004a. Amphibian regeneration and stem cells. *Curr. Top. Microbiol. Immunol.* 280:1–70

Stocum DL. 2004b. Tissue restoration through regenerative biology and medicine. *Adv. Anat. Embryol. Cell Biol.* 176:1–101

Stocum DL. 2006. *Regenerative Biology and Medicine*. New York: Academic. 464 pp.

Stoick-Cooper CL, Moon RT, Weidinger G. 2007a. Advances in signaling in vertebrate regeneration as a prelude to regenerative medicine. *Genes Dev.* 21:1292–315

Stoick-Cooper CL, Weidinger G, Riehle KJ, Hubbert C, Major MB, et al. 2007b. Distinct Wnt signaling pathways have opposing roles in appendage regeneration. *Development* 134:479–89

Straube WL, Brockes JP, Drechsel DN, Tanaka EM. 2004. Plasticity and reprogramming of differentiated cells in amphibian regeneration: partial purification of a serum factor that triggers cell cycle re-entry in differentiated muscle cells. *Cloning Stem Cells* 6:333–44

Streilein JW. 2003. Ocular immune privilege: The eye takes a dim but practical view of immunity and inflammation. *J. Leukoc. Biol.* 74:179–85

Sugiyama T, Fujisawa T. 1978. Genetic analysis of developmental mechanisms in hydra. V. Cell lineage and development of chimera hydra. *J. Cell Sci.* 32:215–32

Tanaka EM, Drechsel DN, Brockes JP. 1999. Thrombin regulates S-phase re-entry by cultured newt myotubes. *Curr. Biol.* 9:792–99

Tanaka EM, Gann AA, Gates PB, Brockes JP. 1997. Newt myotubes reenter the cell cycle by phosphorylation of the retinoblastoma protein. *J. Cell Biol.* 136:155–65

Tassava RA, Olsen-Winner CL. 2003. Responses to amputation of denervated ambystoma limbs containing aneurogenic limb grafts. *J. Exp. Zool. A* 297:64–79

Thornton CS, Thornton MT. 1970. Recuperation of regeneration in denervated limbs of ambystoma larvae. *J. Exp. Zool.* 173:293–301

Tsonis PA, Madhavan M, Tancous EE, Del Rio-Tsonis K. 2004. A newt's eye view of lens regeneration. *Int. J. Dev. Biol.* 48:975–80

Vorontsova MA, Liosner LD. 1960. *Asexual Propagation and Regeneration*. London: Pergamon. 489 pp.

Westfall IA. 1996. Ultrastructure of synapses in the first-evolved nervous systems. *J. Neurocytol.* 25:735–46

Whitehead GG, Makino S, Lien CL, Keating MT. 2005. *fgf20* is essential for initiating zebrafish fin regeneration. *Science* 310:1957–60

Yntema CL. 1959. Blastema formation in sparsely innervated and aneurogenic forelimbs of amblystoma larvae. *J. Exp. Zool.* 142:423–39

Zhao M, Song B, Pu J, Wada T, Reid B, et al. 2006. Electrical signals control wound healing through phosphatidylinositol-3-OH kinase-γ and PTEN. *Nature* 442:457–60

Cell Polarity Signaling in *Arabidopsis*

Zhenbiao Yang

Center for Plant Cell Biology, Department of Botany and Plant Sciences, University of California, Riverside, California 92521-0124; email: zhenbiao.yang@ucr.edu

Annu. Rev. Cell Dev. Biol. 2008. 24:551–75

The *Annual Review of Cell and Developmental Biology* is online at cellbio.annualreviews.org

This article's doi:
10.1146/annurev.cellbio.23.090506.123233

Key Words

ROP GTPase, Rho GTPase, cytoskeleton, exocytosis, actin dynamics, polarized cell growth

Abstract

Cell polarization is intimately linked to plant development, growth, and responses to the environment. Major advances have been made in our understanding of the signaling pathways and networks that regulate cell polarity in plants owing to recent studies on several model systems, e.g., tip growth in pollen tubes, cell morphogenesis in the leaf epidermis, and polar localization of PINs. From these studies we have learned that plant cells use conserved mechanisms such as Rho family GTPases to integrate both plant-specific and conserved polarity cues and to coordinate the cytoskeketon dynamics/reorganization and vesicular trafficking required for polarity establishment and maintenance. This review focuses upon signaling mechanisms for cell polarity formation in *Arabidopsis*, with an emphasis on Rho GTPase signaling in polarized cell growth and how these mechanisms compare with those for cell polarity signaling in yeast and animal systems.

Contents

INTRODUCTION

Cell polarity, broadly defined as asymmetry within a cell, is a fundamental feature of cell function that is tied to developmental and environmental regulation. Polarity formation is initiated by a polarizing signal, which regulates polar distribution of signaling molecules and leads to polarity establishment and maintenance through the cytoskeleton and vesicular trafficking. In plants, cell polarity is fundamental to development, growth, and morphogenesis in every stage of the life cycle. Zygote polarization is required for the first asymmetric division to the embryo axis. Similarly, polarized cell division is essential for cell differentiation and organ initiation and morphogenesis. Polarized cell expansion generates cells with specific shapes that are associated with specialized functions, e.g., polarized and guided pollen tube growth for sperm delivery. Finally, polar localization of auxin-carrier proteins allows directional auxin flow and auxin-gradient formation, processes that are essential for organ and tissue formation and growth.

Given the fundamental importance of cell polarity and its diverse forms, a crucial question in our understanding of this phenomenon is whether there are general principles underlying the various forms of cell polarity in all eukaryotic systems. This question is of particular interest considering the many unique features of plant cells, one of which, the cell wall, is indispensable for polarity formation. Indeed, a paradigm of polarity control centered on Rho GTPase signaling has emerged from investigation of such diverse systems as yeast, worm zygotes, mammalian epithelial cells, plant pollen tubes (PT), and leaf epidermal cells (**Figure 1**). An equally important question is how diverse systems utilize these general rules to build the respective forms of cell polarity within specific developmental and environmental contexts. The answers to these questions have enhanced our understanding of general principles for cell polarity control and of the molecular mechanisms linking fundamental cell polarity to specific growth and developmental processes in plants. In this review, several plant model systems are discussed to illustrate how polarity control mechanisms in plants compare and contrast with those in animal and fungal systems.

MODEL POLARITY SYSTEMS IN PLANTS

Our understanding of the mechanisms underlying plant cell polarity formation has come primarily from several model systems (**Figure 2**), which offer fascinating biology and are accessible to experimental manipulations. Although the zygote of brown algae was formerly a favorite system (Fowler & Quatrano 1997), it has fallen out of favor because it is not amenable to genetic and molecular studies. Along with the development of *Arabidopsis* into a model plant, the single-cell pollen or multicellular epidermal systems (**Figure 2**) from *Arabidopsis* have been the focus of the investigation of the molecular and cellular biological and genetic bases of cell polarity generation in plants.

Tip-Growing Cells

Polar growth due to localized vesicle targeting and exocytosis to the growth site is termed tip growth, which occurs in all eukaryotic kingdoms and is required for the generation of highly elongated tubular cells such as fungal hyphae, animal neurons, PT, and root hairs (**Figure 2**). Although the mechanisms for tip growth in yeast have been extensively studied, it is unclear whether they apply to other tip growth systems, especially those involving rapid growth to an extraordinary length (e.g., neuronal axons, PT, and fungal hyphae). Both PT and root hairs serve as excellent model systems for rapid tip growth. Because root hairs are nonessential, many morphological mutants and concerned genes have been identified. Transcriptome analysis and the candidate gene approach have also identified important genes regulating tip growth. The genes identified by these approaches have provided some important insights into the molecular mechanism of tip growth, including signaling mediated by calcium, reactive oxygen species (ROS), and small GTPases (Bohme et al. 2004; Carol & Dolan 2006; Carol et al. 2005; Foreman et al. 2003; Grierson et al. 1997; Jones et al. 2002, 2006; Molendijk et al. 2001; Parker et al. 2000; Preuss

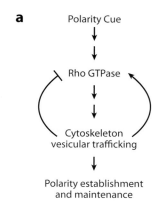

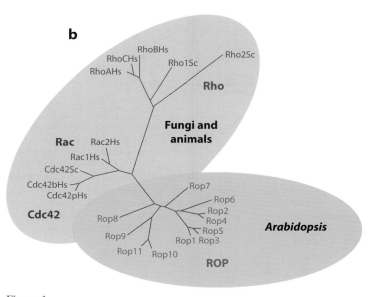

Figure 1

A unifying principle underlying the formation of cell polarity in eukaryotic cells. (*a*) A general signaling mechanism for cell polarity formation. (*b*) A simplified phylogenetic tree showing the major subfamilies of the Rho family small GTPases. All 11 members of the *Arabidopsis* Rho-related GTPase from plants (ROP) family are shown, but only representative members of the Cdc42, Rac, and Rho subfamilies are included.

et al. 2006; Schiefelbein & Somerville 1990; Song et al. 2006; Wen et al. 2005).

To deliver sperm to the ovule, the PT must extend rapidly (as fast as 1 cm h^{-1}) and directionally by navigating through many tissues. This directional growth is remarkably similar to neuronal guidance in animals (Kim et al.

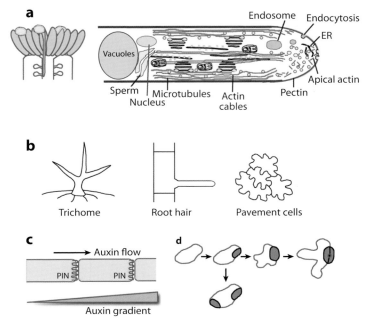

Figure 2

Model cell polarity systems in plants. (*a*) Tip growth model: the pollen tube.
(*Left*) A schematic of the top portion of a pistil with growing pollen tubes.
(*Right*) A schematic showing the polarized cellular structure of pollen tubes.
(*b*) Epidermal cells as a model for the study of planar cell polarity and/or the
polarity of diffuse growth. (*Left*) Single-cell leaf trichome. (*Middle*) Trichoblast
and root hairs. (*Right*) Pavement cells. (*c*) The polar localization of PINs
(PIN-FORMED proteins), which directs auxin flow and produces auxin
gradients, is used as a model for the study of asymmetric distribution of
molecules within a cell. (*d*) Guard cell differentiation as a model for the
investigation of the polarity of cell division.

citing systems for polarity studies in higher
organisms.

Studies of tip growth mechanisms in PT
have focused on two interlinking mechanisms:
the oscillating tip–focused cytosolic calcium
gradient and tip-localized dynamic Rho signaling. Both of these target the actin cytoskeleton that feedback-regulates them, constituting an intricate signaling network known as
LENS (localization-enhancing network, self-
sustaining) (Cole & Fowler 2006). Given that
there are roles for Rho GTPase, actin dynamics, and probably calcium in tip growth in other
systems, LENS may be a useful conceptual
framework for understanding the signaling
mechanisms underpinning tip growth in various systems.

Morphogenesis of Epidermal Cells

Unlike root hairs and PT, most plant cells expand by diffuse growth, whereby they diffusely
or uniformly increase their cell surface while
certain regions or positions of the cell differentially expand owing to differential construction or remodeling of localized regions of the
cell wall. Therefore, the mechanisms for localized cell-wall construction or modification are
the key to the polarity of diffuse growth. These
mechanisms have been investigated using several epidermal cell types amenable to microscopic imaging analyses (**Figure 2**). At least two
forms of cell polarity are important for the morphogenesis of epidermal cells: the apical-basal
polarity formed perpendicularly to the surface
and the planar polarity along the surface. In
Arabidopsis leaves, polarized growth from epidermal cells forming a trichome with three
branches is controlled by apical-basal polarity. Trichomes are nonessential cells, and their
morphology is easily observed, providing an excellent model for genetic analysis of morphogenesis. A large collection of mutants with altered trichome shapes has been isolated, and the
molecular analysis of these mutants has demonstrated a critical role for the ARP2/3 actin
nucleation complex in the regulation of trichome morphogenesis (Hulskamp et al. 1994,

2003, 2004; Lord & Russell 2002; Palanivelu
& Preuss 2006, Palanivelu et al. 2003). Unlike most other cells from multicellular plants,
which dedifferentiate and lose their native polarity upon in vitro culture, cultured pollen
maintains its developmental status and polarity. In vitro tubes grow synchronously and
uniformly. As the growth of PT is genetically
controlled by the haploid genome and involves
many pollen-specific genes, lethal mutations or
pollen-specific transgenes can be maintained in
heterozygous plants, facilitating genetic analysis of the essential genes involved in polarity control. These advantages, combined with
the ease with which live imaging can be performed in PT, make PT one of the most ex-

Schellmann & Hulskamp 2005, Smith & Oppenheimer 2005, Szymanski 2005).

Planar cell polarity, which involves coordination between cells within the plane of a cell layer, is essential for development and morphogenesis in animals (e.g., in convergent extension, wherein cells become intercalated to change the shape of early embryos). In plants, planar cell polarity is also critical for the differentiation of certain epidermal cell types (e.g., guard cells) and for the morphogenesis of most epidermal cells, such as trichoblasts in roots and pavement cells (PC) in leaves. Trichoblasts undergo polar diffuse growth to produce a bulge, from which tip-growing root hair forms. Interestingly, the site of the bulge formation, which is invariably adjacent to the basal end of the cross wall of trichoblasts (**Figure 2**), is regulated by the small-molecule hormone auxin (Fischer et al. 2006, 2007).

PC with a jigsaw-puzzle appearance represent an exciting system for the investigation of polarity involving cell-cell coordination (Fu et al. 2002, 2005; Smith 2003). The development of PC with interdigitating lobes and indentations requires intricate and dynamic polarity formation (**Figures 2**, **3a**) (Fu et al. 2002, 2005). The precise fitting of lobes and indentations among neighboring cells suggests a need for cell-to-cell signaling to spatiotemporally coordinate lobe outgrowth from one cell with the complementary indentation in a neighboring cell. This process bears a striking similarity to animal planar cell polarity, in particular to convergent extension requiring cell-to-cell intercalation (Goto et al. 2005, Klein & Mlodzik 2005, McEwen & Peifer 2001, Price et al. 2006, Settleman 2005). Interestingly, the similarity occurs at the mechanistic level as well. Dynamic gradients of a polarizing signal provide a developmental mechanism that activates the intercalary growth in PC (T. Xu, M. Wen, Y. Fu, J. Friml, J. Chen, M. Wu, A. Jones & Z. Yang, unpublished data); similarly, a gradient of unknown signal is thought to activate planar cell polarity in animals (Klein & Mlodzik 2005). Furthermore, accumulating evidence suggests that Rho GTPase–mediated cytoskeletal reor-

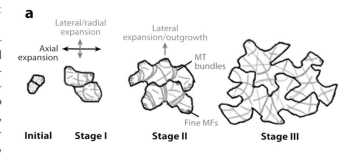

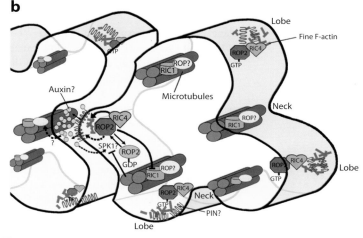

Figure 3

A model for a signaling network regulating the formation of the jigsaw-puzzle appearance of *Arabidopsis* leaf pavement cells (PC). (*a*) The development of PC can be separated into three stages and is associated both with cortical fine actin microfilaments (F-actin) (*red patches*) and with microtubules (MT) (*green lines*) (Fu et al. 2002, 2005). Near-square PC initials first elongate slightly to form near-rectangular cells (stage I), which produce alternating small bumps and indentations, generating cells with multiple shallow lobes and indentations (also termed sinuses or necks) (stage II). Reiterative outgrowing and indenting continue, producing highly lobed interlocking PC that often contain secondary lobes (stage III). From Fu et al. (2005) with permission. (*b*) A model for the ROP GTPase–dependent signaling mechanism for PC morphogenesis. This model includes known components (ROP2, RIC4, F-actin, RIC1, MT, SPK1), speculative factors (auxin and a PIN protein), and their interactions in the ROP (Rho-related GTPase from plants)-signaling network underlying PC morphogenesis. Solid arrows indicate pathways well supported by experiments. Dotted arrows indicate speculative steps/pathways. ER denotes endoplasmic reticulum.

ganization is important for planar cell polarity in animals, as has been shown for PC (Goto et al. 2005, Klein & Mlodzik 2005, McEwen & Peifer 2001, Price et al. 2006, Settleman 2005). Therefore, the study of PC polarity formation may help to shed light onto the mechanistic principles of planar cell polarity in other systems.

Polar Localization of Auxin Transporters

Cell polarity is often expressed as polar distribution of molecules within the cell; these molecules are not necessarily associated with detectable morphological expression in cell polarity. A good example of this type of polarity is polar localization of auxin transporters in plants, including auxin efflux carriers PIN-FORMED proteins (PINs) and influx carrier AUX1 (see Kleine-Vehn & Friml 2008, in this volume). The function of auxin is associated with its flow, its distribution as a gradient, the maximum of its gradient, and/or its specific concentration within a tissue or cell (Grieneisen et al. 2007, Wisniewska et al. 2006). All these features of auxin distribution and dynamics are primarily regulated by the polar distribution of PINs, with the polar distribution of AUX1 playing a secondary role (Kleine-Vehn & Friml 2008). Different PINs exhibit distinct polar localization patterns within the same cell, and the polarity of a PIN within the same cell is controlled by developmental or environmental signals (Leyser 2005). For example, the apical-to-basal reversal of PIN7 polarity in the basal cell of the two-celled embryo is important for *Arabidopsis* embryo axis formation (Friml et al. 2003). Therefore, signaling between PINs and polarity signals is required for polar localization of PINs.

Asymmetric Cell Division

As in other multicellular organisms, asymmetric cell division, found in zygotes and various stem cells, generates two unequal daughter cells with distinct fates in plants. Prior to asymmetric division, polarity must be established to allow this unequal distribution of cellular molecules and structures. For instance, in zygotes of higher plants the apical end is enriched with the cytoplasm, whereas the basal end is primarily occupied by a large vacuole. The mechanism for zygote polarization in plants remains poorly understood owing to the difficulties in visualizing the zygote embedded deep in the ovary and in isolating the mutations affecting this process, because they are lethal to the embryo. However, recent genetic studies on the differentiation of guard cells and root stem cells are beginning to unravel regulatory factors, such as transcriptional factor and signaling molecules, that modulate asymmetric cell division in plants (Aida et al. 2004, Bergmann et al. 2004, Hara et al. 2007, Nadeau & Sack 2002, Pillitteri & Torii 2007, Shpak et al. 2005, Wang et al. 2007, Xu et al. 2006).

THE CYTOSKELETON AND VESICULAR TRAFFICKING IN POLARITY CONTROL

A central aspect of the cell polarity paradigm is the significance of the cytoskeleton and its associated vesicular trafficking: Both serve as an essential cellular linkage to molecular pathways by responding to the initial polarity signal and providing spatial information for feedback regulation of the polarity-signaling pathways (**Figure 1**). Increasing evidence indicates that this paradigm can be extended to the regulation of plant cell polarity formation, although the detailed mechanisms by which the cytoskeleton and vesicular trafficking participate in plant cell polarity formation may vary from those in other systems. As in fungi and animals, both actin microfilaments (F-actin) and microtubules (MT), as well as targeted exocytosis and endocytosis, have been implicated in cell polarity control in plants (Cole & Fowler 2006, Murphy et al. 2005, Smith & Oppenheimer 2005). Given the tight linkage of these cellular events to polarity formation and Rho GTPase signaling, this review includes a discussion of their roles in plant cell polarity. For broader and more detailed descriptions of these cellular events, however, readers are referred to several recent excellent reviews (Campanoni & Blatt 2007, Cole & Fowler 2006, Ehrhardt & Shaw 2006, Murphy et al. 2005, Samaj et al. 2006, Smith & Oppenheimer 2005).

Microtubules

MT act to induce cell polarity formation by targeting and/or locally activating signaling molecules at the polar site in yeast and animal cells (Basu & Chang 2007, Siegrist & Doe 2007). A common signaling molecule regulated by MT in these systems is a Rho family GTPase, which controls actin-based polarity formation (Basu & Chang 2007, Siegrist & Doe 2007). Signaling in the polar site also feedback-regulates MT by stabilizing them. In plants, MT seem to have multiple roles and modes of action in cell polarity, some of which are analogous to polarity control in yeast and animals. Highly ordered paralleled cortical MT form a preprophase band (PPB) that predicts the site and the orientation of cell division, which are critical for asymmetric cell division. The localization of the PPB is determined by an initial polarity signal, which induces the polarization of cells prior to PPB formation. In this sense, the PPB acts to process but not to induce polarity. However, the PPB in turn induces the polarity of cell division, i.e., the position and the orientation of the new cell plate. PPB MT and the associated kinesins POK1 and ROK2 recruit TAN1 to the PPB cortical site, which signals to place and orient the phragmoplast according to the PPB (Muller et al. 2006, Smith et al. 2001, Walker et al. 2007).

Cortical MT modulate the polarity of cell expansion in various plant cells, but their modes of action may vary from one cell type to another. MT induce branching of *Arabidopsis* trichomes with three to four branches. Stabilizing the MT increases the branch number of wild-type trichomes and induces branching of unbranched mutant trichomes, whereas MT disruption causes unbranched trichomes (Mathur & Chua 2000). MT may regulate the localization of the Golgi apparatus or the targeting of specific molecules to induce trichome branching (Lu et al. 2005).

In diffusely growing cells, well-ordered cortical MT are thought to determine the region of the expanding cell surface; e.g., they are associated with the sinuses but excluded from the expanding lobes of PC (**Figure 3**). Removal of cortical MT results in isotropic cell expansion, implying that cortical MT may also directly participate in the formation of cell polarity in plants. Ordered MT are believed to guide the deposition of cellulose microfibrils for the restriction of cell expansion (Ehrhardt & Shaw 2006). This mode of MT action is clearly unique to plant cells. In addition, cortical MT modulate the polarity of cell expansion in plants by regulating Rho GTPase signaling (**Figure 3**) (Fu et al. 2005). This type of MT action in plant cells follows the general theme of the MT induction of cell polarity formation (Basu & Chang 2007, Siegrist & Doe 2007).

Actin Microfilaments

F-actin generally participate in polarity establishment by affecting the biochemical, structural, and biophysical properties of the plasma membrane (PM) at the polar site. Cortical F-actin, which form as patches or dense meshwork by the ARP2/3 actin nucleation complex, directly control PM polarization by regulating both exocytosis and endocytosis in yeast and animals (Basu & Chang 2007, La Carbona et al. 2006, Moseley & Goode 2006). Through vesicular trafficking or direct transport, cortical F-actin target signaling molecules (e.g., Rho GTPases or their activators) to the polar site to promote their own polymerization, forming a positive feedback loop for robust polarity establishment (Charest & Firtel 2006). Cytoplasmic actin bundles, which originate from formin-dependent actin assembly, maintain cell polarity either by targeting post-Golgi vesicles in yeast or by generating the trailing edge in animals.

The picture of F-actin's role in regulating cell polarity in plants is emerging but far from clear. The role of the ARP2/3 complex is limited to shape control in trichomes and in PC (Smith & Oppenheimer 2005). In PC, ARP2/3 knockout mutations do not eliminate but only alter the localization of a lobe-associated actin meshwork that appears as diffuse cortical F-actin (Djakovic et al. 2006, Li et al. 2003).

The formation of these ARP2/3–independent diffuse F-actin requires a Rho GTPase–dependent pathway (Fu et al. 2002, 2005).

The ARP2/3–independent F-actin also control tip growth in PT and root hairs. F-actin in the PT extreme apex have been a subject of debate for decades owing mostly to technical difficulties in visualizing the highly dynamic F-actin. Green fluorescent protein (GFP)-tagged mouse talin was used to visualize highly dynamic F-actin at the tip, which rapidly alternate between the cortex of the apical dome and the cortex immediately adjacent to the extreme apex (Fu et al. 2001, Kost et al. 1998). Rapid-freezing methods confirmed abundant presence of the latter but infrequent occurrence of the former (Lovy-Wheeler et al. 2005), probably reflecting snapshots of the dynamic apical F-actin. The existence of the former, however, is clearly supported by the finding that it is activated by a Rho GTPase signaling pathway localized to the extreme tip of the PM (Fu et al. 2001, Gu et al. 2005, Hwang et al. 2005).

The Rho GTPase–mediated dynamics of the apical F-actin is required for the generation or maintenance of PT polarity (Fu et al. 2001, Gu et al. 2005). In PT, evidence suggests that the actin dynamics regulates tip-targeted exocytosis by coordinating vesicle accumulation and docking/fusion (Lee et al. 2008). Rho GTPase–dependent actin assembly is required for vesicle accumulation to the apex, whereas its disassembly is critical for vesicle docking and/or fusion. Apical F-actin have also been implicated in positive feedback activation of Rho GTPases at PT tips, as in yeast and animals (Hwang et al. 2005). Therefore, at least some roles of dynamic F-actin in polarity formation are conserved in plants at the mechanistic level, although it is not clear whether the apical F-actin regulate endocytosis as they do in yeast and animal cells.

Exocytosis

A role for polarized exocytosis in cell polarity formation has been established in various eukaryotic systems (Brennwald & Rossi 2007, France et al. 2006, Mehta et al. 2005,

Wedlich-Soldner et al. 2004, Zajac et al. 2005). Polarized exocytosis allows for tip growth in root hairs and PT by supplying membrane and wall materials; for instance, loss-of-function mutations on genes encoding the SEC3 and SEC8 subunits of exocyst, which control polar docking of vesicles to the PM, block tip growth (Cole & Fowler 2006). Polar exocytosis also mediates the targeting of signaling molecules. In yeast, polar activation of signaling molecules such as Cdc42 mediates polar exocytosis, which in turn leads to the molecules' own polar targeting, generating a positive feedback loop for robust generation of cell polarity (Wedlich-Soldner et al. 2004, Zajac et al. 2005). As mentioned above, the dynamic tip F-actin appear to participate in the positive feedback activation of ROP1 (where ROP refers to Rho-related GTPase from plants) by regulating exocytosis in pollen tubes. Polar localization of ROP GTPases to the PM involves ADP-ribosylation factor (ARF) GTPase–mediated vesicular trafficking (Molendijk et al. 2001; Xu & Scheres 2005a,b).

Knocking out a Rab4Ab effector depolarizes root hair growth (Preuss et al. 2006). Rab4A GTPases are localized to endosomes/trans-Golgi network (TGN)/exocytic vesicles that have accumulated at the tips of root hairs and PT (de Graaf et al. 2005; Lee et al. 2008; Preuss et al. 2004, 2006). Rab4A belongs to a 29-member subfamily of Rab GTPases that are predicted to localize to TGN/post-Golgi vesicles. The unusually large size of this Rab subfamily is consistent with the notion that these Rabs may be involved in the targeting of functionally distinct vesicles (Vernoud et al. 2003, Zhang et al. 2007). Specific molecules carried on RabA4 vesicles may either mark the site of polarity for tip growth or be involved in limiting or maintaining polarity signaling to the tip. In PT, a ROP1-negative regulator required for growth polarity control appears to be carried on tip-localized vesicles (J. Hwang, V. Vernoud & Z. Yang, unpublished data). Exocytosis-mediated targeting of negative regulators of Rho family GTPases may be a common mechanism for restricting polarity signaling to the polar site, as has been shown for mammalian RICH1 (a CDC42 GTPase–activating protein) in restricting CDC42 signaling to the tight junction (Wells et al. 2006).

Polar localization of PIN and AUX proteins is another example of exocytosis of specialized vesicles that carry specific molecules (Dharmasiri et al. 2006; Geldner et al. 2003; Jaillais et al. 2006, 2007; Kleine-Vehn et al. 2006; Steinmann et al. 1999). Several recent studies clearly demonstrate that different auxin-transporter proteins are targeted to the PM through distinct exocytic routes involving SNX1-dependent and -independent endosome sorting, which are subject to regulation by specific polarity signals (Kleine-Vehn & Friml 2008).

Endocytosis

Endocytosis to retrieve the PM and its associated signaling molecules is a common mechanism for the maintenance of cell polarity in eukaryotes (Engqvist-Goldstein & Drubin 2003, Murphy et al. 2005, Nishimura & Kaibuchi 2007, Pruyne & Bretscher 2000, Yu et al. 2007). In yeast, CDC42 regulates not only polarized exocytosis but also endocytosis in its control of polarity formation. Computational modeling predicts that polarized targeting of PM proteins, their lateral diffusion in the PM, and their internalization by endocytosis are sufficient to generate sustained cell polarity (Marco et al. 2007). Endocytosis has been well documented in plant cells (Dhonukshe et al. 2007, Murphy et al. 2005) and occurs at the tips of PT and root hairs (Lisboa et al. 2007, Monteiro et al. 2005, Ovecka et al. 2005). A recent study in plant cells demonstrated the conservation of clathrin-mediated endocytosis (Dhonukshe et al. 2007), for which phosphatidylinositol 4,5-bisphosphate (PIP2) and its conversion to phosphatidylinositol 4-bisphosphate (PI4P) are required. Both PIP2 and PI4P are localized to the PT-apical PM, and alteration of PIP2 and PI4P levels inhibits the internalization of the PM at PT tips, leading to growth depolariza-

tion (Y. Zhao, A. Yan & Z. Yang, unpublished data). Furthermore, expression of the constitutively active form of ROP induces growth depolarization and inhibits endocytosis (Bloch et al. 2005). Interestingly, a screen designed to identify chemicals that affect the polarity of pollen tube tip growth has led to the identification of endocitin, which impacts the endocytosis of specific PM-localized proteins (Roberts et al. 2008). These observations support a role for endocytosis in maintaining polarized cell growth in plants.

Moreover, a large body of evidence shows that PIN proteins are internalized to endosomes by constitutive endocytosis (Dhonukshe et al. 2007, Richter et al. 2007, Teh & Moore 2007). Interestingly, auxin increases PIN localization to the PM by inhibiting endocytosis, forming a positive feedback loop of auxin efflux–signaling PIN localization (Paciorek et al. 2005).

SIGNALING MECHANISMS BEHIND CELL POLARITY FORMATION

How polarizing signals impinge on cytoskeletal reorganization/dynamics and vesicular trafficking is a central concern in polarity studies. A common theme of polarity signaling in plants has emerged from recent studies of polarized cell growth: Rho GTPase signaling networks, composed of multiple coordinate pathways and feedback loops, provide a robust molecular linkage between cytoskeleton and vesicular trafficking and polarity formation. This signaling mechanism not only resonates with the cell polarity paradigm in yeast and animals but also helps to reveal how Rho GTPases can be used to generate cell polarity in diverse systems. Rho functions as a hub in signaling by integrating numerous signals and coordinating multiple downstream pathways (Nibau et al. 2006, Yang & Fu 2007). To control the plant-specific aspects of cell polarity, Rho has evolved to interact with plant-specific partners or variants of conserved regulators.

ROP GTPases and Partners: Plant Reinvention of Conserved Polarity Signaling

In contrast to the multiple subfamilies of the mammalian Rho family (e.g., Cdc42, Rac, Rho, etc.), all plant Rho-like GTPases fall into a single subfamily, ROP (**Figure 1**) (Brembu et al. 2006, Burridge & Wennerberg 2004, Vernoud et al. 2003, Yang 2002, Yang & Fu 2007, Yang & Watson 1993). Six (ROP1 to ROP6) of the 11 *Arabidopsis* ROPs are known to regulate cell polarity formation (Gu et al. 2004, Yang 2002). Two classes of negative regulators, guanine nucleotide dissociation inhibitors (RhoGDIs) and GTPase-activating proteins (RhoGAPs), are conserved in plants, but they possess unique regulatory functions such as the Cdc42/Rac–interactive binding (CRIB) motif in RhoGAPs (Brembu et al. 2006, Wu et al. 2000). Interestingly, the conventional RhoGEFs (guanine nucleotide exchange factors) with the Dbl-homology (DH) domain are absent from plants, and only a single homolog of DHR2–RhoGEF, SPK1, is present in *Arabidopsis* (Basu et al. 2008, Brembu et al. 2006, Meller et al. 2005, Qiu et al. 2002). However, a novel family of plant-specific RhoGEFs known as RopGEF has recently been identified (Berken et al. 2005, Gu et al. 2006). Several pollen-expressed RopGEFs interact physically and functionally with a pollen-expressed receptor-like kinase (RLK), which belongs to a superfamily of receptor ser/thr kinases in plants (Kaothien et al. 2005, Zhang & McCormick 2007). RopGEFs and RLKs may have coevolved to form a plant-specific signaling module to respond to plant-specific extracellular signals (Yang & Fu 2007).

Plants have reinvented a set of Rho effectors, even though their signaling targets (e.g., the cytoskeleton) are conserved. Plant-specific effectors include two classes of novel proteins: a family of ROP-interactive CRIB motif–containing proteins (RICs) and a family of interactor of constitutively active ROP 1 proteins (ICR1 and ICR1-like) (Lavy et al. 2007, Wu et al. 2001, Xu & Scheres 2005a). RIC3 and RIC4 regulate actin dynamics in a manner apparently independent of the ARP2/3 complex (Fu et al. 2005, Gu et al. 2006, Li et al. 2003). Thus, ROP's regulation of actin dynamics in plants may involve a novel mechanism. ICR1 interacts with SEC3, an exocyst component known to be a direct effector of yeast CDC42. ICR1 is required for polarized growth of PC, consistent with a role in the activation of exocyst; however, direct evidence for this role is lacking (Lavy et al. 2007). These variations from the central theme of Rho signaling in cell polarity provide the basis for Rho GTPase control of cell polarity with various functionalities in diverse cell types and organisms. To elaborate further upon this idea, several examples of ROP signaling in cell polarity are discussed in detail below.

Figure 4

A model for the generation and maintenance of the dynamic and oscillating apical cap of active ROP1 (where ROP refers to Rho-related GTPase from plants) in pollen tubes. (*a*) A time series of images showing the localization of a green fluorescent protein (GFP)-based active ROP1 reporter in a tobacco pollen tube transiently expressing this marker, i.e., GFP fused to the N terminus of a RIC4 deletion mutant (Hwang et al. 2005). Numbers at the bottom of each pollen tube image indicate seconds in the time series shown in the graph at the bottom of this figure. (*Bottom*) Graphs show the oscillation of plasma membrane (PM)-localized GFP-RIC4ΔC. Modified from figure 3 of Hwang et al. (2005). (*b*) Models for positive feedback–mediated lateral propagation of the apical ROP1 activity and for negative feedback–mediated global ROP1 downregulation by the REN1 GTPase–activating protein (RhoGAP) and lateral inhibition by cortical microtubules (MT) and phospholipase C (PLC). Solid arrows indicate pathways supported by experimental evidence. Dotted arrows indicate speculative pathways lacking experimental support. Abbreviations used: CDPK, calcium-dependent protein kinase; F-actin, actin microfilaments; RIC, ROP-interactive Cdc42/Rac-interactive binding (CRIB) motif–containing protein.

ROP GTPase Signaling at the Tip: The Pollen Tube Model

A role for ROPs in cell polarity control in plants was first suggested by a study showing ROP localization to the apical PM of pollen tubes and the essential role of ROPs in tip growth (Lin et al. 1996, Lin & Yang 1997). These initial findings and subsequent studies of ROP signaling have provided us with a road map for addressing key questions about tip growth (**Figure 4**): (*a*) What defines the apical PM domain (i.e., tip growth domain) for tip growth? (*b*) How is the tip growth domain generated and maintained? (*c*) How does this domain signal to exocytic vesicles to control their targeting and exocytosis to the tip?

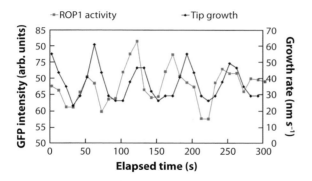

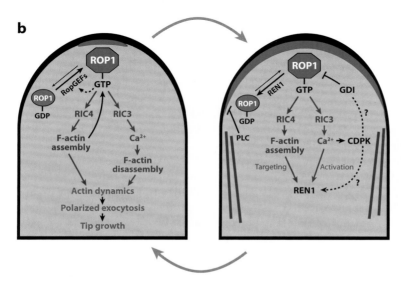

The dynamics of tip-localized ROP activity drives tip growth. Three redundant ROPs (ROP1, -3, and -5), referred to as ROP1 for simplicity, are required for pollen tip growth (Hwang & Yang 2006, Kost et al. 1999, Li et al. 1999). As a positive regulator of tip growth, ROP1 activity is regulated and is critical for the polarity of tip growth (Gu et al. 2003, Hwang & Yang 2006, Kost et al. 1999, Li et al. 1999; J. Hwang, G. Wu, C. Grierson & Z. Yang, unpublished data). Live imaging of active ROP1 reveals the PM distribution of active ROP1 as a dynamic apical cap in normal oscillating PT (**Figure 4***a*). It rises to the maximum size just prior to the growth peak and gradually decreases to the minimum followed by growth rate decreases (Hwang et al. 2005). The maximum of the active ROP1 cap determines the tip growth domain, whereas the dynamics of the apical ROP1 activity drives tip growth (J. Hwang, G. Wu, C. Grierson & Z. Yang, unpublished data).

The dynamics of the active ROP1 controls tip growth in part by regulating the dynamics of apical F-actin (Fu et al. 2001, Gu et al. 2005, Hwang et al. 2005). Two ROP1 downstream pathways check and balance to control actin dynamics; the RIC4 pathway promotes the assembly of the apical F-actin, and the RIC3-calcium pathway promotes the disassembly of the apical F-actin (**Figure 4**). The actin dynamics not only modulates tip-targeted exocytosis for tip growth but also is required for the dynamics of the apical ROP1 cap through feedback regulations (Hwang et al. 2005, Lee et al. 2008).

The generation of the apical cap. ROP1 is first activated at the center of the future apical cap, and then spreads laterally to form the cap until reaching the maximum size (**Figure 4***a*) (J. Hwang, G. Wu, C. Grierson & Z. Yang, unpublished data). Expression of a constitutively active ROP1 mutant (CA-ROP1) induces dramatic lateral spreading of endogenous active ROP1, producing a stable and dramatically enlarged ROP1 cap that is suppressed by RopGAP1 (J. Hwang, G. Wu, C. Grierson &

Z. Yang, unpublished data). Furthermore, knocking out a RhoGAP produces a CA-ROP1-like phenotype (J. Hwang, V. Vernoud & Z. Yang, unpublished data). Finally, the ROP1 or RIC4 overexpression–induced depolarization of ROP1 activity is suppressed by Latrunculin B, which promotes actin depolymerization, implying that F-actin, downstream targets of ROP1 signaling, positively impact ROP1 activation (Fu et al. 2001, Hwang et al. 2005). On the basis of these observations, it was hypothesized that the lateral spreading of ROP1 activation is mediated by positive feedback (J. Hwang, G. Wu, C. Grierson & Z. Yang, unpublished data). One positive feedback mechanism involves apical F-actin (Hwang et al. 2005), similar to the F-actin-mediated positive feedback activation of Cdc42 in yeast (Wedlich-Soldner et al. 2004). Another positive feedback mechanism may involve RopGEF1, an ROP1 activator localized to the apical cap of PT, which was proposed to be directly activated by active ROP1 (Gu et al. 2006). In animal cells, a key feedback loop is Cdc2/Rac activation of phosphoinositide-3-kinase-mediated accumulation of phosphatidylinositol 3,4,5-triphosphate (PIP3) in the PM, which recruits Cdc42/Rac activators (Charest & Firtel 2006). Although there is no evidence for the presence of PIP3 in plants, roles of PI4P and PIP2 in polarized tip growth in root hairs and PTs have been demonstrated and have been implicated in ROP1 activation in PT (Dowd et al. 2006, Helling et al. 2006, Preuss et al. 2006, Stenzel et al. 2008; Y. Zhao, Y. An & Z. Yang, unpublished data). It would be interesting to determine whether these phosphoinositides participate in the positive feedback regulation of the apical ROP1 activity.

The maintenance and the dynamics of the apical cap through downregulation of ROP1. In wild-type PT, as soon as the apical cap of active ROP1 reaches the maximum, it needs to be reduced to confine the ROP1 activity to the tip growth domain and to maintain the dynamics of ROP1 activity (**Figure 4***a*). The downregulation of ROP signaling may be mediated by either global and lateral inhibitions, or both. It has been proposed that the tobacco NtRopGAP1 acts laterally to restrict ROP activity to the apex on the basis of its subapical localization (Klahre & Kost 2006). Knocking out what appears to be the *Arabidopsis* ortholog of NtRopGAP1, however, does not cause the spreading of ROP1 to the subapical region, suggesting that this RopGAP does not play a major role in the downregulation of the apical ROP (J. Hwang, G. Wu, C. Grierson & Z. Yang, unpublished data). However, dramatic lateral spreading of apical ROPs and growth depolarization were induced by knocking out a pleckstrin-homology (PH) domain–containing RhoGAP, REN1 (J. Hwang, V. Vernoud & Z. Yang, unpublished data). REN1 protein is localized to the tube apex, as expected for a global inhibitor. Therefore, REN1 is the major RhoGAP globally inactivating the apical active ROP1.

Another global inhibitor of ROP1 is RhoGDI, which sequesters Rho in the cytosol to prevent it from being activated by the RhoGEFs. RhoGDIs are localized in the PT cytosol, as expected for a global inhibitor (Klahre et al. 2006). Knocking out RhoGDI2a in *Arabidopsis* induces tip swelling and lateral spreading of ROP1 from the tip, indicating that it is an important global inhibitor of the apical ROP1 (J. Hwang, G. Wu, C. Grierson & Z. Yang, unpublished data). A RhoGDI1 knockout also induces ectopic ROP2 localization to the PM, causing growth depolarization in root hairs (Carol et al. 2005).

Apart from global inhibitions, lateral inhibition may also play a role in limiting ROP1 activity to the tip. Cortical MT localized to the subapical region appears to have a minor role in restricting ROP activation to the apex. Stabilization of MT partially suppressed ROP1 overexpression–induced depolarization, whereas MT removal moderately increased lateral spreading of the apical ROP1 activity and growth depolarization (M. Zheng & Z. Yang, unpublished data). Both petunia phospholipase C (PLC1) and tobacco PLC3 are preferentially localized to the subapical region of the PM, and their inhibition induces growth depolarization (Dowd et al. 2006, Helling et al. 2006). Treatments with PLC inhibitors induced lateral spreading of active ROP1 (A. Yan & Z. Yang, unpublished data). These results support a role for PLC in limiting PIP2 and ROP1 activity to the tip.

Calcium: a critical link to feedback loops. As a self-organizing system, the downregulation of the apical ROP1 activity in PT is presumably activated by negative feedback mechanisms. Mathematical modeling predicts that RIC3-dependent calcium, which exhibits as oscillatory tip-high gradients (Holdaway-Clarke et al. 1997, Pierson et al. 1994), is a critical activator of the negative feedback regulation; this has been experimentally validated (A. Yan, G. Xu & Z. Yang, unpublished data). The nature of calcium-signaling targets in the negative feedback regulation is unclear, but mathematical modeling predicts that these targets may be either RhoGAP or an F-actin–disassembling factor, or both (A. Yan, G. Xu & Z. Yang, unpublished data).

Interestingly, calcium also participates in positive feedback regulation of ROS production, which is required for tip growth in root hairs. This growth in turn is catalyzed by the tip-localized RHD2 NADPH oxidase (Takeda et al. 2008). RHD2 appears to act directly downstream of ROP2 in root hair tip growth (Carol & Dolan 2006; Jones et al. 2002, 2007; Molendijk et al. 2001; Wong et al. 2007), and RHD2-mediated ROS activate influxes of tip-localized calcium (Carol & Dolan 2006, Jones et al. 2007), which in turn activates RHD2 to form a positive feedback loop consisting of RHD2, ROS, and calcium (Takeda et al. 2008). A similar ROS-calcium circuit may also regulate tip growth in PT (McInnis et al. 2006, Potocky et al. 2007). Given a role for the RHD2-calcium positive feedback loop in PT tip growth, how could calcium-mediated positive and negative feedback loops coexist in the same system? A simple model is that ROP activation of NADPH oxidase and

RIC3 initiates the ROS-calcium positive feedback loop, which then runs independently of ROPs. This causes a calcium burst, which activates a negative feedback loop to downregulate ROPs.

Identification of calcium sensors will be necessary to test this model. A putative calcium sensor involved in feedback loops is calcium-dependent protein kinase (CDPK). Overexpression of a PM-localized petunia PiCDPK1 induced PT growth depolarization and excessive calcium accumulation (Yoon et al. 2006). Interestingly, a dominant negative mutant of PiCDPK1 also caused growth depolarization, whereas a constitutively active form of PiCDPK1 either blocked pollen germination or severely inhibited growth by reducing both the length and the width of PT. This CDPK may be the calcium sensor involved in both feedback loops.

Identifying ROP signaling–mediated calcium channels may also provide insights into feedback loops. A pollen-expressed putative calcium channel, CNGC18, is required for polarized PT growth (Frietsch et al. 2007). CNGC18 is localized to the apical and subapical regions of PT PM and is permeable to calcium (Chang et al. 2007, Frietsch et al. 2007). ROP signaling enhances CNGC targeting to the PM, most likely through ROP-mediated polarized exocytosis, but it does not directly regulate its activity (Chang et al. 2007).

A model for tip growth signaling in pollen tubes and beyond. As discussed above, a model for tip growth signaling centered on ROP1 GTPase has been developed (**Figure 4**). This model may provide a framework for the understanding of detailed signaling mechanisms for various tip growth systems, e.g., growth of root hairs, fungal hyphae, and neurons. In root hairs, ROP2 probably activates tip growth through F-actin and calcium (Jones et al. 2002, Molendijk et al. 2001). RhoGDI1 plays a similar role in root hair tip growth as does RhoGDI2a in PT (Carol et al. 2005; J. Hwang, G. Wu, C. Grierson & Z. Yang,

unpublished data). Rho family GTPases, actin dynamics, positive feedback loops, and RhoGAP-dependent global inhibition are also important for tip growth in other systems (Alberts et al. 2006; Bidlingmaier & Snyder 2004; Knaus et al. 2007; Ushinsky et al. 2002; Wendland & Philippsen 2000, 2001). It will be interesting to see whether the interlinking feedback loops underlying the dynamics of the apical Rho GTPase cap in pollen represent a general mechanism for the control of tip growth in all systems.

Signaling between ROPs and Microtubules in Polarized Diffuse Growth: The Pavement Cell Model

The striking polarity of PC expansion makes it an ideal system for investigating how polarity is coordinated between cells and is controlled during diffuse growth, which is tightly linked to plant development and morphogenesis. In contrast to tip growth, cortical MT play a predominant role in determining the polarity of diffuse growth. Interestingly, current evidence indicates that polarity of diffuse growth is modulated by signaling mechanisms similar to those for tip growth. This similarity was first suggested by the observation that CA-ROP2 and DN-ROP2 mutants dramatically alter cell shapes in PC (Fu et al. 2002).

The ROP2/4–RIC4 pathway promotes lobe formation. Subsequent studies have shown that functionally redundant ROP2 and ROP4 promote lobe outgrowth (Fu et al. 2005). ROP2/4 are activated locally at the tips of growing lobes, where they promote localized accumulation of RIC4-dependent cortical fine F-actin, similar to the regulation of F-actin by ROP1 in PT tips. In addition, the lobe outgrowth may also require localized exocytosis. ICR1 was recently identified as a putative ROP effector that may link to exocyst recruitment to a polar site (Lavy et al. 2007). A ICR1 knockout generates small PC lacking lobes and indentations. Further studies should determine whether ICR1 is a ROP2/4 effector involved in recruiting exocysts. Active ROP2/4 also need to suppress the organization of ordered cortical MT in the region of outgrowth because ordered MT prevent outgrowth in diffusely growing cells (**Figure 3**) (Fu et al. 2002, 2005). Similarly, MT are also excluded from the tip growth domain in tip-growing cells, and it would be interesting to see whether active ROPs also play a role in excluding MT from the tip.

The signaling pathway promoting indentation. In the indenting region, RIC1 (a novel MT-associated protein) promotes MT ordering that restricts outgrowth, causing narrow necks (**Figure 3**) (Fu et al. 2005). Mutations in the CRIB motif of RIC1 eliminate the function of RIC1 in promoting MT ordering, implying that RIC1 may also be activated by a ROP GTPase to promote the organization of cortical MT (Y. Fu, Z.-L. Zheng & Z. Yang, unpublished data). These results seem to suggest a new ROP-RIC-mediated signaling pathway that activates MT ordering in plants (Fu et al. 2005). An increase in radial expansion of hypocotyl cells in the *ric1* null mutant suggests that this pathway apparently also restricts radial expansion of elongating cells with simple diffuse growth (Y. Fu, Z.-L. Zheng & Z. Yang, unpublished data). Therefore, knowing which signals regulate this RIC1 signaling pathway may provide important insights into plant morphogenesis and development in general.

Microtubule suppression of outgrowth-promoting ROP signaling: a new paradigm for cell morphogenesis? Cortical MT in the indenting region are known to signal back to ROP2/4 in such a way that ROP2/4 activation is repressed by cortical MT in the indenting region (Fu et al. 2005). In tip-growing PT, cortical MT present in the subapical region may also suppress ROP1 activation, probably by lateral inhibition (M. Zheng & Z. Yang, unpublished data). In root hairs, CA-ROP2-induced growth depolarization is enhanced by mutations in a kinesin that affects MT organization (Yang et al.

2007). Therefore, MT-mediated lateral inhibition of tip-localized ROP activation is involved in the regulation of tip growth polarity but is only secondary to the global inhibition. In contrast, cortical MT play a primary role in determining the polarity of diffuse growth, at least in part by suppressing outgrowth-promoting ROPs. This role can be extended to cells with simple diffuse growth, such as differentiating hypocotyls and root cells, in which cortical MT–mediated cell expansion in the direction perpendicular to MT orientation is primary, whereas ROP- and actin-induced cell expansion is secondary or minimal (Fu et al. 2002). On the basis of these observations, I propose that the interregulation between ROP signaling to actin-based polar growth and the polarity determination of cell expansion by cortical MT represents a unifying mechanism governing the polarity of cell expansion in plants, although the degree of significance for each of the two modes varies among tip growth and complex and simple diffuse growth (**Figure 5**).

Auxin: a small molecule acting as a common polarity signal? The initiation of intercalary growth in *Arabidopsis* PC is tightly regulated in time and space during leaf development, as growth starts from the tip and progressively moves along the margin and finally toward the middle of leaves/cotyledons. Auxin forms dynamic gradients that are tightly correlated with the spatiotemporal progression of the intercalary growth, suggesting that auxin may be the polarizing signal that initiates the intercalary growth of PC (T. Xu, M. Wen, Y. Fu, J. Friml, J. Chen, M. Wu, A. Jones & Z. Yang, unpublished data). Auxin has also been implicated in the control of the positioning of root hair–forming sites, which appear to depend on ROP2 localization to those sites (Fischer et al. 2006). Therefore, an auxin-ROP2 pathway may also regulate the planar polarity of root hair positioning. Auxin is implicated in the regulation of the polarity of PIN localization, which is also planar in nature (Paciorek et al. 2005). This raises an important question: Is auxin-ROP

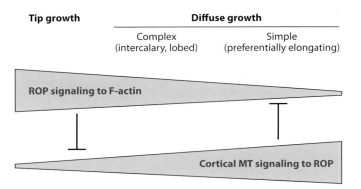

Tip growth — **Diffuse growth**

Complex (intercalary, lobed) — Simple (preferentially elongating)

ROP signaling to F-actin

Cortical MT signaling to ROP

Figure 5

A schematic model for a unifying concept of the mechanisms underlying the control of cell morphogenesis through tip growth or polarized diffuse growth. I propose that the primary mechanism for the control of cell polarity in tip growth is the tip-localized ROP (Rho-related GTPase from plants) activation of actin dynamics, which promotes targeted exocytosis, whereas microtubule (MT)-mediated lateral inhibition plays a secondary role in polarity control. In contrast, MT-dependent mechanisms play a primary role in the control of cell polarity of diffuse growth, whereas ROP activation of actin microfilaments (F-actin) plays a secondary role in polarity control. Cortical MT–mediated polarity control involves its role in aligning cellulose microfibrils and suppression of the ROP-actin pathway. The ROP-actin pathway and the cortical MT counteract one another to fine-tune cell polarity and cell shape formation.

signaling a common mechanism for cell polarity control in plants?

Given a role for auxin as a polarizing signal, an exciting question is how auxin, a diffusible small molecule, locally controls signaling to establish cell polarity. The answer may lie in polar localization of the auxin efflux carrier proteins, PINs. PIN-mediated/localized auxin efflux may lead to a localized accumulation of extracellular auxin, which in turn may locally activate ROP signaling to establish polarity. Auxin promotes PIN localization to the site of auxin accumulation in root cells (Paciorek et al. 2005). Thus, it is tempting to speculate that auxin may activate ROP2, which may promote polar localization of an auxin efflux carrier to the lobe tip to form a positive feedback loop (**Figure 3**). In this speculative model, the auxin receptor responsible for ROP2 activation would most likely be an extracellular receptor, which may directly regulate the potential ROP2 activator, SPK1, a RhoGEF whose knockout produces a PC phenotype similar to that of a *rop2/rop4* mutant (Basu et al. 2008, Fu et al. 2005, Qiu

et al. 2002). PIN-exported auxin, which can diffuse across the cell wall to the indenting region of the neighboring cells, may also activate the ROP-RIC1 pathway as a possible mechanism for coordination between lobe outgrowth and indentation formation (**Figure 3**).

Polar Localization of Proteins: The PIN-FORMED Protein Model

Endosomal recycling and sorting are critical for polar localization and repolarization of PINs (see Kleine-Vehn & Friml 2008). How a recycled PIN decides to localize to a particular domain of the PM must require a signaling mechanism that integrates the specification of the PM domain with endosomal trafficking. Indeed, the PINOID (PID) ser/thr protein kinase and its antagonist, PP2AA phosphatase, are critical for the control of PIN polarity (Benjamins et al. 2001, Christensen et al. 2000, Friml et al. 2004, Michniewicz et al. 2007). Two important questions are how these kinases and phosphatases are regulated and how they are linked to the initial signal that specifies the cell polarity for PIN localization. Both PID and PP2AA partially colocalize with PIN1 in the PM, suggesting that the signaling most likely occurs there. A likely component in this signaling pathway(s) is 3-phosphoinositide-dependent protein kinase 1 (PDK1), which interacts with, phosphorylates, and activates PID (Zegzouti et al. 2006). An analogous signaling pathway involving PDK1 activation of PKC, a ser/thr kinase related to PID, modulates polarized PM localization of the GLUT4 glucose transporter in mammalian cells (Watson et al. 2004). There are also hints that ROP signaling may regulate PIN polarization (Jaillais et al. 2007; Li et al. 2005; Xu & Scheres 2005a,b). GFP-ROP2 localization is polarized in a similar manner to PIN2-GFP, and ROP2 overexpression increases PIN2-GFP polar localization (Li et al. 2005). VPS29-mediated endosome sorting is required for PIN1 repolarization to initiate lateral root formation, and the lateral root formation defect in *vps29* is epistatic to CA-ROP2 induction of lateral root formation (Jaillais et al. 2007). Given these results, it will certainly be worthwhile to test the role of ROP signaling in PIN polarization.

Asymmetric Cell Division: The Guard Cell Model

Signaling to cell polarity formation required for asymmetric cell division in plants may be the least understood polarity system. However, a potential important breakthrough in this area is a series of recent discoveries of the signaling mechanisms regulating guard cell differentiation. The first discovery is the identification of the *TOO MANY MOUTHS* (*TMM*) gene, which encodes an extracellular leucine-rich repeat (LRR) receptor–like protein (Nadeau & Sack 2002). Loss of *TMM* function mutations causes a number of stomatal patterning phenotypes including stomata clustering, suggestive of a defect in responding to positional signals. It was later shown that a triple-knockout mutant for three closely related RLKs, ERRECTA and two ERRECTA-like genes (*ERL1* and *ERL2*), exhibits a *tmm* phenotype and is epistatic to *tmm* (Shpak et al. 2005). A recent report has identified a secreted peptide (EPF1) that genetically acts in the same pathway as TMM and the ERRECTA family (Hara et al. 2007). Interestingly, *EPF1* is only expressed in guard cell precursor cells, whereas both *TMM* and the *ERRECTA* family are expressed in their neighboring cells (Hara et al. 2007, Nadeau & Sack 2002, Shpak et al. 2005). Thus, it was proposed that the secreted EPF1 diffuses to the neighbors of the precursor cells to activate the coreceptor of TMM and the ERRECTA family proteins to regulate asymmetric cell division. Other exciting reports show that a mitogen-activated protein kinase (MAPK) cascade, composed of YODA (a MAPKKK), MKK4/MKK5, and MPK3/MPK6, has a function similar to that of TMM, ERRECTA, and EPF1 and appears to act downstream of them (Bergmann et al. 2004, Lukowitz et al. 2004, Wang et al. 2007). The constitutive activation of the MAP cascade causes an apparent defect in asymmetric cell division, turning all guard cells into PC

(Lukowitz et al. 2004, Wang et al. 2007). The absence of this cascade apparently also abolishes the asymmetric cell division of the zygote, resulting in the elimination of suspensor cell fate (Lukowitz et al. 2004, Wang et al. 2007). Therefore, this apparent positional signal–mediated pathway seems to control the polarity of cell division in *Arabidopsis*.

However, there is an alternative hypothesis that this pathway acts downstream of the polarity signaling to regulate cell fate rather than cell polarity per se. In support of the polarity hypothesis, the loss-of-function *yoda* mutant has a defect in zygote cell elongation, which is likely a defect in zygote polarity establishment (Lukowitz et al. 2004, Wang et al. 2007). Unfortunately, the lack of cell polarity markers for guard cell stem cells or zygotes makes it difficult to directly test the role of this pathway in cell polarity control. Assuming that this signaling pathway regulates the polarity of cell division, some interesting questions remain to be answered. What is the cellular signaling target: polarization of the cytoskeleton, positioning of the nucleus, or polar cell expansion? Is this or another polarity-signaling pathway linked to the control of asymmetric cell division by intrinsic transcriptional factors known to affect asymmetric cell division (Aida et al. 2004, Pillitteri & Torii 2007, Xu et al. 2006)? Do similar pathways regulate asymmetric cell division in other aspects of plant development? What is the connection between RLKs and the MAPK cascade? Given the widespread role of ROPs in cell polarity control and the interaction of RopGEFs with RLKs (see above), it is tempting to speculate that ROP may be involved in bridging this gap.

CONCLUSIONS AND FUTURE PROSPECTS

Investigators have made important breakthroughs in studies of cellular signaling and cell polarity formation, using several plant model systems. In polarized cell growth, localized and dynamic ROP GTPase activity controls polarity establishment through the regulation of the cytoskeleton and vesicular trafficking, providing a framework for addressing many important and interesting questions in cell polarity control. It is yet to be determined whether this signaling paradigm can be extended to other cell polarity systems such as zygote polarization, polar PIN localization, and asymmetric cell division. Cytoskeleton-mediated feedback loops have been implicated in the regulation of localized and dynamic ROP signaling, but it is unclear what the molecular details of the feedback loops are and how they are triggered by an initial polarizing cue. Protein kinases such as plant-specific CDPKs and the conserved PID-related protein kinase family are known to participate in polarity signaling, but it is unknown whether and how they are linked to ROP signaling. PIPs have been implicated in cell polarity regulation in plants, yet their precise role and connection to ROP signaling need to be investigated. Although vesicular trafficking mechanisms, which include processes such as exocytosis and endocytic recycling, are critical for polarity formation, how they are linked to polarity signaling mechanisms remains vague. With existing and expanding genetic tools and molecular and cytological markers combined with proteomic, biochemical, and molecular approaches, exciting insights into these outstanding questions are in sight.

SUMMARY POINTS

1. Cell polarity signaling has been studied through several model systems, including (*a*) single-cell systems such as PT and root hairs and (*b*) multicellular systems such as PC and PIN protein localization in roots.

2. As in animal cells, cortical MT are primarily involved in polarity induction, whereas the polarity-signaling targets, F-actin and associated vesicular trafficking, participate in polarity establishment and feedback-regulate polarity signaling.

3. As in all other eukaryotic cells, the plant subfamily of conserved Rho GTPases, ROP, is the central regulator of cell polarity signaling.

4. ROP is mediated by both conserved and plant-specific regulators, and it controls the dynamics and organization of both F-actin and MT through plant-specific effector proteins such as RICs.

5. In the PT single-cell system, the dynamics of the active ROP1 apical cap is essential for polarized cell growth: It modulates polarized exocytosis and is controlled by interlinking positive feedback–mediated lateral propagation and negative feedback–mediated RhoGAP-dependent global inhibition.

6. In jigsaw-puzzle-shaped PC, the complex polarity of cell expansion is controlled by ROP2 activation of localized F-actin in the lobing domain, which counteracts RIC1 activation of MT arrangement in the indenting domain.

7. Auxin may be a common polarizing signal, activating ROP signaling pathways in its control of cell polarity.

8. Polar localization of PINs is mediated by a cascade of PDK1 and PID ser/thr kinases, whereas asymmetric cell division may be controlled by an RLK-MAPK cascade signaling mechanism. Both of these kinase signaling cascades may be linked to ROP GTPase.

DISCLOSURE STATEMENT

The author is not aware of any biases that might be perceived as affecting the objectivity of this review.

ACKNOWLEDGMENTS

I apologize to those whose relevant work cannot be cited in this review owing to space limitations. I thank Chizuko Morita for her preparation of the artwork used in this review. I thank members of my laboratory for stimulating discussions that helped to formulate the conceptual framework of this review. Work in my laboratory is supported by grants from the National Institutes of Health, the National Science Foundation, and the Department of Energy.

LITERATURE CITED

Aida M, Beis D, Heidstra R, Willemsen V, Blilou I, et al. 2004. The *PLETHORA* genes mediate patterning of the *Arabidopsis* root stem cell niche. *Cell* 119:109–20

Alberts P, Rudge R, Irinopoulou T, Danglot L, Gauthier-Rouviere C, Galli T. 2006. Cdc42 and actin control polarized expression of TI-VAMP vesicles to neuronal growth cones and their fusion with the plasma membrane. *Mol. Biol. Cell* 17:1194–203

Basu R, Chang F. 2007. Shaping the actin cytoskeleton using microtubule tips. *Curr. Opin. Cell Biol.* 19:88–94

Basu R, Le J, Zakharova T, Mallery EL, Szymanski DB. 2008. A SPIKE1 signaling complex controls actin-dependent cell morphogenesis through the heteromeric WAVE and ARP2/3 complexes. *Proc. Natl. Acad. Sci. USA* 105:4044–49

Benjamins R, Quint A, Weijers D, Hooykaas P, Offringa R. 2001. The PINOID protein kinase regulates organ development in *Arabidopsis* by enhancing polar auxin transport. *Development* 128:4057–67

Bergmann DC, Lukowitz W, Somerville CR. 2004. Stomatal development and pattern controlled by a MAPKK kinase. *Science* 304:1494–97

Berken A, Thomas C, Wittinghofer A. 2005. A new family of RhoGEFs activates the ROP molecular switch in plants. *Nature* 436:1176–80

Bidlingmaier S, Snyder M. 2004. Regulation of polarized growth initiation and termination cycles by the polarisome and Cdc42 regulators. *J. Cell Biol.* 164:207–18

Bloch D, Lavy M, Efrat Y, Efroni I, Bracha-Drori K, et al. 2005. Ectopic expression of an activated RAC in *Arabidopsis* disrupts membrane cycling. *Mol. Biol. Cell* 16:1913–27

Bohme K, Li Y, Charlot F, Grierson C, Marrocco K, et al. 2004. The *Arabidopsis COW1* gene encodes a phosphatidylinositol transfer protein essential for root hair tip growth. *Plant. J.* 40:686–98

Brembu T, Winge P, Bones AM, Yang Z. 2006. A RHOse by any other name: a comparative analysis of animal and plant Rho GTPases. *Cell Res.* 16:435–45

Brennwald P, Rossi G. 2007. Spatial regulation of exocytosis and cell polarity: yeast as a model for animal cells. *FEBS Lett.* 581:2119–24

Burridge K, Wennerberg K. 2004. Rho and Rac take center stage. *Cell* 116:167–79

Campanoni P, Blatt MR. 2007. Membrane trafficking and polar growth in root hairs and pollen tubes. *J. Exp. Bot.* 58:65–74

Carol RJ, Dolan L. 2006. The role of reactive oxygen species in cell growth: lessons from root hairs. *J. Exp. Bot.* 57:1829–34

Carol RJ, Takeda S, Linstead P, Durrant MC, Kakesova H, et al. 2005. A RhoGDP dissociation inhibitor spatially regulates growth in root hair cells. *Nature* 438:1013–16

Chang F, Yan A, Zhao L-N, Wu W-H, Yang Z. 2007. A putative calcium-permeable cyclic nucleotide–gated channel, CNGC18, regulates polarized pollen tube growth. *J. Int. Plant. Biol.* 49:1261–70

Charest PG, Firtel RA. 2006. Feedback signaling controls leading-edge formation during chemotaxis. *Curr. Opin. Genet. Dev.* 16:339–47

Christensen SK, Dagenais N, Chory J, Weigel D. 2000. Regulation of auxin response by the protein kinase PINOID. *Cell* 100:469–78

Cole RA, Fowler JE. 2006. Polarized growth: maintaining focus on the tip. *Curr. Opin. Plant Biol.* 9:579–88

de Graaf BH, Cheung AY, Andreyeva T, Levasseur K, Kieliszewski M, Wu HM. 2005. Rab11 GTPase-regulated membrane trafficking is crucial for tip-focused pollen tube growth in tobacco. *Plant Cell* 17:2564–79

Dharmasiri S, Swarup R, Mockaitis K, Dharmasiri N, Singh SK, et al. 2006. AXR4 is required for localization of the auxin influx facilitator AUX1. *Science* 312:1218–20

Dhonukshe P, Aniento F, Hwang I, Robinson DG, Mravec J, et al. 2007. Clathrin-mediated constitutive endocytosis of PIN auxin efflux carriers in *Arabidopsis*. *Curr. Biol.* 17:520–27

Djakovic S, Dyachok J, Burke M, Frank MJ, Smith LG. 2006. BRICK1/HSPC300 functions with SCAR and the ARP2/3 complex to regulate epidermal cell shape in *Arabidopsis*. *Development* 133:1091–100

Dowd PE, Coursol S, Skirpan AL, Kao TH, Gilroy S. 2006. Petunia phospholipase C1 is involved in pollen tube growth. *Plant Cell* 18:1438–53

Ehrhardt DW, Shaw SL. 2006. Microtubule dynamics and organization in the plant cortical array. *Annu. Rev. Plant Biol.* 57:859–75

Engqvist-Goldstein AE, Drubin DG. 2003. Actin assembly and endocytosis: from yeast to mammals. *Annu. Rev. Cell Dev. Biol.* 19:287–332

Fischer U, Ikeda Y, Grebe M. 2007. Planar polarity of root hair positioning in *Arabidopsis*. *Biochem. Soc. Trans.* 35:149–51

Fischer U, Ikeda Y, Ljung K, Serralbo O, Singh M, et al. 2006. Vectorial information for *Arabidopsis* planar polarity is mediated by combined AUX1, EIN2, and GNOM activity. *Curr. Biol.* 16:2143–49

Foreman J, Demidchik V, Bothwell JH, Mylona P, Miedema H, et al. 2003. Reactive oxygen species produced by NADPH oxidase regulate plant cell growth. *Nature* 422:442–46

Fowler JE, Quatrano RS. 1997. Plant cell morphogenesis: plasma membrane interactions with the cytoskeleton and cell wall. *Annu. Rev. Cell Dev. Biol.* 13:697–743

France YE, Boyd C, Coleman J, Novick PJ. 2006. The polarity-establishment component Bem1p interacts with the exocyst complex through the Sec15p subunit. *J. Cell Sci.* 119:876–88

Frietsch S, Wang YF, Sladek C, Poulsen LR, Romanowsky SM, et al. 2007. A cyclic nucleotide–gated channel is essential for polarized tip growth of pollen. *Proc. Natl. Acad. Sci. USA* 104:14531–36

Friml J, Vieten A, Sauer M, Weijers D, Schwarz H, et al. 2003. Efflux-dependent auxin gradients establish the apical-basal axis of *Arabidopsis*. *Nature* 426:147–53

Friml J, Yang X, Michniewicz M, Weijers D, Quint A, et al. 2004. A PINOID-dependent binary switch in apical-basal PIN polar targeting directs auxin efflux. *Science* 306:862–65

Fu Y, Gu Y, Zheng Z, Wasteneys G, Yang Z. 2005. *Arabidopsis* interdigitating cell growth requires two antagonistic pathways with opposing action on cell morphogenesis. *Cell* 120:687–700

Fu Y, Li H, Yang Z. 2002. The ROP2 GTPase controls the formation of cortical fine F-actin and the early phase of directional cell expansion during *Arabidopsis* organogenesis. *Plant Cell* 14:777–94

Fu Y, Wu G, Yang Z. 2001. ROP GTPase-dependent dynamics of tip-localized F-actin controls tip growth in pollen tubes. *J. Cell Biol.* 152:1019–32

Geldner N, Anders N, Wolters H, Keicher J, Kornberger W, et al. 2003. The *Arabidopsis* GNOM ARF-GEF mediates endosomal recycling, auxin transport, and auxin-dependent plant growth. *Cell* 112:219–30

Goto T, Davidson L, Asashima M, Keller R. 2005. Planar cell polarity genes regulate polarized extracellular matrix deposition during frog gastrulation. *Curr. Biol.* 15:787–93

Grieneisen VA, Xu J, Maree AF, Hogeweg P, Scheres B. 2007. Auxin transport is sufficient to generate a maximum and gradient guiding root growth. *Nature* 449:1008–13

Grierson CS, Roberts K, Feldmann KA, Dolan L. 1997. The COW1 locus of *Arabidopsis* acts after RHD2, and in parallel with RHD3 and TIP1, to determine the shape, rate of elongation, and number of root hairs produced from each site of hair formation. *Plant Physiol.* 115:981–90

Gu Y, Fu Y, Dowd P, Li S, Vernoud V, et al. 2005. A Rho family GTPase controls actin dynamics and tip growth via two counteracting downstream pathways in pollen tubes. *J. Cell Biol.* 169:127–38

Gu Y, Li S, Lord EM, Yang Z. 2006. Members of a novel class of *Arabidopsis* Rho guanine nucleotide exchange factors control Rho GTPase-dependent polar growth. *Plant Cell* 18:366–81

Gu Y, Vernoud V, Fu Y, Yang Z. 2003. ROP GTPase regulation of pollen tube growth through the dynamics of tip-localized F-actin. *J. Exp. Bot.* 54:93–101

Gu Y, Wang Z, Yang Z. 2004. ROP/RAC GTPase: an old new master regulator for plant signaling. *Curr. Opin. Plant Biol.* 7:527–36

Hara K, Kajita R, Torii KU, Bergmann DC, Kakimoto T. 2007. The secretory peptide gene *EPF1* enforces the stomatal one-cell-spacing rule. *Genes Dev.* 21:1720–25

Helling D, Possart A, Cottier S, Klahre U, Kost B. 2006. Pollen tube tip growth depends on plasma membrane polarization mediated by tobacco PLC3 activity and endocytic membrane recycling. *Plant Cell* 18:3519–34

Holdaway-Clarke TL, Feijo JA, Hackett GR, Kunkel JG, Hepler PK. 1997. Pollen tube growth and the intracellular cytosolic calcium gradient oscillate in phase while extracellular calcium influx is delayed. *Plant Cell* 9:1999–2010

Hulskamp M, Misra S, Jurgens G. 1994. Genetic dissection of trichome cell development in *Arabidopsis*. *Cell* 76:555–66

Hwang J-U, Yang Z. 2006. Small GTPases and spatiotemporal regulation of pollen tube growth. In *The Pollen Tube*, ed. R Malho, pp. 95–116. Heidelberg, Ger.: Springer-Verlag

Hwang JU, Gu Y, Lee YJ, Yang Z. 2005. Oscillatory ROP GTPase activation leads the oscillatory polarized growth of pollen tubes. *Mol. Biol. Cell* 16:5385–99

Jaillais Y, Fobis-Loisy I, Miege C, Rollin C, Gaude T. 2006. AtSNX1 defines an endosome for auxin-carrier trafficking in *Arabidopsis*. *Nature* 443:106–9

Jaillais Y, Santambrogio M, Rozier F, Fobis-Loisy I, Miege C, Gaude T. 2007. The retromer protein VPS29 links cell polarity and organ initiation in plants. *Cell* 130:1057–70

Jones MA, Raymond MJ, Smirnoff N. 2006. Analysis of the root-hair morphogenesis transcriptome reveals the molecular identity of six genes with roles in root-hair development in *Arabidopsis*. *Plant J.* 45:83–100

Jones MA, Raymond MJ, Yang Z, Smirnoff N. 2007. NADPH oxidase-dependent reactive oxygen species formation required for root hair growth depends on ROP GTPase. *J. Exp. Bot.* 58:1261–70

Jones MA, Shen JJ, Fu Y, Li H, Yang Z, Grierson CS. 2002. The *Arabidopsis* ROP2 GTPase is a positive regulator of both root hair initiation and tip growth. *Plant Cell* 14:763–76

Kaothien P, Ok SH, Shuai B, Wengier D, Cotter R, et al. 2005. Kinase partner protein interacts with the LePRK1 and LePRK2 receptor kinases and plays a role in polarized pollen tube growth. *Plant J.* 42:492–503

Kim S, Dong J, Lord EM. 2004. Pollen tube guidance: the role of adhesion and chemotropic molecules. *Curr. Top. Dev. Biol.* 61:61–79

Kim S, Mollet JC, Dong J, Zhang K, Park SY, Lord EM. 2003. Chemocyanin, a small basic protein from the lily stigma, induces pollen tube chemotropism. *Proc. Natl. Acad. Sci. USA* 100:16125–30

Klahre U, Becker C, Schmitt AC, Kost B. 2006. Nt-RhoGDI2 regulates Rac/ROP signaling and polar cell growth in tobacco pollen tubes. *Plant J.* 46:1018–31

Klahre U, Kost B. 2006. Tobacco RhoGTPase ACTIVATING PROTEIN1 spatially restricts signaling of Rac/ROP to the apex of pollen tubes. *Plant Cell* 18:3033–46

Klein TJ, Mlodzik M. 2005. Planar cell polarization: An emerging model points in the right direction. *Annu. Rev. Cell Dev. Biol.* 21:155–76

Kleine-Vehn J, Dhonukshe P, Swarup R, Bennett M, Friml J. 2006. Subcellular trafficking of the *Arabidopsis* auxin influx carrier AUX1 uses a novel pathway distinct from PIN1. *Plant Cell* 18:3171–81

Kleine-Vehn J, Friml J. 2008. Polar targeting and endocytic recycling in auxin-dependent plant development. *Annu. Rev. Cell Dev. Biol.* 24:447–73

Knaus M, Pelli-Gulli MP, van Drogen F, Springer S, Jaquenoud M, Peter M. 2007. Phosphorylation of Bem2p and Bem3p may contribute to local activation of Cdc42p at bud emergence. *EMBO J.* 26:4501–13

Kost B, Lemichez E, Spielhofer P, Hong Y, Tolias K, et al. 1999. Rac homologues and compartmentalized phosphatidylinositol 4,5-bisphosphate act in a common pathway to regulate polar pollen tube growth. *J. Cell Biol.* 145:317–30

Kost B, Spielhofer P, Chua NH. 1998. A GFP-mouse talin fusion protein labels plant actin filaments in vivo and visualizes the actin cytoskeleton in growing pollen tubes. *Plant J.* 16:393–401

La Carbona S, Le Goff C, Le Goff X. 2006. Fission yeast cytoskeletons and cell polarity factors: connecting at the cortex. *Biol. Cell* 98:619–31

Lavy M, Bloch D, Hazak O, Gutman I, Poraty L, et al. 2007. A novel ROP/Rac effector links cell polarity, root-meristem maintenance, and vesicle trafficking. *Curr. Biol.* 17:947–52

Lee Y-J, Szumlanski A, Nielsen E, Yang Z. 2008. Rho-GTPase-dependent F-actin dynamics coordinates vesicle targeting and exocytosis during tip growth. *J. Cell Biol.* 181:1155–68

Leyser O. 2005. Auxin distribution and plant pattern formation: How many angels can dance on the point of PIN? *Cell* 121:819–22

Li H, Lin Y, Heath RM, Zhu MX, Yang Z. 1999. Control of pollen tube tip growth by a ROP GTPase–dependent pathway that leads to tip-localized calcium influx. *Plant Cell* 11:1731–42

Li L, Xu J, Xu ZH, Xue HW. 2005. Brassinosteroids stimulate plant tropisms through modulation of polar auxin transport in *Brassica* and *Arabidopsis*. *Plant Cell* 17:2738–53

Li S, Blanchoin L, Yang Z, Lord EM. 2003. The putative *Arabidopsis* ARP2/3 complex controls leaf cell morphogenesis. *Plant Physiol.* 132:2034–44

Lin Y, Wang Y, Zhu JK, Yang Z. 1996. Localization of a Rho GTPase implies a role in tip growth and movement of the generative cell in pollen tubes. *Plant Cell* 8:293–303

Lin Y, Yang Z. 1997. Inhibition of pollen tube elongation by microinjected anti-ROP1Ps antibodies suggests a crucial role for Rho-type GTPases in the control of tip growth. *Plant Cell* 9:1647–59

Lisboa S, Scherer GE, Quader H. 2007. Localized endocytosis in tobacco pollen tubes: visualisation and dynamics of membrane retrieval by a fluorescent phospholipid. *Plant Cell Rep.* 27:21–28

Lord EM, Russell SD. 2002. The mechanisms of pollination and fertilization in plants. *Annu. Rev. Cell Dev. Biol.* 18:81–105

Lovy-Wheeler A, Wilsen KL, Baskin TI, Hepler PK. 2005. Enhanced fixation reveals the apical cortical fringe of actin filaments as a consistent feature of the pollen tube. *Planta* 221:95–104

Lu L, Lee YR, Pan R, Maloof JN, Liu B. 2005. An internal motor kinesin is associated with the Golgi apparatus and plays a role in trichome morphogenesis in *Arabidopsis*. *Mol. Biol. Cell* 16:811–23

Lukowitz W, Roeder A, Parmenter D, Somerville C. 2004. A MAPKK kinase gene regulates extraembryonic cell fate in *Arabidopsis*. *Cell* 116:109–19

Marco E, Wedlich-Soldner R, Li R, Altschuler SJ, Wu LF. 2007. Endocytosis optimizes the dynamic localization of membrane proteins that regulate cortical polarity. *Cell* 129:411–22

Mathur J, Chua NH. 2000. Microtubule stabilization leads to growth reorientation in *Arabidopsis* trichomes. *Plant Cell* 12:465–77

McEwen DG, Peifer M. 2001. Wnt signaling: the naked truth? *Curr. Biol.* 11:R524-26

McInnis SM, Desikan R, Hancock JT, Hiscock SJ. 2006. Production of reactive oxygen species and reactive nitrogen species by angiosperm stigmas and pollen: potential signalling crosstalk? *New Phytol.* 172:221–28

Mehta SQ, Hiesinger PR, Beronja S, Zhai RG, Schulze KL, et al. 2005. Mutations in *Drosophila sec15* reveal a function in neuronal targeting for a subset of exocyst components. *Neuron* 46:219–32

Meller N, Merlot S, Guda C. 2005. CZH proteins: a new family of Rho-GEFs. *J. Cell Sci.* 118:4937–46

Michniewicz M, Zago MK, Abas L, Weijers D, Schweighofer A, et al. 2007. Antagonistic regulation of PIN phosphorylation by PP2A and PINOID directs auxin flux. *Cell* 130:1044–56

Molendijk AJ, Bischoff F, Rajendrakumar CS, Friml J, Braun M, et al. 2001. *Arabidopsis thaliana* ROP GTPases are localized to tips of root hairs and control polar growth. *EMBO J.* 20:2779–88

Monteiro D, Castanho Coelho P, Rodrigues C, Camacho L, Quader H, Malho R. 2005. Modulation of endocytosis in pollen tube growth by phosphoinositides and phospholipids. *Protoplasma* 226:31–38

Moseley JB, Goode BL. 2006. The yeast actin cytoskeleton: from cellular function to biochemical mechanism. *Microbiol. Mol. Biol. Rev.* 70:605–45

Muller S, Han S, Smith LG. 2006. Two kinesins are involved in the spatial control of cytokinesis in *Arabidopsis thaliana*. *Curr. Biol.* 16:888–94

Murphy AS, Bandyopadhyay A, Holstein SE, Peer WA. 2005. Endocytotic cycling of PM proteins. *Annu. Rev. Plant Biol.* 56:221–51

Nadeau JA, Sack FD. 2002. Control of stomatal distribution on the *Arabidopsis* leaf surface. *Science* 296:1697–700

Nibau C, Wu HM, Cheung AY. 2006. RAC/ROP GTPases: "hubs" for signal integration and diversification in plants. *Trends Plant Sci.* 11:309–15

Nishimura T, Kaibuchi K. 2007. Numb controls integrin endocytosis for directional cell migration with aPKC and PAR-3. *Dev. Cell* 13:15–28

Ovecka M, Lang I, Baluska F, Ismail A, Illes P, Lichtscheidl IK. 2005. Endocytosis and vesicle trafficking during tip growth of root hairs. *Protoplasma* 226:39–54

Paciorek T, Zazimalova E, Ruthardt N, Petrasek J, Stierhof YD, et al. 2005. Auxin inhibits endocytosis and promotes its own efflux from cells. *Nature* 435:1251–56

Palanivelu R, Brass L, Edlund AF, Preuss D. 2003. Pollen tube growth and guidance is regulated by *POP2*, an *Arabidopsis* gene that controls GABA levels. *Cell* 114:47–59

Palanivelu R, Preuss D. 2006. Distinct short-range ovule signals attract or repel *Arabidopsis thaliana* pollen tubes in vitro. *BMC Plant Biol.* 6:7

Parker JS, Cavell AC, Dolan L, Roberts K, Grierson CS. 2000. Genetic interactions during root hair morphogenesis in *Arabidopsis*. *Plant Cell* 12:1961–74

Pierson ES, Miller DD, Callaham DA, Shipley AM, Rivers BA, et al. 1994. Pollen tube growth is coupled to the extracellular calcium ion flux and the intracellular calcium gradient: effect of BAPTA-type buffers and hypertonic media. *Plant Cell* 6:1815–28

Pillitteri LJ, Torii KU. 2007. Breaking the silence: Three bHLH proteins direct cell-fate decisions during stomatal development. *Bioessays* 29:861–70

Potocky M, Jones MA, Bezvoda R, Smirnoff N, Zarsky V. 2007. Reactive oxygen species produced by NADPH oxidase are involved in pollen tube growth. *New Phytol.* 174:742–51

Preuss ML, Schmitz AJ, Thole JM, Bonner HK, Otegui MS, Nielsen E. 2006. A role for the RabA4b effector protein PI-4Kβ1 in polarized expansion of root hair cells in *Arabidopsis thaliana*. *J. Cell Biol.* 172:991–98

Preuss ML, Serna J, Falbel TG, Bednarek SY, Nielsen E. 2004. The *Arabidopsis* Rab GTPase RabA4b localizes to the tips of growing root hair cells. *Plant Cell* 16:1589–603

Roberts S, Chary SN, Drakakaki G, Li S, Yang Z, Raikhel NV, Hicks GR. 2008. Brassinosteroid receptor BRI1 and the auxin transporters PIN2 and AUX1 are sorted via specific endosomes essential for BRI1 signaling. *Proc. Natl. Acad. Sci. USA.* In press

Price MH, Roberts DM, McCartney BM, Jezuit E, Peifer M. 2006. Cytoskeletal dynamics and cell signaling during planar polarity establishment in the *Drosophila* embryonic denticle. *J. Cell Sci.* 119:403–15

Pruyne D, Bretscher A. 2000. Polarization of cell growth in yeast. *J. Cell Sci.* 113:571–85

Qiu JL, Jilk R, Marks MD, Szymanski DB. 2002. The *Arabidopsis* SPIKE1 gene is required for normal cell shape control and tissue development. *Plant Cell* 14:101–18

Richter S, Geldner N, Schrader J, Wolters H, Stierhof YD, et al. 2007. Functional diversification of closely related ARF-GEFs in protein secretion and recycling. *Nature* 448:488–92

Samaj J, Muller J, Beck M, Bohm N, Menzel D. 2006. Vesicular trafficking, cytoskeleton and signalling in root hairs and pollen tubes. *Trends Plant Sci.* 11:594–600

Schellmann S, Hulskamp M. 2005. Epidermal differentiation: trichomes in *Arabidopsis* as a model system. *Int. J. Dev. Biol.* 49:579–84

Schiefelbein JW, Somerville C. 1990. Genetic control of root hair development in *Arabidopsis thaliana*. *Plant Cell* 2:235–43

Settleman J. 2005. Intercalating *Arabidopsis* leaf cells: a jigsaw puzzle of lobes, necks, ROPs, and RICs. *Cell* 120:570–72

Shpak ED, McAbee JM, Pillitteri LJ, Torii KU. 2005. Stomatal patterning and differentiation by synergistic interactions of receptor kinases. *Science* 309:290–93

Siegrist SE, Doe CQ. 2007. Microtubule-induced cortical cell polarity. *Genes Dev.* 21:483–96

Smith LG. 2003. Cytoskeletal control of plant cell shape: getting the fine points. *Curr. Opin. Plant Biol.* 6:63–73

Smith LG, Gerttula SM, Han S, Levy J. 2001. Tangled1: a microtubule binding protein required for the spatial control of cytokinesis in maize. *J. Cell Biol.* 152:231–36

Smith LG, Oppenheimer DG. 2005. Spatial control of cell expansion by the plant cytoskeleton. *Annu. Rev. Cell Dev. Biol.* 21:271–95

Song XF, Yang CY, Liu J, Yang WC. 2006. RPA, a class II ARFGAP protein, activates ARF1 and U5 and plays a role in root hair development in *Arabidopsis*. *Plant Physiol.* 141:966–76

Steinmann T, Geldner N, Grebe M, Mangold S, Jackson CL, et al. 1999. Coordinated polar localization of auxin efflux carrier PIN1 by GNOM ARF GEF. *Science* 286:316–18

Stenzel I, Ischebeck T, Konig S, Holubowska A, Sporysz M, et al. 2008. The type B phosphatidylinositol-4-phosphate 5-kinase 3 is essential for root hair formation in *Arabidopsis thaliana*. *Plant Cell* 20:124–41

Szymanski DB. 2005. Breaking the WAVE complex: the point of *Arabidopsis* trichomes. *Curr. Opin. Plant Biol.* 8:103–12

Takeda S, Gapper C, Kaya H, Bell E, Kuchitsu K, Dolan L. 2008. Local positive feedback regulation determines cell shape in root hair cells. *Science* 319:1241–44

Teh OK, Moore I. 2007. An ARF-GEF acting at the Golgi and in selective endocytosis in polarized plant cells. *Nature* 448:493–96

Ushinsky SC, Harcus D, Ash J, Dignard D, Marcil A, et al. 2002. CDC42 is required for polarized growth in human pathogen *Candida albicans*. *Eukaryot. Cell* 1:95–104

Vernoud V, Horton AC, Yang Z, Nielsen E. 2003. Analysis of the small GTPase gene superfamily of *Arabidopsis*. *Plant Physiol.* 131:1191–208

Walker KL, Muller S, Moss D, Ehrhardt DW, Smith LG. 2007. *Arabidopsis* TANGLED identifies the division plane throughout mitosis and cytokinesis. *Curr. Biol.* 17:1827–36

Wang H, Ngwenyama N, Liu Y, Walker JC, Zhang S. 2007. Stomatal development and patterning are regulated by environmentally responsive mitogen-activated protein kinases in *Arabidopsis*. *Plant Cell* 19:63–73

Watson RT, Kanzaki M, Pessin JE. 2004. Regulated membrane trafficking of the insulin-responsive glucose transporter 4 in adipocytes. *Endocr. Rev.* 25:177–204

Wedlich-Soldner R, Wai SC, Schmidt T, Li R. 2004. Robust cell polarity is a dynamic state established by coupling transport and GTPase signaling. *J. Cell Biol.* 166:889–900

Wells CD, Fawcett JP, Traweger A, Yamanaka Y, Goudreault M, et al. 2006. A Rich1/Amot complex regulates the Cdc42 GTPase and apical polarity proteins in epithelial cells. *Cell* 125:535–48

Wen TJ, Hochholdinger F, Sauer M, Bruce W, Schnable PS. 2005. The *roothairless1* gene of maize encodes a homolog of *sec3*, which is involved in polar exocytosis. *Plant Physiol.* 138:1637–43

Wendland J, Philippsen P. 2000. Determination of cell polarity in germinated spores and hyphal tips of the filamentous ascomycete *Ashbya gossypii* requires a rhoGAP homolog. *J. Cell Sci.* 113:1611–21

Wendland J, Philippsen P. 2001. Cell polarity and hyphal morphogenesis are controlled by multiple Rho-protein modules in the filamentous ascomycete *Ashbya gossypii*. *Genetics* 157:601–10

Wisniewska J, Xu J, Seifertova D, Brewer PB, Ruzicka K, et al. 2006. Polar PIN localization directs auxin flow in plants. *Science* 312:883

Wong HL, Pinontoan R, Hayashi K, Tabata R, Yaeno T, et al. 2007. Regulation of rice NADPH oxidase by binding of Rac GTPase to its N-terminal extension. *Plant Cell* 19:4022–34

Wu G, Gu Y, Li S, Yang Z. 2001. A genome-wide analysis of *Arabidopsis* ROP-interactive CRIB motif–containing proteins that act as ROP GTPase targets. *Plant Cell* 13:2841–56

Wu G, Li H, Yang Z. 2000. *Arabidopsis* ROP GAPs are a novel family of Rho GTPase-activating proteins that require the Cdc42/Rac-interactive binding motif for ROP-specific GTPase stimulation. *Plant Physiol.* 124:1625–36

Xu J, Hofhuis H, Heidstra R, Sauer M, Friml J, Scheres B. 2006. A molecular framework for plant regeneration. *Science* 311:385–88

Xu J, Scheres B. 2005a. Cell polarity: ROPing the ends together. *Curr. Opin. Plant Biol.* 8:613–18

Xu J, Scheres B. 2005b. Dissection of *Arabidopsis* ADP-RIBOSYLATION FACTOR 1 function in epidermal cell polarity. *Plant Cell* 17:525–36

Yang G, Gao P, Zhang H, Huang S, Zheng ZL. 2007. A mutation in MRH2 kinesin enhances the root hair tip growth defect caused by constitutively activated ROP2 small GTPase in *Arabidopsis*. *PLoS ONE* 2:e1074

Yang Z. 2002. Small GTPases: versatile signaling switches in plants. *Plant Cell* 14(Suppl.):S375–88

Yang Z, Fu Y. 2007. ROP/RAC GTPase signaling. *Curr. Opin. Plant Biol.* 10:490–94

Yang Z, Watson JC. 1993. Molecular cloning and characterization of Rho, a Ras-related small GTP-binding protein from the garden pea. *Proc. Natl. Acad. Sci. USA* 90:8732–36

Yoon GM, Dowd PE, Gilroy S, McCubbin AG. 2006. Calcium-dependent protein kinase isoforms in *Petunia* have distinct functions in pollen tube growth, including regulating polarity. *Plant Cell* 18:867–78

Yu A, Rual JF, Tamai K, Harada Y, Vidal M, et al. 2007. Association of Dishevelled with the clathrin AP-2 adaptor is required for Frizzled endocytosis and planar cell polarity signaling. *Dev. Cell* 12:129–41

Zajac A, Sun X, Zhang J, Guo W. 2005. Cyclical regulation of the exocyst and cell polarity determinants for polarized cell growth. *Mol. Biol. Cell* 16:1500–12

Zegzouti H, Anthony RG, Jahchan N, Bogre L, Christensen SK. 2006. Phosphorylation and activation of PINOID by the phospholipid signaling kinase 3-phosphoinositide-dependent protein kinase 1 (PDK1) in *Arabidopsis*. *Proc. Natl. Acad. Sci. USA* 103:6404–9

Zhang J, Hill DR, Sylvester AW. 2007. Diversification of the RAB guanine triphosphatase family in dicots and monocots. *J. Int. Plant. Biol.* 49:1129–41

Zhang Y, McCormick S. 2007. A distinct mechanism regulating a pollen-specific guanine nucleotide exchange factor for the small GTPase ROP in *Arabidopsis thaliana*. *Proc. Natl. Acad. Sci. USA* 104:18830–35

Hunter to Gatherer and Back: Immunological Synapses and Kinapses as Variations on the Theme of Amoeboid Locomotion

Michael L. Dustin

Helen L. and Martin S. Kimmel Center for Biology and Medicine of the Skirball Institute of Biomolecular Medicine, New York University School of Medicine, New York, New York 10016; email: dustin@saturn.med.nyu.edu

Annu. Rev. Cell Dev. Biol. 2008. 24:577–96

First published online as a Review in Advance on July 3, 2008

The *Annual Review of Cell and Developmental Biology* is online at cellbio.annualreviews.org

This article's doi: 10.1146/annurev.cellbio.24.110707.175226

Key Words

adhesion, polarity, actin, myosin, calcium

Abstract

The immunological synapse was initially defined as a stable cell-cell junction composed of three concentric supramolecular activation clusters (SMACs) enriched in particular components: a central SMAC with clustered antigen receptors and kinases, a peripheral SMAC rich in $\beta2$ integrin adhesion molecule LFA-1, and a distal SMAC marked by a critical tyrosine phosphatase. In the past year the SMACs have each been identified with functional modules of amoeboid motility, and the stability of the immunological synapse has been revealed as a reconfiguration of the motile apparatus from an asymmetric hunting mode, a kinapse, to a symmetric gathering mode, the synapse. The genetic control of this process involves actinomyosin regulators PKCθ and WASp. Crtam is involved in postsynaptic polarity in early kinapses prior to cell division. It is unlikely that the immune system is unique in using symmetrization to stop migration without inactivating motile machinery.

Contents

Lamellipodium:
Rac-dependent
leading-edge structure
that undergoes
extension-retraction
cycles, initiates
retrograde actin flow,
and is used to sense the
environment

Lamella: adhesion
molecule–dependent
structure posterior to
the lamellipodium that
also has retrograde
actin flow coupled to
relative translocation
of the cell body and
adhesion sites

Uropod: myosin
II–rich structure at the
trailing edge of motile
cells that is important
for detaching and
recycling adhesion
molecules

INTRODUCTION

Our fledgling understanding of immunity at
the turn of the previous century emerged
from Mechnikov's microscopic observations of
amoeboid cells of a starfish as they attacked
a thorn that had broken through the ectoderm and the insight that this behavior involved
leukocytes hunting for and engulfing potential
infectious microorganisms (**http://nobelprize.
org/**). Amoeboid locomotion has subsequently
been a major focus of attention, and the mechanisms of this mode of cell movement have
been studied in diverse organisms (De Lozanne
& Spudich 1987, Jay et al. 1995, Ueda et al.
2001, Xu et al. 2003). An amoeboid cell can
be broken down into three tandem functional
modules: the lamellipodium, a sensory module; the lamella, a drive module; and the uropod, a detachment module. Only relatively
recently has it been appreciated that adaptive
immune cells such as naive T cells are relent-
less hunters that continuously travel through
the tissue parenchyma, using amoeboid locomotion, at an average speed of 10–15 μm min^{-1}.
These T cells seem to rest only when they
find antigen, which can stop migration and

lead to the formation of a stable immunological
synapse (IS) that lasts for several hours. However, recent studies suggest that this is not a
period of repose but a highly active gathering
process that involves an overall increase in cell
metabolism (Beeson et al. 1996, Frauwirth &
Thompson 2004). An overview of a simplified
antiviral response provides an initial framework
for thinking about migration in the immune response (**Figure 1**). In vivo, T cells are continually operating as highly polarized amoeboid
cells—even when they form stable junctions
with dendritic cells (DCs) for primary stimulation or with target cells to destroy virally infected cells or tumors. This review focuses on
the relationship between the hunting and gathering phases of a T cell's life and a model that
connects these phases through reorganization
of the three modules.

GO SIGNALS

One of the early breakthroughs made with intravital two-photon laser scanning microscopy
(TPSLM) in the immune system was the discovery of how T cells hunt for antigens (Miller
et al. 2002, 2003). This has been most intensively studied in mouse lymph nodes, which are
subjected to either explanted or in vivo imaging
by TPSLM. Stunning data acquisition and insightful analysis by Cahalan and colleagues led
to the model of stochastic repertoire scanning,
in which T cells in the T cell zones move rapidly
with average speeds of 10–15 μm min^{-1} and
peak speeds of more than 30 μm min^{-1}. DCs, in
contrast, move rapidly in tissues and upon initial entry into lymph nodes but then form networks that are largely sessile, with dynamic process extension and retraction (Lindquist et al.
2004, Mempel et al. 2004, Miller et al. 2004a).
The logic of this behavior becomes clear when
viewed from the perspective of DCs, which
enter the secondary lymphoid tissue with a
cargo of antigens and no means to attract T
cells with the correct receptor other than direct
membrane contact. Cahalan and colleagues estimated that each DC contacts up to 5000 T
cells h^{-1}, using stochastic repertoire scanning

with fast random T cell locomotion and dendrite extension (Miller et al. 2004a). At this rate the chances of a few DCs finding a few of the ~100–1000 T cells specific for any given antigen in a day are excellent. Thus, the basal behavior of T cells makes them the most highly migratory tissue cells in a healthy adult. Germain and colleagues have amended this model in two ways: first, by demonstrating that a reticular fiber scaffold guides T cell migration in the secondary lymphoid tissues (Bajenoff et al. 2006) and second, by showing that at least $CD8^+$ T cells (the precursors of killer T cells) are attracted to subsets of DCs via short-range chemokine gradients (Castellino et al. 2006).

A key characteristic of naive T cell motility is that it appears to be entirely guided by extrinsic signals. Resting small lymphocytes and naive T cells that are placed on a surface coated with extracellular matrix proteins or ICAM-1 or in a 3-D collagen gel are poorly motile (Bromley & Dustin 2002, Gunzer et al. 2000, Wilkinson 1987, Woolf et al. 2007). Naive T cell motility can be induced in 3-D collagen gels by including DCs (Gunzer et al. 2000). In vivo motility of naive T cells is largely inhibited by pertussis toxin, suggesting that such motility depends upon continuous signaling from the environment via $G\alpha_i$ protein–coupled receptors (Huang et al. 2007, Okada & Cyster 2007). Although loss of CCR7 induces only a small decrease in T cell speed in lymph nodes compared with pertussis toxin treatment (Huang et al. 2007, Okada & Cyster 2007, Worbs et al. 2007), this rapid motility of naive T cells can nonetheless be reconstituted in vitro with purified recombinant chemokines CCL19 or CCL21, which are ligands of CCR7, adsorbed to otherwise nonadhesive surfaces (Woolf et al. 2007). There were three interesting observations in this study. First, CCR7 signaling did not desensitize over time, even though the surface density of ligands was high (>500 molecules μm^{-2}). This is consistent with earlier reports (Kohout et al. 2004). Second, integrins were not required, and chemokine receptor interaction with high-density surface-immobilized ligand provided sufficient traction to mediate rapid

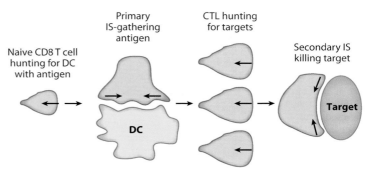

Figure 1

Schematic of an antiviral immune response depicting gross T cell morphology and actin flow patterns in hunting and gathering stages of a T cell's life. Naive T cells hunt for antigen by rapid amoeboid migration in lymphoid tissues. This involves retrograde actin flow (*arrows*). When the T cells encounter an antigen-presenting dendritic cell (DC), the interface rearranges into an immunological synapse (IS) so that retrograde actin flow is directed inward to gather antigens for sustained signaling and stop locomotion. The T cell grows in size, divides multiple times, and generates many effector cells, which use amoeboid locomotion to hunt in tissues for infected target cells. The killing of the infected target cell also involves a stable, secondary IS in which the symmetric retrograde actin flow stops the T cell, sets up a secretory domain, and retains secreted cytotoxic agents. CTL, cytotoxic T cell.

cell locomotion (Woolf et al. 2007). Consistent with this, integrin LFA-1-deficient T cells displayed normal migration speed in intact lymph nodes. The third interesting aspect is the contribution of force to integrin participation in adhesion. Alon and colleagues have emphasized the role of force in LFA-1 activation, and this force can likely be provided either by blood flow or by motile forces induced by the cytoskeleton (Alon & Dustin 2007, Shamri et al. 2005, Woolf et al. 2007). This observation led Woolf et al. (2007) to propose that there is insufficient force to activate LFA-1 during motility in the absence of shear forces encountered in the vasculature. This interpretation, however, is not consistent with the important role of LFA-1 in sensitivity to low levels of antigen, which suggests a direct role for LFA-1 in the hunting process in vivo (Bachmann et al. 1997, Schmits et al. 1996). Therefore, although integrins like LFA-1 may not be required for T cell migration in lymph nodes, they likely contribute to the formation of transient contact areas as cells pass over DC surfaces.

Immunological synapse (IS): a stable immune cell-cell junction mediated by bona fide adhesion molecules organized in a radially symmetrical lamella with a secretory domain

Two-photon laser scanning microscopy (TPLSM): a mode of imaging that allows deep tissue penetration with lower phototoxicity compared with conventional imaging

T cell antigen receptor (TCR): a receptor complex that signals by nonreceptor tyrosine kinase cascade in response to antigenic MHCp

The persistent polarization of effector T cells in vitro does not require chemokines and appears to be a cell-autonomous program that can be activated by a substrate coated with ICAM-1 or serum proteins (Dustin et al. 1997). A number of cell lines, including T cell hybridomas, also have this property. This intrinsic polarity upon chemokine signaling is also dependent on the polarity protein network that includes the PDZ (PSD-95, ZO-1, and Disk large) domain–containing protein Scribble (Ludford-Menting et al. 2005). A complex interplay of cytoskeletal regulators, membrane receptors, and PDZ domain–containing proteins along with atypical protein kinase C ζ (aPKC) are required for apical-basolateral polarity in epithelial cells. Par3, Par6, and aPKC are part of an apically localized complex, and Scribble, Disk large (Dlg), and Lethal giant larvae (Lgl) are part of a basolaterally localized complex, which together are required to form structures such as tight junctions. Scribble knockdown in T cell lines prevented polarization and migration in vitro (Ludford-Menting et al. 2005). The Par proteins interact directly with the actin regulators Cdc-42 and Rac and are implicated in the formation of actin-based projections (Etienne-Manneville & Hall 2003). Furthermore, Scribble links to an exchange factor that activates Cdc-42 and Rac (Audebert et al. 2004, Dow et al. 2007, Osmani et al. 2006). It is possible that these polarity proteins in part mediate the reciprocal inhibition between lamellipodium and uropod characteristics that allow for spontaneous polarity of leukocytes in the absence of an external chemokine gradient (Xu et al. 2003).

Amoeboid cell motility is the product of coordinated function of three actinomyosin-based modules located in the front, middle, and hind sections of the ~10–20-μm-long cells. These modules are a filamentous actin (F-actin)-rich lamellipodium (front), an integrin-rich lamella (middle), and a myosin II–rich uropod (hind) (Jacobelli et al. 2004, Ponti et al. 2004, Smith et al. 2005, Xu et al. 2003). Lamellipodia are sites of rapid actin polymerization and filament turnover linked to myosin II–

based contractility, which leads to retrograde actin flow from the lamellipodium decelerating in the lamella and condensing and dispersing in the uropod (Lin & Forscher 1995, Vallotton et al. 2004). When immobile substrate or cell-cell attachment sites are linked to this retrograde actin flow, the cell is propelled forward (Kruse et al. 2006). The polarity of the T cell likely has an important role in increasing T cell sensitivity to antigen on antigen-presenting cells (APCs) because the leading lamellipodium is 5–10-fold more sensitive than the uropod (Negulescu et al. 1996, Wei et al. 1999).

STOP SIGNALS

Conventional T cell antigen receptors (TCRs) formed from α and β subunit gene rearrangements recognize only peptides bound to membrane proteins encoded in the major histocompatibility complex (MHC). MHC class I presents proteins introduced into the cell cytoplasm during biosynthesis, whereas MHC class II molecules present proteins that remain outside the cell in the endosomal/lysosomal system. The TCR and its ligands are each only 7.5 nm long, and thus this recognition requires the T cell and APC membrane to come within ~13 nm of each other (Garboczi et al. 1996, Garcia et al. 1996, Springer 1990). The cell surface is populated by thousands of glycans per square micrometer of surface; these glycans form a corona-like glycocalyx that must be interwoven by physical pressures and adhesion molecules to allow T cell antigen recognition (Shaw & Dustin 1997). This recognition process is required for functions including signal integration, directed secretion, and asymmetric cell division, which are important at so many levels that it has been difficult to sort out which are the most fundamental functions of the IS.

Prior to direct analysis of ISs by imaging of molecular organization, a number of studies focused on the effects of antigen on migration. The steady-state behavior of T cells in the absence of antigen is rapid, random movement, and this behavior had been foreshadowed by many studies with postmitotic, in vitro–activated effector T cells and T cell hybridomas, which display spontaneous polarity, adhesion, and locomotion in vitro (Donnadieu et al. 1994, Dustin et al. 1997, Negulescu et al. 1996).

In a number of systems, antigen receptor engagement reorients T cell polarity and increases T cell adhesiveness, two changes that favor deceleration or arrest. This was first observed in terms of movement of the microtubule-organizing center (MTOC), which was used as a marker for the secretory apparatus but is also often positioned at the focus of retrograde actin flow near the uropod in a migrating cell (Dustin et al. 1997). The MTOC was observed to translocate to the center of the interface between cytotoxic T cells (CTLs) and target cells, and this behavior was later observed for natural killer cells and helper T cells (Geiger et al. 1982, Kupfer & Dennert 1984, Poenie et al. 2004). Investigators speculated that this reorientation would facilitate directed secretion. The reorientation is also a marker for a 180° reversal of retrograde actin flow, which then becomes targeted at the APC, rather than in the prior direction of migration toward or over the APC (Carpen et al. 1983, Wülfing & Davis 1998). This effect is enhanced by ligation of CD28, a receptor for CD80 and CD86, which are increased on DCs by innate activation. TCR signaling activates LFA-1 and other integrins, which increase adhesion strength and generate an adhesive lamella (Ponti et al. 2004, Smith et al. 2005). Trapping of high-affinity LFA-1, using a combination of activating LFA-1 antibodies, arrested T cell migration in vitro (Dustin et al. 1997). However, this likely is not the manner in which stop signals actually work. Similarly, inhibition of myosin IIA activity results in an inability of T cells to migrate, but this again may not be the mode of stopping induced by antigen (Morin et al. 2008). Cahalan and colleagues determined that antigen recognition by T cell hybridomas results in a Ca^{2+} increase, which is sufficient and necessary for stopping of T cell migration (Negulescu et al. 1996). Effector T cells receive a stop signal from ago-nist MHC-peptide (MHCp) complexes that is Ca^{2+} independent (Dustin et al. 1997), but stopping of naive T cells in lymph nodes appears to be Ca^{2+} dependent (Skokos et al. 2007). Although it is possible to stop T cell migration by locking LFA-1 in its high-affinity form (Dustin et al. 1997), there is no difference in the density or number of LFA-1–ICAM-1 interactions in stopped or migrating cells under more physiological conditions (Grakoui et al. 1999). I further discuss the molecular basis of stopping in the context of the IS. The mechanism by which Ca^{2+} contributes to arrest of T cell movement is unknown.

DEFINITION OF THE IMMUNOLOGICAL SYNAPSE

Kupfer and colleagues employed image deconvolution to resolve structures within the T cell–APC contact area. Applying deconvolution to the painstakingly collected and calibrated images stacks resulted in striking 3-D views of large, micrometer-scale segregated domains (Monks et al. 1998), illustrated schematically in **Figure 2**. The authors observed a micrometer-scale bull's eye with a central zone of TCR-MHCp interaction and a peripheral ring of LFA-1–ICAM-1 interaction. These structures each included hundreds or thousands of molecules and had associated signaling molecule Lck and protein kinase C-θ (PKCθ) for the TCR and talin for LFA-1. Kupfer and colleagues defined these structures as supramolecular activation clusters (SMACs) (**Figure 2**) (Monks et al. 1998). In chemistry a supramolecular assembly is a system held together by a network of noncovalent interactions, and this has proven to be an insightful definition. The central TCR-rich area is referred to as a cSMAC, and the peripheral ring of adhesion molecules is referred to as a pSMAC. Subsequent studies revealed a third zone, the distal SMAC (dSMAC), which is outside the pSMAC and enriched in the large tyrosine phosphatase CD45 (Freiberg et al. 2002). Cell-cell imaging has also led to the elucidation of a distal pole complex, an accumulation of

Major histocompatibility complex–peptide (MHCp) complexes: the form of antigen bound by the TCR

Supramolecular activation cluster (SMAC): noncovalent assemblies at the T cell–antigen-presenting cell interface that are involved in T cell activation and communication

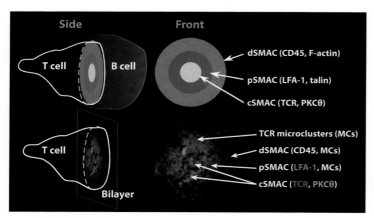

Figure 2

Supramolecular organization of the IS. Schematic side and front views of an IS as formed in the interaction of T cells with B cells or supported planar bilayers containing ICAM-1 and MHC-peptide (MHCp) complexes. The interface can be divided into three well-defined supramolecular activation clusters (SMACs). The central SMAC (cSMAC) can contain 0–50,000 TCRs; the number is linearly related to the density of MHCp complexes and also to the nature of the MHCp complex. The peripheral SMAC (pSMAC) contains thousands of LFA-1-ICAM-1 interactions, and the distal SMAC (dSMAC) is rich in F-actin and CD45. The cSMAC also accumulates PKCθ in a CD28-dependent fashion, and the pSMAC contains the integrin regulator and cytoskeletal linker talin. At the resolution achieved in most cell-cell imaging studies, these structures appear solid, but at the higher resolution attained with a supported planar bilayer system, additional nuances are revealed with the SMAC framework. Signaling in the planar bilayer system is clearly sustained by TCR microclusters (MCs), which are continuously formed in the dSMAC, translocate through the pSMAC, and join the cSMAC, where signaling is inactivated and TCR recycling or degradation is initiated. The TCR and PKCθ in the cSMAC can be resolved, and the pSMAC is revealed as a lattice with MCs in the interstitial spaces. The dSMAC is not well stained in this image but has abundant MCs. Image courtesy of S. Vardhana.

proteins opposite the synapse (Cullinan et al. 2002). These proteins include CD43, CD44, and PKCζ, an important molecule in the control of cell polarity (Cullinan et al. 2002, Ludford-Menting et al. 2005).

We acquired the first dynamic views of SMAC formation, using supported planar bilayers, a technology pioneered by McConnell et al. (1986). T cell interactions with planar bilayers containing glycosylphosphatidylinositol (GPI)-anchored ICAM-1 (ICAM-1-GPI) and CD58-GPI reconstituted some characteristics of the SMAC patterns described by Kupfer, even when the T cells were activated by other means than through the TCR (Dustin et al.

1998). We proposed the extant term immunological synapse (IS) to describe the "combination of a specialized junction, cell polarization, and positional stability" (Dustin et al. 1998). Subsequently, this definition was expanded to include directed secretion as a fourth criterion for an IS (Dustin & Colman 2002).

IMMUNOLOGICAL SYNAPSE FORMATION AND THE ACTIN CYTOSKELETON

Using the planar bilayer system, we next reconstituted the IS to enable more dynamic studies with live T cells (Grakoui et al. 1999) (**Figure 3**; see **Supplemental Video** online for an explanation of this protocol). Bilayers with ICAM-1-GPI and I-E^k-GPI (or using His-tagged soluble I-E^k and Ni^{2+} chelating lipids) were functional in the stimulation of T cell proliferation and cytokine production, indicating that any resulting interaction patterns were functionally relevant. A key characteristic of the GPI-anchored proteins in the supported planar bilayer system is that they are laterally mobile, and labeling of the proteins with fluorescent dyes allows direct visualization of receptor-ligand interactions (Dustin et al. 1996). This system, which allowed time-lapse imaging of live T cells interacting with the bilayers, revealed that the cSMAC was formed by initial symmetrical cell spreading with concurrent formation of a central zone of LFA-1 interaction with ICAM-1 and a peripheral zone of TCR interaction with MHCp, followed by centripetal transport of peripherally engaged TCRs and a concurrent process of LFA-1 and ICAM-1 exclusion from the center. The end point was remarkably similar to the patterns observed by Kupfer and colleagues (Monks et al. 1998) in cell-cell interactions, but visualizing synapse formation provided new insight into the dynamics of the process that has held up remarkably well in explaining synapse formation and establishing the importance of planar symmetry for a stable synapse. Thus, the formation of SMACs was fully reconstituted with planar bilayers containing agonist MHCp.

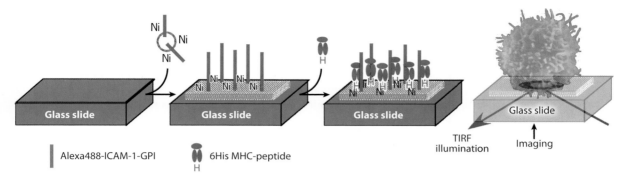

Figure 3

Formation of an IS on a planar bilayer. A clean glass substrate is incubated with a liposome suspension containing fluorescent ICAM-1 and Ni^{2+} chelating lipids. The bilayer is then incubated with His-tagged fluorescent MHCp. A T cell with the appropriate TCR to recognize the MHCp will form an IS with a bull's eye–like pattern of ICAM-1 and MHCp. Total internal reflection fluorescence (TIRF) microscopy can be used to increase the signal-to-noise ratio, particularly for molecules in the cell.

Formation of the IS is actin dependent, with an early block in contact formation with cytochalasin D or latrunculin A treatment (Grakoui et al. 1999). Signaling is initiated prior to cSMAC formation on the basis of early Ca^{2+} elevation, but the maintenance of the IS was postulated to be important for sustained signaling and full activation (Grakoui et al. 1999). Although Grakoui et al. (1999) did not use the term lamellipodium to describe the distal part of the IS in which TCR-MHCp engagement was initiated, they described the structure as a cytoskeletal protrusive mechanism to ensure close membrane contact. Contemporary studies by Wülfing & Davis (1998) also revealed an actinomyosin transport mechanism acting to deliver protein complexes to the IS, although this delivery was detected using large beads that could not enter the IS junction. However, models for actin dynamics in all the early studies between 1998 and 2005 viewed the actin-dependent lamellipodial process as a transient phase that promoted initial engagement but that then would end within a few minutes and follow the TCR into the cSMAC (Bunnell et al. 2001, Dustin & Cooper 2000, Krummel et al. 2000).

A surprising characteristic of the cSMAC was the stability of the TCR interactions with MHCp relative to the dynamics of these interactions reported from solution measurements (Grakoui et al. 1999, Lyons et al. 1996). To determine whether these interactions were stable or dynamic, we performed fluorescence recovery after photobleaching (FRAP) experiments. Contact area FRAP experiments had been used previously to demonstrate that short-lived molecular interactions turn over rapidly in contact areas as expected (Dustin 1997). In contrast, TCR-MHCp interactions in the cSMAC appeared to be stable because MHCp fluorescence did not recover after bleaching despite a large pool of fluorescence MHCp diffusing through the cSMAC area. This stability did not fit with a conventional signaling role for much of the TCR accumulated in the cSMAC because earlier studies had demonstrated that TCR signaling required continuous new TCR-MHCp interaction (Beeson et al. 1996, Valitutti et al. 1995). Another technological advance was needed to appreciate that both actin dynamics and new TCR engagement are ongoing processes in the IS.

This technological advance was the application of total internal reflection fluorescence microscopy (TIRFM). Initially developed by Axelrod (1981), TIRFM was employed by McConnell and colleagues in 1986 to study MHC-peptide associations, although not in an imaging mode (Watts et al. 1986). The method is based on illuminating the interface between a coverslip and cell-containing media with a laser beam at an acute angle such the light is reflected off the interface and fluorescence excitation can take place only through a shallow, evanescent wave that penetrates <200 nm into the cell (**Figure 3**). The development of commercial objectives with numerical aperture of 1.45 or greater enables the convenient use of TIRFM with live cells (Mattheyses & Axelrod 2006). This method decreases background and increases contrast on events at the cell–planar bilayer interface but is not helpful for cell-cell interface imaging because such interfaces tend to be more than 200 nm from the coverslip media interface. Application of TIRFM to immunological synapses formed on supported bilayers revealed that signaling is sustained by the formation of peripheral microclusters (MCs) that are continually formed at the periphery and transported to the cSMAC (Campi et al. 2005, Varma et al. 2006, Yokosuka et al. 2005). Both the formation of the MCs and the transport of the MCs are actin dependent (Campi et al. 2005, Varma et al. 2006). The peripheral MCs contain active ZAP-70, active Lck, phosphorylated LAT, and SLP-76 (Campi et al. 2005, Yokosuka et al. 2005). We utilized the classical experiment introduced by Valitutti et al. (1995), in which anti-MHCp antibodies that prevent new TCR-MHCp interactions are added to T cells that are engaged in signaling, resulting in rapid cessation of signaling. Previously, Huppa et al. (2003) had used this experiment to demonstrate that ISs dissolved over a period of minutes following the addition of MHC-peptide interactions, but TCR MCs had not been visualized in this study. When we repeated this experiment with visualization of Ca^{2+} signaling, MC dynamics, and cSMAC integrity, we determined that the decay in Ca^{2+} signaling was exactly matched by the loss of new MCs but was not correlated with decomposition of the cSMAC, which required 20–30 min (Varma et al. 2006). Thus, signaling is sustained in the IS by continual new engagement of TCRs by agonist MHCp in the periphery of the IS. Understanding how these MCs function in the context of self-MHCp ligands will be important for a more complete under-

standing of T cell sensitivity (Krogsgaard et al. 2005).

TIRFM studies of model IS contact area dynamics also revealed new aspects of cytoskeletal dynamics (Dobereiner et al. 2006, Sims et al. 2007). The periphery of the IS formed on planar bilayers undergoes contractile oscillations similar to those of the lamellipodium of spreading fibroblasts. This highly conserved and stereotypical behavior is based on cycles of actin polymerization–dependent extension and myosin II–dependent contraction to allow receptor interactions and mechanical testing of these connections (Giannone et al. 2004). These observations have led us to a model that relates the SMACs to the cortical actin modules in a migrating cell. Waterman-Storer and colleagues defined two actin-rich modules as the lamellipodium and the lamella on the basis of different roles in sensing and adhesion (Ponti et al. 2004). Sheetz and colleagues have shown that a continuous sheet of dynamic cortical actin spans the lamellipodium and lamella, whereas a second top layer of dynamic actin in the lamellipodium allows the lamellipodium to be articulated three-dimensionally rather than simply extending or retracting on a two-dimensional substrate (Giannone et al. 2007). The uropod is a relatively F-actin-depleted zone that is enriched in myosin II (Xu et al. 2003). We have proposed that the dSMAC is analogous to a lamellipodium, the pSMAC is analogous to a lamella, and the cSMAC is analogous to a uropod in a migrating cell (Sims et al. 2007) (**Figure 4**, left). This model predicts that TCR MCs are formed in the dSMAC and translocated by retrograde actin flow through the pSMAC to the cSMAC, where the TCRs are recycled or targeted to multivesicular bodies (Varma et al. 2006). Consistent with the picture that TCR MCs are pushed toward the center by retrograde actin flow, rather than transported along microtubules, the path taken by a MC to the center is flexible, and MCs can negotiate barriers to reach the cSMAC as long as they can move toward the center without needing to back up (Demond et al. 2007). Recently, we have collaborated with Vale to

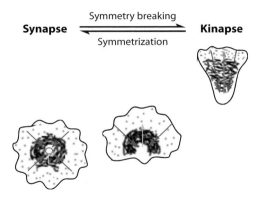

Synapse ⇌ **Kinapse**
Symmetry breaking / Symmetrization

Figure 4

Schematic of an IS breaking symmetry and becoming a kinapse. All three structures have a lamellipodium, lamella, and uropod region. The uropod of the IS is a secretory/endocytic domain in addition to a zone of integrin detachment. The gray pattern denotes LFA-1-ICAM-1 interaction, which begins as MCs in the lamellipodium/dSMAC and then consolidates into a lacy network of interaction in the lamella/pSMAC. The blue arrows indicate the direction of actin flow. In the IS the forces generated by linkage of actin flow to integrins cancel out, resulting in very slow movement (<0.1 μm min^{-1}; *red circle*). During symmetry breaking the loss of half of the pSMAC results in net forces that start to move the cell in the vector defined by the negative sum of the actin flow vectors (0.1–1 μm min^{-1}; *yellow arrow*). When the lamella fully focuses, the resulting kinapse moves the T cell rapidly (1−>15 μm min^{-1}; *green arrow*).

explicitly demonstrate centripetal actin flow by speckle microscopy with GFP actin in a model IS formed by Jurkat T cells (Kaizuka et al. 2007). This model is consistent with other data regarding F-actin dynamics in Jurkat spreading on anti-CD3 and the molecular requirements for Vav, Rac, and WAVE2 for F-actin accumulation at the synapse (Gomez et al. 2005, 2006; Nolz et al. 2006; Zeng et al. 2003).

The cSMAC is relatively free of F-actin, as shown by phalloidin staining (Sims et al. 2007), speckle microscopy data (Kaizuka et al. 2007), and recently published electron micrographs of CTL-mediated ISs (Stinchcombe et al. 2006). The cSMAC has been long been thought to contain a secretory domain into which cargo such as cytotoxic agents can be released into the confined synaptic space (Das et al. 2004,

Stinchcombe et al. 2001). The absence of F-actin in the cSMAC raised the problem of how actin-dependent receptor clusters would persist in this area to form the cSMAC. We have addressed this by demonstrating that many TCR MCs become actin independent as they grow and traverse the pSMAC (Varma et al. 2006). We did not determine if this phenomenon was due to size alone or if other modifications were needed to achieve this stability, but we did note that the smallest TCR MCs appear to disperse when actin is depolymerized, suggesting that events leading to actin independence may be determinative of whether TCRs are incorporated into the cSMAC and degraded or recycle back to the dSMAC to form new MCs.

A striking characteristic of the IS is that the cSMAC is usually free of LFA-1-ICAM-1 interactions, which accumulate in the pSMAC with the integrin-binding protein talin. Sims et al. (2007) noted that the pSMAC is continuously F-actin dependent because the pSMAC can be disbanded by latrunculin A within minutes and then reforms rapidly when latrunculin A is washed out. However, the resolution of this imaging was not adequate to detect individual LFA-1-ICAM-1 MCs. In the Jurkat study, Kaizuka et al. (2007) directly observed the formation of LFA-1 microdomains in the dSMAC and translocation to the pSMAC, where they dispersed at its inner edge. The failure of LFA-1-ICAM-1 interactions to enter into the cSMAC was attributed to two different phenomena. First, the LFA-1-ICAM-1 microdomains remain actin dependent even after they enter and traverse the pSMAC. Thus, when F-actin disperses in the cSMAC, the LFA-1 clusters lose their scaffolding and fall apart. Second, the high density of anti-CD3 bound to TCR clustered in the cSMAC of the Jurkat synapse sets up a diffusing barrier that in most cases prevents diffusion of free ICAM-1 into the cSMAC. This decrease in free ICAM-1 concentration would also contribute to loss of interactions in the cSMAC, although it is not clear if TCR-MHCp interactions would generate cSMACs with similar barrier properties. Free ICAM-1 concentration was substantially reduced in areas in which the smaller adhesion molecules CD2 and CD58 interact (Dustin et al. 1998).

PKCθ has an unexpected role in the control of pSMAC symmetry. Kupfer and colleagues identified PKCθ as the only PKC isoform that is recruited to the IS between T cells and B cell tumors (Monks et al. 1997). Subsequent studies, including our own, suggested that CD28 is required for PKCθ recruitment to the synapse (Huang et al. 2002, Sanchez-Lockhart et al. 2004, Tseng et al. 2005). The generation of PKCθ knockout mice confirmed the importance of PKCθ in T cell activation (Sun et al. 2000). Recently, we carefully analyzed the effect of PKCθ on IS stability (Sims et al. 2007). We found that PKCθ-deficient T cells form synapses on planar bilayers with agonist MHCp, ICAM-1, and CD80. In fact, the synapses are hyperstable. Through the first long-term analysis of naive T cell synapse formation, we learned that wild-type T cells form and break synapses repeatedly, with a period of approximately 20 min. Synapses were disrupted by breaking the symmetry of the pSMAC (Sims et al. 2007). Eighty percent of wild-type T cells formed, broke, and reformed synapses within 90 min. In contrast, 80% of PKCθ-deficient T cells continuously maintained synapses over the same period. This suggests that PKCθ promotes symmetry breaking. We also examined the impact of Wiscott-Aldrich syndrome protein (WASp) deficiency on synapse stability. WASp-deficient T cells formed synapses normally but then broke symmetry, started migrating, and could not reform synapses. In fact, the cells detached from the substrate by 90 min. This phenotype was converted to that of the PKCθ-deficient mouse by the application of a PKCθ inhibitor. These results suggest that WASp promotes the symmetrization of the contact area. We think that WASp is not needed for the initial round of synapse formation in vitro because the initial spreading process is often symmetric by default. However, WASp may be more important in vivo because the default behavior of naive T cells is rapid migration rather than symmetric spreading. We propose a mechanistic model wherein PKCθ promotes myosin II contraction in the pSMAC region, promoting symmetry breaking, whereas WASp suppresses pSMAC myosin II contraction, allowing symmetrization. Researchers have suggested that myosin II regulation by myosin light-chain kinase is important for lamellipodium formation and that Rho kinase–mediated myosin II activation in the uropod is important for the disengagement of integrins at the trailing edge of migrating cells. We propose that PKCθ and WASp are important for myosin II regulation in the pSMAC/lamella region. The consequence of high myosin II activity in this region is to break open and collapse the LFA-1-ICAM-1 interaction in the pSMAC to one side of the cSMAC, causing the T cell to move in that direction and converting the cSMAC into a uropod and the dSMAC into a leading lamellipodium (**Figure 4**).

FUNCTIONS OF THE IMMUNOLOGICAL SYNAPSE

The action of the IS as a brake on T cell motility to allow DCs with a particular MHCp to capture specific T cells has implications for both priming and tolerance induction. Foreign antigens and some self-antigens may appear on only a few DCs in secondary lymphoid tissues. Because naive T cells need to integrate TCR signals for hours to exit the G_0 stage of the cell cycle, the advantages of staying with one antigen-positive DC for at least long enough to advance to G_1 is clear. However, this postulate has not been clearly tested because it is difficult to prevent synapse formation in vivo.

Directed secretion is likely to be important for both CTLs and helper T cells (Geiger et al. 1982, Kupfer et al. 1986, Poo et al. 1988). There are IS-directed and -nondirected secretion pathways operative in the same cell (Huse et al. 2006). Cortical F-actin inhibits granule secretion in mast cells. Consistent with this finding, the secretory domain of the CTL IS is relatively free of F-actin (Stinchcombe et al. 2006). This relative actin depletion has also been observed in CD4 T cells during early stages of activation prior to the acquisition of effector function (Sims et al. 2007). Thus, actin depletion from the cSMAC may not be unique to effector T cells but may be a more general property of stable ISs. These studies also highlight that the cSMAC is a site of bidirectional membrane traffic; TCR internalization also is an important function (Varma et al. 2006). TCRs may also be delivered to the IS via the cSMAC, but how this relates to signal initiation in peripheral TCR clusters is not clear (Das et al. 2004). The molecular mechanisms of directed secretion have been partly elucidated through analysis of patients with defects in melanosome trafficking and cellular immunity (Clark & Griffiths 2003). The proteins Rab23a and Munc 14-3 have been implicated in this process. Cytolytic granules are essentially secretory lysosomes. The process by which the secretory lysosomes fuse to the plasma membrane may involve a priming step in which earlier endosome compartments containing Munc14-3 bridge the secretory lysosomes to the plasma membrane (Menager et al. 2007). Efficient targeting of granules to the interface requires LFA-1-ICAM-1 interactions (Anikeeva et al. 2005), perhaps because the pSMAC has an important role in orientation of the MTOC (Kuhn & Poenie 2002). The MTOC position is dependent on formins, proteins involved in the addition of actin monomers to the barbed ends of F-actin (Gomez et al. 2007). The integrity of the pSMAC is very important for the efficiency of killing. Sykulev and colleagues have demonstrated that classical CD8[+] CTLs have more stable pSMACs than do less common CD4[+] CTLs, which emerge in viral infections. The stabilization of the pSMAC with a PKCθ inhibitor, on the basis of the results of Sims et al. (2007), increased the effectiveness of CD4[+] CTLs (A.M. Beal, N. Anikeeva, R. Varma, T.O. Cameron, P.J. Norris, M.L. Dustin & Y. Sykulev, manuscript submitted). The role of the pSMAC in containing and focusing cytolytic granules may depend upon actin dynamics. Speckle microscopy studies on GFP-actin demonstrate that the cortical actin cytoskeleton in the pSMAC flows toward the

cSMAC at a velocity of 19.2 μm min^{-1} (Kaizuka et al. 2007). This centripetal flow drives TCR MCs and LFA-1-ICAM-1 interaction domains toward the cSMAC. Such continual centripetal movement of LFA-1-ICAM-1 complexes may produce a "raking" effect, which moves macromolecules in the synaptic cleft toward the center.

Asymmetric cell division is a mechanism by which stem cells can maintain their stem cell characteristics while giving rise to daughter cells that can differentiate into distinct lineages (Knoblich et al. 1999). In T cells only ~100 naive precursors recognize even dominant antigenic determinants (Hataye et al. 2006, Moon et al. 2007). When a response to one of these determinants is activated, there is a need to maintain a few copies of these original naive cells in an undifferentiated state as central memory cells while generating many more effector cells to respond to the invader (Lanzavecchia & Sallusto 2001). Asymmetric cell divisions are often organized by an external spatial cue like a basement membrane or cellular niche (Lechler & Fuchs 2005). Chan and I had speculated in 2000 that termination of the IS by mitosis could result in asymmetric cell divisions that set up the generation of central memory and differentiated effector cells (Dustin & Chan 2000). Subsequently, in vivo imaging studies suggested that T cells break ISs prior to the first cell division, raising questions about this speculation (Mempel et al. 2004, Miller et al. 2004b, Shakhar et al. 2005). Nonetheless, Chang et al. (2007) showed that lymphocytes undergo asymmetric early cell divisions in vivo in the context of bacterial infection. One of the markers that underwent asymmetric partitioning in this study was CD8, which would not be engaged during migration in the absence of contact with specific MHC-peptide ligands (Chang et al. 2007). Although Chang et al. (2007) focused on the decision between memory and effector, it is also possible that asymmetric cell division influences decisions between different CD4[+] helper T cell fates (Maldonado et al. 2004). How the polarized distribution of an IS marker would be retained in the migrating cell until the first

Kinapse: mobile cell-cell junction mediated by bona fide adhesion molecules organized in an asymmetrical lamella by immunoreceptor signaling

cell division is not clear, but polarity networks established by proteins like Scribble and Dlg are active in migrating cells (Ludford-Menting et al. 2005). There are also unanswered questions as to how the simple protein asymmetry assayed by surface fluorescence is maintained for days after the first division. Some process related to the asymmetrically distributed proteins or epigenetic changes in the nucleus during IS formation must alter gene expression to maintain this asymmetry at this level in the actively metabolizing cells. This will be an interesting area to watch in the near future.

SIGNAL INTEGRATION THROUGH MIGRATORY JUNCTIONS: KINAPSES

There are now numerous examples in which T cells have been shown to integrate signals while migrating. One of the early studies on T cell activation by APCs describes T cells searching the surface of APCs in a highly dynamic fashion (Valitutti et al. 1995). While we, Trautmann and colleagues, and Cahalan and colleagues reported stop signals associated with antigen recognition in model systems (Donnadieu et al. 1994, Dustin et al. 1997, Negulescu et al. 1996), in vitro studies with macrophages or DCs reported highly dynamic interactions in which the velocity of T cell migration was not reduced compared with baseline migration (Gunzer et al. 2000, Underhill et al. 1999). These dynamic interactions are currently thought to be driven by chemokines presented on surfaces of the APCs and tissue stroma (Asperti-Boursin et al. 2007, Okada & Cyster 2007, Stachowiak et al. 2006, Woolf et al. 2007, Worbs et al. 2007). We introduced the concept that certain chemokines could be dominant over antigen receptor stop signals in the context of transwell migration assays (Bromley et al. 2000). The dominant chemokines in this assay—ligands for CCR7 and CXCR3—are important in intranodal migration of naive T cells and memory T cells, respectively. Therefore, DCs presenting antigen to T cells need to overcome these chemokinetic signals to form an IS. In many cases these go signals are either slowly or never overcome by TCR stop signals, in which case T cells integrate signals during rapid migration. In this situation the junction between the T cell and APC is short-lived, and the T cell never polarizes toward the APC. This does not fit the two key criteria of a synapse: stability and polarity. Rather than broadening the definition of synapse, I prefer a modification of the term. The word synapse can be dissected into two components: syn-, meaning same, and -apse, indicating joining in the same place. If we change syn- to the root for movement, kin- from kinesis, we can construct the new term kinapse to define a moving cell-cell junction that allows vectoral communication but lacks the stability and vectoral secretion characteristic of ISs (**Figure 4**, right). From here on I refer to mobile T cell–APC junctions across which TCR signals are relayed as kinapses.

Naive T cells form both synapses and kinapses during antigen recognition, and T cells recognizing ligands in vitro interconvert these structures periodically under the control of PKCθ, which helps convert synapses into kinapses, and WASp, which helps converts kinapses into synapses (Sims et al. 2007). This rapid interconversion emphasizes the fundamental similarity in membrane-cytoskeletal modules between synapses and kinapses: Both are based on actin-myosin machines common to cell motility, but synapses are symmetric whereas kinapses are asymmetric, leading to net migration (**Figure 4**). Naive T cells scan APCs in the steady state, using a kinapse interface, and there is evidence that critical homeostatic signals are received through the TCR under these conditions (Fischer et al. 2007, Stefanova et al. 2002). Upon recognition of agonist ligand, naive T cells integrate signals via kinapses for a variable period from a few minutes to 8 h (Mempel et al. 2004, Shakhar et al. 2005). It is not clear what determines the duration of this period, but the number of agonist MHCp per APC and the number of APCs bearing that density of MHCp both may be important factors. It is also not clear what specifically is happening in this early phase within the T cells while they integrate these signals. Lanzavecchia and colleagues noted that antigen recognition downregulates homeostatic chemokine receptors like CCR7 (Sallusto et al. 1999), so it is possible that integration of TCR signals via kinapses allows T cells to progressively downregulate CCR7 and reduce chemokinetic signals, allowing the T cells to eventually symmetrize the synapse with APCs expressing the same level of MHCp that had been unable to arrest the T cell earlier. T cell signaling for proliferation appears to require a period of IS formation prior to proliferation under conditions of immune activation or tolerance induction (Shakhar et al. 2005). Therefore, the kinapse can serve as a preliminary interaction to the IS. The balance between synapse and kinapse modes during priming may further alter differentiation.

We have recently described a functional response of T cells that appears to take place purely via kinapses. In this system naive T cells that recognize low-potency MHCp are fully tolerized via anergy induction within three days but never alter their migration pattern from the basal serial kinapse formation (Skokos et al. 2007). The lack of arrest corresponds to a lack of Ca^{2+} elevation with these ligands both in vitro and in vivo. This led to a paradox in that conventional mechanisms of tolerance induction rely on Ca^{2+}-dependent activation of calcineurin and translocation of NFAT into the nucleus, where it activates transcription of ubiquitin ligases and disrupts synapse formation by effector T cells (Heissmeyer et al. 2004). Consistent with our Ca^{2+} data, we found that anergy induction by low-potency MHCp was resistant to inhibition by cyclosporin A, whereas anergy induction by high-potency MHCp, which does induce Ca^{2+} elevation and IS formation, was blocked by cyclosporin A (Skokos et al. 2007). Interestingly, when a farnesylation inhibitor is applied, it attenuates anergy induction by low-potency ligands, but not by the high-potency ligands. Thus, low-potency ligands induce anergy by a biochemically distinct mechanism that likely involves Ras activation. This

insight was driven by our initial observations from imaging studies. Therefore, T cells can use a pure kinapse-based signal integration process for both homeostasis and tolerance induction by weak, ubiquitous ligands. The Achilles's heel of peripheral tolerance based on such dynamic interactions is that a high proportion of APCs may be needed to present the low-potency MHCp to sustain TCR signaling in the absence of a stable synapse.

CRTAM AS A MODIFIER OF KINAPSE FUNCTION IN T CELL DIFFERENTIATION

The type I transmembrane protein Crtam (class I MHC–restricted T cell–associated molecule) links the polarity network in T cells to the control of T cell cytokine production in migrating post-IS, premitotic T cell blasts (enlarged T cells that are preparing for mitosis). In early priming, T cells may swarm around clusters of antigen-positive DCs such that this may represent a kinapse. Crtam has an intriguing property: It appears to take polarized components from the IS and maintain their polar distribution in the cell after the synapse is broken. Yeh et al. (2008) analyzed activation and cytokine production by T cells in Crtam knockout mice. Yeh et al. found that Crtam-deficient T cells were hyperproliferative but failed to make cytokines interferon-γ and interleukin-22, two proinflammatory cytokines that are not usually associated with primary T cell activation. These investigators also found that Crtam is not expressed in naive T cells but is induced in a small subset of helper T cells and in all CTLs (Yeh et al. 2008). This subset of $Crtam^+$ helper T cells is a discrete population that can make proinflammatory cytokines early in a response, which may be relevant to the differentiation of these and neighboring T cells to become stably proinflammatory effector T cells (Maldonado et al. 2004, Szabo et al. 2003). The onset of Crtam expression corresponds to the G_0-G_1 transition; expression ends after M phase in the first cell cycle. The mechanism by which Crtam modulates inflammatory

Interleukin: soluble molecules secreted by immune and tissue cells to facilitate autocrine, paracrine, and systemic communication within the context of immunity

cytokine production by a small subset of helper T cells is based on the recruitment of the polarity network protein Scribble. Scribble contains 16 NH$_2$-terminal leucine-rich repeats, 4 PDZ domains, and an uncharacterized COOH-terminal region. Scribble interacts with Crtam through one of the PDZ domains. The hyperproliferative effects of Crtam deficiency are consistent with the role of Scribble as a tumor suppressor in epithelial cells and suggest that Crtam is a major binding partner for Scribble in the control of cell growth. It is not known precisely how Scribble regulates cytokine production, but this activity also correlates with the requirement for Crtam to maintain polarity of CD3, talin, Cdc-42, and PKCζ to the same pole and CD44 to the opposite pole. The images in papers on polarity networks in T cells suggest that these proteins are not restricted to the plasma membrane and are also associated extensively with cytoplasmic membrane systems. I am intrigued by the possibility that Crtam and Scribble may sequester internalized IS components like LFA-1, TCR, CD4 (or CD8), and talin until these components can be partitioned to one of the daughter cells during asymmetric cell division (see above).

SUMMARY POINTS

1. Amoeboid locomotion is utilized by immune cells to hunt for antigen.

2. Amoeboid lymphocytes can be divided into three modules: lamellipodium, lamella, and uropod.

3. The immunological synapse is based on reorganizing the lamellipodium, lamella, and uropod into a radially symmetrical system, which stops motility and creates the central secretory domain.

4. TCR signaling without symmetrizing the lamella results in a moving kinapse-type junction.

5. PKCθ favors the conversion of synapse to kinapse, and WASp favors the conversion of kinapse to synapse.

6. Directed secretion into a secretory domain surrounded by an intact pSMAC is important for optimal T cell–mediated killing.

7. T cell polarity during early activation in the G_0-G_1-M period of the first cell cycle appears to set up an asymmetric cell division.

8. Crtam maintains stable polarity in the G_1-M period after the synapse, but before the first cell division.

FUTURE ISSUES

1. The mechanisms by which PKCθ and WASp control the synapse/kinapse transitions need to be determined. These transitions may be based on myosin II regulation in the lamella/pSMAC, but this hypothesis needs to be tested.

2. Additional genetic factors controlling synapse stability need to be identified to test more precisely the importance of the immunological synapse. These may be lymphocyte-specific factors that manipulate the core modules in ways that are unique to immune system cells.

3. The role of Crtam in asymmetric cell division should be tested. If a role is found, then what performs this function in CD4$^+$ T cells that do not express Crtam?

4. Better methods for in vivo study of immunological synapses need to be developed to evaluate the impact of tissue microenvironments on cell-cell communication.

DISCLOSURE STATEMENT

The author is not aware of any biases that might be perceived as affecting the objectivity of this review.

ACKNOWLEDGMENTS

I thank my many collaborators on these studies, including members of my lab, Y. Sykulev, and R. Vale. This writing project was supported by NIH AI44931 and AI43549.

LITERATURE CITED

Alon R, Dustin ML. 2007. Force as a facilitator of integrin conformational changes during leukocyte arrest on blood vessels and antigen-presenting cells. *Immunity* 26:17–27

Anikeeva N, Somersalo K, Sims TN, Thomas VK, Dustin ML, Sykulev Y. 2005. Distinct role of lymphocyte function-associated antigen-1 in mediating effective cytolytic activity by cytotoxic T lymphocytes. *Proc. Natl. Acad. Sci. USA* 102:6437–42

Asperti-Boursin F, Real E, Bismuth G, Trautmann A, Donnadieu E. 2007. CCR7 ligands control basal T cell motility within lymph node slices in a phosphoinositide 3-kinase-independent manner. *J. Exp. Med.* 204:1167–79

Audebert S, Navarro C, Nourry C, Chasserot-Golaz S, Lecine P, et al. 2004. Mammalian Scribble forms a tight complex with the βPIX exchange factor. *Curr. Biol.* 14:987–95

Axelrod D. 1981. Cell-substrate contacts illuminated by total internal reflection fluorescence. *J. Cell Biol.* 89:141–45

Bachmann MF, McKall-Faienza K, Schmits R, Bouchard D, Beach J, et al. 1997. Distinct roles for LFA-1 and CD28 during activation of naive T cells: adhesion versus costimulation. *Immunity* 7:549–57

Bajenoff M, Egen JG, Koo LY, Laugier JP, Brau F, et al. 2006. Stromal cell networks regulate lymphocyte entry, migration, and territoriality in lymph nodes. *Immunity* 25:989–1001

Beeson C, Rabinowitz J, Tate K, Gutgemann I, Chien YH, et al. 1996. Early biochemical signals arise from low affinity TCR-ligand reactions at the cell-cell interface. *J. Exp. Med.* 184:777–82

Bromley SK, Dustin ML. 2002. Stimulation of naive T-cell adhesion and immunological synapse formation by chemokine-dependent and -independent mechanisms. *Immunology* 106:289–98

Bromley SK, Peterson DA, Gunn MD, Dustin ML. 2000. Cutting edge: hierarchy of chemokine receptor and TCR signals regulating T cell migration and proliferation. *J. Immunol.* 165:15–19

Bunnell SC, Kapoor V, Trible RP, Zhang W, Samelson LE. 2001. Dynamic actin polymerization drives T cell receptor-induced spreading: a role for the signal transduction adaptor LAT. *Immunity* 14:315–29

Campi G, Varma R, Dustin ML. 2005. Actin and agonist MHC-peptide complex-dependent T cell receptor microclusters as scaffolds for signaling. *J. Exp. Med.* 202:1031–36

Carpen O, Virtanen I, Lehto VP, Saksela E. 1983. Polarization of NK cell cytoskeleton upon conjugation with sensitive target cells. *J. Immunol.* 131:2695–98

Castellino F, Huang AY, Altan-Bonnet G, Stoll S, Scheinecker C, Germain RN. 2006. Chemokines enhance immunity by guiding naive CD8$^+$ T cells to sites of CD4$^+$ T cell-dendritic cell interaction. *Nature* 440:890–95

Chang JT, Palanivel VR, Kinjyo I, Schambach F, Intlekofer AM, et al. 2007. Asymmetric T lymphocyte division in the initiation of adaptive immune responses. *Science* 315:1687–91

Clark R, Griffiths GM. 2003. Lytic granules, secretory lysosomes and disease. *Curr. Opin. Immunol.* 15:516–21

Cullinan P, Sperling AI, Burkhardt JK. 2002. The distal pole complex: a novel membrane domain distal to the immunological synapse. *Immunol. Rev.* 189:111–22

Das V, Nal B, Dujeancourt A, Thoulouze MI, Galli T, et al. 2004. Activation-induced polarized recycling targets T cell antigen receptors to the immunological synapse: involvement of SNARE complexes. *Immunity* 20:577–88

De Lozanne A, Spudich JA. 1987. Disruption of the *Dictyostelium* myosin heavy chain gene by homologous recombination. *Science* 236:1086–91

Demond AL, Mossman KD, Starr T, Dustin ML, Groves JT. 2008. T cell receptor microcluster transport through molecular mazes reveals mechanism of translocation. *Biophys. J.* 94:3286–92

Dobereiner HG, Dubin-Thaler BJ, Hofman JM, Xenias HS, Sims TN, et al. 2006. Lateral membrane waves constitute a universal dynamic pattern of motile cells. *Phys. Rev. Lett.* 97:038102

Donnadieu E, Bismuth G, Trautmann A. 1994. Antigen recognition by helper T cells elicits a sequence of distinct changes of their shape and intracellular calcium. *Curr. Biol.* 4:584–95

Dow LE, Kauffman JS, Caddy J, Zarbalis K, Peterson AS, et al. 2007. The tumour-suppressor Scribble dictates cell polarity during directed epithelial migration: regulation of Rho GTPase recruitment to the leading edge. *Oncogene* 26:2272–82

Dustin ML. 1997. Adhesive bond dynamics in contacts between T lymphocytes and glass-supported planar bilayers reconstituted with the immunoglobulin-related adhesion molecule CD58. *J. Biol. Chem.* 272:15782–88

Dustin ML, Bromley SK, Kan Z, Peterson DA, Unanue ER. 1997. Antigen receptor engagement delivers a stop signal to migrating T lymphocytes. *Proc. Natl. Acad. Sci. USA* 94:3909–13

Dustin ML, Chan AC. 2000. Signaling takes shape in the immune system. *Cell* 103:283–94

Dustin ML, Colman DR. 2002. Neural and immunological synaptic relations. *Science* 298:785–89

Dustin ML, Cooper JA. 2000. The immunological synapse and the actin cytoskeleton: molecular hardware for T cell signaling. *Nat. Immunol.* 1:23–29

Dustin ML, Ferguson LM, Chan PY, Springer TA, Golan DE. 1996. Visualization of CD2 interaction with LFA-3 and determination of the two-dimensional dissociation constant for adhesion receptors in a contact area. *J. Cell Biol.* 132:465–74

Dustin ML, Olszowy MW, Holdorf AD, Li J, Bromley S, et al. 1998. A novel adapter protein orchestrates receptor patterning and cytoskeletal polarity in T cell contacts. *Cell* 94:667–77

Etienne-Manneville S, Hall A. 2003. Cell polarity: Par6, aPKC and cytoskeletal crosstalk. *Curr. Opin. Cell Biol.* 15:67–72

Fischer UB, Jacovetty EL, Medeiros RB, Goudy BD, Zell T, et al. 2007. MHC class II deprivation impairs CD4 T cell motility and responsiveness to antigen-bearing dendritic cells in vivo. *Proc. Natl. Acad. Sci. USA* 104:7181–86

Frauwirth KA, Thompson CB. 2004. Regulation of T lymphocyte metabolism. *J. Immunol.* 172:4661–65

Freiberg BA, Kupfer H, Maslanik W, Delli J, Kappler J, et al. 2002. Staging and resetting T cell activation in SMACs. *Nat. Immunol.* 3:911–17

Garboczi DN, Ghosh P, Utz U, Fan QR, Biddison WE, Wiley DC. 1996. Structure of the complex between human T-cell receptor, viral peptide and HLA-A2. *Nature* 384:134–41

Garcia KC, Degano M, Stanfield RL, Brunmark A, Jackson MR, et al. 1996. An $\alpha\beta$ T cell receptor structure at 2.5 Å and its orientation in the TCR-MHC complex. *Science* 274:209–19

Geiger B, Rosen D, Berke G. 1982. Spatial relationships of microtubule-organizing centers and the contact area of cytotoxic T lymphocytes and target cells. *J. Cell Biol.* 95:137–43

Giannone G, Dubin-Thaler BJ, Dobereiner HG, Kieffer N, Bresnick AR, Sheetz MP. 2004. Periodic lamellipodial contractions correlate with rearward actin waves. *Cell* 116:431–43

Giannone G, Dubin-Thaler BJ, Rossier O, Cai Y, Chaga O, et al. 2007. Lamellipodial actin mechanically links myosin activity with adhesion-site formation. *Cell* 128:561–75

Gomez TS, Hamann MJ, McCarney S, Savoy DN, Lubking CM, et al. 2005. Dynamin 2 regulates T cell activation by controlling actin polymerization at the immunological synapse. *Nat. Immunol.* 6:261–70

Gomez TS, Kumar K, Medeiros RB, Shimizu Y, Leibson PJ, Billadeau DD. 2007. Formins regulate the actin-related protein 2/3 complex-independent polarization of the centrosome to the immunological synapse. *Immunity* 26:177–90

Gomez TS, McCarney SD, Carrizosa E, Labno CM, Comiskey EO, et al. 2006. HS1 functions as an essential actin-regulatory adaptor protein at the immune synapse. *Immunity* 24:741–52

Grakoui A, Bromley SK, Sumen C, Davis MM, Shaw AS, et al. 1999. The immunological synapse: a molecular machine controlling T cell activation. *Science* 285:221–27

Gunzer M, Schafer A, Borgmann S, Grabbe S, Zanker KS, et al. 2000. Antigen presentation in extracellular matrix: Interactions of T cells with dendritic cells are dynamic, short lived, and sequential. *Immunity* 13:323–32

Hataye J, Moon JJ, Khoruts A, Reilly C, Jenkins MK. 2006. Naive and memory CD4$^+$ T cell survival controlled by clonal abundance. *Science* 312:114–16

Heissmeyer V, Macian F, Im SH, Varma R, Feske S, et al. 2004. Calcineurin imposes T cell unresponsiveness through targeted proteolysis of signaling proteins. *Nat. Immunol.* 5:255–65

Huang J, Lo PF, Zal T, Gascoigne NR, Smith BA, et al. 2002. CD28 plays a critical role in the segregation of PKCθ within the immunologic synapse. *Proc. Natl. Acad. Sci. USA* 99:9369–73

Huang JH, Cardenas-Navia LI, Caldwell CC, Plumb TJ, Radu CG, et al. 2007. Requirements for T lympho-cyte migration in explanted lymph nodes. *J. Immunol.* 178:7747–55

Huppa JB, Gleimer M, Sumen C, Davis MM. 2003. Continuous T cell receptor signaling required for synapse maintenance and full effector potential. *Nat. Immunol.* 4:749–55

Huse M, Lillemeier BF, Kuhns MS, Chen DS, Davis MM. 2006. T cells use two directionally distinct pathways for cytokine secretion. *Nat. Immunol.* 7:247–55

Jacobelli J, Chmura SA, Buxton DB, Davis MM, Krummel MF. 2004. A single class II myosin modulates T cell motility and stopping, but not synapse formation. *Nat. Immunol.* 5:531–38

Jay PY, Pham PA, Wong SA, Elson EL. 1995. A mechanical function of myosin II in cell motility. *J. Cell Sci.* 108(Pt. 1):387–93

Kaizuka Y, Douglass AD, Varma R, Dustin ML, Vale RD. 2007. Mechanisms for segregating T cell receptor and adhesion molecules during immunological synapse formation in Jurkat T cells. *Proc. Natl. Acad. Sci. USA* 104:20296–301

Knoblich JA, Jan LY, Jan YN. 1999. Deletion analysis of the *Drosophila* Inscuteable protein reveals domains for cortical localization and asymmetric localization. *Curr. Biol.* 9:155–58

Kohout TA, Nicholas SL, Perry SJ, Reinhart G, Junger S, Struthers RS. 2004. Differential desensitization, receptor phosphorylation, βarrestin recruitment, and ERK1/2 activation by the two endogenous ligands for the CC chemokine receptor 7. *J. Biol. Chem.* 279:23214–22

Krogsgaard M, Li QJ, Sumen C, Huppa JB, Huse M, Davis MM. 2005. Agonist/endogenous peptide-MHC heterodimers drive T cell activation and sensitivity. *Nature* 434:238–43

Krummel MF, Sjaastad MD, Wulfing C, Davis MM. 2000. Differential clustering of CD4 and CD3 ζ during T cell recognition. *Science* 289:1349–52

Kruse K, Joanny JF, Julicher F, Prost J. 2006. Contractility and retrograde flow in lamellipodium motion. *Phys. Biol.* 3:130–37

Kuhn JR, Poenie M. 2002. Dynamic polarization of the microtubule cytoskeleton during CTL-mediated killing. *Immunity* 16:111–21

Kupfer A, Dennert G. 1984. Reorientation of the microtubule-organizing center and the Golgi apparatus in cloned cytotoxic lymphocytes triggered by binding to lysable target cells. *J. Immunol.* 133:2762–66

Kupfer A, Swain SL, Janeway CA Jr, Singer SJ. 1986. The specific direct interaction of helper T cells and antigen-presenting B cells. *Proc. Natl. Acad. Sci. USA* 83:6080–83

Lanzavecchia A, Sallusto F. 2001. Antigen decoding by T lymphocytes: from synapses to fate determination. *Nat. Immunol.* 2:487–92

Lechler T, Fuchs E. 2005. Asymmetric cell divisions promote stratification and differentiation of mammalian skin. *Nature* 437:275–80

Lin CH, Forscher P. 1995. Growth cone advance is inversely proportional to retrograde F-actin flow. *Neuron* 14:763–71

Lindquist RL, Shakhar G, Dudziak D, Wardemann H, Eisenreich T, et al. 2004. Visualizing dendritic cell networks in vivo. *Nat. Immunol.* 5:1243–50

Ludford-Menting MJ, Oliaro J, Sacirbegovic F, Cheah ET, Pedersen N, et al. 2005. A network of PDZ-containing proteins regulates T cell polarity and morphology during migration and immunological synapse formation. *Immunity* 22:737–48

Lyons DS, Lieberman SA, Hampl J, Boniface JJ, Chien Y, et al. 1996. A TCR binds to antagonist ligands with lower affinities and faster dissociation rates than to agonists. *Immunity* 5:53–61

Maldonado RA, Irvine DJ, Schreiber R, Glimcher LH. 2004. A role for the immunological synapse in lineage commitment of CD4 lymphocytes. *Nature* 431:527–32

Mattheyses AL, Axelrod D. 2006. Direct measurement of the evanescent field profile produced by objective-based total internal reflection fluorescence. *J. Biomed. Opt.* 11:14006

McConnell HM, Watts TH, Weis RM, Brian AA. 1986. Supported planar membranes in studies of cell-cell recognition in the immune system. *Biochim. Biophys. Acta* 864:95–106

Mempel TR, Henrickson SE, Von Andrian UH. 2004. T-cell priming by dendritic cells in lymph nodes occurs in three distinct phases. *Nature* 427:154–59

Menager MM, Menasche G, Romao M, Knapnougel P, Ho CH, et al. 2007. Secretory cytotoxic granule maturation and exocytosis require the effector protein hMunc13-4. *Nat. Immunol.* 8:257–67

Miller MJ, Hejazi AS, Wei SH, Cahalan MD, Parker I. 2004a. T cell repertoire scanning is promoted by dynamic dendritic cell behavior and random T cell motility in the lymph node. *Proc. Natl. Acad. Sci. USA* 101:998–1003

Miller MJ, Safrina O, Parker I, Cahalan MD. 2004b. Imaging the single cell dynamics of CD4$^+$ T cell activation by dendritic cells in lymph nodes. *J. Exp. Med.* 200:847–56

Miller MJ, Wei SH, Cahalan MD, Parker I. 2003. Autonomous T cell trafficking examined in vivo with intravital two-photon microscopy. *Proc. Natl. Acad. Sci. USA* 100:2604–9

Miller MJ, Wei SH, Parker I, Cahalan MD. 2002. Two-photon imaging of lymphocyte motility and antigen response in intact lymph node. *Science* 296:1869–73

Monks CR, Freiberg BA, Kupfer H, Sciaky N, Kupfer A. 1998. Three-dimensional segregation of supramolecular activation clusters in T cells. *Nature* 395:82–86

Monks CR, Kupfer H, Tamir I, Barlow A, Kupfer A. 1997. Selective modulation of protein kinase C-Θ during T-cell activation. *Nature* 385:83–86

Moon JJ, Chu HH, Pepper M, McSorley SJ, Jameson SC, et al. 2007. Naive CD4$^+$ T cell frequency varies for different epitopes and predicts repertoire diversity and response magnitude. *Immunity* 27:203–13

Morin NA, Oakes PW, Hyun YM, Lee D, Chin EY, et al. 2008. Nonmuscle myosin heavy chain IIA mediates integrin LFA-1 deadhesion during T lymphocyte migration. *J. Exp. Med.* 205:195–205

Negulescu PA, Krasieva TB, Khan A, Kerschbaum HH, Cahalan MD. 1996. Polarity of T cell shape, motility, and sensitivity to antigen. *Immunity* 4:421–30

Nolz JC, Gomez TS, Zhu P, Li S, Medeiros RB, et al. 2006. The WAVE2 complex regulates actin cytoskeletal reorganization and CRAC-mediated calcium entry during T cell activation. *Curr. Biol.* 16:24–34

Okada T, Cyster JG. 2007. CC chemokine receptor 7 contributes to Gi-dependent T cell motility in the lymph node. *J. Immunol.* 178:2973–78

Osmani N, Vitale N, Borg JP, Etienne-Manneville S. 2006. Scrib controls Cdc42 localization and activity to promote cell polarization during astrocyte migration. *Curr. Biol.* 16:2395–405

Poenie M, Kuhn J, Combs J. 2004. Real-time visualization of the cytoskeleton and effector functions in T cells. *Curr. Opin. Immunol.* 16:428–38

Ponti A, Machacek M, Gupton SL, Waterman-Storer CM, Danuser G. 2004. Two distinct actin networks drive the protrusion of migrating cells. *Science* 305:1782–86

Poo WJ, Conrad L, Janeway CA Jr. 1988. Receptor-directed focusing of lymphokine release by helper T cells. *Nature* 332:378–80

Sallusto F, Kremmer E, Palermo B, Hoy A, Ponath P, et al. 1999. Switch in chemokine receptor expression upon TCR stimulation reveals novel homing potential for recently activated T cells. *Eur. J. Immunol.* 29:2037–45

Sanchez-Lockhart M, Marin E, Graf B, Abe R, Harada Y, et al. 2004. Cutting edge: CD28-mediated transcriptional and posttranscriptional regulation of IL-2 expression are controlled through different signaling pathways. *J. Immunol.* 173:7120–24

Schmits R, Kundig TM, Baker DM, Shumaker G, Simard JJ, et al. 1996. LFA-1-deficient mice show normal CTL responses to virus but fail to reject immunogenic tumor. *J. Exp. Med.* 183:1415–26

Shakhar G, Lindquist RL, Skokos D, Dudziak D, Huang JH, et al. 2005. Stable T cell-dendritic cell interactions precede the development of both tolerance and immunity in vivo. *Nat. Immunol.* 6:707–14

Shamri R, Grabovsky V, Gauguet JM, Feigelson S, Manevich E, et al. 2005. Lymphocyte arrest requires instantaneous induction of an extended LFA-1 conformation mediated by endothelium-bound chemokines. *Nat. Immunol.* 6:497–506

Shaw AS, Dustin ML. 1997. Making the T cell receptor go the distance: a topological view of T cell activation. *Immunity* 6:361–69

Sims TN, Soos TJ, Xenias HS, Dubin-Thaler B, Hofman JM, et al. 2007. Opposing effects of PKCθ and WASp on symmetry breaking and relocation of the immunological synapse. *Cell* 129:773–85

Skokos D, Shakhar G, Varma R, Waite JC, Cameron TO, et al. 2007. Peptide-MHC potency governs dynamic interactions between T cells and dendritic cells in lymph nodes. *Nat. Immunol.* 8:835–44

Smith A, Carrasco YR, Stanley P, Kieffer N, Batista FD, Hogg N. 2005. A talin-dependent LFA-1 focal zone is formed by rapidly migrating T lymphocytes. *J. Cell Biol.* 170:141–51

Springer TA. 1990. Adhesion receptors of the immune system. *Nature* 346:425–34

Stachowiak AN, Wang Y, Huang YC, Irvine DJ. 2006. Homeostatic lymphoid chemokines synergize with adhesion ligands to trigger T and B lymphocyte chemokinesis. *J. Immunol.* 177:2340–48

Stefanova I, Dorfman JR, Germain RN. 2002. Self-recognition promotes the foreign antigen sensitivity of naive T lymphocytes. *Nature* 420:429–34

Stinchcombe JC, Bossi G, Booth S, Griffiths GM. 2001. The immunological synapse of CTL contains a secretory domain and membrane bridges. *Immunity* 15:751–61

Stinchcombe JC, Majorovits E, Bossi G, Fuller S, Griffiths GM. 2006. Centrosome polarization delivers secretory granules to the immunological synapse. *Nature* 443:462–65

Sun Z, Arendt CW, Ellmeier W, Schaeffer EM, Sunshine MJ, et al. 2000. PKC-θ is required for TCR-induced NF-κB activation in mature but not immature T lymphocytes. *Nature* 404:402–7

Szabo SJ, Sullivan BM, Peng SL, Glimcher LH. 2003. Molecular mechanisms regulating Th1 immune responses. *Annu. Rev. Immunol.* 21:713–58

Tseng SY, Liu M, Dustin ML. 2005. CD80 cytoplasmic domain controls localization of CD28, CTLA-4, and protein kinase Cθ in the immunological synapse. *J. Immunol.* 175:7829–36

Ueda M, Sako Y, Tanaka T, Devreotes P, Yanagida T. 2001. Single-molecule analysis of chemotactic signaling in *Dictyostelium* cells. *Science* 294:864–67

Underhill DM, Bassetti M, Rudensky A, Aderem A. 1999. Dynamic interactions of macrophages with T cells during antigen presentation. *J. Exp. Med.* 190:1909–14

Valitutti S, Dessing M, Aktories K, Gallati H, Lanzavecchia A. 1995. Sustained signaling leading to T cell activation results from prolonged T cell receptor occupancy. Role of T cell actin cytoskeleton. *J. Exp. Med.* 181:577–84

Vallotton P, Gupton SL, Waterman-Storer CM, Danuser G. 2004. Simultaneous mapping of filamentous actin flow and turnover in migrating cells by quantitative fluorescent speckle microscopy. *Proc. Natl. Acad. Sci. USA* 101:9660–65

Varma R, Campi G, Yokosuka T, Saito T, Dustin ML. 2006. T cell receptor-proximal signals are sustained in peripheral microclusters and terminated in the central supramolecular activation cluster. *Immunity* 25:117–27

Watts TH, Gaub HE, McConnell HM. 1986. T-cell-mediated association of peptide antigen and major histocompatibility complex protein detected by energy transfer in an evanescent wave-field. *Nature* 320:179–81

Wei X, Tromberg BJ, Cahalan MD. 1999. Mapping the sensitivity of T cells with an optical trap: polarity and minimal number of receptors for Ca^{2+} signaling. *Proc. Natl. Acad. Sci. USA* 96:8471–76

Wilkinson PC. 1987. Lymphocyte locomotion "in vitro": the role of growth activators and chemoattractants. *Biomed. Pharmacother.* 41:329–36

Woolf E, Grigorova I, Sagiv A, Grabovsky V, Feigelson SW, et al. 2007. Lymph node chemokines promote sustained T lymphocyte motility without triggering stable integrin adhesiveness in the absence of shear forces. *Nat. Immunol.* 8:1076–85

Worbs T, Mempel TR, Bolter J, von Andrian UH, Forster R. 2007. CCR7 ligands stimulate the intranodal motility of T lymphocytes in vivo. *J. Exp. Med.* 204:489–95

Wülfing C, Davis MM. 1998. A receptor/cytoskeletal movement triggered by costimulation during T cell activation. *Science* 282:2266–69

Xu J, Wang F, Van Keymeulen A, Herzmark P, Straight A, et al. 2003. Divergent signals and cytoskeletal assemblies regulate self-organizing polarity in neutrophils. *Cell* 114:201–14

Yeh Y-H, Sidhu SS, Chan AC. 2008. Regulation of a late phase of T cell polarity and effector functions by Crtam. *Cell* 132:846–59

Yokosuka T, Sakata-Sogawa K, Kobayashi W, Hiroshima M, Hashimoto-Tane A, et al. 2005. Newly generated T cell receptor microclusters initiate and sustain T cell activation by recruitment of Zap70 and SLP-76. *Nat. Immunol.* 6:1253–62

Zeng R, Cannon JL, Abraham RT, Way M, Billadeau DD, et al. 2003. SLP-76 coordinates Nck-dependent Wiskott-Aldrich syndrome protein recruitment with Vav-1/Cdc42-dependent Wiskott-Aldrich syndrome protein activation at the T cell-APC contact site. *J. Immunol.* 171:1360–68

Dscam-Mediated Cell Recognition Regulates Neural Circuit Formation

Daisuke Hattori, S. Sean Millard, Woj M. Wojtowicz, and S. Lawrence Zipursky*

Department of Biological Chemistry, Howard Hughes Medical Institute, David Geffen School of Medicine, University of California, Los Angeles, California 90095; email: lzipursky@mednet.ucla.edu

Annu. Rev. Cell Dev. Biol. 2008. 24:597–620

The *Annual Review of Cell and Developmental Biology* is online at cellbio.annualreviews.org

This article's doi:
10.1146/annurev.cellbio.24.110707.175250

1081-0706/08/1110-0597$20.00

*Authors are listed alphabetically.

Key Words

self-avoidance, tiling, immunoglobulin domain, homophilic repulsion, binding specificity

Abstract

The Dscam family of immunoglobulin cell surface proteins mediates recognition events between neurons that play an essential role in the establishment of neural circuits. The *Drosophila Dscam1* locus encodes tens of thousands of cell surface proteins via alternative splicing. These isoforms exhibit exquisite isoform-specific binding in vitro that mediates homophilic repulsion in vivo. These properties provide the molecular basis for self-avoidance, an essential developmental mechanism that allows axonal and dendritic processes to uniformly cover their synaptic fields. In a mechanistically similar fashion, homophilic repulsion mediated by *Drosophila* Dscam2 prevents processes from the same class of cells from occupying overlapping synaptic fields through a process called tiling. Genetic studies in the mouse visual system support the view that vertebrate DSCAM also promotes both self-avoidance and tiling. By contrast, DSCAM and DSCAM-L promote layer-specific targeting in the chick visual system, presumably through promoting homophilic adhesion. The fly and mouse studies underscore the importance of homophilic repulsion in regulating neural circuit assembly, whereas the chick studies suggest that DSCAM proteins may mediate a variety of different recognition events during wiring in a context-dependent fashion.

Contents

INTRODUCTION

The patterns of synaptic connections between neurons in an animal's brain are key determinants of behavior. How these patterns are established during development remains a central question in neurobiology. More than one hundred years ago, Ramón y Cajal, the father of neuroanatomy, proposed a chemical basis for wiring specificity based on his extensive studies on the structure and organization of the developing nervous system and mature nervous system in a wide variety of species. He argued that a dynamic structure at the leading edge of an extending axon, which he called the growth cone (Ramón y Cajal 1890), detects signals in the developing brain produced by targets that promote directed motility. This chemotactic model fell into disfavor during the 1930s and 1940s with the rise of behaviorally based explanations for circuit assembly; during this period, circuits were viewed as initially rather coarse, with their refinement being determined by an animal's interaction with the environment.

In the 1960s, Roger Sperry resurrected the notion that neural circuit formation relies on interactions between specific chemical signals expressed by different neurons (Sperry 1963). Working with lower-vertebrate preparations, Sperry damaged nerves, scrambled nerve fibers, and then assessed the restoration of specific behaviors and connection patterns following nerve regeneration. Sperry demonstrated that damaged neurons in the visual system restored patterns of normal connectivity. Importantly, regenerating axons frequently extended over uninnervated, inappropriate targets to form connections in the appropriate location. To explain this specificity, Sperry proposed that each neuron "must carry some kind of individual identification tags, presumably cytochemical in nature, by which they are distinguished one from another almost at the level, in many regions, of the single neuron." He proposed that these tags would provide the basis for synaptic specificity, with "each axon linking only with certain neurons to which it becomes selectively attached by specific chemical affinities." He argued that not only were "synaptic terminals . . . selectively determined" but also the "route by which growing fibers reach those terminals, is selectively determined, presumably on the basis of similar or identical chemoaffinity factors." These chemoaffinity factors are what we now call cell recognition molecules. Sperry envisioned that wiring specificity emerges through the combined action of long-range (i.e., secreted) signals, as Ramón y Cajal had proposed, and short-range "identification tags" (i.e., cell surface molecules) that mediate contact-dependent signals.

Since Sperry proposed his chemoaffinity model some 45 years ago, investigators have identified various cell surface recognition molecules that contribute to the patterning of neural circuits (Tessier-Lavigne & Goodman 1996). These recognition molecules allow neurons to exchange information, thus providing cells with patterning instructions. Recognition molecules include proteins that bind to the same protein (homophilic binding) or to different proteins (heterophilic binding) on opposing membranes (**Figure 1a**). The interactions between these recognition proteins, in turn, influence the motility of developing axons and dendrites by activating intracellular signaling pathways. In some cases, these interactions promote adhesion between cells, whereas in others they activate repulsion (**Figure 1b,c**). Both adhesion and repulsion play crucial roles in specifying neural circuitry.

Adhesive and repulsive cellular responses to recognition molecules mediate every aspect of neuronal patterning from the initial neurite outgrowth events through all the guidance and targeting steps that ultimately culminate in the formation of precise synaptic connections. Although we frequently broadly categorize interactions between proteins expressed on two opposing cell surfaces as either adhesive or repulsive, and indeed this categorization can be of considerable value, adhesive and repulsive cellular signaling events can elicit a variety of complex responses during the assembly of neural circuits (**Figure 1b**). For example, adhesive interactions between recognition molecules expressed on opposing neurites can promote growth of an axon along the surface of another axon, a process commonly called fasciculation. Binding between recognition molecules may also transiently inhibit growth as cells interact with intermediate targets or guidepost

cells, and finally, adhesive interactions can lead to the formation of specific synapses. Repulsive interactions can promote defasciculation, thereby directing neurites into divergent paths; can prevent neurites from crossing one another; and can generate boundaries between distinct populations of neurons. We wish to remind the reader that, although considerable progress has been made in identifying cell recognition molecules in the developing nervous system, in no case do we know how neurons choose to make synaptic connections with one target neurite over another.

Perhaps a useful starting point is to ask how many cell recognition molecules there are and what developmental strategies have evolved to achieve specificity in the face of the extensive cellular complexity in the developing nervous system. Sperry's notion that a vast number of specific chemical labels play a role in wiring was criticized at the time as being inconsistent with information theory. It was difficult to envision enough chemical labels being available in the developing brain to regulate the formation of neural circuits on this basis. Indeed, in the human brain there are 10^{12} neurons and some 10^{15} connections, yet, as we now know, our genomes harbor only some 3×10^4 genes. One solution envisioned by Sperry was to use the graded expression of cell surface molecules in target cells and matched graded expression of their receptors on growth cones. The discovery by Bonhoeffer and colleagues (Drescher et al. 1995) and Cheng & Flanagan (1994) that topographic maps in the vertebrate visual system are, indeed, assembled through the use of graded expression of Eph receptors and their ligands, the ephrins, validated this idea (Flanagan & Vanderhaeghen 1998). The vertebrate immune system provides an example of a different mechanism for generating large numbers of recognition proteins on the surface of cells from a limited number of genes. Here gene families, gene rearrangement, and assembly of multisubunit recognition proteins conspire to generate large families of related proteins with different recognition specificities (i.e., antibodies and T cell

Homophilic adhesion or repulsion: interactions between the same protein on two opposing membranes. This can result in adhesion or repulsion

Heterophilic binding: binding between two different proteins on opposing membranes

Fasciculation: the assembly of axons into bundles

Ephrins and Ephs: cell surface recognition molecules that bind to each other in a heterophilic fashion and that can promote repulsion and attraction

receptors). Do similar strategies for generating diverse cell recognition proteins exist in the nervous system? The discovery that alternative splicing at the *Dscam1* (*Down syndrome cell adhesion molecule*) locus in *Drosophila* generates literally tens of thousands of molecularly distinct axon guidance receptors of the immunoglob-ulin (Ig) superfamily with distinct recognition specificities raised the intriguing possibility that large diverse families of chemical labels do exist in the developing nervous system and that they contribute to the assembly of precisely interconnected neural circuits (Schmucker et al. 2000, Wojtowicz et al. 2004).

a Cell surface proteins mediate interactions between neuronal processes

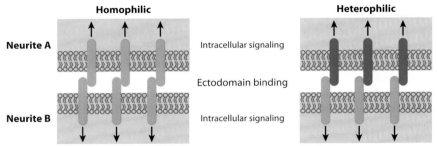

b Functional outputs of contact-dependent signaling

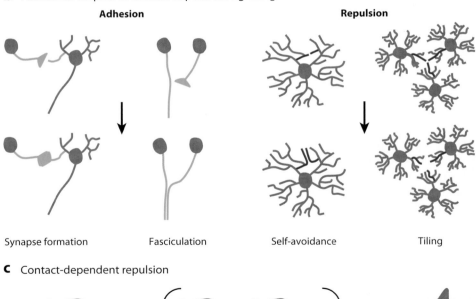

c Contact-dependent repulsion

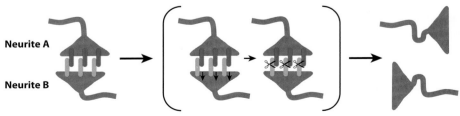

Although Sperry envisioned that chemoaffinity tags mediate interactions between the neuronal processes of neighboring cells that encounter one another as they migrate through the developing nervous system, the Sperry-like tags encoded by fly *Dscam1* function in an entirely unexpected way. As we discuss here, Dscam1 provides each cell with a unique cell surface identity (Neves et al. 2004). This allows both axonal and dendritic branches to distinguish between branches emanating from the same cell, so-called sister branches, and branches from different cells (Hughes et al. 2007, Matthews et al. 2007, Soba et al. 2007, Zhan et al. 2004, Zhu et al. 2006). Self-recognition leads to a repulsive response between processes of the same cell, a phenomenon known as self-avoidance (**Figure 1b**) (Kramer et al. 1985). Self-avoidance allows sister branches to spread out over a large target area, thus maximizing the receptive field of each neuron while simultaneously allowing multiple neurons to have overlapping fields. This process is necessary for patterning dendritic and axonal branches in both the peripheral nervous system and the central nervous system. A second *Dscam* gene in flies, *Dscam2*, promotes a related repulsive function called tiling (Millard et al. 2007). Here, processes from different cells of the same class use

Dscam2 to repel each other and to promote growth away from one another. Tiling ensures that the receptive fields of neurons from the same class do not overlap with one another, thus restricting connections to specific circuits. Recent studies in mouse demonstrate that DSCAM is selectively expressed in subclasses of cells and suggest that it uses homophilic repulsion to simultaneously promote both self-avoidance and tiling (Fuerst et al. 2008). Thus, Dscam proteins sculpt local circuitry by preventing inappropriate interactions between processes. These studies underscore the importance of homophilic repulsion in establishing neural circuitry.

Dscam1 ISOFORMS EXHIBIT EXQUISITE ISOFORM-SPECIFIC HOMOPHILIC BINDING PROPERTIES

Dscam was identified as an open reading frame from a region of human chromosome 21 implicated in Down syndrome, which arises from triploidy of all or part of this chromosome. There are four *Dscam* paralogs in *Drosophila* (*Dscam1-4*). We now refer to the founding member of the *Drosophila Dscam* family as *Dscam1* instead of *Dscam*. Diversity in *Dscam* generated through alternative splicing is unique

Sister branches: axonal or dendritic neurites extending from the same cell

Self-avoidance: mediates recognition between sister branches and promotes repulsion

Receptive field: the region of tissue innervated by a neuron

Dscam2: *Drosophila* paralog of *Dscam1*. It promotes tiling in a subset of visual system neurons in *Drosophila*

Tiling: phenomenon in which axonal or dendritic processes of different cells of the same class repel each other

---

Figure 1

(*a*) Cell surface proteins mediate interactions between neurons. Interactions between neuronal processes are mediated by direct contact between cell surface molecules. Two interacting neurites (i.e., neurite A and neurite B) are shown. Binding between the extracellular regions of cell surface proteins is translated to changes in the cytoplasmic domain and elicits intracellular signaling events (*black arrows*), which lead to directed changes in neurite motility through cytoskeletal rearrangements. Binding between identical proteins is referred to as homophilic, whereas binding between different proteins is referred to as heterophilic. (*b*) Cell surface protein interactions have different signaling outputs. Contact-dependent interactions between cell surface proteins elicit signal transduction cascades within the cytoplasm that lead to two different outputs: adhesion (also called attraction) and repulsion. (*Left*) The neurites of two different neurons expressing adhesive molecules (*green*) encounter one another. Adhesion can lead to various responses, two of which, synapse formation and fasciculation, are depicted. (*Right*) Neurites of the same neuron (*left*) or two different neurons (*right*) expressing repulsive molecules (*red*) encounter one another. Repulsion causes the neurites to grow away from one another and mediates patterning events such as self-avoidance and tiling. (*c*) Discrete steps underlying contact-dependent repulsion. First, recognition cell surface molecules expressed on opposing neurites bind to each other. Next, intracellular signaling promotes downregulation of receptor binding and activation of cytoskeletal rearrangements that promote repulsion. Two mechanisms have been described to mediate dissociation: proteolytic cleavage of the interacting molecules (shown) and endocytosis (not shown).

to *Dscam1*, and although highly conserved within arthropods, vertebrate *DSCAMs* do not exhibit this feature. Dscam1 isoforms share a common domain structure with 10 Ig domains and 6 fibronectin type III domains, a single transmembrane segment, and a C-terminal cytoplasmic domain (**Figure 2*a***) (Schmucker et al. 2000, Yamakawa et al. 1998). Three of the Ig domains are encoded by blocks of alternative exons, and as such they contain variable amino acid sequences. There are 12 alternative exons that encode the first half of Ig2, 48 alternative exons that encode the first half of Ig3, and 33 alternative exons that encode Ig7. Splicing at each of the exon blocks is independent of splicing at the other blocks; therefore, alternative splicing of the *Dscam1* gene can potentially give rise to 19,008 different ectodomains (i.e., 12 Ig2s × 48 Ig3s × 33 Ig7s). Each ectodomain is tethered to the membrane by one of two different alternative transmembrane domains to give rise to 38,016 different Dscam1 isoforms (i.e., 19,008 ectodomains × 2 transmembrane domains).

Each Dscam1 ectodomain has a distinct and exquisite binding specificity (**Figure 2*b***). A series of in vitro binding experiments (Wojtowicz et al. 2004, 2007) and cell aggregation assays (Matthews et al. 2007) established that Dscam1 isoforms engage in homophilic binding. By

---

Figure 2

(*a*) *Drosophila Dscam1* encodes a vast repertoire of cell surface recognition proteins. The *Drosophila Dscam1* gene encodes a large family of single-pass transmembrane proteins of the immunoglobulin (Ig) superfamily. *Dscam1* contains four blocks of alternative exons that encode 12 different variants for the N-terminal half of Ig2 (*red*), 48 different variants for the N-terminal half of Ig3 (*blue*), 33 different variants for Ig7 (*green*), and two different variants for the transmembrane domain (TM) (*yellow*). Splicing leads to the incorporation of one alternative exon from each block, and as such, *Dscam1* encodes 19,008 (i.e., 12 × 48 × 33) different ectodomains linked to one of two different transmembrane domains. (*b*) Dscam1 proteins exhibit isoform-specific homophilic binding. Each isoform binds to itself but rarely, if at all, to other isoforms. The three variable Ig domains mediate homophilic binding specificity. Variants of each domain engage in self-binding but do not bind to other variants (with rare exceptions). Therefore, homophilic binding occurs between identical isoforms that match at all three variable Ig domains. Isoform pairs that contain only two matches and differ at the third variable domain do not bind to one another. The quaternary structure of the first four Ig domains constrains the Ig2 and Ig3 domains, literally tethering them to one another. As such, if opposing Ig2 domains do not match, Ig3 self-binding is sterically inhibited, even if the Ig3 domains match, and vice versa. Additional intramolecular interactions between constant domains in the linker region between Ig3 and Ig7 are formed when the three variable domains match; such interactions play a crucial role in stabilizing the homophilic dimer (see panel *d*). An asterisk indicates that Ig2 difference is shown. (*c*) Electrostatic and shape complementarity underlies self-binding of each variant. Complementarity is illustrated by the Ig2 interface as an example. The Ig2 self-binding interface occurs between identical segments in opposing Ig2 domains. These segments are oriented in an antiparallel fashion. The interface comprises a symmetry center (SC) residue and flanking left and right networks. The interface segments of two different Ig2 variants (i.e., A and B) are shown in red and pink, respectively. Each self-binding interface exhibits electrostatic and shape complementarity at the SC and the left and right networks (complementarity is illustrated by the *yellow boxes*). The heterophilic interface formed between these two Ig2 variants does not exhibit complementarity at the SC, the left network (note the three negatively charged residues), or the right network (note the three positively charged residues), and thus these different Ig2 variants do not bind to one another. (*d*) A conformational change occurs upon homophilic binding. (*Right*) The Dscam1$_{1-8}$ crystal structure reveals a dimer of two S-shaped monomers with direct contacts between opposing Ig2, Ig3, and Ig7 variable domains. Electron micrographs of Dscam1$_{1-8}$ demonstrated that, whereas the first four Ig domains form a compact horseshoe structure, the remainder of the domains are highly flexible. (*Left*) These differences in structure suggest that the bottom half of the S shape observed in the crystal structure forms upon homophilic binding as opposing Ig2, Ig3, and Ig7 domains interact. Stabilizing intramolecular contacts are formed between regions within constant domains Ig5 and Ig6. This large conformational change that occurs within the Dscam ectodomain upon homophilic binding may provide a molecular mechanism for transducing the signal of homophilic binding to the cytoplasmic domain, where subsequent signaling events occur.

contrast, no heterophilic binding was observed between isoforms that differ at all three variable Ig domains. To assess which of the three variable domains contributes to this binding specificity of Dscam1 isoforms, three pairs of isoforms were tested for binding: (*a*) a pair containing different Ig2 variants but the same Ig3 and Ig7 variants, (*b*) a pair containing different Ig3 variants but the same Ig2 and Ig7, and (*c*) a pair containing different Ig7 variants but the same Ig2 and Ig3 (Wojtowicz et al. 2004). Although each isoform bound homophilically to itself, no binding was observed between any of the three pairs of isoforms differing at

a Alternative splicing of *Dscam1* can give rise to 38,016 cell surface proteins

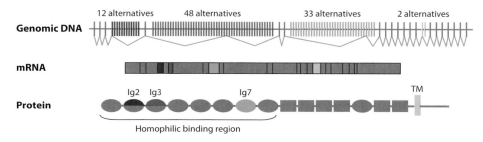

b Dscam1 proteins exhibit isoform-specific homophilic binding

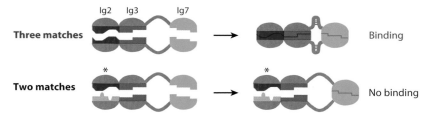

c Variants of each domain exhibit electrostatic and shape self-complementarity

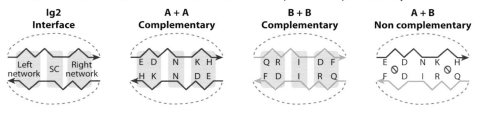

d Conformational change occurs upon homophilic binding

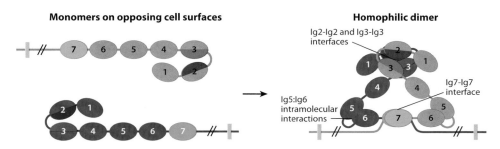

ELISA (Enzyme-Linked ImmunoSorbent Assay): measures binding between proteins or other molecules

only a single variable Ig domain (Wojtowicz et al. 2004). These studies demonstrated that all three variable domains contribute to Dscam1 binding specificity. On the basis of these studies, we proposed that each variable domain binds to an identical domain in an opposing molecule—i.e., Ig2 binds to Ig2, Ig3 binds to Ig3, and Ig7 binds to Ig7 (**Figure 2b**). In this way, isoform-specific homophilic binding arises from matching of the three self-binding variable domains between molecules expressed on opposing cell surfaces.

If Dscam1 homophilic binding is indeed mediated by matching of three, self-binding domains, then whether or not all 19,008 isoforms exhibit isoform-specific homophilic binding depends upon whether each of the 12 Ig2 variants, 48 Ig3 variants, and 33 Ig7 variants exhibits specific self-binding. To analyze the binding properties of these variable domains, a high-throughput ELISA-based binding assay was developed (Wojtowicz et al. 2007). The variants of each variable domain within an otherwise common ectodomain were tested for binding in a grid (i.e., 12×12 for Ig2, 47×47 for Ig3, and 33×33 for Ig7). The grids demonstrated that each variable domain binds to itself (with the exception of Ig7.33) but weakly, if at all, to other variants. As each variable domain preferentially binds to itself, each isoform comprising three self-binding variable domains preferentially binds to itself.

Matching of all three variable domain pairs is required for isoform binding, and thus isoforms identical at two domain pairs but differing at the third domain pair do not bind to one another. Rare exceptions to this rule occur when the differing domain pair exhibits high amino acid sequence identity. Although heterophilic binding is observed in these rare cases, heterophilic binding is always weaker than the homophilic binding of each isoform to itself. On the basis of the self-binding properties of each Ig2, Ig3, and Ig7 variant, the *Dscam1* gene is proposed to give rise to 18,048 proteins that engage in isoform-specific homophilic binding (i.e., 12 Ig2s × 47 Ig3s × 32 Ig7s = 18,048) (Wojtowicz et al. 2007).

THE STRUCTURAL BASIS FOR Dscam1 HOMOPHILIC RECOGNITION

Crystal structures of the Dscam1 ectodomain have confirmed the modular model for Dscam1 isoform–specific homophilic binding (**Figure 2d**). Meijers et al. (2007) described the structure of the N-terminal four Ig domains ($Dscam1_{1-4}$) for two isoforms, and Sawaya et al. (2008) described the structure of the N-terminal eight Ig domains ($Dscam1_{1-8}$) for one isoform. The $Dscam1_{1-8}$ structure was solved, in part, by molecular replacement through the use of the $Dscam1_{1-4}$ structure. In both $Dscam1_{1-4}$ structures and the $Dscam1_{1-8}$ structure, the molecules associate as dimers with direct contacts between opposing variable domains. Indeed, greater than 80% of the surface area buried by the $Dscam1_{1-8}$ dimer is derived from variable residues. The eight-domain structure comprises a region sufficient for homophilic binding (Wojtowicz et al. 2004), and extensive agreement between the structure and biochemical experiments (Meijers et al. 2007, Wojtowicz et al. 2007) strongly suggests that the eight-domain structure represents the structure formed upon homophilic binding in vivo.

Modular Ig2-Ig2, Ig3-Ig3, and Ig7-Ig7 interactions are observed in the $Dscam_{1-8}$ homophilic dimer (Sawaya et al. 2008). Each of the three variable domains binds to its identical counterpart in an antiparallel fashion, giving rise to twofold symmetric interfaces. Self-binding of Ig2 occurs via an eight-residue peptide along the first strand in the Ig fold (Meijers et al. 2007, Sawaya et al. 2008). Similarly, self-binding of Ig3 occurs via a transition segment along the first strand (Meijers et al. 2007, Sawaya et al. 2008). In contrast to the Ig2-Ig2 and Ig3-Ig3 interfaces, which occur along a single strand located at the edge of the Ig fold, the Ig7 self-binding interface comprises an entire face of the Ig fold involving multiple strands (Wojtowicz et al. 2007, Sawaya et al. 2008). Extensive biochemical studies demonstrated that these self-binding interface regions observed in the crystal structures can be generalized to most, if not all, Ig2, Ig3, and Ig7 variants (Wojtowicz et al. 2007). Interface residues were swapped between Ig2 domains and shown to be sufficient to confer the binding specificity of Ig2 variants. Similar experiments were conducted for Ig3 and Ig7. The crystal structures and additional modeling studies of the Ig2, Ig3, and Ig7 interface regions demonstrate that each self-binding variable domain pair fits snugly together (**Figure 2c**). Self-binding of each variable domain is mediated by exquisite electrostatic and shape complementarity. This complementarity does not exist between different alternatives of each variable domain, thus preventing binding between them. These studies demonstrate that variants of each domain have evolved a unique self-complementary interface that is incompatible with the interfaces of other variants (Sawaya et al. 2008).

In the crystal structure, $Dscam1_{1-8}$ monomers fold into an S shape, which positions the three variable domains on one side of the molecule poised for self-binding interactions with their counterparts in the opposing molecule (**Figure 2d**) (Sawaya et al. 2008). These interactions give rise to a double-S homophilic dimer formed by two symmetrically paired S-shaped monomers. The overall S shape is composed of two halves. Ig1–Ig4 fold into a compact horseshoe structure in the top half of the S curve, similar to the Ig1–Ig4 structures of other Ig superfamily cell surface adhesion molecules, including hemolin (Su et al. 1998) and axonin-1/TAG-1 (transiently expressed axonal surface glycoprotein-1) (Freigang et al. 2000). The horseshoe fold is accommodated by a long linker region between Ig2 and Ig3, which allows a sharp bend in the backbone, and extensive intramolecular interactions between Ig1:Ig4 and Ig2:Ig3. The bottom turn of the S is formed by a long linker region between Ig5 and Ig6, which similarly adopts a sharp bend and allows Ig5:Ig6 interactions.

Previous biochemical studies demonstrated that isoforms sharing identity at two variable domains and differing by only a single inter-face residue at the third variable domain do not bind to one another. The $Dscam1_{1-8}$ structure illuminates how a small number of residue differences can have such a dramatic effect on the overall binding properties of isoforms. For Ig7, residue differences change the interface slightly, but like perfectly crafted puzzle pieces, a small change in one piece prevents it from fitting with its partner. Although Ig2 and Ig3 engage in modular self-binding with their counterparts, the horseshoe structure constrains Ig2 and Ig3 within the monomer such that the Ig2-Ig2 and Ig3-Ig3 contacts form one composite interface. Therefore, if one-half of the composite Ig2-Ig3 interface does not fit with its counterpart, then the other half cannot fit—i.e., small differences between opposing Ig2 domains lead to the loss of both the Ig2-Ig2 and the Ig3-Ig3 contacts. The homophilic dimer buries 4500 Å^2 of surface area, 1300 Å^2 of which is contributed by the Ig7-Ig7 interface and 1659 Å^2 of which is contributed by the combined Ig2-Ig2 and Ig3-Ig3 interfaces. As such, small differences between variants, which result in loss of an entire variable domain interface, lead to loss of binding. These findings illuminate the molecular basis for the extraordinary all-or-none homophilic binding properties of Dscam1 isoforms.

Comparison of electron micrographs of single $Dscam1_{1-8}$ molecules (Meijers et al. 2007) and $Dscam1_{1-8}$ monomers within the dimer in the crystal structure revealed a marked difference in shape. Negative-stained images of single $Dscam1_{1-8}$ molecules revealed that the four N-terminal domains form a rigid horseshoe structure consistent with the crystal structure. By contrast, the rest of the molecule (i.e., Ig5–Ig8) adopts a large range of different shapes, suggesting that in the absence of homophilic binding this region is relatively unstructured. This comparison suggests that the C-terminal half of the structure undergoes a marked conformational change upon formation of the homophilic dimer.

On the basis of these structures, we have proposed the following model for Dscam1 binding in vivo (**Figure 2d**). In the absence of homophilic binding, Ig1–Ig4 exhibit a stable horseshoe structure at the end of a flexible trunk comprising the remaining Ig and fibronectin type III domains. Self-binding of the three variable domain pairs between isoforms expressed on opposing cells induces a conformational change, leading to formation of the sharp bend between Ig5 and Ig6 and formation of the symmetric double-S structure. This double-S shape is formed only when all three pairs of variable domains match. The sharp bend between Ig5 and Ig6 allows intramolecular interactions to form between these constant domains, which stabilize the double-S homophilic dimer structure. This large conformational change in the ectodomain may provide a mechanism for transducing the signal of homophilic binding to the cytoplasmic domain, thereby triggering intracellular signaling, which leads to changes in the motility of axonal and dendritic processes.

Together these structural and biochemical studies demonstrate that the *Dscam1* gene gives rise to tens of thousands of isoform-specific homophilic binding proteins through the

a Dscam1 mediates self-avoidance in MB axons

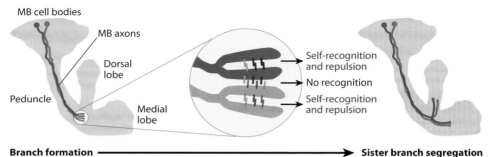

b The morphology of MB neurons of different genotypes

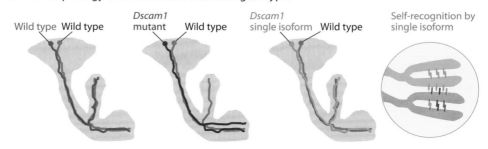

c Dscam1 mediates self-avoidance in da neurons

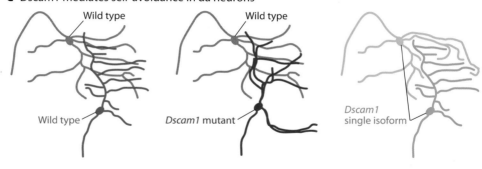

combinatorial association of different sets of three modular, self-binding variable domains. Finely tuned complementarity at each of the variable domains provides extraordinary specificity, which ensures all-or-none binding of Dscam1 isoforms.

ISOFORM-SPECIFIC HOMOPHILIC RECOGNITION PROVIDES THE MOLECULAR BASIS FOR SELF-AVOIDANCE

How is this extraordinary binding specificity of Dscam1 isoforms used in vivo? Dscam1 is broadly expressed, and many isoforms have been found in the developing nervous system (Schmucker et al. 2000). The elimination of ectodomain diversity leads to defects in wiring, demonstrating that Dscam1 diversity and the vast recognition specificities that it provides contribute to establishing neural circuits (Hattori et al. 2007). Extensive loss-of-function analyses revealed a common function for Dscam1. In many cases, loss of Dscam1 results in defects in the segregation of branches that extend from the same neuron, or sister branches (Hughes et al. 2007, Hummel et al. 2003, Matthews et al. 2007, Soba et al. 2007, Wang et al. 2002, Zhu et al. 2006). This led to the view that Dscam1 pro-

teins promote self-recognition between sister branches through their isoform-specific homophilic binding properties (Zhan et al. 2004). This recognition and selective binding are followed by disengagement and repulsion of sister branches. Thus, the extraordinary binding specificity of Dscam1 provides the molecular recognition underlying self-avoidance. Below, we review findings that established the central role of Dscam1 in self-avoidance.

Early studies by Lee and colleagues demonstrated that Dscam1 plays a crucial role in the segregation of axon branches in mushroom body (MB) neurons (Wang et al. 2002). The MB is a central brain structure involved in learning and memory. During development, MB neurons project axons through the brain in a large nerve bundle called the peduncle (**Figure 3a**) (Kurusu et al. 2002). At the base of the peduncle, each axon bifurcates (i.e., splits in two), giving rise to two sister branches. Each sister branch segregates to a different pathway, either dorsally or medially, where again it fasciculates with and extends along other MB axon branches. The MARCM technique was used to generate single mutant cells in an otherwise wild-type background to show that Dscam1 has a discrete function in MB axons. Although *Dscam1* mutant MB axons bifurcate, the two sister branches often fail to segregate to different pathways and frequently grow in parallel along the same

Mushroom body (MB): a structure in the fly brain comprising thousands of neurons

MARCM (mosaic analysis with a repressible cell marker): facilitates the generation and visualization of single mutant cells in an otherwise wild-type background

Figure 3

Dscam1 regulates self-avoidance. (*a*) Dscam1 mediates self-avoidance in mushroom body (MB) neurons. The MB is a central brain structure comprising thousands of neurons. Each MB extends a single axon within a nerve bundle called the peduncle. At the base of the peduncle MB axons bifurcate and extend one branch medially and the other dorsally. Each MB neuron expresses a unique combination of isoforms. As a consequence, sister branches recognize each other through Dscam1 matching. This signals repulsion and subsequent segregation of axons to separate pathways. (*b*) Axon branching patterns of MB neurons of different genotypes. (*Left*) Wild-type MB axon branches segregate with high fidelity. (*Middle*) The branches of a single *Dscam* mutant neuron in a wild-type background frequently do not segregate appropriately. (*Right*) Expression of a single arbitrarily chosen isoform promotes branch segregation in a single *Dscam1* null mutant cell. These and other experiments demonstrated that, although it is unimportant which isoform a single MB neuron expresses for appropriate branch segregation, it is crucial that each MB neuron express isoforms different from its neighbors. (*c*) Dscam1 mediates self-avoidance in dendritic arborization (da) neurons. Different classes of da neurons elaborate overlapping dendritic fields in the body wall of *Drosophila* larva. (*Left*) Two wild-type neurons are shown. (*Middle*) The dendrites of a *Dscam1* null mutant cell form fascicles, supporting the notion that Dscam1 binding promotes repulsion. (*Right*) Overexpression of the same Dscam1 isoform in both neurons leads to nonoverlapping receptive fields, consistent with homophilic binding inducing repulsion.

pathway (**Figure 3*b***) (Wang et al. 2002). Thus, Dscam1 is required, not for branch formation itself, but rather for the segregation of the sister branches to different pathways.

How do Dscam1 diversity and isoform-specific homophilic binding contribute to MB sister branch segregation? Gain-of-function studies suggested that Dscam1 isoform–specific homophilic binding mediates repulsion (see below). This raised the possibility that Dscam1-mediated homophilic repulsion promotes sister branch segregation in MB neurons (Zhan et al. 2004). For Dscam1 to serve this function, each MB neuron must express isoforms that enable them to distinguish between sister branches and the branches of neighboring MB neurons. Assessment of alternative exon expression in MB neurons by the use of customized microarrays comprising all alternative exons provided evidence that most alternative exons are expressed in MB neurons, and that each MB neuron expresses multiple Dscam1 isoforms (Zhan et al. 2004). Sequencing analysis of Dscam1 cDNA revealed that most isoforms expressed in MB neurons are distinct from each other (89 distinct isoforms were identified from 93 cDNA sequenced). Quantitative RT-PCR and an independent statistical analysis showed that each MB neuron expresses $\sim$10–30 Dscam1 mRNAs. Collectively, these data indicate that different MB neurons express different sets of Dscam1 isoforms, thereby providing each neuron with a unique Dscam1 identity. Thus, at the branch point where many different MB axons bifurcate, sister branches selectively recognize each other by isoform-specific homophilic binding (i.e., self-recognition) and, in turn, disengage and extend away from each other along different pathways (i.e., self-avoidance). Branches of different neurons do not recognize each other because they express few, if any, common isoforms. Homophilic repulsion therefore occurs only between sister branches. Thus, the unique Dscam1 identity in each MB neuron allows each branch to selectively recognize its sister branch and distinguish it from all other branches and thus to segregate accordingly (**Figure 3*a***).

Two additional observations confirmed that Dscam1 is a self-avoidance receptor. Hattori et al. (2007) generated *Dscam1^single^* knock-in mutants, in which only one isoform is encoded by the *Dscam1* locus and therefore all neurons share the same Dscam1 identity. As expected, these mutants exhibited defects in MB formation, consistent with loss of sister branch segregation. Even animals carrying a wild-type *Dscam1* allele in *trans* to a *Dscam1^single^* allele displayed similar defects, exemplifying the necessity for each MB neuron to express different isoforms from its neighbors. In sharp contrast, when a single MB neuron was engineered to express Dscam1^single^ in an otherwise wild-type background, it retained normal sister branch segregation (Hattori et al. 2007) (**Figure 3*b***). This observation confirmed the findings of previous studies in which exogenously supplied single isoforms were sufficient to restore sister branch segregation at the single-cell level (Wang et al. 2004, Zhan et al. 2004). These findings are consistent with the notion that the identity of the isoforms expressed in a given neuron is not important as long as the isoforms expressed are different from those expressed by neighboring neurons. These data firmly established the model that Dscam1 diversity and its recognition specificity provide the molecular basis for self-avoidance in MB axons.

Studies by Zhu et al. (2006) suggested that Dscam1 also mediates self-avoidance in dendrites in the CNS. Using the MARCM technique, these researchers showed that dendrites of single projection neurons and interneurons in the olfactory system form clumps and fail to uniformly innervate their targets in the absence of Dscam1. Owing to the complexity of the neuropil, it was not possible to determine whether Dscam1 promotes self-avoidance between these dendrites or whether it is required for other aspects of dendritogenesis, such as outgrowth.

A compelling argument for Dscam1's function in regulating dendrite self-avoidance has been made in dendritic arborization (da) neurons in the peripheral nervous system (Hughes et al. 2007, Matthews et al. 2007, Soba et al.

2007). There are four classes of da neurons, classes I–IV, which elaborate dendritic fields in a two-dimensional pattern within the body wall of the larva. Whereas the dendrites of one class of da neurons overlap with the processes of other da classes, the dendrites of the same neuron, or sister dendrites, do not overlap with each other (**Figure 3c**). Indeed, the dendrites of all four classes of da neurons exhibit self-avoidance properties. Given Dscam1's function in MB neurons, it seemed plausible that Dscam1 might provide the recognition specificity that enables sister dendrites to selectively recognize and segregate from each other while allowing them to overlap with the dendrites of other da neurons.

Genetic studies established that Dscam1 is essential for self-avoidance in all four classes of da neurons. In the absence of Dscam1, sister dendrites adhered to each other and extended across the body wall in fascicles (**Figure 3c**). The number and length of the dendrites were the same as for wild type; only the dendrites' spatial relationship was altered. Self-avoidance was restored when single arbitrarily chosen isoforms were supplied in single *Dscam1* mutant neurons, showing that, as in MB neurons, the identity of isoforms expressed in these neurons is not important. To assess whether expression of the same isoform on opposing dendrites is sufficient to mediate self-recognition, neurons with overlapping dendritic fields in wild type were engineered to express the same isoform. Expression of the same isoform caused the dendrites of these neurons to repel each other, leading to nonoverlapping dendritic fields (**Figure 3c**). This finding provided evidence that repulsion ensues when opposing dendrites express the same Dscam1 isoform. In summary, these data suggest that sister dendrites of da neurons exhibit self-avoidance as they express the same Dscam1 isoforms, whereas dendrites of different da neurons overlap as they express different Dscam1 isoforms.

These studies led to the view that self-avoidance is achieved by a molecular mechanism in which Dscam1 isoforms on opposing dendrites bind to each other and then this

binding, in turn, activates a repulsive response. The repulsive response is likely mediated by signaling events through the cytoplasmic domain. To test this hypothesis, Matthews et al. (2007) utilized a chimeric Dscam1 isoform, in which the cytoplasmic domain was substituted with GFP, presumably resulting in the loss of cytoplasmic signaling events required for a repulsive response. Using the same genetic strategy described above, Matthews et al. (2007) engineered da neurons with overlapping dendritic fields in wild type to express this chimeric Dscam1 isoform. Whereas dendrites engineered to express a single wild-type Dscam1 isoform repel each other and no longer overlap, dendrites expressing this chimeric Dscam1-GFP not only overlap but extensively bind to each other, in a sense trapping an intermediate in the repulsive pathway. This argues that, during the self-avoidance process, binding of Dscam1 isoforms on opposing sister dendrites activates a repellent response mediated by the cytoplasmic domain. The repulsive response involves disengagement of the homophilic receptor complex at the cell surface and activation of cytoskeletal reorganization events. In summary, these studies demonstrate that Dscam1 acts as an isoform-specific homophilic repulsive molecule and that this function of Dscam1 is essential for mediating self-avoidance.

Self-avoidance critically depends upon the acquisition of a unique Dscam1 identity in each neuron. How is Dscam1 isoform expression controlled to ensure this? In principle, a unique Dscam1 identity can arise if each neuron expresses isoforms in a deterministic fashion, reliably making one neuron different from another. This requires strictly regulated expression of isoforms. Microarray expression studies revealed that different types of neurons (e.g., photoreceptor neurons and MB neurons) express different spectra of alternative exons (Neves et al. 2004, Zhan et al. 2004). Consistent with this notion, Graveley and colleagues identified specific splicing factors regulating the expression of particular alternative exons (Park et al. 2004). At least one of the splicing factors is known to be expressed in a tissue-specific manner, suggesting that these splicing factors may contribute to regulating the expression of specific isoforms in vivo. Alternatively, unique Dscam1 identities may be obtained through stochastic expression of multiple isoforms from the large number of isoforms. In theory, if a given neuron expresses 20 isoforms at random from 19,008 possible isoforms, more than 10^{67} unique Dscam1 identities, which far exceeds the total number of neurons in a fly, can be generated. The stochastic nature of isoform expression may arise from the intrinsic variability in the splicing machinery from one neuron to another. Additionally, some sequence elements within alternative exon clusters of the *Dscam1* gene may contribute to stochastic expression. Sequence analysis of the Ig3 alternative exon cluster by Graveley identified a docking site in the intron preceding the cluster that is partially complementary to selector sequences immediately upstream of every alternative exon (Graveley 2005). The random pairing of this docking site and a selector sequence in pre-mRNA may contribute to generating the randomness of the alternative exon utilization. In summary, although it is clear in the case of MB neurons that each neuron expresses a unique set of Dscam1 isoforms, it remains unclear how the isoform expression is controlled to ensure self-avoidance. Analysis of the isoform expression in the same cell identifiable from one animal to another is necessary to address whether Dscam1 splicing is regulated in a deterministic or a stochastic fashion.

How much Dscam1 diversity is required for self-avoidance? We envision that different neural tissues require different degrees of diversity depending upon the complexity of the tissue. For example, neurons in a less complex tissue (e.g., da neurons in the body wall) that encounter processes of only a small number of nonself neurons would likely require fewer isoforms than those in an environment with the processes of many different nonself neurons (e.g., MBs). Studies on deletion mutants in which the ectodomain diversity was reduced from 19,008 to 4752 did not identify defects in self-avoidance in either the MB (Wang et al. 2004) or the da systems (Matthews et al. 2007). Thus, although *Dscam1single* studies clearly showed that Dscam1 diversity is essential for self-avoidance in many tissues, how much Dscam1 diversity is required to provide a robust system for self-avoidance in each system is not known.

In summary, studies in the central and the peripheral nervous systems provide strong evidence that Dscam1 diversity endows neurites with the ability to distinguish between self and nonself neurites. Dscam1 isoform–specific homophilic repulsion between sister branches provides a molecular basis for self-avoidance. Kramer, Stent, and colleagues first described the phenomenon of self-avoidance some 20 years ago on the basis of studies in the leech peripheral nervous system (Kramer et al. 1985). They proposed that self-avoidance would play a more general role in patterning circuits in both vertebrate and invertebrate brains. However, its general importance in regulating the patterning of neural circuits had remained unclear, largely because the molecular basis for self-avoidance remained to be identified and additional experimental evidence for the existence of self-avoidance was lacking. Studies on fly *Dscam1* underscore the widespread requirement for self-avoidance in establishing neural circuits. We propose that self-avoidance is an essential step in wiring, providing an initial driving force for the formation of intricate branch patterns in both the peripheral and the central nervous systems.

Dscam2 IS A TILING RECEPTOR IN THE FLY VISUAL SYSTEM

The prominent role played by Dscam1 in self-avoidance raised the possibility that homophilic repulsion might be a more general property of Dscam proteins. This was supported by the finding that Dscam2 mediates tiling between processes of a subset of neurons in the fly visual system (Millard et al. 2007) (**Figure 4a**).

In contrast to *Dscam1*, the three fly *Dscam1* paralogs, *Dscam2*, *Dscam3*, and *Dscam4*, do not undergo extensive alternative splicing. *Dscam2* encodes two alternative Ig7 domains, but *Dscam3* and *Dscam4* encode only a single ectodomain (Millard et al. 2007). Like Dscam1 isoforms, the two different Dscam2 proteins exhibit isoform-specific homophilic binding. In addition, Dscam3 and Dscam4 bind homophilically but not heterophilically to other family members. As a first step toward understanding how the binding properties of Dscam paralogs function in the developing brain, Millard et al. (2007) generated mutants in *Dscam2*. These mutants showed marked defects in the organization of the visual system.

The fly visual system contains the compound eye, comprising an array of photoreceptor neurons that detect light, and four neuropil regions that process visual information, including the lamina and medulla (Meinertzhagen & Hanson 1993). The medulla is organized into ~750 reiterated columns. Columnar organization preserves the spatial quality of information received at the retina. This information can then be transferred to cells that connect multiple columns and interpret the combined data as a specific visual stimulus, such as motion. Each column contains axons from R7 and R8 photoreceptor neurons, 5 different types of lamina neurons called L1–L5, and ~50 other neuronal cell types (Fischbach & Dittrichi 1989).

Using MARCM techniques, Millard et al. (2007) assessed the role of Dscam2 in R7, R8, L1, and L2 neurons. In wild type, the synaptic connections made by these cells are restricted to a single column and form at specific layers. Dscam2 was not required in R7, R8, or L2 cells for either layer specificity or columnar restriction. By contrast, although the terminal arbors and interstitial branches of L1 formed in the appropriate layers, they aberrantly extended into neighboring columns (**Figure 4a**). Thus, Dscam2 is required for restricting L1 axons to a single column. Because Dscam2 mediates interactions between cells, loss of Dscam2 homophilic binding should generate phenotypes in both mutant cells and the nonmutant cells with which they interact. We exploited this bio-chemical property to determine how Dscam2 restricts L1 axons to columns.

Columnar restriction may reflect either adhesion between L1 axons and another cell within the same column or, alternatively, repulsion between the processes of L1 neurons in adjacent columns. To distinguish between these possibilities, we focused on the directionality of the L1 phenotype. *Dscam2* mutant L1 axons extend bidirectionally into adjacent columns the majority of the time. If another lamina neuron within the same column anchors L1 through Dscam2-mediated adhesive interactions, then the loss of Dscam2 in this cell should lead to a bidirectional phenotype in the wild-type L1 cell. Alternatively, if L1 cells in adjacent columns restrict L1 axons through homophilic repulsive interactions, then the loss of Dscam2 in one of the adjacent columns should lead to unidirectional growth toward that mutant column. The technique of reverse MARCM (Lee et al. 2000) provided a way to distinguish between these two possibilities. Here wild-type neurons were labeled, and the consequence of having neighboring mutant neurons was assessed. Consistent with the repulsion model, wild-type neurons with mutant cells in adjacent columns extended unidirectionally (**Figure 4a**). These studies established that Dscam2 mediates cell-type-specific avoidance between L1 axons in adjacent columns.

In summary, Millard et al. (2007) argue that Dscam2 promotes repulsion between processes of adjacent cells, thus preventing inappropriate connections from being formed in neighboring columns. Because each column contains similar L1 target cells, cell-type-specific avoidance provides a mechanism for restricting connections to a single circuit. The restriction of axonal or dendritic processes from the same cell types to nonoverlapping spatial domains is referred to as tiling (Perry & Linden 1982, Wassle et al. 1981). Tiling is mechanistically similar to self-avoidance. Interestingly, self-avoidance maximizes the number of connections that an individual neuron can make, whereas tiling limits the extent of neuronal connections. Both of

Medulla: a region of the *Drosophila* visual system that is organized into reiterated columns and multiple layers

Lamina 1 (L1) neurons: receive synaptic input from photoreceptor neurons and make connections in the medulla

Reverse MARCM: facilitates the generation and visualization of single wild-type cells near unlabeled mutant cells

these mechanisms ensure precise wiring of the brain. Thus, Dscam1 and Dscam2 proteins regulate two very different aspects of neural connectivity through a common, homophilic repulsive mechanism.

MOUSE DSCAM PROMOTES HOMOPHILIC REPULSION

A recent study by Burgess and coworkers supports the notion that mammalian DSCAMs also mediate homophilic repulsion (Fuerst et al.

a Dscam2 regulates tiling in the fly visual system

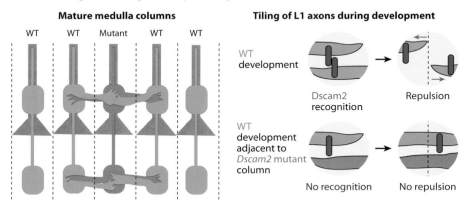

b DSCAM regulates tiling and self-avoidance in the mouse visual system

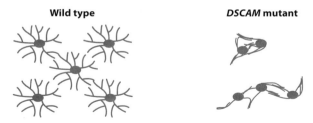

c DSCAM regulates layer specificity in the chick visual system

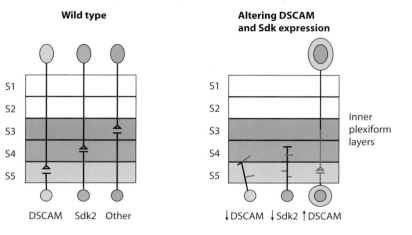

2008). There are two *DSCAM* homologs in vertebrates (Agarwala et al. 2001, Yamakawa et al. 1998). These proteins mediate homophilic binding, but neither gene is alternatively spliced. Fuerst et al. (2008) identified a spontaneous mutation disrupting the mouse *DSCAM* locus that resulted in an overt neurological phenotype. These animals exhibit anatomical defects in the cerebellum and retina. In the vertebrate retina, visual input is processed by interneurons, including amacrine cells. Different classes of amacrine cells (~30 classes) extend dendrites into specific layers of the inner plexiform layer (Masland 2004), where they make connections with retinal ganglion cells. Amacrine cells of the same class appear to be tiled across the layer, generating a sheet of evenly spaced cells. In addition, sister dendrites from the same amacrine cell are patterned by self-avoidance. The *DSCAM* mutant has profound defects in dendritic organization in distinct subsets of amacrine cells (Fuerst et al. 2008) (**Figure 4***b*).

DSCAM expression is restricted to two subclasses of amacrine cells: tyrosine hydroxylase (TH)-expressing, dopaminergic amacrine cells and nitric oxide synthase (bNOS)-expressing amacrine cells. TH and bNOS amacrine cells arborize in different layers. In *DSCAM* mutant animals, a quantitative measurement of spacing between cells of the same type demonstrated that tiling is lost in the TH and bNOS cells at stage P13. Importantly, two other cell types that do not express DSCAM did not exhibit defects in *DSCAM* mutants. In addition to the tiling defect, examination of mutant TH and bNOS cells revealed that sister neurites are fasciculated, indicative of a deficit in self-avoidance. Thus, both self-avoidance and tiling are disrupted, and the combination of these two defects results in a hyperfasciculation phenotype in the mutant animals. The simplest interpretation of these findings is that DSCAM promotes repulsive interactions between sister neurites and between processes of the same cell types, an amalgam of the *Drosophila* Dscam1 and Dscam2 functions.

These data argue that the role of Dscam in mediating homophilic repulsion is evolutionarily conserved. In insects, Dscam1 is broadly expressed. Diversity has evolved to ensure that each neuron expresses a unique Dscam1 identity, thereby allowing sister neurites to selectively recognize and repel each other. This

---

Figure 4

Dscam proteins participate in several aspects of neuronal wiring. (*a*) *Drosophila* Dscam2 is a tiling receptor. (*Left panel*) Schematic of Dscam2 phenotypes in lamina 1 (L1) axons in the fly medulla region of the visual system. L1 axons (*pink* and *green*) elaborate processes in two distinct layers. Interactions between these processes mediated by Dscam2 restrict the formation of connections to a single column, as indicated in the far left and right columns. Mutant (*pink*) L1 axons are not restricted to a single column. Similarly, the processes of wild-type (WT) (*green*) axons extend axons into columns with a mutant L1. Columns are delineated with dashed lines. (*Right panel*) Schematic of L1 column development. Dscam2 homophilic binding (*blue bars*) occurs between wild-type L1 neurites during pupal development. This induces a repulsive signal that results in the retraction of neurites back to their column of origin and the formation of columnar boundaries. Mutant neurites (*pink*) cannot interact with wild-type L1 neurites (*green*) because the former lack Dscam2. Without Dscam2 homophilic binding, neither mutant nor wild-type L1 neurites are restricted to their column of origin, and both can form connections in neighboring columns. (*b*) Mouse DSCAM mediates both self-avoidance and tiling. (*Left panel*) DSCAM-positive amacrine cells exhibit both self-avoidance and tiling properties. (*Right panel*) In the absence of DSCAM, both self-avoidance and tiling are lost. Branches from individual amacrine cells fasciculate with one another and with other cells of the same type. (*c*) Chick DSCAM contributes to layer-specific targeting. (*Left panel*) Ganglion cells (*bottom*) and amacrine cells (*top*) in the chick retina, which express the same DSCAM protein or a related Ig superfamily protein in the Sidekick (Sdk) family, target to the same layer. (*Right panel*) When either DSCAM or Sdk2 is knocked down in ganglion cells that normally express these proteins, dendritic targeting is less precise. Similarly, when cells that do not normally express DSCAM are engineered to misexpress it, they target to the DSCAM-positive S5 layer.

Dscam1 identity enables the protein to function throughout the nervous system because repulsion only occurs between processes of the same cell. By contrast, mouse DSCAM is expressed in subsets of neurons. As these subsets arborize in nonoverlapping layers, DSCAM functions in both self- and cell-type-specific avoidance. Thus, self-avoidance does not require extraordinary diversity if the repulsive receptors are restricted to cell subtypes. This argues that many cell recognition molecules that mediate homophilic repulsion in the vertebrate nervous system remain to be identified. It is also possible, however, that diversity in other families of cell recognition molecules contributes to self-avoidance. One notable example is the protocadherin family (Kohmura et al. 1998, Wu & Maniatis 1999). Stochastic expression of these genes occurs in Purkinje cells, thereby providing each neuron with a unique identity (Esumi et al. 2005). Whether these proteins promote homophilic recognition and repulsion is not yet known.

CHICK DSCAM PROMOTES LAYER-SPECIFIC TARGETING

Many axon guidance molecules can both attract and repel neurons, depending upon the nature of the signaling pathways operating within the growth cone. Even the heterophilic interactions between Eph and ephrin, which have been classically defined as repulsive molecules (Flanagan & Vanderhaeghen 1998), signal attractive or adhesive functions when these molecules are expressed at lower levels (Hansen et al. 2004). Thus, it is not surprising that recent results suggest that DSCAM may also function in an adhesive fashion.

Yamagata & Sanes (2008) used the chick retina as a model system for analyzing cell recognition molecules that play a role in layer-specific targeting. As in the mouse, interneurons (i.e., amacrine and bipolar cells) form synaptic connections with retinal ganglion cells in specific layers. DSCAM and DSCAM-L appear to play a role in this layer-specific tar-

geting (**Figure 4c**). DSCAM and DSCAM-L are expressed in different subsets of interneurons and ganglion cells. Interestingly, interneurons and ganglion cells that target to the same layer express the same DSCAM protein. Knocking down DSCAM levels through retrovirally mediated expression of interfering RNAs disrupted layer-specific targeting of DSCAM-expressing neurons. Conversely, misexpression of DSCAM in retinal cells led to respecification of neurites to the layers expressing the same DSCAM protein. The simplest model for DSCAM function in regulating layer-specific targeting is one in which DSCAM promotes adhesion between the dendrites of the retinal ganglion cells and the processes of interneurons.

On the basis of these and previous studies demonstrating that Sidekick1 and Sidekick2 proteins play a similar role in layer-specific targeting (Yamagata et al. 2002) (**Figure 4c**), Yamagata & Sanes (2008) proposed that layer recognition is controlled, in part, by an Ig family homophilic recognition code. The finding that vertebrate DSCAMs may act instructively by mediating adhesive interactions between processes of different cells raises the question of whether the extraordinary isoform diversity of fly Dscam1 could be used in a similar manner in some developmental contexts.

DOES Dscam1 MEDIATE SELECTIVE INTERACTIONS BETWEEN PROCESSES OF DIFFERENT CELLS?

Many lines of evidence support the view that self-avoidance, mediated by isoform-specific homophilic repulsion, is a major function of Dscam1 diversity. However, given the extraordinary complexity of the fly brain and the handful of neuronal cell types analyzed so far, it remains plausible that in some developmental contexts isoform-specific homophilic binding may mediate recognition events other than self-avoidance, such as adhesive interactions between different neurons. In this scenario, specific isoforms should be required in specific neurons to form appropriate connections. In this context, a study by Schmucker and coworkers (Chen et al. 2006) is particularly provocative. They generated two deletion mutants in which 5 of the 12 Ig2 alternative exons were removed. Because different subsets of alternative exons were deleted in each mutant, these mutants encode different isoforms, although they have the potential to generate the same degree of diversity (i.e., ~11,000 ectodomain isoforms). Intriguingly, each of these two mutants showed a different spectrum of abnormalities in the complex branching patterns of a mechanosensory neuron in the thorax. These defects included an increase in the frequency of branches that occurred at low frequency in wild type and the appearance of ectopic branches not seen in wild type. Thus, different isoforms deleted in each mutant may play distinct roles in regulating the pattern of branching in this neuron.

These findings raise the possibility that, in addition to mediating self-avoidance, Dscam1 diversity may also play an instructive role in which specific isoforms mediate interactions between neurons. It remains unclear, however, which neurons require these deleted isoforms because the analysis was performed in mutant animals in which isoforms were deleted in all neurons rather than in genetically mosaic animals. This also raises the possibility that neurons that normally selectively express the deleted isoforms lose Dscam1 expression altogether and thus are rendered null mutant. Indeed, this phenomenon occurred for the alternatively spliced cell surface protein N-cadherin (Nern et al. 2005). If this is the case in these *Dscam1* deletion mutants, then the deletion-specific defects observed in the mechanosensory neuron may represent an indirect consequence of defects in target neuropil organization resulting from a loss of self-avoidance in specific subsets of target neurons. Thus, additional studies are necessary to demonstrate whether neurons utilize specific isoforms to mediate interactions with different cells in establishing neural circuits.

PERSPECTIVE

A Combinatorial Mechanism Generates Dscam1 Binding Specificities

By the end of the 1990s it was generally believed that, although cell recognition is an integral part of neural circuit assembly, it was highly unlikely that the vast number of individual identification tags envisioned by Sperry existed. It was thus a considerable surprise that, in the course of assessing the role of Dscam1 in axon guidance, we serendipitously discovered that alternative splicing generates an array of some 19,000 different ectodomains each comprising three variable domains embedded in a common scaffold. This molecular theme is reminiscent of antibodies and T cell receptors and raised the intriguing notion that these different isoforms would exhibit different recognition specificities that, in turn, would regulate the assembly of neural circuits. Genetic analysis demonstrated that Dscam1 diversity plays a crucial and widespread role in neural circuit formation, and biochemical studies established that different Dscam1 isoforms exhibit exquisite isoform-specific recognition. Together these studies make a compelling case that Dscam1 proteins function as Sperry-like identity tags.

Although vertebrate DSCAMs share a common function with fly Dscam1 in promoting contact-dependent repulsion and self-avoidance, vertebrate genomes do not encode multiple isoforms of DSCAM. In fact, blocks of tandemly arranged alternative exons as are present in fly *Dscam1* have not been observed in any vertebrate gene characterized so far. Therefore, if similar recognition diversity exists in vertebrates, then other types of combinatorial mechanisms must generate large families of recognition proteins. Similar levels of diversity may be generated by combining modules contained within polypeptide chains encoded by different genes, rather than within a single polypeptide as in fly Dscam1. Indeed, the combinatorial association of different polypeptides contributes to the diverse recognition specificities in vertebrate antibodies and T cell receptors. Here, heavy- and light-chain regions come together in three-dimensional space to generate a unique binding site. Because there are families of related polypeptides in small gene clusters expressed in the developing vertebrate nervous system [e.g., protocadherins (Kohmura et al. 1998, Wu & Maniatis 1999)], it will be interesting to see whether they associate in a combinatorial fashion to give rise to a large number of neuronal recognition molecules.

Repulsive Interactions Between Other Homophilic Molecules May Function in Neural Circuit Assembly

The pioneering studies of Edelman and Takeichi and their colleagues on N-CAM and cadherins led to the view that homophilic adhesive interactions regulate the interactions between neuronal processes in the developing nervous system (Rutishauser 1984, Takeichi 1988). These contact-dependent mechanisms for intercellular communication may drive different types of adhesive interactions, including growth along the surface of axon fascicles in some contexts and, in others, the stable association of cell surfaces to form synaptic contacts. These classic studies led to the implicit assumption that homophilic adhesion in vitro will lead inexorably to adhesive interactions in vivo.

That Dscam-mediated homophilic repulsion plays a key role in patterning neural circuits raises the question of whether other proteins characterized as homophilic adhesion molecules on the basis of in vitro assays promote patterning in vivo through repulsive signaling mechanisms. Many cell culture systems used to characterize adhesion molecules, such as the S2 cell system in flies, may not express the signaling or cytoskeletal proteins that promote repulsion. For example, whereas Dscam1 isoforms mediate repulsion in vivo, in cultured S2 cells they promote aggregation. Thus, other classically defined homophilic adhesion proteins that are characterized by their ability to mediate aggregation in cultured cells in vitro

may act in vivo to promote repulsion. Indeed, two other homophilic proteins, the protocadherin Flamingo in *Drosophila* (Lee et al. 2003, Usui et al. 1999) and the Lar phosphatase in the leech (Baker & Macagno 2000), which promote aggregation in vitro, have been proposed to mediate homophilic repulsion in vivo. These studies underscore the importance of both gain- and loss-of-function studies in different developmental contexts to explore the mechanisms by which homophilic binding between proteins on opposing cellular processes mediates neural circuit assembly.

Tiling and Self-Avoidance Are Key Regulators of Neural Circuit Assembly

When, in the early 1980s, the phenomenon of self-avoidance was discovered (see above) (Kramer & Stent 1985, Kramer et al. 1985), it was speculated that self-avoidance is a general property of neurons in the central and peripheral nervous systems in both vertebrate and invertebrate species. Studies of Dscam1 function in flies revealed that, indeed, many neuronal cell types in both the central and the peripheral nervous systems require self-avoidance to elaborate their branches. In addition, mouse studies support the view that vertebrate DSCAM also promotes self-avoidance. On the basis of these findings, we propose that self-avoidance is a universal mechanism regulating neural circuit formation and that the Dscam family of proteins plays a crucial role in this process.

The notion that fly Dscam1 promotes self-avoidance raised the obvious possibility that regulated splicing could provide neurons with a code to promote tiling, a process that, analogous to self-avoidance, promotes repulsion between processes of different cells rather than between processes of the same cell. The finding that fly Dscam2 and mouse DSCAM serve this function in subsets of neurons in the fly and vertebrate visual systems, respectively, reinforced the notion that the *Dscam* family evolved to promote repulsive interactions between processes of the same cell and processes of the same neuronal subclass.

Self-avoidance and tiling sculpt circuits in complementary ways. Self-avoidance promotes the extension of processes away from one another and allows a cell to maximize its connections. By contrast, tiling provides a means of restricting connections to specific circuits. In the fly visual system, for instance, visual information is initially confined to individual columns for signal processing prior to integrating signals from adjacent columnar units. Restriction of L1 synapses to single columns by Dscam2 prevents the elaboration of synapses in inappropriate columns; if not prevented, such elaboration would lead to abnormalities in processing visual information. The study of Dscam proteins not only has provided a molecular basis for self-avoidance and tiling but has helped to establish them as fundamental developmental processes contributing to the establishment of precise neural circuitry in both vertebrate and invertebrate species.

SUMMARY POINTS

1. Alternative splicing at the *Dscam1* locus has the potential to generate 38,016 different isoforms. This includes 19,008 ectodomains tethered to the membrane by one of two alternative transmembrane domains.

2. Biochemical experiments reveal that 18,048 different ectodomains exhibit isoform-specific homophilic binding. Identical isoforms bind to themselves. Homophilic binding requires matching of three variable Ig domains. A small fraction of heterophilic pairs exhibit binding, but this is always weaker than their corresponding homophilic binding.

3. Dscam1 diversity is essential for the patterning of neural circuits, as demonstrated in mutant animals expressing only a single ectodomain from the endogenous locus.

4. Molecular experiments support a model in which each neuron expresses a unique combination of Dscam1 isoforms, thereby endowing each neuron with a unique cell surface identity.

5. Homophilic binding between identical Dscam1 isoforms on opposing membranes signals repulsion and results in branch segregation. This homophilic repulsion promotes a phenomenon called self-avoidance.

6. A Dscam1 paralog in fly, Dscam2, promotes tiling. Homophilic binding between Dscam2 molecules on two opposing membranes from different cells promotes repulsion, thereby preventing overlap of their processes.

7. Mouse DSCAM is expressed in discrete sets of amacrine cells that arborize in different layers. Loss-of-function studies reveal that DSCAM promotes both self-avoidance and tiling within these layers.

8. Chick DSCAM and DSCAM-L are expressed in different populations of neurons that form synapses in discrete layers in the inner plexiform layers in the retina. Both gain- and loss-of-function studies support a model in which DSCAM and DSCAM-L contribute to layer-specific targeting. It is likely that in this developmental context DSCAM and DSCAM-L promote adhesion rather than repulsion.

FUTURE ISSUES

1. Although a number of studies argue that Dscam1 diversity plays a key role in promoting self-avoidance, it remains unclear whether Dscam1 also promotes recognition between processes of different cells. It will be important to assess whether Dscam1 diversity, in some developmental contexts, specifies interactions between processes of different cells.

2. The characterization of Dscam1 isoform expression in individual cells is challenging and so far has been assessed with customized microarrays on single cells isolated by fluorescent sorting. It will be important in future experiments to develop more robust methods for isoform expression analysis. Such methods may include splicing reporter constructs. This would facilitate the characterization of splicing patterns in single cells at multiple stages of development. RNA isolation from single identified cells and methods to characterize the isoforms expressed in them should address the question of whether specific neurons express the same sets of isoforms in different individuals.

3. Dscam1 and Dscam2 promote contact-dependent repulsion. Genetic and biochemical approaches should provide effective ways of dissecting the mechanisms by which homophilic binding promotes this process through interactions with the cytoplasmic signaling domain.

4. Dscam1 diversity is not present in its mammalian homologs. If a similar degree of diversity in cell surface recognition molecules exists in vertebrates, these molecules remain to be identified.

DISCLOSURE STATEMENT

The authors are not aware of any biases that might be perceived as affecting the objectivity of this review.

LITERATURE CITED

Agarwala KL, Ganesh S, Tsutsumi Y, Suzuki T, Amano K, Yamakawa K. 2001. Cloning and functional characterization of DSCAML1, a novel DSCAM-like cell adhesion molecule that mediates homophilic intercellular adhesion. *Biochem. Biophys. Res. Commun.* 285:760–72

Baker MW, Macagno ER. 2000. The role of a LAR-like receptor tyrosine phosphatase in growth cone collapse and mutual-avoidance by sibling processes. *J. Neurobiol.* 44:194–203

Chen BE, Kondo M, Garnier A, Watson FL, Puettmann-Holgado R, et al. 2006. The molecular diversity of Dscam is functionally required for neuronal wiring specificity in *Drosophila*. *Cell* 125:607–20

Cheng HJ, Flanagan JG. 1994. Identification and cloning of ELF-1, a developmentally expressed ligand for the Mek4 and Sek receptor tyrosine kinases. *Cell* 79:157–68

Drescher U, Kremoser C, Handwerker C, Loschinger J, Noda M, Bonhoeffer F. 1995. In vitro guidance of retinal ganglion cell axons by RAGS, a 25 kDa tectal protein related to ligands for Eph receptor tyrosine kinases. *Cell* 82:359–70

Esumi S, Kakazu N, Taguchi Y, Hirayama T, Sasaki A, et al. 2005. Monoallelic yet combinatorial expression of variable exons of the protocadherin-alpha gene cluster in single neurons. *Nat. Genet.* 37:171–76

Fischbach KF, Dittrich APM. 1989. The optic lobe of *Drosophila melanogaster*. I. A Golgi analysis of wild type structure. *Cell Tissue Res.* 258:441–75

Flanagan JG, Vanderhaeghen P. 1998. The ephrins and Eph receptors in neural development. *Annu. Rev. Neurosci.* 21:309–45

Demonstrated branching defects in *Dscam1* mutants lacking specific exon 4 variants, suggesting a role for specific isoforms in patterning connections.

Freigang J, Proba K, Leder L, Diederichs K, Sonderegger P, Welte W. 2000. The crystal structure of the ligand binding module of axonin-1/TAG-1 suggests a zipper mechanism for neural cell adhesion. *Cell* 101:425–33

Fuerst PG, Koizumi A, Masland RH, Burgess RW. 2008. Neurite arborization and mosaic spacing in the mouse retina require DSCAM. *Nature* 451:470–74

Graveley BR. 2005. Mutually exclusive splicing of the insect *Dscam* pre-mRNA directed by competing intronic RNA secondary structures. *Cell* 123:65–73

Hansen MJ, Dallal GE, Flanagan JG. 2004. Retinal axon response to ephrin-As shows a graded, concentration-dependent transition from growth promotion to inhibition. *Neuron* 42:717–30

Hattori D, Demir E, Kim HW, Viragh E, Zipursky SL, Dickson BJ. 2007. Dscam diversity is essential for neuronal wiring and self-recognition. *Nature* 449:223–27

Hughes ME, Bortnick R, Tsubouchi A, Baumer P, Kondo M, et al. 2007. Homophilic Dscam interactions control complex dendrite morphogenesis. *Neuron* 54:417–27

Hummel T, Vasconcelos ML, Clemens JC, Fishilevich Y, Vosshall LB, Zipursky SL. 2003. Axonal targeting of olfactory receptor neurons in *Drosophila* is controlled by Dscam. *Neuron* 37:221–31

Kohmura N, Senzaki K, Hamada S, Kai N, Yasuda R, et al. 1998. Diversity revealed by a novel family of cadherins expressed in neurons at a synaptic complex. *Neuron* 20:1137–51

Kramer AP, Goldman JR, Stent GS. 1985. Developmental arborization of sensory neurons in the leech *Haementeria ghilianii*. I. Origin of natural variations in the branching pattern. *J. Neurosci.* 5:759–67

Kramer AP, Stent GS. 1985. Developmental arborization of sensory neurons in the leech *Haementeria ghilianii*. II. Experimentally induced variations in the branching pattern. *J. Neurosci.* 5:768–75

Kurusu M, Awasaki T, Masuda-Nakagawa LM, Kawauchi H, Ito K, Furukubo-Tokunaga K. 2002. Embryonic and larval development of the *Drosophila* mushroom bodies: concentric layer subdivisions and the role of fasciclin II. *Development* 129:409–19

Lee RC, Clandinin TR, Lee CH, Chen PL, Meinertzhagen IA, Zipursky SL. 2003. The protocadherin Flamingo is required for axon target selection in the *Drosophila* visual system. *Nat. Neurosci.* 6:557–63

Lee T, Winter C, Marticke SS, Lee A, Luo L. 2000. Essential roles of *Drosophila* RhoA in the regulation of neuroblast proliferation and dendritic but not axonal morphogenesis. *Neuron* 25:307–16

Masland RH. 2004. Neuronal cell types. *Curr. Biol.* 43:497–500

Matthews BJ, Kim ME, Flanagan JJ, Hattori D, Clemens JC, et al. 2007. Dendrite self-avoidance is controlled by Dscam. *Cell* 129:593–604

Meijers RP-HR, Skiniotis G, Liu JH, Walz T, Wang JH, Schmucker D. 2007. Structural basis of Dscam isoform specificity. *Nature* 449:487–91

Meinertzhagen IA, Hanson TE. 1993. The development of the optic lobe. In *The Development of* Drosophila melanogaster, ed. M Bate, A Martinez-Arias, pp. 1363–491. Cold Spring Harbor: Cold Spring Harb. Press

Millard SS, Flanagan JA, Pappu KS, Wu W, Zipursky SL. 2007. Dscam2 mediates axonal tiling in the *Drosophila* visual system. *Nature* 447:720–24

Nern A, Nguyen LV, Herman T, Prakash S, Clandinin TR, Zipursky SL. 2005. An isoform-specific allele of *Drosophila* N-cadherin disrupts a late step of R7 targeting. *Proc. Natl. Acad. Sci. USA* 102:12944–49

Neves G, Zucker J, Daly M, Chess A. 2004. Stochastic yet biased expression of multiple Dscam splice variants by individual cells. *Nat. Genet.* 36:240–46

Park JW, Parisky K, Celotto AM, Reenan RA, Graveley BR. 2004. Identification of alternative splicing regulators by RNA interference in *Drosophila*. *Proc. Natl. Acad. Sci. USA* 101:15974–79

Perry VH, Linden R. 1982. Evidence for dendritic competition in the developing retina. *Nature* 297:683–85

Ramón y Cajal S. 1890. Sur l'origine et les ramifications des fibres nerveuses de la moelle embryonaire. *Anat. Ang.* 5:609–13

Rutishauser U. 1984. Developmental biology of a neural cell adhesion molecule. *Nature* 310:549–54

Sawaya MR, Wojtowicz WM, Andre I, Qian B, Wu W, et al. 2008. A double S-shape provides the structural basis for the extraordinary binding specificity of Dscam isoforms. *Cell.* In press

Demonstrated that a *DSCAM* mutation in mouse leads to defects in patterning of amacrine cell processes.

Showed that Dscam1 diversity is essential for patterning neural circuits.

Along with Hughes et al. (2007) and Soba et al. (2007), demonstrated that Dscam1 is required for self-avoidance in fly da neurons.

X-ray crystal structure of the N-terminal 4 Ig domains of Dscam1 revealed dimer interfaces in Ig2 and Ig3.

Demonstrated that Dscam2 is required for tiling of axonal processes of L1 neurons in the fly visual system.

X-ray crystal structure of the N-terminal eight Ig domains of Dscam1 elucidates the structural basis for isoform-specific homophilic binding.

Reported the finding of Dscam1 diversity and the requirement for Dscam1 in wiring.

Schmucker D, Clemens JC, Shu H, Worby CA, Xiao J, et al. 2000. *Drosophila* **Dscam is an axon guidance receptor exhibiting extraordinary molecular diversity.** *Cell* **101:671–84**

Soba P, Zhu S, Emoto K, Younger S, Yang SJ, et al. 2007. *Drosophila* sensory neurons require Dscam for dendritic self-avoidance and proper dendritic field organization. *Neuron* 54:403–16

Sperry RW. 1963. Chemoaffinity in the orderly growth of nerve fiber patterns and connections. *Proc. Natl. Acad. Sci. USA* 50:703–10

Su XD, Gastinel LN, Vaughn DE, Faye I, Poon P, Bjorkman PJ. 1998. Crystal structure of hemolin: a horseshoe shape with implications for homophilic adhesion. *Science* 281:991–95

Takeichi M. 1988. The cadherins: cell-cell adhesion molecules controlling animal morphogenesis. *Development* 102:639–55

Described branch segregation defects in mushroom body neurons in *Dscam1* mutants.

Tessier-Lavigne M, Goodman CS. 1996. The molecular biology of axon guidance. *Science* 274:1123–33

Usui T, Shima Y, Shimada Y, Hirano S, Burgess RW, et al. 1999. Flamingo, a seven-pass transmembrane cadherin, regulates planar cell polarity under the control of Frizzled. *Cell* 98:585–95

Wang J, Ma X, Yang JS, Zheng X, Zugates CT, et al. 2004. Transmembrane/juxtamembrane domain-dependent Dscam distribution and function during mushroom body neuronal morphogenesis. *Neuron* 43:663–72

Showed Dscam1 isoform-specific homophilic binding and that it requires matching at all three variable domains.

Wang J, Zugates CT, Liang IH, Lee CH, Lee T. 2002. *Drosophila* **Dscam is required for divergent segregation of sister branches and suppresses ectopic bifurcation of axons.** *Neuron* **33:559–71**

Wassle H, Peichl L, Boycott BB. 1981. Dendritic territories of cat retinal ganglion cells. *Nature* 292:344–45

Wojtowicz WM, Andre I, Qian B, Baker D, Zipursky SL. 2007. A vast repertoire of Dscam binding specificities arises from modular interactions of variable Ig domains. *Cell* 130:1134–45

Wojtowicz WM, Flanagan JJ, Millard SS, Zipursky SL, Clemens JC. 2004. Alternative splicing of *Drosophila* **Dscam generates axon guidance receptors that exhibit isoform-specific homophilic binding.** *Cell* **118:619–33**

Demonstrated that DSCAM and DSCAM-L contribute to layer-specific targeting in the chick visual system.

Wu Q, Maniatis T. 1999. A striking organization of a large family of human neural cadherin-like cell adhesion genes. *Cell* 97:779–90

Yamagata M, Sanes JR. 2008. Dscam and Sidekick proteins direct lamina-specific synaptic connections in vertebrate retina. *Nature* **451:465–69**

Yamagata M, Weiner JA, Sanes JR. 2002. Sidekicks: synaptic adhesion molecules that promote lamina-specific connectivity in the retina. *Cell* 110:649–60

Proposed that Dscam1 mediates self-recognition and repulsion in mushroom body neurons. This phenomenon is now called self-avoidance.

Yamakawa K, Huot YK, Haendelt MA, Hubert R, Chen XN, et al. 1998. DSCAM: A novel member of the immunoglobulin superfamily maps in a Down syndrome region and is involved in the development of the nervous system. *Hum. Mol. Genet.* 7:227–37

Zhan XL, Clemens JC, Neves G, Hattori D, Flanagan JJ, et al. 2004. Analysis of Dscam diversity in regulating axon guidance in *Drosophila* **mushroom bodies.** *Neuron* **43:673–86**

Zhu H, Hummel T, Clemens JC, Berdnik D, Zipursky SL, Luo L. 2006. Dendritic patterning by Dscam and synaptic partner matching in the *Drosophila* antennal lobe. *Nat. Neurosci.* 9:349–55

Cumulative Indexes

Contributing Authors, Volumes 20–24

Ohgami N, 22:129–57
Oliver G, 21:457–83
Onn I, 24:105–29
Oppenheimer DG, 21:271–95
Orci L, 20:87–123
Orr-Weaver TL, 24:475–99
Osborne AR, 21:529–50
Owen DJ, 20:153–91

P

Page SL, 20:525–58
Panstruga R, 23:147–74
Papa FR, 22:487–508
Pardue M-L, 23:1–22
Patel NH, 24:425–46
Pathak MM, 22:23–52
Peaper DR, 24:343–68
Pearson BJ, 20:619–47
Pelkmans L, 24:501–23
Pesin JA, 24:475–99
Piper M, 20:505–23
Piper RC, 23:519–47
Pokutta S, 23:237–61
Poo M-m, 23:375–404
Protas ME, 24:425–46
Pruyne D, 20:559–91

Q

Qian D, 23:675–99

R

Rachubinski RA, 23:321–44
Ramirez J, 20:125–51
Rämö P, 24:501–23
Rapoport TA, 21:529–50
Rawn SM, 24:159–81
Reber M, 21:551–80
Reddien PW, 20:193–221,
  725–57
Relaix F, 23:645–73
Richter D, 21:223–45
Rikitake Y, 24:309–42
Römisch K, 21:435–56

Roop DR, 23:93–113

S

Sabatini DD, 21:1–33
Salio M, 24:369–95
Sanchez Alvarado A, 20:725–57
Sancho E, 20:695–723
Sandhoff K, 21:81–103
Schäfer M, 23:69–92
Schekman R, 20:87–123
Schroer TA, 20:759–79
Seedorf M, 24:287–308
Segall JE, 21:695–718
Shepherd JD, 23:613–43
Shi Y, 21:35–56
Shimono Y, 23:675–99
Shin K, 22:207–35
Si-Ammour A, 21:297–318
Siekhaus DE, 22:237–65
Silk JD, 24:369–95
Sillitoe RV, 23:549–77
Singer R, 21:695–718
Singh SB, 20:367–94
Smith HMS, 20:125–51
Smith LG, 21:271–95
Somerville C, 22:53–78
Spudich G, 20:649–76
Steinkraus KA, 24:29–54
Stewart SA, 22:531–57
Stinchcombe JC, 23:495–517
Sumen C, 21:581–603
Sundquist WI, 20:395–425

T

Takai Y, 24:309–42
Tanaka T, 20:593–618
Theurkauf W, 21:411–34
Tiedge H, 21:223–45
Tombola F, 22:23–52
Tontonoz P, 20:455–80
Trainor PA, 22:267–86
Tran TS, 23:263–92
Tsai B, 23:23–43

U

Ünal E, 24:105–29

V

van den Berg B, 21:529–50
Vergne I, 20:367–94
Vert G, 21:177–201
von Andrian UH, 21:581–603

W

Walter P, 22:487–508
Walther TC, 21:347–80
Wang H, 21:223–45
Waters CM, 21:319–46
Wei C-J, 20:811–38
Weinberg RA, 22:531–57
Weis WI, 23:237–61
Werner S, 23:69–92
West AP, 22:409–37
Winey M, 20:1–28
Wojtowicz WM, 24:597–620

X

Xie T, 21:605–31
Xiong J-P, 21:381–410
Xu X, 20:811–38

Y

Yamauchi Y, 22:129–57
Yan N, 21:35–56
Yang Z, 24:551–75
Yurchenco PD, 20:255–84

Z

Zheng JQ, 23:375–404
Zheng Y, 20:867–94
Zipursky SL, 24:597–620
Zúñiga-Pflücker JC,
  23:463–93

Chapter Titles, Volumes 20–24

Gene Expression, Posttranscriptional Regulation